MICROBIAL
TRANSFORMATIONS
OF STEROIDS

A Handbook

MICROBIAL TRANSFORMATIONS OF STEROIDS

A Handbook

William Charney
Manager, Industrial Microbiology, Schering Corporation, Union, New Jersey

and

Hershel L. Herzog
Director of Chemical Development, Schering Corporation, Bloomfield, New Jersey

1967

ACADEMIC PRESS *New York and London*

ACADEMIC PRESS INC.
111 Fifth Avenue, New York, New York 10003

United Kingdom Edition published by
ACADEMIC PRESS INC. (LONDON) LTD.
Berkeley Square House, London W.1

LIBRARY OF CONGRESS CATALOG CARD NUMBER: 68-18661

PRINTED IN THE UNITED STATES OF AMERICA

To Mita and Levonna

PREFACE

The principal purpose of this volume is to provide those who wish to use microbial transformations of steroids with a single source book for the period from 1937 to the present. This handbook should answer the following questions: Has a particular compound been prepared with the aid of microorganisms? If so, how efficient are these methods, and which among them is likely to be the best? Has a particular microbial genus (or species) been used with a particular substrate (or substrates), and what was the observed result? Where can the required culture be obtained? Is there a United States Patent or a published scientific article (through December 31, 1963, with selected entries thereafter) which discloses the product of the organism in question in a detailed example?

The literature of this field has been spread widely in chemical and biological journals throughout the world. To the extent that we have been able, we have combed this literature and tabulated selected data which we believe may be useful. We have continued our scrutiny to the present, and all important developments subsequent to December, 1963, are discussed, with references appropriately noted in the Bibliographical Appendix. The Tables contain essentially no reference to this later work.

A secondary purpose of ours has been to survey the historical development and present status of the field. We have been closely associated with the commercial production of steroids for 15 years and have participated in some of the events which influenced the evolution of microbial transformations. It has been our intention to interpret the many developments in the theory and practice of the field from our largely applied viewpoint.

To the extent that we have considered theory, we have concentrated on the processes occurring within the steroid and have given little attention to the nature of the enzymes responsible for the observed changes or to the chemical changes which they might experience.

We extend our special thanks to the management of the Schering Corporation and to our colleague and guide, Dr. E. B. Hershberg, for their aid and understanding during the lengthy preparation of this volume. We also thank Miss Lisette Harris, Mrs. Marie Marshall, and Mrs. Elizabeth Wesson for their cheerful completion of the arduous task of typing the manuscript, and Miss Dorothy Mizoguchi for the translation of articles published in Japanese.

We are grateful to Dr. C. H. Robinson and Dr. A. L. Nussbaum for reading and criticizing the historical and chemical transformation sections.

William Charney
Hershel L. Herzog

October, 1967

CONTENTS

Preface   vii

Chapter I
INTRODUCTION

Earliest Work – Nonsteroid   1

Earliest Work – Steroid   2

Significance of Discovery of Antiinflammatory Action of Cortisone   4

First Hydroxylations   5

First Dehydrogenations   6

Manufacture of Natural and Synthetic Corticosteroids   9

New Trends in Research   11

Chapter II
CHEMICAL CLASSIFICATION OF MICROBIAL TRANSFORMATIONS
        OF STEROIDS

The Role of Enzymes in Microbial Transformations   14

   Practical Implications   14

The Classes of Chemical Reactions   16

   Oxidation   17

      Hydroxylation   18

      Dehydrogenation   37

      Epoxidation   43

      Oxidation of Alcohols to Ketones or Aldehydes   45

      Oxidation of Ketones to Esters and Lactones   46

      Oxidation of Sulfides to Sulfoxides   47

      Oxidation of Amines to Ketones   48

      Oxidative Degradation – a Composite   48

   Reduction   55

      Reduction of Carbonyl Compounds to Alcohols   55

Reduction of Carbon–Carbon Double Bonds   60

Reduction of Steroidal Bromide   63

Esterification and Hydrolysis.   63

Hydrolysis of Esters to Give Steroid Alcohols.   63

Esterification of Steroid Alcohols   65

N–Acetate Formation from Amines   65

Hydrolysis of Oxides to Alcohols   66

Hydrolysis of Glycosides.   67

Isomerization of Double Bonds   67

Miscellaneous Addition, Rearrangement, and Elimination Processes . .   69

Wagner–Meerwein Rearrangement   69

Decarboxylation.   69

Reverse Aldol Reaction.   70

Michael Addition   70

D–Homoannulation   71

Enolization of Carbonyl Compounds – Inversion at the α–Carbon . . .   71

Dehydration   71

Amination.   72

Resolution of Steroids from Total Synthesis   73

Chapter III

THE CONSTRUCTION AND USE OF TABLE I

Order of the Table   74

Nomenclature   74

Description of the Transformation Leading to the Product.   76

Yield.   78

Organism   78

Constants   78

References   79

Table I: Transformations by Product   80

Chapter IV

TAXONOMY

System of Classification 220

Classes and Major Orders of Fungi and Bacteria (reported to
    transform steroids) 222

Hydroxylation – Taxonomic Distribution According to Order 223

Hydroxylation – Taxonomic Distribution According to Genus 224

Δ^1-Dehydrogenation – Taxonomic Distribution According to Genus 236

Table II: Taxonomy to Species............................. 237

Chapter V

THE CONSTRUCTION AND USE OF TABLE III – TRANSFORMATIONS
    BY GENUS

Order of the Table 262

Specific Notes on Divisions of the Table...................... 262

    Genera.. 262

    Species 263

    Sources 263

    Substrates 263

    Reactions 264

    References 265

Culture Collections (source of cultures)....................... 265

Table III: Transformations by Genus 269

Chapter VI

BIBLIOGRAPHY 681

Chapter VII

BIBLIOGRAPHICAL APPENDIX 721

MICROBIAL
TRANSFORMATIONS
OF STEROIDS

A Handbook

CHAPTER I

Introduction

Microbial transformations of organic compounds have been known in an empirical way from the dawn of history. In almost every civilization, primitive or advanced, man has practiced the fermentation of fruit, grain, or milk to obtain intoxicating and nourishing dietary factors. Evidence of wine production from as early as approximately 3000 B. C. has been found in excavations at Lachish and other sites.[1]

The rational application of these early techniques could come only after the scientific practice of organic chemistry and microbiology was begun. A sufficient understanding had developed by 1857 to provide the necessary background for the work of Louis Pasteur on the fermentation of sugar to lactic acid and ethanol. Herein was elucidated for the first time the concept that individual microbial species were responsible for discrete chemical alterations of selected substrates.[2-5] These experiments and their publication have been called "the birth of microbiology."[5]

EARLIEST WORK - NONSTEROID

After Pasteur and until the end of the 19th century, few studies of the application of microorganisms to organic chemistry were carried out. None of these were of an intensive, systematic nature, which might have emphasized the broader possibilities of a fusion of the two sciences,[6,7] although Brown recognized that such possibilities did exist. He gave individual examples of the oxidation of secondary alcohols to ketones and of primary alcohols to aldehydes and carboxylic acids.

Beginning in 1896, Bertrand carried out extensive studies of the simple, oxidative process resulting from the action of *Acetobacter xylinum* on a series of polyhydric alcohols, and thereby established the generality of the illustrated scheme.[8-10]

---

[1] Wooley, L., "The Beginnings of Civilization," Vol. I, Part II, p. 234. The New American Library, New York, 1965.

[2] Pasteur, L., Compt. Rend. 45, 913 (1857).

[3] Pasteur, L., Ann. Chim. Phys. [1] 58, 323 (1860).

[4] Pasteur, L., Ann. Sci. Nat. 16, 5 (1861).

[5] Vallery-Radot, L. P., "Pasteur Fermentation Centennial," p. 4. Chas. Pfizer and Co., Inc., New York, 1957.

[6] Boutroux, L., Compt. Rend. 86, 605 (1878).

[7] Brown, A. J., J. Chem. Soc., pp. 172 and 432 (1886).

[8] Bertrand, G., Compt. Rend. 122, 900 (1896); 126, 984 (1898).

[9] Bertrand, G., Ann. Chim. Phys. [7] 8, 3 (1904).

[10] Bertrand, G., Bull. Soc. Chim. France 15, 627 (1896); 19, 502 (1898).

As "Bertrand's rule" was finally elaborated, it was shown that a pair of adjacent, *cis*, secondary hydroxyl groups, next to a primary hydroxyl group, suffice to establish conditions favorable for the oxidation.[11] The reaction eventually became important for the conversion of sorbitol to *l*-sorbose,[12] an intermediate in the manufacture of vitamin C. Dihydroxyacetone, which has been used extensively in recent times to tan human skin *in vivo* (for cosmetic reasons), can also be made on a commercial scale in the same way.[13] A favored organism for these reactions is *Acetobacter suboxydans.*

Following the work of Bertrand, the next major development in the field arose from the finding of Lintner and von Liebig[14] that a fermenting yeast reduced furfuraldehyde to the alcohol. Neuberg and his school explored the application of yeasts to a wide variety of substrates. Their studies are summarized *in extenso* by Fischer (F-245) and Stodola.[15]

EARLIEST WORK - STEROID

Steroidal substrates were used first, in 1937, by Mamoli and Vercellone (M-550, M-551), who began by extending the findings of the Neuberg school. They showed that fermenting yeast may be used to reduce 17-ketosteroids to 17β-hydroxysteroids. This method had some passing importance in the manufacture of the male hormone,

testosterone (M-543), and later of the female hormone, estradiol (W-1085), but was superseded by more convenient and efficient nonenzymatic procedures.

Through the use of impure yeast cultures, Mamoli and Vercellone (M-538, M-540, M-542, M-552) discovered a useful class of sequential oxidation-isomerization reactions which they later attributed correctly to the action of the bacterial contaminants (M-553). A representative transformation of this type (including a hydrolysis step, as well) is the conversion of 3β,21 -dihydroxy-5-pregnen-20-one 21-acetate to deoxycorticosterone by *Corynebacterium mediolanum* (*Corynebacterium helvolum*) (M-541, M-546). Schering (USA) employed a similar process to manufacture Reichstein's Compound S (17α, 21-dihydroxy-4-pregnene-3, 20-dione) for a time. It is now clear that nonenzymatic methods are more efficient for the synthesis of Compound S.

---

[11] Some later modifications of the rule are summarized by Sowden, J. S., in "The Carbohydrates" (W. Pigman, ed.), p. 132. Academic Press, New York, 1957.

[12] Wells, P. A., Stubbs, J. J., Lockwood, L. B., and Roe, E. T., Ind. Eng. Chem. 29, 1385 (1937).

[13] Underkofler, L. A., and Fulmer, E. I., J. Am. Chem. Soc. 59, 301 (1937).

[14] Lintner, C. J., and von Liebig, H. J., Z. Physiol. Chem. 72, 449 (1911).

[15] Stodola, F. H., "Chemical Transformations by Microorganisms," Chapter 2. Wiley, New York, 1958.

Mamoli and his colleagues also recognized a class of bacterial reductions, which they attributed to an anaerobic bacterial species identified as *Bacillus putrificus*. Al-

though this culture has since been lost, the same (5β) and related (5α) reductions have been demonstrated with a variety of aerobic and anaerobic microbial species and have some academic interest since they parallel normal modes of mammalian metabolism of 3-keto-Δ^4-steroids.

Considered in the historical context, the timing of Mamoli's pioneering application of microbial methods to the organic chemistry of steroids was logical. Just a few years earlier the correct structure of the steroid nucleus had been established. In 1935 testosterone was isolated from steer testis by Laqueur and was shown to be a powerful male hormone in a variety of animal tests. The structure was established by Butenandt and Ruzicka during the same year. The possibility of important medical

Testosterone

application was on the horizon. We appreciate the element of inevitability in the development of microbiological transformations in the steroid field, arising as it did from the knowledge of the chemistry of yeasts developed by Neuberg and from the availability of 17-ketosteroid intermediates.

The period from 1940-1949, following the early efforts of the Mamoli school, was rather quiet with respect to the further evolution of microbial transformations. Economic incentive for further study was absent because adequate nonenzymatic methodology had been devised for the synthesis of testosterone and related male hormone products, and estradiol. Also, the war disrupted scientific activity in Italy and Germany, where all the work had been done. Nevertheless, key observations which foreshadowed the subsequent explosive growth of the field were made.

Horvath and Kramli (H-406) in 1947 reported the 7-dehydrogenation of cholesterol with *Azotobacter* sp. and in 1948 (K-474, K-475) they reported the 7-hydroxylation of cholesterol with *Proactinomyces* sp. These reactions, both novel at this time, were the first examples of what later proved to be the most important contributions of microbiology to steroid chemistry. There was no basis, at the time these observations were made, to appreciate their future import.

Turfitt (T-1029, T-1030, T-1031, T-1032, T-1034) studied the use of steroids, as a sole source of carbon for microbial growth, and the steroid transformation products produced thereby. The key observations he made, which lay fallow until greater understanding of the field developed [cf. the work of Whitmarsh (W-1111) and particularly of Sih and his collaborators (Ap-79, Ap-83, Ap-95)] were that cholestenone and 3-keto-4-cholenic acid were transformed by *Proactinomyces erythropolis*, albeit to a very minor degree, into 3-keto-4-androstene-17β-carboxylic acid. The idea which this illustrated was that cholesterol conceivably might be transformed by a microbiological degradative method into useful steroid entities of substantially lower molecular weight.[16]

SIGNIFICANCE OF DISCOVERY OF ANTIINFLAMMATORY ACTION OF CORTISONE

The most important chapter in the history of microbial transformations of steroids has had to do with the synthesis of the hormones of the adrenal gland and of their more powerful and therapeutically selective synthetic analogs. Studies of the composition of steroids in bovine and other mammalian adrenal glands by Kendall, Reichstein, and Wintersteiner, and their respective collaborators, begun in the early 1930's, led eventually to the isolation, characterization, and structural proof of cortisone (1938).

Cortisone

Understanding of the therapeutic possibilities of this agent did not begin to develop until 1949, when Hench and associates[17] announced the successful use of cortisone 21-acetate as a palliative in rheumatoid arthritis. For their contributions to this discovery Hench, Kendall, and Reichstein shared the Nobel Prize.

Since rheumatoid arthritis was (and is) a grave and crippling disease, with a high incidence, there was a tremendous incentive to provide cortisone by an efficient synthetic technique. Sarett, among others, had been working on the partial synthesis of adrenocorticoid hormones, and in 1946 he achieved the first synthesis of cortisone. The cortisone for the Hench-Kendall clinical experiment was prepared at Merck based on synthetic methods devised by Sarett and by Kendall and his co-workers. The starting material was deoxycholic acid, which was readily available from bovine

---

[16] At this time cholesterol was still the major starting material for steroid hormone synthesis. It was transformed by oxidation with chromic acid into dehydroepiandrosterone in about 10% yield. In the late 1940's cholesterol was supplanted by diosgenin as the preferred starting material.

[17] Hench, P. S., Kendall, E. C., Slocumb, C. H., and Polley, H. F., A. M. A. Arch. Internal Med. 85, 545 (1950).

bile. The introduction of the 11-oxygen atom, an essential element of structure, was a major task.[18]

While Merck, beginning in 1949, and Schering, in 1951, manufactured cortisone from deoxycholic acid, Peterson and Murray, biochemist and microbiologist, respectively, with the Upjohn Company, chose to attack the problem of the introduction of 11-oxygen by the potentially more direct, microbiological method. They have said (P-723) that they were stimulated to enter this field by the successes of the Mamoli school. They were also encouraged, early in their work, by the report of Hechter and collaborators[19] that perfusion of deoxycorticosterone through isolated adrenal glands resulted in the formation of corticosterone by enzymatic 11β-hydroxylation.

FIRST HYDROXYLATIONS

In 1950 Peterson and Murray observed the first microbial 11-hydroxylation, namely, the 11α-hydroxylation of progesterone with the fungus, *Rhizopus arrhizus*. "The culture was isolated from the air when an agar plate was exposed on a window sill" (P-721). Shortly thereafter, *Rhizopus nigricans* was found to 11α-hydroxylate progesterone in high yield. The first publication of this work *in extenso* was in a U. S.

patent which was issued in July 1952 (M-601) and described, with a wealth of detail, the hydroxylations at 6β and 11α of a variety of substrates by fungi of the order Mucorales. Selected examples of 7ξ- and 14ξ-hydroxylations were also given.[20] Emphasis was placed on 11α-hydroxylation, since it was apparent that herein lay the great economic value of this invention.

The importance of the Murray-Peterson discovery was manyfold. It led to a new technology for the manufacture of adrenocortical hormones and, eventually, of their synthetic analogs. It introduced the use of fungi, heretofore unexplored as a source of enzymes for microbiological transformations. And perhaps most important of all, it caused a surge of interest in the field. Much new, basic information for science was developed subsequently from the study of microbiological transformation of steroids.

Colingsworth, Brunner, and Haines (C-134), also of the Upjohn Company, discovered the 11β-hydroxylation of Compound S with the actinomycete, *Streptomyces fradiae* shortly after the original Murray-Peterson findings were made. This was to

[18] Flow chart 26 from "Steroids" (L. F. Fieser and M. Fieser, p. 644, compounds I to IX. Reinhold, New York, 1959), is an accurate representation of the complexity of this process, as it was actually practiced on an industrial scale. More generally, the background for all important early developments in steroid chemistry is given in detail by the Fiesers.

[19] Hechter, O., Jacobsen, R. P., Jeanloz, R., Levy, H., Marshall, C. W., Pincus, G., and Schenker, V., J. Am. Chem. Soc. 71, 3261 (1949).

[20] Hydroxylation at the 8-position was also described. These assignments were later revised to 9α, and in some cases 7β.

be the prototype for a second class of hydroxylation of considerable commercial
significance.

Compound S   Hydrocortisone

The same investigators also found that *Cunninghamella blakesleeana* was considerably more efficient at promoting this same reaction (H-339).

The motives which induced Murray, Peterson, and their Upjohn colleagues to
enter this field were equally impelling for Perlman, Titus, and Fried of Squibb. Independently,[21] they discovered the 16α-hydroxylation of progesterone with an actinomycete later shown to be *Streptomyces argenteclus*. In 1956, when the antiinflammatory activity of triamcinolone was reported by Bernstein (B-60), the considerable
value of this hydroxylation was first appreciated (T-1002). Fried and his colleagues

Triamcinolone

also discovered the useful 11α-hydroxylation of progesterone by *Aspergillus niger*
early in their studies.

FIRST DEHYDROGENATIONS

An immediate and major result from all of these early findings was the improvement of the methodology of steroid chemistry and the opening of a new avenue for research. Microbiological transformation studies were begun in the laboratories of
most of the pharmaceutical houses with interests in steroid chemistry (Lederle, Merck,
Pfizer, Schering, and Syntex, among others). Since Schering was producing cortisone
acetate at this time and was attempting to develop a useful synthesis for hydrocortisone
(cortisol), we were prompted to extend the investigations of the early workers into new
lines which might improve our production techniques. In this connection we began, in
1953, the study of the enzymatic hydrolysis of hydrocortisone 11, 21-diacetate. The
diacetate had been prepared[22] in the hope that a chemical hydrolysis might afford

---

[21] The first Squibb patent application in this field was filed in July 1951.

[22] Oliveto, E. P., Gerold, C., and Hershberg, E. B., Arch. Biochem. Biophys. 43, 234
(1953).

hydrocortisone. The 11-ester was then found to be exceptionally difficult to hydrolyze, and we turned to the use of microorganisms.

One of the early experiments, which was run by Nobile in our laboratories, was the treatment of the diacetate with *Corynebacterium simplex*. The rationale was that an apparently related and then unavailable culture, *Corynebacterium mediolanum*, had been shown by Mamoli to have a good esterase (M-541, M-546). As it turned out, *C. simplex* afforded an interesting new reaction product in high yield, but that product was *not* hydrocortisone. More detailed investigation with other substrates, particularly Compound S, showed that the major transformation was 1-dehydrogenation (H-389, N-671).

The microbial 1-dehydrogenation reaction was not new, having been described at a Gordon Conference in the summer of 1953 by Fried [23] and published in November of the same year (F-284). Vischer and Wettstein had also observed 1-dehydrogenation (V-1056). In none of the cases described by Fried, Thoma, and Klingsberg or Vischer

---

[23] Josef Fried, not to be confused with his brother, John Fried, also a steroid chemist. All the early work in microbial transformations reported by J. Fried was done by Josef Fried.

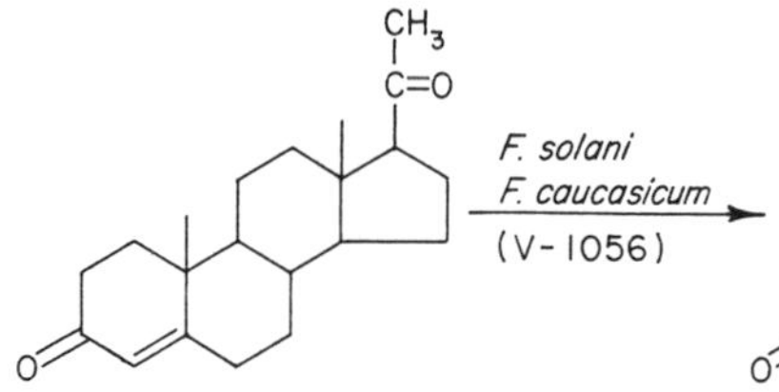

CH$_3$
C=O

F. solani
F. caucasicum
(V-1056)

and Wettstein, several of which are illustrated here, did a steroid with a pregnane skeleton pass through the dehydrogenation process to an identified product with side-chain intact. In all instances wherein a 1-dehydro product was characterized, either 1, 4-androstadiene-3, 17-dione, 17β-hydroxy-1, 4-androstadien-3-one, or 1-dehydro-testololactone was formed, the side chain having been altered in the illustrated way.[24]

Since we had shown that *C. simplex* dehydrogenated without concomitant side-chain degradation, we were able to use this transformation to prepare the previously unknown 1-dehydro analogs of cortisone and hydrocortisone, later named prednisone and prednisolone, respectively. These were tested in animals by Tolksdorf, Perlman,

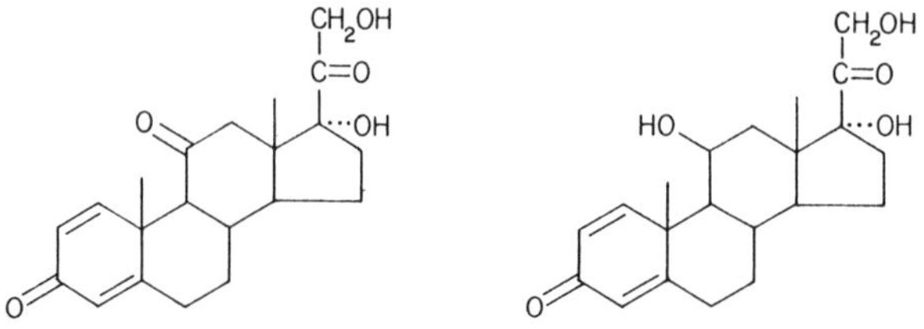

CH$_2$OH
C=O
···OH

CH$_2$OH
C=O
···OH

Prednisone   Prednisolone

and their collaborators at Schering[25] and found to be three to five times more potent than the parent 1, 2-dihydro compounds by a variety of criteria (H-387, H-389). In July 1954, prednisolone was given to M. M. Pechet, then at the National Institutes of Health, who with J. J. Bunim and A. Bollett tested the compound in an arthritic human. This first test and the many subsequent tests with both prednisone and prednisolone in corticoid-responsive diseases confirmed the enhanced potency predicted from the animal experiments. In addition, and even more important, they showed that there was essentially no drug-induced salt retention at therapeutic dose levels. Since salt retention had been a significant complication resulting from the use of cortisone and hydrocortisone, the improved therapeutic index of prednisone and prednisolone encouraged a much wider use of adrenocorticoids in the treatment of dermatologic, allergic, and collagen diseases.

Using fermentation techniques, the Schering Corporation made prednisone and prednisolone broadly available early in 1955. These agents quickly supplanted cortisone and hydrocortisone for most indications requiring systemic (as opposed to topical) treatment. These 1-dehydro compounds continue to be used widely (1966) in spite of the many additional synthetic corticoids which have been produced. In the

---

[24] Vischer and Wettstein mentioned chromatographic evidence for the formation of products, from Compound S and cortisone, which had suffered no degradation.

[25] Tolksdorf, S., Battin, M. L., Cassidy, J. W., McLeod, R. M., Warren, F. H., and Perlman, P. L., Proc. Soc. Exptl. Biol. Med. 92, 207 (1956).

subsequent development of the corticoid field, 1-dehydrogenation played a vital role. All synthetic corticoids for systemic use contain this structural unit.

The other contributions from microbiology toward the realization of new structures have been in providing improved technology for manufacture. Triamcinolone, whose preparation and properties were announced by Bernstein and his collaborators

Triamcinolone

of Lederle in 1956 (B-60), was the first useful antiinflammatory agent to embody the potency-enhancing effort of the 9α-fluorine atom, discovered by Fried and Sabo in 1954. To counteract the concomitant, increased, salt-retention component, also contributed by the halogen, the insertion of Δ^1-unsaturation was insufficient. Bernstein found that the presence of a 16α-hydroxyl group effectively blocked salt retention in 9α-fluorosteroids, at the expense of the potency enhancement normally found in 9α-fluorocorticoids. Triamcinolone has essentially the same milligram potency as prednisone and prednisolone, but has been found to be somewhat more active in the treatment of certain, rather common dermatologic conditions, particularly psoriasis. This property has led to its widespread use. The considerably poorer therapeutic index of triamcinolone (as measured in dogs) does not seem to have become a problem in human medicine, although the pattern of side effects varies somewhat from that usually observed with other synthetic corticoids.

Bernstein and his associates achieved the introduction of the 16α-hydroxyl group by chemical means in their first synthesis, and hence microbiology cannot be said to have contributed significantly to this aspect of the discovery. In the ultimate commercial exploitation, however, advantage was taken of the findings of Perlman, Titus, and Fried (P-718), and subsequent improvements by Thoma and Fried (T-1002), to introduce the 16α-hydroxyl group microbiologically. Lederle eventually cross-licensed with Squibb, exchanging triamcinolone rights for rights to use the 9α-fluoro discovery of Fried and Sabo and the 16α-hydroxylation technology.

Many synthetic corticoids were introduced following the discovery of triamcinolone. These include triamcinolone 16,17-acetonide, 6α-methylprednisolone, 16α-methyl-9α-fluoroprednisolone (dexamethasone), 16β-methyl-9α-fluoroprednisolone (betamethasone), 6α-fluoro-16α-methylprednisolone (paramethasone), 16-methylene-prednisolone, and 6α,9α-difluoro-16α-hydroxyprednisolone 16,17-acetonide (fluocinolone acetonide). Microbiology played no essential role in their discovery, although in some cases microbiological technology has been employed to advantage in their manufacture.

MANUFACTURE OF NATURAL AND SYNTHETIC CORTICOSTEROIDS

As far as we are able to determine, the present status of manufacture of the important *bulk* corticoids is illustrated in the flow diagrams which follow. Since manufacturing details are rarely available for public inspection, there is an element of guesswork in some of these charts. Paramethasone and fluocinolone acetonide are thought to require microbial 11β-hydroxylation steps in their manufacture.

Hydrocortisone and Cortisone

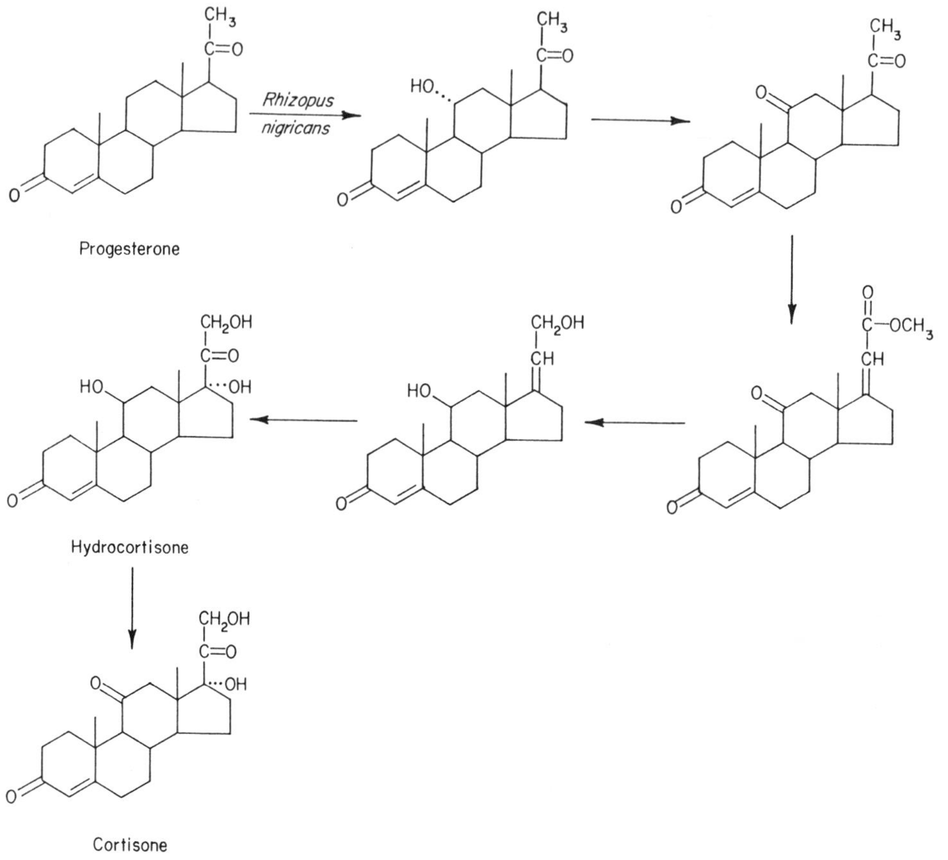

Upjohn

Rhizopus nigricans

Progesterone

Hydrocortisone

Cortisone

Schering A.G. and Pfizer

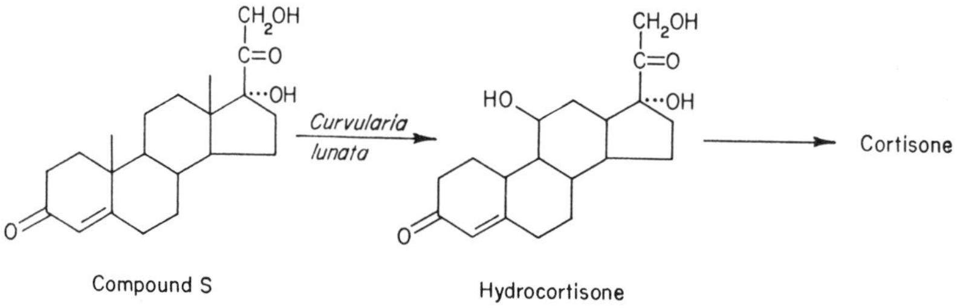

Curvularia lunata

Compound S   Hydrocortisone   Cortisone

Dexamethasone and betamethasone have been made principally from deoxycholic acid and hecogenin, respectively, by nonmicrobiological routes.

Microbiology has had a passing role in the discovery of the anabolic agent, 1-dehydromethyltestosterone. First prepared by Nobile in our laboratories by the action of *Cornybacterium simplex* on methyltestosterone (N-667a), and independently

Prednisolone and Prednisone

Upjohn

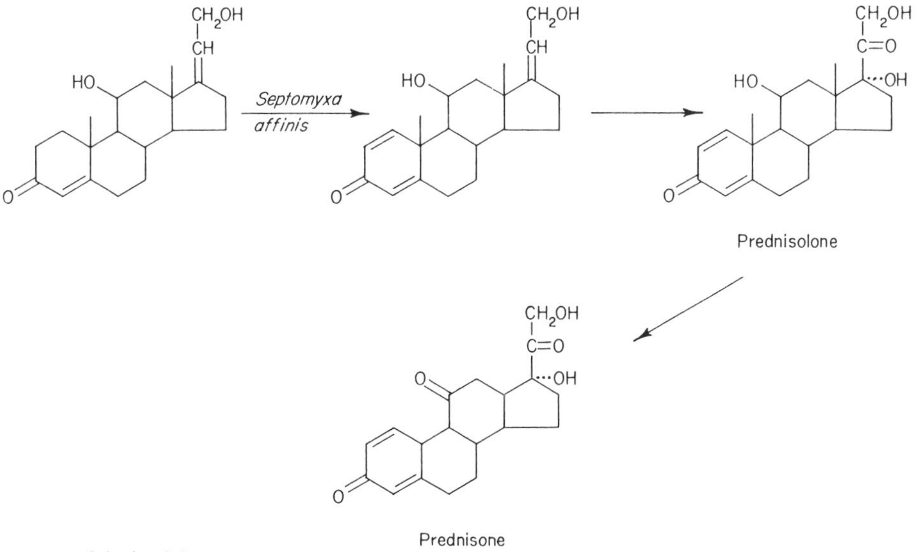

Prednisolone

Prednisone

Schering A.G.

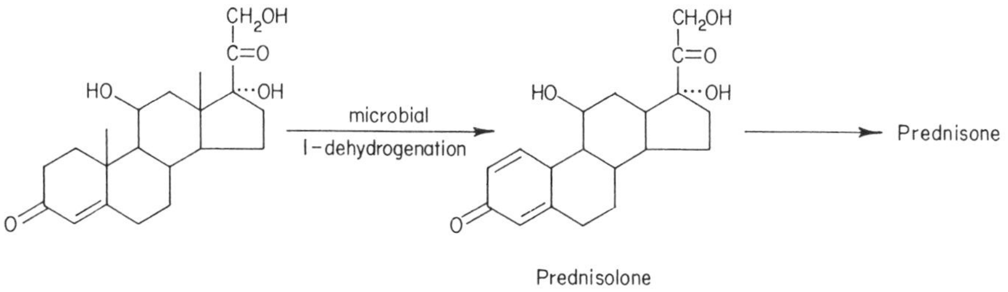

Prednisolone

by Vischer, Meystre, and Wettstein (V-1052), its application to medicine was pioneered by Ciba. It is questionable whether the microbiological route to this compound has any current commercial importance.

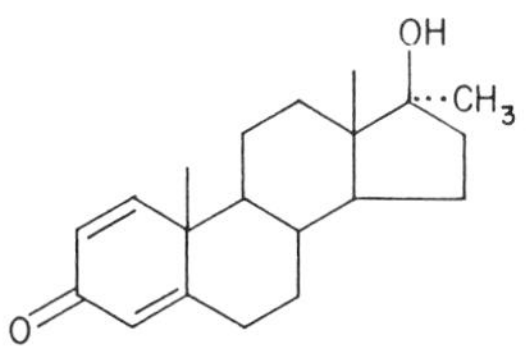

1-Dehydromethyltestosterone

NEW TRENDS IN RESEARCH

The most interesting new prospect for the commercial application of microbiological transformations comes from the work of Sih and his collaborators. In the course of his studies on the microbiological degradation of steroids, Sih observed that estrone and estradiol were very resistant to attack by *Nocardia restrictus*, which he showed degraded nonaromatic steroids readily (e.g., androstenedione) (Ap-83).[26] Since *N. restrictus* was also capable of using cholesterol as a sole carbon source, Sih conceived that a suitable cholesterol-like substrate might be devised which would suffer side-chain degradation to a 17-ketosteroid, followed by A-ring aromatization, to afford estrone. From earlier studies by Dodson and Muir (D-170, S-849) of the aromatization of 19-hydroxy-4-androstene-3,17-dione, taken together with these new observations, he concluded that 19-hydroxy-4-cholesten-3-one would be a suitable substrate for conversion to estrone. In the first tests reported, Sih and Wang (Ap-83) obtained

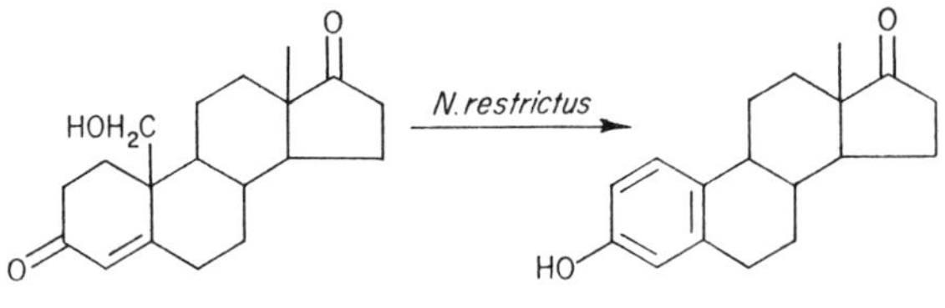

Estrone

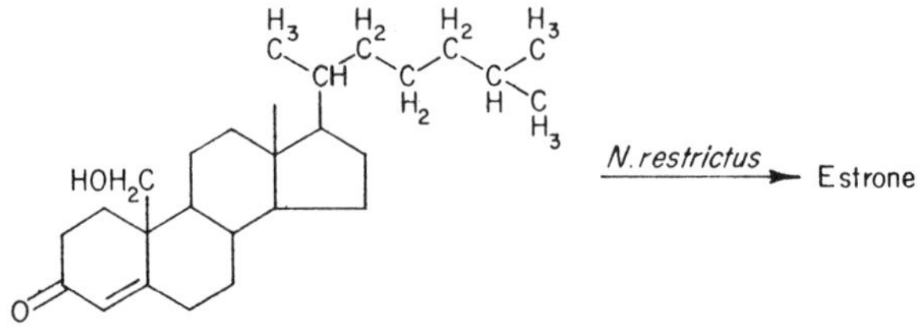

N. restrictus → Estrone

an 8% yield of estrone from the action of *N. restrictus*. Later improvements both in choice of substrate (19-hydroxycholesterol 3-acetate) and culture (CSD-10, an unidentified organism isolated from soil) have given estrone in 72% yield (Ap-81).

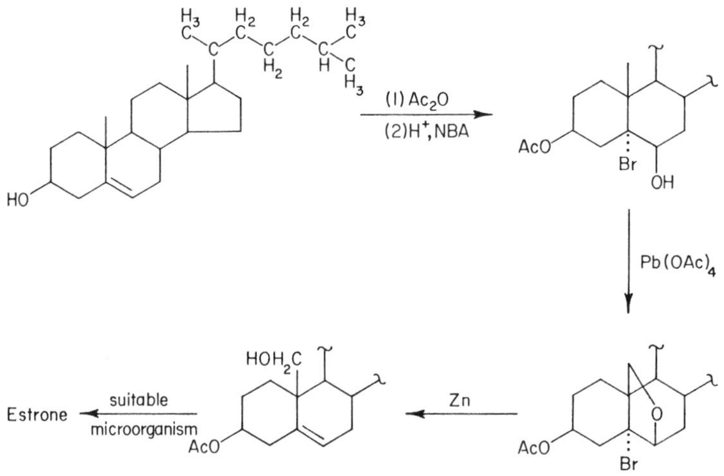

The work of Sih depended in great part on the earlier findings of Dodson and Muir (D-169, D-170, D-171, D-172), who established the fundamentals of microbial A-ring aromatization and B-ring cleavage of androstenedione and related structures.

Since 19-hydroxycholesterol 3-acetate is readily available from cholesterol by the illustrated synthesis, it is possible to predict that this method or one closely allied to it will supplant presently used technology for estrone manufacture to some degree. Estrone, in addition to its uses as a female hormone is a key intermediate for the commercial synthesis of many widely used contraceptive agents. It has been selling for a price in the range of $0.50-$1.00/gram (1965).

In a broader sense, Sih and others have shown that a number of microbial genera, e.g., *Pseudomonas, Mycobacterium, Corynebacterium, Proactinomyces*, etc., are also able to use cholesterol as a sole carbon source. It is reasonable to assume that representative species of all these genera will be useful for estrone production in the same way that *Nocardia restrictus* has been (Ap-95). Sih has also shown that substrates related in structure to cholesterol, like β-sitosterol, can act as sole carbon sources for *Nocardia*. By analogy with the cholesterol case, 19-hydroxy-4-stigmasten-3-one has been used to prepare estrone (Ap-83). The importance of this finding is that β-sitosterol is a somewhat cheaper and more readily available raw material than cholesterol. It occurs widely in plants and has been accumulated for many years by the Upjohn Company as a by-product of stigmasterol purification. Upjohn has been purchasing soybean sterols (from General Mills), from which they separate stigmasterol for use as a starting material in progesterone manufacture. The combined β-sitosterol-campesterol by-product, which is produced in considerably larger amounts than the desired stigmasterol, has been cast in large blocks and buried in the ground for want of a better application. This sterol mine, which up to now has had essentially no value, may become the major source for estrone in the future.

β-Sitosterol   Campesterol

This brief history has emphasized those discoveries which have had the greatest impact on commerce, because these findings were also pivotal in stimulating the subsequent studies of mechanism, and thereby had also the greatest impact on science. A more highly developed appreciation for the mechanistic basis of microbiological transformations was developed by Hayano, Talalay, Bloom, and Shull and their respective collaborators, and most recently by Ringold and Sih, all following the breakthrough discoveries and applications of the 1949-1954 period. Although this appreciation has until now had no decisive effect on the development of the field, which was shaped principally by the earlier, empirical findings, we may see in the work of Sih and his students the first instance of the successful synthesis of theory and practice.

In summary, microbiology applied to steroid chemistry has resulted in major contributions to technology, medicine, and science. Murray and Peterson, and Perlman and Fried laid the basis for the efficient application of microbiology to the synthesis of antiinflammatory steroids. The renewed interest in the field which they provoked led then to the one finding which was directly implicated in an improvement of therapy, namely, the application of microbial 1-dehydrogenation to the preparation of synthetic adrenocorticoid substances in our laboratory. Studies of mechanism which followed have clarified certain aspects of the stereochemistry and mechanism of microbial transformations and have established relationships with the larger corpus of knowledge of enzymatic chemistry.

CHAPTER II

CHEMICAL CLASSIFICATION OF MICROBIAL
TRANSFORMATIONS OF STEROIDS

THE ROLE OF ENZYMES IN MICROBIAL TRANSFORMATIONS

Practical Implications

Microbial transformations of steroids are part of the larger class of organic chemical reactions which are catalyzed by enzymes. The microorganism functions as a convenient source of the required enzymes and, in some cases, provides identifiable reagent species (cofactors) which act on the steroid in the presence of the enzyme or contribute to the regeneration of the active site on the enzyme. That the reactions are indeed enzymatic has been proved in several cases by the isolation of the crystalline enzyme from the microbial species and by the subsequent transformation of the steroid *in vitro*, using the crystalline enzyme and an added reagent. The resulting transformation was identical with that obtained employing the intact microbial system with the same substrate.

Hübener and collaborators have isolated a crystalline "20β-hydroxy steroid dehydrogenase" (H-410) from *Streptomyces hydrogenans*, which on incubation with a wide variety of 20-ketosteroids (S-803) afforded the corresponding 20β-hydroxy compounds in high yields, but at rates which varied with the functional groups elsewhere in the molecule. The enzyme also catalyzed the oxidation of 20β-hydroxysteroids back to 20-ketosteroids in the appropriate medium (H-410). NADH or another hydrogen source, e.g., NADPH, is required for the reduction (H-408), the stoichiometry of which is illustrated. In the microbial culture the NADH (or NAD$^+$) is regenerated by an appropriate reducing (or oxidizing) system already functioning to supply the other needs of the organism for the same coenzyme.

Another crystalline enzyme which has been studied is the isomerase of Kawahara, Wang, and Talalay (K-437, K-438), an induced enzyme isolated from *Pseudomonas testosteroni*. In this case, Malhotra and Ringold (Ap-44) have proved that the reaction

is entirely intramolecular and that no reagent or cofactor is required. The mechanism of this reaction is discussed in the section on isomerization.

An interesting example of an endogenous reagent class was described by Gale, and associates (G-291), who have shown that vitamin $K_{2(35)}$ can be isolated from *Bacillus sphaericus*. These investigators concluded on the basis of rate and inactivation-reactivation studies with a cellfree Δ^1-dehydrogenating system derived from *B. sphaericus* that vitamin $K_{2(35)}$ is the natural cofactor for this reaction. Talalay[27]

prefers to view the role of vitamin $K_{2(35)}$ as that of a secondary hydrogen acceptor with a flavin acting as the primary oxidizing agent.

The regeneration of the oxidized forms of coenzymes or reagents of the NAD, flavin, or vitamin K types depends in the final analysis on oxygen from the air. For efficient transformation to take place, oxygen must be placed in intimate contact with the cellular material so that diffusion into the cells can occur. The solubility of oxygen in aqueous media is limited, which means that efficient aeration and agitation may be required to maintain an oxygen-saturated medium. Shake-flask agitation may be inadequate, which sometimes explains the observed superiority of the aerated, internally agitated fermentor in achieving the desired transformation.

As a practical matter, the microorganism of choice provides the necessary enzymes and cofactors for the desired transformation. It has never been necessary to do more than provide the organism with a medium which is both suitable for growth and known to provide adequate levels of enzymes and cofactors by direct test with the steroid substrate in question. The knowledge of the enzymatic nature of these reactions, however, does serve to instruct the user to seek optimum pH and temperature conditions, known to be important factors in controlling enzymatic reaction rates. These optima are not necessarily the same as the optima for enzyme production, and so, the phasing of steroid transformations as a function of the microbial growth cycle can be quite important. An illustration of this idea is the separation of the growth of the organism from the transformation of the steroid. This is accomplished by filtration of the mycelium (S-871) [or spores (V-1048)] after growth under optimum conditions, followed by washing, and resuspension of the cellular material in a medium selected as optimum for transformation (often one in which there is no further microbial growth).

In some instances it has been proved that microorganisms produce enzymes for the transformation of steroids in response to a steroidal enzyme inducer contained in, or added to, the medium. *Septomyxa affinis* has been shown by Murray and Sebek (M-647) and Koepsell (K-456) to produce its 1-dehydrogenase best in the presence of 3-ketobisnor-4-cholen-22-al. This inducer did not, however, induce the enzyme(s) responsible for the Baeyer-Villiger type reaction which *S. affinis* is also known to cause.

On the other hand, in the many cases in which microbial cultures are grown in steroidfree media, filtered to separate the mycelium [e.g., *Curvularia lunata* (S-871)] or spores [e.g., *Aspergillus ochraceus* (V-1048)], and the resulting, cellular material resuspended in water to which steroid is *then* added, no enzyme induction is likely to be involved. The transformation with these resting cells most probably results from

[27] Talalay, P., Ann. Rev. Biochem. <u>34</u>, 347 (1965).

the action of enzyme synthesized during an earlier growth stage when exogenous steroid was absent.

To achieve optimum results with a given culture on a commercial level it is obviously desirable to know whether the required enzymes are induced or constitutive. In the laboratory it is judicious to avoid conclusions concerning a failure to transform until it is clear that this failure does not arise from inadequate conditions for enzyme induction.

Many organisms produce an overabundance of steroid-transforming enzymes, which lead, in turn, to multiple transformations. (e.g., *Rhizopus arrhizus* hydroxylates progesterone at both the 6β- and 11α-positions). It is sometimes desirable to suppress selectively the formation of the enzyme which leads to by-product formation or to inhibit the competing reactions after the enzymes have been formed. This has been accomplished in a few instances, but expectation for success in a previously untried case is modest at best. Dulaney, Stapley, and Hlavac (D-193) showed that the 6β-hydroxylating enzyme of *Aspergillus ochraceus* requires zinc ion for its formation. Growth of cultures in zinc-deficient media effectively abolished the 6β-hydroxylating ability of the culture without damaging its 11α-hydroxylating power. Sih and Weisenborn (S-897) have described the partial inhibition with cyanide ion of the 1-dehydrogenation of progesterone by *Nocardia restrictus*. In this case the major steroidal product became 9α-hydroxyprogesterone. Sih attributed the diminished rate of 1-dehydrogenation to inhibition of a coenzymatic oxidation-reduction system by the cyanide (S-885).

As far as we know, transformations of steroids, carried out with intact microbial cells, occur within the cell and not in the medium surrounding the cell.[28] To enter the cell the steroid being transformed must dissolve to some extent in the medium so that it can diffuse through the cell wall and into the enzyme-rich interior. The practical implication of this requirement is that solubility and rate of diffusion may become the rate-limiting factors for transformation. Most steroid substrates ordinarily employed have modest, though measurable, solubilities in water and in the aqueous media used for microbial culture. To ensure saturation of the medium and to minimize this rate-limiting effect, steroids are often introduced into reactions in micronized form or, more conveniently, in solution in a water-miscible solvent from which precipitation in very fine particles occurs upon dilution with the aqueous medium containing the microorganism.

The experimental findings summarized in this treatise may be interpreted reasonably to show that microbial enzymes are not highly substrate specific.[29] The alternate explanation for the diversity of substrates which a given species can transform is that the organism has a different enzyme for each new substrate. The latter explanation is much less satisfying, and no evidence has been adduced in its support.

THE CLASSES OF CHEMICAL REACTIONS

It is probably true that any class of enzyme-catalyzed reaction presently known, or to be discovered, will eventually find an illustration in the microbial transformation of steroids. At the present time examples of all of the listed categories are known.

[28]An apparent exception is the report of Krider, Cordon, and Wall (K-478) that cultures of Aspergilli and Penicillia produce an induced, extracellular saponase in response to the presence of saponins.

[29]Very recent transformations of steroids of 9β,10α-configuration ("retrosteroids") illustrate that there is no requirement for anything approaching a "natural" steroid structure. Cf. French Patents 1,372,850, 1,372,851, and 1,372,852 issued to N. V. Philips Co. of The Netherlands (see also Ap-16, Ap-92, Ap-93).

1.   Oxidation

    a. Hydroxylation
    b. Dehydrogenation
    c. Epoxidation
    d. Oxidation of alcohols to ketones or aldehydes
    e. Oxidation of ketones to esters or lactones
    f. Oxidation of sulfides to sulfoxides
    g. Oxidation of amines to ketones
    h. Oxidative degradation – a composite

2.   Reduction

    a. Reduction of ketones, aldehydes, and acids to alcohols
    b. Reduction of double bonds
    c. Reduction of bromide

3.   Esterification, amide formation, and hydrolysis

    a. Hydrolysis of esters to give steroid alcohols
    b. Esterification of steroid alcohols to esters
    c. Hydrolysis of oxides to alcohols
    d. Hydrolysis of acetals to steroid alcohols
    e. N-Acylation of amines

4.   Isomerization

5.   Miscellaneous addition, rearrangement, and elimination processes

6.   Resolution of d,l-mixtures

In the application of these reactions to problems in organic chemistry, one must recognize that each reaction class is likely to have substrate limitations. Superimposed on these limitations are the normal difficulties associated with reproducing experimental conditions in, and results derived from, biological systems. In the likely event of the absence of precisely applicable earlier findings, it is desirable to select an organism for the transformation being sought, which prior work has shown to be suitably nonspecific in substrate requirement. To help with these choices the tabular material presented in the later chapters has been provided.

The discussion of reaction classes with illustrations is offered here to give a concise overall view of the historical basis of the field, and its present condition, with particular reference to applications in organic chemistry and technology.

Oxidation

The most important single category of microbiological transformations is oxidation. The impetus for the recent, explosive development of the entire field came from the discovery of the fungal hydroxylation process by Murray and Peterson. At present, the only steroid transformations with continuing technological significance are hydroxylation and dehydrogenation, because of the ways in which they are used as parts of the syntheses of adrenocortical hormones and analogs. A promising new application, which remains to be proved on a commercial scale, is the oxidative degradation of sterols to estrone. This transformation may have great significance for the manufacture of estrogens, progestins, and related contraceptive drugs. The many other transformations which are described here have special interest for the insights they provide into the biochemistry of microbial systems and for their applications to difficult synthetic problems.

Hydroxylation

It is known that enzymatic hydroxylation processes for steroids observe these rules. (a)The entering oxygen atom is provided by gaseous oxygen (usually from the air), and not by water or any other oxygen-containing compound present in the medium prior to the initiation of the aeration process. (b) The stereochemistry of the carbon atom which is hydroxylated is always preserved. The newly formed hydroxyl group has the same configuration as had the hydrogen atom which occupied the same site prior to reaction. Thus, 11α-hydrogen is transformed into 11α-hydroxyl, 11β-hydrogen into 11β-hydroxyl, etc.

The evidence for the first rule comes from the work of Hayano, Dorfman, and associates. In the earliest studies they showed that beef adrenal homogenates could be used to 11β-hydroxylate a variety of steroids which were saturated at C-11 (H-372). When labeled oxygen and ordinary water were used in the incubation system, the label was incorporated in the resulting 11-oxygenated steroid. When oxygen-labeled water and ordinary oxygen were used, no label was introduced in the resulting 11-oxygenated product. It was also proved that $\Delta^{9(11)}$-steroids are not precursors of 11β-hydroxylated steroids produced using beef adrenal homogenates as the enzyme source.[30] Hayano, Dorfman, and collaborators showed later that the conclusions about the source of incorporated oxygen were equally true for *microbial* hydroxylations at 6β, 11α, 11β, 12β, 15α, 17α, and 21 (H-374, K-485).

Hayano, Peterson, and collaborators (H-371) and Corey, Gregoriou, and Peterson (C-137) demonstrated that stereochemistry is preserved at the carbon atom which undergoes substitution. The former carried out the 11α-hydroxylation of pregnane-3,20-dione-11α,12α-H³ with *Rhizopus nigricans* and showed that tritium was lost at the 11- but not at the 12-position. Complementary experiments by Corey, using 11β-deuterated pregnane-3,20-dione and *Rhizopus nigricans* afforded 11α-hydroxypregnane-3,20-dione-11β-H² (*label retained*). This proved that deuterium on carbon which becomes substituted will survive the oxygenation process if the deuterium configuration is not the same as that taken by the entering oxygen. Taken together, the cited studies provide the basis for rules (a) and (b), and no contradictory evidence has, as yet, been found.

Ringold[31] has put forward the interesting proposition that hydroxylation at 2β, 6β, 10β, and 17α, in systems capable of being enolized toward these positions, involves the enol as an activated species. Ringold then suggests that both the enolization process and oxygen introduction involve enzyme participation, the OH⁺ attacking

---

[30] Hayano, M., and Dorfman, R. I., J. Biol. Chem. **211**, 227 (1954).

[31] Hayano, M., in "Oxygenases" (O. Hayaishi, ed.), pp. 225-229. Academic Press, New York, 1962.

reagent being generated by the action of enzyme on oxygen. It seems to us that it may only be necessary to assume that enzyme is responsible for generating the enol. At this point undissociated oxygen can react with the enol, as has already been shown by Barton[32] for the nonenzymatic 17α-oxygenation of 20-ketopregnanes in the presence of strong base (t-butoxide ion) and oxygen. If our proposal were indeed true, the first product of this type of microbial oxygenation would be hydroperoxide, as observed by Barton in the chemical process, and not the hydroxy compound. Completion of the reaction would then require the enzyme-mediated reduction of hydroperoxide to hydroxyl (e.g., by NADPH). Stable compounds bearing hydroperoxide at the 10β- and 17α-positions have been described by Shapiro, Legatt, and Oliveto[33] and Barton,[32] respectively. These intermediates might be used to establish whether hydroperoxides can be reduced by a hydroxylating culture.

The rather surprising paucity of microbially induced 2α-, 6α-, 10α-, and 17β-hydroxylations is consistent with the thesis that the enzymes which lead to 2β-, 6β-, 10β-, and 17α-hydroxylations are concerned principally with the enolization process and that the oxygenation stage is controlled by purely chemical factors. It is well established, for example, that electrophilic chemical attack at the 6-position, under kinetic control, is directly entirely to 6β, even though the thermodynamically more stable species is the 6α-substituted product.

We believe it might be instructive to attempt the independent confirmation of the enolization hypothesis according to either one of the following schemes.

If a 17α-20-ketopregnane (e.g., 17α-deoxycorticosterone) is subjected to the action of a 17α-hydroxylating organism (e.g., *Trichothecium roseum*) the isolation of either a 17α-hydroxy-20-ketopregnene (e.g., Compound S) or a 17β-20-ketopregnane (e.g., deoxycorticosterone) would give important evidence for the enolization hypothesis. Since the formation of the former would be an apparent violation of the rule for

---

[32] Bailey, E. J., Elks, J., and Barton, D. H. R., Proc. Chem. Soc., p. 214 (1960).

[33] Shapiro, E. L., Legatt, T., and Oliveto, E. P., Tetrahedron Letters, p. 663 (1964).

preservation of configuration in the hydroxylation process, it would be best explained by the prior enolization of the starting material, thereby destroying configuration at the 17-position. If the oxygenation process were incomplete, it might still be possible to detect deoxycorticosterone formed by the reketonization of the enol to the normal, more stable 17β-form.

The second scheme involves the use of a 10α-3-keto-Δ^4-estrene as the substrate for what is normally a 10β-hydroxylation process. The reasoning follows the same line developed for the first scheme.

At those sites which cannot be activated by enolization, a mechanism for hydroxylation other than that proposed for 2β, 6β, 10β, and 17α must be operating. Hayano has enumerated the sequence of steps as follows: (a) oxygen activation, (b) substrate activation, if any, and oxygen transfer, and (c) regeneration of coenzymes. She suggested that the hydroxylation enzyme acts by providing the species OH^+ from oxygen, NADPH, and a proton. The resulting ion then displaces the hydrogen atom by OH, with retention of configuration, at the site in the steroid under attack.

While this hypothesis is interesting, it is not compelling. Since it is already well recognized that molecular oxygen can react with electron-rich centers or radicals without the intervention of an agent (e.g., enzyme) whose purpose might be to activate oxygen, one may argue that the oxygenation process at a saturated carbon atom seems to require activation of the C−H link only. One might therefore postulate that the function of the oxygenation enzyme is to confer upon the C−H link either radical or ionic character.

$$C-H \longrightarrow C-\!\cdot\!-\cdot\!-H$$
$$\longrightarrow C^{-}\!---H^{+} \quad (C^{+}\!---H^{-})$$

The dashed line symbolizes the bond which is incompletely broken, but polarized, as a result of enzyme action. Given one of these premises, one may then depict the oxygenation process in the illustrated terms below. The first product of such a reaction will be a hydroperoxide which then requires reduction with NADH or an equivalent

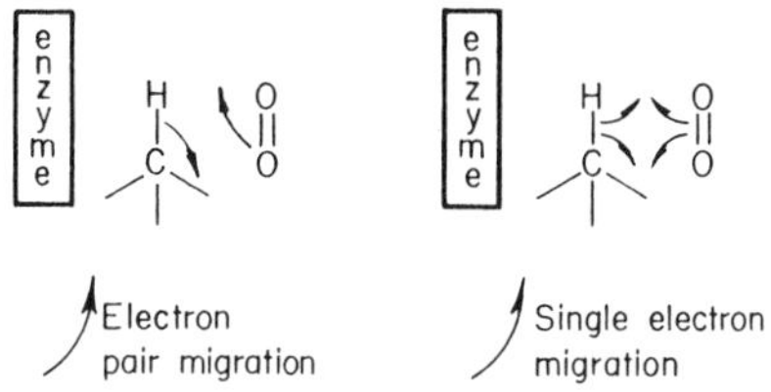

Electron
pair migration

Single electron
migration

reducing system.[34] This scheme embodies the 1 : 1 molar relationship of oxygen to NADH which Cooper, Estabrook, and Rosenthal[35] find exists for steroid hydroxylations.

$$\begin{array}{c} H \\ | \\ R-C-O-O-H \\ | \\ R' \end{array} + NADH + H^{+} \longrightarrow \begin{array}{c} H \\ | \\ R-C-OH \\ | \\ R' \end{array} + NAD^{+} + H_2O$$

One merit of the hydroperoxide proposal is that it might be subject to experimental test. As has already been pointed out, reasonably stable 10β- and 17α-hydroperoxides have been prepared. One might prepare 17α-hydroperoxyprogesterone as a reference and carrier substance to identify the hydroperoxy intermediate, if indeed one be formed, from the 17α-hydroxylation of C¹⁴-labeled progesterone with a suitable microorganism [e.g., *Cephalothecium roseum* (H-374)]. Incubation of a

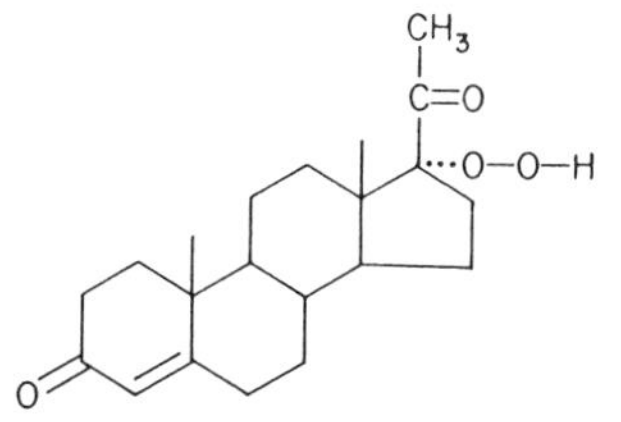

---

[34] S. Kaufman [in "Oxygenases" (O. Hayaishi, ed.), p. 170. Academic Press, New York, 1962] has summarized four proposals for a general mechanism of oxygenation, of which one is the formation and reduction of an intermediate hydroperoxide depicted here. B. Imelik [Compt. Rend. 226, 2082 (1948)] reported that Pseudomonas aeruginosa caused the transient formation of cyclohexane hydroperoxide when cyclohexane was the substrate.

[35] Cooper, D. Y., Estabrook, R. E., and Rosenthal, O., J. Biol. Chem. 238, 1320 (1963).

17α-hydroperoxy substrate with a 17α-hydroxylating culture would help to decide whether 17α-hydroperoxyl can indeed be reduced to 17α-hydroxyl under these conditions.

　　Sites of Reaction. 1α-Hydroxylation. Dodson, Goldkamp, and Muir (D-162, D-163) observed 1α-hydroxylation with *Penicillium* sp. on 4-androstene-3,17-dione, 5α-androstane-3,17-dione, and 3β-hydroxy-5-androsten-17-one (dehydroepiandrosterone). The organism also oxidizes the 3-hydroxyl and isomerizes the double bond,

but hydroxylation *precedes* these reactions. Few instances of 1α-hydroxylation are known. Some recent, interesting examples were given by Sax and associates (Ap-68). These are discussed in greater detail under 2α-hydroxylation.

　　1β-Hydroxylation. Greenspan and Schaffner, in association with our laboratory, reported 1β-hydroxylation of Compound S with *Rhizoctonia ferrugena* (G-315). The configuration of the entering group was established by Nussbaum (N-688, N-689)

through comparison with the same product synthesized from ruscogenin (1β-hydroxy-diosgenin), a sapogenin from *Ruscus aculeatus*. The same transformation has been seen in the androstane series with *Haplosporella* and *Xylaria* sp. (D-165). Nozaki has demonstrated 1β-hydroxylation of digitoxigenin (N-679) and 3β,14β, 21-trihydroxy-5β-pregnan-20-one (Ap-59) using *Absidia orchidis*. In these latter instances, the site of hydroxylation seems to be influenced by the configuration or nature of the substituent(s) at the 5- and/or 14-position, since *Absidia* hydroxylates principally at the 11α- and 11β-positions in the 4-pregnene series (H-334, N-682, S-841).

　　2α-Hydroxylation. This transformation was recently seen for the first time by Sax and co-workers (Ap-68) and Modelli (Ap-51). The former reported that *Nocardia corallina* afforded simultaneous 1α- and 2α-hydroxylation of ethisterone (I), 9α-fluoro-11β,17β-dihydroxy-17α-methyl-4-androsten-3-one (II) (together with oxidation at the 11-position), and 11β,16α,17α,21-tetrahydroxy-4-pregnene-3,20-dione 16,17-acetonide. No monohydroxylated products were isolated. Since *N. corallina* is normally (and in these cases, also) a Δ¹-dehydrogenating organism, Sax has proposed that the Δ¹-compounds are intermediates in these hydroxylation processes. This was proved with the Δ¹-containing compound (III), which was dihydroxylated under the same fermentation condition as (II). A different mechanism from those normally operating in hydroxylations must be involved. Sax has suggested for consideration a number of pathways from the Δ¹,⁴-dien-3-one to the 1α,2α-dihydroxy product. To his suggestions might also be added direct *cis* hydroxylation of the Δ¹ double bond in the way that chemical

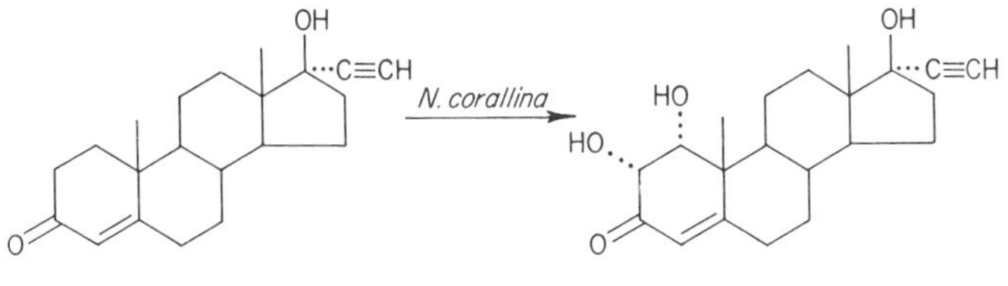

(I)

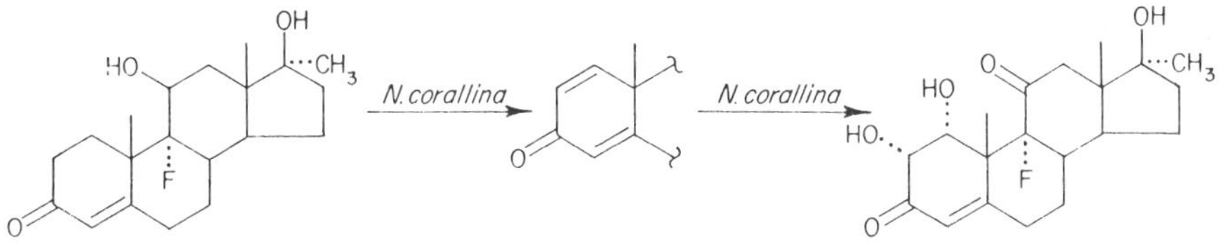

(II)   (III)

agents like permanganate do in related unsaturated systems. This question remains to be settled.

Modelli (Ap-51) has described the 2α-hydroxylation of 19-nortestosterone (17β-hydroxy-4-estren-3-one) and 19-nor-4-androstene-3,17-dione with *Nocardia italica*. These are the only examples of 2α-hydroxylation which arise from a "normal" mechanism of hydroxylation at a saturated carbon (as distinct from the Sax results).

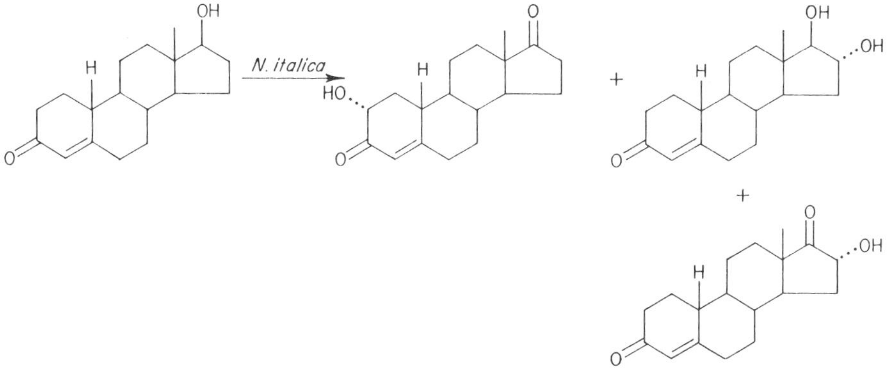

Satisfactory, conventional chemical methods for introducing the 2α-hydroxyl group are available.

2β-Hydroxylation. Simultaneous reports from our laboratories (G-315, H-383) and by Dodson, Goldkamp, and Muir (D-162, D-163) contained the first descriptions of 2β-hydroxylation. We found that *Streptomyces* sp. and *Rhizoctonia ferrugena* transformed Compound S. The Searle workers used 4-androstene-3,17-dione as the

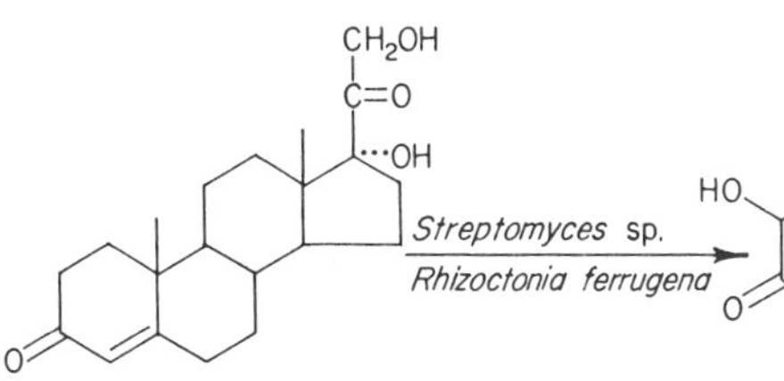

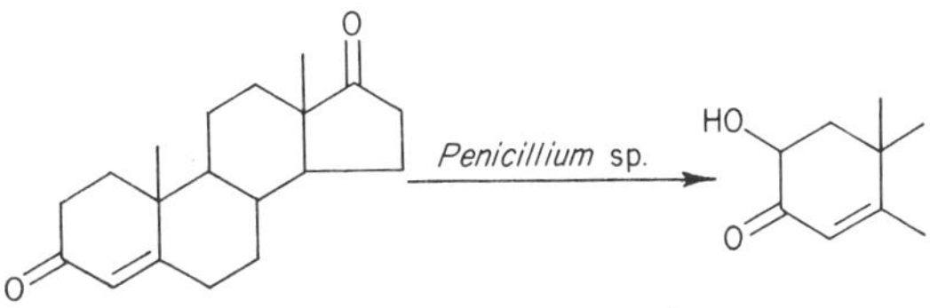

substrate with *Penicillium* sp.   In actuality, 2β-hydroxylation of progesterone (together with 16α-hydroxylation) was among the first hydroxylations which were carried
out (P-716, P-718), though no assignment was made until recently (Ap-42).

3-Hydroxylation.   No hydroxylation at the 3-position had been described until
very recently, when Cherry, Jones, and Meakins (Ap-12) reported the 3β,12β-dihy-
droxylation of 5-androsten-7-one by *Calonectria decora*.   Since all naturally occurring steroidal raw materials are oxygenated at the 3-position, the problem has had
only academic implications.

4-Hydroxylation.   No hydroxylation at the 4-position has been reported.[36]   The
usual substrates for microbial transformations are Δ[4]-3-ketosteroids.   The double
bond at the 4-position interferes with normal modes of hydroxylation, accounting for
the bulk of the experience to date. Saturated substrates might reasonably be hydroxylated at the 4-position with appropriate microorganisms. Substrates of the 3-keto-
5β-pregnane series might be preferred since their normal mode of enolization is toward the 4-position, thereby offering the possibility of more than one mechanism of
hydroxylation.

5α-Hydroxylation.   One organism has been reported to cause 5α-hydroxylation.
Pan and co-workers (P-706a) described the 5α-hydroxylation of A-nor-5α-pregnane-
2,20-dione by *Cokeromyces recurvatus*.   The paucity of observed 5α-hydroxylations
is probably a function of the infrequent use of 5α-steroids as substrates.

5β-Hydroxylation.   Hydroxylation at the 5β-position is limited to the 5β-hydrox-
ylation of cardiac aglycones (e.g., digitoxigenin) with *Absidia orchidis*, and was discovered by Nozaki (N-679).

---

[36] Cherry, Jones, and Meakins (Ap-12) have recently made a tentative assignment of
4β,12β-dihydroxylation to one of the products from the action of Calonectria decora on 5-andro-
sten-7-one.

6α-Hydroxylation. No microorganism is known to cause enzymatic 6α-hydroxylation.[37] Mallett, Fukuda, and Guynes (Ap-45; see also M-536, M-537) described the transformation of 3β-hydroxy-5-androsten-17-one into 6α(and 6β-)-hydroxy-1,4-androstadiene-3,17-dione with *Actinoplanes missouriensis*. These transformations depend on the *nonenzymatic* oxygenation of 5-androstene-3,17-dione, a reaction intermediate. *Actinoplanes missouriensis* seems to be deficient in Δ⁵-isomerase, which is an uncommon situation.

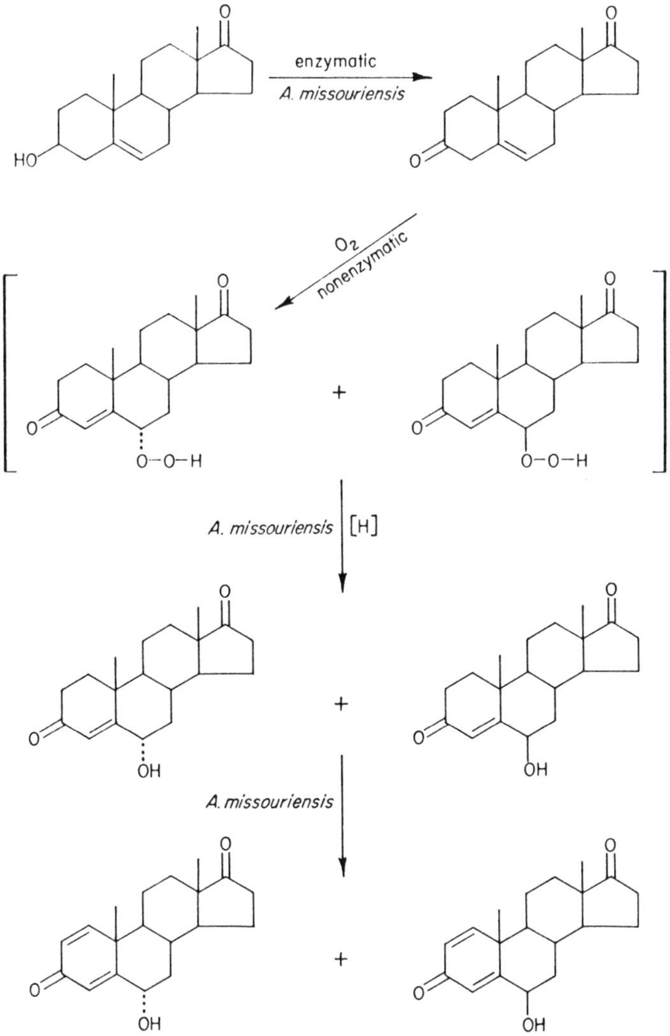

enzymatic
A. missouriensis

O₂
nonenzymatic

+

A. missouriensis [H]

+

A. missouriensis

+

+

+

O–O–H   O–O–H

OH   OH

OH   OH

---

[37] Bridgeman and associates have mentioned the transformation of 5α-androstan-17-one into the 1β,6α-diol by an unnamed organism in connection with structural studies of the product thus formed (Ap-6).

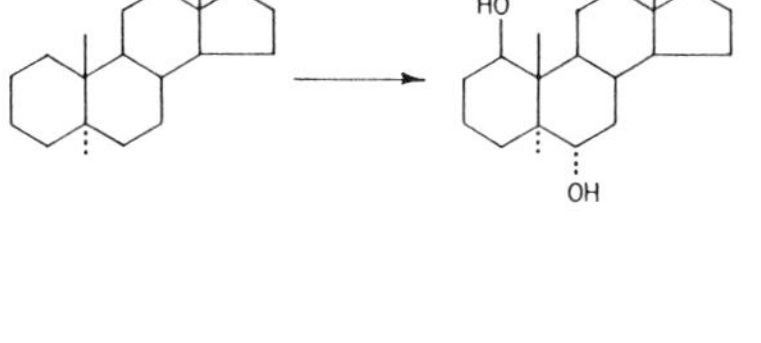

HO

OH

6β-Hydroxylation.   One of the most common transformations is 6β-hydroxyla-tion.   It is often, though not always, associated with 11α-hydroxylation, 14α-hydrox-ylation, or 17α-hydroxylation.   Peterson, Murray, and their collaborators discovered that *Rhizopus arrhizus* transforms progesterone into $6\beta,11\alpha$-dihydroxyprogesterone (M-601, M-616, P-729), 17α-hydroxyprogesterone into $6\beta,17\alpha$-dihydroxyprogesterone (M-580), and Compound S into $6\beta,17\alpha,21$-trihydroxy-4-pregnene-3,20-dione (M-601, M-615, P-725).   They reported the action of many other genera of the order

Mucorales on a variety of steroidal substrates, observing 6β-hydroxylation as a fre-quent occurrence (M-601).   From our own experience, corticosteroids and their ana-logs (e.g., prednisone) are 6β-hydroxylated efficiently by *Chaetomium* sp. (C-108).

7α-Hydroxylation.   This transformation was first seen by Meystre, Vischer, and Wettstein with *Peziza* sp. on deoxycorticosterone (M-585) and by Fried and asso-ciates with *Phycomyces blakesleeanus* on progesterone (F-285, F-286).

The questions of assignment of configuration at the 7-position have been reviewed thoroughly by Tweit, Goldkamp, and Dodson (T-1037).   From their analysis of rota-tional data, together with appropriate chemical information, unambiguous assign-ments can be made.

7β-Hydroxylation.   The first microbial hydroxylation, reported by Kramli and Horvath (K-474), was that at the 7 ξ-position by *Proactinomyces* sp. on cholesterol. Although this may have been 7β, no unambigious assignment can be made.   Kahnt and collaborators (K-433) reported the unequivocal 7β-hydroxylation of 21-hydroxy-5α-pregnane-3,20-dione by *Rhizopus* sp.   Some confusion, which crept into the later assignments of 7α- and 7β-hydroxy-3-keto-Δ^4-steroids, was resolved by Tweit, Goldkamp, and Dodson (T-1037).

8α-Hydroxylation. There is no 8α-hydrogen in the normal steroid structure. Considerations of mechanism therefore rule out 8α-hydroxylation as a reasonable event. With steroids of abnormal skeleton, bearing an 8α-hydrogen atom, there is no a priori reason for excluding the possibility of 8α-hydroxylation. Such a reaction remains to be discovered.

8β-Hydroxylation. Kondo and his collaborators have observed the only 8β-hydroxylation described thus far (K-472, T-1014), from the action of *Cercospora melonis* on Compound S. Earlier transformations, for which 8β-hydroxylation was

proposed as one of several alternatives [e.g., *Helicostylum piriforme* on Compound S (M-601)], have since been shown to be 9α-hydroxylations.

9α-Hydroxylation. This transformation was observed first by Peterson and Murray (E-204, M-601) with *Helicostylum piriforme* on Compound S, although the choice of assignment between 8β and 9α was not made. Schubert and associates (S-815) developed chemical methodology from which a more precise assignment could be made and deduced thereby the 9α-hydroxylation or progesterone by *Circinella* sp.

Dodson and Muir provided the first completely unambiguous evidence for both position and configuration (D-172) in the 9α-hydroxylation of progesterone by *Nocardia* sp. The formation of the illustrated 3,9-oxide can only occur if the hydroxyl at the 9-position is α.

The 9α-hydroxylation has considerable theoretical and practical significance. Dodson and Muir (D-169 – D-171) recognized it as a key stage in a major path of microbial degradation of the steroid nucleus. The cleavage of ring B results from a

spontaneous reverse aldol reaction, following 1-dehydrogenation and 9α-hydroxylation. Bacterial 1-dehydrogenating genera have, by and large, been shown to act also as 9α-hydroxylators. Examples include *Nocardia* (D-172), *Pseudomonas* (D-171), *Arthro-bacter*, or *Corynebacterium* sp. (C-138, D-171), and others. As a consequence, an inherent hazard in the use of these cultures as 1-dehydrogenators for the preparation of synthetic adrenocorticoids and other hormonal agents has been the loss of product through 9α-hydroxylation and degradation. This phenomenon has been attributed generically to a "destructase" (F-230), and techniques for suppression of the secondary reactions have been suggested. The quinonoid species used for this purpose probably act by suppressing 9α-hydroxylation (or the formation of the required enzyme).

It is probably also true that the many bacteria, which can use cholesterol (or steroids generally) as a sole carbon source, break down the steroid nucleus by approximately the same sequence of reactions. This will be taken up in greater detail in a later section devoted to degradation.

9β-Hydroxylation. On mechanical grounds, steroids with conventional skeletons should not give this transformation. "Retro" steroids [38] of the 9β,10α-configuration, however, could lead to 9β-hydroxy products. Microbiological transformation studies with representative structures of this type have been made at the Phillips-Duphar Laboratories.[39] In the light of the interesting hormonal activities found within this class (e.g., dydrogesterone-progestational agent) further developments may reasonably be anticipated.

Dydrogesterone

10α-Hydroxylation. Some 19-norsteroids with the 10α-configuration have been prepared.[40] These have yet to be oxygenated microbiologically.

---

[38] Westerhof, P., and Reerink, E. H., Rec. Trav. Chim. 79, 771 (1960).

[39] French Patent 1,372,851 (Sept. 18, 1964); see also Ap-16.

[40] Wenger, R., Dutler, H., Wehrli, H., Schaffner, K., and Jeger, O., Helv. Chim. Acta 45, 2420 (1962).

10β-Hydroxylation. Peterson, Murray, and their collaborators (M-642, P-708) described the 10β-hydroxylation of 19-nortestosterone by *Rhizopus nigricans*. The major product, however, was 11α,17β-dihydroxy-4-estren-3-one. More recently,

DeFlines and co-workers (D-150) reported the efficient use of *Botrytis paeoniae* and other organisms for uncomplicated 10β-hydroxylation of the same substrate.

11α-Hydroxylation. One of the first hydroxylations described and also one of the most important for industry is 11α-hydroxylation. Peterson and Murray discovered 11α-hydroxylation by *Rhizopus* sp. and other members of the Mucorales order, using a wide variety of substrates (e.g., progesterone, 17α-hydroxyprogesterone,

Compound S), as part of a rational program to improve the synthesis of cortisone (M-601). This goal was realized through their work and that of the Levin and Hogg chemical groups at Upjohn. The hydrocortisone synthesis via the 11α-hydroxylation of progesterone remains the cornerstone of the most efficient method for the preparation of a variety of natural and synthetic adrenal hormones. The price of natural glucocorticoids has fallen from in excess of \$200/gram (1949) to about \$0.45/gram (1965) as a result of the perfection of both the chemical and microbiological stages of the hydrocortisone synthesis.

Subsequently, it was shown that 11α-hydroxylation is one of the most common transformations. The better cultures may be identified in Table I, "Transformation by Products," by the high yields recorded for the illustrated conversions (e.g., 11α-hydroxylated products in the $C_{21}H_{30}O_3$, $C_{21}H_{30}O_4$, and $C_{21}H_{30}O_5$ series).

11β-Hydroxylation. Although many claims for 11β-hydroxylation are made in the literature, very few organisms afford a clean reaction in high yield. The first recorded 11β-hydroxylation, by Colingsworth, Brunner, and Haines (C-134), was the transformation of Compound S into hydrocortisone with *Streptomyces fradiae*. The yield with this organism was very low. The first practical 11β-hydroxylation processes were those of Shull, Kita, and Davisson (S-871, S-875) using *Curvularia lunata* and those of Hanson, Mann, and co-workers (H-339, M-556) using *Cunninghamella blakesleeana*. The former has continued to be important for the commercial production of hydrocortisone from Compound S, as practiced by Charles Pfizer, Inc. and its licensees (particularly Schering A.G.). In contrast with the 11α-hydroxylation of progesterone by *Rhizopus nigricans*, which affords yields in excess of 90%, 11β-hydroxylation of Compound S by *Curvularia lunata* has rarely been reported to be better than 60-65%. Further improvement of this yield or a related 11β-hydroxylation would have significant consequences for industry.

12α-Hydroxylation. This rare transformation has been seen in our laboratories, also by Fried and Thoma and by Kondo and Tori in rather special cases. We observed that testosterone was transformed into 12α,17β-dihydroxy-4,14-androstadien-3-one in very low yield by *Wojnowicia graminis* (H-381). The presumed precursor of the 12α-hydroxylated product is the 12α,14α-diol (in view of the formation of 14α-hydroxy-4-androstene-3,17-dione in the fermentation). The required elimination of the 14α-hydroxy

group to give the Δ^{14}-unsaturation is logically, though not necessarily, an artifact from the processing of the fermentation. Fried and Thoma (F-277) observed that fermentation of 9(11)-dehydroprogesterone with *Colletotrichum phomoides, Thamnidium elegans,* or *Aspergillus nidulans* gave 6β,12α-dihydroxy-4,9(11)-pregnadiene-3,20-dione as a major product. This product was transformed in part into the corresponding 9β,11β-oxide, presumably through the action of an 11β-hydroxylating enzyme. Kondo and Tori (K-473) reported the 12α-hydroxylation of 9α-hydroxy-4-androstene-3,17-dione by *Cercospora melonis*. The same culture also transformed 4-androstene-3,17-dione to the same 9α,12α-dihydroxy product.

12β-Hydroxylation. First reported by A. Schubert, Siebert, and collaborators by the action of *Calonectria decora* on progesterone and 15α-hydroxyprogesterone (S-814; see also S-810, S-816, S-817), this transformation remains infrequent with conventional 3-keto-Δ^4-steroidal substrates (D-152, T-1036). The reaction is somewhat

more common with cardiac aglycone substrates. The earliest examples of the latter
were described by Gubler and Tamm (G-320, T-977, T-979) and include the 12β-
hydroxylation of digitoxigenin to digoxigenin by *Fusarium lini*.

Hydroxylation at the 15α-position often co-occurs with that at the 12β-position.

13-Hydroxylation. No studies with 13-demethylsteroids have been reported.

14α-Hydroxylation. The earliest example of 14α-hydroxylation was reported
by Murray and Peterson (M-601) with *Helicostylum piriforme* on Compound S. This
transformation is quite common with progesterone, deoxycorticosterone and Compound S. *Mucor* sp. are among the more effective 14α-hydroxylators (E-204, M-614,
M-635, T-980).

14β-Hydroxylation. No reports of transformations with steroids bearing a 14β-H
(C-D *cis* ring fusion) have been recorded. Cardiac aglycones customarily contain a
14β-hydroxyl group. Microbiological conversion studies with 14β,17α-progesterone or
a related substrate might conceivably lead into the former series.

15α-Hydroxylation. This hydroxylation was discovered by Fried and colleagues
with *Colletotrichum antirrhini* on progesterone (F-285, F-287, F-288) and by Meystre,
Vischer, and Wettstein with *Gibberella baccata* on deoxycorticosterone (M-585, U-1043,
W-1087). It can be accomplished efficiently with a variety of substrates (B-58, C-139,
D-158, G-319, T-980).

15β-Hydroxylation. The first reports of 15β-hydroxylation were from Fried and associates with *Phycomyces blakesleeanus* on progesterone (F-285 – F-288) and from Meystre, Vischer, and Wettstein with *Lenzites abietina* on deoxycorticosterone (M-585, W-1087). The 15β-hydroxylation of Compound S goes especially well with *Bacillus megaterium* (H-382).

16α-Hydroxylation. One of the earliest examples of microbial hydroxylation, reported by Perlman, Titus, and Fried (P-718) in 1952, was the 16α-hydroxylation of progesterone by an actinomycete later shown to be *Streptomyces argenteolus*. This

class of hydroxylation has been studied carefully subsequent to the discovery of triamcinolone, a widely used antiinflammatory steroid. (The manufacture of triamcinolone incorporates more microbiological manipulation than that of any other steroid presently in commerce.) Many streptomycetes (e.g., *S. roseochromogenus*) are not very substrate specific, 16α-hydroxylating a wide range of steroids from testosterone (F-288) and 1-dehydrotestololactone (P-706, T-1000), on the one hand, to 9α-fluorohydrocortisone (G-297, S-912, T-1002), on the other, with good efficiency in many instances.

16β-Hydroxylation. This transformation has been seen infrequently. It was reported from our laboratory using *Wojnowicia graminis* with testosterone (H-381). Dodson and Mizuba (D-166) have described the 16β-hydroxylation of androstenedione

(minor)   (major)

with *Corticium centrifugum.* In their discussion they make the point that introduction of the 16β-hydroxyl group in their (and our) case cannot be ascribed unambiguously to a 16β-hydroxylation reaction. They suggest the illustrated, alternative path, which proceeds via 16α-hydroxylation, rearrangement, and reduction. Evidence for this

(I)

proposal is that the 16-keto-17β-hydroxy intermediate (I) was isolated from the fermentation by Dodson and Mizuba. In our case, *all* the intermediates between testosterone and 16β-hydroxytestosterone required by the Dodson-Mizuba proposal were isolated from the reaction mixture.

Nawa and co-workers (N-651) have described the 16β-hydroxylation of digitoxigenin to gitoxigenin by *Helicostylum piriforme.* Identification was by paper chromatography. This example cannot be accommodated within the Dodson-Mizuba proposal.

H. piriforme

17α-Hydroxylation. This transformation was considered at one time to have potential importance as a stage in the preparation of adrenocorticoids bearing the dihydroxyacetone side chain. Meystre, Vischer, and Wettstein (M-584) described the 17α-hydroxylation of deoxycorticosterone by *Trichothecium roseum*. A strain of the same culture with similar properties (*Cephalothecium roseum*) was reported at

T. roseum

about the same time by Meister and co-workers (M-581). The Meister culture was distinguished from the Meystre culture by its ability to 11α-hydroxylate also.

In practice, chemical methods of 17α-hydroxylation have turned out to be superior to microbiological methods. This fact, combined with the relative rarity of 17α-hydroxylating species, has led to neglect of serious study of this reaction, and it is not employed for other than research applications today.

17β-Hydroxylation. Substrates with which this reaction might be observed have not been studied. There has been little incentive to look for this reaction since good chemical methods are available for the synthesis of 17β-hydroxy-17α-pregnanes and 17β-hydroxyandrostanes.

18-Hydroxylation. For a time some interest was attached to the search for an 18-hydroxylator. After Reichstein and co-workers [41] showed that aldosterone, one of the adrenal hormones regulating salt metabolism in the human, was substituted at the

Aldosterone

18-position, a convenient synthetic route to this compound was sought. Several brilliant and versatile chemical solutions to the problem were found, which have resulted

---

[41] Simpson, S. A., Tait, J. F., Wettstein, A., Neher, R., von Euw, J., Schindler, O., and Reichstein, T., Helv. Chim. Acta **37**, 1200 (1954).

in greatly diminished interest in this potential application for microbiological transformations. Kondo and Tori (K-473) reported the first 18-hydroxylation with *Cercospora* (*Corynespora*) *melonis* on androstenedione and 9α-hydroxyandrostendione.

Kondo, Mitsugi, and Tori (Ap-38) extended this finding to develop a synthesis of aldosterone, using *Corynespora cassiicola*.

(I)

(II)   Aldosterone

The conversion of 18-hydroxycorticosterone (I) into the 11,18-oxide (II) was accomplished by chemical means. This step, taken together with the two microbiological stages, completes a novel partial synthesis of aldosterone from corticosterone.

19-Hydroxylation. Hasegawa and Takahashi (H-347) first described the 19-hydroxylation of Compound S with *Corticium sasakii*. The structure was established by Hagiwara (H-326). This hydroxylation remains quite rare.

The 19-hydroxylation process has become an object of renewed interest in the light of the findings of Sih concerning the efficient microbial conversion of 19-hydroxycholesterol 3-acetate to estrone. Excellent chemical methods, however, which were developed during the search for techniques of 18-oxygenation, exist for the introduction of the 19-hydroxyl group. It is unlikely that microbiology will make an important contribution to this aspect of the new estrone technology.

CH₂OH
|
C=O
···OH

C. sasakii →

CH₂OH
|
C=O
···OH

HOH₂C

O

O

Hydroxylation at the 20- and 22-positions and beyond. The 20-position is usually occupied by a carbonyl group in the commonly employed pregnane substrates and is thereby not available for reaction; C-22 and beyond are absent. With the work of Sih, interest has revived in C_{27} and higher sterol substrates.

Working with two *Nocardia* sp., Sih has shown that cholesterol is degraded by fission between C-24 and C-25, C-22 and C-23, and C-17 and C-20.[41a]

One may speculate that hydroxylations at C-26 and perhaps at C-24 and C-22 are involved in the degradative sequence, although Sih has not chosen to reach these conclusions as yet, nor is there any evidence in their support. His evidence and proposals are discussed in greater detail in the section on degradation.

Mammalian hydroxylations of cholesterol at C-20 and C-22 have been demonstrated.[41b] It would not be surprising to find microorganisms with the same capacities.

21-Hydroxylation. Just as 17α-hydroxylation is of interest for corticoid synthesis, so too is 21-hydroxylation. Here again, excellent chemical methods were available for oxygenation which inhibited any continuing, deep study of this problem. The microbial process was first shown by Meystre, Vischer, and Wettstein (M-584) using *Ophiobolus herpotrichus* on progesterone and 17α-hydroxyprogesterone, among

CH₃
|
C=O
···OH

O. herpotrichus →

CH₂OH
|
C=O
···OH

O

O

others. This hydroxylation was later applied to the total synthesis of aldosterone, as an ingenious method of simultaneously introducing the required 21-oxygen function and resolving the *d,l*-mixture (W-1102). Only the natural form of the starting material was transformed.

OH CH₃
| |
O——CH C=O

d,l-

O. herpotrichus → *d-*

OH CH₂OH
| |
O——CH C=O

+ *l*- starting material

O

O

[41a] Sih, C. J., Wang, K. C., and Tai, H. H., J. Am. Chem. Soc. 89, 1956 (1967); Sih, C. J., Tai, H. H., and Tsong, Y. Y., ibid., p. 1957.

[41b] Chaudhuri, A. C., Harada, Y., Shimizu, K., Gut, M., and Dorfman, R. I., J. Biol. Chem. 237, 703 (1962).

Dehydrogenation

Following the discovery of 1-dehydrogenation by Fried, Thoma, and Klingsberg (F-284) and Vischer and Wettstein (V-1056), alternative formulations of the path for this reaction were presented (V-1053, W-1087). Levy and Talalay, from studies with

the dehydrogenating enzyme mixture isolated from *Pseudomonas testosteroni*, concluded that direct dehydrogenation (no intermediate hydroxylation) is the most probable path with this organism (L-509). The evidence was that the *in vitro* dehydrogenation reaction did not require oxygen, whereas the enzymatic hydroxylation process with steroids has been shown to require oxygen. They also demonstrated that phenazine methosulfate is an efficient oxidizing agent for Δ^4-3-ketosteroids, when acting in concert with an enzyme preparation from *Pseudomonas testosteroni* under anaerobic

conditions.[42] These results, together with the observations of Levy and Talalay that suitable 1α- and 1β-hydroxylated substrates (e.g., 1α-hydroxy-4-androstene-3,17-dione) were not converted to 1-dehydro species with the same enzyme mixture in the presence of phenazine methosulfate, can be taken to affirm the dehydrogenation mechanism and to exclude the hydroxylation-dehydration mechanism.

The dehydrogenation mechanism is also supported by the work of Gale and associates (G-291). They showed that *Bacillus sphaericus* contained a quinone, characterized by them as vitamin $K_{2(35)}$, which was essential for the dehydrogenation of hydrocortisone to prednisolone. In a cellfree preparation derived from *B. sphaericus*, photoinactivation of vitamin $K_{2(35)}$ destroyed the dehydrogenation power of the system. The system was reactivated fully by the addition of vitamin $K_{2(35)}$ or related quinoid structures (e.g., menadione or hexahydrocoenzyme Q). Gale and collaborators concluded that vitamin $K_{2(35)}$ is the cofactor for dehydrogenation with *B. sphaericus*.

---

[42] Other oxidizing agents which were ineffective in this system were NAD, NADP, riboflavin monophosphate, FAD, ferricyanide ion, and cytochrome c. The inference should not be made that in vivo transformation with Ps. testosteroni can be run anaerobically with any degree of efficiency. Since the necessary oxidizing reagent species are rarely present in stoichiometric quantities, oxygen is required to regenerate the natural equivalent(s) of phenazine methosulfate.

From his studies with *Ps. testosteroni*, Talalay[43] favors the views that flavins are required intermediates in the oxidation-reduction chain and that they are truly coenzymatic, whereas quinones are, more likely, secondary oxidizing agents, playing their role later in the oxidation-reduction cycle. For the present, at least, there is no evidence for a unity of mechanism in the diverse microbial dehydrogenation processes.

Most recently, Iida and colleagues (Ap-31) have prepared a cellfree enzyme system with reversible Δ^1-hydrogenase-dehydrogenase activity. The enzyme mixture was isolated from cultures of *Bacterium cyclo-oxydans*, and the production of enzyme was promoted by the addition of steroidal inducers (e.g., 1,4-androstadiene-3,17-dione).[44] The dehydrogenation reaction was stimulated by a quinone (menadione) and hydrogenation by NADH. The activities could not be separated by enzyme fractionation techniques. Further detailed studies with *B. cyclo-oxydans* might throw more light on dehydrogenation mechanisms.

The stereochemistry of the microbial dehydrogenation process at the 1- and 2-positions has been studied with one microorganism, *Bacillus sphaericus*, by Ringold, Hayano, Stefanovic, and co-workers (H-373, R-769). The relevant indirect evidence is that substrates with 1β- or 2α-substituents are dehydrogenated successfully by *B. sphaericus*, whereas those with 1α- or 2β-substituents are not. From these findings

R = OH or CH$_3$

it was inferred that the 1α- and 2β-hydrogen atoms are required for the microbial dehydrogenation to take place (H-373).

This conclusion was supported by the observation (R-769) that 1β-deuterium largely survives the dehydrogenation process, whereas 1α-deuterium is lost.

---

[43] Talalay, P., Ann. Rev. Biochem. **34**, 347 (1965).

[44] The ability of B. cyclo-oxydans to produce both hydrogenase and dehydrogenase activity was first recognized by Goodman, May, and Smith (G-296).

Ringold, Hayano, and Stefanovic then proposed that the dehydrogenation process takes place via the illustrated reaction sequence, the first step of which is the enzyme-mediated enolization of the 3-ketone toward the 2-position. This is followed by hydride transfer of the α-hydrogen at the 1-position to the coenzyme, with subsequent collapse

of the enzyme-substrate complex. That enolization occurs readily in the fermentation medium was established by isotope exchange studies. This evidence was then used to support the contention that enolization is a necessary stage in the dehydrogenation process. The failure of the attempted dehydrogenation of 5β-androstane-3, 17-dione by *B. sphaericus,* in contrast to the successful dehydrogenation of 5α-androstane-3,17-dione, was explained in terms of the normal modes of enolization of the two substrates. The former enolizes toward the 4-position and thereby fails to provide the necessary intermediate for elimination of the hydrogen at the 1α-position. The latter enolizes toward the 2-position, leading to the completion of the anticipated reaction.

A subsequent refinement of this proposal has been made by Jerussi and Ringold (Ap-33). The crux of the refinement is that the enzyme which promotes enolization is also implicated in the oxidation-reduction process, in that it has bound to it a flavin or some other redox system, which acts to abstract hydride ion from 1α as the second stage of the process. Jerussi and Ringold illustrated the reaction system as follows:

(A = proton donor, B= proton acceptor, C = hydride acceptor)

The conclusions were derived from the study of deuterium isotope effects on reaction rates at the 1α- and 2β-positions.

These proposals are very satisfying in many ways. An obstacle, however, to the extension of the proposed mechanism to all microbiological dehydrogenation of 3-ketosteroids at the 1-position is the work of Fonken and Murray (F-253). They showed that the 20-ketal of 5β-pregnane-3,11,20-trione is dehydrogenated at the 1-position by *Septomyxa affinis.* Either the illustrated 3-keto-5β-pregnane (I) enolizes abnormally

(I)

P. 40

(toward 2- instead of toward 4-), or the Ringold-Hayano-Stefanovic proposal does not extend to *S. affinis* and organisms which behave like it. This qualification applies only to the enolization part of the hypothesis for the time being. It might be desirable to establish the direction of enolization of the 3-ketone in (I). A more ambitious undertaking, which could be justified if enolization is indeed toward the 4-position, would be to show the stereochemistry of hydrogen abstraction in the Fonken-Murray case by appropriate labeling techniques.

Sites of Reaction. Dehydrogenation has been reported at the 1-, 4-(5α- and 5β-), 7-, 9(11), 14-, and 16-positions. The dehydrogenation reaction was described first by Horvath and Kramli in 1947 (H-406, H-407) for the conversion of cholesterol into 7-dehydrocholesterol with *Azotobacter* sp. No other examples of this reaction have been

reported, and this method is of significance only as a milestone in the evolution of microbial transformations.

In 1953, after the resurgence of interest in the field, Fried, Thoma, and Klingsberg (F-284) and Vischer and Wettstein (V-1056) discovered the 1-dehydrogenation reaction. The former, using *Cylindrocarpon radicicola* with progesterone, testosterone, and Compound S showed that in all instances 1-dehydrotestololactone was

R = OH (R' = H), R = $\overset{\text{O}}{\overset{\|}{\text{C}}}$—CH$_3$ (R' = H), R = $\overset{\text{O}}{\overset{\|}{\text{C}}}$—CH$_2$OH (R' = OH)

formed in about 50% yield. *Streptomyces lavendulae*, with progesterone, on the other hand, gave a mixture of 1,4-androstadiene and 17β-hydroxy-1,4-androstadien-3-one.

Vischer and Wettstein reported the use of *Fusarium solani* and *Fusarium cau-casicum* to dehydrogenate 4-androstene-3,17-dione and related C_{19} species to 1,4-

androstadiene-3,17-dione.   Progesterone and deoxycorticosterone were also dehydro-genated and degraded to the same product.   Saturated substrates and 3β-hydroxy-Δ^5-

steroids were transformed to 1,4-androstadiene-3,17-dione, as well, but in poorer yield.   Wix and Albrecht (W-1116, W-1118) investigated the use of *F. caucasicum* as a practical tool for the preparation of 1,4-androstadiene-3,17-dione, which has been an important precursor in the manufacture of estrone.

After the discovery of prednisone and prednisolone through the use of *Coryne-bacterium simplex* (N-671) with cortisone and hydrocortisone, respectively, many 1-dehydrogenating cultures were described.   Among the most significant of these were *Bacillus sphaericus* (S-942), *Bacterium cyclo-oxydans* (K-480), and *Septomyxa affinis* (M-573), all of which have been or are being used for the manufacture of antiinflam-matory steroids.

In general, preferred substrates for 1-dehydrogenation are Δ^4-3-ketosteroids. Saturated 3-ketosteroids have also been used, but chemical methods of dehydrogena-tion are usually superior to microbial methods for these substrates.

The 1-dehydrogenation reaction is also a very convenient way to aromatize a 19-norsteroid (C-128, H-386). Ordinarily, the reverse sequence has been the

economically significant one, insofar as phenols have been the precursors of 19-nor-steroids. The total synthesis of 19-norsteroids, however, by Velluz and his collaborators at Roussel[45] has made these compounds available by a route independent of aromatic antecedents. Hence the microbial synthesis of steroidal phenols can become more than academic.

Dehydrogenation at the 4-position was first described by Vischer and Wettstein (V-1056) with the conversion of 5α-androstane-3,17-dione and related species into 1,4-androstadiene-3,17-dione by *Fusarium solani*. This class of transformation has

also been reported in the pregnane series by Stoudt and associates (S-943) with *Nocardia blackwellii* and by Coronelli, Kluepfel, and Sensi (C-138, K-451) with *Corynebacterium simplex*, and in the bile acid series by Hayakawa and collaborators (H-359, H-365, T-975) with *Streptomyces* and *Corynebacterium* sp. The work of Coronelli, Kluepfel, and Sensi raises an interesting problem. In each of the illustrated cases the A-ring saturated substrate is transformed into a 1,4-diene[46] as the

---

[45] Chem. Eng. News **42**, 42 (1964).

[46] With concomitant 9α,11α-epoxidation of the $\Delta^{9,11}$ substrate.

major product. With 16β-methyl-17α,21-dihydroxy-5α-pregnane-3,11,20-trione, the minor product is the monounsaturated Δ^1-compound, which is implicated as an intermediate in the formation of the 1,4-diene (K-451). From 16β-methyl-17α,21-dihydroxy-$\Delta^{9(11)}$-5α-pregnene-3,20-dione 21-acetate, the products of dehydrogenation are the $\Delta^{1,4}$- and the Δ^4-species. The Δ^4-species might be formed either as a primary product of reaction from the A-ring saturated substrate or as a product of reduction of the $\Delta^{1,4}$-diene (G-296). If the former were true, it would present yet another dilemma with which the enolization hypothesis of the microbial dehydrogenation process must contend.

Dehydrogenation at the 9(11)-position has been reported from the action of *Glomerella fusaroides* on estrone (L-494). *Glomerella* is orginarily a good hydroxylating species, with no hint of dehydrogenating activity. The course of this dehydrogenation, which is also accompanied by a bizarre inversion at the 14-position, remains to be clarified.

We observed dehydrogenation at the 14-position with *Wojnowicia graminis* on testosterone (H-381), together with 12α-hydroxylation. It is our view that this is not a true dehydrogenation, but is an artifact arising from prior formation of the 12α,14α-diol,[47] followed by elimination (not necessarily enzymatic) of the labile 14α-hydroxyl. The driving force for the postulated elimination may come from the 1,3-diaxial interaction of the hydroxyl groups at 12α and 14α.

Dehydrogenation at the 16-position by *Trichothecium roseum* on digitoxigenin has been reported (T-1013). Since this organism is normally a 17α-hydroxylator, the question remains whether the 17α-hydroxy derivative of digitoxigenin is the precursor of the observed product.

Epoxidation

Bloom and Shull deduced the generalization that microorganisms which can cause *axial* hydroxylation at a given carbon atom can also cause epoxidation of a double bond attached to the same carbon atom (B-66). The epoxide oxygen will have the same configuration as the hydroxyl group which is normally introduced at the saturated carbon atom. Their explanation of this thesis was that the pi electrons of the double

bond assume an orientation similar to that of the electrons of the axial C,H bond and that the hydroxylating enzyme does not differentiate between the two situations. The initial stage of reaction, namely attack by oxygen (originating in the gas phase), is the same for hydroxylation and epoxidation. The natures of the transition state and any reaction intermediates remain to be elucidated.

Sites of Reaction. Bloom and Shull (B-66) showed that *Curvularia lunata* epoxidized 17α,21-dihydroxy-4,9(11)-pregnadiene-3,20-dione to the 9β,11β-epoxide and

---

[47] 14α-Hydroxy-4-androstene-3,17-dione is also a product of the same fermentation.

$17\alpha,21$-dihydroxy-4,14-pregnadiene-3,20-dione to the $14\alpha,15\alpha$-epoxide. They also indicated that other known axial hydroxylators at the 11-position (*Cunninghamella blakesleeana*) and at the 14-position (*Helicostylum piriforme, Mucor griseocyanus,* etc.) also formed epoxides with the appropriate substrates.

Prochazka and colleagues (P-741) have reported the formation of a 5,6-oxide of unspecified configuration from the action of *Rhizopus nigricans* on 3β-hydroxy-B-nor-5-androsten-17-one. Based on the known ability of *Rhizopus* sp. to 6β-hydroxylate, we think the oxide must be $5\beta,6\beta$. This is consistent with the observed formation, in

the same transformation, of a $5\alpha,6\beta$-dihydroxy product, which probably arises from the diaxial opening of the oxide with water (possibly enzymatic; cf. C-87).

From the action of *Nocardia* sp. on $\Delta^{9(11)}$ compounds, $9\alpha,11\alpha$-epoxides have been formed (S-886). This is attributable to the 9α-hydroxylating ability of *Nocardia*.

Corynebacterium simplex behaves in a similar fashion (C-138). Kurosawa, Hayano, and Bloom (K-484) reported the $11\beta,12\beta$-epoxidation of 4,11-pregnadiene-3,20-dione with *Curvularia lunata.*

In general, chemical methods of epoxidation are superior to the microbiological. The principal significance of the latter has been to provide a better understanding of the chemical mechanism of the microbial oxygenation process.

Oxidation of Alcohols to Ketones or Aldehydes

The oxidation-reduction process for the conversion of hydroxysteroids to keto-steroids (and the reverse reaction) has been studied in detail by Talalay and his collaborators [48] with induced enzymes isolated from *Pseudomonas testosteroni*. They purified one enzyme system which oxidized the 3α-hydroxyl group and another which oxidized both 3β- and 17β-hydroxyl groups. Talalay has characterized the oxidation-reduction reaction with these enzymes as NAD-linked and illustrated the general reaction as:

There is little substrate specificity among microorganisms producing hydroxy-steroid dehydrogenases. The only limitation which is usually found is that the *formal* stereochemistry and position of the hydroxyl group to be oxidized should be the same as that in the model from which the proposed transformation is derived. For example, 3α-hydroxysteroid dehydrogenase studied by Talalay is effective irrespective of whether the 3α-hydroxyl group is axial or equatorial. The same is also true for the 3β-hydroxysteroid hydrogenase.

There is some evidence from the work of Ringold and collaborators with *Pseudomonas testosteroni* that the presence of electron-withdrawing groups at the 6-position in 3-keto-Δ^4-substrates shifts the direction of net change (and hence the equilibrium) from oxidation to reduction. From these results it may be inferred that electron density at the carbonyl group can be decisive in determining equilibrium. This is also consistent with the formulation of the oxidation-reduction process as hydride ion transfer between diphosphopyridine nucleotide and substrate.[49] These findings are discussed in greater detail in the section on reduction of carbonyl groups.

---

[48] Talalay has reviewed his work in extenso, in "The Enzymes" (P. D. Boyer, H. Lardy, and K. Myrbäck, eds.) 2nd ed., Vol. 7, p. 177. Academic Press, New York, 1963.

[49] H. R. Levy, P. Talalay, and B. Vennesland [Progr. Stereochem. 3, 299 (1962)], have reviewed the evidence for the chemical change in NAD^+ which accompanies the oxidation of an alcohol to a ketone or aldehyde.

Useful oxidation of alcohols to ketones has been known since the work of Bertrand in 1896.[8-10] The application of this reaction to steroid chemistry was first made by Mamoli and his collaborators (S-808, V-1047), who showed that 5-androstene-3β,17β-diol could be oxidized to 4-androstene-3,17-dione with bacteria isolated from contaminated yeast. The same crude culture also oxidized 5-pregnen-3β-ol-20-one to

progesterone (M-540). Various pure strains identified as *Micrococcus dehydrogenans* (E-215), *Corynebacterium mediolanum* (A-1, M-546), and *Flavobacterium dehydrogenans* (N-688, N-689) have been very useful in the laboratory for the oxidation of the 3β-hydroxyl group, often together with deacetylation at the 3-position (and elsewhere) and isomerization of a double bond at the 5- to 4-position. This technique remains the method of choice for combined deacetylation-oxidation-isomerization (3β-acetoxy-$\Delta^5 \rightarrow$ 3-keto-Δ^4) in the presence of oxidation-sensitive or pH-labile groups elsewhere in the molecule.

Oxidations of hydroxyl groups have also been observed at the 3α- (S-799, S-800, S-818, S-943), 6β- (B-32), 7α- (S-799, S-800), 11β- (H-344, M-556), 12α- (S-799, S-800, S-810), 15β- (T-1036), 16α- and/or 16β- (S-793a), 18 (Ap-38), and 20β-positions (C-128, N-665). In general, chemical methods of oxidation have been preferred for reaction at these sites.

The many instances of apparent direct introduction of carbonyl groups at unsubstituted sites are almost certainly hydroxylation followed by oxidation. There are as yet no grounds for believing that a mechanism exists for the direct transformation of the methylene group into carbonyl by microorganisms.

Oxidation of Ketones to Esters and Lactones

The microbiological counterpart of the Baeyer-Villiger oxidation of ketones to esters or lactones was discovered by Fried, Thoma, and Klingsberg (F-284) and Peterson, Murray, and co-workers (P-726). Fried and his co-workers appreciated the parallel with the Baeyer-Villiger reaction and suggested correctly the sequential nature of the degradation of progesterone into testololactone by *Penicillium chrysogenum*. Using *Streptomyces lavendulae* with progesterone, Fried was able to isolate

(3)

17β-hydroxy-1,4-androstadien-3-one (equivalent to stage 2) and 1,4-androstadiene-3,17-dione (equivalent to stage 3). He also observed that the presence of the 17α-hydroxyl group in a 20-ketopregnane did not prevent the reaction (e.g., *Cylindrocarpon radicicola* with Compound S).

Fonken, Murray, and Reineke (F-254) isolated testosterone acetate (stage 1) from the degradation of progesterone with *Cladosporium resinae*, thereby substantiating further the thesis of Fried, Thoma, and Klingsberg. They proved unequivocally, with appropriately labeled progesterone, that the 21-carbon atom of progesterone is the precursor of the methyl carbon atom of acetate in testosterone acetate.

Prairie and Talalay (P-737) showed that the ether oxygen of testololactone (as distinct from carbonyl oxygen) is provided by oxygen from air in the transformation of testosterone into testololactone by *P. lilacinum* (P-726).

If one makes a judicious choice of organism and fermentation conditions, any of the intermediates between progesterone and testololactone (or 1-dehydrotestololactone) may become a major product. The potential value of this degradative technique was appreciated in the early, independent report of Vischer and Wettstein (V-1056) concerning the degradation of progesterone into 1,4-androstadiene-3,17-dione by *Fusarium* sp. They proposed that a more efficient synthesis of estrone than the one employing dehydroepiandrosterone as starting material might incorporate the progesterone degradation as a key stage. This possibility was investigated in some detail by Wix and Albrecht (W-1116, W-1117, W-1118) using *Fusarium solani.* In the final analysis, the purely chemical routes to androstadienedione and estrone have been more economical, although the question has been reopened again recently by the findings of Sih concerning the microbial degradation of 19-hydroxycholesterol.

Oxidation of Sulfides to Sulfoxides

This reaction has been reported by Holmlund and co-workers (H-405) and Dodson and Sollman (D-174, D-176). Holmlund converted 17β-hydroxy-7α-thiomethyl-4-androsten-3-one 17-acetate into the corresponding deacetylated 7α-sulfoxidomethyl compound by the action of *Calonectria decora*. Dodson and Sollman described the transformation of 17α-thiomethyl-4-androsten-3-one into *two* sulfoxides (and an 11α-hydroxylated sulfoxide) whose configurations differed at sulfur. Nothing is known about the mechanism of this reaction, but it is reasonable to suppose that the entering oxygen is provided by air.

Oxidation of Amines to Ketones

Only one example of this interesting and possible useful transformation has been reported. DeFlines and co-workers (D-148) described the conversion of conessine to Δ⁴-conenin-3-one by *Gloeosporium cyclaminis* and *Hypomyces haematococcus*. Rich sources of 3-aminosteroids have been found in the *Funtumia* sp. of African plants.[50]

While no evidence has been adduced in support of a mechanism for this reaction, one may speculate that a complex chain of events is involved. We think that enzymatic *N*-demethylation is a likely, early stage,[51] followed by some form of transamination process.

Oxidative Degradation – a Composite

Many microbiol genera can degrade a variety of steroidal substrates to carbon dioxide and water (T-965 and references cited therein). This degradative ability is particularly prominent among the genera which dehydrogenate Δ⁴-3-keto-steroids into the corresponding Δ¹ compounds, such as *Corynebacterium*, *Mycobacterium*, *Pseudomonas*, and *Nocardia*. As a consequence, the production of the

[50] Goutarel, R., "Les alcaloids steroidiques des apocynacées." Hermann, Paris, 1964.

[51] Cf. Williams, R. T., Proc. European Soc. Study Drug Toxicity 4, 9 (1964); McMahon, R. F., J. Pharm. Sci. 55, 457 (1966).

antiinflammatory 1-dehydrocorticoids by this route requires careful control to prevent loss. The paths whereby degradation occurs have been elucidated through the combined efforts of Dodson and Muir (D-171, D-172), Schubert, Böhme, and Hörhold (S-818 – S-821), and Sih, Wang, and their collaborators (Ap-79, Ap-81, Ap-83), and these paths are illustrated in the charts which follow. The first of these had to do with the degradation of the steroid nucleus.

Note: Stereochemistry remains the same at all centers in the degradation products as in the parent.

Dodson and Muir were the first to show that degradation followed the paths $1 \rightarrow 3 \rightarrow 5$ or $1 \rightarrow 2 \rightarrow 5$, depending on the organism used. For selected *Nocardia* sp.

it is obligatory that 9α-hydroxylation precede 1-dehydrogenation (D-172). For certain *Pseudomonas* sp., on the other hand, 1-dehydrogenation must precede 9α-hydroxylation (D-171). In both instances the 9,10-<u>seco</u> species 5 results from the spontaneous, presumably nonenzymatic, reverse aldol reaction of postulated intermediate 4. These conclusions were confirmed later by Schubert and Sih using other organisms.

A later stage of degradation, namely, the opening of ring A, was first appreciated by Schubert, Böhme, and Hörhold (S-819), who isolated the degradation product having partial structure 8 from the action of *Mycobacterium* sp. on progesterone. This pathway was later confirmed by Sih and Wang (S-895), who used *Nocardia restrictus* with androstenedione.

Sih, Wang, and their collaborators elucidated the pathway whereby 5 is transformed into 8 via 6 and 7. A key reaction is the 4-hydroxylation of the phenolic intermediate 5. Sih has recently shown that the same process is also implicated in the microbial degradation of estrone by a particular *Nocardia* sp. (Ap-13), which is illustrated here. Intermediate B corresponds to 6 and C to 7. The probable structure of

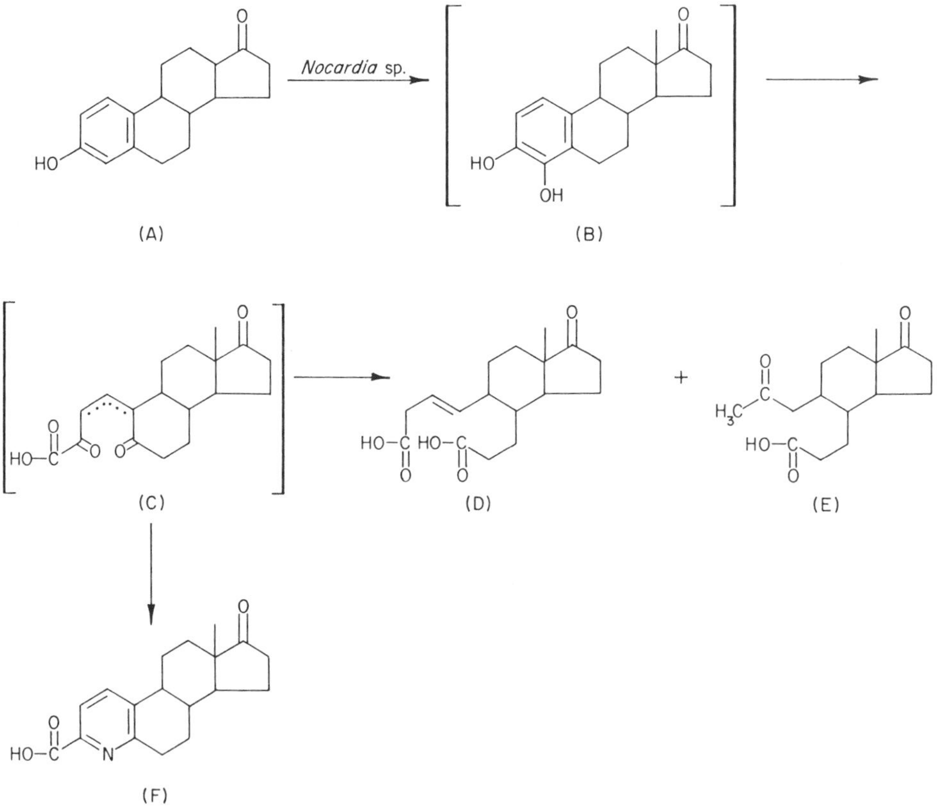

C (and 7) was deduced by the formation of the heterosteroid F (or its equivalent from 7) by reaction with ammonia. The processes which lead from C to D and from 7 to 8 have been rationalized by Sih in identical chemical terms. Compound E is presumed to arise from D by further degradation. Sih and Wang and their collaborators also showed that 8 is further fragmented into 9 and thence to propionaldehyde and pyruvic acid.

A second problem of great current interest has to do with the microbial degradation of the side chains of cholesterol and related sterols. In 1948, Turfitt (T-1034) observed that *Proactinomyces erthropolis* degraded cholestenone and bile acids to a very minor degree to the corresponding etio acids. No further transformations of

this class were disclosed until 1964, when Whitmarsh (W-1111) reported that cholesterol was degraded in poor yield by *Nocardia* sp. into 3-ketobisnor-4-cholenic acid, 3-ketobisnor-1,4-choladienic acid, 4-androstene-3,17-dione, and 1,4-androstadiene-3,17-dione.

In apparently unrelated investigations, which were to assume importance later on, Dodson and Muir (D-171) showed that 19-hydroxy-4-androstene-3,17-dione was converted into estrone readily and in good yield by *Pseudomonas* sp. Sih and Rahim (S-894) showed that this was also true for *Nocardia restrictus*. Sih recognized that estrone thus produced was singularly stable to further microbial attack, in contrast with 3-keto-Δ^4-androstenes or 3-keto-Δ^4-pregnenes. He reasoned that it might be possible to ferment an appropriate substrate in such a way that side-chain degradation to a 17-ketone and A-ring aromatization would occur. If attack on the steroid nucleus could then be directed toward aromatization via retro-aldol loss of the angular substituent at the 19-position rather than by 9α-hydroxylation and 9,10-secosteroid formation, estrone would result.

For this purpose he chose 19-hydroxy-4-cholesten-3-one, which might yield 19-hydroxy-4-androstene-3,17-dione as the sought-after intermediate of degradation. When he incubated the former with *Nocardia restrictus*, estrone was indeed formed in 8% yield. A culture (CSD-10), isolated from soil using cholesterol as the sole

source of carbon, gave estrone in 30% yield from the same 19-oxygenated substrate, the greatest part of the remainder being unreacted starting material. In the same way, 19-hydroxy-β-sitost-4-en-3-one was also converted into estrone in 10% yield, thereby illustrating a desirable lack of side-chain specificity in CSD-10. In a later

study, Sih, Wang, and their collaborators (Ap-81) made further refinements of their method consisting principally of the replacement of 19-hydroxy-4-cholesten-3-one by 3β,19-dihydroxy-5-cholestene 3-acetate (5) as substrate for CSD-10. Thereby estrone was produced in 72% yield. The proposed process for estrone manufacture from cholesterol is illustrated on the next page. Stages 1 → 5 employ methodology worked out to a high degree of perfection by a Ciba group.[52] Sih has told us that the entire process, 1 → estrone, has been carried out in his laboratory in an overall yield of 50%. Because of the brevity and efficiency of this process, one may anticipate that it or a variant will become a commercially significant method of estrone manufacture.

---

[52] Kalvoda, J., Heusler, K., Ueberwasser, H., Anner, G., and Wettstein, A., Helv. Chim. Acta 46, 1361 (1963).

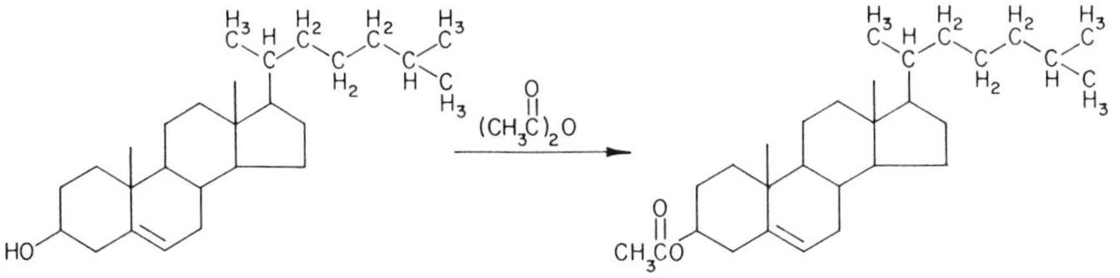

(1)   (2)

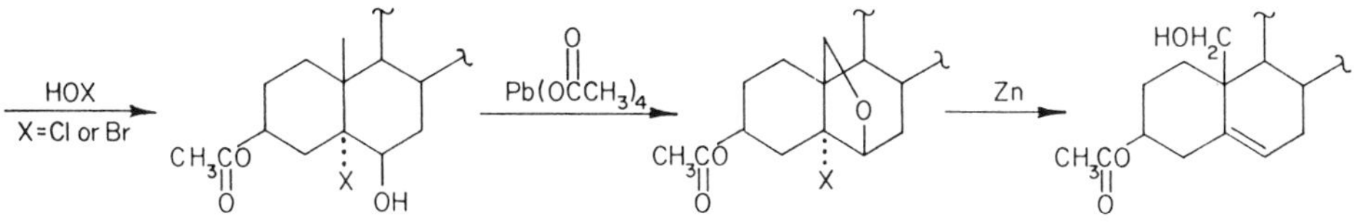

(3)   (4)   (5)

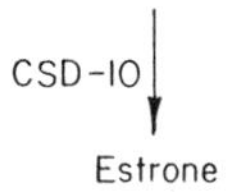

CSD-IO

Estrone

In later investigations, Sih and his collaborators [52a] proved that cholesterol is degraded to a 17-ketosteroid by *Nocardia, Mycobacterium, Corynebacterium* and *Arthrobacter* via a sequence which involves a cholanic acid and a <u>bisnor</u>cholanic acid as intermediates. They also established unequivocally, using labeled substrates, the nature of the fragments to which the side chain is degraded. The pathway and label locations are illustrated.

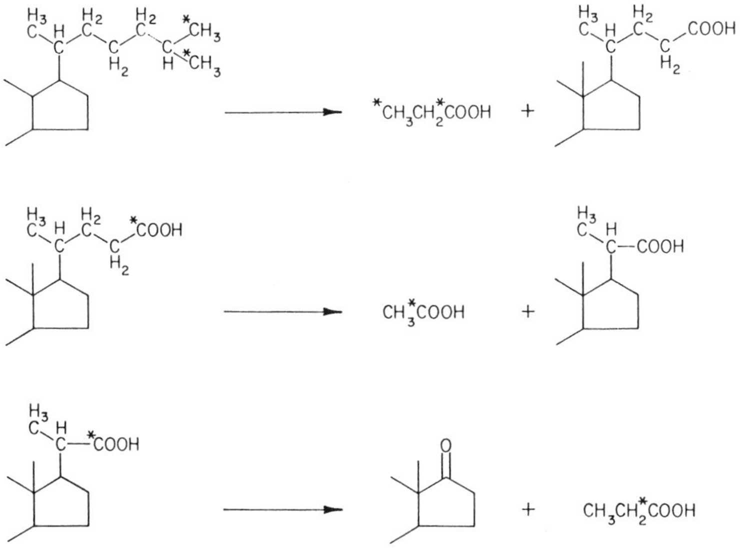

[52a] Sih, C. J., Wang, K. C., and Tai, H. H., J. Am. Chem. Soc. 89, 1956 (1967); Sih, C. J., Tai, H. H. and Tsong, Y. Y., ibid., p. 1957.

From these findings Sih has inferred the details of the mode of microbial degradation of the bisnorcholanic acid in the following manner. He reports that this latter
sequence does not require oxygen, on which basis he presumably excludes hydroxylation of the bisnorcholanic acid as an alternative path.[52b]

He has not reached similar conclusions about the degradation of the cholanic
acid to the bisnor acid. The location of the labels in the propionic acid derived from
the degradation of the cholestane to the cholanic acid require that oxidative attack
occur at C-26. This need not necessarily be the initiating stage of the entire degradation, but if it is, the repetitive dehydrogenation[52c]-hydration-reverse aldol mechanism
could be the means of degrading C_{27} to C_{19} steroids with the indicated microbial
species. Hypotheses involving hydroxylation stages at C-24 and C-22 can be constructed which are the equivalent of the dehydrogenation-hydration sequence, but there
is no evidence for such hydroxylations.

The efficient microbial degradation of the spiroketal side chain in diosgenin and
tigogenin to give 1,4-androstadiene-3,16-dione (I), 16α-hydroxy-1,4-androstadien-3-
one (II), and 16β-hydroxy-1,4-androstadien-3-one (III) has been described by Kondo

(I)   (II)

[52b] A proof of his proposal is possible using H_2O^{18} as the medium, thereby leading to a
17-ketosteroid labeled at the 17-carbonyl oxygen.

[52c] The organisms reported here to degrade cholesterol are known to be active 1-dehydro-
genation species for 3-ketosteroids.

and Mitsugi (Ap-37). This degradation is effected with the representative 1-dehydro-genating species, *Fusarium solani* and *Corynebacterium simplex*. In these instances there are both parallels with and differences from the degradation of the cholesterol side chain. The pathway proposed by Kondo and Mitsugi is illustrated as follows.

(1) $\xrightarrow{\text{hydrolysis}}$ (2)

(3) $\xrightarrow{\text{oxidation}}$ ... $\xrightarrow{\text{Baeyer-Villiger}}$ (4)

(5) $\xrightarrow{\text{hydrolysis}}$ ... $\xrightarrow{\text{reverse aldol}}$ (6)

Evidence for the intermediate stages is that the listed substrates are also transformed to (I): stage 3, kryptogenin (*F. solani*); stage 5, 3β-acetoxy-20α-hydroxy-5-pregnen-16-one (*F. solani*). The parallel with the cholesterol degradation lies in the apparent requirement for an aldolase in both sequences. The structures of the end-products of degradation in the two cases appear to require different chemistry at C-20 and C-22 to rationalize their formation.

Reduction

Reduction of Carbonyl Compounds to Alcohols

Reduction of carbonyl to hydroxyl is part of the equilibrium process described in the section on oxidation of alcohols to ketones. The same mechanistic principles apply. Evidence for the correctness of the stoichiometry of the illustrated representation of this reaction has been provided, using crystalline enzyme, by Hübener, Schmidt-Thome, and co-workers (H-410, N-657, S-803).

$$\text{C=O} + \text{NADH} + \text{H}^+ \underset{\text{enzyme}}{\rightleftharpoons} \text{H-C-OH} + \text{NAD}^+$$

If it is assumed that hydride ion transfer from NADH to carbonyl is the rate-controlling step for the forward reaction, it would be expected that decreasing the electron density at the carbonyl group should increase the rate of the reduction process. Ringold and associates (R-767) have shown that cellfree extracts of *Pseudo-monas testosteroni,* which do not reduce the 3-carbonyl of testosterone, 2α-methyl-testosterone, or 6β-methyltestosterone to any significant degree, do reduce testos-terones bearing fluorine at the 2α-, 4-, 6α-, or 6β-positions, or chlorine at the 4-position to a mixture of the corresponding 3α- and 3β-ols. Robinson, Bruce, and

Oliveto (R-774) have shown that *Flavobacterium dehydrogenans*, which does not reduce a 17-ketosteroid unsubstituted at the 16-position, does indeed reduce 16,16-difluorode-hydroepiandrosterone and 16,16-difluoroestrone methyl ether to 17α-hydroxysteroids.

Since the presence of these highly electronegative species at positions where they may, by induction, withdraw electrons from carbonyl does have the anticipated effect, we infer support for the interpretation that hydride ion transfer is rate-controlling in this oxidation-reduction mechanism.

Sites of Reaction. Reduction of the carbonyl groups at the 3- and 17-positions by yeasts (mainly *Saccharomyces cerevisiae*) were among the first microbial transformations recognized by Mamoli and Vercellone (M-549, M-551, V-1046). Estradiol was synthesized conveniently from estrone (W-1085) and testosterone from androstenedione using this method (M-543). Following the early work, many additional examples of reduction at the 3- and 17-positions have been reported, and also instances of reduction at the 7-, 9-, 16-, 19-, 20-, 21-, and 22-positions.

In general, and where applicable, the use of yeast is the preferred mode of microbial reduction of carbonyl compounds, since it is unlikely to cause other transformations simultaneously. This specificity is equally true of protozoa, but the latter are much less convenient to use. The bacteria, fungi, and actinomycetes, in addition to their many other abilities, will often oxidize or reduce at the same site with greater facility. The direction of the change is a function of the substrate and the medium, as well as the organism.

Ordinarily the conjugated 3-carbonyl resists reduction by yeast at both the carbonyl and unsaturated sites. An apparent exception is the case reported by Butenandt, Dannenberg, and Suranyi (B-80) of the reduction of 5α-1-androstene-3,17-dione to

5α-androstane-$3\beta,17\beta$-diol.   An instructive group of reductions at the 3-position by *Saccharomyces cerevisiae* was reported by Camerino, Alberti, and Vercellone (C-83).

(1)

(2)

(3)

Although a major stereochemical change at the 5-position (5α in 1 vs. 5β in 2), which alters the geometry of the A- and B-rings profoundly, does not interfere with the reduction at the 3-position or alter the formal stereochemistry of the resulting carbinol, the apparently minor change at the 11-position in compound 3 (11α-ol in 3 vs. 11-C = O in 1) leads to a carbonyl of opposite stereochemistry at the 3-position.

A more predictable approach to reduction, developed by Schubert, involves the anaerobic application of *Clostridium paraputrificum* to Δ^4-3-ketosteroids (Ap-71, S-823). In all instances (testosterone, progesterone, corticosterone, cortisone) the product is the corresponding 3α-hydroxy-5β-steroid. From $\Delta^{1,4}$-3-ketosteroids the corresponding Δ^1-3α-hydroxy-5β-steroid is formed in good yield, with a lesser amount of fully saturated hexahydrosteroid as a by-product. From $\Delta^{1,4,6}$-3-keto-steroids or $\Delta^{4,6}$-3-ketosteroids the end-product of hydrogenation is the Δ^6-3α-hy-droxy-5β-steroid.

Reduction of 7-ketone to 7α-hydroxyl has been reported with *Streptomyces gelaticus* (H-363) and *Corynebacterium* sp. (T-975) among others. Reductions of this type are commonly seen with substrates in the bile acid series.

In the 9,10-seco series, 9-ketones of the type of Compound 5 (p. 49) are converted into 9α- and 9β-hydroxy products by the action of *Nocardia restrictus* (W-1063) or *Mycobacterium* sp. (S-818, S-820).

Several examples of simultaneous 16α- and 16β-hydroxylation, accompanied by formation of the corresponding 16-ketone, have been reported. We described the action of *Wojnowicia graminis* on testosterone (H-381) leading to the aforementioned three species, and Sax and co-workers (S-793a) reported the same processes from the action of *Bacillus megaterium* on 4-estren-3-one. Dodson and Mizuba (D-166)

presented an ingenious argument to the effect that 16β-hydroxy products need not arise from 16β-hydroxylation, but could be formed equally well from an initial 16α-hydroxylation of a 17-ketosteroid followed by Marker-Lawson rearrangement and reduction at the 16-position in the illustrated way. This argument cannot account for the

results of Sax, since no possibility for Marker-Lawson rearrangement exists. It is not possible, however, to exclude an alternative formulation involving one oxidation and reduction stage, following 16α-hydroxylation. In any event, evidence for reduction at the 16-position remains hypothetical.

Reduction of the 17-ketone to 17β-hydroxyl has been demonstrated with a wide variety of substrates and organisms. *Saccharomyces cerevisiae* is a very convenient and reliable reducing culture for this reaction. Reduction to 17α-hydroxyl has been reported only once in the special case of 16,16-difluoro-17-ketosteroids (R-774), discussed in the mechanism section.

Reduction of 19-carbonyl to hydroxyl has been described by Sih and co-workers (S-892) from the action of *Penicillium thomii* on 14β-hydroxy-3,19-dioxo-4,20(22)-cardadienolide. This reaction was described as reversible, with the equilibrium favoring the alcohol.

Reduction of the 20-carbonyl in pregnanes of widely varied structure has been reported by many investigators. The reduction to 20β-ol was first described by Fried, Thoma, and Klingsberg with *Streptomyces lavendulae* (F-284). The product of reduction accumulated in the mycelium, whereas the products of oxidation remained in the

broth. For synthetic purposes, the preferred organisms for this reduction are *Streptomyces hydrogenans* (L-522) and other *Streptomyces* sp. (C-110), which afford the desired process, uncomplicated by major competing reactions. Hübener and collaborators (H-410, N-657, S-803) isolated an inducible, *crystalline* 20β-hydrogenase from *S. hydrogenans*, which they demonstrated could be used to catalyze reduction *or* oxidation at the 20-position with a wide variety of substrates.

Reduction of 20-ketopregnanes to 20α-hydroxyl compounds, by a microbial process free from unrelated coincident reactions, was first reported in our laboratory with the use of *Rhodotorula longissima* (C-110). The application of this organism to a

broader selection of 20-ketopregnanes was described subsequently by Idler and co-workers (C-122, I-413a). No examples of this reduction have been reported with fungi, actinomycetes, or bacteria. Thus far, yeasts (C-88), algae (L-527), alfalfa seedlings (L-526), and many mammalian species have been shown to give reduction products with this stereochemistry.

Reduction of 22-aldehydes to the respective carbinols was first described by Murray, Peterson, and their collaborators (M-578) with *Rhizopus nigricans* and *Rhizopus arrhizus*, concomitant with hydroxylation at the 11α- and 6β-positions. *Penicillium lilacinum* (E-202) and *Gliocladium catenulatum* (W-1068) have been reported to give reduction at the 22-position, free of major side reaction. Ambiguity in the descriptions of the starting materials in these reactions make it uncertain as to whether the reductions occur principally with retention of configuration at the 20-position or with inversion. It is clear, however, that *G. catenulatum* leads to an equilibration of the starting material at the 20-position, at least in part.

Reduction of Carbon-Carbon Double Bonds

This type of reaction may be divided into two categories: (1) reduction of isolated double bonds and (2) reduction of conjugated double bonds. There are very few examples of the former in the steroid field, all involving the use of unidentified fecal anaerobes to reduce Δ^5-compounds to the 5β-series (C-133, S-914), and there is no adequate basis for the presentation of arguments about mechanism.[53]

The reduction of double bonds conjugated with keto groups may be viewed as part of the illustrated equilibrium process, the reverse of which is the dehydrogenation of ketosteroids. The nature of the reagent X, be it protein-bound flavin, quinone,

or another oxidizing agent, has been discussed in the section on dehydrogenation. If this view is accepted, then the stereochemical restrictions developed for dehydrogenation should apply.[53a] These restrictions are that the leaving (or entering) hydrogens at the 1- and 2-positions are axial and *trans* (1α,2β). The evidence for the equilibrium

---

[53] The conversion of cholic acid into 7-deoxy bile acids by mixed intestinal microorganisms is considered to proceed via elimination of the 7α-hydroxyl group followed by reduction. These reductions have not been demonstrated with pure cultures. Bergstrom, S., Danielsson, H., and Samuelson, B., in "Lipid Metabolism" (K. Bloch, ed.), p. 316. Wiley, New York, 1960.

[53a] Whether these may be generalized from the studies with one organism, B. sphaericus, remains to be established.

nature of the reaction comes from Goodman, May, and Smith (G-296) who showed that *C. simplex* and *B. cyclo-oxydans* interconvert triamcinolone and 1,2-dihydrotriamcinolone.

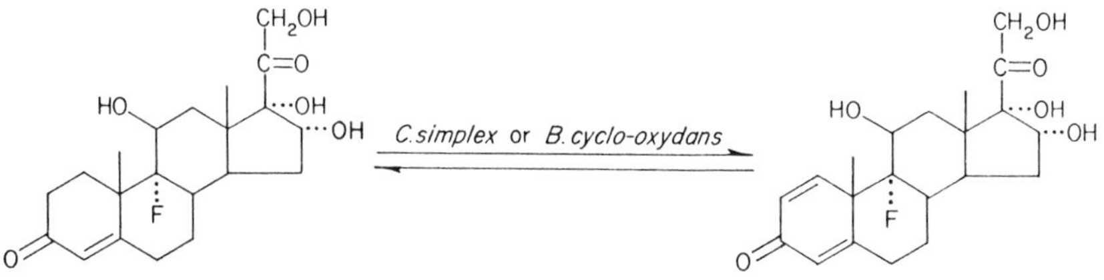

Sites of Reaction. Reduction of conjugated double bonds was first observed by Mamoli and Schramm (M-548) with a crude culture of putrefactive bacteria. The pure culture, described as *Bacillus putrificus*, reduced 3-keto-Δ^4-androstenes to 3-keto-5β-androstanes and 3α-hydroxy-5β-androstanes (M-545). This culture is no longer available (E-202), but a modern equivalent is *Clostridium paraputrificum*, described by Schubert (Ap-71, S-823). The properties of the latter are described in greater detail in the section on reduction of carbonyl groups.

Butenandt, Dannenberg, and Suranyi (B-80) reported the reduction of Δ^1-3-keto-5α-steroids to 3β-hydroxysteroids with yeast.

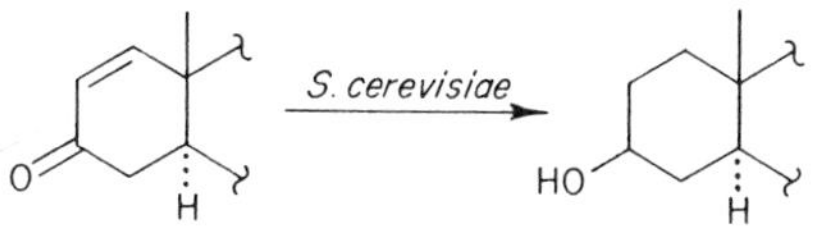

Reductions of 3-keto-Δ^4-substrates with fungi or actinomycetes may lead to either 4,5α- or 4,5β-dihydro products, but these reactions are usually incidental to hydroxylation elsewhere in the substrates (E-201, P-718, P-725, P-729). Selective reduction of $\Delta^{1,4}$-3-ketosteroids to Δ^1-5β-steroids with *Streptomyces* sp. has also been described (G-314).

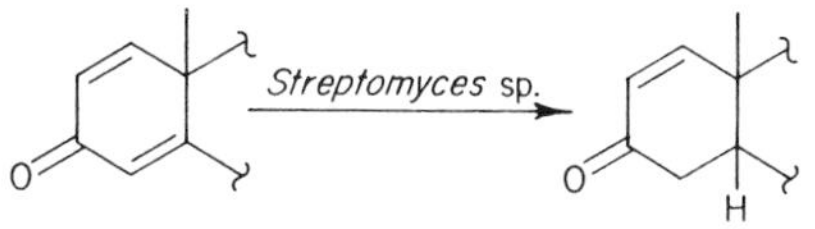

There is indirect evidence for the reduction of 12α-hydroxy-3-keto-4,6-choladienic acid at Δ^6. Hayakawa and collaborators (H-358, H-367, T-974) have shown that cholic acid is transformed into the illustrated products (1-5) by *Corynebacterium simplex* and other *Corynebacterium* sp.

If one places the products in the sequence shown here, the elimination of the 7α-hydroxyl group in 2 need not necessarily be enzyme-catalyzed. Conversion of 3 into 4 follows logically and requires enzyme mediation. Other routes to the formation of the same products are not excluded.

The reduction of 16-dehydroprogesterone, accompanied by 11α-hydroxylation, from the action of *Rhizopus nigricans* (M-579, M-601, M-605) or *Aspergillus niger*

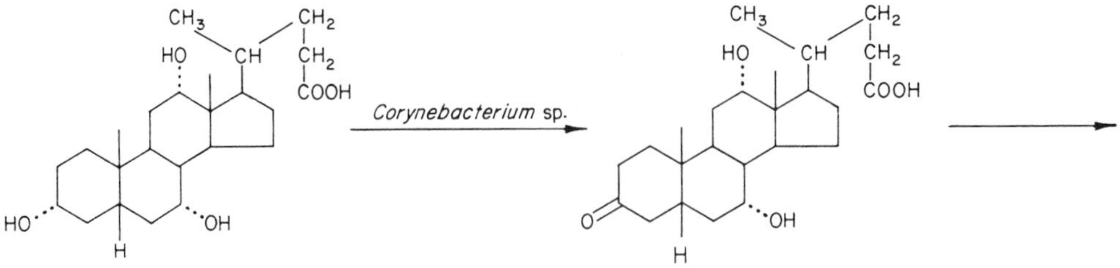

(1)

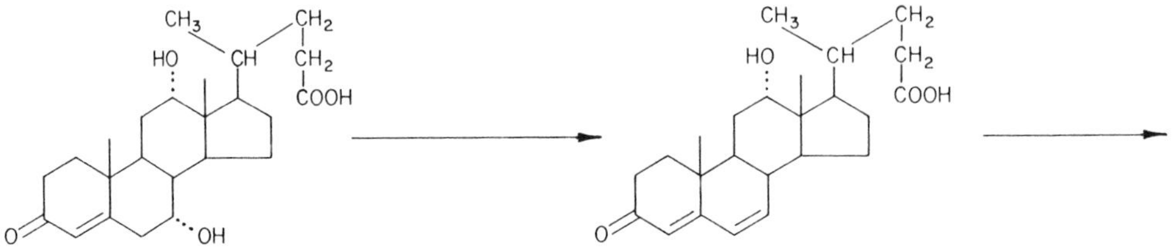

(2)

(3)

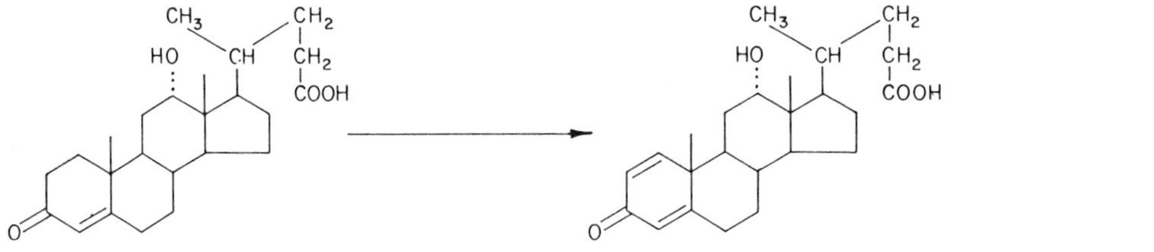

(4)

(5)

(M-603) affords 11α-hydroxy-17α-4-pregnene-3,20-dione. The thermodynamically more stable configuration of the side chain in pregnenolone and 3β-hydroxy-5α-pregnan-20-one is the β-form.[54] If one makes the reasonable assumption that this

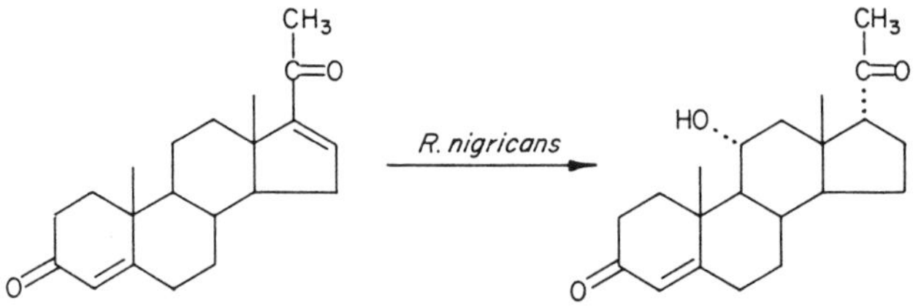

is also true for 11α-hydroxyprogesterone vs. its 17α-epimer, it becomes possible to develop a speculative argument about the stereochemistry of the attachment of the steroid to the enzyme. If one chooses to argue that reaction is complete at the enzyme surface by 1,2-addition in the illustrated sense, then the hydrogen at the 17-position must have been delivered from the β-side, and the product thus produced must be free to alter the angle of attachment at the 17-position from the initial planarity of the starting material to the quasi-axial of the product without steric interference from the enzyme. This may be accommodated if the steroid is attached to the enzyme by its β-face.

---

[54] Butenandt, A., and Fleischer, G., Ber. 70, 96 (1937); Butenandt, A., and Mamoli, L., ibid., 68, 1847 (1935).

An alternative treatment of the problem is to assume the reversal of the Ringold mechanism for dehydrogenation (as developed for A-ring transformations) to account for the observed reaction. In specific terms this involves enzyme-mediated attack by hydride ion on the 16-position as the initiating stage. The mechanism requires the formation of the illustrated enol as the intermediate. The enol must then be *protonated*

and go back to the ketone before it leaves the enzyme surface in order to attain the thermodynamically less favorable 17α-stereochemistry. This treatment again implies attachment of the substrate and the transition state derived from it to the enzyme by the β-face. The Ringold mechanism has the apparent merit of requiring no change in geometry at the 17-position during the enzyme-mediated, hydride ion transfer stage. Protonation of the enol would be spontaneous, and it would be necessary to invoke only a *steric but not a catalytic* role for the enzyme during this part of the process.

Reduction of Steroidal Bromide

Laskin and Diassi (L-492) have reported the only example of reduction of a steroidal bromide. *Cylindrocarpon radicicola* transformed 9α-bromo-11-ketoprogesterone into 1-dehydro-11-ketotestololactone. Reductive removal of halide from an α-haloketone is well known in organic chemistry and can be done very efficiently with a variety of reducing systems.

Esterification and Hydrolysis

Hydrolysis of Esters to Give Steroid Alcohols

The mechanism of catalysis for hydrolysis of steroid esters to steroid alcohols has not been elucidated in particular. In view of the nonspecific nature of esterases, however, it might be possible to carry over mechanistic conclusions from the studies with simpler esters. A favored formulation of this process by Bender and Kezdy[55] is

---

[55] Bender, M. L., and Kezdy, F. J., Ann. Rev. Biochem. **34**, 49 (1965).

shown here. The enzyme provides the required imidazole and hydroxyl groups. Water may participate in the cleavage of the steroid ester and is involved in the regeneration of the enzyme hydroxyl site.

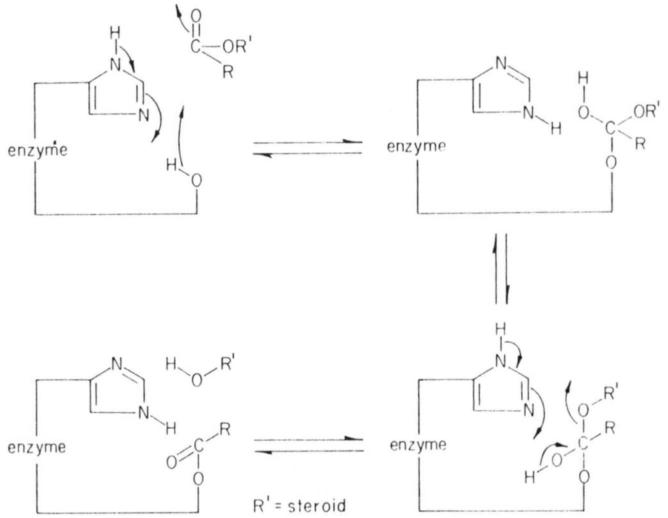

Hydrolysis of steroidal 21-acetates was among the earliest transformations recognized. Mamoli (M-541) found that *Corynebacterium mediolanum* could be used to transform 21-acetoxypregnenolone into deoxycorticosterone. Since then it has been shown that nonspecific esterases are common among bacteria, fungi, and actinomycetes.

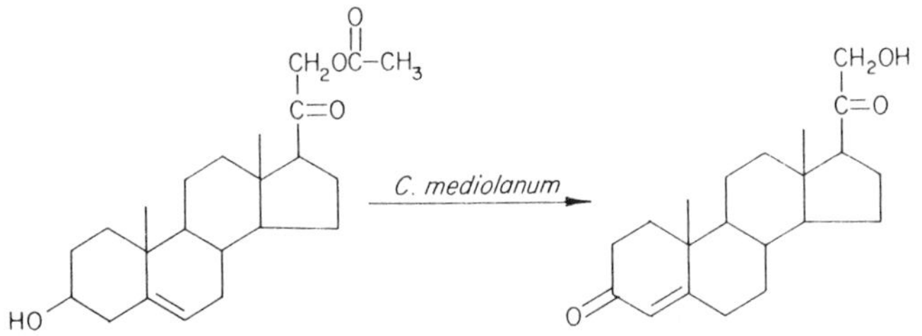

Acetylation is employed widely as a protective device for hydroxyl groups during the chemical manipulation of steroids. Successful use in this way implies the ability to remove the protective group following completion of the synthetic program. We have found that *Flavobacterium dehydrogenans* (A-16) contains what we believe to be a "universal" system of deacetylase(s). The acetates which we have hydrolyzed with its aid include 1β- (N-689), 3β- (N-689),[56] 11α- (unpublished), 11β- (C-129), 15α- (unpublished), 16α- (S-839), 16β- (S-839), 17α- (N-690), 17β- (G-304), 20β- (unpublished), and 21- (C-129).[56] The yields are usually very high, and major coincident reactions, namely, oxidation of 3-hydroxyl to ketone and isomerization of Δ^5 to Δ^4, are often useful.

While microbial hydrolysis of esters other than acetates might be expected to be equally common, relatively little reliable documentation of these reactions exists in the steroid field. The reason for this is clearly that acetates are the preferred esters

-----

[56] See also South African Patent 3462 (1955).

for most synthetic purposes, and consequently other esters have been subjected only rarely to study in microbial transformations. Among the few examples are the hydrolyses of testololactone to testolic acid by *Penicillium lilacinum* (P-737), other *Penicillium* sp. (H-398), *Cephalosporium acremonium* (H-398), and *Aspergillus flavipes* (H-398).

A convenient source of esterase for *"in vitro"* laboratory use is malt enzyme (diastase, J. P.) the application of which was described by Noguchi (N-672, N-673). Noguchi reported the successful hydrolysis of acetates at the 16α-, 17β-, 20α-, 20β-, and 21-positions (N-672). He also extended this method to 21-esters of other straight-chain aliphatic carboxylic acids (formate, butyrate, and caprylate), dibasic aliphatic hemiesters (hemisuccinate and hemitartrate) and N-substituted amino acid esters (dimethylaminoacetate and diethylaminoacetate) (N-673). 17β-Formate was hydrolyzed, but 17β-propionate was not.

Esterification of Steroid Alcohols

Only two reports of examples of this reaction class have been made. McGuire, Maxwell, and Tomkins (M-572) described the action of *Saccharomyces fragilis* on androstenedione, which afforded testerone acetate. The product arose from sequential

reduction followed by acetylation. Holmlund and collaborators (H-404) observed the acetylation of the 16,17-acetonide of 9α-fluoro-16α-hydroxyhydrocortisone by

Trichoderma glauca. These examples are principally of academic interest as further evidence of the reversibility of enzymatic reactions. The mechanism which operates here is possibly the reverse of that illustrated for hydrolysis.

N-Acetate Formation from Amines

The only example of this reaction class was described by Smith and co-workers (S-911) from the action of *Streptomyces roseochromogenus* on 21-amino-9α-fluoro-11β,17α-dihydroxy-1,4-pregnadiene-3,20-dione to give the 21-N-acetate.

The mechanism of acylation may be related to that of esterification of hydroxyl groups.

Hydrolysis of Oxides to Alcohols

The simple hydrolysis of oxides with *Saccharomyces cerevisiae*, first described by Camerino and Sciaky (C-87), leads to glycols with diaxial opening. This reaction is then the mechanistic equivalent of a normal, acid-catalyzed opening of an oxide,

with water acting as the nucleophile. One may speculate that the enzyme is acting as a reversible proton donor-proton acceptor species, perhaps involving an imidazole as the combined proton source-proton sink. The stereochemical problems attendant to the formation of a cyclic 9-member ring transition state might be mitigated by considering that the participating water need not be a single molecule, but may be a hydrogen-bonded agglomerate.

A special case of oxide opening involving Wagner-Meerwein rearrangement was described by Camerino and Vercellone (C-88). This is analogous to a nonenzymatic, acid-catalyzed process studied by Heusler and Wettstein[57] and in our laboratory.[58]

---

[57] Heusler, K., and Wettstein, A., Ber. **87**, 1301 (1954).

[58] Shapiro, E. S., Steinberg, M., Gould, D., Gentles, M. J., Herzog, H. L., Gilmore, M., Charney, W., Hershberg, E. B., and Mandell, L., J. Am. Chem. Soc. **81**, 6483 (1959) (and preceding papers in the series).

The initiating stage here appears to be identical with the normal oxide opening. Molecular geometry then favors intramolecular methyl migration $(13 \rightarrow 17)$ over nucleophilic, intermolecular hydration at the 17-position. The reaction is completed by proton loss from the 14-position.

Hydrolysis of Glycosides

Cleavage of glucose from selected steroidal glycosides by fungi was recognized and studied by Stoll, Renz, and Brack (S-936a). Ability to perform this transformation is especially prominent among *Aspergillus* and *Penicillium* sp. It is not clear from the available evidence whether the reaction in question is hydrolysis or a transglycosylation. The generic form of the reaction, which embodies this uncertainty, can be given as follows:

$$R-O-R' + R''-OH \longrightarrow R'-O-R'' + R-OH$$

R = steroid portion of glycoside
R'= sugar portion of glycoside
R''= sugar moiety *or* hydrogen

The substantial literature on transglycosylation has been reviewed by Stodola.[59]

The Stoll group observed the selective cleavage of glucose from several cardioactive glycosides. In each case (scilliroside, digilanide A, and deacetyldigilanide A) glucose was an end group, the cleavage leading thereby to a partially degraded glycoside. Such a result is difficult to obtain by other than enzymatic techniques. Later work by Krider, Cordon, and Wall (K-478), using the same fungal genera, showed that this technique could be applied to steroidal saponins to give sapogenins.

Isomerization of Double Bonds

Isomerization of the double bond from Δ^5 to Δ^4 was among the reactions first recognized by Mamoli. With *Corynebacterium mediolanum* he converted $3\beta,21$-dihydroxy-5-pregnen-20-one 21-acetate into deoxycorticosterone (M-541). From our

experience *Flavobacterium dehydrogenans* can be used very efficiently in the same way (N-688, N-689). In general, enzymes which promote the isomerization reaction are

[59]Stodola, F., "Chemical Transformations by Microorganisms," p. 65. Wiley, New York, 1958.

widely distributed among oxidizing microorganisms. We know of only one oxidizing organism, *Actinoplanes missouriensis* (Ap-45), which does not also sequentially isomerize Δ^5 to Δ^4.[60]

The mechanism of the enzyme-catalyzed isomerization has been studied in detail by Talalay and Ringold. Talalay, Wang, and Kawahara isolated and crystallized the induced isomerase from *Pseudomonas testosteroni* (K-437, T-972)[61] and showed that its use required no cofactor. From study of the isomerization in deuterium oxide, they demonstrated no deuterium incorporation into the steroid and inferred that the isomerization involved a transfer of hydrogen from C-4 to C-6. Malhotra and Ringold proved that hydrogen is transferred from the 4β- to the 6β-position by using appropriate, deuterium-labeled substrates (Ap-44). They also established that the transfer is intramolecular. The present view of the mechanism which represents a synthesis of the Talalay and Ringold findings is illustrated here.[62] This formulation requires 8-member ring (1) and 10-membered ring (2) transition states

which Talalay has asserted are shown to be accommodated easily, in appropriate scale models.[62] Talalay has inferred the histidine catalysis from enzyme inactivation studies with methylene blue. Some evidence for probable reversibility comes from the work of Ward and Engel[63] with sheep adrenal enzymes. They showed that 4-androstene-3,17-dione could be transformed into dehydroepiandosterone. The first

stage of this reaction is presumed to be the deconjugation of Δ^4 to Δ^5. It has also been reported that *Bacillus pulvifaciens* converts 6β-hydroxy-4-androstene-3,17-dione into 5α-androstane-3,6,17-trione (I-420), which may be accounted for by the action of an isomerase.

---

[60] While Flavobacterium dehydrogenans isomerizes the double bond smoothly in a 3β-hydroxy-Δ^5-substrate, presumably after oxidation at the 3-position, it does not isomerize the double bond in a 3-keto-$\Delta^{1,5}$-substrate (N-690).

[61] Kawahara, F. S., Wang, S. F., and Talalay, P., J. Biol. Chem. 237, 1500 (1962); Wang, S. F., Kawahara, F. S., and Talalay, P. ibid., 238, 567 (1963).

[62] Talalay, P., Ann. Rev. Biochem. 34, 352 (1965).

[63] Ward, M. G., and Engel, L. L., J. Biol. Chem. 239, PC3604 (1964).

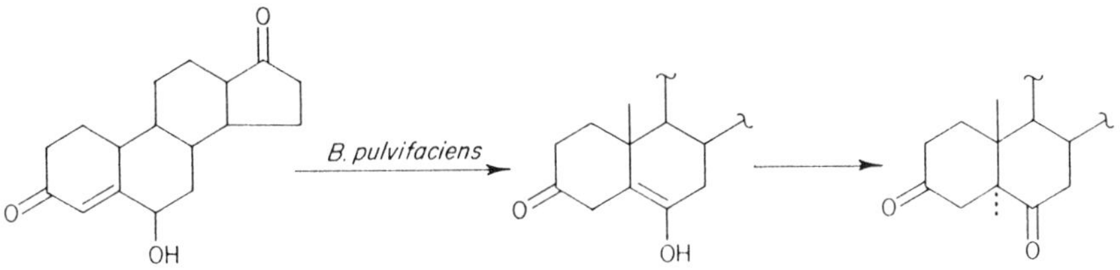

The isomerase from *Ps. testosteroni* has also transformed $\Delta^{5(10)}$-3-ketosteroids into their Δ^4-counterparts *in vitro* (T-972). The appropriate substrates have not been investigated with intact cultures, but there is no reason to doubt than an equivalent reaction would take place *in vivo*.

Miscellaneous Addition, Rearrangement, and Elimination Processes

The following reaction classes have been identified in the presence of microbial systems. The necessity for enzymatic catalysis is not proved in many of these cases and is specifically excluded in two.

    a. Wagner-Meerwein rearrangement
    b. Decarboxylation
    c. Aldol and reverse aldol reactions
    d. Michael addition
    e. D-Homoannulation
    f. Enolization of carbonyl compounds
    g. Dehydration
    h. Amination

Wagner-Meerwein Rearrangement

Saccharomyces cerevisiae was used by Camerino and Vercellone (C-88) to transform 16α,17α-oxido-20-ketopregnanes. The products thus produced are those which have also resulted from acid-catalyzed, hydrolytic attack on the oxide[64] followed by

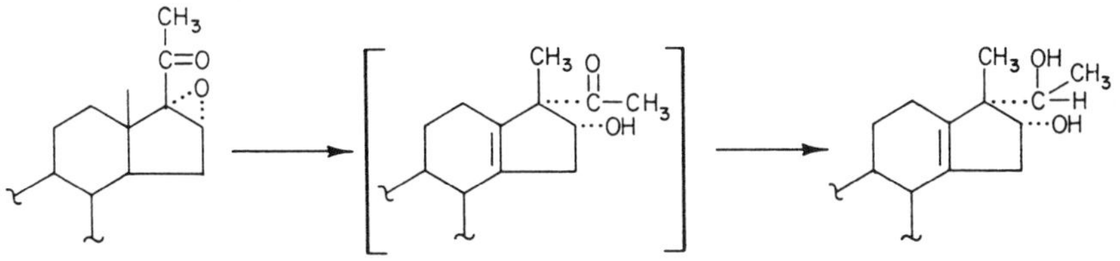

reduction at the 20-position. The Wagner-Meerwein rearrangement of the angular methyl group from the 13- to the 17-position is presumably not under enzymatic control per se, but follows as a consequence of the enzyme-catalyzed opening of the oxide, a reaction which has been demonstrated in other cases (cf. p. 66) with yeasts.

Decarboxylation

Decarboxylation of a β-ketolactone has been shown by Urech, Vischer, and Wettstein (U-1044) in the illustrated case. The reaction also proceeded in the medium alone, in the absence of *Fusarium solani* or enzymes from it, when the appropriate 17-keto-(18 → 11) lactone was used as substrate.

---

[64] Heusler, K., and Wettstein, A., Ber. **87**, 1301 (1954).

Reverse Aldol Reaction

Dodson and Muir showed that the reverse aldol reaction is a key step in the degradation of the B-ring (D-171, D-172). In the illustration, 9α-hydroxylation of a $\Delta^{1,4}$-3-ketosteroid with *Pseudomonas* sp. affords an intermediate which then experiences cleavage between the 9- and 10-positions. The same investigators also reported another

variant of the same reaction, in which formaldehyde is lost from 19-hydroxy-1,4-androstadiene-3,17-dione, which was produced *in situ* by the Δ^1-dehydrogenation of 19-hydroxy-4-androstene-3,17-dione. The latter sequence represents a key transition in the conversion of cholesterol into estrone as described by Sih.

There is no evidence that an enzyme is required for the reverse aldol stage of either of the illustrated reactions. It is likely that an aldolase is required for the reverse aldol reactions described in the section on degradation of the cholesterol and diosgenin side chains (Ap-37; Sih and collaborators[52a]).

Michael Addition

Intramolecular Michael addition of an 11β-hydroxyl group to a 3-keto-Δ^1-system has been reported by Gnoj and associates (G-292). There is no reason to believe that an enzyme is required for the addition, which follows enzymatic deacetylation at the 11-position.

D-Homoannulation

D-Homoannulation was among the first transformations described by Fried and his collaborators (F-283) using *Aspergillus niger* with 17α-hydroxyprogesterone.

Later work by Goodman and Smith (G-297) with triamcinolone and related 16α-hydroxycorticoids established that, for the examples studied, D-homoannulation is non-enzymatic, the reaction being promoted by ferrous or ferric ion in the presence of

calcium carbonate and inhibited by phosphate ion. Whether this mechanism also applies to the reaction of 17α-hydroxyprogesterone is open to some question, since 17α-hydroxy-20-ketosteroids D-homoannulate much less readily than do 16α-hydroxycorticoids.

Enolization of Carbonyl Compounds — Inversion at the α-Carbon

From deuterium exchange experiments with 3-ketosteroids, it has been inferred that enolization is a common, microbially induced process. The same conclusion is also supported by the observed isomerization at 20- of 22-aldehydes. Wechter (W-1068) has described the inversion of 3-ketobisnor-4-cholen-22-al to the 20-iso compound by *Gliocladium catenulatum*, for which a reasonable mechanism is the illustrated enolization.

Dehydration

Dehydrative elimination of hydroxyl groups is well known from the enzymatic conversion of saturated to monounsaturated fatty acids.[65] Incubation of cholic acid with rat feces under anaerobic conditions gives a mixture of 7-deoxy products, which were presumed to have arisen through dehydration of the 7α-hydroxyl group, followed

---

[65] Hayano, M., in "Oxygenases" (O. Hayaishi, ed.), p. 229. Academic Press, New York, 1962.

by reduction of the resulting Δ^6 double bond.[66] A related process has been seen by
Hayakawa and his collaborators from the action of *Corynebacterium simplex* (H-358,
H-367, T-974) and *Streptomyces rubescens* (H-362) on cholic acid. One may infer

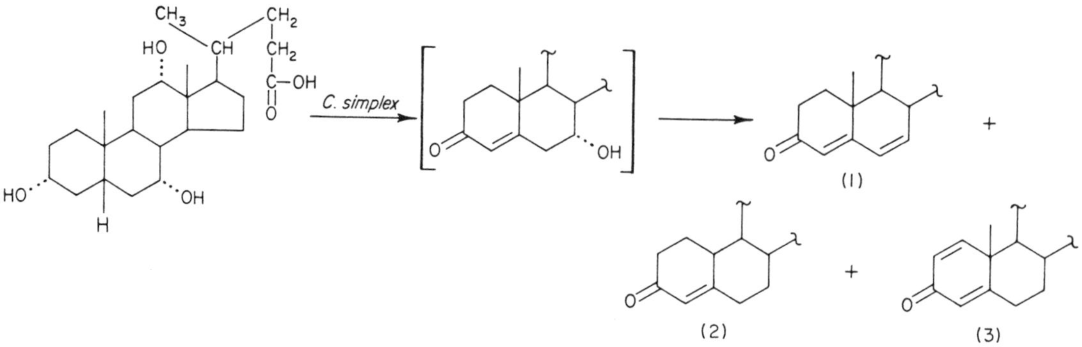

that the antecedent of the three illustrated products is 7α,12α-dihydroxy-3-keto-4-
cholenic acid [actually isolated from the reaction (H-365, H-367)], which then suffers
dehydrative elimination to give the $\Delta^{4,6}$-diene (1), followed by reduction to the 3-keto-
Δ^4 (2), and finally dehydrogenation to the $\Delta^{1,4}$-diene (3).

Whether the elimination at the 7-position is enzyme-catalyzed or merely a purely
chemical reverse Michael reaction has not been established.

Dehydration of the 5β-hydroxyl group in cardiac aglycones has been reported by
Nozaki (N-679) with *Absidia orchidis* and by Sih and associates (S-891) with *Chaetomium globosum*. In each case elimination presumably followed oxidation of the 3β-
hydroxyl to ketone and may be nonenzymatic.

Amination

The only example of amination in the steroid field has been reported by Smith
and collaborators (S-911). *Streptomyces roseochromogenus* on 9α-fluoroprednisolone
afforded the 21-deoxy-21-acetylamino product. This reaction may be following
the illustrated path.

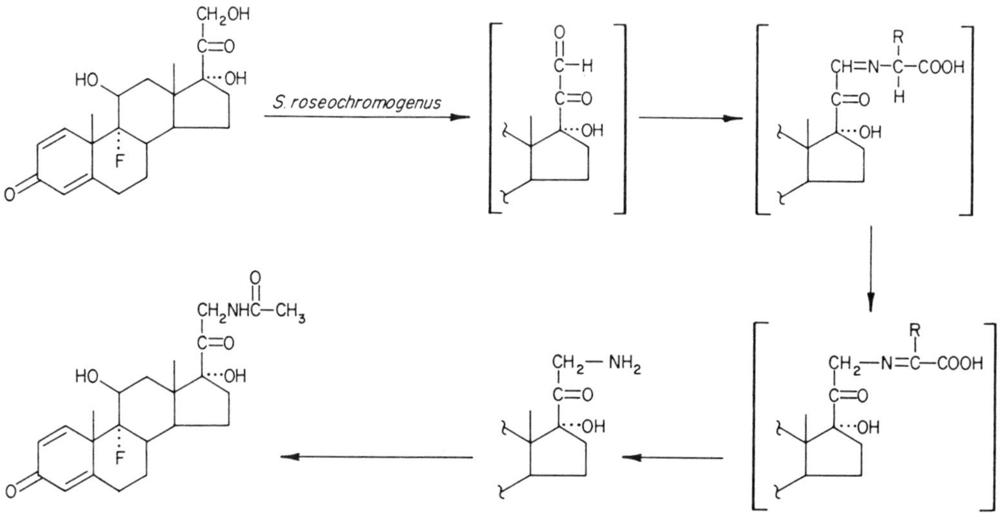

---

[66]Bergstrom, S., Danielsson, H., and Samuelsson, B., in "Lipide Metabolism" (K.
Bloch, ed.), p. 305. Wiley, New York, 1960.

Resolution of Steroids from Total Synthesis

Total synthesis has become an important factor in the commercial production of steroids. Velluz and collaborators at Roussel have devised a practical method for the manufacture of 19-norsteroids and estrogens.[67] Implicit in any total synthesis is the requirement for either a resolution or a stage of asymmetric reaction. Both methods have been used successfully to provide steroids of natural configuration. Of the two techniques the latter is to be preferred, since it is capable of converting all the substrate into useful product, whereas the former can only provide half of the product in natural configuration.

Gibian and collaborators (Ap-24) succeeded in devising an efficient asymmetric microbiological stage as part of a synthesis of estradiol methyl ether. The optically

inactive diketone 1 was reduced to the optically active, natural series (d) ketol 2 with the aid of *Saccharomyces pastorianus*, *S. carlsbergensis*, or, best of all, *S. uvarum*. *Bacillus thuringiensis*, on the other hand, afforded exclusively the epimer at the 13-position.

The first successful use of a microbial stage to separate a racemic mixture was described by Vischer, Schmidlin, and Wettstein (V-1055) who prepared natural (d)-aldosterone by 21-hydroxylation of a d,l-precursor with *Ophiobolus herpotrichus*.

The natural series of steroids is not necessarily the preferred substrate for all microorganisms. Greenspan and collaborators (Ap-28) have described oxidation of 17β-hydroxysteroids with *Flavobacterium dehydrogenans* and Δ^1-dehydrogenations with *Corynebacterium hoagii*, which resulted in the transformation of both d and l substrates.

---

[67] Chem. Eng. News 42, 42 (1964).

CHAPTER III

THE CONSTRUCTION AND USE OF TABLE I

ORDER OF THE TABLE

The entries in Table I are all products of microbial transformation. With few exceptions, compounds are recorded in this table only when a detailed procedure has been given in the cited reference. Specifically excluded are the lists of transformation products, given without experimental detail, which occur often in the patent literature. As a general rule, one is better advised to use the scientific literature, as distinct from the patent literature, as the prime guide.

The table entries are recorded in an order determined by the following rules, which are applied sequentially:

    (a) According to increasing carbon content
    (b) According to increasing hydrogen content
    (c) According to increasing oxygen content
    (d) According to the alphabetic placement of hetero atoms, e.g., Br, Cl, F, I, N, S; for compounds of identical C, H, and O content; BrCl (as in $C_{21}H_{28}O_3BrCl$) precedes Br_2 (as in $C_{21}H_{28}O_3Br_2$); FS precedes N (e.g., $C_{21}H_{28}O_3FS$ precedes $C_{21}H_{28}O_3N$)

Products of known empirical formula, but unknown structure, are shown at the end of each group of entries having common empirical formulas. Systematic organic chemical nomenclature has been used, except for sapogenins and steroidal alkaloids. Common names of the principal hormones are given parenthetically.

Where an isotope (other than the most common) of a given element is present, the empirical formula is constructed without special reference to the label (e.g., $C_{21}H_{29}H^3O_3$ is given under $C_{21}H_{30}O_3$). The label is indicated by the use of a suffix symbol in the product name (e.g., 21-hydroxy-4-pregnene-3,20-dione 21-O^{18}).

NOMENCLATURE

The following systematic stem names were used for the indicated structures.

Estrone   Androstane   Pregnane

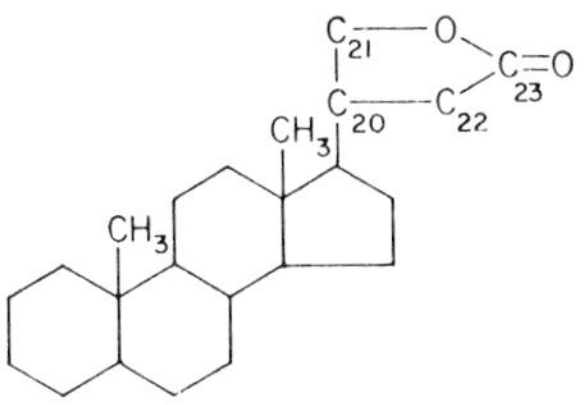

Cardanolide

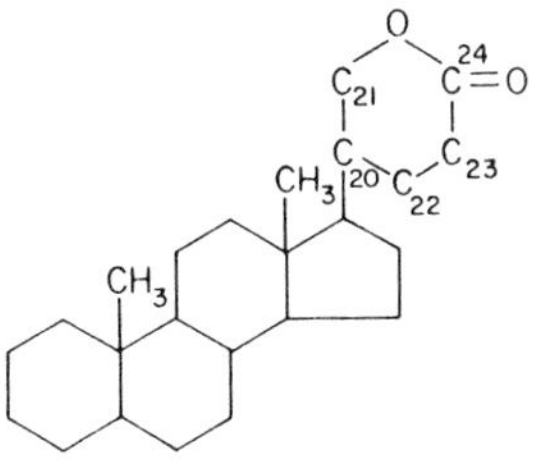

Bufanolide

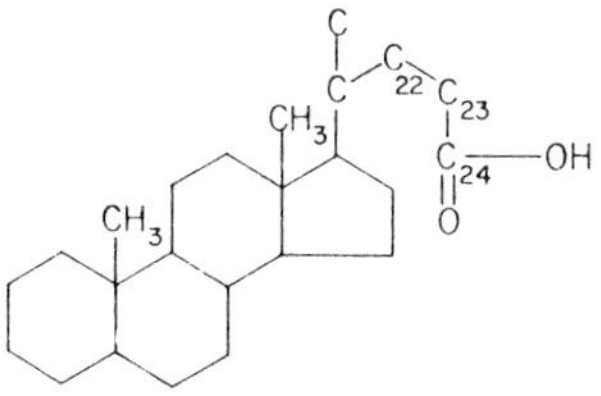

Cholanic acid

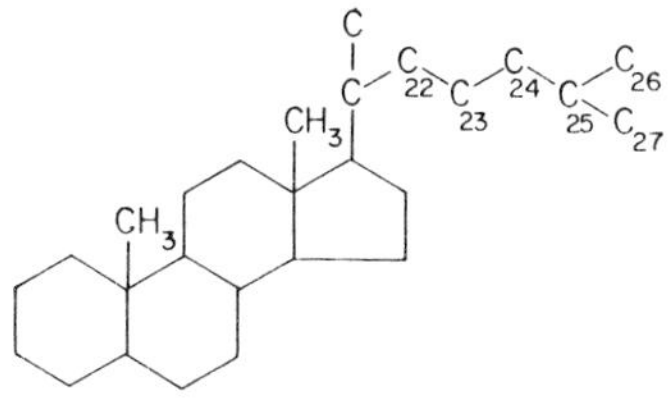

Cholestane

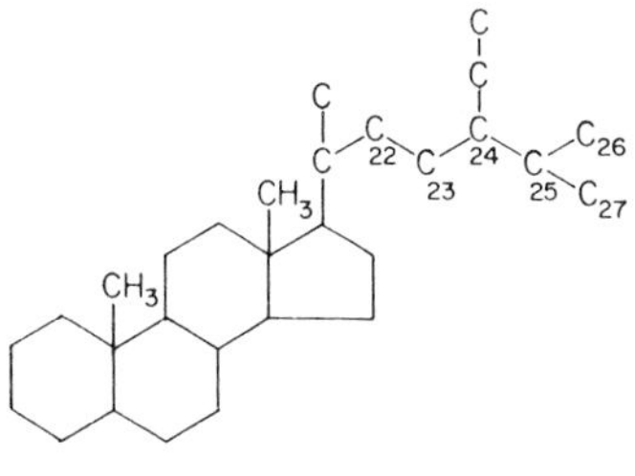

Stigmastane

The problem of the nomenclature of the few sapogenin and steroidal alkaloid entries was evaded by the use of common stem names. These are defined elsewhere.[68]

Configuration of any substituent attached to a ring carbon of the steroid nucleus is defined as β when that substituent projects above the plane of the steroid nucleus and as α when the substituent projects below the plane. Substituents which have the β-configuration are shown attached to the nucleus by solid lines, and those which have the α-configuration, by dotted lines. Configuration of hydrogen at the 5-position is always defined by 5α- or 5β- preceding the stem. Configurations at the 8-, 10-, 13-, and 17-positions are understood to be β unless otherwise indicated, and configurations at the 9- and 14-positions are understood to be α. Configuration at the 20-position is specified as α or β following the Fieser convention.[68]

No more than one class of suffix designation for substituents is affixed to any stem. All remaining substituents are expressed in prefixes, arranged alphabetically. The alphabetical arrangement of prefixes depends only on the root term for the prefix and is independent of the number of substituents of the particular type. For example, *fluoro* precedes *hydroxy*, *fluoro* precedes *dihydroxy*, *hydroxy* precedes *methyl*, and *trihydroxy* precedes *methyl*.

---

[68] Fieser, L. F., and Fieser, M., "Steroids." Reinhold, New York, 1959.

The prefix nor defines a steroid with cne less carbon atom than the stem indicates (bisnor — two carbon atoms less, etc.). Where no number or letter precedes nor, the carbon which has been dropped is the highest-numbered stem member. In other instances, the carbon atom which is missing is shown by the number or letter preceding nor (e.g., 19-nor-4-pregnene-3,20-dione or A-nor-3-androstene-2-one). Where the letter designation is used, ring contraction of the indicated ring is present, and the highest numbered carbon atom in that ring is absent.

The prefix homo defines a steroid with one more atom than the stem indicates. The rules for definition of the locus of the change follow those for norsteroids. The homo atom, which is usually a ring member in the compounds treated here, is given a number designation of the highest-numbered atom of the given ring, followed by the letter a.

D-homo-17a-oxa

Oxa, aza, and thia designate the replacement of an actual or hypothetical carbon by oxygen, nitrogen, and sulfur, respectively.

Seco defines a bond normally present in the steroid skeleton, which is broken in the case in question.

9,10-seco-

Retro defines a steroid with the 9β,10α-configuration (in place of the normal 9α,10β).

Entries of the same empirical formula are placed in alphabetical sequence according to the name defined by the stem plus the suffix: androstadiene, androstane, androstene, pregnadiene, pregnane, and pregnene.

For compounds with identical stem names, ranking is determined by the alphabetical position of the prefix: bromo, ethyl, fluoro, hydroxy, methyl, etc. Where there is more than one prefix, that which begins with the letter closest to a determines the rank of the compound. Designations such as di and tri are ignored for this purpose, e.g., dihydroxy is an h prefix, not a d prefix. For compounds with identical prefixes and stem names, the order is determined by the position of the lowest-numbered substitutent, e.g., 1α-hydroxy-4-pregnene-3,20-dione precedes 6β-hydroxy-4-pregnene-3,20-dione. For identically positioned substituents α always precedes β.

DESCRIPTION OF THE TRANSFORMATION LEADING TO THE PRODUCT

A shorthand notation is used to show the transformation(s) which led to the illustrated product. Symbols are defined as follows.

Δ^x	Insertion of a double bond between the numbered carbon (x=1, 2, 3, etc.) and that of next higher number
$\Delta^{x,y}$	Insertion of <u>two</u> double bonds, x defining the unsaturation of the lower number and y the unsaturation of the higher number (according to the preceding rule)
$\Delta^{x(y)}$	Insertion of a double bond between the indicated, nonconsecutively numbered carbon atoms
$\Delta^x (y\text{-}\alpha)$	Insertion of a double bond into a precursor with hydrogen or another substituent in the illustrated configuration, e.g., $\Delta^4 (5\beta\text{-H})$ means double bond introduction into a 5β-steroid at Δ^4
x-OH	Hydroxylation at the indicated site
$\longrightarrow$	The illustrated functional group is transformed in the indicated way
x-OH $\longrightarrow$ x-C=O	The indicated hydroxyl group is oxidized to ketone
x-C=O $\longrightarrow$ x-OH	The indicated ketone is reduced to hydroxyl
$\Delta^x \longrightarrow y\beta\text{-H}$	The indicated double bond is reduced and hydrogen enters in the noted configuration, e.g., $\Delta^4 \longrightarrow 5\beta$-H means that the Δ^4 double bond has been reduced, with the hydrogen at the 5-position entering β-
enol. or enoliz.	Enolization of a carbonyl group
ketoniz.	Reversion of an enol to the corresponding ketone
degradation [X,Y] (substrate)	The degradation of the indicated rings [X,Y] of the illustrated substrate has occurred. The chemical changes here are so numerous and, in some cases, incompletely understood that individual steps are not shown
Me	CH_3
Fo	$\overset{\displaystyle O}{\overset{\displaystyle \|}{H\text{-}C\text{-}}}$
Ac	$\overset{\displaystyle O}{\overset{\displaystyle \|}{CH_3 C\text{-}}}$
Pr	$\overset{\displaystyle O}{\overset{\displaystyle \|}{CH_3\text{-}CH_2\text{-}C\text{-}}}$
Bu	$\overset{\displaystyle O}{\overset{\displaystyle \|}{CH_3\text{-}CH_2\text{-}CH_2\text{-}C\text{-}}}$
i-Bu	$\overset{\displaystyle O}{\overset{\displaystyle \|}{(CH_3)_2\text{-}CH\text{-}C\text{-}}}$

rev. aldol or
reverse aldol

YIELD

Where a yield is reported by the investigators, it is recorded in the table. The term (cr.) following yield means that the figure applies to a product which in our judgment is significantly less pure than the analytical sample of the indicated compound. Where no yield has been reported, the yield column shows a dash (–). Where the yield is less than 1%, it has sometimes been given as "trace" (tr.).

ORGANISM

The organism is described in the language of the particular reference, with few exceptions (*Corynebacterium* is used in preference to *Arthrobacter*, and *Streptomyces* in place of *Actinomyces*). When an organism has been unidentified in early work, but characterized in later reports, the final assignment is used. For a more exact description of the organism (source or culture number), it is necessary to consult Table III "Transformation by Genus." Where the author has catalogued a list of identical transformations, using different species from the same genus, we have sometimes abbreviated his report as a single entry with a generic description (e.g., *Aspergillus* sp. for a list of Aspergilli which all 11α-hydroxylate Compound S). These cultures are listed individually in Table III "Transformation by Genus" and are marked with an asterisk in that table.

Transformations with mixed cultures have been omitted from this table except in a few cases of historical interest.

In general, reactions with cellfree enzymes and enzyme systems, which have not also been reported for the intact culture, have not been included in this table.

CONSTANTS

Melting points are given to the nearest degree (centigrade), excepting those values which have been reported by the investigators to the half degree (e.g., 244.5-246). Rotations are rounded off to the nearest degree, with the same exception. The rotation solvent is given in brackets after the reading: a, acetone; c, chloroform; d, dioxane; e, ethanol; m, methanol; and p, pyridine.

In several instances a rotatory dispersion curve has been reported by the investigator with no sodium D line read-out. An asterisk has been entered in the rotation column in these cases. No temperatures have been recorded for rotations on account of the lack of space in the table and the relative insensitivity of rotations to minor temperature changes. Almost all rotations were reported at 25 ± 5°C.

REFERENCES

The reference for each entry is given by coded citation in the reference column. These citations are arranged alphabetically in the Bibliography. None of these references are listed in the Bibliographical Appendix. The references are drawn from the scientific literature and the United States Patent literature through January 1964, with a few subsequent inclusions.

Many later references to the scientific literature (not patent literature) through December 1966 are in the Bibliographical Appendix. These are annotated briefly in most cases and have been used, where pertinent, in the discussion sections but not in the tabular sections of this book.

TABLE I

Transformations by Product

EMPIRICAL FORMULA	NAME OF REACTION PRODUCT	TRANSFORMATION	YIELD %	ORGANISM	CONSTANTS m. p.°	[α]$_D$	REF
$C_{13}H_{18}O_3$	3aα-H-4α-[3'-propionic acid]-5α-hydroxy-7aβ-methyl-hexahydro-1-indanone lactone	degradation [A, B] (testosterone); 17β-OH → C=O	2	Nocardia restrictus	124-127	+ 24[c]	W-10
	3aα-H-4α-[3'-propionic acid]-5β-hydroxy-7aβ-methyl-hexahydro-1-indanone lactone	degradation [A, B] (testosterone); 17β-OH → C=O	—	Nocardia restrictus	128.5-130.5	—	W-10
$C_{13}H_{18}O_4$	3aα-H-4α-[3'-propionic acid]-7aβ-methylhexahydro-1,5-indanedione	degradation [A, B] (4-androstene-3,17-dione)	12	Nocardia restrictus	110-111.5	+121[c]	S-895
		degradation [A, B] (testosterone); 17β-OH → C=O	13	Nocardia restrictus	109-110	—	W-10
$C_{13}H_{20}O_3$	3aα-H-4α-[3'-n-propanol]-7aβ-methylhexahydro-1,5-indanedione	degradation [A, B] (progesterone)	—	Mycobacterium smegmatis	110-114	—	S-821
$C_{15}H_{22}O_4$	1β-acetyl-3aα-H-4α-[3'-propionic acid]-7aβ-methyl-hexahydro-5-indanone	degradation [A, B] (progesterone)	2-10	Mycobacterium smegmatis	90-93	+ 79[c]	S-819
$C_{15}H_{24}O_3$	1β-acetyl-3aα-H-4α-[3'-n-propanol]-7aβ-methylhexahydro-5-indanone	degradation [A, B] (progesterone)	—	Mycobacterium smegmatis	112-116	+ 86[c]	S-821
$C_{18}H_{19}O_3Br$	9α-bromo-3-hydroxy-1,3,5(10)-estratriene-11,17-dione	Δ^1; enol.	—	Corynebacterium simplex	—	—	R-76
$C_{18}H_{19}O_3F$	6α-fluoro-3-hydroxy-1,3,5(10)-estratriene-11,17-dione	Δ^1; enol.	—	Septomyxa affinis	—	—	P-70
$C_{18}H_{20}O_2$	3-hydroxy-1,3,5(10),6-estratetraene-17-one	Δ^1; enol.	—	Corynebacterium simplex	—	—	Z-11
	3-hydroxy-1,3,5(10),7-estra-tetraene-17-one (equilin)	Δ^1; enol.	>60	Corynebacterium simplex	237-240	+295[c]	Z-11 Z-11
			—	Septomyxa affinis	—	—	B-72
			—	Corynebacterium simplex	—	—	B-72
	3-hydroxy-14β-1,3,5(10),9(11)-estratetraene-17-one	Δ$^{9(11)}$; 14α-H → 14β-H	<1	Glomerella fusaroides	250-252	+299[e]	L-49
$C_{18}H_{20}O_3$	3-hydroxy-9β,11β-oxido-1,3,5(10)-estratrien-17-one	Δ^1; enol.	—	Corynebacterium simplex	—	—	R-76
$C_{18}H_{21}O_2F$	6α-fluoro-3-hydroxy-1,3,5(10)-estratrien-17-one	Δ^1; enol.	—	Septomyxa affinis	—	—	P-70
$C_{18}H_{22}O_2$	3-hydroxy-1,3,5(10)-estratrien-16-one	Δ^1; enol.	67	Nocardia corallina	244.5-246	—	S-793
		Δ^1; enol.; 16α-OH → 16-C=O	—	Nocardia corallina	—	—	S-793
		Δ^1; enol.; 16β-OH → 16-C=O	—	Nocardia corallina	—	—	S-793

TABLE I

Transformations by Product

EMPIRICAL FORMULA	NAME OF REACTION PRODUCT	TRANSFORMATION	YIELD %	ORGANISM	CONSTANTS m. p.°	$[\alpha]_D$	REF.
$_{18}H_{22}O_2$	3-hydroxy-1,3,5(10)-estratrien-17-one (estrone)	3-OAc→3-OH	17	Saccharomyces cerevisiae	–	–	M-539
		3-OPr→3-OH	17	Saccharomyces cerevisiae	–	–	M-539
		3-OBu→3-OH	18	Saccharomyces cerevisiae	–	–	M-539
		17β-OH→17-C=O	32	Bacterium steroidiclasium	254-255	–	A-23
			–	Corynebacterium sp.	–	–	Z-1133
			50	Micrococcus dehydrogenans	254	–	M-546
			tr.	Proactinomyces erythropolis	–	–	T-1034
			95	Streptomyces albus	–	–	W-1082
			–	Streptomyces diastaticus	–	–	S-835; V-1048
			–	Streptomyces rimosus	–	–	S-835; U-1048
		d,l -17β-OH→ d-17-C=O + l-17β-OH	–	Streptomyces albus	257-259	+161	W-1102
		Δ^1; enol.; 17β-OH→17-C=O	60	Bacillus sphaericus	262-264	+162[d]	G-317
			22	Corynebacterium simplex	258-262	–	K-487
			–	Nocardia corallina	–	–	H-399
			67	Pseudomonas testosteroni	253-256	+154[d]	L-507; L-508
			55	Septomyxa affinis	–	–	M-573; W-1072
		Δ^4 (5α); enol.	–	Pseudomonas testosteroni	–	–	L-508
		Δ^1; reverse aldol (formaldehyde↑); enol.	–	Arthrobacter simplex	260-262	–	M-597
			–	Nocardia corallina	260-262	–	M-597
			–	Pseudomonas cruciviae	260-262	–	M-597
			–	Pseudomonas dacunhae	260-262	–	M-597
			–	Pseudomonas sp.	260-262	–	D-169; D-171; M-597
$C_{18}H_{22}O_3$	18-nor-13α-H-11β-hydroxy-1,4-andro-stadiene-3,17-dione	17β-Ac→17-C=O; 13β-COOH→13α-H; Δ^1	20	Fusarium solani	248-251	*	U-1044

TABLE I

Transformations by Product

EMPIRICAL FORMULA	NAME OF REACTION PRODUCT	TRANSFORMATION	YIELD %	ORGANISM	CONSTANTS m. p.°	$[\alpha]_D$	REF.
$C_{18}H_{22}O_3$	18-nor-13β-H-11β-hydroxy-1,4-androstadiene-3,17-dione	17β-Ac→17-C=O; 13β-COOH→13β-H; Δ^1	6	Fusarium solani	199-202	*	U-104
	3,7α-dihydroxy-1,3,5(10)-estratrien-17-one	7α-OH	2	Aspergillus carneus	—	—	L-497
			—	Glomerella cingulata	—	—	L-494
			15	Glomerella fusaroides	260-262	+111[e] +117[d]	L-497
			≳10	Glomerella fusaroides	258-260	—	L-494
			3	Glomerella glycines	258-260	—	L-497
			—	Glomerella glycines	—	—	L-494
		7α-OH; 17β-OH→17-C=O	—	Aspergillus carneus	—	—	L-497
			—	Glomerella fusaroides	—	—	L-497
			—	Glomerella glycines	—	—	L-497
	3,15α-dihydroxy-1,3,5(10)-estratrien-17-one	15α-OH	—	Aspergillus carneus	—	—	L-497
			32	Fusarium moniliforme	232-233	+212[e]	C-139
			—	Glomerella cingulata	—	—	L-494
			5	Glomerella fusaroides	228-230	+197[e]	L-497
			5	Glomerella fusaroides	228-230	+202[e]	L-494
			—	Glomerella glycines	—	—	L-494
			—	Glomerella glycines	228-230	—	L-497
		15α-OH; 17β-OH→17-C=O	—	Aspergillus carneus	—	—	L-497
			—	Glomerella fusaroides	—	—	L-497
	3,16α-dihydroxy-1,3,5(10)-estratrien-17-one	16α-OH	—	Streptomyces californicus	—	—	L-491
			—	Streptomyces halstedii	214-216	+175[m]	K-448
			—	Streptomyces mediocidicus	—	—	K-448
		16α-OH; 17β-OH→17-C=O	—	Streptomyces halstedii	—	—	K-448
			—	Streptomyces mediocidicus	—	—	K-448

TABLE I

Transformations by Product

EMPIRICAL FORMULA	NAME OF REACTION PRODUCT	TRANSFORMATION	YIELD %	ORGANISM	CONSTANTS m.p.°	$[\alpha]_D$	REF.
$C_{18}H_{22}O_3$	3-hydroxy-D-homo-17a-oxa-1,3,5(10)-estratrien-17-one	17β-Ac→ 17a-oxa-17-C≡O; Δ^1; enol.	3	Streptomyces lavendulae	338-339	−	G-317
$C_{18}H_{24}O_2$	1,3,5(10)-estratriene-3,17β-diol (estradiol)	Δ^1; enol.	−	Actinoplanes missouriensis	−	−	M-536
			52	Corynebacterium simplex	174-180	−	K-487
			75	Corynebacterium simplex	171-173	−	C-128
			−	Pseudomonas testosteroni	−	−	L-508
			12	Septomyxa affinis	−	−	M-573
			−	Septomyxa affinis	−	−	W-1072
		Δ^1; enol.; 17β-Ac→17β-OH	−	Streptomyces lavendulae	−	−	G-317
		17-C≡O→17β-OH	60-75	Rhizobium sp.	−	−	C-114
			70	Saccharomyces cerevisiae	177-179.5	+ 83[e]	W-1085
			−	Saccharomyces cerevisiae	174	−	S-806
			77	Trichomonas gallinae	−	−	S-830; S-829
		d,l-17-C≡O → d-17β-OH + l-17-C≡O	−	Saccharomyces cerevisiae	177-178	+ 82[e]	W-1094; V-1055
		17-C≡O→17β-OH; 3-OAc→3-OH	68	Saccharomyces cerevisiae	173-174	−	M-539
		17-C≡O→17β-OH; 3-OPr→3-OH	−	Saccharomyces cerevisiae	−	−	M-539
		17-C≡O→17β-OH; 3-OBu→3-OH	−	Saccharomyces cerevisiae	−	−	M-539
		3-OPr→3-OH	71	Saccharomyces cerevisiae	173-174	−	M-539
	1-5α-estrene-3,17-dione	Δ^1; 17β-OH→ 17-C≡O	33	Pseudomonas testosteroni	188-189	+221[c]	L-508
	4-estrene-3,16-dione	16-C≡O; (via 16α-OH and 16β-OH)	33	Bacillus megaterium	139.5-149.5	−	S-793a
			−	Cephalosporium acremonium	−	−	S-793a

TABLE I

Transformations by Product

EMPIRICAL FORMULA	NAME OF REACTION PRODUCT	TRANSFORMATION	YIELD %	ORGANISM	CONSTANTS m. p.°	$[\alpha]_D$	REF.
$C_{18}H_{24}O_2$	4-estrene-3,16-dione	16-C=O (via 16α-OH and 16β-OH)	–	Streptomyces roseochromogenus	–	–	S-793a
		16α-OH→16-C=O	–	Bacillus megaterium	–	–	S-793a
			–	Cephalosporium acremonium	–	–	S-793a
			–	Streptomyces roseochromogenus	–	–	S-793a
		16β-OH→16-C=O	–	Bacillus megaterium	–	–	S-793a
			–	Cephalosporium acremonium	–	–	S-793a
			–	Streptomyces roseochromogenus	–	–	S-793a
	4-estrene-3,17-dione	17β-OH→17-C=O	–	Bacillus sphaericus	162-166	–	G-317
			2	Corynebacterium simplex	170-173	–	K-487
			–	Trichomonas gallinae	–	–	S-829
		17β-Ac→17-C=O	–	Streptomyces lavendulae	163-166	–	G-317
$C_{18}H_{24}O_3$	9α-hydroxy-A-nor-3-androstene-2,17-dione	9α-OH; 17β-OH→17-C=O	–	Bacterium cyclooxydans	–	–	S-885
			–	Corynebacterium simplex	–	–	S-885
			–	Mycobacterium rhodocrous	–	–	S-885
			76	Nocardia restrictus	279-280	+ 46[e]	S-885
			71	Nocardia restrictus	281-283	+ 76[c]	W-1080
			–	Pseudomonas testosteroni	–	–	S-885
	D-homo-17a-oxa-A-nor-3-androstene-2,17-dione	17β-OH→ 17β-oxa-17-C≠O	36	Penicillium citrinum	229-230	- 91[c]	L-500; L-502
	6ξ-hydroxy-B-nor-4-androstene-3,17-dione	6ξ-OH	34	Absidia orchidis	210-213	+57.5[c]	P-741
	11α-hydroxy-B-nor-4-androstene-3,17-dione	11α-OH	4	Absidia orchidis	115-180	+ 23[c]	P-741
	10β,17β-dihydroxy-1,4-estradien-3-one	Δ^1	32	Corynebacterium simplex	230-234	- 28[m]	D-150
	1,3,5(10)-estratriene-3,6β,17β-triol	6β-OH	–	Mortierella alpina	–	–	L-493; L-497
		6β-OH; 17-C=O→ 17β-OH	–	Mortierella alpina	–	–	L-493

TABLE I

Transformations by Product

EMPIRICAL FORMULA	NAME OF REACTION PRODUCT	TRANSFORMATION	YIELD %	ORGANISM	CONSTANTS m.p.°	$[\alpha]_D$	REF.
$C_{18}H_{24}O_3$	1,3,5(10)-estratriene-3,7α,17β-triol	7α-OH	3	Aspergillus carneus	225-257	–	L-497
			–	Glomerella fusaroides	–	–	L-497
			–	Glomerella glycines	–	–	L-497
		7α-OH; 17-C=O→17β-OH	–	Aspergillus carneus	–	–	L-497
			–	Glomerella fusaroides	–	–	L-497
			–	Glomerella glycines	–	–	L-497
	1,3,5(10)-estratriene-3,15α,17β-triol	15α-OH	1	Aspergillus carneus	–	–	L-497
			21(cr.)	Fusarium moniliforme	250-251	+150[e]	C-139
			–	Glomerella fusaroides	–	–	L-497
			–	Glomerella glycines	–	–	L-497
		15α-OH; 17-C=O→17β-OH	–	Aspergillus carneus	–	–	L-497
			1-2	Glomerella fusaroides	248-250	–	L-494; L-497
			1-2; 4	Glomerella glycines	248-250	–	L-494; L-497
	1,3,5(10)-estratriene-3,16α,17β-triol	16α-OH	–	Streptomyces halstedii	281-283	+ 56[d]	K-448
			–	Streptomyces mediocidicus	281-283	+ 56[d]	K-448
			–	Streptomyces sp.	–	–	S-788
		16α-OH; 17-C=O→17β-OH	–	Streptomyces halstedii	–	–	K-488
			–	Steptomyces mediocidicus	–	–	K-488
	17β-hydroxy-4-estrene-3,16-dione	16-C=O (via 16β-OH)	1	Mycosphaerella latebrosa	120-130	- 90[c]	D-149
	11α-hydroxy-4-estrene-3,17-dione	11α-OH	69	Aspergillus ochraceus	–	–	D-150
		11α-OH; 17β-OH→17-C=O	9	Aspergillus ochraceus	212-214	+ 5[c]	D-150
	12β-hydroxy-4-estrene-3,17-dione	12β-OH; 17β-OH→17-C=O	4	Colletotrichum derridis	185-187	+121[c]	D-152
	15α-hydroxy-4-estrene-3,17-dione	15α-OH; 17β-OH→17-C=O	8	Fusarium orthoceras	200-201	+162[c]	D-151
			10	Penicillium sp.	200-201	+162[c]	D-151
$C_{18}H_{24}O_4$	16α-hydroxy-A-nor-D-homo-17a-oxa-3-androstene-2,17-dione	16α-OH	75	Streptomyces roseochromogenus	202-203	-114[c]	L-503

TABLE I

Transformations by Product

EMPIRICAL FORMULA	NAME OF REACTION PRODUCT	TRANSFORMATION	YIELD %	ORGANISM	m. p.°	$[\alpha]_D$	REF.
$C_{18}H_{26}O_2$	16α-hydroxy-4-estren-3-one	16α-OH	7	Bacillus megaterium	163-164	+ 21[m]	S-793a
			–	Cephalosporium acremonium	–	–	S-793a
			13	Streptomyces roseochromogenus	163-163.5	+20[m]	S-793a
	16β-hydroxy-4-estren-3-one	16β-OH	2	Bacillus megaterium	149-150.5	+23[m]	S-793a
			–	Cephalosporium acremonium	–	–	S-793a
			–	Streptomyces roseochromogenus	–	–	S-793a
		16-C=O→16β-OH	–	Bacillus megaterium	–	–	S-793a
			–	Cephalosporium acremonium	–	–	S-793a
			–	Streptomyces roseochromogenus	–	–	S-793a
		16α-OH→16β-OH (via 16-C=O)	–	Bacillus megaterium	–	–	S-793a
			–	Cephalosporium acremonium	–	–	S-793a
			–	Streptomyces roseochromogenus	–	–	S-793a
$C_{18}H_{26}O_3$	1β,17β-dihydroxy-A-nor-3-androsten-2-one	1β-OH	–	Gnomonia fragariae	–	–	L-496
	3β-hydroxy-5,6-oxido-B-nor-androstan-17-one	$\Delta^5 \to 5\xi,6\xi$-oxide	17	Rhizopus nigricans	192-200	+11.5[c]	P-741
	3β,11α-dihydroxy-B-nor-5-androsten-17-one	11α-OH	17	Rhizopus nigricans	110-150	- 85[c]	P-741
	3β,X-dihydroxy-B-nor-5-androsten-17-one	X-OH	1	Rhizopus nigricans	268-270	- 10[e]	P-741
	17β-hydroxy-5α-estrane-3,6-dione	6β-OH; $\Delta^4 \to \Delta^5$; ketoniz.	–	Rhizopus reflexus	–	–	M-623
	6β,17β-dihydroxy-4-estren-3-one	6β-OH	29	Helminthosporium kusanoi	209-213	- 53[c]	D-153
			18	Rhizopus nigricans	217-219	- 63[m]	P-708
			16	Rhizopus nigricans	–	–	M-642
			–	Rhizopus relexus	–	–	M-618
	10β,17β-dihydroxy-4-estren-3-one	10β-OH	46	Botrytis paeoniae	205-210	+ 70[c]	D-150
			19	Curvularia lunata	205-210	+ 70[c]	D-150
			tr.	Helminthosporium buchloes	209-211	–	D-153
			1	Rhizopus nigricans	199-205	+ 76[m]	P-708; M-642

TABLE I

Transformations by Product

EMPIRICAL FORMULA	NAME OF REACTION PRODUCT	TRANSFORMATION	YIELD %	ORGANISM	CONSTANTS m.p.°	$[\alpha]_D$	REF.
$C_{18}H_{26}O_3$	$11\alpha,17\beta$-dihydroxy-4-estren-3-one	11α-OH	34	Aspergillus ochraceus	165-166	- 43[c]	D-150
			4	Rhizopus nigricans	167-168; 185-187[p]	- 46[c]	P-708
			—	Rhizopus reflexus	—	—	M-618
	$11\beta,17\beta$-dihydroxy-4-estren-3-one	11β-OH	3	Curvularia lunata	214-219	+ 92[c]	D-150
	$12\beta,17\beta$-dihydroxy-4-estren-3-one	12β-OH	19	Colletotrichum derridis	163-165	+ 92[c]	D-152
	$14\alpha,17\beta$-dihydroxy-4-estren-3-one	14α-OH	2	Curvularia lunata	—	—	D-150
			15	Helminthosporium buchloes	192-194	+ 84[c]	D-153
			—	Mucor griseocyanus	—	—	M-610
	$15\alpha,17\beta$-dihydroxy-4-estren-3-one	15α-OH	2	Fusarium orthoceras	136-139	+ 95[c]	D-151
			—	Fusarium orthoceras	—	—	M-599
			9	Penicillium sp.	136-139	+ 95[c]	D-151
	$15\xi,17\beta$-dihydroxy-4-estren-3-one	15ξ-OH	—	Penicillium urticae	—	—	M-639
	$16\alpha,17\beta$-dihydroxy-4-estren-3-one	16α-OH	35	Hypomyces aurantius	185-186	+ 30[c]	D-149
	$16\beta,17\beta$-dihydroxy-4-estren-3-one	16β-OH	32	Mycosphaerella latebrosa	153-154	+ 51[c]	D-149; S-950
$C_{18}H_{26}O_4$	$3\beta,11\alpha$-dihydroxy-$5\xi,6\xi$-oxido-B-nor-androstan-17-one	11α-OH; $\Delta^5\rightarrow5\xi,6\xi$-oxide	2	Rhizopus nigricans	235-240	- 18[e]	P-741
	$10\beta,11\beta,17\beta$-trihydroxy-4-estren-3-one	10β-OH; 11β-OH	ca. 1	Curvularia lunata	—	—	D-150
$C_{18}H_{28}O_4$	$3\beta,5\alpha,6\beta$-trihydroxy-B-nor-androstan-17-one	$\Delta^5\rightarrow5\xi,6\xi$-oxide$\rightarrow$ $5\alpha,6\beta$-diol	12	Rhizopus nigricans	170-173	+ 61	P-741
$C_{19}H_{20}O_4$	11β-hydroxy-3,17-diketo-1,4-androstadien-18-oic acid (18→11)-lactone	17β-Ac$\rightarrow$17-C=O	35	Fusarium solani	320-322d.	—	U-1044
		Δ^1; 17β-Ac$\rightarrow$17-C=O	—	Fusarium solani	—	—	U-1044
$C_{19}H_{21}O_3F$	6α-fluoro-1,4-androstadiene-3,11,17-trione	Δ^1	—	Septomyxa affinis	—	—	P-709
	9α-fluoro-17β-hydroxy-1,4,6-androstatriene-3,11-dione	17-C=O$\rightarrow$17β-OH	—	Saccharomyces cerevisiae	—	—	G-305
$C_{19}H_{22}O_2$	1,4,7-androstatriene-3,17-dione	Δ^1	—	Septomyxa affinis	—	—	B-72
$C_{19}H_{22}O_2Cl_2$	$9\alpha,11\beta$-dichloro-1,4-androstadiene-3,17-dione	Δ^1	—	Corynebacterium simplex	—	—	G-308

TABLE I

Transformations by Product

EMPIRICAL FORMULA	NAME OF REACTION PRODUCT	TRANSFORMATION	YIELD %	ORGANISM	CONSTANTS m. p.°	[α]_D	REF.
$C_{19}H_{22}O_3$	1,4-androstadiene-3,11,17-trione	17α-OH-17β-(20-C=O-21-OH) →17-C=O; Δ^1	40	Septomyxa affinis	186-190	–	S-901
		17β-Ac→17-C=O; Δ^1	–	Septomyxa affinis	–	–	W-1072
	1,4-androstadiene-3,11,17-trione-4C^{14}	Δ^1; 17α-OH-17β-(20-C=O-21-OAc)→17-C=O	96	Bacillus sphaericus	–	–	C-120
	17β-hydroxy-1,4,6-andro-statriene-3,11-dione	17-C=O→17β-OH	–	Saccharomyces cerevisiae	–	–	G-305
$C_{19}H_{22}O_4$	14α-hydroxy-1,4-andro-stadiene-3,11,17-trione	Δ^1	–	Bacillus sphaericus	300-305d.	–	T-955
		11-C=O (probably via 11β-OH); 14α-OH	–	Pellicularia filamentosa	308-310d.	+212 (c-m,1:1)	T-955
		11β-OH→11-C=O; 14α-OH	–	Pelliculoria filamentosa	305-307	–	T-955
	11β,17β-dihydroxy-3-keto-1,4-androstadien-18-oic acid (18→11) lactone	Δ^1; 17β-Ac→17β-OH	3	Fusarium solani	310-314	–	U-1044
		17β-Ac→17β-OH	–	Fusarium solani	–	–	U-1044
$C_{19}H_{23}O_3Cl$	9α-chloro-11β-hydroxy-1,4-androstadiene-3,17-dione	17β-(20-C=O-21-OH)→17-C=O; Δ^1	–	Septomyxa affinis	–	–	H-399
$C_{19}H_{23}O_3F$	6α-fluoro-11β-hydroxy-1,4-androstadiene-3,17-dione	Δ^1	–	Septomyxa affinis	–	–	P-709
	6β-fluoro-11β-hydroxy-1,4-androstadiene-3,17-dione	Δ^1	–	Septomyxa affinis	–	–	P-709
	6α-fluoro-17β-hydroxy-1,4-androstadiene-3,11-dione	Δ^1	–	Septomyxa affinis	–	–	P-709
	12α-fluoro-11β-hydroxy-1,4-androstadiene-3,17-dione	Δ^1; 17β-OH→17-C=O	–	Corynebacterium simplex	–	–	R-772
	9α-fluoro-11β,17β-dihydroxy-1,4,6-androstatrien-3-one	17-C=O→17β-OH	–	Saccharomyces cerevisiae	–	–	G-305
$C_{19}H_{23}O_4F$	9α-fluoro-16α-hydroxy-4-androstene-3,11,17-trione	16α-OH	–	Streptomyces roseochromogenus	–	–	T-1008
$C_{19}H_{24}O_2$	1,4-androstadiene-3,17-dione	Δ^1	47	Actinoplanes missouriensis	132-135	–	M-536; M-537
			–	Arthrobacter simplex	–	–	M-597
			8	Arthrobacter sp.	141-143	–	D-171; D-170
			–	Bacillus lentus	143-144.5	+115[c]	R-750
			–	Bacillus pulvifaciens	–	–	I-420
			–	Bacillus sphaericus	–	–	S-942; H-399; H-373

TABLE I

Transformations by Product

EMPIRICAL FORMULA	NAME OF REACTION PRODUCT	TRANSFORMATION	YIELD %	ORGANISM	CONSTANTS m. p.°	$[\alpha]_D$	REF.
$C_{19}H_{24}O_2$	1,4-androstadiene-3,17-dione	Δ^1	–	Fusarium caucasicum	–	–	V-1056; W-1117; C-97; H-399; W-1116; W-1118
			–	Fusarium solani	–	–	V-1056
			–	Mycobacterium flavum	–	–	C-100
			–	Pseudomonas dacunhae	142-143.5	–	M-597
			4	Pseudomonas sp.	142-143.5	–	D-171
			42-44	Pseudomonas testosteroni	140.5-141	+123[c]	L-507; L-508
			–	Pycnodothis sp.	–	–	K-450
			–	Septomyxa affinis	–	–	W-1072; H-399
		Δ^1 (from 1α-H³, 2β-H)	–	Bacillus sphaericus	–	–	B-75a; G-323
		Δ^4 (from 5α-H)	–	Pseudomonas testosteroni	–	–	L-507; L-508
		$\Delta^{1,4}$ (from 5α-H)	–	Calonectria decora	145-146	+110[c]	W-1096
			–	Fusarium caucasicum	–	–	W-1116; V-1056
			–	Fusarium solani	–	–	V-1056
			–	Protaminobacter alboflavum	–	–	S-866
			–	Protaminobacter rubrum	–	–	S-866
			–	Pseudomonas testosteroni	–	–	L-507; L-508
		17β-OH→17-C=O	–	Cylindrocarpon radicicola	–	–	P-733
			–	Streptomyces lavendulae	–	–	P-733
		Δ^1; 17β-OH→17-C=O	–	Actinoplanes sp.	–	–	M-537
			–	Bacillus pulvifaciens	–	–	I-420
			–	Bacillus sphaericus	–	–	H-373
			8	Corynebacterium simplex	–	–	N-665
			–	Corynebacterium simplex	–	–	C-128
			–	Fusarium caucasicum	–	–	W-1118; C-97

TABLE I

Transformations by Product

EMPIRICAL FORMULA	NAME OF REACTION PRODUCT	TRANSFORMATION	YIELD %	ORGANISM	CONSTANTS m. p.°	[α]$_D$	REF.
$C_{19}H_{24}O_2$	1,4-androstadiene-3,17-dione	Δ^1; 17β-OH→17-C=O	–	Fusarium lateritium	–	–	C-97
			–	Fusarium solani	–	–	C-97
			–	Mycobacterium flavum	–	–	C-100
			–	Nocardia corallina	–	–	H-399
			–	Pseudomonas chlororaphis	–	–	N-648
			–	Pseudomonas testosteroni	–	–	L-507
			–	Septomyxa affinis	–	–	S-835; W-1072
		Δ^1; 17β-OF$_0$→17-C=O	–	Fusarium caucasicum	–	–	C-97
			–	Fusarium lateritium	–	–	C-97
			–	Fusarium solani	–	–	C-97
		Δ^1; 17β-OAc→17-C=O	–	Fusarium caucasicum	–	–	C-97
			–	Fusarium lateritium	–	–	C-97
			–	Fusarium solani	–	–	C-97
		Δ^1; 17β-OPr→17-C=O	–	Fusarium caucasicum	–	–	C-97
			–	Fusarium lateritium	–	–	C-97
			–	Fusarium solani	–	–	C-97
		3α-OH→3-C=O; $\Delta^{1,4}$ (from 5α-H)	–	Mycobacterium fortuitum	–	–	S-818
			–	Mycobacterium smegmatis	–	–	S-818
			–	Mycobacterium tuberculosis	–	–	S-818
		$\Delta^{1,4}$ (from 5β-H); 3α-OH→3-C=O	–	Mycobacterium fortuitum	–	–	S-818
			–	Mycobacterium smegmatis	–	–	S-818
			–	Mycobacterium tuberculosis	–	–	S-818
		17β-OH→17-C=O; $\Delta^{1,4}$ (from 5β-H)	–	Pseudomonas testosteroni	–	–	L-507
		Δ^1; 3β-OH→3-C=O; $\Delta^5 \to \Delta^4$	–	Actinoplanes missouriensis	–	–	M-537; M-536
			–	Bacillus lentus	140-142	+111[c]	R-750
			45	Bacillus pulvifaciens	139.5-140	–	T-1027; I-420

TABLE I

Transformations by Product

EMPIRICAL FORMULA	NAME OF REACTION PRODUCT	TRANSFORMATION	YIELD %	ORGANISM	CONSTANTS m. p.°	$[\alpha]_D$	REF.
$C_{19}H_{24}O_2$	1,4-androstadiene-3,17-dione	Δ^1; 3β-OH$\rightarrow$3-C=O; $\Delta^5 \rightarrow \Delta^4$	—	Fusarium caucasicum	—	—	W-1118
			—	Fusarium caucasicum	—	—	V-1056
			—	Mycobacterium fortuitum	—	—	S-818
			—	Mycobacterium smegmatis	—	—	S-818
			—	Mycobacterium tuberculosis	—	—	S-818
		Δ^1; 3β-OAc$\rightarrow$3β-OH; 3β-OH$\rightarrow$3-C=O; $\Delta^5 \rightarrow \Delta^4$	—	Bacillus lentus	140-142	+112[c]	R-750
			—	Bacillus pulvifaciens	—	—	I-420
		Δ^1; 3β-OH$\rightarrow$3-C=O; 17β-OH$\rightarrow$17-C=O; $\Delta^5 \rightarrow \Delta^4$	17	Corynebacterium simplex	139-140	+110[c]	N-665; C-128
		Δ^1; 17β-Ac$\rightarrow$17-C=O	—	Calonectria decora	—	—	V-1053
			—	Cylindrocarpon radicicola	—	—	P-733
			—	Fusarium caucasicum	145-146	+110	V-1056
			—	Fusarium caucasicum	—	—	W-1116; W-1117; W-1118; C-97
			—	Fusarium lateritium	—	—	C-97
			80	Fusarium solani	145-146	+110[c] +112[a]	W-1095; V-1056
			—	Fusarium solani	140-141	—	N-663
			—	Fusarium solani	—	—	S-949; C-97
			—	Mycobacterium flavum	—	—	C-100
			—	Mycobacterium smegmatis	—	—	S-820
			—	Pycnodothis sp.	139-140	+119[c]	K-450
			27-37	Septomyxa affinis	143-144.5	+115[c]	W-1072
			39	Septomyxa affinis	—	—	S-901
			7	Streptomyces lavendulae	138-139.5	+115[c]	F-284; F-271
			—	Streptomyces lavendulae	—	—	P-733; P-719

TABLE I

Transformations by Product

EMPIRICAL FORMULA	NAME OF REACTION PRODUCT	TRANSFORMATION	YIELD %	ORGANISM	CONSTANTS		REF.
					m.p.°	$[\alpha]_D$	
$C_{19}H_{24}O_2$	1,4-androstadiene-3,17-dione	Δ^1; Δ^{16}-17-Ac→17-C=O	—	Fusarium caucasicum	—	—	W-1118
			—	Pycnodothis sp.	—	—	K-450
		Δ^1; $16\alpha,17\alpha$-oxido-17β-Ac→17-C=O	—	Fusarium caucasicum	—	—	W-1118
		Δ^1; 17α-OH-17β-Ac→17-C=O	42	Septomyxa affinis	—	—	S-901
		Δ^1; 17β(-20-C=O-21-OH)→17-C=O	—	Fusarium caucasicum	—	—	W-1118; V-1056
			—	Fusarium solani	—	—	V-1056
			—	Mycobacterium flavum	—	—	C-100
			—	Pycnodothis sp.	—	—	K-450
			—	Septomyxa affinis	—	—	W-1072
			40	Septomyxa affinis	—	—	S-901
		Δ^1; 17β(-20-C=O-21-F)→17-C=O	46	Septomyxa affinis	—	—	S-901
		Δ^1; 17α-OH-17β(-20-C=O-21-OH)→17-C=O	10-15	Septomyxa affinis	—	—	S-901
		Δ^1; 17β-(20β-OH-21-H)→17-C=O	—	Mycobacterium flavum	—	—	C-100
		Δ^1; $\Delta^5 \to \Delta^4$; 17β-Ac→17-C=O; 3β-OH→3-C=O	—	Fusarium caucasicum	—	—	W-1118 V-1056
			—	Fusarium solani	—	—	V-1056; W-1095
		$\Delta^5 \to \Delta^4$; Δ^1; Δ^{16}-17-Ac → 17-C=O; 3β-OH → 3-C=O	—	Fusarium caucasicum	—	—	W-1118
		$\Delta^{1,4}$-(5α-H); 17β-Ac→17-C=O	—	Fusarium caucasicum	—	—	W-1116 W-1118 V-1056
			—	Fusarium solani	—	—	V-1056; W-1095
		$\Delta^{1,4}$-(5α-H); Δ^{16}-17-Ac→17-C=O	—	Fusarium caucasicum	—	—	W-1118
		$\Delta^{1,4}$-(5α-H); 3β-OH→3-C=O; 17β-Ac→17-C=O	—	Fusarium caucasicum	—	—	W-1118
		$\Delta^{1,4}$-(5α-H); 3β-OAc→3-C=O; 17β-Ac→17-C=O	—	Fusarium caucasicum	—	—	V-1056
			—	Fusarium solani	—	—	V-1056

TABLE I

Transformations by Product

EMPIRICAL FORMULA	NAME OF REACTION PRODUCT	TRANSFORMATION	YIELD %	ORGANISM	m. p. °	$[\alpha]_D$	REF.
$C_{19}H_{24}O_2$	1,4-androstadiene-3,17-dione	17β-(2'-isooctyl) $\rightarrow$17-C=O; 3β-OH$\rightarrow$ 3-C=O; $\Delta^5\rightarrow\Delta^4$; Δ'	–	Nocardia sp.	–	–	W-1111
	1,4-androstadiene-3,17-dione-1-H³	Δ^1	–	Bacillus sphaericus	–	–	B-75a
	17β-hydroxy-1,4,9(11)-androstatrien-3-one	17-C=O$\rightarrow$17β-OH	55	Saccharomyces cerevisiae	145-148	- 28[d]	R-775
	3-hydroxy-2-methyl-1,3,5(10)-estratrien-17-one	$\Delta^1(2\alpha$-CH$_3$); enol.; 17β-OH$\rightarrow$17-C=O	17	Septomyxa affinis	243-244	+167[c]	P-731
	3-hydroxy-4-methyl-1,3,5(10)-estratrien-17-one	Δ^1; enol.; 17β-OH$\rightarrow$17-C=O	13	Septomyxa affinis	244-247	+147[c]	P-731
$C_{19}H_{24}O_2F_2$	16,16-difluoro-1,3,5(10)-estratriene-3,17α-diol-3-methyl ether	17-C=O$\rightarrow$17α-OH	35(cr.)	Flavobacterium dehydrogenans	111-113	+ 48[d]	R-774
$C_{19}H_{24}O_2N_2$	16-diazo-4-androstene-3,17-dione	3β-OH$\rightarrow$3-C=O; $\Delta^5\rightarrow\Delta^4$	–	Flavobacterium dehydrogenans	217-218	-112[d]	R-763
$C_{19}H_{24}O_3$	17β-hydroxy-1,4-androstadiene-3,11-dione	Δ^1; 17β-Ac$\rightarrow$17β-OH	–	Septomyxa affinis	–	–	W-1072
		Δ^1; 17α-OH-17β(-20-C=O-21-OH)$\rightarrow$ 17β-OH	9	Septomyxa affinis	208-210d.	–	S-901
		$\Delta^{1,4}$-(5α-H); 17β-Ac$\rightarrow$17β-OH	29	Hypomyces haematococcus	233.5-234.5	+169	M-574
			–	Septomyxa affinis	–	–	M-574
	2-hydroxy-1,4-androstadiene-3,17-dione	Δ^1-(2α-OH); 17β-OH$\rightarrow$17-C=O	13	Bacillus sphaericus	148-150	+ 67[c]	G-318; H-373
			–	Nocardia corallina	–	–	H-399
		Δ^1-(2α-OH); 2α-OAc$\rightarrow$2α-OH; 17β-OAc$\rightarrow$17-C=O	–	Bacillus sphaericus	–	–	H-399
			–	Nocardia corallina	–	–	H-399
		Δ^1-(2β-OH); 2β-OAc$\rightarrow$2β-OH; 17β-OAc$\rightarrow$17-C=O	–	Nocardia corallina	–	–	H-399
	6α-hydroxy-1,4-androstadiene-3,17-dione	3β-OH$\rightarrow$3-C=O; $\Delta^5\rightarrow\Delta^4$; Δ^1; 6α-OH	–	Actinoplanes missouriensis	255-259	–	M-536; M-537
	6β-hydroxy-1,4-androstadiene-3,17-dione	3β-OH$\rightarrow$3-C=O; $\Delta^5\rightarrow\Delta^4$; Δ^1; 6β-OH	–	Actinoplanes missouriensis	200-204	–	M-536; M-537
	11α-hydroxy-1,4-androstadiene-3,17-dione	11α-OH	37	Sporotrichum bombycinum	212-214	+86.5[c]	M-582
		Δ^1; 17β-Ac$\rightarrow$17-C=O	–	Fusarium javanicum	190-192	+ 79[c]	F-276
			–	Septomyxa affinis	–	–	W-1072
		Δ^1; 11α-OH; 17β-Ac$\rightarrow$17-C=O	14	Fusarium javanicum	–	–	F-278; F-274

TABLE I

Transformations by Product

EMPIRICAL FORMULA	NAME OF REACTION PRODUCT	TRANSFORMATION	YIELD %	ORGANISM	CONSTANTS m. p.°	$[\alpha]_D$	REF.
$C_{19}H_{24}O_3$	11α-hydroxy-1,4-andro-stadiene-3,17-dione	Δ^1; 17β-OH→17-C=O	—	Actinoplanes missouriensis	—	—	M-536
	11β-hydroxy-1,4-andro-stadiene-3,17-dione	Δ^1	70-80 (cr.)	Corynebacterium simplex	176-179	—	C-128; N-666; N-667
		Δ^1; 17β-Ac→17-C=O	—	Septomyxa affinis	—	—	W-1072
		Δ^1; 17β-(20-C=O-21-OH)→17-C=O	55	Septomyxa affinis	185-186	—	S-901
		17α-OH-17β-(20-C=O-21-OH)→17-C=O	—	Pseudomonas chlororaphis	—	—	N-648
		Δ^1; 17α-OH-17β-(20-C=O-21-OH)→17-C=O	—	Pseudomonas chlororaphis	—	—	N-648
	14α-hydroxy-1,4-andro-stadiene-3,17-dione	Δ^1	—	Bacillus pulvifaciens	—	—	I-420
		$\Delta^5 \to \Delta^4$; Δ^1; 3β-OH→3-C=O; 14α-OH	—	Bacillus pulvifaciens	284-287d.	+ 69[a]	S-792; I-420
	D-homo-17a-oxa-1,4-andro-stadiene-3,17-dione	Δ^1	—	Bacillus lentus	207.5-208	- 45	R-750
		17-C=O→17a-oxa-17-C=O	—	Cylindrocarpon radicicola	—	—	P-733
			60	Fusarium caucasicum	219-220	-49[c]	W-1095
		17β-OH→17a-oxa-17-C=O	—	Cylindrocarpon radicicola	—	—	P-733
		Δ^1; 17-C=O→17a-oxa-17-C=O	—	Fusarium caucasicum	—	—	C-97
			—	Fusarium lateritium	—	—	C-97
			—	Fusarium solani	—	—	C-97
			—	Septomyxa affinis	—	—	W-107
		Δ^1; 17β-OH→17a-oxa-17-C=O	—	Cylindrocarpon radicicola	216-218	- 46[c]	F-269; F-274; F-284
			—	Fusarium caucasicum	—	—	C-97
			—	Fusarium lateritium	—	—	C-97
			—	Fusarium solani	—	—	C-97
			—	Hypomyces solani	—	—	L-525
			—	Septomyxa affinis	—	—	W-107

TABLE I

Transformations by Product

EMPIRICAL FORMULA	NAME OF REACTION PRODUCT	TRANSFORMATION	YIELD %	ORGANISM	CONSTANTS m. p.°	$[\alpha]_D$	REF.
$C_{19}H_{24}O_3$	D-homo-17a-oxa-1,4-andro-stadiene-3,17-dione	Δ^1; 17β-OFo→ 17a-oxa-17-C=O	–	Fusarium caucasicum	–	–	C-97
			–	Fusarium lateritium	–	–	C-97
			–	Fusarium solani	–	–	C-97
		Δ^1; 17β-OAc→ 17a-oxa-17-C=O	–	Fusarium caucasicum	–	–	C-97
			–	Fusarium lateritium	–	–	C-97
			–	Fusarium solani	–	–	C-97
		Δ^1; 17β-OPr → 17a-oxa-17-C=O	–	Fusarium caucasicum	–	–	C-97
			–	Fusarium lateritium	–	–	C-97
			–	Fusarium solani	–	–	C-97
		Δ^1; 17β-Ac → 17a-oxa-17-C=O	31-50	Cylindrocarpon radicicola	218-219	- 44[c]	F-269; F-274; F-284; P-733
			–	Fusarium caucasicum	–	–	E-202; C-97; W-1116
			33	Fusarium javanicum	220-222	- 47[c]	F-274; F-278
			–	Fusarium lateritium	–	–	C-97
			75	Fusarium solani	213-215	- 44[c]	K-462; N-663
			–	Fusarium solani	–	–	S-949; C-97
			21	Septomyxa affinis	–	–	S-901
			–	Septomyxa affinis	221-223	–	W-1072
		Δ^1; 17α-OH-17β-Ac→ 17a-oxa-17-C=O	19	Septomyxa affinis	–	–	S-901
		Δ^1; 17β-(20-C=O-21-OH)→17a-oxa-17-C=O	60	Fusarium solani	–	–	K-462
			20	Fusarium solani	–	–	S-901
		Δ^1; 17β-(-20-C=O-21-F)→17a-oxa-17-C=O	35	Septomyxa affinis	–	–	S-901
		Δ^1; 17α-OH-17β-(20-C=O-21-OH)→ 17a-oxa-17-C=O	–	Cylindrocarpon radicicola	–	–	F-269; F-275; F-284

TABLE I

Transformations by Product

EMPIRICAL FORMULA	NAME OF REACTION PRODUCT	TRANSFORMATION	YIELD %	ORGANISM	CONSTANTS m. p.°	[α]$_D$	REF.
C$_{19}$H$_{24}$O$_3$	D-homo-17a-oxa-1,4-androstadiene-3,17-dione	Δ^1; 17α-OH-17β-(20-C=O-21-OH)→17a-oxa-17-C=O	–	Pseudomonas chloraraphis	–	–	N-648
		Δ^1; $\Delta^5\to\Delta^4$; 3β-OH→3-C=O; 17β-(20-C=O-21-OAc)→17a-oxa-17-C=O	–	Fusarium solani	–	–	K-462
		$\Delta^{1,4}$-(5α-H); 17β-Ac→17a-oxa-17-C=O	–	Fusarium caucasicum	–	–	W-1116
	11β,17β-dihydroxy-1,4,6-androstatrien-3-one	17-C=O→17β-OH	–	Saccharomyces cerevisiae	–	–	G-305
	9,10-seco-3-hydroxy-1,3,5(10)-androstatriene-9,17-dione	Δ^1; rev. aldol; enol.	46	Arthrobacter sp.	123-129	–	D-170; D-172
			–	Bacillus sphaericus	122-129	+96[c]	K-473
		9α-OH; Δ^1; rev. aldol; enol.	10	Arthrobacter sp.	120-126	–	D-171; M-597
			ca. 20	Nocardia corallina	145.5-147	–	D-172; M-597
			–	Nocardia corallina	124-129	–	M-597
			1	Nocardia restrictus	122-124	–	S-895;
			26	Pseudomonas sp.	123.5-125	+100.5[c]	D-169; D-171; M-597
		9α-OH; Δ^1; rev. aldol; enol.; 17β-OH→17-C=O	1	Nocardia restrictus	122-124	–	W-1063
		9α-OH; Δ^1; rev. aldol; enol.; 17β-Ac→17-C=O	<1	Mycobacterium smegmatis	–	–	S-820
		9α-OH; Δ^1; $\Delta^5\to\Delta^4$; 3β-OH→3-C=O; rev. aldol; enol.	–	Mycobacterium sp.	–	–	S-818
		9α-OH; 3α-OH→3-C=O; $\Delta^{1,4}$-(5α-H); rev. aldol; enol.	–	Mycobacterium sp.	–	–	S-818
		9α-OH; 3α-OH→C=O; $\Delta^{1,4}$-(5β-H); rev. aldol; enol.	–	Mycobacterium sp.	–	–	S-818
	1-5α-androstene-3,11,17-trione	17β-Ac→17-C=O; Δ^1	–	Septomyxa affinis	–	–	W-1072

TABLE I

Transformations by Product

EMPIRICAL FORMULA	NAME OF REACTION PRODUCT	TRANSFORMATION	YIELD %	ORGANISM	CONSTANTS m.p.°	$[\alpha]_D$	REF.
$C_{19}H_{24}O_3$	1-5α-androstene-3,11,17-trione	Δ^1; 17β-Ac→17-C=O	28-45	Septomyxa affinis	244.5-246.5	+188[c]	E-207; M-573
	1-5β-androstene-3,11,17-trione	17β-Ac→17-C=O; Δ^1	—	Septomyxa affinis	—	—	W-1072
		Δ^1; 17β-Ac→17-C=O	5-10	Septomyxa affinis	174.5-177.5	+205[c]	E-207; M-573
	9α,11α-oxido-4-androstene-3,17-dione	$\Delta^{9(11)}$→9α,11α-oxido	53	Nocardia sp.	273-275	+180[c]	S-886
	4-androstene-3,6,17-trione	6-C=O	—	Euglena gracilis	—	—	G-322
	4-androstene-3,6,17-trione-7-H[3]	6-C=O (via 6β-OH)	2	Rhizopus arrhizus	205-208	—	B-32
	4-androstene-3,11,17-trione	11β-OH→11-C=O	—	Gibberella saubinetti	—	—	U-1043
		17β-OH→17-C=O	—	Trichomonas gallinae	—	—	S-829
		17β-Ac→17-C=O	—	Aspergillus oryzae	—	—	C-102
			—	Gliocladium catenulatum	—	—	M-633
			—	Penicillium expansum	—	—	M-637
		17α-OH-17β-(20-C=O-21-OH)→ 17-C=O	—	Gliocladium catenulatum	—	—	M-633
			—	Penicillium lilacinum	—	—	M-637
		17α-OH-17β-(20-C=O-21-OAc)→ 17-C=O	—	Gliocladium catenulatum	—	—	M-633
			—	Penicillium lilacinum	—	—	M-637
	unknown	unknown	0.3-5	Bacillus pulvifaciens	284-287	—	T-1027
$C_{19}H_{24}O_4$	11α-hydroxy-D-homo-17a-oxa-1,4-androstadiene-3,17-dione	Δ^1; 17β-Ac → 17a-oxa-17-C=O; 11α-OH	< 1	Fusarium javanicum	251-253	- 58[c]	F-274; F-278
	15α-hydroxy-D-homo-17a-oxa-1,4-androstadiene-3,17-dione	15α-OH	42	Penicillium sp.	260-262	- 55[c]	D-158; P-706
	16α-hydroxy-D-homo-17a-oxa-1,4-androstadiene-3,17-dione	16α-OH	45	Streptomyces roseochromogenus	196-198; 213-214	- 68[c]	T-1000; P-706
	3,18-dihydroxy-9,10-seco-1,3,5(10)-androstatriene-9,17-dione	Δ^1; rev. aldol. enol.	—	Bacillus sphaericus	148-150	+ 91[c]	K-473
	14α-hydroxy-4-androstene-3,11,17-trione	14α-OH	—	Pellicularia filamentosa	—	—	K-473

TABLE I

Transformations by Product

EMPIRICAL FORMULA	NAME OF REACTION PRODUCT	TRANSFORMATION	YIELD %	ORGANISM	CONSTANTS m.p.°	$[\alpha]_D$	REF.
$C_{19}H_{24}O_4$	14α-hydroxy-4-androstene-3,11,17-trione	14α-OH; 11β-OH→11-C=O	–	Pellicularia filamentosa	301-304d.	+263 |c; m -1; 1|	T-955
	15α-hydroxy-4-androstene-3,11,17-trione	11-C=O	–	Pellicularia filamentosa	199-201	–	T-955
$C_{19}H_{25}O_2F$	6α-fluoro-17α-methyl-1,3,5(10)-estratriene-3,17β-diol	Δ¹; enol.	–	Septomyxa affinis	–	–	C-93
$C_{19}H_{25}O_3F$	9α-fluoro-11β,17β-dihydroxy-1,4-androstadien-3-one	17-C=O→17β-OH	–	Saccharomyces cerevisiae	–	–	N-666
	12α-fluoro-11β,17β-dihydroxy-1,4-androstadien-3-one	Δ¹	–	Corynebacterium simplex	–	–	R-772
	9α-fluoro-11β-hydroxy-4-androstene-3,17-dione	17β-Ac→17-C=O	–	Cylindrocarpon radicicola	260-262	+177[c]	T-996
$C_{19}H_{25}O_4F$	9α-fluoro-11β,16α-dihydroxy-4-androstene-3,17-dione	16α-OH	58(cr.)	Streptomyces roseochromogenus	280-282	+173[c]	T-1008
			57(cr.)	Streptomyces roseochromogenus	262-270	+157[m]	B-62
$C_{19}H_{26}O_2$	17β-hydroxy-1,4-androstadien-3-one	Δ¹	21	Corynebacterium simplex	159-165	–	N-665
			–	Corynebacterium simplex	165-167	–	C-128
			–	Fusarium caucasicum	–	–	C-97
			–	Fusarium lateritium	–	–	C-97
			–	Fusarium solani	–	–	C-97
			–	Mycobacterium smegmatis	–	–	S-873
			–	Nocardia corallina	–	–	H-399
			–	Pseudomonas testosteroni	–	–	L-507
			–	Ramularia robusta	–	–	L-525
			–	Septomyxa affinis	–	–	W-1072
			–	Volutella ciliata	–	–	L-525
		17-C=O→17β-OH	84	Saccharomyces cerevisiae	168	–	D-143
			82	Saccharomyces cerevisiae	163-167	–	C-128
			–	Trichomonas gallinae	–	–	S-829
		Δ¹; 17-C=O→17β-OH	–	Fusarium caucasicum	–	–	C-97
			–	Fusarium lateritium	–	–	C-97

TABLE I

Transformations by Product

EMPIRICAL FORMULA	NAME OF REACTION PRODUCT	TRANSFORMATION	YIELD %	ORGANISM	CONSTANTS m. p.°	$[\alpha]_D$	REF.
$C_{19}H_{26}O_2$	17β-hydroxy-1,4-andro-stadien-3-one	Δ^1 ; 17-C=O→17β-OH	—	Fusarium solani	—	—	C-97
			—	Mycobacterium flavum	—	—	C-100
			—	Pseudomonas testosteroni	—	—	L-508
			—	Septomyxa affinis	—	—	W-1072
		Δ^4 ; 17-C=O→17β-OH	—	Pseudomonas testosteroni	—	—	L-508
		$\Delta^{1,4}$-(5β-H)	—	Pseudomonas testosteroni	—	—	L-508
		$\Delta^{1,4}$-(5α-H) ; 17-C=O→17β-OH	—	Pseudomonas testosteroni	—	—	L-508
		Δ^1 ; Δ^5→Δ^4 ; 3β-OH→3-C=O	7	Corynebacterium simplex	164-166	+ 25[c]	N-665 ; C-128
		Δ^1 ; 17β-Ac→17β-OH	—	Cylindrocarpon radicicola	—	—	P-733
			—	Fusarium caucasicum	—	—	C-97
			—	Fusarium lateritium	—	—	C-97
			—	Fusarium solani	—	—	C-97
			—	Fusarium solani	167-168	—	N-663
			—	Mycobacterium flavum	—	—	C-100
			8	Septomyxa affinis	172-173	+ 23	W-1072
			18	Septomyxa affinis	—	—	S-901
			12	Streptomyces lavendulae	167-168	+ 21[c]	F-284 ; F-271 ; P-733
		Δ^1 ; 17β-(20β-OH-21-H) →17β-OH	—	Mycobacterium flavum	—	—	C-100
		Δ^1 ; 17α-OH-17β-Ac→ 17β-OH	50	Septomyxa affinis	—	—	W-1072
			14	Septomyxa affinis	—	—	S-901
		Δ^1 ; 17β-(20-C=O-21-OH)→17β-OH	—	Mycobacterium flavum	—	—	C-100
			—	Septomyxa affinis	—	—	W-1072
			20	Septomyxa affinis	—	—	S-901
		Δ^1 ; 17β-(20-C=O-21-F) →17β-OH	11	Septomyxa affinis	—	—	S-901
		Δ^1 ; 17α-OH-17β-(20-C=O-21-OH)→17β-OH	< 1	Septomyxa affinis	—	—	S-901

TABLE I

Transformations by Product

EMPIRICAL FORMULA	NAME OF REACTION PRODUCT	TRANSFORMATION	YIELD %	ORGANISM	CONSTANTS m. p.°	$[\alpha]_D$	REF.
$C_{19}H_{26}O_2$	1-5α-androstene-3,17-dione	Δ^1	–	Bacillus sphaericus	–	–	H-373
		Δ^1-(1α-H^2)	–	Bacillus sphaericus	–	–	R-768; R-769
		Δ^1-(1α-H^3)	–	Bacillus sphaericus	–	–	G-323; B-75a
		Δ^1; 17β-OH→17-C=O	–	Bacillus sphaericus	–	–	H-373
	1-5β-androstene-3,17-dione	Δ^4→5β-H	80	Clostridium paraputrificum	168-169	+222[e]	S-824
	4-androstene-3,17-dione	17β-OH→17-C=O	6	Aspergillus oryzae	167-169	–	K-482
			–	Bacillus pulvifaciens	–	–	I-420
			–	Cladosporium resinae	–	–	F-254
			–	Corynebacterium simplex	–	–	C-128
			–	Fusarium caucasicum	–	–	C-97
			–	Fusarium lateritium	–	–	C-97
			–	Fusarium solani	–	–	C-97
			–	Nocardia corallina	–	–	H-399
			–	Penicillium lilacinum	–	–	P-737
			47	Proactinomyces erythropolis	171	–	T-1032
			–	Pseudomonas chlororaphis	–	–	N-648
			–	Pseudomonas testosteroni	–	–	L-508
			–	Trichomonas gallinae	–	–	S-829
			1	Wojnowicia graminis	160-167	–	H-381
		3β-OH→3-C=O; Δ^5→Δ^4	–	Acetobacter pasteurianum	173	+198[c]	K-457
			18	Bacillus pulvifaciens	169-170	+216[c]	T-1027 I-420
			–	Corynebacterium helvolum	–	–	M-546
			47	Corynebacterium simplex	167-169	–	N-665; C-128
			–	Flavobacterium androstenedionicum	–	–	E-219
			87	Micrococcus dehydrogenans	168-169	–	E-214

TABLE I

Transformations by Product

EMPIRICAL FORMULA	NAME OF REACTION PRODUCT	TRANSFORMATION	YIELD %	ORGANISM	CONSTANTS m. p.°	$[\alpha]_D$	REF.
$C_{19}H_{26}O_2$	4-androstene-3,17-dione	3β-OH→3-C=O; $\Delta^5 \to \Delta^4$	70	"Milan yeast"	168-169	−	M-552
			−	Mycobacterium fortuitum	−	−	S-818
			−	Mycobacterium smegmatis	−	−	S-818
			−	Mycobacterium tuberculosis	−	−	S-818
			96	Proactinomyces erythropolis	169	−	T-1032
		3β-OAc→3-C=O; $\Delta^5 \to \Delta^4$	84	Streptomyces globisporus	171-172	+192[c]	H-335
			−	Streptomyces viridochromogenes	−	−	H-335
		3β-OH→3-C=O; $\Delta^5 \to \Delta^4$; 17β-OH→17-C=O	−	Corynebacterium simplex	−	−	C-128
			−	Corynebacterium sp.	−	−	Z-1133
			40	Flavobacterium androstenedionicum	165-169	−	E-220; E-219
			18	Flavobacterium carbonilicum	170-171	−	M-592
			4	Micrococcus dehydrogenans	167-168	−	E-217
			6	Proactinomyces erythropolis	170	−	T-1032
			76	Streptomyces globisporus	−	−	H-337
			−	Streptomyces viridochromogenes	−	−	H-337
		3α-OH→3-C=O; Δ^4-(5α-H)	−	Mycobacterium fortuitum	−	−	S-818
			−	Mycobacterium smegmatis	−	−	S-818
			−	Mycobacterium tuberculosis	−	−	S-818
		3α-OH→3-C=O; Δ^4-(5β-H)	−	Mycobacterium fortuitum	−	−	S-818
			−	Mycobacterium smegmatis	−	−	S-818
			−	Mycobacterium tuberculosis	−	−	S-818
		17β-OH→17-C=O; Δ^4-(5β-H)	−	Pseudomonas testosteroni	−	−	L-508
		17β-Ac→17-C=O	−	Aspergillus chevalieri	−	−	C-102

TABLE I

Transformations by Product

EMPIRICAL FORMULA	NAME OF REACTION PRODUCT	TRANSFORMATION	YIELD %	ORGANISM	CONSTANTS m.p.°	$[\alpha]_D$	REF.
$C_{19}H_{26}O_2$	4-androstene-3,17-dione	17β-Ac→17-C=O	–	Aspergillus flavus	–	–	P-726
			–	Aspergillus oryzae	–	–	C-102
			–	Cephalosporium acremonium	–	–	H-398
			–	Cephalosporium subverticillatum	–	–	B-67
			–	Cladosporium resinae	–	–	F-254
			–	Cylindrocephalum aureum	–	–	S-880
			–	Fusarium caucasicum	–	–	C-97; W-1116
			–	Fusarium lateritium	–	–	C-97
			–	Fusarium solani	–	–	C-97; S-949
			–	Gliocladium catenulatum	174-176	+194[c]	P-726
			4	Gliocladium catenulatum	169-171	–	M-633
			–	Nocardia sp.	170-172	–	D-172
			–	Penicillium brevicompactum	–	–	M-637
			–	Penicillium chrysogenum	–	–	C-102
			–	Penicillium citrinum	–	–	C-102
			–	Penicillium frequentans	–	–	M-637
			16	Penicillium lilacinum	175-176.5	+194[c]	M-637
			–	Penicillium lilacinum	–	–	P-726; S-832
			–	Penicillium steckii	–	–	C-102
			–	Penicillium sp.	–	–	C-102
			–	Pycnodothis sp.	–	–	K-450
		17β-Pr→17-C=O	–	Gliocladium catenulatum	–	–	M-633
		17α-OH-17β-Ac→17-C=O	–	Aspergillus oryzae	–	–	C-102
			–	Penicillium lilacinum	–	–	M-637
		17β-(20-C=O-21-OH)→17-C=O	–	Cylindrocephalum aureum	–	–	S-880

TABLE I

Transformations by Product

EMPIRICAL FORMULA	NAME OF REACTION PRODUCT	TRANSFORMATION	YIELD %	ORGANISM	CONSTANTS m.p.°	$[\alpha]_D$	REF.
$C_{19}H_{26}O_2$	4-androstene-3,17-dione	17β-(20-C=O-21-OH) $\rightarrow$17-C=O	–	Gliocladium catenulatum	–	–	M-633
			–	Penicillium nigricans	–	–	M-637
		17β-(20-C=O-21-OAc)$\rightarrow$17-C=O	–	Gliocladium deliquescens	–	–	M-633
			–	Gliocladium luteolum	–	–	M-633
			–	Gliocladium roseum	–	–	M-633
			–	Penicillium canescens	–	–	M-637
			–	Penicillium charlesii	–	–	M-637
			–	Penicillium lividum	–	–	M-637
		17β-(20-C=O-21-OPr)$\rightarrow$17-C=O	–	Cylindrocephalum aureum	–	–	S-880
		17α-OH-17β-(20-C=O-21-OH)$\rightarrow$ 17-C=O	–	Didymella lycopersici	–	–	V-1048
			–	Gliocladium catenulatum	–	–	M-633
			–	Penicillium chrysogenum	–	–	V-1048
			–	Penicillium lilacinum	–	–	M-637
			–	Pseudomonas chlororaphis	–	–	N-648
		17β-Ac$\rightarrow$17-C=O; Δ^4-(5α-H)	–	Fusarium caucasicum	–	–	W-1116
		17β-(2'-isooctyl) $\rightarrow$17-C=O; 3β-OH$\rightarrow$ 3-C=O; $\Delta^5\rightarrow\Delta^4$	–	Nocardia sp.	–	–	W-1111
$C_{19}H_{26}O_2F_2$	16,16-difluoro-17α-hydroxy-4-androsten-3-one	17-C=O$\rightarrow$17α-OH; 3β-OH$\rightarrow$3-C=O; $\Delta^5\rightarrow\Delta^4$	46	Flavobacterium dehydrogenans	190-193	+ 64[d]	R-774
$C_{19}H_{26}O_3$	11α,17β-dihydroxy-1,4-androstadien-3-one	11α-OH	59	Sporotrichum sulfurescens	174-175	- 7[c]	M-582
		11α-OH; 17β-(20-C=O-21-OH) $\rightarrow$17β-OH	44	Sprortrichum epigaeum	–	–	M-582
		Δ^1; 17β-Ac$\rightarrow$17β-OH	–	Fusarium javanicum	183-185	- 15[c]	W-1072
			–	Septomyxa affinis	–	–	W-1072
		Δ^1; 17β-Ac$\rightarrow$17β-OH; 11α-OH	–	Fusarium javanicum	183-185	–	F-274; F-278
	11β,17β-dihydroxy-1,4-androstadien-3-one	Δ^1; 17β-Ac$\rightarrow$17β-OH	–	Septomyxa affinis	–	–	W-1072

TABLE I

Transformations by Product

EMPIRICAL FORMULA	NAME OF REACTION PRODUCT	TRANSFORMATION	YIELD %	ORGANISM	CONSTANTS m. p.°	[α]$_D$	REF.
C$_{19}$H$_{26}$O$_3$	11β,17β-dihydroxy-1,4-androstadien-3-one	Δ^1; 17β-(20-C=O-21-OH) →17β-OH	13	Septomyxa affinis	156	–	S-901
	12α,17β-dihydroxy-4,14-androstadien-3-one	Δ^{14}; 12α-OH	<1	Wojnowicia graminis	166-168	+136[c]	H-381
	5α-androstane-3,6,17-trione	Δ^4→Δ^5; ketoniz.	–	Bacillus pulvifaciens	–	–	I-420
		6-C=O; 3β-OH→3-C=O; Δ^5→5α-H	7-9	Bacillus pulvifaciens	196-196.5	+79.5[c]	T-1027; I-420
		6-C=O; Δ^4→5α-H	–	Rhizopus arrhizus	195-196	–	M-604
	5β-androstane-3,6,17-trione	17β-Ac→17-C=O	–	Gliocladium catenulatum	–	–	M-633
			–	Penicillium novae zeelandiae	–	–	M-637
	5α-androstane-3,11,17-trione	17β-Ac→17-C=O	–	Gliocladium catenulatum	–	–	M-633
			–	Penicillium lilacinum	–	–	M-637
	5β-androstane-3,12,17-trione	17β-Ac→17-C=O	–	Penicillium lilacinum	–	–	M-637
	3,17β-dihydroxy-9,10-<u>seco</u>-1,3,5(10)-androstatrien-<u>9</u>-one	9α-OH; Δ^1; rev. aldol.; enol.; 17-C=O→17β-OH	<1	Pseudomonas sp.	133-134	+16[c]	D-171; M-597
	3,9α-dihydroxy-9,10-<u>seco</u>-1,3,5(10)-androstatrien-17-one	9α-OH; Δ^1; rev. aldol.; enol.; 9-C=O→9α-OH; 17β-OH→17-C=O	<1	Nocardia restrictus	195-197	+48[e]	W-1063
	3,9β-dihydroxy-9,10-<u>seco</u>-1,3,5(10)-androstatrien-17-one	9α-OH; Δ^1; rev. aldol.; enol.; 9-C=O→9β-OH; 17β-OH→17-C=O	7(cr.)	Nocardia restrictus	155-157	+90[e]	W-1063
	3,9ξ-dihydroxy-9,10-<u>seco</u>-1,3,5(10)-androstatrien-17-one	3β-OH→3-C=O; Δ^5→Δ^4; Δ^1; 9α-OH; rev. aldol.; enoliz.; 9-C=O→9ξ-OH	–	Mycobacterium fortuitum	–	–	S-818
			–	Mycobacterium smegmatis	–	–	S-818
			–	Mycobacterium tuberculosis	–	–	S-818
		3α-OH→3-C=O; Δ^{1,4}-(5α-H); 9α-OH; rev. aldol.; enoliz.; 9-C=O→9ξ-OH	–	Mycobacterium fortuitum	–	–	S-818
			–	Mycobacterium smegmatis	–	–	S-818
			–	Mycobacterium tuberculosis	–	–	S-818
		3α-OH→3-C=O; Δ^{1,4}-(5β-H); 9α-OH; rev. aldol.; enoliz.; 9-C=O→9ξ-OH	–	Mycobacterium fortuitum	–	–	S-818
			–	Mycobacterium smegmatis	–	–	S-818

TABLE I

Transformations by Product

EMPIRICAL FORMULA	NAME OF REACTION PRODUCT	TRANSFORMATION	YIELD %	ORGANISM	CONSTANTS m.p.°	$[\alpha]_D$	REF.
$C_{19}H_{26}O_3$	3,9ξ-dihydroxy-9,10-seco-1,3,5(10)-androstatrien-17-one	3α-OH→3-C=O; $\Delta^{1,4}$(5β-H); 9α-OH; rev. aldol.; enoliz.; 9-C=O→9ξ-OH	—	Mycobacterium tuberculosis	—	—	S-818
		17β-Ac→17-C=O; Δ^1; 9α-OH; rev. aldol.; enoliz.; 9-C=O→9ξ-OH	< 1	Mycobacterium smegmatis	—	—	S-820
	17β-hydroxy-4-androstene-3,11-dione	17-C=O→17β-OH	62	Saccharomyces cerevisiae	177-180	+182[a]	H-385
			—	Trichomonas foetus	—	—	S-830
			94	Trichomonas gallinae	—	—	S-830; S-829
		17β-Ac→17β-OH	12	Aspergillus oryzae	—	—	C-102
			—	Neocosmospora vasinfecta	—	—	S-881
			51	Penicillium notatum	182-184	+200[c] +183.5[a]	H-336
	17β-hydroxy-4-androstene-3,16-dione	16-C=O	3	Wojnowicia graminis	153-155	- 54[c]	H-381
		16-C=O; 17-C=O→17β-OH	12	Corticium centrifugum	161-162.5	- 66[c]	D-166
	1α-hydroxy-4-androstene-3,17-dione	1α-OH	7	Penicillium sp.	215.5-218	+184[c]	D-163; D-167; D-168
		1α-OH 3β-OH→3-C=O; Δ^5→Δ^4	3	Penicillium sp.	216-218	—	D-163; D-168
	1β-hydroxy-4-androstene-3,17-dione	1β-OH	10(cr.)	Haplosporella sp.	155-156.5	+127.5[c]	D-165
			25	Xylaria sp.	—	+126 [c]	D-165
	2α-hydroxy-4-androstene-3,17-dione	2α-OAc→2α-OH; 17β-OAc→17-C=O	—	Bacillus sphaericus	—	—	H-399
			—	Nocardia corallina	—	—	H-399
	2β-hydroxy-4-androstene-3,17-dione	2β-OH	1	Penicillium sp.	143-145	- 37[c]	D-163; D-167; D-168
		2β-OAc→2β-OH; 17β-OAc→17-C=O	—	Bacillus sphaericus	—	—	H-399
			—	Corynebacterium simplex	—	—	H-399
			—	Nocardia corallina	—	—	H-399
			—	Septomyxa affinis	—	—	H-399
	6β-hydroxy-4-androstene-3,17-dione	6β-OH	—	Aspergillus niger	194-195	+109	F-288
			—	Fusarium caucasicum	—	—	C-97
			—	Fusarium lateritium	—	—	C-97

TABLE I

Transformations by Product

EMPIRICAL FORMULA	NAME OF REACTION PRODUCT	TRANSFORMATION	YIELD %	ORGANISM	CONSTANTS m. p.°	CONSTANTS $[\alpha]_D$	REF.
$C_{19}H_{26}O_3$	6β-hydroxy-4-androstene-3,17-dione	6β-OH	—	Fusarium solani	—	—	C-97
			13	Gibberella saubinetti	192-193.5	+107[c]	U-1043
			4	Haplosporella sp.	183-187	—	D-165
			8(cr.)	Rhizopus arrhizus	191-194	+ 99[c]	E-201
			—	Rhizopus nigricans	—	—	E-201
			—	Rhizopus reflexus	—	—	E-201
			2(cr.)	Wojnowicia graminis	—	—	H-381
		3β-OH→3-C=O; $\Delta^5 \to \Delta^4$; 6β-OH	< 1	Bacillus pulvifaciens	194-195	+115.5[c]	T-1027; Y-420
		17β-Ac→17-C=O	—	Gliocladium catenulatum	—	—	M-633
			—	Penicillium citrinum	—	—	M-637
		17β-Ac→17-C=O; 6β-OH	1	Gliocladium catenulatum	190-192	+107[c]	M-633; P-726
		17β-(20-C=O-21-OH) →17-C=O; 6β-OH	—	Gliocladium catenulatum	—	—	M-633
		17β-(20-C=O-21-OAc) →17-C=O; 6β-OH	—	Gliocladium deliquescens	—	—	M-633
			—	Gliocladium luteolum	—	—	M-633
			—	Gliocladium roseum	—	—	M-633
		17α-OH-17β-(20-C=O-21-OH)→ 17-C=O; 6β-OH	—	Gliocladium catenulatum	—	—	M-633
	6β-hydroxy-4-androstene-3,17-dione-6α,7ξ-H^3	6β-OH	12(cr.)	Rhizopus arrhizus	185-187	—	B-32
	7α-hydroxy-4-androstene-3,17-dione	7α-OH	—	Diplodia natalensis	—	—	T-997
			4	Neurospora sp.	255-256.5	+164[c]	T-1037
	7β-hydroxy-4-androstene-3,17-dione	7β-OH	10	Haplosporella sp.	225.5-228.5	—	D-165
			< 1	Pseudomonas sp.	221-225	—	D-171; M-597
			—	Rhizopus stolonifer	220.5-222.5	+186	T-1037
			10	Xylaria sp.	218-223	—	D-165
	9α-hydroxy-4-androstene-3,17-dione	9α-OH	10	Cylindrocarpon radicicola	—	—	S-898; P-740
			31	Nocardia sp.	223.5-224.5	+183[c]	D-170; D-172; M-597
		9α-OH; 17β-OH→17-C=O	17	Ascochyta linicola	218-220	—	S-828
			—	Circinella muscae	—	—	R-748
		17β-Ac→17-C=O	52	Arthrobacter sp.	223-224	—	D-172

TABLE I

Transformations by Product

EMPIRICAL FORMULA	NAME OF REACTION PRODUCT	TRANSFORMATION	YIELD %	ORGANISM	CONSTANTS m. p.°	[α]$_D$	REF.
$_{19}H_{26}O_3$	9α-hydroxy-4-androstene-3,17-dione	9α-OH; 17β-Ac→17-C=O	7	Nocardia restrictus	220-222	–	S-885
	11α-hydroxy-4-androstene-3,17-dione	11α-OH	< 1	Pseudomonas sp.	212-216	–	D-171; M-597
			19-23	Rhizopus arrhizus	226-227	+162[c]	M-601; M-604; E-201
			–	Rhizopus nigricans	–	–	M-601; E-201
			–	Rhizopus reflexus	–	–	E-201
		17β-Ac→17-C=O	20	Aspergillus oryzae	–	–	C-102
			–	Penicillium lilacinum	–	–	S-832
		Δ^{16}-17-Ac→17-C=O; 11α-OH	–	Aspergillus ochraceus	–	–	V-1048; S-835
		17α-OH-17β-Ac→17-C=O	–	Penicillium thomii	–	–	M-637
		17α-OH-17β-(20-C=O-21-OH)→17-C=O	–	Gliocladium catenulatum	–	–	M-637
			–	Penicillium lilacinum	–	–	M-637
	11α-hydroxy-4-androstene-3,17-dione-6α,7ξ-H³	11α-OH	19	Rhizopus arrhizus	216-225	–	B-32
	11β-hydroxy-4-androstene-3,17-dione	17β-OH→17-C=O	–	Trichomonas gallinae	–	–	S-829
		17α-OH-17β-(20-C=O-21-OH)→17-C=O	–	Pseudomonas chlororaphis	–	–	N-648
	14α-hydroxy-4-androstene-3,17-dione	14α-OH; 17β-OH→17-C=O	2	Wojnowicia graminis	246-252	+166[c]	H-381
		14α-OH; 3β-OH→3-C=O; Δ⁵→Δ⁴	4	Bacillus pulvifaciens	260-261.5	+162[c]	I-420; S-792; T-1027
		17β-Ac→17-C=O	5-11	Penicillium lilacinum	252-258	–	M-637; E-204
		17β-(20-C=O-21-OH)→17-C=O	–	Penicillium lilacinum	–	–	M-637
		17α-OH-17β-(20-C=O-21-OH)→17-C=O	–	Penicillium lilacinum	–	–	M-637
	15α-hydroxy-4-androstene-3,17-dione	15α-OH	–	Fusarium caucasicum	–	–	C-97
			–	Fusarium lateritium	–	–	C-97
			33-50	Fusarium lini	190-198	+217[c]	G-319; T-980

TABLE I

Transformations by Product

EMPIRICAL FORMULA	NAME OF REACTION PRODUCT	TRANSFORMATION	YIELD %	ORGANISM	CONSTANTS m. p.°	$[\alpha]_D$	RE
$C_{19}H_{26}O_3$	15α-hydroxy-4-androstene-3,17-dione	15α-OH	—	Fusarium oxysporum	—	—	M-59
			—	Fusarium solani	—	—	C-97
			2	Gibberella baccata	—	—	U-10
			21	Gibberella saubinetti	195-196	—	U-10
		15α-OH; 17β-OH→17-C=O	—	Fusarium lini	—	—	G-31
		17α-OH-17β-(20-C=O-21-OH)→ 17-C=O	—	Pseudomonas chlororaphis	—	—	N-64
	15β-hydroxy-4-androstene-3,17-dione	15β-OH	4	Xylaria sp.	192-197	+136[c]	D-16
	16α-hydroxy-4-androstene-3,17-dione	16α-OH	—	Staurophoma sp.	180-183	—	H-39
			—	Streptomyces argenteolus	185-187	+194[c]	F-26
			—	Streptomyces californicus	—	—	L-49
			—	Streptomyces olivaceus	—	—	F-26
			25	Streptomyces roseochromogenus	185-187	+194[c]	F-26 F-28
			—	Streptomyces viridis	—	—	F-26
	19-hydroxy-4-androstene-3,17-dione	19-OH	—	Corticium microsclerotia	165	+180[c]	H-35
	17a-oxa-D-homo-4-androstene-3,17-dione	17-C=O→ 17a-oxa-17-C=O	—	Cephalosporium acremonium	—	—	H-39
			—	Fusarium caucasicum	—	—	C-97
			—	Fusarium lateritium	—	—	C-97
			—	Fusarium solani	—	—	C-97
			80	Penicillium lilacinum	211-212	—	P-73
			34	Penicillium citrinum	203-208	+ 51[c]	S-84
			—	Pythium ultimum	—	—	S-84
		17β-OH→ 17a-oxa-17-C=O	—	Penicillium lilacinum	—	—	P-73
			—	Fusarium caucasicum	—	—	C-97
			—	Fusarium lateritium	—	—	C-97
			—	Fusarium solani	—	—	C-97
		17β-OAc→ 17a-oxa-17-C=O	—	Fusarium sp.	—	—	C-97

TABLE I

Transformations by Product

EMPIRICAL FORMULA	NAME OF REACTION PRODUCT	TRANSFORMATION	YIELD %	ORGANISM	CONSTANTS m. p.°	$[\alpha]_D$	REF.
$C_{19}H_{26}O_3$	17a-oxa-D-homo-4-andro-stene-3,17-dione	17β-OPr→ 17a-oxa-17-C=O	–	Fusarium sp.	–	–	C-97
		17β-OFo→ 17a-oxa-17-C=O	–	Fusarium sp.	–	–	C-97
		17β-Ac→ 17a-oxa-17-C=O	–	Aspergillus flavipes	207-209	+ 43[c]	F-270
			–	Aspergillus flavus	210-212	+ 43[c]	P-726
			–	Aspergillus chevalieri	–	–	C-102
			60-65	Aspergillus oryzae	202-206	+ 42[c]	K-461
			73	Aspergillus oryzae	–	–	C-102
			–	Aspergillus sp.	–	–	C-104
			–	Cephalosporium acremonium	–	–	H-398
			50	Cephalosporium subverticillatum	–	–	B-67
			–	Collybia dryophila	–	–	S-825
			–	Fusarium sp.	–	–	C-97
			–	Penicillium adametzi	–	–	P-726
			70	Penicillium chrysogenum	207-209	+ 43[c]	F-284
			–	Penicillium citrinum	–	–	S-846
			–	Penicillium lilacinum	–	–	S-832; P-726
			–	Penicillium sp.	–	–	C-99; C-102
			–	Pythium ultimum	–	–	S-846; S-849
			–	Plutus granularis	–	–	S-825
		17α-OH-17β-Ac→ 17a-oxa-17-C=O	–	Aspergillus flavus	–	–	P-726
			–	Aspergillus oryzae	–	–	C-102
			–	Penicillium citrinum	–	–	S-846
			–	Pythium ultimum	–	–	S-846; S-849
		17β-(20-C=O-21-OH) →17a-oxa-17-C=O	60	Aspergillus oryzae	–	–	K-461
			–	Penicillium citrinum	–	–	S-846
			–	Pythium ultimum	–	–	S-846; S-849
			–	Rhizopus suinus	203-206	+ 40[c]	W-1095

TABLE I

Transformations by Product

EMPIRICAL FORMULA	NAME OF REACTION PRODUCT	TRANSFORMATION	YIELD %	ORGANISM	CONSTANTS m.p.°	$[\alpha]_D$	REF.
$C_{19}H_{26}O_3$	17a-oxa-D-homo-4-andro-stene-3,17-dione	3β-OH$\to$3-C=O; $\Delta^5\to\Delta^4$; 17β-(20-C=O-21-OAc) $\to$17a-oxa-17-C=O	35	Aspergillus oryzae	–	–	K-461
	3β-hydroxy-5-androstene-7,17-dione	7-C=O	5	Rhizopus sp.	243-244.5	- 83[c]	D-175
	1,3,5(10)-estratriene-3,6β,17β-triol 3-methyl ether	6β-OH	15	Fusarium moniliforme	190-192	+ 45[m]	C-139
$C_{19}H_{26}O_4$	13α-hydroxy-13,17-seco-1,4-androstadiene-16-carboxylic acid	17a-oxa-17-C=O$\to$ 17,17a-seco-13α-OH-16-COOH	–	Cephalosporium acremonium	–	–	H-398
	1β,6β-dihydroxy-4-andro-stene-3,17-dione	1β-OH; 6β-OH	2	Xylaria sp.	237-239	+ 68[c]	D-165
	6β,9α-dihydroxy-4-andro-stene-3,17-dione	6β-OH	–	Pellicularia filamentosa	225-227	+ 77 [c-m, 1:1]	T-955
	6β,11β-dihydroxy-4-andro-stene-3,17-dione	6β-OH	tr.	Gibberella saubinetti	–	–	U-1043
		6β-OH	20	Rhizoctonia solani	275-284	+132	U-1043
	6β,X-dihydroxy-4-andro-stene-3,17-dione	6β-OH; X-OH; 3β-OH$\to$3-C=O; $\Delta^5\to\Delta^4$	tr.	Bacillus pulvifaciens	271-273	+ 86[m]	T-1027 S-792
	9α,12α-dihydroxy-4-andro-stene-3,17-dione	9α-OH	–	Cercospora melonis	–	–	K-473
		12α-OH	–	Cercospora melonis	–	–	K-473
		9α-OH; 12α-OH	–	Cercospora melonis	253-257	+214[c]	K-473
	9α,14α-dihydroxy-4-andro-stene-3,17-dione	9α-OH	–	Cercospora melonis	–	–	K-473
		14α-OH	–	Cercospora melonis	–	–	K-473
			–	Pellicularia filamentosa	243-247	+137[c]	T-955
		9α-OH; 14α-OH	–	Cercospora melonis	241-244	+139[c]	K-473
	9α,15β-dihydroxy-4-andro-stene-3,17-dione	9α-OH	–	Cercospora melonis	–	–	K-473
		15β-OH	–	Cercospora melonis	–	–	K-473
		9α-OH; 15β-OH	–	Cercospora melonis	236-238	+138[c]	K-473
	9α,18-dihydroxy-4-andro-stene-3,17-dione	18-OH	–	Cercospora melonis	–	–	K-473
		9α-OH; 18-OH	–	Cercospora melonis	224-226	+144[d]	K-473
	11α,14α-dihydroxy-4-andro-stene-3,17-dione	11α-OH	–	Pellicularia filamentosa	–	–	T-955
	11β,14α-dihydroxy-4-andro-stene-3,17-dione	11β-OH	–	Pellicularia filamentosa	–	–	T-955
	11β,15α-dihydroxy-4-andro-stene-3,17-dione	11β-OH	–	Cunninghamella elegans	218-220	–	U-104
		–		Pellicularis filamentosa	215-216.5	+217 [c-m, 1:1]	T-955

TABLE I

Transformations by Product

EMPIRICAL FORMULA	NAME OF REACTION PRODUCT	TRANSFORMATION	YIELD %	ORGANISM	CONSTANTS m. p.	$[\alpha]_D$	REF.
$_{19}H_{26}O_4$	$11\beta,15\alpha$-dihydroxy-4-andro-stene-3,17-dione	15α-OH	28	Gibberella saubinetti	221-222	$+222 c $	U-1043
	2β-hydroxy-17a-oxa-D-<u>homo</u>-4-androstene-3,17-dione	2β-OH	--	Gnomonia fragariae	--	--	L-496
			5	Penicillium sp.	180-182	$-182 c $	T-1036
	6β-hydroxy-17a-oxa-D-<u>homo</u>-4-androstene-3,17-dione	6β-OH	27	Coniothyrium helleborine	235-236	$- 13 c $	F-282; F-281; T-994
	7α-hydroxy-17a-oxa-D-<u>homo</u>-4-androstene-3,17-dione	7α-OH	30	Coniothyrium helleborine	275-280	$+ 27 c $	T-994; F-282; F-281
	11α-hydroxy-17a-oxa-D-<u>homo</u>-4-androstene-3,17-dione	17β-Ac→17a-oxa-17-C=O	—	Penicillium lilacinum	—	--	S-832
	16α-hydroxy-17a-oxa-D-<u>homo</u>-4-androstene-3,17-dione	$16\alpha,17\alpha$-oxido-17β-Ac→16α-OH-17a-oxa-17-C=O	--	Cylindrocarpon radicicola	--	--	E-195
$_{19}H_{28}O_2$	5α-androstane-3,17-dione	Δ^4→5α-H	—	Streptomyces griseus	--	--	V-1059
		d,l -3α-OH→ d-3-C=O+l-3α-OH	—	Pseudomonas sp.	130-132	+109	W-1102
		17β-Ac→17-C=O	—	Fusarium caucasicum	--	—	V-1056
			—	Fusarium solani	--	—	V-1056; W-1095
		17β-Ac→17-C=O; 3β-OAc→3-C=O	—	Fusarium caucasicum	--	--	V-1056
			—	Fusarium solani	--	—	V-1056
	5β-androstane-3,17-dione	Δ^4→5β-H	76	Bacillus putrificus	130-131	—	M-545
		Δ^1_4→H; Δ^4→5β-H	—	Clostridium paraputrificum	—	—	S-824
		17β-Ac→17-C=O	—	Penicillium canescens	—	—	M-637
	17β-hydroxy-3α,5α-<u>cyclo</u>-androstan-6-one	17-C=O →17β-OH	50	Saccharomyces cerevisiae	182-183	—	B-81
	17β-hydroxy-5α-1-andro-sten-3-one	17-C=O →17β-OH	83	Saccharomyces cerevisiae	158-159	$- 42 e $	B-78
	17α-hydroxy-4-androsten-3-one	3β-OH→3-C=O; $\Delta^5 \rightarrow \Delta^4$	—	Aspergillus flavus	—	--	H-337
			80	Penicillium notatum	215-218	$+ 68 e $	H-337
			—	Streptomyces globisporus	—	--	H-337
			—	Streptomyces viridochromogenes	—	--	H-337
	17β-hydroxy-4-androsten-3-one (testosterone)	17-C=O→17β-OH	8.5	Chlorella pyrenoidosa	150-152.5	—	G-321

TABLE I

Transformations by Product

EMPIRICAL FORMULA	NAME OF REACTION PRODUCT	TRANSFORMATION	YIELD %	ORGANISM	CONSTANTS m. p.°	$[\alpha]_D$	RE
$C_{19}H_{28}O_2$	17β-hydroxy-4-androsten-3-one (testosterone)	17-C=O →17β-OH	–	Euglena gracilis	–	–	G-32
			–	Fusarium sp.	–	–	C-97
			–	Hydrogenomonas facilis	–	–	F-22
			–	Penicillium sp.	–	–	H-33
			60-75	Rhizobium sp.	–	–	C-11
			–	Saccharomyces cerevisiae	150-151	–	M-54 M-55
			–	Saccharomyces cerevisiae	152-154	+109[e]	H-33 H-33
			–	Saccharomyces fragilis	–	–	M-57
			91	Trichomonas gallinae	–	–	S-82 S-83
			41(cr.)	Wojnowicia graminis	144-147	–	H-38
		$\Delta^5 \to \Delta^4$; 17-C=O →17β-OH	–	Saccharomyces cerevisiae	151	–	M-55
		3β-OH→3-C=O; $\Delta^5 \to \Delta^4$	–	Acetobacter pasteurianum	152	+108[e]	K-45
			78	Aspergillus flavus	152-154	+109[e]	H-33
			–	Corynebacterium sp.	–	–	Z-11
			11	Flavobacterium carbonilicum	151	–	M-59
			64	Micrococcus dehydrogenans	151	–	E-21
			–	Penicillium notatum	–	–	H-33
			68	Proactinomyces erythropolis	–	–	T-10
		3β-OAc→3-C=O; $\Delta^5 \to \Delta^4$; 17-C=O →17β-OH	7.5	Streptomyces globisporus	152-154	+109[e]	H-33
			–	Streptomyces viridochromogenes	–	–	H-33
		17β-Ac→17β-OH	–	Aspergillus oryzae	–	–	C-10
			–	Cephalosporium acremonium	–	–	H-39
			–	Cladosporium resinae	–	–	F-25
			–	Cylindrocephalum aureum	–	–	S-88
			–	Fusarium sp.	–	–	C-97
			–	Neocosmospora vasinfecta	–	–	S-88

TABLE I

Transformations by Product

EMPIRICAL FORMULA	NAME OF REACTION PRODUCT	TRANSFORMATION	YIELD %	ORGANISM	CONSTANTS m. p.°	[α]$_D$	REF.
$_9H_{28}O_2$	Testosterone	17β-Ac →17β-OH	—	Penicillium lilacinum	—	—	S-832
			62	Penicillium notatum	154-155	+110[e]	H-336
			--	Penicillium sp.	—	—	H-336; C-102; C-99
		17α-OH-17β-Ac→ 17β-OH	—	Aspergillus oryzae	—	—	C-102
			—	Penicillium sp.	—	—	H-336
		17β-(20-C=O-21-OH) →17β-OH	—	Cylindrocephalum aureum	—	—	S-880
			69	Neocosmospora vasinfecta	153.5-155.5	+108[c]	S-881
		17β-(20-C=O-21- OAc)→17β-OH	—	Neocosmospora vasinfecta	—	—	S-881
		17β-(20-C=O-21- OPr)→17β-OH	—	Cylindrocephalum aureum	—	—	S-880
	3β-hydroxy-5-androsten-17-one	3β-OAc→3β-OH	—	Trichomonas gallinae	—	—	S-829
		17β-Ac→17-C=O	—	Fusarium caucasicum	—	—	V-1056
			—	Fusarium solani	—	—	V-1056; W-1095
		17β-Bu→17-C=O	—	Gliocladium catenulatum	—	—	M-633
H$_{28}$O$_3$	17β-hydroxy-5α-androstane-3,6-dione	3-C=O-Δ^4 → 5α-H-3,6-di-C=O; (via 6β-OH; Δ^4→Δ^5; ketoniz.)	6	Rhizopus reflexus	233-234	- 9[c]	E-201; M-623
	1α-hydroxy-5α-androstane-3,17-dione	1α-OH	7	Penicillium sp.	211-213.5	+110[c]	D-163
		1α-OH; Δ^4→5α-H	1	Penicillium sp.	204-206	+114[c]	D-163
	11α-hydroxy-5α-androstane-3,17-dione	11α-OH	—	Sporotrichum epigaeum	—	—	M-582
	11α-hydroxy-5β-androstane-3,17-dione	11α-OH	—	Sporotrichum sulfurescens	—	—	M-582
	9,10-seco-1,3,5(10)-androstatriene-3,9β,17β-triol	17-C=O→17β-OH; 9α-OH; Δ^1; rev. aldol.; enol.; 9-C=O →9β-OH	tr.	Nocardia restrictus	171.5 -172.5	+ 19[e]	W-1063
	1α,17β-dihydroxy-4-androsten-3-one	1α-OH	tr.	Penicillium sp.	239-240	—	T-1036
	2α,17β-dihydroxy-4-androsten-3-one	2α-OAc →2α-OH; 17β-OAc →17β-OH	—	Bacillus sphaericus	—	—	H-399
			—	Septomyxa affinis	—	—	H-399
	2β,17β-dihydroxy-4-androsten-3-one	2β-OH	—	Gnomonia fragariae	—	—	L-496

TABLE I

Transformations by Product

EMPIRICAL FORMULA	NAME OF REACTION PRODUCT	TRANSFORMATION	YIELD %	ORGANISM	CONSTANTS m. p.°	$[\alpha]_D$	REF
$C_{19}H_{28}O_3$	2β,17β-dihydroxy-4-androsten-3-one	2β-OAc→2β-OH; 17β-OAc→17β-OH	–	Bacillus sphaericus	–	–	H-399
			–	Corynebacterium simplex	–	–	H-399
			–	Septomyxa affinis	–	–	H-399
	6β,17β-dihydroxy-4-androsten-3-one	6β-OH	–	Fusarium roseum	–	–	R-747
			11	Penicillium sp.	212-214	+30[c]	T-103
			–	Rhizopus arrhizus	–	–	E-201
			–	Rhizopus nigricans	–	–	E-201
			6	Rhizopus reflexus	216-222	+32[c]	E-201 M-618
			3	Wojnowicia graminis	205; 215-218	+29[c]	H-381
	9α,17β-dihydroxy-4-androsten-3-one	9α-OH	14	Ascochyta linicola	196-197	+79[d]	S-828
			10	Bacterium cyclooxydans	–	–	S-898; P-740
			–	Circinella muscae	209-211	+103[c]	R-748
		9α-OH; 17β-Ac→17β-OH	1	Nocardia sp.	197-199	+104[c]	D-172
	11α,17β-dihydroxy-4-androsten-3-one	11α-OH	–	Aspergillus ochraceus	–	–	V-104 S-835
			–	Rhizopus arrhizus	–	–	E-201
			11	Rhizopus nigricans	181-181.5	+93[c]	E-201 M-601
			43	Rhizopus reflexus	181-181.5	+93[c]	E-201
		17-C=O→17β-OH	90	Trichomonas gallinae	–	–	S-830 S-829
		17β-Ac→17β-OH	45	Aspergillus oryzae	–	–	C-102
			–	Penicillium lilacinum	–	–	S-832
			–	Penicillium notatum	–	–	H-336
		11α-OH; 17β-Ac→17β-OH	50	Sporotrichum epigaeum	178-182	+90[c]	M-582
		11α-OH; 17α-OH-17β-(20-C=O-21-OH)→17β-OH	50	Sporotrichum sulfurescens	–	–	M-582
	11β,17β-dihydroxy-4-androsten-3-one	17-C=O→17β-OH	86	Trichomonas gallinae	–	–	S-830 S-829
	12β,17β-dihydroxy-4-androsten-3-one	12β-OH	–	Penicillium sp.	121-125°d	+120[c]	T-103
		17-C=O→17β-OH	–	Saccharomyces cerevisiae	117-119	–	R-749
	14α,17β-dihydroxy-4-androsten-3-one	14α-OH	38	Mucor griseocyanus	183.5-186	+124[c]	E-204 M-610

TABLE I

Transformations by Product

EMPIRICAL FORMULA	NAME OF REACTION PRODUCT	TRANSFORMATION	YIELD %	ORGANISM	CONSTANTS m. p.°	[α]$_D$	REF.
$C_{19}H_{28}O_3$	14α,17β-dihydroxy-4-andro-sten-3-one	17β-Ac→17β-OH	—	Neocosmospora vasinfecta	—	—	S-881
	15α,17β-dihydroxy-4-andro-sten-3-one	15α-OH	8	Fusarium lini	102-110; 204-206	+136[m]	T-980; G-319
			—	Fusarium udum	199-201	+153[c]	M-599
			—	Penicillium urticae	199-201	+155[c]	M-639
	15β,17β-dihydroxy-4-andro-sten-3-one	15β-OH	4	Penicillium sp.	216-218	+ 67[e]	T-1036
		17-C=O→17β-OH	40(cr.)	Saccharomyces cerevisiae	220-222	+ 57[e]	H-382
	16α,17β-dihydroxy-4-andro-sten-3-one	16α-OH	—	Pestalotia funerea	183-184	+ 76[c]	F-266
			—	Streptomyces roseochromogenus	183-184	+ 76	F-288
			—	Streptomyces sp.	—	—	S-788
			42	Wojnowicia graminis	183-187	+ 63[d]	H-381
		16α-OH; 17-C=O→17β-OH	—	Wojnowicia graminis	—	—	H-381
		3β-OH→3-C=O; Δ^5→Δ^4	—	Corynebacterium mediolanum	191-192	+ 80[c]	A-1
		17β-Ac→17β-OH	—	Streptomyces lavendulae	182-184	+ 66[c]	F-271
			—	Streptomyces lavendulae	183-184	+ 76	F-288
	16β,17β-dihydroxy-4-andro-sten-3-one	16β-OH	5	Wojnowicia graminis	179-182	+101[c] + 94[d]	H-381
		16β-OH; 17-C=O→17β-OH	7(cr.)	Corticium centrifugum	183.5-185.5	+103[c]	D-166
	3ξ,19-dihydroxy-4-andro-sten-17-one	19-OH	—	Hypochnus sasakii	—	—	S-869
	1α,3β-dihydroxy-5-andro-sten-17-one	1α-OH	24	Penicillium sp.	288-290	+ 11[c] +31.5[e]	D-163; D-168
			—	Penicillium sp.	275-277	+ 11[c]	G-293
	3β,7α-dihydroxy-5-andro-sten-17-one	7α-OH	18	Fusidium sp.	181.5-183.5	- 71[c]	D-175
			—	Rhizopus sp.	—	—	D-175
	3β,7β-dihydroxy-5-andro-sten-17-one	7β-OH	12	Rhizopus sp.	214-216	+67.5[c]	D-175
	11α,17β-dihydroxy-17α-methyl-4-estren-3-one	11α-OH	—	Rhizopus nigricans	—	—	M-608
$C_{19}H_{28}O_4$	1α,6β,17β-trihydroxy-4-androsten-3-one	1α-OH; 6β-OH	tr.	Pencillium sp.	256-260	+ 19[m]	T-1036
	13α-hydroxy-3-keto-13,17-seco-4-androstene-16-carboxylic acid	17a-oxa-17-C=O→ 13,17-seco-13α-OH-16-COOH	—	Aspergillus flavipes	—	—	H-398
			—	Penicillium sp.	—	—	H-398

TABLE I

Transformations by Product

EMPIRICAL FORMULA	NAME OF REACTION PRODUCT	TRANSFORMATION	YIELD %	ORGANISM	CONSTANTS m. p.°	$[\alpha]_D$	REF
$C_{19}H_{28}O_1$	13α-hydroxy-3-keto-13,17-seco-4-androstene-16-carboxylic acid	17-C=O →13,17-seco-13α-OH-16-$\overline{COOH}$	–	Aspergillus flavipes	–	–	H-398
			2	Cephalosporium acremonium	138.5-139.5	–	H-398
			–	Penicillium lilacinum	–	–	P-737
		17β-OH→13,17-seco-13α-OH-16-$\overline{COOH}$	–	Penicillium lilacinum	–	–	P-737
		17β-Ac→13,17-seco-13α-OH-16-$\overline{COOH}$	–	Aspergillus flavipes	–	–	H-398
			–	Cephalosporium acremonium	–	–	H-398
			–	Penicillium sp.	–	–	H-398
$C_{19}H_{30}O_2$	17β-hydroxy-5β-androstan-3-one	Δ^4→5β-H	70	Bacillus putrificus	139	–	M-545
		17β-Ac→17β-OH	–	Neocosmospora vasinfecta	–	–	S-881
	3α-hydroxy-5α-androstan-17-one	Δ^4→5α-H; 3-C=O→3α-OH	–	Euglena gracilis	–	–	G-322
	3β-hydroxy-5α-androstan-17-one	3-C=O→3β-OH	–	Streptomyces griseus	–	–	V-105
		Δ^4→5α-H; 3-C=O→3β-OH	–	Streptomyces griseus	–	–	V-105
		17α-OH-17β-(20α-OH-21-H)→17-C=O	–	Gliocladium roseum	–	–	M-633
	3α-hydroxy-5β-androstan-17-one	Δ^1→H; Δ^4→5β-H; 3-C=O→3α-OH	–	Clostridium paraputrificum	–	–	S-824
	5-androstene-3β,17β-diol	17-C=O→17β-OH	4	Fusidium sp.	180.5-183	–	D-175
			18	Saccharomyces cerevisiae	178-179	–	M-549 M-543
			86	Trichomonas foetus	–	–	S-830
			–	Trichomonas gallinae	–	–	S-829
		17-C=O→17β-OH; 3β-OAc→3β-OH	–	Trichomonas gallinae	–	–	S-829
$C_{19}H_{30}O_3$	1α,3β-dihydroxy-5α-andro-stan-17-one	1α-OH; Δ^4→5α-H; 3-C=O→3β-OH	1	Penicillium sp.	200-201	+ 93[c]	D-163
	3α,11α-dihydroxy-5β-andro-stan-17-one	17α-OH-17β-Ac→17-C=O	–	Penicillium lilacinum	–	[–]	M-637
	5ξ-androstane-X,16α,17β-triol	16α-OH; Δ^4→5ξ-H; 3-C=O→ ?	3	Wojnowicia graminis	196-199	+ 10[d] + 10[c]	H-381
$C_{19}H_{30}O_4$	X,16α,17β-trihydroxy-4-androsten-3-one	16α-OH; X-OH	–	Pestalotia funerea	279-286	–	F-266
$C_{19}H_{32}O_2$	5α-androstane-3α,17β-diol	Δ^4→5α-H; 3-C=O→3α-OH; 17-C=O→17β-OH	–	Euglena gracilis	–	–	G-322
	5α-androstane-3β,17β-diol	3-C=O→3β-OH; 17-C=O→17β-OH	–	Saccharomyces cerevisiae	163-164	–	V-104 M-54

TABLE I

Transformations by Product

EMPIRICAL FORMULA	NAME OF REACTION PRODUCT	TRANSFORMATION	YIELD %	ORGANISM	CONSTANTS m. p.°	$[\alpha]_D$	REF.
$_{19}H_{32}O_2$	5α-androstane-3β,17β-diol	$\Delta^1 \to H$; 3-C=O→3β-OH	6	Saccharomyces cerevisiae	163	–	B-80
		$\Delta^1 \to H$; 3-C=O→3β-OH; 17-C=O→17β-OH	24	Saccharomyces cerevisiae	163	–	B-80
		$\Delta^5 \to 5\alpha$-H; 3-C=O→3β-OH; 17-C=O→17β-OH	–	Saccharomyces cerevisiae	163-164	+ 4	M-551
	5β-androstane-3α,17β-diol	$\Delta^4 \to 5\beta$; 3-C=O→3α-OH	73	Clostridium paraputrificum	229-230	+ 24[e]	S-823
			–	Clostridium tertium	–	–	S-823
	5β-androstane-3α,17β-diol	17-C=O→17β-OH	–	Trichomonas vaginalis	–	–	S-830
$_{20}H_{23}O_2F$	17α-ethinyl-6α-fluoro-1,3,5(10)-estratriene-3,17β-diol	Δ^1; enol.	–	Septomyxa affinis	–	–	C-93
$_{20}H_{24}O_3$	6α-methyl-1,4-androstadiene-3,11,17-trione	Δ^1; 17β-Ac→17-C=O	9	Septomyxa affinis	274-276d	+230[c]	R-780
	16β-methyl-1,4-androstadiene-3,11,17-trione	Δ^1	–	Corynebacterium simplex	–	–	R-752
	3-hydroxy-19-nor-1,3,5(10)-pregnatriene-11,20-dione	Δ^1; enol.	–	Corynebacterium hoagii	–	–	H-386
			43	Corynebacterium simplex	229-232	+324[d]	B-73
$_{20}H_{24}O_4$	3,17α-dihydroxy-19-nor-1,3,5(10)-pregnatriene-11,20-dione	Δ^1; enol.	–	Corynebacterium hoagii	–	–	H-386
	3,21-dihydroxy-19-nor-1,3,5(10)-pregnatriene-11,20-dione	Δ^1; enol.	–	Corynebacterium simplex	–	–	H-386
$_{20}H_{24}O_5$	3,17α,21-trihydroxy-19-nor-1,3,5(10)-pregnatriene-11,20-dione	Δ^1; enol.	–	Corynebacterium simplex	–	–	H-386
$_{20}H_{25}O_2F$	6α-fluoro-17β-hydroxy-17α-methyl-1,4,9(11)-androstatrien-3-one	Δ^1	–	Corynebacterium simplex	–	–	G-308
$_{20}H_{25}O_3F$	9α-fluoro-17β-hydroxy-16α-methyl-1,4-androstadiene-3,11-dione	17-C=O→17β-OH	–	Saccharomyces cerevisiae	–	–	R-752
$_{20}H_{26}O_2$	2-methyl-1,4-androstadiene-3,17-dione	Δ^1 (2α-methyl); 17β-OH → 17-C=O	–	Bacillus sphaericus	–	–	H-373
	16α-methyl-17β-hydroxy-1,4,9(11)-androstatrien-3-one	17-C=O→17β-OH	–	Saccharomyces cerevisiae	172-174	- 46[d]	R-775
	17β-hydroxy-17α-methyl-1,4,9(11)-androstatrien-3-one	Δ^1	37	Bacillus sphaericus	136-139 (solvate)	- 52[d]	R-775
			–	Corynebacterium simplex	–	–	G-308

TABLE I

Transformations by Product

EMPIRICAL FORMULA	NAME OF REACTION PRODUCT	TRANSFORMATION	YIELD %	ORGANISM	CONSTANTS m.p.°	$[\alpha]_D$	REF.
$C_{20}H_{26}O_2$	16-methylene-4-androstene-3,17-dione	3β-OH→3-C=O; $\Delta^5 \to \Delta^4$	63	Flavobacterium dehydrogenans	161-162	–	B-76
	D-nor-1,4-pregnadiene-3,20-dione	$\overset{1}{\Delta}$	–	Bacillus sphaericus	193-194	+110[d]	R-763
	3-hydroxy-19-nor-1,3,5(10)-pregnatrien-20-one	$\overset{1}{\Delta}$; enol.	62	Corynebacterium simplex	238-240	+164[c]	B-73
			20	Streptomyces lavendulae	242-244	–	G-317
$C_{20}H_{26}O_2Cl_2$	$9\alpha,11\beta$-dichloro-17β-hydroxy-17α-methyl-1,4-androstadien-3-one	$\overset{1}{\Delta}$	–	Corynebacterium simplex	–	–	G-308
$C_{20}H_{26}O_3$	17β-hydroxy-6α-methyl-1,4-androstadiene-3,11-dione	$\overset{1}{\Delta}$; 17β-Ac→17β-OH	26	Septomyxa affinis	209-210	+148[c]	R-780
	11α-hydroxy-16α-methyl-1,4-androstadiene-3,17-dione	$\overset{1}{\Delta}$	–	Corynebacterium simplex	–	–	R-752
	11β,17β-dihydroxy-17α-methyl-1,4,6-androstatrien-3-one	11β-OAc→11β-OH; 17β-OAc→17β-OH	–	Flavobacterium dehydrogenans	–	–	G-305
	1,3,5(10)-estratriene-3,17β-diol 17-acetate	$\overset{1}{\Delta}$; enol.	59-79	Corynebacterium simplex	218-222	–	K-487
	11α-hydroxy-D-nor-1,4-pregnadiene-3,20-dione	11α-OH	–	Glomerella cingulata	227-230	+ 77[d]	R-763
	3,11β-dihydroxy-19-nor-1,3,5(10)-pregnatrien-20-one	$\overset{1}{\Delta}$; enol.	–	Corynebacterium hoagii	–	–	H-386
$C_{20}H_{26}O_4$	3,11β,17α-trihydroxy-19-nor-1,3,5(10)-pregnatrien-20-one	$\overset{1}{\Delta}$; enol.	–	Corynebacterium hoagii	–	–	H-386
	3,11β,21-trihydroxy-19-nor-1,3,5(10)-pregnatrien-20-one	$\overset{1}{\Delta}$; enol.	–	Corynebacterium hoagii	–	–	H-386
$C_{20}H_{26}O_5$	3,7,12-triketo-5β-androstane-17β-carboxylic acid	17β-CH(CH$_3$)CH$_2$-CH$_2$COOH → 17β-COOH	tr.	Proactinomyces erythropolis	240	–	T-103
	3,11β,17α,21-tetrahydroxy-19-nor-1,3,5(10)-pregnatrien-20-one	$\overset{1}{\Delta}$; enol.	–	Corynebacterium simplex	–	–	H-386
	17α,21-dihydroxy-18-nor-4-pregnene-3,11,20-trione	21-OH	–	Colletotrichum lindemuthianum	–	–	A-10; A-13
$C_{20}H_{27}O_2F$	6α-fluoro-17β-hydroxy-17α-methyl-1,4-androstadien-3-one	$\overset{1}{\Delta}$	–	Septomyxa affinis	–	–	C-93
$C_{20}H_{27}O_3F$	9α-fluoro-11β,17β-dihydroxy-16α-methyl-1,4-androstadien-3-one	17-C=O→17β-OH	–	Saccharomyces cerevisiae	–	–	R-752
	21-fluoro-11β-hydroxy-19-nor-4-pregnene-3,20-dione	11β-OH	–	Curvularia lunata	–	–	R-755

TABLE I

Transformations by Product

EMPIRICAL FORMULA	NAME OF REACTION PRODUCT	TRANSFORMATION	YIELD %	ORGANISM	CONSTANTS m. p.°	$[\alpha]_D$	REF.
$C_{20}H_{28}O_2$	17β-hydroxy-17α-methyl-1,4-androstadien-3-one	Δ^1	21	Actinoplanes missouriensis	–	–	M-536
			–	Bacillus lentus	162-163	0	R-750
			–	Corynebacterium simplex	–	–	N-665; N-667a
			–	Didymella lycopersici	163-164	0|c|	V-1052; W-1096
			39	Flavobacterium sp.	–	–	I-430
			–	Hypomyces solani	–	–	L-525
			–	Ramularia robusta	–	–	L-525
			–	Pseudomonas testosteroni	164-166	- 3|c|	L-508
			75(cr.)	Septomyxa affinis	169-171	0|c|	W-1072; E-205
			–	Stereum fasciatum	164-166	0|c|	T-959
			–	Volutella ciliata	–	–	L-525
	1-methyl-1-5α-androstene-3,17-dione	Δ^1 (1β-CH$_3$); 17β-OH→17-C=O	–	Bacillus sphaericus	–	–	H-373
	D-<u>nor</u>-4-pregnene-3,20-dione	3β-OH→3-C=O; $\Delta^5 \to \Delta^4$	–	Flavobacterium dehydrogenans	153-155	+209|c|	R-763
$C_{20}H_{28}O_3$	11α,17β-dihydroxy-17α-methyl-1,4-androstadien-3-one	11α-OH	33	Sporotrichum sulfurescens	250-253	- 33|c|	E-205; M-582
	11β,17β-dihydroxy-17α-methyl-1,4-androstadien-3-one	Δ^1	–	Bacillus sphaericus	–	–	G-305
			–	Septomyxa affinis	262-265	+ 40|c|	E-206
	3-keto-4-androstene-17β-carboxylic acid	17β-CH(CH$_3$)CH$_2$-CH$_2$COOH→ 17β-COOH	tr.	Proactinomyces erythropolis	–	–	T-1034
		17β-CH(CH$_3$)CH$_2$ CH$_2$CH$_2$CH(CH$_3$)$_2$ →17β-COOH	tr.	Proactinomyces erythropolis	245	–	T-1034
	17β-hydroxy-17α-methyl-4-androstene-3,16-dione	16-C=O	–	Curvularia lunata	–	–	S-950
	6β-hydroxy-A-<u>nor</u>-3-pregnene-2,20-dione	6β-OH	6(cr.)	Aspergillus nidulans	217-219	–	T-1006; W-1076
			27	Cokeromyces recurvatus	214-215	+ 24|c|	L-503a
	7α-hydroxy-A-<u>nor</u>-3-pregnene-2,20-dione	7α-OH	44	Diplodia natalensis	161-161.5	+ 65|c|	W-1078; L-502
	9α-hydroxy-A-<u>nor</u>-3-pregnene-2,20-dione	9α-OH	5	Nocardia restrictus	227-229	+ 94|c|	W-1079
	11α-hydroxy-A-<u>nor</u>-3-pregnene-2,20-dione	11α-OH	28	Aspergillus nidulans	183-184	+ 93|c|	W-1076; T-1006

TABLE I

Transformations by Product

EMPIRICAL FORMULA	NAME OF REACTION PRODUCT	TRANSFORMATION	YIELD %	ORGANISM	CONSTANTS m.p.°	$[\alpha]_D$	REF
$C_{20}H_{28}O_3$	16α-hydroxy-A-nor-3-pregnene-2,20-dione	16α-OH	59	Streptomyces roseochromogenus	213-214	+ 32[c]	L-506 L-502
	21-hydroxy-A-nor-3-pregnene-2,20-dione	21-OH	25	Aspergillus niger	148-149	+ 76[c]	W-107 L-502
	9α-hydroxy-19-nor-4-pregnene-3,20-dione	9α-OH	–	Cylindrocarpon radicicola	–	–	S-898; P-740
	11α-hydroxy-19-nor-4-pregnene-3,20-dione	11α-OH	66	Rhizopus nigricans	171-173	+ 62[c]	B-73; C-117
	11β-hydroxy-19-nor-4-pregnene-3,20-dione	11β-OH	20	Curvularia lunata	215-217	+158[c]	B-73
	14α-hydroxy-19-nor-4-pregnene-3,20-dione	14α-OH	15	Helicostylum piriforme	202-204	+166[c]	B-73
	21-hydroxy-19-nor-4-pregnene-3,20-dione	21-OH	46	Aspergillus niger	–	–	Z-112 Z-112 R-783
		dl → d-21-OH + l	–	Ophiobolus herpotrichus	–	–	W-110
$C_{20}H_{28}O_4$	11β,17α-dihydroxy-19-nor-4-pregnene-3,20-dione	11β-OH	–	Curvularia lunata	–	–	R-773
	X-hydroxy-3-keto-4-androstene-17β-carboxylic acid	17β-CH(CH₃)-CH₂CH₂COOH → 17β-COOH; 3β-OH→3-C=O; Δ⁵→Δ⁴; X-OH	1	Streptomyces gelaticus	255-258d	–	H-364
	1ξ,17β-dihydroxy-4-estren-3-one 17-acetate	1ξ-OH	25	Corynebacterium simplex	149-151	–	K-487
$C_{20}H_{28}O_5$	11β,17α,21-trihydroxy-18-nor-4-pregnene-3,20-dione	21-OH	–	Colletotrichum lindemuthianum	–	–	A-12
$C_{20}H_{29}O_2Cl$	3β-chloro-16α-hydroxy-19-nor-5-pregnen-20-one	16α-OH	–	Streptomyces roseochromogenus	–	–	Z-112
$C_{20}H_{30}O_2$	17β-hydroxy-17α-methyl-1-5α-androsten-3-one	Δ¹	–	Actinoplanes missouriensis	–	–	M-536
	17β-hydroxy-17α-methyl-4-androsten-3-one	3β-OH → 3-C=O; Δ⁵→Δ⁴	–	Corynebacterium helvolum	–	–	M-546
$C_{20}H_{30}O_2S$	17α-methylsulfinyl-4-androsten-3-one (stereochemistry at S uncertain)	17α-SCH₃→ 17α-S(O)CH₃	–	Rhizopus stolonifer	–	–	D-174
	17α-methylsulfinyl-4-androsten-3-one (opposite stereochemistry at S from preceding compound)	17α-SCH₃→ 17α-S(O)CH₃	–	Rhizopus stolonifer	–	–	D-174
$C_{20}H_{30}O_3$	6β,17β-dihydroxy-4-methyl-4-androsten-3-one	6β-OH	tr.	Rhizopus nigricans	218-220	+ 10[c]	K-445
	7α,17β-dihydroxy-4-methyl-4-androsten-3-one	7α-OH	2	Rhizopus nigricans	190-192	+105[d]	K-445
	7β,17β-dihydroxy-4-methyl-4-androsten-3-one	7β-OH	12	Rhizopus nigricans	189-190.5	+106[c]	K-445

TABLE I

Transformations by Product

EMPIRICAL FORMULA	NAME OF REACTION PRODUCT	TRANSFORMATION	YIELD %	ORGANISM	CONSTANTS m.p.°	$[\alpha]_D$	REF.
$_{20}H_{30}O_3$	$11\alpha,17\beta$-dihydroxy-4-methyl-4-androsten-3-one	11α-OH	7.5	Rhizopus nigricans	179.5-180.5	+ 72[c]	K-445
	$1\alpha,17\beta$-dihydroxy-17α-methyl-4-androsten-3-one	3β-OH→3-C=O; $\Delta^5 \to \Delta^4$	–	Penicillium sp.	–	–	G-293
	$2\beta,17\beta$-dihydroxy-17α-methyl-4-androsten-3-one	2β-OH	–	Gnomonia fragariae	–	–	L-496
	$6\beta,17\beta$-dihydroxy-17α-methyl-4-androsten-3-one	6β-OH	90	Gibberella saubinetti	–	–	U-1043
			–	Rhizopus arrhizus	–	–	E-201
			4	Rhizopus nigricans	252-253	+ 3[c]	E-201; M-619
			–	Rhizopus reflexus	–	–	E-201
	$9\alpha,17\beta$-dihydroxy-17α-methyl-4-androsten-3-one	9α-OH	16	Ascochyta linicola	190-191	–	S-828
	$11\alpha,17\beta$-dihydroxy-17α-methyl-4-androsten-3-one	11α-OH	–	Rhizopus arrhizus	–	–	E-201
			47	Rhizopus nigricans	160-161.5	+ 66[c] + 59[e]	E-201; M-608
			–	Rhizopus reflexus	–	–	E-201
			49-70	Sporotrichum sulfurescens	154-156	–	M-582
	$16\beta,17\beta$-dihydroxy-17α-methyl-4-androsten-3-one	16β-OH	–	Curvularia lunata	–	–	S-950
$_{20}H_{30}O_3S$	17β-hydroxy-7α-methyl-sulfinyl-4-androsten-3-one	7α-SCH$_3$→7α-S(O)CH$_3$ 17β-OAc→17β-OH	29	Calonectria decora	189.5-190	+ 11[m]	H-405
	11α-hydroxy-17α-methyl-sulfinyl-4-androsten-3-one (stereochemistry at S unknown)	11α-OH; 17α-SCH$_3$→ 17α-S(O)CH$_3$	–	Rhizopus stolonifer	225-226	- 88[c]	D-174; D-176
	11α-hydroxy-17β-methyl-sulfinyl-4-androsten-3-one (stereochemistry at S unknown)	11α-OH	–	Rhizopus stolonifer	223-224	–	D-176
	11α-hydroxy-17β-methyl-sulfinyl-4-androsten-3-one (opposite stereochemistry at S from preceding compound)	11α-OH;	–	Rhizopus stolonifer	297-299d	–	D-176
$_{20}H_{30}O_4S$	11α-hydroxy-17β-methyl-sulfonyl-4-androsten-3-one	11α-OH	–	Rhizopus stolonifer	267-268	+105	D-176
$_{20}H_{32}O_3$	$3\beta,16\alpha$-dihydroxy-19-nor-5α-pregnan-20-one	16α-OH	–	Streptomyces roseochromogenus	–	–	W-1093
			–	Streptomyces sp.	–	–	W-1093
$_{21}H_{22}O_3$	17α-ethinyl-17β-hydroxy-1,4,6-androstatriene-3,11-dione	Δ^1	–	Bacillus sphaericus	–	–	G-304

TABLE I

Transformations by Product

EMPIRICAL FORMULA	NAME OF REACTION PRODUCT	TRANSFORMATION	YIELD %	ORGANISM	CONSTANTS m. p.°	$[\alpha]_D$	REF
$C_{21}H_{23}O_6Cl$	9α-chloro-$14\alpha,17\alpha,21$-trihydroxy-$1,4,6$-pregna-triene-$3,11,20$-trione	14α-OH	—	Curvularia lunata	—	—	G-302
$C_{21}H_{23}O_6F$	9α-fluoro-$14\alpha,17\alpha,21$-trihydroxy-$1,4,6$-pregna-triene-$3,11,20$-trione	14α-OH	—	Curvularia lunata	—	—	G-302
$C_{21}H_{24}O_2Cl_2F_2$	$9\alpha,11\beta$-dichloro-$6\alpha,21$-difluoro-$1,4$-pregnadiene-$3,20$-dione	Δ^1	—	Corynebacterium simplex	—	—	R-758
$C_{21}H_{24}O_2Cl_2FI$	$9\alpha,11\beta$-dichloro-6α-fluoro-21-iodo-$1,4$-pregnadiene-$3,20$-dione	Δ^1	—	Corynebacterium simplex	—	—	R-758
$C_{21}H_{24}O_2FI$	6α-fluoro-21-iodo-$1,4,9(11)$-pregnatriene-$3,20$-dione	Δ^1	—	Corynebacterium simplex	—	—	R-758
$C_{21}H_{24}O_3$	17α-ethinyl-17β-hydroxy-$1,4$-androstadiene-$3,11$-dione	Δ^1	—	Bacillus sphaericus	—	—	G-304
	17α-ethinyl-$11\beta,17\beta$-dihydroxy-$1,4,6$-androstatrien-3-one	Δ^1	—	Bacillus sphaericus	—	—	G-304
		11β-OAc→11β-OH; 17β-OAc→17β-OH	—	Flavobacterium dehydrogenans	—	—	G-304
$C_{21}H_{24}O_4$	11β-hydroxy-$3,20$-diketo-$1,4$-pregnadien-18-oic acid $(18\to11)$ lactone	Δ^1	75	Corynebacterium simplex	194-195	—	U-104
$C_{21}H_{24}O_5$	$17\alpha,21$-dihydroxy-$1,4,6$-pregnatriene-$3,11,20$-trione	Δ^1	—	Bacillus sphaericus	225°d 235°d (polymorph)	+246[d]	G-310
		21-OAc→21-OH; Δ^1	—	Bacillus sphaericus	—	—	G-310
$C_{21}H_{24}O_5F_2$	$6,9\alpha$-difluoro-$11\beta,17\alpha,21$-trihydroxy-$1,4,6$-pregna-triene-$3,20$-dione	Δ^1	—	Corynebacterium simplex	—	—	A-7
$C_{21}H_{24}O_6$	$9\alpha,17\alpha,21$-trihydroxy-$1,4,6$-pregnatriene-$3,11,20$-trione	9α-OH	—	Helicostylum piriforme	—	—	G-302
	$14\alpha,17\alpha,21$-trihydroxy-$1,4,6$-pregnatriene-$3,11,20$-trione	14α-OH	—	Helicostylum piriforme	—	—	G-302
$C_{21}H_{24}O_6ClF$	12α-chloro-6α-fluoro-$16\alpha,17\alpha,21$-trihydroxy-$1,4$-pregnadiene-$3,11,20$-trione	Δ^1	—	Nocardia aurantia	—	—	F-261
$C_{21}H_{25}O_2F$	17α-ethinyl-6α-fluoro-17β-hydroxy-$1,4$-androstadien-3-one	Δ^1	—	Septomyxa affinis	—	—	C-93
	6β-fluoro-$1,4,9(11)$-pregna-triene-$3,20$-dione	Δ^1	—	Corynebacterium simplex	—	—	R-757
	21-fluoro-$1,4,9(11)$-pregna-triene-$3,20$-dione	Δ^1	—	Corynebacterium simplex	—	—	R-773
$C_{21}H_{25}O_3Br$	9α-bromo-$1,4$-pregnadiene-$3,11,20$-trione	Δ^1	—	Corynebacterium hoagii	—	—	H-379

TABLE I
Transformations by Product

EMPIRICAL FORMULA	NAME OF REACTION PRODUCT	TRANSFORMATION	YIELD %	ORGANISM	CONSTANTS m. p. °	$[\alpha]_D$	REF.
$C_{21}H_{25}O_3Cl$	9α-chloro-1,4-pregnadiene-3,11,20-trione	Δ^1	—	Corynebacterium hoagii	—	—	H-379
$C_{21}H_{25}O_3Cl_2F$	9α,11β-dichloro-21-fluoro-17α-hydroxy-1,4-pregnadiene-3,20-dione	Δ^1	—	Corynebacterium simplex	—	—	R-756
$C_{21}H_{25}O_3Cl_2I$	9α,11β-dichloro-17α-hydroxy-21-iodo-1,4-pregnadiene-3,20-dione	Δ^1	—	Corynebacterium simplex	—	—	R-756
$C_{21}H_{25}O_3F$	17α-ethinyl-9α-fluoro-11β,17β-dihydroxy-1,4-androstadien-3-one	Δ^1	—	Bacillus sphaericus	—	—	N-667
	6α-fluoro-1,4-pregnadiene-3,11,20-trione	Δ^1	—	Septomyxa affinis	—	—	C-91
	6β-fluoro-1,4-pregnadiene-3,11,20-trione	Δ^1	—	Septomyxa affinis	—	—	C-91
	9α-fluoro-1,4-pregnadiene-3,11,20-trione	Δ^1	—	Corynebacterium simplex	—	—	H-379
	6α-fluoro-17α-hydroxy-1,4,9(11)-pregnatriene-3,20-dione	Δ^1	—	Corynebacterium simplex	—	—	H-391
$C_{21}H_{25}O_3I$	17α-hydroxy-21-iodo-1,4,9(11)-pregnatriene-3,20-dione	Δ^1	—	Corynebacterium simplex	—	—	R-756
$C_{21}H_{25}O_3Cl_2I$	9α,11β-dichloro-17α-hydroxy-21-iodo-1,4-pregnadiene-3,20-dione	Δ^1	—	Corynebacterium simplex	—	—	R-756
$C_{21}H_{25}O_4F$	9α-fluoro-17α-hydroxy-1,4-pregnadiene-3,11,20-trione	Δ^1	—	Corynebacterium simplex	—	—	H-379
	9α-fluoro-21-hydroxy-1,4-pregnadiene-3,11,20-trione	Δ^1	—	Corynebacterium simplex	—	—	N-668
	12α-fluoro-21-hydroxy-1,4-pregnadiene-3,11,20-trione	Δ^1; 21-OAc→21-OH	—	Bacillus sphaericus	—	—	W-1083
$C_{21}H_{25}O_4FS$	9α-fluoro-17α-hydroxy-21-mercapto-1,4-pregnadiene-3,11,20-trione	21-SAc →21-SH	—	Flavobacterium dehydrogenans	—	—	N-685
$C_{21}H_{25}O_4F_3$	6α,9α,21-trifluoro-11β,17α-dihydroxy-1,4-pregnadiene-3,20-dione	Δ^1	—	Septomyxa affinis	267-272	—	M-534
$C_{21}H_{25}O_5Br$	9α-bromo-17α,21-dihydroxy-1,4-pregnadiene-3,11,20-trione	Δ^1	—	Corynebacterium simplex	—	—	N-668
	9α-bromo-17α,21-dihydroxy-1,5-pregnadiene-3,11,20-trione	21-OAc→21-OH	—	Flavobacterium dehydrogenans	—	—	N-690
$C_{21}H_{25}O_5Cl$	9α-chloro-17α,21-dihydroxy-1,4-pregnadiene-3,11,20-trione	Δ^1	—	Corynebacterium simplex	—	—	N-668

TABLE I

Transformations by Product

EMPIRICAL FORMULA	NAME OF REACTION PRODUCT	TRANSFORMATION	YIELD %	ORGANISM	CONSTANTS m.p.°	$[\alpha]_D$	REF.
$C_{21}H_{25}O_5Cl$	9α-chloro-17α, 21-dihydroxy-1, 5-pregnadiene-3, 11, 20-trione	21-OAc→21-OH	—	Flavobacterium dehydrogenans	—	—	N-690
$C_{21}H_{25}O_5F$	2-fluoro-17α, 21-dihydroxy-1, 4-pregnadiene-3, 11, 20-trione	$\Delta^1(2\alpha F)$	23	Nocardia corallina	232-236	+145[m]	H-402 H-401
	9α-fluoro-17α, 21-dihydroxy-1, 4-pregnadiene-3, 11, 20-trione	Δ^1	39	Corynebacterium simplex	—	—	N-668 N-669
	9α-fluoro-17α, 21-dihydroxy-1, 5-pregnadiene-3, 11, 20-trione	21-OAc→21-OH	—	Flavobacterium dehydrogenans	—	—	N-690
$C_{21}H_{25}O_5N$	21-hydroxy-17β, 20α-oxido-16-oximino-1, 4-pregna-diene-3, 11-dione	Δ^1	—	Bacillus sphaericus	—	—	N-686
$C_{21}H_{25}O_6Br$	9α-bromo-11β, 14α, 17α, 21-tetrahydroxy-1, 4, 6-pregna-triene-3, 20-dione	14α-OH	—	Curvularia lunata	—	—	G-302
$C_{21}H_{25}O_6F$	9α-fluoro-6ξ, 17α, 21-trihydroxy-1, 4-pregnadiene-3, 11, 20-trione	6ξ-OAc→6ξ-OH; 21-OAc→21-OH	—	Flavobacterium dehydrogenans	—	—	G-309
	9α-fluoro-14α, 17α, 21-trihydroxy-1, 4-pregnadiene-3, 11, 20-trione	14α-OH	—	Helicostylum piriforme	—	—	N-669
	9α-fluoro-11β, 14α, 17α, 21-tetrahydroxy-1, 4, 6-pregna-triene-3, 20-dione	14α-OH	—	Curvularia lunata	—	—	G-302
	9α-fluoro-11β, 16α, 17α, 21-tetrahydroxy-1, 4, 6-pregna-triene-3, 20-dione	16α-OAc→16α-OH; 21-OAc→21-OH	—	Flavobacterium dehydrogenans	—	—	G-29
$C_{21}H_{26}O_2$	17α-ethinyl-17β-hydroxy-1, 4-androstadien-3-one	Δ^1	—	Corynebacterium simplex	—	—	N-66
	1, 4, 9(11)-pregnatriene-3, 20-dione	Δ^1	—	Corynebacterium simplex	135-138; 147-150	+ 75[c]	R-77 R-75
	1, 4, 11-pregnatriene-3, 20-dione	Δ^1	—	Didymella lycopersici	166-168	+ 112[a]	V-10 W-10
	1, 4, 16-pregnatriene-3, 20-dione	Δ^1	—	Corynebacterium simplex	—	—	H-38 O-70
$C_{21}H_{26}O_2BrCl$	9α-bromo-11β-chloro-1, 4-pregnadiene-3, 20-dione	Δ^1	—	Corynebacterium simplex	—	—	R-75
$C_{21}H_{26}O_2BrF$	9α-bromo-11β-fluoro-1, 4-pregnadiene-3, 20-dione	Δ^1	—	Corynebacterium simplex	—	—	R-75
$C_{21}H_{26}O_2Br_2$	9α, 11β-dibromo-1, 4-pregna-diene-3, 20-dione	Δ^1	—	Corynebacterium simplex	—	—	R-75
$C_{21}H_{26}O_2ClF$	9α-chloro-11β-fluoro-1, 4-pregnadiene-3, 20-dione	Δ^1	—	Corynebacterium simplex	—	—	R-75

TABLE I
Transformations by Product

EMPIRICAL FORMULA	NAME OF REACTION PRODUCT	TRANSFORMATION	YIELD %	ORGANISM	CONSTANTS m.p.°	$[\alpha]_D$	REF.
$_{21}H_{26}O_2ClI$	9α-iodo-11β-chloro-1,4-pregnadiene-3,20-dione	Δ^1	—	Corynebacterium simplex	—	—	R-754
$_{21}H_{26}O_2Cl_2$	9α,11β-dichloro-1,4-pregnadiene-3,20-dione	Δ^1	—	Corynebacterium simplex	198-208d	+184[c]	R-754
$_{21}H_{26}O_2FI$	9α-iodo-11β-fluoro-1,4-pregnadiene-3,20-dione	Δ^1	—	Corynebacterium simplex	—	—	R-754
$_{21}H_{26}O_3$	17α-ethinyl-11β,17β-dihydroxy-1,4-androstadien-3-one	Δ^1	—	Bacillus sphaericus	—	—	G-304
	17α-ethinyl-11β,17β-dihydroxy-4,6-androstadien-3-one	11β,17β-diOAc→11β,17β-diOH	—	Flavobacterium dehydrogenans	—	—	G-304
	1,4-pregnadiene-3,11,20-trione	Δ^1	71	Actinoplanes missouriensis	156-159	—	M-536
		Δ^1	30	Septomyxa affinis	179-181	+224[c]	E-208; W-1072
	21-hydroxy-1,4,6-pregnatriene-3,20-dione	Δ^1; 21-OAc→21-OH	—	Didymella lycopersici	166-168	+112[a]	W-1096; V-1052
	17α-hydroxy-1,4,9(11)-pregnatriene-3,20-dione	Δ^1	—	Corynebacterium simplex	233-235	-19[c]	R-773
	21-hydroxy-1,4,9(11)-pregnatriene-3,20-dione	Δ^1	—	Corynebacterium simplex	—	—	R-755
	11α-hydroxy-1,4,16-pregnatriene-3,20-dione	11α-OH	—	Rhizopus nigricans	—	—	H-388; O-700
	11β-hydroxy-1,4,16-pregnatriene-3,20-dione	11β-OH	—	Curvularia lunata	—	—	H-388; O-700
	21-hydroxy-1,4,16-pregnatriene-3,20-dione	21-OAc→21-OH; 3β-OAc→3-C=O; $\Delta^5\to\Delta^4$; Δ'	—	Corynebacterium simplex	—	—	H-388; O-700
$_{21}H_{26}O_4$	21-hydroxy-11β,12β-oxido-1,4-pregnadiene-3,20-dione	21-OH	—	Wojnowicia graminis	—	—	D-157
	11α-hydroxy-16α,17α-oxido-1,4-pregnadiene-3,20-dione	Δ^1	—	Bacterium mycoides	—	—	F-240
			—	Bacterium havaniensis	—	—	F-233
	21-hydroxy-16α,17α-oxido-1,4-pregnadiene-3,20-dione	3β-OH→3-C=O; $\Delta^5\to\Delta^4$; Δ^1	—	Bacillus lentus	206-208	+88[d]	R-750
	21-hydroxy-1,4-pregnadiene-3,11,20-trione	Δ^1	—	Bacillus sphaericus	—	—	S-942
			—	Calonectria decora	220-222d	—	W-1096
			—	Corynebacterium simplex	—	—	N-665
	17α,20α-dihydroxy-9β,11β-oxido-1,4,6-pregnatrien-3-one	20-C=O→20α-OH	—	Rhodotorulla longissima	—	—	G-303

TABLE I

Transformations by Product

EMPIRICAL FORMULA	NAME OF REACTION PRODUCT	TRANSFORMATION	YIELD %	ORGANISM	CONSTANTS m. p.°	$[\alpha]_D$	REF.
$C_{21}H_{26}O_4$	17α,20β-dihydroxy-9β,11β-oxido-1,4,6-pregnatrien-3-one	20-C=O→20β-OH	—	Corynebacterium simplex	—	—	G-303
	11α,21-dihydroxy-1,4,16-pregnatriene-3,20-dione	21-OH	—	Ophiobolus herpotrichus	—	—	O-700; H-388
	11β,21-dihydroxy-1,4,16-pregnatriene-3,20-dione	21-OH	—	Ophiobolus herpotrichus	—	—	O-700; H-388
	1-11β-hydroxy-3,20-diketo-4-pregnen-18-oic acid (18→11) lactone	dl-21-H→ d-21-OH+1-21-H	—	Ophiobolus herpotrichus	—	-154	V-1055
$C_{21}H_{26}O_4BrCl$	9α-bromo-11β-chloro-17α,21-dihydroxy-1,5-pregnadiene-3,20-dione	21-OAc→21-OH	—	Flavobacterium dehydrogenans	—	—	N-691
	9α-chloro-11β-bromo-17α,21-dihydroxy-1,5-pregnadiene-3,20-dione	21-OAc→21-OH	—	Flavobacterium dehydrogenans	—	—	N-691
$C_{21}H_{26}O_4BrF$	9α-bromo-11β-fluoro-17α,21-dihydroxy-1,5-pregnadiene-3,20-dione	21-OAc→21-OH	—	Flavobacterium dehydrogenans	—	—	N-691
	9α-fluoro-11β-bromo-17α,21-dihydroxy-1,5-pregnadiene-3,20-dione	21-OAc··→21-OH	—	Flavobacterium dehydrogenans	—	—	N-691
$C_{21}H_{26}O_4Br_2$	9α,11β-dibromo-17α,21-dihydroxy-1,5-pregnadiene-3,20-dione	21-OAc→21-OH	—	Flavobacterium dehydrogenans	—	—	N-691
$C_{21}H_{26}O_4ClF$	9α-chloro-11β-fluoro-17α,21-dihydroxy-1,5-pregnadiene-3,20-dione	21-OAc→21-OH	—	Flavobacterium dehydrogenans	—	—	N-691
	9α-fluoro-11β-chloro-17α,21-dihydroxy-1,5-pregnadiene-3,20-dione	21-OAc→21-OH	—	Flavobacterium dehydrogenans	—	—	N-691
$C_{21}H_{26}O_4ClI$	9α-iodo-11β-chloro-17α,21-dihydroxy-1,5-pregnadiene-3,20-dione	21-OAc→21-OH	—	Flavobacterium dehydrogenans	—	—	N-691
$C_{21}H_{26}O_4Cl_2$	9α,11β-dichloro-17α,21-dihydroxy-1,5-pregnadiene-3,20-dione	21-OAc→21-OH	—	Flavobacterium dehydrogenans	—	—	N-691
$C_{21}H_{26}O_4FI$	9α-iodo-11β-fluoro-17α,21-dihydroxy-1,5-pregnadiene-3,20-dione	21-OAc→21-OH	—	Flavobacterium dehydrogenans	—	—	N-691
$C_{21}H_{26}O_4F_2$	9α,11β-difluoro-17α,21-dihydroxy-1,5-pregnadiene-3,20-dione	21-OAc→21-OH	—	Flavobacterium dehydrogenans	—	—	N-691
	6α,9α-difluoro-15α-hydroxy-4-pregnene-3,11,20-trione	15α-OH	—	Penicillium urticae	—	—	A-31
$C_{21}H_{26}O_4S$	17α-hydroxy-21-mercapto-1,4-pregnadiene-3,11,20-trione	21-SAc→21-SH	—	Flavobacterium dehydrogenans	—	—	N-685

TABLE I

Transformations by Product

EMPIRICAL FORMULA	NAME OF REACTION PRODUCT	TRANSFORMATION	YIELD %	ORGANISM	CONSTANTS m.p.°	$[\alpha]_D$	REF.
$_{21}H_{26}O_5$	$11\beta,21$-dihydroxy-3,20-diketo-1,4-pregnadien-18-al(18→11) hemiacetal	Δ^1	—	Calonectria decora	—	—	W-1096
		$d,1→d-\Delta^1+1$	—	Didymella lycopersici	—	—	V-1055; W-1102
	$17\alpha,21$-dihydroxy-9β,11β-oxido-1,4-pregnadiene-3,20-dione	Δ^1; 21-OAc→21-OH	—	Didymella lycopersici	—	—	W-1096
	$16\alpha,21$-dihydroxy-11β,12β-oxido-1,4-pregnadiene-3,20-dione	16α-OH	—	Streptomyces roseochromogenus	—	—	D-157
	$17\alpha,21$-dihydroxy-1,4-pregnadiene-3,11,20-trione (prednisone)	Δ^1	—	Bacillus lentus	224-225	+170[d]	R-750
			—	Bacillus pulvifaciens	—	—	I-420
			62	Bacillus sp.	225-230	+164[m]	S-848
			—	Bacillus sphaericus	—	—	S-942
			—	Bacillus subtilis	232-233	+166[d]	L-521
			—	Bacterium cyclooxydans	—	—	K-480
			—	Calonectria decora	231-234	+169[d]	V-1053; W-1096
			—	Calonectria decora	—	—	S-951
			58-85 (cr.)	Corynebacterium simplex	233-235d	+172[d]	N-671; N-665; H-389; H-387
			90	Didymella lycopersici	231-234	—	W-1096
			—	Didymella lycopersici	226-232	—	V-1052
			64	Fusarium oxysporum	229-231d	—	C-125
			—	Fusarium solani	231-234	+169[d]	V-1053
			—	Fusarium solani	229-233	+170[d]	K-462
			72(cr.)	Gliocladium roseum	230-234	+164[c]	S-857
			—	Gloeosporium olivarum	229-233	+171[d]	K-465
			—	Graphiola cylindrica	—	—	K-465
			—	Helminthosporium gramineum	—	—	K-465
			—	Helminthosporium turcicum	—	—	S-857
			—	Helminthosporium zizaniae	—	—	K-465

TABLE I

Transformations by Product

EMPIRICAL FORMULA	NAME OF REACTION PRODUCT	TRANSFORMATION	YIELD %	ORGANISM	CONSTANTS m.p.°	$[\alpha]_D$	REF
$C_{21}H_{26}O_5$	prednisone	Δ^1	—	Hypomyces solani	—	—	L-525
			—	Micromonospora chalcea	—	—	S-864 S-867
			—	Mycobacterium flavum	—	—	C-100 C-101
			—	Mycobacterium smegmatis	—	—	S-873
			75-81	Mycobacterium sp.	—	—	K-47
			—	Nocardia corallina	—	—	H-39
			—	Ophiobolus heterostropus	—	—	S-857
			—	Protaminobacter alboflavum	—	—	S-863
			—	Protaminobacter rubrum	—	—	S-863
			—	Septomyxa affinis	—	—	W-107 K-45
			3	Septomyxa affinis	—	—	S-901
			52	Streptomyces olivochromogenus	—	—	C-125
		$d,1 \rightarrow d-\Delta^1 + 1$	—	Didymella lycopersici	231-234	+170[d]	V-105 W-110
		$21-OAc \rightarrow 21-OH$	—	Bacillus megaterium	—	—	S-948
		$21-OH$	—	Colletotrichum lindemuthianum	—	—	H-324
			—	Ophiobolus herpotrichus	231-233	—	W-110 O-70 H-388
			—	Sclerotinia fructicola	—	—	W-110
		$\Delta^{1,4}$ $(5\alpha-H)$	—	Calonectria decora	—	—	W-109
			—	Didymella lycopersici	—	—	W-109
			—	Nocardia blackwelli	—	—	S-943
		$\Delta^{1,4}(5\beta-H)$	—	Protaminobacter alboflavum	—	—	S-866
			—	Protaminobacter rubrum	—	—	S-866
		$\Delta^{1,4}(5\beta-H);$ $21-OAc \rightarrow 21-OH$	—	Nocardia blackwelli	235-239	—	S-943
		$3\alpha-OH \rightarrow 3-C=O;$ $\Delta^{1,4}$ $(5\beta-H)$	—	Nocardia blackwelli	—	—	S-943

TABLE I

Transformations by Product

EMPIRICAL FORMULA	NAME OF REACTION PRODUCT	TRANSFORMATION	YIELD %	ORGANISM	CONSTANTS m.p.°	$[\alpha]_D$	REF.
$_{21}H_{26}O_5$	prednisone	3α-OH$\rightarrow$3-C=O; $\Delta^{1,4}$(5β-H); 21-OAc$\rightarrow$21-OH	—	Nocardia blackwelli	—	—	S-939
	prednisone - 4-C^{14}	Δ^1	54	Corynebacterium simplex	—	—	C-120
	$17\alpha,21$-dihydroxy-1,5-pregnadiene-3,11,20-trione	21-OAc$\rightarrow$21-OH	—	Flavobacterium dehydrogenans	—	—	N-690
		21-O-i-Bu$\rightarrow$21-OH	—	Flavobacterium dehydrogenans	—	—	N-690
	$11\alpha,17\alpha,21$-trihydroxy-1,4,6-pregnatriene-3,20-dione	11α-OH	—	Fusarium equisetti	—	—	M-557
	$11\beta,17\alpha,21$-trihydroxy-1,4,6-pregnatriene-3,20-dione	Δ^1	—	Bacillus sphaericus	239-243	+100[d]	G-310
	$17\alpha,20\alpha,21$-trihydroxy $9\beta,11\beta$-oxido-1,4,6-pregnatrien-3-one	20-C=O$\rightarrow$20α-OH	—	Rhodotorulla rubra	—	—	G-303
	$17\alpha,20\beta,21$-trihydroxy-$9\beta,11\beta$-oxido-1,4,6-pregnatrien-3-one	20-C=O$\rightarrow$20β-OH	—	Corynebacterium simplex	—	—	G-303
	$16\alpha,17\alpha,21$-trihydroxy-1,4,9(11)-pregnatriene-3,20-dione	3β-OAc$\rightarrow$3-C=O; 21-OAc$\rightarrow$21-OH; $\Delta^{1,4}$(5α-H)	—	Bacterium havaniensis	—	+9[c]	O-705
	$11\beta,14\alpha$-dihydroxy-3,20-diketo-4-pregnen-18-oic acid (18$\rightarrow$11) lactone	14α-OH	—	Pleospora gaeumanni	—	—	W-1108
	$11\beta,21$-dihydroxy-3,20-diketo-4-pregnen-18-oic acid (18$\rightarrow$11) lactone	d,1$\rightarrow$d-21-OH+1	—	Ophiobolus herpotrichus	—	—	W-1101; W-1102
			—	Wojnowicia graminis	205-222	+117[a]	W-1102
$_{21}H_{26}O_6$	$11\beta,14\alpha,21$-trihydroxy-3,20-diketo-1,4-pregnadien-18-al	14α-OH	—	Pleospora gaeumanni	—	—	W-1108
	$6\beta,17\alpha,21$-trihydroxy-1,4-pregnadiene-3,11,20-trione	6β-OH	—	Chaetomium funicolum	—	—	C-108
	$7\alpha,17\alpha,21$-trihydroxy-1,4-pregnadiene-3,11,20-trione	Δ^1; 21-OAc $\rightarrow$ 21-OH	—	Bacillus sphaericus	—	—	N-687
	$14\alpha,17\alpha,21$-trihydroxy-1,4-pregnadiene-3,11,20-trione	Δ^1	—	Mycobacterium smegmatis	—	—	S-874; S-873
	$15\beta,17\alpha,21$-trihydroxy-1,4-pregnadiene-3,11,20-trione	Δ^1	—	Bacillus sphaericus	—	—	C-126
	$9\alpha,11\beta,17\alpha,21$-tetrahydroxy-1,4,6-pregnatriene-3,20-dione	9α-OH	—	Helicostylum piriforme	—	—	G-302
	$11\beta,14\alpha,17\alpha,21$-tetrahydroxy-1,4,6-pregnatriene-3,20-dione	14α-OH	—	Helicostylum piriforme	—	—	G-302

TABLE I

Transformations by Product

EMPIRICAL FORMULA	NAME OF REACTION PRODUCT	TRANSFORMATION	YIELD %	ORGANISM	CONSTANTS m. p.°	$[\alpha]_D$	REF.
$C_{21}H_{26}O_6$	$11\beta,16\alpha,21$-trihydroxy-3,20-diketo-4-pregnen-18-oic acid (18→11) lactone	16α-OH	—	Pestalotia funera	—	—	W-109
		21-OH	—	Ophiobolus herpotrichus	—	—	W-109
$C_{21}H_{26}O_6ClF$	12α-chloro-6α-fluoro-$16\alpha,17\alpha$,21-trihydroxy-4-pregnene-3,11,20-trione	16α-OH	—	Streptomyces roseochromogenus	—	—	F-261
$C_{21}H_{26}O_6F_2$	$6\alpha,12\alpha$-difluoro-$11\beta,16\alpha,17\alpha$,21-tetrahydroxy-1,4-pregnadiene-3,20-dione	Δ^1	—	Nocardia aurantia	—	—	F-261
$C_{21}H_{27}O_3Br$	9α-bromo-11β-hydroxy-1,4-pregnadiene-3,20-dione	Δ^1	—	Corynebacterium simplex	—	—	H-379
$C_{21}H_{27}O_3Cl$	9α-chloro-11β-hydroxy-1,4-pregnadiene-3,20-dione	Δ^1	—	Corynebacterium hoagii	—	—	H-379
$C_{21}H_{27}O_3F$	6α-fluoro-11α-hydroxy-1,4-pregnadiene-3,20-dione	Δ^1	—	Septomyxa affinis	—	—	C-91
	6α-fluoro-11β-hydroxy-1,4-pregnadiene-3,20-dione	Δ^1	—	Septomyxa affinis	—	—	C-91
	6α-fluoro-17α-hydroxy-1,4-pregnadiene-3,20-dione	Δ^1	—	Septomyxa affinis	—	—	B-34
	6β-fluoro-11α-hydroxy-1,4-pregnadiene-3,20-dione	Δ^1	—	Septomyxa affinis	—	—	C-91
	6β-fluoro-11β-hydroxy-1,4-pregnadiene-3,20-dione	Δ^1	—	Septomyxa affinis	—	—	C-91
	9α-fluoro-11β-hydroxy-1,4-pregnadiene-3,20-dione	Δ^1	—	Corynebacterium simplex	—	—	H-379
	9α-fluoro-14α-hydroxy-4-pregnene-3,11,20-trione	14α-OH	—	Pleospora gaeumanni	—	—	W-1108
$C_{21}H_{27}O_3N$	$17\beta,20\alpha$-oxido-16-oximino-1,4-pregnadien-3-one	Δ^1	—	Bacillus sphaericus	—	—	N-686
	12a-aza-C-homo-1,4-pregnadiene-3,$\overline{12,20}$-trione	3β-OH→3-C=O; $\Delta^{1,4}$ (5α-H)	62	Nocardia sp.	183-185	+48[m]	M-563
$C_{21}H_{27}O_4Br$	9α-bromo-11β,21-dihydroxy-1,4-pregnadiene-3,20-dione	Δ^1; 21-OAc→21-OH	—	Corynebacterium hoagii	—	—	N-668
	12α-bromo-16α-hydroxy-4-pregnene-3,11,20-trione	16α-OH	—	Streptomyces roseochromogenus	—	—	F-256
$C_{21}H_{27}O_4Cl$	9α-chloro-$11\beta,17\alpha$-dihydroxy-1,4-pregnadiene-3,20-dione	Δ^1	—	Corynebacterium hoagii	—	—	H-379
	9α-chloro-11β,21-dihydroxy-1,4-pregnadiene-3,20-dione	Δ^1	—	Corynebacterium hoagii	—	—	N-668
		Δ^1	—	Nocardia corallina	—	—	H-399
	12α-chloro-16α-hydroxy-4-pregnene-3,11,20-trione	16α-OH	—	Streptomyces roseochromogenus	—	—	F-257

TABLE I

Transformations by Product

EMPIRICAL FORMULA	NAME OF REACTION PRODUCT	TRANSFORMATION	YIELD %	ORGANISM	CONSTANTS m. p.°	[α]$_D$	REF.
$C_{21}H_{27}O_4F$	9α-fluoro-11β,17α-dihydroxy-1,4-pregnadiene-3,20-dione	Δ^1	—	Corynebacterium simplex	—	—	H-379; N-668
	9α-fluoro-11β,21-dihydroxy-1,4-pregnadiene-3,20-dione	Δ^1;	—	Nocardia corallina	—	—	H-399
	12α-fluoro-11β,21-dihydroxy-1,4-pregnadiene-3,20-dione	Δ^1; 21-OAc→21-OH	—	Bacillus sphaericus	—	—	T-985; W-1083
	6α-fluoro-15-hydroxy-4-pregnene-3,11,20-trione	15α-OH	—	Penicillium urticae	—	—	A-31
	6α-fluoro-16-hydroxy-4-pregnene-3,11,20-trione	16α-OH	—	Streptomyces roseochromogenus	—	—	B-35
	9α-fluoro-21-hydroxy-4-pregnene-3,11,20-trione	21-OH	—	Cercosporella herpotrichoides	—	—	L-490
$C_{21}H_{27}O_4FS$	9α-fluoro-11β,17α-dihydroxy-21-mercapto-1,4-pregnadiene-3,20-dione	21-S Ac→21-SH	—	Flavobacterium dehydrogenans	—	—	N-685
$C_{21}H_{27}O_4N$	12a-aza-17α-hydroxy-C-homo-1,4-pregnadiene-3,12,20-trione	3β-OAc→3-C=O; $\Delta^{1,4}$(5α-H)	17	Nocardia sp.	260-262	+45[c]	M-563
$C_{21}H_{27}O_5Br$	6β-bromo-11β,17α,21-trihydroxy-1,4-pregnadiene-3,20-dione	11β,17α,21-triOAc →11β,17α,21-triOH	—	Flavobacterium dehydrogenans	—	—	N-690
	9α-bromo-11β,17α,21-trihydroxy-1,4-pregnadiene-3,20-dione	Δ^1	—	Corynebacterium simplex	—	—	N-668
$C_{21}H_{27}O_5Cl$	6α-chloro-11β,17α,21-trihydroxy-1,4-pregnadiene-3,20-dione	11β-OH	—	Cunninghamella bainieri	195-196	+61[d]	R-770
	9α-chloro-11β,17α,21-trihydroxy-1,4-pregnadiene-3,20-dione	Δ^1	—	Corynebacterium simplex	—	—	N-668
$C_{21}H_{27}O_5F$	2-fluoro-11β,17α,21-trihydroxy-1,4-pregnadiene-3,20-dione	Δ^1 (2α-F)	—	Nocardia corallina	—	—	H-401
	6α-fluoro-11β,17α,21-trihydroxy-1,4-pregnadiene-3,20-dione	Δ^1; 21-OAc→21-OH	53	Septomyxa affinis	202-204	+73[d]	S-924
			—	Septomyxa affinis	202-204	+92[d]	M-647
			—	Septomyxa affinis	208-213	+92[d]	H-396
	9α-fluoro-11β,16α,17α-trihydroxy-1,4-pregnadiene-3,20-dione	Δ^1	64	Bacterium havaniensis	275-279	+51	F-238
			—	Bacterium mycoides	—	—	F-238
	9α-fluoro-11β,17α,21-trihydroxy-1,4-pregnadiene-3,20-dione	Δ^1	—	Bacillus lentus	265-269	+109[c]	R-750
			—	Bacillus sphaericus	—	—	S-942; N-669
			—	Bacterium cyclo-oxydans	—	—	K-480
			—	Bacterium havaniensis	—	—	F-233

TABLE I

Transformations by Product

EMPIRICAL FORMULA	NAME OF REACTION PRODUCT	TRANSFORMATION	YIELD %	ORGANISM	m. p.°	$[\alpha]_D$	REF.
$C_{21}H_{27}O_5F$	9α-fluoro-11β,17α,21-tri-hydroxy-1,4-pregnadiene-3,20-dione	Δ^1	—	Bacterium mycoides	—	—	F-240
			20	Corynebacterium simplex	265-269d	+111[e]	H-389; N-671
			41	Corynebacterium simplex	247-250	—	N-668; N-665; N-669
			—	Didymella lycopersici	263-266	+108[e]	W-1096
			36	Nocardia corallina	254-256	+ 92[m]	H-403; H-399
			70	Nocardia restrictus	265-269	+111[e]	S-885
			—	Nocardia sp.	—	—	T-1005
		Δ^1; 21-OAc→21-OH	—	Bacterium havaniensis	—	—	F-233
			—	Bacterium mycoides	—	—	F-240
			—	Didymella lycopersici	263-266	+108[d]	V-1052
		20β-OH→20-C=O	—	Mycobacterium rhodocrous	—	—	G-294
	12α-fluoro-11β,14α,17α-tri-hydroxy-1,4-pregnadiene-3,20-dione	14α-OH	—	Pleospora gaeumanni	—	—	W-1103
	12α-fluoro-11β,17α,21-tri-hydroxy-1,4-pregnadiene-3,20-dione	Δ^1	—	Bacillus sphaericus	—	—	H-380
	16β-fluoro-11β,17α,21-tri-hydroxy-1,4-pregnadiene-3,20-dione	Δ^1	—	Protaminobacter alboflavum	—	—	B-51
	9α-fluoro-11β,17α,21-tri-hydroxy-1,5-pregnadiene-3,20-dione	11β,17α,21-triOAc →11β,17α,21-triOH	—	Flavobacterium dehydrogenans	—	—	N-690
	2α-fluoro-17α,21-dihydroxy-4-pregnene-3,11,20-trione	$\Delta^1 \to H$	8	Streptomyces sp.	—	—	H-402
$C_{21}H_{27}O_5N$	21-hydroxy-17β,20α-oxido-16-oximino-4-pregnene-3,11-dione	21-OAc→21-OH	—	Flavobacterium dehydrogenans	—	—	N-686
$C_{21}H_{27}O_6Cl$	9α-chloro-11β,16α,17α,21-tetrahydroxy-1,4-pregna-diene-3,20-dione	Δ^1	—	Nocardia corallina	—	—	H-399
	12α-chloro-16α,17α,21-tri-hydroxy-4-pregnene-3,11,20-trione	16α-OH	—	Streptomyces roseochromogenus	—	—	F-256
$C_{21}H_{27}O_6F$	9α-fluoro-11β,16α,17aα-tri-hydroxy-17aβ-hydroxy-methyl-D-homo-1,4-andro-stadiene-3,17-dione	Δ^1; 16α,17α,21-tri-OH-20-C=O→16α,17aα-dihydroxy-17aβ-hydroxymethyl-D-homo-17-C=O	—	Bacterium cyclooxydans	—	—	G-297

TABLE I

Transformations by Product

EMPIRICAL FORMULA	NAME OF REACTION PRODUCT	TRANSFORMATION	YIELD %	ORGANISM	CONSTANTS m.p.°	[α]$_D$	REF.
$_{21}H_{27}O_6F$	9α-fluoro-11β,16α,17aα-trihydroxy-17aβ-hydroxymethyl-D-homo-1,4-androstadiene-3,17-dione	Δ¹	—	Nocardia corallina	254-255d	—	S-910
	6α-fluoro-11α,16α,17α,21-tetrahydroxy-1,4-pregnadiene-3,20-dione	11α-OH	—	Rhizopus nigricans	—	—	R-771
	6α-fluoro-11β,16α,17α,21-tetrahydroxy-1,4-pregnadiene-3,20-dione	11β-OH	—	Cunninghamella bainieri	—	—	R-771
		16α-OH	—	Streptomyces roseochromogenus	—	—	H-399; M-531
	9α-fluoro-6ξ,11β,17α,21-tetrahydroxy-1,4-pregnadiene-3,20-dione	6ξ,11β,17α,21-tetraOAc→6ξ,11β,17α,21-tetraOH	—	Flavobacterium dehydrogenans	—	—	G-309
	9α-fluoro-11β,14α,17α,21-tetrahydroxy-1,4-pregnadiene-3,20-dione	14α-OH	48	Helicostylum piriforme	—	—	N-669
			—	Pleospora gaeumanni	—	—	W-1108a
	9α-fluoro-11β,15β,17α,21-tetrahydroxy-1,4-pregnadiene-3,20-dione	Δ¹	5	Bacillus sphaericus	—	—	N-669
	9α-fluoro-11β,15β,16α,21-tetrahydroxy-1,4-pregnadiene-3,20-dione	Δ¹	—	Bacillus sphaericus	—	—	N-669
	9α-fluoro-11β,16α,17α,21-tetrahydroxy-1,4-pregnadiene-3,20-dione (triamcinolone)	Δ¹	43	Bacterium cyclooxydans	—	—	G-296; G-297; L-505; R-779; S-908
			10	Bacterium havaniensis	253-255	—	F-233
			—	Bacterium mycoides	—	—	F-240
			—	Corynebacterium simplex	—	—	B-61; S-908; G-296; H-399
			65	Mycobacterium rhodocrous	—	—	T-1002; G-296
			—	Nocardia corallina	—	—	B-61; H-399; O-704
			—	Nocardia sp.	—	—	T-1005
		16α-OH	30-70	Nocardia italica	—	—	S-918
			—	Streptomyces californicus	—	—	L-491
			20	Streptomyces roseochromogenus	248-250	+ 71[a]	T-1002
		20β-OH→20-C=O	—	Bacterium cyclooxydans	—	—	G-294; G-296

TABLE I

Transformations by Product

EMPIRICAL FORMULA	NAME OF REACTION PRODUCT	TRANSFORMATION	YIELD %	ORGANISM	CONSTANTS m. p.°	$[\alpha]_D$	REF.
$C_{21}H_{27}O_6F$	triamcinolone	20β-OH→20-C=O	—	Corynebacterium simplex	—	—	G-294; G-296
			—	Mycobacterium rhodocrous	—	—	G-294; G-296
		20β-OH→20-C=O; Δ^1	—	Bacterium cyclo-oxydans	—	—	G-294; G-296
			—	Corynebacterium simplex	—	—	G-296
	12α-fluoro-11β,16α,17α,21-tetrahydroxy-1,4-pregnadiene-3,20-dione	16α-OH	—	Streptomyces argenteolus	—	—	H-380
			—	Streptomyces roseochromogenus	—	—	F-257
	9α-fluoro-16α,17α,21-trihydroxy-4-pregnene-3,11,20-trione	16α-OH	—	Streptomyces sp.	—	—	S-788
$C_{21}H_{28}O_2$	17β-hydroxy-17α-methyl-16-methylene-1,4-androstadien-3-one	Δ^1	51	Corynebacterium simplex	145-148	-101[d]	B-76
	17β-hydroxy-17α-vinyl-1,4-androstadien-3-one	Δ^1	—	Didymella lycopersici	165-166	—	W-1109
	17α-ethinyl-17β-hydroxy-4-androsten-3-one	3β-OH → 3-C=O; $\Delta^5 \to \Delta^4$	70	Micrococcus dehydrogenans	264-266	—	C-84
	1,4-pregnadiene-3,20-dione	Δ^1	—	Actinoplanes missouriensis	144-147	—	M-536
			—	Bacillus sphaericus	—	—	S-942; H-399
			—	Bacterium havaniensis	—	—	F-233
			—	Bacterium mycoides	—	—	F-240
			—	Calonectria decora	151-152	+120[e]	V-1053 W-1096
			—	Corynebacterium simplex	—	—	H-399
			—	Cylindrocarpon radicicola	—	—	P-733
			—	Fusarium solani	151	+122[c]	N-663
			60	Gloeosporium olivarum	149-151	+120[e]	K-465
			—	Mycobacterium smegmatis	150-153	—	S-820; S-873
			—	Nocardia corallina	—	—	H-399
			17	Nocardia restrictus	150-151	—	S-885

TABLE I

Transformations by Product

EMPIRICAL FORMULA	NAME OF REACTION PRODUCT	TRANSFORMATION	YIELD %	ORGANISM	CONSTANTS m. p.°	$[\alpha]_D$	REF.
$C_{21}H_{28}O_2$	1,4-pregnadiene-3,20-dione	Δ^1	20	Nocardia sp.	150-151	—	S-897; S-888
			—	Septomyxa affinis	—	—	W-1072; H-399; V-1048
			—	Streptomyces lavendulae	—	—	P-733
		$\Delta^{1,4}$ (5α)	—	Nocardia sp.	—	—	S-888
		$\Delta^{1,4}$ (5β)	45	Nocardia sp.	150-152	—	S-888
		3β-OH→3-C=O; Δ^1	49	Corynebacterium simplex	150-152	—	N-665
		3β-OH→3-C=O; Δ^5→Δ^4; Δ^1	50	Bacillus pulvifaciens	150-155	+112[e]	T-1027; I-420
		3β-OAc→3-C=O; Δ^5→Δ^4; Δ^1	1	Bacillus pulvifaciens	—	—	T-1027; I-420
		20β-OH→20-C=O; 3β-OH→3-C=O; Δ^5→Δ^4; Δ^1	41	Corynebacterium simplex	152-153	+122[c]	N-665; C-128
	1,4-pregnadiene-3,20-dione-7α-H³	Δ^1	—	Bacillus sphaericus	—	—	G-323
	1,4-pregnadiene-3,20-dione-16α-H³	Δ^1	—	Bacillus sphaericus	—	—	G-323
	1,4-pregnadiene-3,20-dione-11α-H³, 12α-H³	Δ^1	—	Bacillus sphaericus	—	—	G-323
$C_{21}H_{28}O_3$	11α-hydroxy-1,4-pregnadiene-3,20-dione	Δ^1	—	Bacterium cyclooxydans	228-230	+ 93[c]	K-480
			—	Bacterium havaniensis	—	—	F-233
			—	Bacterium mycoides	—	—	F-240
			8(cr.)	Corynebacterium simplex	228-230	+ 93[c]	T-995
			73	Septomyxa affinis	232.5-234	+117[c]	E-208; W-1072; K-456
	11β-hydroxy-1,4-pregnadiene-3,20-dione	Δ^1	—	Bacillus sphaericus	232-234	—	S-942
			—	Septomyxa affinis	—	—	W-1072
	17α-hydroxy-1,4-pregnadiene-3,20-dione	Δ^1	—	Septomyxa affinis	—	—	W-1072
	21-hydroxy-1,4-pregnadiene-3,20-dione	Δ^1	49	Actinoplanes missouriensis	179-180	—	M-536
			66(cr.)	Bacillus sp.	183-187	+108[a]	S-848
			—	Bacillus sphaericus	—	—	S-942
			—	Bacterium havaniensis	—	—	F-233

TABLE I

Transformations by Product

EMPIRICAL FORMULA	NAME OF REACTION PRODUCT	TRANSFORMATION	YIELD %	ORGANISM	CONSTANTS m.p.°	$[\alpha]_D$	REF.
$C_{21}H_{28}O_3$	21-hydroxy-1,4-pregnadiene-3,20-dione	Δ^1	—	Calonectria decora	189-195d	+120[c]	V-1053
			ca. 100	Calonectria decora	185-192	—	W-1096
			—	Corynebacterium simplex	—	—	N-665
			88	Didymella lycopersici	185-195	—	W-1096
			60(cr.)	Gliocladium roseum	185-191	+110[m]	S-857
			—	Helminthosporium turcicum	—	—	S-857
			—	Ophiobolus heterostropus	—	—	S-857
			26	Pseudomonas dacunhae	184-189	+110[a]	S-848
			—	Septomyxa affinis	—	—	W-1072
		Δ^1; 21-OAc→21-OH	—	Mycobacterium smegmatis	—	—	S-873
	21-hydroxy-1,4-pregnadiene-3,20-dione	$\Delta^{1,4}$ (5β-H)	—	Micromonospora chalcea	—	—	S-867
			—	Protaminobacter alboflavum	—	—	S-866
			—	Protaminobacter rubrum	—	—	S-866
		21-OH	68(cr.)	Ophiobolus herpotrichus	185-192	+120[c]	W-1101
	11α-hydroxy-4,6-pregnadiene-3,20-dione	11α-OH	22-51	Rhizopus nigricans	160-162	+111[c]	P-730; M-601
	15α-hydroxy-4,9(11)-pregnadiene-3,20-dione	15α-OH	—	Gibberella saubinetti	—	—	M-599
	16α-hydroxy-17β-methyl-18-nor-4,13-17α-pregnadiene-3,20-dione	3β-OH→3-C=O; $\Delta^5 \to \Delta^4$	7	Flavobacterium dehydrogenans	138-140	+187[d] +82[c]	S-839
	16β-hydroxy-17β-methyl-18-nor-4,13-17α-pregnadiene-3,20-dione	3β-OH→3-C=O; $\Delta^5 \to \Delta^4$	27	Flavobacterium dehydrogenans	128-129	+141[d] +136[c]	S-839
	21-hydroxy-4,14-pregnadiene-3,20-dione	21-OH	—	Ophiobolus herpotrichus	182-184	—	M-576
	21-hydroxy-4,16-pregnadiene-3,20-dione	21-OH	—	Cercosporella herpotrichoides	—	—	L-490
			—	Kabatiella phoradendri	—	—	L-498
	3-hydroxy-9,10-seco-1,3,5(10)-pregnatriene-3,20-dione	Δ^1; 9α-OH; rev. aldol.; enol.	<1	Mycobacterium smegmatis	—	—	S-820

TABLE I

Transformations by Product

EMPIRICAL FORMULA	NAME OF REACTION PRODUCT	TRANSFORMATION	YIELD %	ORGANISM	CONSTANTS m. p.°	[α]$_D$	REF.
$C_{21}H_{28}O_3$	11β,21-dihydroxy-1,4,17(20)-pregnatrien-3-one	Δ^1	80(cr.)	Septomyxa affinis	149-153	—	W-1072; M-647; K-456; R-766
	11β,12β-oxido-4-pregnene-3,20-dione	Δ^{11}→11β,12β-oxide	1	Curvularia lunata	—	—	K-484
$C_{21}H_{28}O_3BrF$	17α-bromo-6α-fluoro-11β-hydroxy-4-pregnene-3,20-dione	11β-OH	—	Curvularia lunata	—	—	R-759
$C_{21}H_{28}O_4$	17β-hydroxy-4-androstene-3,11-dione acetate	17β-Ac→17β-OAc	12	Cladosporium resinae	167.5-169	—	F-250
	6β,17α-dihydroxy-1,4-pregnadiene-3,20-dione	6β-OH	—	Chaetomium funicolum	—	—	C-108
			—	Chaetomium succineum	—	—	C-108
	11β,21-dihydroxy-1,4-pregnadiene-3,20-dione	Δ^1	—	Bacillus pulvifaciens	—	—	I-420
			42	Bacillus sp.	210-218	+150[e]	S-848
			—	Bacillus sphaericus	—	—	S-942
			—	Calonectria decora	216-220	+158[e]	V-1053; W-1096
			33(cr.)	Corynebacterium simplex	227.5-230.5	+173[m]	H-389; N-671; N-665
			44	Gliocladium roseum	208-218	+140[e]	S-857
			—	Helminthosporium turcicum	—	—	S-857
			—	Mycobacterium phlei	217-218	+154[e]	S-873
			—	Nocardia corallina	—	—	H-399
			—	Ophiobolus heterostropus	—	—	S-857
			3	Pseudomonas dacunhae	207-211	+136[e]	S-848
	16α,21-dihydroxy-1,4-pregnadiene-3,20-dione	Δ^1	—	Bacterium havaniensis	—	—	F-233
			—	Bacterium mycoides	—	—	F-240
			—	Corynebacterium simplex	—	—	H-376
	17α,21-dihydroxy-1,4-pregnadiene-3,20-dione	Δ^1	33	Azotomonas fluorescens	—	—	T-989
			—	Bacillus lentus	240-242	+80[d]	R-750
			—	Bacillus pulvifaciens	—	—	I-420
			42	Bacillus pulvifaciens	217.5-219	+70[c]	T-1027

TABLE I

Transformations by Product

EMPIRICAL FORMULA	NAME OF REACTION PRODUCT	TRANSFORMATION	YIELD %	ORGANISM	CONSTANTS m. p.°	$[\alpha]_D$	REF
$C_{21}H_{28}O_4$	17α,21-dihydroxy-1,4-pregnadiene-3,20-dione	Δ^1	56	Bacillus sp.	234-238	+75|c|	S-848
			—	Bacillus sphaericus	—	—	S-942; H-399
			43	Bacillus sphaericus	226-230	+77|e|	K-444
			—	Bacillus subtilis	—	—	L-522
			—	Bacterium cyclooxydans	—	—	K-480
			—	Bacterium havaniensis	—	—	F-233
			—	Bacterium mycoides	—	—	F-240
			—	Calonectria decora	227-233d	+76|e|	W-109 V-105
			53	Corynebacterium simplex	246-250d	+76|c|	H-389 N-671 N-665
			—	Corynebacterium simplex	—	—	H-399 L-522
			32	Cylindrocarpon radicicola	240-242	+57|c|	F-275
			65	Flavobacterium sp.	—	—	I-430
			—	Fusarium javanicum	242-244	—	F-275
			—	Fusarium solani	229-233	+76|e|	V-105
			—	Fusarium solani	—	—	V-104 S-835
			—	Fusarium solani	226-230	+77|e|	K-462
			60(cr.)	Gliocladium roseum	232-236	+80[c]	S-857
			—	Gloeosporium olivarum	225-230	+77|e|	K-464 K-465
			—	Graphiola cylindrica	—	—	K-465
			—	Helminthosporium gramineum	—	—	K-460
			—	Helminthosporium sp.	—	—	S-857
			—	Helminthosporium zizaniae	224-229	+77|e|	K-460
			—	Hypomyces solani	—	—	L-525
			—	Mycobacterium flavum	—	—	C-100
			24	Mycococcus sp.	—	—	I-429
			—	Nocardia corallina	—	—	H-399

TABLE I

Transformations by Product

EMPIRICAL FORMULA	NAME OF REACTION PRODUCT	TRANSFORMATION	YIELD %	ORGANISM	CONSTANTS m. p.°	$[\alpha]_D$	REF.
$_{21}H_{28}O_4$	$17\alpha,21$-dihydroxy-1,4-pregnadiene-3,20-dione	Δ^1	—	Ophiobolus heterostropus	—	—	S-857
			—	Pseudomonas boreopolis	—	—	T-960
			—	Pseudomonas chlororaphis	—	—	N-648
			12	Pseudomonas dacunhae	220-231	+82.5[m]	S-848
			—	Pseudomonas oleovorans	—	—	T-960
			—	Pseudomonas sp.	—	—	N-652; U-1039; I-414
			—	Rhizoctonia solani	221	+72[c]	T-956
			—	Septomyxa affinis	—	—	S-835; V-1048
			20	Septomyxa affinis	238-242	+70[c]	W-1072
			70-80	Septomyxa affinis	—	—	S-901
			—	Serratia marcescens	—	—	T-960
			—	Stereum fasciatum	233-234	+80[c]	T-959
			—	Streptomyces flaveolus	235-239d	+75[e]	K-470
			—	Streptomyces lavendulae	—	—	S-835; V-1048
			—	Streptomyces sp.	—	—	K-470
			—	Volutella ciliata	—	—	L-525
		Δ^1; 21-OAc → 21-OH	—	Cylindrocarpon radicicola	—	—	F-275
			—	Mycobacterium smegmatis	235-236	+72[a]	S-873
		$\Delta^{1,4}$ (5αH)	—	Nocardia blackwellii	—	—	S-943
		$\Delta^{1,4}$ (5βH)	—	Nocardia blackwellii	—	—	S-943
		3β-OAc→3-C = O; $\Delta^5 \to \Delta^4$; Δ^1; 21-OAc → 21-OH	10-15	Corynebacterium simplex	238-240	—	C-128; C-115
			25	Corynebacterium simplex	246-249	+76[c]	N-665
	$6\beta,12\alpha$-dihydroxy-4,9(11)-pregnadiene-3,20-dione	6β-OH; 12α-OH	—	Aspergillus nidulans	—	—	F-277
			51(cr.)	Colletotrichum phomoides	231-232	+107[c]	F-277
			—	Thamnidium elegans	—	—	F-277

TABLE I

Transformations by Product

EMPIRICAL FORMULA	NAME OF REACTION PRODUCT	TRANSFORMATION	YIELD %	ORGANISM	CONSTANTS m. p.°	$[\alpha]_D$	REF.
$C_{21}H_{28}O_4$	6β, X-dihydroxy-4,9(11)-pregnadiene-3,20-dione	6β-OH; X-OH	—	Colletotrichum phomoides	250-252	+23[c]	F-277
	17α,21-dihydroxy-4,9(11)-pregnadiene-3,20-dione-11,12α-H³	21-OAc → 21 - OH	—	Curuvularia lunata	—	—	K-484
	6β,21-dihydroxy-4,17(20)-pregnadiene-3,11-dione	6β-OH ; 11β-OH → 11-C=O	14-29	Rhizopus arrhizus	252-254	+107[d]	H-344; H-341
	9α,21-dihydroxy-4,17(20)-pregnadiene-3,11-dione	9α-OH; 11β-OH → 11-C= O	—	Cunninghamella blakesleeana	—	—	H-344; H-342
			59	Helicostylum piriforme	219.5-221	+173[d]	H-344; H-342
	21-hydroxy-11β,12β-oxido-4-pregnene-3,20-dione	21-OH	—	Cercosporella herpotrichoides	—	—	L-490
			32	Wojnowicia graminis	164-166	+179[c]	D-157
	7β-hydroxy-16α,17α-oxido-4-pregnene-3,20-dione	7β-OH	19	Penicillium sp.	229-232	+158.5[c]	T-1036
	11α-hydroxy-16α,17α-oxido-4-pregnene-3,20-dione	11α-OH	—	Botryodiplodia theobromae	—	—	P-746
			9	Didymocladium ternatum	246-247	—	P-746
			31-73	Rhizopus nigricans	247-249	+136[c]	P-727; M-644
			78	Rhizopus nigricans	235-237	+146[c]	E-223
			—	Rhizopus nigricans	238-238.5	+137[c]	B-52 ; D-161
			—	Rhizopus reflexus	—	—	M-644
	9α-hydroxy-4-pregnene-3,11,20-trione	9α-OH	—	Ascochyta linicola	—	—	S-828
	15α-hydroxy-4-pregnene-3,11,20-trione	15α-OH	—	Calonectria decora	224-228	+289[c]	S-810
			—	Fusarium concolor	—	—	M-599
			—	Penicillium urticae	227-229	+257[e]	B-44; A-31
	17α-hydroxy-4-pregnene-3,11,20- trione	17α-OH	—	Aspergillus sp.	—	—	T-1010
			—	Cephalothecium roseum	—	—	M-600
	21-hydroxy-4-pregnene-3,11,20-trione	21-OH	38	Aspergillus niger	178-179	—	Z-1124 Z-1123
			—	Aspergillus niger	—	—	R-783
			51(cr.)	Ophiobolus herpotrichus	170-176	—	M-584; W-1101
	15α-hydroxy-4-pregnene-3,12,20-trione	15α-OH; 12α-OH → 12-C= O	—	Calonectria decora	235-239	+261[c]	S-810

TABLE I

Transformations by Product

EMPIRICAL FORMULA	NAME OF REACTION PRODUCT	TRANSFORMATION	YIELD %	ORGANISM	CONSTANTS m. p.°	[α]$_D$	REF.
$_{21}H_{28}O_4$	6β-hydroxy-4-pregnene-3,15,20-trione	6β-OH; 15-C=O; (via 15β-OH)	0.5	Penicillium sp.	280-286	+122[e]	T-1036
	7ξ,20β-dihydroxy-3-keto-4-pregnen-18-oic acid (18→20) lactone	7ξ-OH	—	Rhizopus nigricans	—	—	L-488; L-489
	11α,20β-dihydroxy-3-keto-4-pregnen-18-oic acid (18→20) lactone	11α-OH	—	Rhizopus nigricans	—	—	L-488; L-489
$_{21}H_{28}O_4Cl_2$	9α,11β-dichloro-17α,21-dihydroxy-5-pregnene-3,20-dione	21-OAc→21-OH	—	Flavobacterium dehydrogenans	—	—	N-691
$_{21}H_{28}O_4F_2$	9α,11β-difluoro-17α,21-dihydroxy-5-pregnene-3,20-dione	21-OAc→21-OH	—	Flavobacterium dehydrogenans	—	—	N-691
$_{21}H_{28}O_4S$	11β,17α-dihydroxy-21-mercapto-1,4-pregnadiene-3,20-dione	21-SAc → 21-SH	—	Flavobacterium dehydrogenans	—	—	N-685
$_{21}H_{28}O_5$	17α,20α,21-trihydroxy-1,4-pregnadiene-3,11-dione	20-C=O→20α-OH	22	Rhodotorula longissima	238-240d	+117[d]	C-110
	17α,20β,21-trihydroxy-1,4-pregnadiene-3,11-dione	20-C=O→20β-OH	—	Calonectria decora	—	—	S-951
			—	Fusarium sp.	—	—	S-951
			—	Mycobacterium flavum	—	—	C-100
			69	Streptomyces albus	184-185	+117[d]	K-459
			75	Streptomyces griseus	184-185	+118[d]	C-110
			60	Streptomyces hydrogenans	—	—	L-522
		Δ^1	—	Calonectria decora	—	—	S-951
			—	Fusarium sp.	—	—	S-951
		Δ^1; 20-C=O→20β-OH	—	Calonectria decora	177-180	—	S-951
			—	Corynebacterium simplex	—	—	H-389
			—	Fusarium sp.	—	—	S-951
			—	Gloeosporium olivarum	—	—	K-465
			—	Mycobacterium flavum	—	—	C-100
	6β,17α,21-trihydroxy-1,4-pregnadiene-3,20-dione	Δ^1	—	Bacillus lentus	229-231	—	R-750
		6β-OH	—	Chaetomium funicolum	—	—	C-108
	7α,17α,21-trihydroxy-1,4-pregnadiene-3,20-dione	7α-OH	—	Diplodia natalensis	—	—	T-997

TABLE I

Transformations by Product

EMPIRICAL FORMULA	NAME OF REACTION PRODUCT	TRANSFORMATION	YIELD %	ORGANISM	CONSTANTS m.p.°	$[\alpha]_D$	REF
$C_{21}H_{28}O_5$	$11\alpha,17\alpha,21$-trihydroxy-1,4-pregnadiene-3,20-dione	Δ^1	25-50	Corynebacterium simplex	246-247d	+ 73[m]	H-389; H-384; N-665
		11α-OH	—	Aspergillus ochraceus	—	—	V-104 S-835
			—	Beauveria sp.	—	—	I-421
			61(cr.)	Fusarium equiseti	206-208	+ 76[d]	M-557
			—	Glomerella cingulata	—	—	C-109
			—	Glomerella lagenarium	—	—	C-109
			12	unidentified fungus	222-223	+ 76[m]	T-990
		11α-OH; 21-OAc→21-OH	—	Glomerella cingulata	—	—	C-109
			—	Glomerella lagenarium	—	—	C-109
	$11\beta,17\alpha,21$-trihydroxy-1,4-pregnadiene-3,20-dione (prednisolone)	Δ^1	—	Azotobacter agilis	—	—	T-989
			42	Azotobacter indicus	—	—	T-989
			70	Azotomonas fluorescens	—	—	T-989
			—	Bacillus lentus	235-237	+100[d]	R-750
			46	Bacillus pulvifaciens	220-222	+ 99[d]	T-1027
			—	Bacillus pulvifaciens	—	—	I-420
			62	Bacillus sp.	228-231	+ 98[m]	S-848
			—	Bacillus sphaericus	—	—	S-942; H-399
			—	Bacillus sphaericus	233-236d	+100[d]	K-468
			—	Bacterium cyclo-oxydans	—	—	K-480
			—	Bacterium havaniensis	—	—	F-233
			—	Bacterium mycoides	—	—	F-240
			—	Calonectria decora	238-241	—	W-1096
			—	Corynebacterium hoagii	—	—	N-665
			80	Corynebacterium simplex	239-241d	+107[d]	N-665
			94(cr.)	Corynebacterium simplex	240-241d	+102[d]	H-389; N-671
			90	Corynebacterium simplex	235d	+100[d]	K-467
			—	Corynebacterium simplex	—	—	H-399

TABLE I

Transformations by Product

EMPIRICAL FORMULA	NAME OF REACTION PRODUCT	TRANSFORMATION	YIELD %	ORGANISM	CONSTANTS m.p.°	$[\alpha]_D$	REF.
$_{21}H_{28}O_5$	Prednisolone	Δ^1	—	Didymella lycopersici	234-236	+ 98[d]	V-1052
			84	Didymella lycopersici	238-241	—	W-1096
			75	Flavobacterium sp.	—	—	I-430
			—	Gloeosporium olivarum	—	—	K-465
			—	Graphiola cylindrica	236	+100[d]	K-465
			46-68	Micrococcus sp.	—	—	I-431
			—	Micromonospora chalcea	—	—	S-864; S-867
			—	Mycobacterium smegmatis	196-198	+108[e]	S-873
			77-80	Mycobacterium sp.	—	—	K-476
			55-62	Mycococcus sp.	—	—	I-429
			—	Nocardia corallina	—	—	H-399
			—	Nocardia sp.	—	—	S-939
			—	Protaminobacter alboflavum	—	—	S-863
			—	Protaminobacter rubrum	—	—	S-863
			—	Pseudomonas chlororaphis	—	—	N-648
			—	Septomyxa affinis	—	—	W-1072; M-647; K-456
			—	Serratia plymuthica	—	—	T-960
			—	Streptomyces flaveolus	232-236d	+100[d]	K-470
			—	Streptomyces lavendulae	235-237	—	F-272
			—	Streptomyces sp.	—	—	K-470
		$d,l \rightarrow d-\Delta^1 + l$	—	Didymella lycopersici	234-236	+ 98[d]	W-1102
		$\Delta^{1,4}$ (5α-H)	—	Calonectria decora	—	—	W-1096
		$\Delta^{1,4}$ (5β-H)	—	Nocardia blackwellii	—	—	S-943
			—	Protaminobacter alboflavum	—	—	S-866
			—	Protaminobacter rubrum	—	—	S-866

TABLE I

Transformations by Product

EMPIRICAL FORMULA	NAME OF REACTION PRODUCT	TRANSFORMATION	YIELD %	ORGANISM	CONSTANTS m. p. °	$[\alpha]_D$	REF
$C_{21}H_{28}O_5$	Prednisolone	3α-OH→3-C=O; $\Delta^{1,4}(5\beta$-H)	—	Nocardia blackwellii	—	—	S-943
		11β-OH	—	Coniothyrium helleborine	—	—	T-100
			19	Corticium sasakii	232-236d	—	H-350
			11	Unidentified fungus	230-231	—	T-990
		21-OH	—	Ophiobolus herpotrichus	—	—	W-110 H-388 O-700
		Δ^1; 11β-OH	—	Corticium sasakii	227-231	—	H-327
			—	Pseudomonas oleovorans	—	—	T-960
			20-30	Pseudomonas sp.	—	—	T-961; U-104
	$12\beta,17\alpha,21$-trihydroxy-1,4-pregnadiene-3,20-dione	Δ^1	—	Bacillus lentus	232-234	—	R-750
			—	Corynebacterium simplex	232-234	—	R-749
	$14\alpha,17\alpha,21$-trihydroxy-1,4-pregnadiene-3,20-dione	Δ^1	—	Bacillus lentus	229-230	—	R-750
			2	Mycobacterium smegmatis	217-218	+132[c]	S-872; S-873
		14α-OH	10	Unidentified fungus	234-234.5	+107[m]	T-990
	$15\beta,17\alpha,21$-trihydroxy-1,4-pregnadiene-3,20-dione	Δ^1	—	Bacillus sphaericus	—	—	C-126; C-127
	$16\alpha,17\alpha,21$-trihydroxy-1,4-pregnadiene-3,20-dione	Δ^1	—	Bacterium havaniensis	—	—	F-233
			—	Bacterium mycoides	—	—	F-240
	$11\beta,17\alpha,21$-trihydroxy-1,5-pregnadiene-3,20-dione	21-OAc→21-OH	—	Flavobacterium dehydrogenans	—	—	N-690
		$11\beta,17\alpha,21$-triOAc →$11\beta,17\alpha,21$-triOH	—	Flavobacterium dehydrogenans	—	—	N-690
	$17\alpha,20\beta,21$-trihydroxy-4,6-pregnadiene-3,11-dione	20-C=O → 20β-OH	26	Curvularia lunata	208-209; 204-205 (polymorph)	+126 [d]	G-306
	$14\alpha,17\alpha,21$-trihydroxy-4,9(11)-pregnadiene-3,20-dione	14α-OH	—	Curvularia lunata	191-194	—	B-65
	$17\alpha,21$-dihydroxy-$1\beta,11\beta$-oxido-5,9-cyclopregnane-3,20-dione	$11\beta,21$-diOAc→ $11\beta,21$-diOH; Δ^1-11β-OH → 1β, 11β-oxide	—	Flavobacterium dehydrogenans	208-213	- 14	G-292
			—	Flavobacterium dehydrogenans	200-206	- 14	R-777
	$11\beta,21$-dihydroxy-3,20-diketo-4-pregnen-18-al (18→11) hemiacetal (aldosterone)	11β-OH	—	Cunninghamella blakesleeana	165-168	—	W-110
		d,1→d-21-OH + 1	—	Ophiobolus herpotrichus	162-168	+142[a]	W-1102 V-1055

TABLE I

Transformations by Product

EMPIRICAL FORMULA	NAME OF REACTION PRODUCT	TRANSFORMATION	YIELD %	ORGANISM	CONSTANTS m.p.°	[α]$_D$	REF.
$_1H_{28}O_5$	$17\alpha,21$-dihydroxy-$9\alpha,11\alpha$-oxido-4-pregnene-3,20-dione	$\Delta^{9(11)} \to 9\alpha,11\alpha$-oxide	20	Nocardia sp.	213-215	+ 85[d]	S-886
	$17\alpha,21$-dihydroxy-$9\alpha,11\alpha$-oxido-4-pregnene-3,20-dione-$11\beta,12\alpha$-H³	$\Delta^{9(11)} \to 9\alpha,11\alpha$-oxide; 21-OAc→21-OH	46	Curvularia sp.	223	—	K-484
	$6\beta,12\alpha$-dihydroxy-$9\beta,11\beta$-oxido-4-pregnene-3,20-dione	$\Delta^{9(11)} \to 9\beta,11\beta$-oxide; 6β-OH; 12α-OH	41(cr.)	Colletotrichum phomoides	202-204	+ 5[c]	F-277
	$17\alpha,21$-dihydroxy-$9\beta,11\beta$-oxido-4-pregnene-3,20-dione	$\Delta^{9(11)} \to 9\beta,11\beta$-oxide	—	Cunninghamella blakesleeana	210-211	+ 13[d]	B-66
			—	Curvularia brachysporia	—	—	S-865
			—	Curvularia lunata	—	—	B-66; S-865; B-65
	$17\alpha,21$-dihydroxy-$9\beta,11\beta$-oxido-4-pregnene-3,20-dione-$11\alpha,12\alpha$-H³	$\Delta^{9(11)} \to 9\beta,11\beta$-oxide; 21-OAc→21-OH	11	Curvularia lunata	208-211	—	K-484
	$16\alpha,21$-dihydroxy-$11\beta,12\beta$-oxido-4-pregnene-3,20-dione	16α-OH	26	Streptomyces roseochromogenus	212-214	+158[c]	D-157
	$17\alpha,21$-dihydroxy-$14\alpha,15\alpha$-oxido-4-pregnene-3,20-dione	$\Delta^{14} \to 14\alpha,15\alpha$-oxide	—	Cunninghamella blakesleeana	—	—	B-66; S-865
			—	Curvularia lunata	230-232	+135[d]	B-66; S-865
			—	Helicostylum piriforme	—	—	B-66; S-865
			—	Mucor griseocyanus	—	—	B-66; S-865
			—	Mucor parasiticus	—	—	B-66; S-865
			—	Phycomyces blakesleeanus	—	—	S-865
	$2\beta,21$-dihydroxy-$16\alpha,17\alpha$-oxido-4-pregnene-3,20-dione	2β-OH	—	Gnomonia fragariae	—	—	L-496
	$11\alpha,21$-dihydroxy-$16\alpha,17\alpha$-oxido-4-pregnene-3,20-dione	11α-OH; 21-OAc→21-OH	—	Rhizopus nigricans	218-220	+127[m]	A-8
	$17\alpha,21$-dihydroxy-1-5β-pregnene-3,11,20-trione	$\Delta^4 \to 5\beta$-H	14(cr.)	Streptomyces sp.	—	—	G-314
	$6\beta,21$-dihydroxy-4-pregnene-3,11,20-trione	6β-OH; 11β-OH→11-C=O	16(cr.)	Sclerotium hydrophilum	195-200	+146.5 [m]	S-856
	$14\alpha,21$-dihydroxy-4-pregnene-3,11,20-trione	14α-OH	36(cr.)	Absidia regnieri	208-214	—	S-841
		14α-OH; 11β-OH→11-C=O	40(cr.)	Absidia regnieri	210-215	+ 69[m]	S-841; S-851

TABLE I

Transformations by Product

EMPIRICAL FORMULA	NAME OF REACTION PRODUCT	TRANSFORMATION	YIELD %	ORGANISM	CONSTANTS m. p.°	$[\alpha]_D$	REF
$C_{21}H_{28}O_5$	15β,21-dihydroxy-4-pregnene-3,11,20-trione	15β-OH; 11β-OH→11-C=O	28(cr.)	Botrytis cinerea	189-195	+180[m]	S-842
			21(cr.)	Sclerotium hydrophilum	195-200	+190[m]	S-856
	17α,21-dihydroxy-4-pregnene-3,11,20-trione (cortisone)	Δ^1→H	1	Bacillus megaterium	215-220d	—	H-382
		21-OAc→21-OH	—	Bacillus megaterium	—	—	S-948
		11β-OH→11-C=O	—	Cunninghamella blakesleeana	—	—	H-344
			59	Cunninghamella elegans	211-213	—	E-225
		11β-OH→11-C=O; 21-OAc→21-OH	—	Cunninghamella elegans	—	—	E-225
		17α-OH	3	Cephalothecium roseum	—	—	M-600
			—	Trichothecium roseum	206-216	—	M-584
		17α-OH; 11β-OH→11-C=O	—	Cephalothecium roseum	—	—	M-600
			—	Trichothecium roseum	—	—	M-584
		11β-OH; 11β-OH→11-C=O	—	Absidia sp.	—	—	C-98; H-334
			—	Botrytis cinerea	—	—	C-98
			—	Corticium sasakii	226-227	—	H-327
			13	Cunninghamella blakesleeana	—	—	M-601
			—	Cunninghamella blakesleeana	—	—	M-556 O-696 H-339 M-555 M-641 S-919
			—	Cunninghamella sp.	—	—	C-98
			—	Curvularia lunata	—	—	C-98
			—	Rhizoctonia sp.	—	—	G-312 G-313
			—	Streptomyces fradiae	—	—	H-328
	17α,21-dihydroxy-16α-methyl-18-nor-4-pregnene-3,11,20-trione	21-OH	—	Colletotrichum lindemuthianum	—	—	A-11
$C_{21}H_{28}O_5F_2$	6α,21-difluoro-11β,16α,17α-trihydroxy-4-pregnene-3,20-dione	16α-OH	—	Streptomyces roseochromogenus	—	—	M-532

TABLE I

Transformations by Product

EMPIRICAL FORMULA	NAME OF REACTION PRODUCT	TRANSFORMATION	YIELD %	ORGANISM	CONSTANTS m. p.°	[α]_D	REF.
$C_{21}H_{28}O_6$	$11\beta,16\alpha,17a\alpha$-trihydroxy-$17a\beta$-hydroxymethyl-D-homo-1,4-androstadien-3,17-dione	16α-OH; 17α-OH-17β-(20-C = O-21-OH) → $17a\alpha$-OH-$17a\beta$-CH_2OH-17-C=O	—	Streptomyces roseochromogenus	—	—	G-297
	*$6\beta,11\beta,17\alpha$.21-tetrahydroxy-1,4-pregnadiene-3,20-dione	6β-OH	—	Chaetomium cochliodes	—	—	C-108
	$7\alpha,11\beta,17\alpha,21$-tetrahydroxy-1,4-pregnadiene-3,20-dione	7α-OH	—	Diplodia natalensis	—	—	T-997
	$11\beta,14\alpha,17\alpha,21$-tetrahydroxy-1,4-pregnadiene-3,20-dione	Δ^1	—	Mycobacterium smegmatis	227-229	+103.5[d]	S-873; S-874
	$11\alpha,15\beta,17\alpha,21$-tetrahydroxy-1,4-pregnadiene-3,20-dione	Δ^1	—	Bacillus sphaericus	—	—	C-126; C-127
	$11\beta,15\beta,17\alpha,21$-tetrahydroxy-1,4-pregnadiene-3,20-dione	Δ^1	—	Bacillus sphaericus	—	—	C-127; C-126
	$11\beta,16\alpha,17\alpha,21$-tetrahydroxy-1,4-pregnadiene-3,20-dione	Δ^1	—	Bacterium havaniensis	—	—	F-233
			—	Bacterium mycoides	—	—	F-240
			28	Corynebacterium simplex	231-232	+77[m]	B-61; B-59; B-54
			10	Nocardia corallina	229-231	—	B-61; H-399
		16α-OH	—	Streptomyces californicus	—	—	L-491
			—	Streptomyces roseochromogenus	—	—	G-297; F-257
	$11\beta,14\alpha,21$-trihydroxy-3,20-diketo-4-pregnen-18-al (18 → 11) hemiacetal	14α-OH	—	Pleospora gaeumanni	—	—	W-1108
	$11\beta,17\alpha,21$-trihydroxy-3,20-diketo-4-pregnen-18-al (18 - 11) hemiacetal	d,l → d-17α-OH + l	—	Trichothecium roseum	—	—	W-1102
	$14\alpha,17\alpha,21$-trihydroxy-9β,11β-oxido-4-pregnene-3,20-dione	14α-OH; $\Delta^{9(11)}$ → $9\beta,11\beta$-oxide	—	Curvularia lunata	—	—	B-65
	$11\beta,17\alpha,21$-trihydroxy-14α,15α-oxido-4-pregnene-3,20-dione	11β-OH; Δ^{14} → $14\alpha,15\alpha$-oxide	—	Cunninghamella blakesleeana	—	—	S-865
			—	Curvularia lunata	—	—	S-865
	$2\beta,17\alpha,21$-trihydroxy-4-pregnene-3,11,20-trione (tentative)	11-C = O (via 11β-OH); 2β-OH	—	Rhizoctonia solani	181-200	—	G-312
	$6\beta,17\alpha,21$-trihydroxy-4-pregnene-3,11,20-trione (tentative)	6β-OH; 11-C = O (via 11β-OH)	—	Rhizoctonia solani	210-215d	+113[d]	G-312
	$7\alpha,17\alpha,21$-trihydroxy-4-pregnene-3,11,20-trione	7α-OH	—	Diplodia natalensis	—	—	T-997

*Later, unpublished work has shown this product to be $6\beta,17\alpha,21$-trihydroxy-1,4-pregnadiene-3,11,20-trione.

TABLE I

Transformations by Product

EMPIRICAL FORMULA	NAME OF REACTION PRODUCT	TRANSFORMATION	YIELD %	ORGANISM	CONSTANTS		REF.
					m. p.°	$[\alpha]_D$	
$C_{21}H_{28}O_6$	$15\alpha,17\alpha,21$-trihydroxy-4-pregnene-3,11,20-trione	15α-OH; 21-OAc → 21-OH	—	Fusarium oxysporium	—	—	M-599
	$15\beta,17\alpha,21$-trihydroxy-4-pregnene-3,11,20-trione	15β-OH	—	Bacillus megatherium	—	—	C-126
$C_{21}H_{28}O_6F_2$	$6\alpha,9\alpha$-difluoro-$11\beta,16\alpha,17\alpha,21$-tetrahydroxy-4-pregnene-3,20-dione	16α-OH	18	Streptomyces roseochromogenus	242-248	+58[d]	M-586
	$6\alpha,12\alpha$-difluoro-$11\beta,16\alpha,17\alpha,21$-tetrahydroxy-4-pregnene-3,20-dione	16α-OH	—	Streptomyces roseochromogenus	—	—	F-261
$C_{21}H_{29}O_3Br$	17α-bromo-11α-hydroxy-4-pregnene-3,20-dione	11α-OH	—	Aspergillus ochraceus	—	—	V-104 S-835
	17α-bromo-11β-hydroxy-4-pregnene-3,20-dione	11β-OH	—	Curvularia lunata	—	—	R-756 R-773
$C_{21}H_{29}O_3F$	6α-fluoro-17α-hydroxy-1-5α-pregnene-3,20-dione	Δ^1	—	Septomyxa affinis	—	—	B-34
	6α-fluoro-17α-hydroxy-1-5β-pregnene-3,20-dione	Δ^1	—	Septomyxa affinis	—	—	B-34
	6α-fluoro-11α-hydroxy-4-pregnene-3,20-dione	11α-OH	—	Aspergillus ochraceus	—	—	V-104 S-835
$C_{21}H_{29}O_3N$	12a-aza-C-homo-1-5α-pregnene-3,12,20-trione	3β-OAc → 3-C = O; Δ'	26	Arthrobacter sp.	206-207.5	+32[m]	M-563
$C_{21}H_{29}O_4Br$	12α-bromo-$11\beta,16\alpha$-dihydroxy-4-pregnene-3,20-dione	16α-OH	—	Streptomyces roseochromogenus	211-212	+101[c]	F-256
$C_{21}H_{29}O_4F$	6α-fluoro-$11\beta,16\alpha$-dihydroxy-4-pregnene-3,20-dione	16α-OH	—	Streptomyces roseochromogenus	—	—	B-35
	6α-fluoro-$11\alpha,17\alpha$-dihydroxy-4-pregnene-3,20-dione	11α-OH	—	Aspergillus nidulans	—	—	F-268
	6β-fluoro-$11\alpha,17\alpha$-dihydroxy-4-pregnene-3,20-dione	11α-OH	—	Rhizopus nigricans	—	—	H-391
	6β-fluoro-$11\beta,17\alpha$-dihydroxy-4-pregnene-3,20-dione	11β-OH	—	Chaetomella oblonga	—	—	H-391
	9α-fluoro-$2\beta,11\beta$-dihydroxy-4-pregnene-3,20-dione	2β-OH	—	Gnomonia fragariae	—	—	L-496
	9α-fluoro-$11\beta,21$-dihydroxy-4-pregnene-3,20-dione	d,l → d-21-OH + l	—	Ophiobolus herpotrichus	—	—	W-110
	12α-fluoro-$11\beta,14\alpha$-dihydroxy-4-pregnene-3,20-dione	14α-OH	—	Pleospora gaeumanni	—	—	W-110
	12α-fluoro-$11\beta,16\alpha$-dihydroxy-4-pregnene-3,20-dione	16α-OH	—	Streptomyces roseochromogenus	—	—	F-256 F-257
$C_{21}H_{29}O_5Cl$	6α-chloro-$11\alpha,17\alpha,21$-trihydroxy-4-pregnene-3,20-dione	11α-OH	—	Aspergillus nidulans	—	—	F-268

TABLE I

Transformations by Product

EMPIRICAL FORMULA	NAME OF REACTION PRODUCT	TRANSFORMATION	YIELD %	ORGANISM	m. p.°	$[\alpha]_D$	REF.
$C_{21}H_{29}O_5Cl$	6α-chloro-11β,17α,21-trihydroxy-4-pregnene-3,20-dione	11β-OH; 21-OAc → 21-OH	—	Cunninghamella bainieri	—	—	R-770
$C_{21}H_{29}O_5F$	6α-fluoro-2β,17α,21-trihydroxy-4-pregnene-3,20-dione	2β-OH	—	Gnomonia fragariae	—	—	L-496
	6α-fluoro-11β,16α,17α-trihydroxy-4-pregnene-3,20-dione	16α-OH	—	Streptomyces roseochromogenus	—	—	M-530
	6α-fluoro-11α, 17α, 21-trihydroxy-4-pregnene-3,20-dione	11α-OH	32	Aspergillus nidulans	201-203	+100[e]	F-268
	6α-fluoro-15β,17α,21-trihydroxy-4-pregnene-3,20-dione	15β-OH	—	Aspergillus nidulans	225-228	+79[e]	F-268
	9α-fluoro-11β,16α,21-trihydroxy-4-pregnene-3,20-dione	16α-OH	24	Streptomyces roseochromogenus	241.5-244.5	+127[m]	H-403
	9α-fluoro-11β,17α,21-trihydroxy-4-pregnene-3,20-dione	21-C=O → 21-OH	—	Streptomyces roseochromogenus	—	—	S-907
		21-OAc → 21-OH	—	Streptomyces olivochromogenus	—	—	S-941
	12α-fluoro-11β,14α,17α-trihydroxy-4-pregnene-3,20-dione	14α-OH	—	Pleospora gaeumanni	—	—	W-1103
$C_{21}H_{29}O_6Cl$	9α-chloro-2β,11β,17α,21-tetrahydroxy-4-pregnene-3,20-dione	2β-OH	—	Streptomyces roseochromogenus	—	—	S-913
	9α-chloro-11β,16α,17α,21-tetrahydroxy-4-pregnene-3,20-dione	16α-OH	—	Streptomyces roseochromogenus	—	—	S-913
$C_{21}H_{29}O_6F$	9α-fluoro-11β,16α,17aα-trihydroxy-17aβ-hydroxy-methyl-D-homo-4-androstene-3,17-dione	16α-OH; 17α-OH-17β-(20-C=O-21-OH) → 17aα-OH-17aβ-CH₂OH-17-C=O	—	Streptomyces roseochromogenus	252-254	+84[m]	S-910; S-912; G-297; G-295
	9α-fluoro-11β,16α,17α,20β,21-pentahydroxy-1,4-pregnadien-3-one	Δ¹	—	Bacterium cyclooxydans	—	—	G-296; G-294
		20-C=O → 20β-OH	—	Bacterium cyclooxydans	—	—	G-296; S-908
				Corynebacterium simplex	—	—	G-296; S-908
				Mycobacterium rhodochorus	—	—	G-296
		Δ¹; 20-C=O → 20β-OH	—	Bacterium cyclooxydans	—	—	S-908
			<1	Corynebacterium simplex	262-264	—	S-908

TABLE I

Transformations by Product

EMPIRICAL FORMULA	NAME OF REACTION PRODUCT	TRANSFORMATION	YIELD %	ORGANISM	CONSTANTS m.p.°	$[\alpha]_D$	REF.
$C_{21}H_{29}O_6F$	6α-fluoro-$11\beta,16\alpha,17\alpha,21$-tetrahydroxy-4-pregnene-3,20-dione	16α-OH	26(cr.)	Streptomyces roseochromogenus	234-236	+ 95[d]	M-586; M-533
	9α-fluoro-$1\xi,11\beta,17\alpha,21$-tetrahydroxy-4-pregnene-3,20-dione	1ξ-OH	—	Mortierella sp.	—	—	F-237
			38	Streptomyces antibioticus	—	—	F-234
			5	Streptomyces ruber	248-254	+122[m]	F-234
		1ξ-OH; 21-OAc→21-OH	2	Streptomyces olivochromogenus	247-252	—	M-569; S-941
	9α-fluoro-$2\beta,11\beta,17\alpha,21$-tetrahydroxy-4-pregnene-3,20-dione	2β-OH	—	Streptomyces roseochromogenus	245-249	+ 1.5[m]	S-912; S-913
	9α-fluoro-$6\beta,11\beta,17\alpha,21$-tetrahydroxy-4-pregnene-3,20-dione	6β-OH	—	Streptomyces rimosus	224-227	+ 56[m]	S-909
		6β-OH; 21-OAc→21-OH	—	Streptomyces olivochromogenus	—	—	M-569; S-941
	9α-fluoro-$7\alpha,11\beta,17\alpha,21$-tetrahydroxy-4-pregnene-3,20-dione	7α-OH	—	Diplodia natalensis	—	—	T-997
	9α-fluoro-$11\beta,14\alpha,17\alpha,21$-tetrahydroxy-4-pregnene-3,20-dione	14α-OH	—	Pleospora gaeumanni	—	—	W-1108
	9α-fluoro-$11\beta,15\beta,16\alpha,21$-tetrahydroxy-4-pregnene-3,20-dione	15β-OH	—	Bacillus megaterium	—	—	N-669
	9α-fluoro-$11\beta,15\beta,17\alpha,21$-tetrahydroxy-4-pregnene-3,20-dione	15β-OH	—	Bacillus megaterium	—	—	N-669
	9α-fluoro-$11\beta,16\alpha,17\alpha,21$-tetrahydroxy-4-pregnene-3,20-dione	Δ^1→H	—	Bacterium cyclo-oxydans	—	—	G-296
			—	Corynebacterium simplex	—	—	G-296
		16α-OH	30-70	Nocardia italica	—	—	S-918
			—	Streptomyces californicus	—	—	L-491
			50	Streptomyces roseochromogenus	250-252	+ 97[p]	T-1002 G-297; G-295; L-505; S-913
			—	Streptomyces sp.	—	—	S-788
		16α-OH; 21-OAc→21-OH	—	Streptomyces halstedii	235-238	+ 94.5[p]	K-447
	12α-fluoro-$11\beta,16\alpha,17\alpha,21$-tetrahydroxy-4-pregnene-3,20-dione	16α-OH	—	Streptomyces argenteolus	—	—	H-380
			—	Streptomyces roseochromogenus	—	—	F-256; F-257

TABLE I

Transformations by Product

EMPIRICAL FORMULA	NAME OF REACTION PRODUCT	TRANSFORMATION	YIELD %	ORGANISM	CONSTANTS m.p.°	$[\alpha]_D$	REF.
$C_{21}H_{29}O_7Cl$	9α-chloro-$2\beta,11\beta,16\alpha,17\alpha,21$-pentahydroxy-4-pregnene-3,20-dione	2β-OH	—	Streptomyces roseochromogenus	—	—	S-913
		16α-OH	—	Streptomyces roseochromogenus	—	—	S-913
$C_{21}H_{29}O_7F$	9α-fluoro-$1\xi,11\beta,16\alpha,17\alpha,21$-pentahydroxy-4-pregnene-3,20-dione	1ξ-OH	—	Mortierella zonata	—	—	F-237
	9α-fluoro-$2\beta,11\beta,16\alpha,17\alpha,21$-pentahydroxy-4-pregnene-3,20-dione	16α-OH	—	Streptomyces roseochromogenus	—	—	S-912
		2β-OH; 16α-OH	3(cr.)	Streptomyces roseochromogenus	220-223	- 26.5[m]	S-912; S-913
$C_{21}H_{30}O_2$	17α-ethyl-17β-hydroxy-1,4-androstadien-3-one	Δ^1	—	Corynebacterium simplex	—	—	N-667a
	17β-hydroxy-17α-methyl-16-methylene-4-androsten-3-one	3β-OH→3-C=O; $\Delta^5 \rightarrow \Delta^4$	24	Flavobacterium dehydrogenans	144-146	- 5[d]	B-76
	4-pregnene-3,20-dione	3β-OH→3-C=O; $\Delta^5 \rightarrow \Delta^4$	—	Aspergillus sp.	—	—	C-104; P-710
			30	Bacillus pulvifaciens	129-130	+175[d]	T-1027; I-420
			—	Corynebacterium helvolum	—	—	M-546
			—	Eremothecium ashbyii	—	—	P-710
			82	Micrococcus dehydrogenans	127-128	—	E-214
			—	Penicillium sp.	—	—	P-710
			—	Streptomyces sp.	—	—	P-710; P-712; P-716; F-267
			—	Ustilago zeae	—	—	P-710
		d,1-3β-OH→ d-3-C=O+1; d,1-Δ^5→d-Δ^4+1	—	Aspergillus niger	123-126	+191	W-1102
			—	Streptomyces fradiae	125-127	+190	W-1102
		3β-OAc→3-C=O; $\Delta^5 \rightarrow \Delta^4$	2	Bacillus pulvifaciens	—	—	T-1027; I-420
$C_{21}H_{30}O_3$	17α-ethyl-$11\beta,17\beta$-dihydroxy-1,4-androstadien-3-one	11β-OH	—	Curvularia lunata	—	—	N-667a
	17β-hydroxy-4-androsten-3-one acetate	17β-Ac→17β-OAc	10-15	Cladosporium resinae	138.5-140	+ 85[a]	F-254; F-250
		17-C=O →17β-OAc	—	Saccharomyces fragilis	—	—	M-572
	5-androstene-3,17-dione 3-ethylene ketal	17β-OH→17-C=O	88	Nocardia restrictus	196-198	+ 16[c]	S-885

TABLE I

Transformations by Product

EMPIRICAL FORMULA	NAME OF REACTION PRODUCT	TRANSFORMATION	YIELD %	ORGANISM	CONSTANTS		REF.
					m.p.°	$[\alpha]_D$	
$C_{21}H_{30}O_3$	$11\alpha,20\beta$-dihydroxy-1,4-pregnadien-3-one	Δ^1 ; $20\text{-}C\text{=}O \rightarrow 20\beta\text{-OH}$	—	Bacterium cyclo-oxydans	227-229	+ 41[c]	K-480
			57	Corynebacterium simplex	227-229	+ 41[c]	T-995
	$16\alpha,20\beta$-dihydroxy-1,4-pregnadien-3-one	Δ^1 ; $20\text{-}C\text{=}O \rightarrow 20\beta\text{-OH}$	—	Streptomyces lavendulae	226-227	- 15[c]	F-288; F-271; F-273
	$16\alpha,20\alpha$-dihydroxy-17β-methyl-18-<u>nor</u>-17α-4,13-pregnadien-3-one	$20\text{-}C\text{=}O \rightarrow 20\alpha\text{-OH}$; $13\text{-Me-}16\alpha,17\alpha\text{-}$ oxido$\rightarrow\Delta^{13}\text{-}16\alpha\text{-OH-}$ $17\beta\text{-Me}$	34	Saccharomyces cerevisiae	172-175	- 15[c]	C-88; C-90
	$3,9\xi$-dihydroxy-9,10-<u>seco</u>-1,3,5(10)-pregnatrien-20-one	Δ^1 ; $9\alpha\text{-OH}$; rev. aldol.; enol.; $9\text{-}C\text{=}O \rightarrow 9\xi\text{-OH}$	<1	Mycobacterium smegmatis	—	—	S-820
	20α-hydroxy-4-pregnene-3,11-dione	$20\text{-}C\text{=}O \rightarrow 20\alpha\text{-OH}$	—	Rhodotorula longissima	—	—	C-122
	11α-hydroxy-17α-4-pregnene-3,20-dione	$11\alpha\text{-OH}$; $\Delta^{16}\text{-}17\text{-Ac} \rightarrow 17\alpha\text{-Ac}$	—	Aspergillus niger	—	—	M-603
			24	Rhizopus nigricans	209-211.5	- 12[c]	M-579; M-601; M-605
	1β-hydroxy-4-pregnene-3,20-dione	$3\beta\text{-OH} \rightarrow 3\text{-}C\text{=}O$; $\Delta^5 \rightarrow \Delta^4$	—	Corynebacterium mediolanum	153	+192[c]	B-77
			35	Flavobacterium dehydrogenans	154-156	+142[c]	N-689
	1ξ-hydroxy-4-pregnene-3,20-dione	$1\xi\text{-OH}$	—	Cladosporium sp.	—	—	S-941
	2β-hydroxy-4-pregnene-3,20-dione	$2\beta\text{-OH}$	tr.	Penicillium sp.	184-186	—	T-1036
	6β-hydroxy-4-pregnene-3,20-dione	$6\beta\text{-OH}$	—	Mortierella alpina	—	—	F-239
			—	Mortierella pusilla	—	—	F-239
			—	Penicillium urticae	—	—	E-202
			—	Streptomyces aureofaciens	175-176	+108	F-288; P-713
			10	Streptomyces sp.	172-173	+ 98[c]	S-854; S-847
	7α-hydroxy-4-pregnene-3,20-dione	$7\alpha\text{-OH}$	—	Cephalosporium sp. (see footnote)	—	—	B-56
			—	Diplodia natalensis	—	—	T-997
			18	Helminthosporium sp.	227-231	+154[d]	M-570
			4(cr.)	Phycomyces blakesleeanus	229-230	+167[c]	F-288; F-285; F-286
	7β-hydroxy-4-pregnene-3,20-dione	$7\beta\text{-OH}$	15	Cladosporium sp.	188-191	+141[c] +158[d]	M-570 S-941
	(Footnote) revise to 7β- ref. T-1037						

TABLE I

Transformations by Product

EMPIRICAL FORMULA	NAME OF REACTION PRODUCT	TRANSFORMATION	YIELD %	ORGANISM	CONSTANTS m.p.°	$[\alpha]_D$	REF.
$C_{21}H_{30}O_3$	7β-hydroxy-4-pregnene-3,20-dione	7β-OH	17-36	Diplodia tubericola	190.5-192.5	+144[d]	T-1023; T-1025; A-28
		7β-OH; 3β-OH→3-C=O; $\Delta^5 \to \Delta^4$	6-12	Diplodia tubericola	—	—	T-1025; A-28
	9α-hydroxy-4-pregnene-3,20-dione	9α-OH	31	Ascochyta linicola	191-194	—	S-828
			—	Bacterium cyclo-oxydans	—	—	S-885
			49	Circinella sp.	190-192	+204[c]	S-815
			—	Corynebacterium simplex	—	—	S-885; P-740
			—	Mycobacterium rhodocrous	—	—	S-885
			—	Nocardia corallina	193-194.5	+185	D-173
			13-17	Nocardia restrictus	190-191	+188[c]	S-898; S-885; P-740; S-897
			33	Nocardia sp.	193-194.5	+185[c]	D-172
			—	Pseudomonas testosteroni	—	—	S-885
			—	Streptomyces aureofaciens	189-191	+202[c] +150[a]	P-713; F-288
	11α-hydroxy-4-pregnene-3,20-dione	11α-OH	—	Absidia sp.	—	—	C-98; N-682
			35	Aspergillus niger	166-167	+178[c]	F-283
			—	Aspergillus niger	—	—	W-1121; W-1120
			9	Aspergillus ochraceus	165-168	—	D-190
			90	Aspergillus ochraceus	—	—	W-1067; W-1065
			—	Aspergillus ochraceus	—	—	D-193; K-436; M-562; S-797; V-1048; D-182; S-835; S-900; D-181; W-1066; K-454
			15	Aspergillus saitoi	168-170	+169[c]	I-417

TABLE I

Transformations by Product

EMPIRICAL FORMULA	NAME OF REACTION PRODUCT	TRANSFORMATION	YIELD %	ORGANISM	CONSTANTS m. p.°	$[\alpha]_D$	REF.
$C_{21}H_{30}O_3$	11α-hydroxy-4-pregnene-3,20-dione	11α-OH	—	Aspergillus sp.	—	—	D-190; M-603; C-104; I-417; W-1081 T-1010
			3	Bacillus cereus	161-165	—	M-568
			—	Botrytis cinerea	—	—	C-98
			34	Cunninghamella echinulata	165-166	—	Z-1125
			—	Cunninghamella sp.	—	—	C-98
			—	Dactylium dendroides	—	—	D-189
			34(cr.)	Gloeosporium kaki	164-167	+180|c|	S-855
			—	Glomerella lagenarium	—	—	S-855
			—	Penicillium sp.	—	—	D-190; C-99
			>25	Pestalotia foedans	—	—	S-882
			—	Pestalotia royenae	—	—	S-882
			—	Psilocybe caerulescens	—	—	C-113
			17	Rhizopus arrhizus	166-168	+176|c|	P-729
			16-28	Rhizopus arrhizus	166-167	+176|c|	M-601; N-649
			12	Rhizopus cambodjae	164-165	—	C-84
			50(cr.)	Rhizopus chinensis	168.5-169.5	+178|c|	A-29; A-26
			15	Rhizopus javanicus	165-167	+177|c|	N-682
			80-83	Rhizopus nigricans	166-167	+180|c|	P-729; M-601
			68-82	Rhizopus nigricans	166-168	+176-180|c|	T-1028 T-1009 B-42; T-1011
			50	Rhizopus nigricans	168-170	+169|c|	A-26
			—	Rhizopus nigricans	—	—	C-103; R-766; W-1066
			—	Rhizopus sp.	—	—	M-554; T-1010 A-29; N-682; K-433
			70	Rhizopus stolonifer	—	—	T-1011

TABLE I

Transformations by Product

EMPIRICAL FORMULA	NAME OF REACTION PRODUCT	TRANSFORMATION	YIELD %	ORGANISM	CONSTANTS m. p.°	$[\alpha]_D$	REF.
$_{21}H_{30}O_3$	11α-hydroxy-4-pregnene-3,20-dione	11α-OH	—	Sporotrichum epigaeum	166-168	+180[c]	M-582
			—	Stachylidium theobromae	—	—	V-1048; S-835
			2	Trichoderma viride	153-161	—	W-1119
			—	Trichothecium roseum	—	—	W-1122
		d,l→d-11α-OH+1	—	Rhizopus nigricans	169-171	+176[c]	W-1102
		3β-OH→3-C=O; $\Delta^5 \to \Delta^4$; 11α-OH	—	Aspergillus niger	—	—	F-288
			—	Psilocybe caerulescens	—	—	C-113
	11β-hydroxy-4-pregnene-3,20-dione	11β-OH	—	Absidia sp.	—	—	C-98
			—	Botrytis cinerea	—	—	C-98
			—	Coniothyrium hellebori	—	—	R-749
			—	Cunninghamella blakesleeana	—	—	E-202; C-98
			—	Cunninghamella sp.	—	—	C-98
			—	Curvularia lunata	185-187	+214[a]	S-871
			—	Curvularia lunata	—	—	C-98; Z-1130
			—	Curvularia sp.	185-188	+217[a]	Z-1132
			—	Pycnosporium sp.	—	—	D-147
	12β-hydroxy-4-pregnene-3,20-dione	12β-OH	—	Coniothyrium hellebori	—	—	R-749
	14α-hydroxy-4-pregnene-3,20-dione	14α-OH	—	Absidia regnieri	192.5-194	+197.5[c] +186[e]	T-982
			—	Bacillus cereus	191-193	+190	F-288
			4	Circinella sp.	185-188	+190[c]	S-815
			15(cr.)	Cunninghamella blakesleeana	187-191	—	N-661
			33	Curvularia lunata	190-192	—	N-661
			—	Curvularia sp.	198-200	+190[c]	Z-1132
			3	Helicostylum piriforme	191-199	+215[c]	M-614; E-204
			7-12	Mucor griseocyanus	180-187	+200[c]	M-614; E-204
			—	Mucor griseocyanus	—	—	S-835; V-1048
			19	Mucor parasiticus	195-200	+188[c]	M-614; E-204

TABLE I

Transformations by Product

EMPIRICAL FORMULA	NAME OF REACTION PRODUCT	TRANSFORMATION	YIELD %	ORGANISM	CONSTANTS m.p.°	$[\alpha]_D$	REF.
$C_{21}H_{30}O_3$	14α-hydroxy-4-pregnene-3,20-dione	14α-OH	24	Mucor parasiticus	184-195	+200[c]	I-424
			—	Mucor parasiticus	—	—	N-682
			—	Stachylidium theobromae	—	—	S-835; V-1048
			23	Stemphylium botryosum	187-192	+186[a]	N-661
	15α-hydroxy-4-pregnene-3,20-dione	15α-OH	—	Colletotrichum antirrhini	231-232	+219	F-288; F-285; F-287
			24-34	Fusarium lini	220-228	+220[c]	G-319; T-980
			—	Fusarium lini	230-234	+224[c]	M-599
			—	Fusarium lycopersici	231-232	+218[c]	K-452
			—	Fusarium lycopersici	—	—	S-858
			—	Fusarium roseum	—	—	R-747
			—	Fusarium sp.	—	—	K-452
			—	Gibberella saubinetti	219-221	+190[c]	S-858
			7	Helminthosporium sativum	228-230	+213[c]	T-1022
			—	Hypholoma sp.	231-232	+219	M-568; D-191
			—	Nigrospora oryzae	228-230	+226[c]	M-596
			—	Nigrospora sp.	—	—	M-596
			7	Penicillium notatum	233-235	+235[e]	C-86
			3	Penicillium sp.	231-232	+219[c]	F-285; F-287
			1	Penicillium urticae	230-234	+224[c]	M-576; M-602; E-202
			—	Streptomyces sp.	—	—	F-285; F-287
	15β-hydroxy-4-pregnene-3,20-dione	15β-OH	9	Bacillus megaterium	195-199	+158[c]	H-382
			—	Bacillus megaterium	203-205	+155	M-568; D-191
			2	Helminthosporium sativum	202-204	+149[c]	T-1022
			18	Penicillium sp.	198-202	—	T-1030
			—	Penicillium sp.	—	—	C-99
			9(cr.)	Phycomyces blakesleeanus	204-205	+151[c]	F-288; F-285; F-286; F-287

TABLE I

Transformations by Product

EMPIRICAL FORMULA	NAME OF REACTION PRODUCT	TRANSFORMATION	YIELD %	ORGANISM	CONSTANTS m. p.°	$[\alpha]_D$	REF.
$C_{21}H_{30}O_3$	16α-hydroxy-4-pregnene-3,20-dione	16α-OH	25	Pestalotia funera	224-225	+126[c]	F-266
			—	Streptomyces argenteolus	225-226	+158[c]	F-267; P-718
			—	Streptomyces argenteolus	225-226	+170[c]	P-716; P-719
			19	Streptomyces globosus	215-219	+155[c]	V-1060
			—	Streptomyces olivaceus	225-226	+158[c]	F-267
			—	Streptomyces roseochromogenus	223-225	+152[c]	F-267
			13	Streptomyces sp.	214-218	+160[c]	S-847
			—	Streptomyces sp.	—	—	V-1060; S-847; S-788; L-491
			—	Streptomyces viridis	223-225	+152[c]	F-267
		3β-OH→3-C=O; Δ⁵→Δ⁴; 16α-OH	—	Streptomyces argenteolus	—	—	P-716; F-267
	17α-hydroxy-4-pregnene-3,20-dione	17α-OH	—	Sporormia minima	—	—	D-182a
			—	Trichoderma viride	210-214	—	M-565; D-185
		3β-OH→3-C=O; Δ⁵→Δ⁴	68(cr.)	Flavobacterium androstenedionicum	214-215	—	E-222
	17α-hydroxy-4-pregnene-3,20-dione 17-O¹⁸	17α-OH(O₂¹⁸)	—	Cephalothecium roseum	—	—	H-374
	19-hydroxy-4-pregnene-3,20-dione	19-OH	—	Corticium microsclerotia	170-171	+175[e]	H-350
	21-hydroxy-4-pregnene-3,20-dione (desoxycorticosterone)	21-OH	50	Aspergillus niger	142-143	+185[e]	Z-1123; Z-1124; R-783
			—	Cercosporella herpotrichoides	—	—	L-490
			—	Coniothyrium sp.	—	—	D-186
			—	Hendersonia rubi	—	—	D-183
			—	Kabatiella phoradendri	—	—	L-498
			58-77	Ophiobolus herpotrichus	140-142	+175	M-584; W-1101; W-1081
			—	Sclerotinia fructicola	—	—	W-1101
			—	Wojnowicia graminis	138-141	—	M-564; D-183; D-184

TABLE I

Transformations by Product

EMPIRICAL FORMULA	NAME OF REACTION PRODUCT	TRANSFORMATION	YIELD %	ORGANISM	CONSTANTS		REF.
					m.p.°	$[\alpha]_D$	
$C_{21}H_{30}O_3$	21-hydroxy-4-pregnene-3,20-dione	d,l→d-21-OH + 1	—	Ophiobolus herpotrichus	140-143	+180[e]	W-110
		21-OAc→21-OH	—	Bacillus megaterium	—	—	S-948
		3β-OH→3-C=O; $\Delta^5 \to \Delta^4$	—	Flavobacterium sp.	—	—	P-742
		21-OAc→21-OH; 3β-OH→3-C=O; $\Delta^5 \to \Delta^4$	34	Corynebacterium mediolanum	139-140	—	M-541 M-544
		$\Delta^4(5\xi$-H)	—	Micromonospora chalcea	—	—	S-867
			—	Protaminobacter alboflavum	—	—	S-866
			—	Protaminobacter rubrum	—	—	S-866
	21-hydroxy-4-pregnene-3,20-dione 21-O¹⁸	21-OH(O_2^{18})	—	Ophiobolus herpotrichus	—	—	H-374
	X-hydroxy-4-pregnene-3,20-dione	X-OH	4	Neurospora sitophila	165-172	—	M-624
	20S-11α,20-dihydroxy-4-18,20-cyclopregnen-3-one	11α-OH	63	Aspergillus ochraceus	205-206	+113[d]	W-107
	16α-hydroxy-17β-methyl-18-nor-13-5ξ,17α-pregnene-3,20-dione	3β-OH→3-C=O; $\Delta^5 \to 5\xi$-H	—	Flavobacterium dehydrogenans	151.5-153	+145[d] + 37[c]	S-839
	16β-hydroxy-17β-methyl-18-nor-13-5ξ,17α-pregnene-3,20-dione	3β-OH→3-C=O; $\Delta^5 \to 5\xi$-H	17	Flavobacterium dehydrogenans	172-173	+ 93[c] +104[d]	S-839
$C_{21}H_{30}O_4$	11α,17aξ-dihydroxy-17aξ-methyl-D-homo-4-androstene-3,17-dione	11α-OH; 17α-OH-17β-Ac → D-homo-17aξ-OH-17aξ-Me-17-C=O	25	Aspergillus niger	261-262	+ 46[c]	F-283
	17α,20α,21-trihydroxy-1,4-pregnadien-3-one	20-C=O→20α-OH	55	Rhodotorula glutinis	212-213	+ 13[c]	T-958
	17α,20β,21-trihydroxy-1,4-pregnadien-3-one	20-C=O→20β-OH	71(cr.)	Candida pulcherrima	193-195	+ 17[c]	T-958
			29	Sporotrichum gougeroti	192-193	—	T-958
		Δ^1; 20-C=O→20β-OH	26	Alcaligenes sp.	190-193	—	S-945
			—	Bacillus subtilis	—	—	L-522
			25-60	Corynebacterium simplex	195-196	+ 33[m]	H-389 N-665
			—	Corynebacterium simplex	—	—	L-522
			—	Fusarium javanicum	193-194	+ 27[c]	F-275
			—	Mycobacterium flavum	—	—	C-100

TABLE I

Transformations by Product

EMPIRICAL FORMULA	NAME OF REACTION PRODUCT	TRANSFORMATION	YIELD %	ORGANISM	CONSTANTS m. p.°	[α]_D	REF.
$_{21}H_{30}O_4$	$17\alpha,20\beta,21$-trihydroxy-1,4-pregnadien-3-one	Δ^1; 20-C=O→20β-OH	—	Mycobacterium lacticola	—	—	S-945
			—	Pseudomonas boreopolis	—	—	T-960
			—	Pseudomonas oleovorans	—	—	T-960
			—	Pseudomonas sp.	—	—	N-652; U-1038; U-1039; U-1040
			—	Stereum fasciatum	—	—	T-959
			—	Streptomyces flaveolus	—	—	K-470
			—	Streptomyces sp.	—	—	K-470
		3β-OAc→3-C=O; Δ^5→Δ^4; Δ^1; 20-C=O→20β-OH; 21-OAc→21-OH	35	Corynebacterium simplex	—	—	C-115
	11α-hydroxy-$16\alpha,17\alpha$-oxido-5α-pregnane-3,20-dione	11α-OH	—	Aspergillus ochraceus	—	—	K-439
			60	Rhizopus nigricans	205-207	+ 49[c]	K-439
	11α-hydroxy-$16\alpha,17\alpha$-oxido-5β-pregnane-3,20-dione	11α-OH	30-40	Aspergillus ochraceus	—	—	K-440; W-1066
			24-44	Rhizopus nigricans	170-172	+ 57[c]	K-440; W-1066
	15α-hydroxy-5β-pregnane-3,11,20-trione	15α-OH	—	Fusarium vasinfectum	—	—	M-599
	16α-hydroxy-5β-pregnane-3,11,20-trione	16α-OH	19	Sepedonium ampullosporum	220-225	—	F-252
	$17\alpha,20\alpha$-dihydroxy-4-pregnene-3,11-dione	20-C=O→20α-OH	—	Rhodotorula longissima	—	—	C-122
	$1\xi,15\xi$-dihydroxy-4-pregnene-3,20-dione	1ξ-OH; 15ξ-OH	—	Rhizoctonia solani	217-222	—	G-312
	$2\beta,15\beta$-dihydroxy-4-pregnene-3,20-dione	2β-OH; 15β-OH	1	Penicillium sp.	217-219	- 51.5[c]	T-1036
			37(cr.)	Sclerotinia libertiana	206-216	- 67[c]	T-983
	$2\beta,16\alpha$-dihydroxy-4-pregnene-3,20-dione	2β-OH	—	Gnomonia fragariae	—	—	L-496
		2β-OH; 16α-OH	—	Streptomyces argenteolus	215.5-216.5	- 39[c]	P-718; P-716; F-267
	$2\beta,17\alpha$-dihydroxy-4-pregnene-3,20-dione	2β-OH	6	Sclerotinia libertiana	219-221	-125[c]	T-983
	$2\beta,21$-dihydroxy-4-pregnene-3,20-dione	2β-OH	—	Gnomonia fragariae	196-198	- 22.5[c]	L-496
	$2\beta,X$-dihydroxy-4-pregnene-3,20-dione	2β-OH; X-OH	3(cr.)	Sclerotinia libertiana	210-216	- 65[c]	T-983

TABLE I

Transformations by Product

EMPIRICAL FORMULA	NAME OF REACTION PRODUCT	TRANSFORMATION	YIELD %	ORGANISM	CONSTANTS m. p.°	$[\alpha]_D$	REF.
$C_{21}H_{30}O_4$	6β,9α-dihydroxy-4-pregnene-3,20-dione	6β-OH; 9α-OH	—	Streptomyces aureofaciens	208-211	+ 79[c]	P-714
	6β,11α-dihydroxy-4-pregnene-3,20-dione	6β-OH	—	Aspergillus ochraceus	—	—	V-1048
			—	Cunninghamella blakesleeana	—	—	E-202
			10	Syncephalastrum racemosum	245-247	+152[c]	A-27
		6β-OH; 11α-OH	20	Aspergillus niger	250-253	+100[c]	F-283
			30	Aspergillus ochraceus	—	+100[m]	D-190
			50-60	Aspergillus ochraceus	—	—	K-436
			—	Aspergillus ochraceus	—	—	D-193; D-181; M-562; S-797; V-1048 D-182; S-900
			3	Aspergillus saitoi	232-234	+152[c]	I-417
			—	Aspergillus sp.	—	—	I-417; T-1010 D-190
			—	Boletus luteus	—	—	S-825
			—	Dermoloma sp.	—	—	S-825
			10	Gloeosporium kaki	238-242	+130[p]	S-855
			—	Glomerella lagenarium	—	—	S-855
			—	Hygrophorus conicus	—	—	S-825
			—	Leucopaxillus paradoxus	—	—	S-825
			7	Rhizopus arrhizus	245-248	+144[p]	P-729; M-601; M-616
			30	Rhizopus cambodjae	250-254	+155[p] +114[d]	C-84
			12	Rhizopus javanicus	246-248	+142[p]	N-682
			10	Rhizopus kansho	232-234	+152[c]	A-26
			< 1	Rhizopus nigricans	—	—	P-729
			—	Rhizopus nigricans	—	—	T-1009
			—	Rhizopus sp.	—	—	N-682; T-1010

TABLE I

Transformations by Product

EMPIRICAL FORMULA	NAME OF REACTION PRODUCT	TRANSFORMATION	YIELD %	ORGANISM	CONSTANTS m. p.°	$[\alpha]_D$	REF.
$_{21}H_{30}O_4$	$6\beta,11\alpha$-dihydroxy-4-pregnene-3,20-dione	6β-OH; 11α-OH	40	Sclerotium hydrophilum	236-241	+100[m]	S-856
			36	Streptomyces sp.	234-240	+110[m]	S-854; S-847
			—	Trichoderma sp.	—	—	T-1010
			—	Trichothecium roseum	—	—	T-1010
		3β-OH→3-C=O; $\Delta^5 \rightarrow \Delta^4$; 6β-OH; 11α-OH	—	Aspergillus niger	—	—	F-288
	$6\beta,14\alpha$-dihydroxy-4-pregnene-3,20-dione	6β-OH	—	Naematoloma sublateritium	—	—	S-811
		6β-OH; 14α-OH	—	Absidia regnieri	242-246	+132[p] +114[c]	T-982
			—	Absidia sp.	—	—	N-682
			14	Achromobacter kashiwasakiensis	245	+125[c]	T-1026
			—	Cunninghamella blakesleeana	246-249	+124[c]	S-811
			—	Cunninghamella elegans	—	—	S-811
			—	Curvularia lunata	—	—	S-811
			—	Curvularia sp.	246-249	—	Z-1132
			20	Mucor corymbifer	255-265	+142[d]	C-82
			—	Mucor hiemalis	—	—	D-177
			—	Mucor mucedo	—	—	S-811
			—	Naematoloma sublateritium	—	—	S-811
			—	Trichothecium roseum	—	—	S-811
	$6\beta,15\alpha$-dihydroxy-4-pregnene-3,20-dione	15α-OH	—	Fusarium oxysporum	—	—	M-599
		6β-OH; 15α-OH* *(corrected structure - 12β, 15α-dihydroxy-4-pregnene-3,20-dione ref. Ap-18)	8	Fusarium lini	192-203	+130[c]	G-319; T-980
			—	Fusarium roseum	—	—	R-747
	$6\beta,16\alpha$-dihydroxy-4-pregnene-3,20-dione	6β-OH	30	Aspergillus nidulans	230-232	+ 75	F-267; F-288
	$6\beta,17\alpha$-dihydroxy-4-pregnene-3,20-dione	6β-OH	29(cr.)	Botrytis cinerea	237-240	+ 15[c]	S-842
			—	Fusarium lycopersici	—	—	S-858
			30	Gibberella saubinetti	230-242	+ 10[a]	S-858

TABLE I

Transformations by Product

EMPIRICAL FORMULA	NAME OF REACTION PRODUCT	TRANSFORMATION	YIELD %	ORGANISM	CONSTANTS m. p.°	[α]$_D$	REF.
$C_{21}H_{30}O_4$	6β,17α-dihydroxy-4-pregnene-3,20-dione	6β-OH	46	Rhizopus arrhizus	244-246	+6[c]	M-580
			—	Rhizopus nigricans	256-258	+4[c]	M-601 M-607
			17(cr.)	Sclerotium hydrophilum	238-240	+8[c]	S-856
		6β-OH; 17α-OH	—	Naucoria confragosa	—	—	S-825
	6β,21-dihydroxy-4-pregnene-3,20-dione	6β-OH	29(cr.)	Botrytis cinerea	198-205	+96[c]	S-842
			6	Gibberella saubinetti	—	—	U-104
			5	Lenzites abietina	—	—	M-585
			1	Rhizopus arrhizus	190-192	—	M-601
			2-3	Streptomyces fradiae	181-183	+110[e]	H-328
			34	Streptomyces sp.	198-202	+115[c]	S-847
			9	Trichothecium roseum	—	+97[c]	M-584
		6β-OH; 21-OAc → 21-OH	13	Rhizopus arrhizus	198-202; 206-210 (solvate)	+97[c]	E-203
			8(cr.)	Sclerotium hydrophilum	190-198	+105[m]	S-856
		21-OH	25	Aspergillus niger	198-200	—	Z-1124 Z-1123 R-783
	6β,21-dihydroxy-4-pregnene-3,20-dione-6β-O^{18}	6β-OH (O_2^{18})	—	Rhizopus arrhizus	—	—	H-374
	7α,14α-dihydroxy-4-pregnene-3,20-dione	7α-OH	—	Curvularia sp.	252-255	+175[c]	S-813
		7α-OH; 14α-OH	—	Curvularia lunata	—	—	Z-1130 Z-1132
			—	Curvularia lunata	280	+177[m]	D-187
			—	Curvularia sp.	252-255	+175[c]	S-813
			—	Mucor hiemalis	234-238	—	D-177
	7α,15β-dihydroxy-4-pregnene-3,20-dione	7α-OH; 15β-OH	< 1	Helminthosporium sativum	250-253	+121[m]	T-1022
	7α,21-dihydroxy-4-pregnene-3,20-dione	7α-OH	—	Cephalosporium sp.* *(revise to 7β - ref.	— T-1037)	—	B-56
			—	Curvularia sp.	—	—	M-585
			—	Diplodia natalensis	—	—	T-997
			58	Helminthosporium sp.	216-225	+144[c]	M-570
			60	Peziza sp.	216-226	+158	M-585
		d,l→d-7α-OH + l	—	Peziza sp.	—	+155	W-1102

TABLE I

Transformations by Product

EMPIRICAL FORMULA	NAME OF REACTION PRODUCT	TRANSFORMATION	YIELD %	ORGANISM	CONSTANTS m. p.°	[α]_D	REF.
$C_{21}H_{30}O_4$	7β,14α-dihydroxy-4-pregnene-3,20-dione (revised structure - ref. T-1037)	7β-OH ; 14α-OH	—	Absidia regnieri	208-214	+154|c|	T-982
	7β,15β-dihydroxy-4-pregnene-3,20-dione	15β-OH	5	Diplodia tubericola	231-233	+136|c|	T-1025
			6	Diplodia tubericola	231-232	+122|c|	A-28
		7β-OH ;15β-OH	8	Diplodia tubericola	231-233	+136|c|	T-1025
			1	Diplodia tubericola	231-232	+122|c|	A-28
			5	Helminthosporium sativum	230-232	+130|c|	T-1022
			10	Penicillium sp.	232-234	+122|c|	T-1036; T-1037; D-177
			19-25	Syncephalastrum racemosum	225-226	+122|c|	T-1020; A-26; A-27
		3β-OH→3-C=O; Δ⁵ → Δ⁴; 7β-OH; 15β-OH	21-42	Diplodia tubericola	—	—	T-1025; A-28
	7β,21-dihydroxy-4-pregnene-3,20-dione	7β-OH	32	Cladosporium sp.	178-181.5	+151|c|	M-570
	9α,14α-dihydroxy-4-pregnene-3,20-dione	9α-OH	3	Circinella sp.	—	—	S-815
		14α-OH	44	Circinella sp.	—	—	S-815
		9α-OH; 14α-OH	—	Absidia regnieri (assignment of structure is doubtful)	249-253d	+149|c|	T-982
			10	Circinella sp.	272-273	+179[c]	S-815
	9α,15α-dihydroxy-4-pregnene-3,20-dione	15α-OH	—	Calonectria decora	240-242	+212[c]	S-810
	9α,17α-dihydroxy-4-pregnene-3,20-dione	9α-OH	—	Nocardia sp.	—	—	D-173
	9α,21-dihydroxy-4-pregnene-3,20-dione	9α-OH	—	Mucor parasiticus	182-184	+167[c]	S-937
			10-20	Neurospora crassa	182-184	+163[c]	S-937
			7(cr.)	Nocardia sp.	180-182	+168[c]	S-796
			—	Nocardia sp.	—	—	D-173
			10	Pseudomonas testosteroni	—	—	S-898; P-740
		9α-OH; 21-OAc → 21-OH	44	Ascochyta linicola	187-188	—	S-828
			tr.	Helicostylum piriforme	—	—	E-204
			1	Mucor parasiticus	180-183	+167[c]	E-204; M-640

TABLE I

Transformations by Product

EMPIRICAL FORMULA	NAME OF REACTION PRODUCT	TRANSFORMATION	YIELD %	ORGANISM	CONSTANTS m.p.°	$[\alpha]_D$	REF.
$C_{21}H_{30}O_4$	$11\alpha,15\alpha$-dihydroxy-4-pregnene-3,20-dione	15α-OH	—	Calonectria decora	182-183	+180[m]	S-814
			—	Gibberella zeae	—	—	M-599
	$11\alpha,15\beta$-dihydroxy-4-pregnene-3,20-dione	11α-OH; 15β-OH	6(cr.)	Aspergillus giganteus	173-175	+134[c]	D-179 D-180
			—*(revise to 12β-OH; 15α-OH - ref. Ap-18)	Nigrospora oryzae*	202-203	+134[c]	M-596
	$11\alpha,16\alpha$-dihydroxy-4-pregnene-3,20-dione	11α-OH	42(cr.)	Aspergillus niger	213-215	+128[c]	F-267; F-283
	$11\alpha,17\alpha$-dihydroxy-4-pregnene-3,20-dione	11α-OH	15	Aspergillus niger	219-221	+87[c]	F-283
			—	Aspergillus niger	—	—	M-603
			—	Aspergillus ochraceus	—	—	V-1048 S-835
			41	Absidia regnieri	216-221	+80[c]	S-841
			22	Cunninghamella echinulata	215-217	—	Z-1125
			—	Dactylium dendroides	—	—	D-189
			30(cr.)	Gloeosporium kaki	219-222	+80[c]	S-855
			—	Glomerella lagenarium	—	—	S-855
			2	Rhizopus arrhizus	220-223	—	M-601
			75	Rhizopus nigricans	220-222	+76[c]	M-580; M-601; M-607; H-391
			ca. 14	Sclerotinia libertiana	218-221	+73[c]	T-983
			21(cr.)	Sclerotium hydrophilum	214-224	+80[c]	S-856
		17α-OH	—	Dactylium dendroides	—	—	D-189
			27	Sepedonium ampullosporum	210-214	—	M-646
		11α-OH; 17α-OH	—	Aspergillus sp.	—	—	D-190
			6	Cephalothecium roseum	218-222	+74[c]	M-600
			8-15	Dactylium dendroides	224-227; 248-251	+74[m]	D-189; D-188
			—	Trichothecium roseum	—	—	T-1010
	$11\alpha,18$-dihydroxy-4-pregnene-3,20-dione	11α-OH	—	Aspergillus ochraceus	195-197	—	W-1110
			—	Rhizopus nigricans	—	—	W-1100

TABLE I

Transformations by Product

EMPIRICAL FORMULA	NAME OF REACTION PRODUCT	TRANSFORMATION	YIELD %	ORGANISM	CONSTANTS m.p.°	$[\alpha]_D$	REF.
$C_{21}H_{30}O_4$	$11\alpha,21$-dihydroxy-4-pregnene-3,20-dione	11α-OH	67	Aspergillus niger	153-154	+168[c]	F-283
			—	Aspergillus niger	—	—	M-603
			—	Aspergillus ochraceus	—	—	D-193; D-182; V-1048; S-835
			—	Coniothyrium helleborine	—	—	T-1003
			28	Cunninghamella echinulata	150-152	—	Z-1125
			—	Dactylium dendroides	—	—	D-189
			—	Gloeosporium kaki	—	—	S-855
			40	Glomerella lagenarium	153-161	+180[m]	S-855
			—	Rhizopus sp.	158-159	+171[e]	K-433
			17	Streptomyces sp.	153-156	+165[c]	S-847
		11α-OH; 21-OAc → 21-OH	16	Aspergillus nidulans	153-158	+166[c]	M-603
			—	Aspergillus ustus	—	—	M-603
			6	Rhizopus arrhizus	154-158	—	E-203
			65	Rhizopus nigricans	153-155	+166[c] +165[e]	E-203; M-601
			9(cr.)	Sclerotium hydrophilum	156-160	+173[m]	S-856
		21-OH	28	Aspergillus niger	147-150	—	Z-1124; Z-1123
			—	Hendersonia aberrans	—	—	D-183
			—	Wojnowicia graminis	—	—	D-183; D-184
		11α-OH; 21-OH	—	Aspergillus niger	153-154	+163[e]	W-1121; W-1120; W-1081
			—	Psilocybe caerulescens	—	—	C-113
		3β-OH→3-C = O; $\Delta^5 \to \Delta^4$; 11α-OH; 21-OH	—	Psilocybe caerulescens	—	—	C-113
	$11\alpha,21$-dihydroxy-4-pregnene-3,20-dione-11α-O^{18}	11α-OH (O_2^{18})	—	Rhizopus nigricans	—	—	H-374
	$11\beta,14\alpha$-dihydroxy-4-pregnene-3,20-dione	11β-OH; 14α-OH	—	Curvularia lunata	224-229	+211[m]	D-187
			—	Curvularia lunata	—	—	Z-1130

TABLE I

Transformations by Product

EMPIRICAL FORMULA	NAME OF REACTION PRODUCT	TRANSFORMATION	YIELD %	ORGANISM	CONSTANTS m. p.°	$[\alpha]_D$	REF.
$C_{21}H_{30}O_4$	11β,14α-dihydroxy-4-pregnene-3,20-dione	11β-OH; 14α-OH	—	Curvularia sp.	224-227	+219[m]	Z-1132
	11β,15α-dihydroxy-4-pregnene-3,20-dione	15α-OH	—	Calonectria decora	173-175	+230[c]	S-817
	11β,17α-dihydroxy-4-pregnene-3,20-dione	11β-OH	32	Curvularia lunata	226-228	+135.5[a]	S-871
			—	Rhodoseptoria sp.	—	—	K-446
			—	Spondylocladium australe	—	—	H-391
			—	Stachylidium theobromae	—	—	D-146
		17α-OH	—	Cephalothecium roseum	—	—	M-600
			—	Sporormia minima	—	—	D-182a
			—	Trichoderma viride	—	—	D-185
	11β,21-dihydroxy-4-pregnene-3,20-dione (corticosterone)	11β-OH	—	Colletotrichum sp.	—	—	T-1003
			—	Coniothyrium helleborine	—	—	T-1003
			29	Corticium sasakii	178-180	+216[e]	H-350
			—	Cunninghamella blakesleeana	—	—	M-555
			28	Curvularia lunata	178-180	+210.5[e]	S-871; S-875
			—	Pycnosporium sp.	—	—	D-147
			—	Rhodoseptoria sp.	—	—	K-446
			10(cr.)	Stachylidium bicolor	177-179	+220[e]	S-843
			—	Trichothecium roseum	—	—	T-1003
		21-OH	19	Aspergillus niger	179-182	—	Z-1124; Z-1123; R-783
			—	Coniothyrium sp.	—	—	D-186
			—	Hendersonia acicola	—	—	D-183
			—	Wojnowicia graminis	—	—	D-184
		11β-OH; 21-OH	—	Curvularia lunata	—	—	R-783
		d,l →d-11β-OH + l	—	Curvularia lunata	178-181	+220[e]	W-1102
	11β,21-dihydroxy-4-pregnene-3,20-dione-11β-O^{18}	11β-OH (O$_2^{18}$)	—	Cunninghamella blakesleeana	—	—	H-374
	12β,14α-dihydroxy-4-pregnene-3,20-dione	12β-OH	—	Calonectria decora	240-242	+129[c]	S-810

TABLE I

Transformations by Product

EMPIRICAL FORMULA	NAME OF REACTION PRODUCT	TRANSFORMATION	YIELD %	ORGANISM	CONSTANTS m.p.°	$[\alpha]_D$	REF.
$C_{21}H_{30}O_4$	12β,15α-dihydroxy-4-pregnene-3,20-dione	12β-OH	—	Calonectria decora	—	—	S-814
		12β-OH; 15α-OH	77	Calonectria decora	218	+139[c] +186[m]	S-814; G-319; M-596*
				*(corrected structures - see 6β,15α-diol and 11α, 15β-diol entries)			
		3β-OH → 3-C=O $\Delta^5 \to \Delta^4$; 12β-OH; 15α-OH	10	Calonectria decora	—	—	S-816
	12β,15α-dihydroxy-4-pregnene-3,20-dione-11α 12α-H³	12β-OH; 15α-OH	—	Calonectria decora	—	—	H-370
	12β,15α-dihydroxy-4-pregnene-3,20-dione-12β,15α-O¹⁸	12β-OH; 15α-OH (O$_2^{18}$)	—	Calonectria decora	—	—	K-485
	14α,15β-dihydroxy-4-pregnene-3,20-dione	14α-OH; 15β-OH	1	Helminthosporium sativum	259-263	+136[m]	T-1022
	14α,21-dihydroxy-4-pregnene-3,20-dione	14α-OH	—	Cunninghamella blakesleeana	—	—	M-555
			32	Mucor parasiticus	174-179	—	E-204
			44(cr.)	Mucor parasiticus	166-169	—	T-980
			—	Stachylidium bicolor	172-177	—	S-843
		14α-OH; 21-OAc → 21-OH	36(cr.)	Absidia regnieri	170-175	+171[c]	S-841
			17	Helicostylum piriforme	167-173.5	—	E-204
			26	Mucor griseocyanus	175-176 (solvate) 167-170.5 (unsolvated)	+190[c]	E-204;
			—	Mycobacterium smegmatis	—	—	S-873
		21-OH	—	Aspergillus niger	—	—	Z-1123
		d,l → d-14α-OH + l	—	Pleospora gaeumanni	—	—	W-1102
	15α,21-dihydroxy-4-pregnene-3,20-dione	15α-OH	83-87	Fusarium lini	198-214	+202.5[c]	G-319; T-980; W-1074
			—	Fusarium lycopersici	—	—	S-858
			81	Fusarium oxysporum	222-227	+212[c]	M-599
			20-70	Gibberella baccata	216-222	+196[e]	M-585; U-1043

TABLE I

Transformations by Product

EMPIRICAL FORMULA	NAME OF REACTION PRODUCT	TRANSFORMATION	YIELD %	ORGANISM	m. p.°	$[\alpha]_D$	REF
$C_{21}H_{30}O_4$	15α,21-dihydroxy-4-pregnene-3,20-dione	15α-OH	25	Gibberella saubinetti	215-220	+217[c]	S-858
			50	Gibberella saubinetti	—	—	U-104
			—	Gibberella zeae	—	—	M-59
			—	Penicillium notatum	215-220	+186[e]	C-86
		15α-OH; 21-OAc → 21-OH	—	Nigrospora oryzae	210-213	+214[c]	M-59
		d,l → d-15α-OH +l	—	Gibberella baccata	—	+195	W-110
	15β,17α-dihydroxy-4-pregnene-3,20-dione	15β-OH	—	Nigrospora oryzae	213-215	+74[c]	M-59
			2	Sclerotinia libertiana	258-259d	+54[c]	T-983
	15β,21-dihydroxy-4-pregnene-3,20-dione	15β-OH	10(cr.)	Botrytis cinerea	202-209	+147[c]	S-842
			19	Lenzites abietina	206-216	+141.5	M-58
		d,l → d-15β-OH+l	—	Lenzites abietina		+141	W-110
	16α,21-dihydroxy-4-pregnene-3,20-dione	16α-OH	—	Streptomyces argenteolus	—	—	F-288
			—	Streptomyces roseochromogenus	201-203	+129[c]	F-288 F-267
			—	Streptomyces sp.	—	—	F-267
			15	Streptomyces sp.	203-205	+114.5[e]	V-105
		16α-OH; 21-OAc → 21-OH	4	Streptomyces argenteolus	202-203	+130[c]	F-267
			—	Streptomyces californicus	—	—	L-491
		d,l → d-16α-OH+l	—	Streptomyces sp.	—	+144	W-110
	17α,21-dihydroxy-4-pregnene-3,20-dione (Reicnstein's Compound S)	17α-OH	—	Sporormia minima	—	—	D-182
			—	Trichoderma viride	—	—	D-185
			27(cr.)	Trichothecium roseum	202-213	+132[c]	M-584
		21-OH	17	Aspergillus niger	204-207	—	Z-1124 R-783
			—	Coniothyrium sp.	—	—	D-186
			—	Hendersonia phragmitis	—	—	D-183
			—	Ophiobolus herpotrichus	—	—	M-584 W-110
			—	Wojnowicia graminis	—	—	D-184

TABLE I

Transformations by Product

EMPIRICAL FORMULA	NAME OF REACTION PRODUCT	TRANSFORMATION	YIELD %	ORGANISM	CONSTANTS m. p.°	CONSTANTS $[\alpha]_D$	REF.
$C_{21}H_{30}O_4$	Reichstein's Compound S	21-OAc → 21-OH	—	Bacillus megaterium	—	—	S-948
		3β-OH → 3-C = O; $\Delta^5 \to \Delta^4$	—	Flavobacterium sp.	—	—	P-742
		3β-OH → 3-C= O; $\Delta^5 \to \Delta^4$; 21-OAc→21-OH	87	Flavobacterium dehydrogenans	208-210	+110[c]	H-378
		3β-OAc → 3-C =O; $\Delta^5 \to \Delta^4$; 21-OAc → 21-OH	93	Flavobacterium dehydrogenans	209	+110[c]	H-378
		3β-OH → 3- C= O; $\Delta^5 \to \Delta^4$; 20β-OH → 20-C=O	—	Acetobacter suboxydans	—	—	L-523
	19,21-dihydroxy-4-pregnene-3,20-dione	19-OH	—	Corticium microsclerotia	153-156	—	H-350
	3β,11α-dihydroxy-5-pregnene-7,20-dione	11α-OH; 7 - C=O	18	Rhizopus arrhizus	228-230	—	E-202; M-630; M-601
	3β,11α-dihydroxy-16α,17α-oxido-5-pregnen-20-one	11α-OH	—	Fusarium solani	—	—	P-746
			—	Myrothecium roridum	—	—	P-746
	Products of unknown or questionable structure	Substrate Progesterone	—	Absidia regnieri	212-213.5	+154[e]	T-982
			—	Absidia regnieri	227-228.5	+88[p]	T-982
			—	Curvularia sp.	—	—	Z-1132
			10	Mucor corymbifer	270-275	—	C-82
			5	Mucor corymbifer	218-223	—	C-82
			0.5	Mucor corymbifer	275-280	—	C-82
			0.2	Mucor corymbifer	217-220	—	C-82
			0.3	Mucor corymbifer	240-250	—	C-82
			0.5	Mucor corymbifer	275-280	—	C-82
			0.3	Mucor corymbifer	210-215	—	C-82
			1	Penicillium sp.	251-253	+202	F-285; F-287
			26(cr.)	Sclerotinia libertiana	216-224	-18[p]	T-983
			4(cr.)	Sclerotinia libertiana	228-238d	+190[c]	T-983
		desoxycorticosterone 21- acetate		Mucor parasiticus	180-197; 200-225	+152[c]	T-980
$C_{21}H_{30}O_5$	11β,17α,20β,21-tetrahydroxy-1,4-pregnadien-3-one	20-C = O→20β-OH	—	Streptomyces griseus	—	—	C-110
	12β,17α,20β,21-tetrahydroxy-1,4-pregnadien-3-one	Δ^1; 20-C=O → 20β-OH	—	Corynebacterium simplex	245-247	—	R-749

TABLE I

Transformations by Product

EMPIRICAL FORMULA	NAME OF REACTION PRODUCT	TRANSFORMATION	YIELD %	ORGANISM	CONSTANTS m.p.°	$[\alpha]_D$	REF.
$C_{21}H_{30}O_5$	$17\alpha, 21$-dihydroxy-5β-pregnane-3,11,20-trione	$\Delta^4 \to 5\beta$-H	—	Alternaria bataticola	214-217	+ 92	S-852
	$11\beta, 17\alpha, 20\beta, 21$-tetrahydroxy-1,4-pregnadien-3-one	20-C=O→20β-OH	—	Streptomyces albus	—	—	K-459
			95	Streptomyces hydrogenans	—	—	L-522
		$\overset{1}{\Delta}$; 20-C=O→20β-OH	—	Streptomyces sp.	—	—	K-470
	$17\alpha, 20\alpha, 21$-trihydroxy-4-pregnene-3,11-dione	20-C=O→20α-OH	32	Rhodotorula longissima	240-242d	+158[d]	C-110; C-122
	$17\alpha, 20\beta, 21$-trihydroxy-4-pregnene-3,11-dione	20-C=O→20β-OH	—	Calonectria decora	—	—	S-951
			—	Fusarium solani	—	—	S-949
			—	Fusarium sp.	—	—	S-951
			—	Gloeosporium olivarum	—	—	K-465
			—	Hydrogenomonas facilis	—	—	F-228
			—	Mycobacterium sp.	—	—	S-917
			57	Streptomyces albus	202.5-205.5	+137[d]	K-459
			50(cr.)	Streptomyces griseus	206-207	—	C-110
			68	Streptomyces hydrogenans	190; 204	—	L-522
	$17\alpha, 20\xi, 21$-trihydroxy-4-pregnene-3,11-dione	20-C=O→20ξ-OH	40-60	Rhizobium sp.	—	—	C-114
	$1\beta, 17\alpha, 21$-trihydroxy-4-pregnene-3,20-dione	1β-OH	5	Rhizoctonia ferrugena	193-207d	+ 89[d]	G-315; G-312; G-313
			—	Rhizoctonia sp.	—	—	S-793b; G-313
		1β-OAc→1β-OH; 21-OAc→21-OH; 3β-OAc→3-C=O; $\Delta^5 \to \Delta^4$	68	Flavobacterium dehydrogenans	203-207	—	N-689
	$2\beta, 11\beta, 21$-trihydroxy-4-pregnene-3,20-dione	2β-OH	19(cr.)	Sclerotinia libertiana	183-186	- 7[m]	S-840; S-853
	$2\beta, 15\beta, 21$-trihydroxy-4-pregnene-3,20-dione	2β-OH; 15β-OH; 21-OAc→21-OH	20(cr.)	Sclerotinia libertiana	210-219	- 47[m]	S-849; S-853
	$2\beta, 17\alpha, 21$-trihydroxy-4-pregnene-3,20-dione	2β-OH	<1	Conidiobolus sp.	232-235	- 88[e]	W-1073
			—	Gnomonia fragariae	—	—	L-496
			35	Helminthosporium tritici-vulgaris	208-213	- 59[d]	K-460
			<1	Rhizoctonia ferrugena	225.5-228d	- 58[d]	G-313

TABLE I

Transformations by Product

EMPIRICAL FORMULA	NAME OF REACTION PRODUCT	TRANSFORMATION	YIELD %	ORGANISM	CONSTANTS m.p.°	$[\alpha]_D$	REF.
$H_{30}O_5$	2β,17α,21-trihydroxy-4-pregnene-3,20-dione	2β-OH	3	Rhizoctonia ferrugena	220-222	—	G-315; G-312
			—	Rhizoctonia sp.	209-211	—	G-312
			—	Sclerotinia libertiana	215-222	- 64[d]	S-860; T-983
			—	Sclerotinia sclerotiorum	—	—	S-860
			6	Streptomyces sp.	225.5-228	- 58[d]	H-383
		2β-OH; 21-OAc→21-OH	—	Streptomyces argenteolus	224-227	—	P-716; F-267
	6β,11α,21-trihydroxy-4-pregnene-3,20-dione	6β-OH; 11α-OH; 21-OAc→21-OH	19(cr.)	Sclerotium hydrophilum	220-226	+105[m]	S-856
	6β,11β,21-trihydroxy-4-pregnene-3,20-dione	6β-OH	1	Trichothecium roseum	225-227	+118[d]	N-654
		11β-OH	3	Curvularia lunata	225-227	+118[d]	N-654
	6β,17α,21-trihydroxy-4-pregnene-3,20-dione	6β-OH	—	Absidia sp.	—	—	N-682
			33	Achromobacter kashiwasakiensis	224-226	+ 60.5[e]	T-1026
			4-6	Arthrobotrys superba	—	—	E-226
			30	Bacillus cereus	222	+ 58[m]	S-944
			5(cr.)	Botrytis cinerea	228-235	+ 42[c]	S-842
			—	Coniothyrium hellebori	—	—	R-749
			—	Coriolus versicolor	—	—	B-63
			—	Corticium sasakii	223	—	H-327
			—	Cunninghamella blakesleeana	—	—	S-919
			—	Cunninghamella sp.	—	—	C-98; N-682
			35-40	Curvularia lunata	229-232	+ 57[e]	K-469
			—	Curvularia sp.	—	—	K-469
			—	Fusarium dimerum	228-232	+ 55[d]	K-462
			—	Fusarium lycopersici	—	—	S-858
			—	Fusarium roseum	—	—	R-747
			39	Gibberella saubinetti	230-236	+ 72[m]	S-858
			26	Gibberella saubinetti	—	—	U-1043
			—	Gloeosporium foliicolum	—	—	K-464
			—	Glomerella cingulata	—	—	K-464

TABLE I

Transformations by Product

EMPIRICAL FORMULA	NAME OF REACTION PRODUCT	TRANSFORMATION	YIELD %	ORGANISM	CONSTANTS m. p. °	$[\alpha]_D$	REF
$C_{21}H_{30}O_5$	6β,17α,21-trihydroxy-4-pregnene-3,20-dione	6β-OH	2	Helicostylum piriforme	228-232	—	E-204 M-60
			—	Helminthosporium leersii	225-231	+55[d]	K-460
			—	Mucor sp.	—	—	N-682
			—	Pellicularia filamentosa	219-221	—	T-957
			—	Phoma sp.	—	—	I-422
			—	Polyporus tulipiferus	—	—	B-63
			—	Poria cocos	—	—	B-63
			—	Rhizoctonia solani	233-234	+67[a]	T-956
			—	Rhizoctonia solani	—	—	S-793
			—	Rhizoctonia sp.	—	—	G-312
			30	Rhizopus arrhizus	230-233	+58.5[e]	P-725 M-601 M-615
			3	Rhizopus nigricans	230-234	—	P-725 M-615
			—	Rhizopus sp.	—	—	N-682
			—	Scenedesmus sp.	—	—	L-527
			24 (cr.)	Sclerotium hydrophilum	231-238	+62[c]	S-856
			30	Streptomyces sp.	230-235	+51[m]	S-854 S-847
			35-40	Streptomyces sp.	—	—	C-112
			40	Verticillium malthousi	230-233	+57[e]	K-468
			36	Verticillium niveostratosum	—	—	K-468
		6β-OH; 17α-OH	—	Cephalothecium roseum	234-236	+53	M-581
		6β-OH; 17α-OH; 21-OAc → 21-OH	<1	Cephalothecium roseum	—	—	M-600
	7α,14α,21-trihydroxy-4-pregnene-3,20-dione	7α-OH	20	Mucor griseocyanus	—	—	C-94
		7α-OH; 14α-OH	24	Mucor griseocyanus	245-248	+146[d]	C-94
	7α,17α,21-trihydroxy-4-pregnene-3,20-dione	7α-OH	19	Diplodia natalensis	248-240	+97[e]	T-997 T-999 T-998
			>30	Diplodia tubericola	228-230	+146[m]	T-102 A-28

TABLE I

Transformations by Product

EMPIRICAL FORMULA	NAME OF REACTION PRODUCT	TRANSFORMATION	YIELD %	ORGANISM	CONSTANTS m. p.°	$[\alpha]_D$	REF.
$C_{21}H_{30}O_5$	$7\beta,14\alpha,15\beta$-trihydroxy-4-pregnene-3,20-dione	14α-OH	38(cr.)	Syncephalastrum racemosum	—	—	T-1021
		7β-OH; 14α-OH; 15β-OH	—	Absidia regnieri	267-269	+75[p]	T-982
			8	Syncephalastrum racemosum	263-265	+103[m]	T-1021; A-27
			5	Syncephalastrum sp.	263-265	+170[m]	A-26
	$7\beta,17\alpha,21$-trihydroxy-4-pregnene-3,20-dione	7β-OH	—	Cephalosporium asperum	—	—	B-56
			16(cr.)	Cephalosporium sp.	209-211	+94[m]	B-56; B-55
			—	Penicillium sp.	—	—	T-1037; T-1036
	$7\xi,17\alpha,21$-trihydroxy-4-pregnene-3,20-dione	7ξ-OH	—	Rhizoctonia sp.	—	—	G-312
	$8\beta,17\alpha,21$-trihydroxy-4-pregnene-3,20-dione	8β-OH	—	Cercospora melonis	219-223	+109[d]	K-472
	$9\alpha,11\beta,21$-trihydroxy-4-pregnene-3,20-dione	9α-OH	10	Ascochyta linicola	—	—	S-828
	$9\alpha,17\alpha,21$-trihydroxy-4-pregnene-3,20-dione	9α-OH	10	Ascochyta linicola	235-240	—	S-828
			60(cr.)	Curvularia lunata	231-235	+103[d]	K-469
			8-15	Helicostylum piriforme	248-252	+107[d]	E-204; M-601; M-609
			10	Nocardia aurantia	—	—	S-898; P-740
			—	Nocardia corallina	—	—	D-173
			21	Nocardia restrictus	236-238	+103[d]	P-740
			—	Streptomyces aureofaciens	218-220	+120[e]	P-715
	$11\alpha,17\alpha,21$-trihydroxy-4-pregnene-3,20-dione	11α-OH	37	Absidia glauca	205-209	+110[c]	N-682
			44	Absidia orchidis	—	—	H-334
			70	Absidia regnieri	206-209	+120[m]	S-841
			—	Absidia sp.	—	—	N-682; C-98; S-801
			40-50	Arthrobotrys superba	—	—	E-226
			70	Aspergillus nidulans	—	—	F-288
			25	Aspergillus niger	217-219	+117[e]	F-283
			—	Aspergillus niger	—	—	M-603

TABLE I

Transformations by Product

EMPIRICAL FORMULA	NAME OF REACTION PRODUCT	TRANSFORMATION	YIELD %	ORGANISM	CONSTANTS m. p. °	$[\alpha]_D$	REF
$C_{21}H_{30}O_5$	11α,17α,21-trihydroxy-4-pregnene-3,20-dione	11α-OH	60-85	Aspergillus ochraceus	—	—	K-43
			—	Aspergillus ochraceus	—	—	D-19 D-18 V-104 S-835
			50	Aspergillus sp.	—	—	D-19
			28	Bacillus cereus	203-209	+110[m]	S-944
			88	Beauveria sp.	212-214	—	I-421
			>70	Cercospora melongenae	215-218	+120[e]	K-47
			—	Cercospora scirpicola	211-216	—	K-47
			—	Cercospora zinniae	—	—	K-47
			—	Colletotrichum sp.	—	—	T-10
			2	Conidiobolus sp.	206-209	+82[m]	W-10
			—	Coniothyrium helleborine	—	—	T-100 T-10
			—	Conocybe siligenoides	—	—	C-11
			3	Corticium sasakii	212-216	+120[e]	H-32
			—	Corticium sasakii	—	—	H-34
			13(cr.)	Corticium vagum	212-216	+120[e]	H-35
			88	Coryneum cardinale	219-220	—	T-99
			30	Cunninghamella echinulata	216-217	—	Z-112
			—	Cunninghamella echinulata	—	—	K-46
			—	Cunninghamella sp.	—	—	N-68
			3-5	Curvularia lunata	213-215	+120[e]	K-46 K-44
			—	Curvularia sp.	—	—	K-46
			—	Dactylium dendroides	—	—	D-18
			30	Didymella lycopersici	210-212	—	S-83 S-835 V-104
			70(cr.)	Fusarium equiseti	210-213	+117[e]	M-55
			—	Fusarium sp.	—	—	M-55

TABLE I

Transformations by Product

EMPIRICAL FORMULA	NAME OF REACTION PRODUCT	TRANSFORMATION	YIELD %	ORGANISM	CONSTANTS m.p.°	$[\alpha]_D$	REF.
$_1H_{30}O_5$	11α,17α,21-trihydroxy-4-pregnene-3,20-dione	11α-OH	—	Gloeosporium foliicolum	214-218	+120[e]	K-464
			38	Gloeosporium kaki	204-208	+115[e]	S-859; S-855
			88	Glomerella cingulata	212-214	—	C-109
			49	Glomerella lagenarium	200-209	+110[m]	S-855
			—	Glomerella sp.	—	—	C-109; K-464
			tr.	Helicostylum piriforme	206-211	—	E-204; M-601
			>70	Helminthosporium sigmoideum	210-213	+120[e]	K-460
			—	Mucor sp.	—	—	N-682
			—	Pellicularia filamentosa	210-212	+112[d]	T-957
			—	Phoma sp.	—	—	I-422
			—	Psilocybe sp.	—	—	C-113
			—	Rhizoctonia sp.	—	—	G-313; G-312; S-793b
			55	Rhizopus nigricans	209-212; 217-219 (polymorphs)	+113[c] +113[m]	P-725; M-601; M-641
			30	Rhizopus sp.	207-211	+115[e]	K-433
			—	Rhizopus sp.	—	—	N-682
			—	Sclerotinia libertiana	205-209	+115[e]	S-860
			—	Sclerotinia sclerotiorum	—	—	S-860
			23(cr.)	Sclerotium hydrophilum	205-210	+112[m]	S-856
			61	Sporotrichum sulfurescens	205-210	—	M-582
			15	Stachylidium bicolor	—	—	K-468
			—	Stachylidium theobromae	—	—	D-146
			11	Streptomyces sp.	205-210	+117[m]	S-854; S-847
			—	Stropharia cubensis	—	—	C-113
			27	Sycephalastrum racemosum	208-210	+107[c]	A-27

TABLE I

Transformations by Product

EMPIRICAL FORMULA	NAME OF REACTION PRODUCT	TRANSFORMATION	YIELD %	ORGANISM	CONSTANTS m.p.°	$[\alpha]_D$	REF
$C_{21}H_{30}O_5$	$11\alpha,17\alpha,21$-trihydroxy-4-Pregnene-3,20-dione	11α-OH	—	Trichothecium roseum	—	—	T-100 M-60
			9	Verticillium theobromae	213-215	+120[e]	K-468
		11α-OH; 21-OAc → 21-OH	—	Coryneum cardinale	—	—	T-991
			—	Rhizopus nigricans	—	—	M-60 M-64
		11α-OH; 17α-OH	—	Cephalothecium roseum	206-211	+121[m]	M-58
			—	Dactylium dendroides	—	—	D-189 D-188
		21-OAc → 21-OH; 11α-OH; 17α-OH	1	Trichothecium roseum	—	—	M-60
	$11\beta,12\beta,15\alpha$-trihydroxy-4-pregnene-3,20-dione	12β-OH; 15α-OH	—	Calonectria decora	229-231	+148[c]	S-817
	$11\beta,14\alpha,17\alpha$-trihydroxy-4-pregnene-3,20-dione	11β-OH; 14α-OH	ca. 20	Curvularia lunata	247-250	+181[e]	S-876
	$11\beta,14\alpha,21$-trihydroxy-4-pregnene-3,20-dione	11β-OH	37	Stachylidium bicolor	206-215	+180[m]	S-841 S-843 S-851
	$11\beta,15\alpha,21$-trihydroxy-4-pregnene-3,20-dione	15α-OH	—	Fusarium moniliforme	—	—	M-59
	$11\beta,15\beta,21$-trihydroxy-4-pregnene-3,20-dione	15β-OH	20	Botrytis cinerea	235-244	+180[p]	S-842
			—	Sclerotinia libertiana	230-235	+180[p]	S-853 S-840
	$11\beta,16\alpha,21$-trihydroxy-4-pregnene-3,20-dione	16α-OH	—	Streptomyces roseochromogenus	—	—	H-399
	$11\beta,17\alpha,21$-trihydroxy-4-pregnene-3,20-dione (hydrocortisone)	11β-OH	—	Absidia glauca	206-210	+163[e]	N-682
			—	Absidia orchidis	—	—	H-334 N-682
			—	Absidia sp.	—	—	S-801 C-98
			6-8	Arthrobotrys superba	—	—	E-226
			33(cr.)	Botrytis cinerea	213-216	+162[e]	F-229
			2(cr.)	Botrytis cinerea	201-209	+156[m]	S-842
			—	Botrytis cinerea	—	—	C-98
			19	Botrytis fabae	200-208	+155[e]	S-859
			—	Botrytis peoniae	—	—	F-229
			—	Cercospora zinniae	207-210	+160[e]	K-472
			—	Chaetomella oblonga	—	—	S-789

TABLE I

Transformations by Product

EMPIRICAL FORMULA	NAME OF REACTION PRODUCT	TRANSFORMATION	YIELD %	ORGANISM	CONSTANTS m. p.°	$[\alpha]_D$	REF.
$C_{21}H_{30}O_5$	hydrocortisone	11β-OH	—	Chaetomella raphigera	—	—	S-789
			—	Colletotrichum sp.	—	—	T-1003
			—	Coniothyrium hellebori(ne)	—	—	T-1003; T-1004; T-993; F-288; R-749
			—	Corticium microsclerotium	205-207	+162[e]	H-350
			—	Corticium practicola	—	—	H-350
			—	Corticium sasakii	—	—	H-350; H-347; H-325
			37	Corticium vagum	205-207	—	H-350
			19	Cunninghamella blakesleeana	208-210	+160[a]	H-339
			65	Cunninghamella blakesleeana	—	—	M-556
			5-20	Cunninghemella blakesleeana	—	—	M-601; M-641; M-555; O-696; S-919
			—	Cunninghamella sp.	—	—	C-98
			—	Curvularia falcata	—	—	S-878
			39	Curvularia lunata	208.5-209.5	+166[e]	S-871; S-875
			40-55	Curvularia lunata	—	—	K-443; K-466
			—	Curvularia lunata	212-215d	+160[e]	K-469
			—	Curvularia lunata	—	—	D-192; C-98
			—	Curvularia pallescens	—	—	S-875
			—	Dothichiza ferruginosa	—	—	K-449
			—	Epicoccum sp.	—	—	R-782
			—	Helminthosporium sigmoideum	208-212	+160[e]	K-460
			<10	Pellicularia filamentosa	204-207	+178[e]	T-957
			—	Phoma sp.	—	—	I-422

TABLE I

Transformations by Product

EMPIRICAL FORMULA	NAME OF REACTION PRODUCT	TRANSFORMATION	YIELD %	ORGANISM	CONSTANTS m. p.°	$[\alpha]_D$	REF.
$C_{21}H_{30}O_5$	hydrocortisone	11β-OH	—	Pseudomonas boreopolis	—	—	T-960
			—	Pseudomonas sp.	—	—	N-652; U-1038
			—	Pycnosporium sp.	—	—	D-147
			—	Rhizoctonia sp.	—	—	G-312; G-313; S-793b
			—	Rhodoseptoria sp.	—	—	K-446
			—	Sclerotinia libertiana	201-206	+160[e]	S-860
			—	Sclerotinia sclerotiorum	—	—	S-860
			20(cr.)	Spondylocladium australe	—	—	S-790
			—	Spondylocladium xylogenum	—	—	S-790
			46	Stachylidium bicolor	—	—	K-468
			50(cr.)	Stachylidium bicolor	202-208	+162[m]	S-843
			—	Stachylidium bicolor	—	—	D-146
			—	Stachylidium theobromae	201	+163[c]	D-146
			—	Stachylidium theobromae	—	—	S-835
			1	Streptomyces fradiae	202-204	+164.5[e]	C-134 C-135 H-328
			5-10	Streptomyces fradiae	—	—	C-112
			—	Trichothecium roseum	—	—	S-878 T-100
			28	Verticillium theobromae	210-213	+160[e]	K-468
		d,1→d-11β-OH+1	—	Curvularia lunata	209-212	+171[e]	W-11
		11β-OH; 21-OAc→21-OH	—	Botrytis cinerea	—	—	F-229
			—	Corticium microslerotium	—	—	H-350
			—	Curvularia lunata	—	—	Z-113
			—	Stachylidium theobromae	—	—	D-146
		17α-OH	—	Cephalothecium roseum	—	—	M-60

TABLE I
Transformations by Product

EMPIRICAL FORMULA	NAME OF REACTION PRODUCT	TRANSFORMATION	YIELD %	ORGANISM	CONSTANTS m. p.°	$[\alpha]_D$	REF.
$H_{30}O_5$	hydrocortisone	17α-OH	—	Sporormia minima	—	—	D-182a
			—	Trichothecium roseum	202-210	—	M-584
		21-OH	—	Coniothyrium sp.	—	—	D-186
			—	Hendersonia herpotricha	—	—	D-183
			—	Wojnowicia graminis	—	—	D-184
		$\Delta^1 \to H$	2	Bacillus megaterium	210-215	—	H-382
		21-OAc → 21-OH	—	Cunninghamella elegans	—	—	E-225
		11β-OAc → 11β-OH; 21-OAc → 21-OH	90	Flavobacterium dehydrogenans	—	—	C-129
		Δ^4 (5β-H)	—	Nocardia asteroides	—	—	S-939
	11β,18,21-trihydroxy-4-pregnene-3,20-dione	11β-OH	—	Cunninghamella blakesleeana	—	—	W-1100
		d,1 → d-21-OH + 1	—	Ophiobolus herpotrichus	—	—	W-1102
	11β,19,21-trihydroxy-4-pregnene-3,20-dione	11β-OH	21	Cunninghamella blakesleeana	163-164	+210[c]	B-40
			7	Curvularia lunata	—	—	N-654
	12β,17α,21-trihydroxy-4-pregnene-3,20-dione	12β-OH	25	Coniothyrium hellebori	179-181	—	R-749
	14α,15α,21-trihydroxy-4-pregnene-3,20-dione	15α-OH	29	Fusarium lini	208-222	+172[c]	T-980
	14α,17α,21-trihydroxy-4-pregnene-3,20-dione	14α-OH	—	Absidia regnieri	213-218	+155[m]	S-841
			—	Coriolus versicolor	—	—	B-63
			—	Cunninghamella blakesleeana	—	—	E-202; S-919
			—	Curvularia lunata	229-233d	+147[d]	K-469
			15-20	Curvularia lunata	227-230	+150[d]	K-469
			—	Curvularia lunata	—	—	K-443
			—	Curvularia sp.	—	—	K-469
			3-6	Helicostylum piriforme	234-237	+155[m]	E-204; M-601
			—	Helminthosporium avenae	227-230	+148[m]	K-460
			—	Mucor sp.	—	—	N-682
			—	Poria cocos	—	—	B-63
			—	Polyporus tulipiferus	—	—	B-63

TABLE I

Transformations by Product

EMPIRICAL FORMULA	NAME OF REACTION PRODUCT	TRANSFORMATION	YIELD %	ORGANISM	CONSTANTS m.p.°	[α]$_D$	RE
C$_{21}$H$_{30}$O$_5$	14α,17α,21-trihydroxy-4-pregnene-3,20-dione	14α-OH	5 (cr.)	Stemphylium botryosum	227-228d	+144[m]	N-6
		14α-OH; 21-OAc → 21-OH	—	Mycobacterium smegmatis	226-228	+130[a]	S-87
	15α,17α,21-trihydroxy-4-pregnene-3,20-dione	15α-OH	—	Calonectria decora	225-227	+146[m]	S-81
			—	Fusarium roseum	—	—	R-7
			2-4	Gibberella baccata	—	—	U-1
			5	Gibberella saubinetti	—	—	U-1
			42(cr.)	Helminthosporium sativum	216-218	+145[m]	T-1
			29(cr.)	Hormodendrum olivaceum	227-230	+146[m]	B-5 A-9
			—	Rhizoctonia sp.	—	—	G-3
		15α-OH; 21-OAc → 21-OH	3	Fusarium lini	176-178	+146[m]	T-9
	15β,17α,21-trihydroxy-4-pregnene-3,20-dione	15β-OH	15	Aspergillus niger (our assignment - questionable)	248-250	+97[e]	F-2
			50	Bacillus megaterium	218-220d; 240-241d (polymorphs)	+103[e]	H-38 C-12 C-12
			—	Coriolus versicolor	—	—	B-63
			2	Penicillium sp.	219-222	+88[e]	T-1
			—	Phoma sp.	—	—	I-42
			—	Poria cocos	—	—	B-63
			—	Polyporus tulipiferus	—	—	B-63
			15(cr.)	Spicaria simplicissima	240-242	+96[m]	B-58 A-9
	16α,17α,21-trihydroxy-4-pregnene-3,20-dione	16α-OH	30-70	Nocardia italica	—	—	S-91
			—	Pestalotia funarea	—	—	S-83
			—	Streptomyces roseochromogenus	—	—	H-39 V-10 S-83
			—	Streptomyces viridis	—	—	V-10 S-83
		16α-OH; 21-OAc → 21-OH	—	Streptomyces californicus	—	—	L-49
	17α,19,21-trihydroxy-4-pregnene-3,20-dione	19-OH	42	Corticium microsclerotium	235-236	+121[e] +123[e]	H-35
			3	Corticium sasakii	233-236d	+127[d] +144[e]	H-32 H-32 H-34
			8 (cr.)	Corticium vagum	233-236	+143[e] +128[d]	H-35

TABLE I

Transformations by Product

EMPIRICAL FORMULA	NAME OF REACTION PRODUCT	TRANSFORMATION	YIELD %	ORGANISM	CONSTANTS m.p.°	$[\alpha]_D$	REF.
$H_{30}O_5$	$17\alpha,19,21$-trihydroxy-4-pregnene-3,20-dione	19-OH	—	Hypochnus sasakii	—	—	S-869
			33	Pellicularia filamentosa	234-235	+123[e]	T-957
		19-OH; 21-OAc → 21-OH	—	Corticium microsclerotium	—	—	H-350
	X,$17\alpha,21$-trihydroxy-4-pregnene,3,20-dione	X-OH	—	Sclerotinia libertiana	219-225d	—	T-983
$H_{30}O_6$	$11\alpha,16\alpha,17a\alpha$-trihydroxy-$17a\beta$-hydroxymethyl-D-homo-4-androstene-3,17-dione	16α-OH; $16\alpha,17\alpha$-diOH-17β (-20-C=O-21-OH) → D-homo-$16\alpha,17a\alpha$-diOH-$17a\beta$-CH_2OH-17-C=O	—	Streptomyces roseochromogenus	—	—	G-297
	$11\beta,16\alpha,17a\alpha$-trihydroxy-$17a\beta$-hydroxymethyl-D-homo-4-androstene-3,17-dione	16α-OH; $16\alpha,17\alpha$-diOH-17β (-20-C=O-21-OH) → D-homo-$16\alpha,17a\alpha$-diOH-$17a\beta$-CH_2OH-17-C=O	—	Streptomyces roseochromogenus	—	—	G-297
	$1\xi,11\beta,17\alpha,21$-tetrahydroxy-4-pregnene-3,20-dione	1ξ-OH	17(cr.)	Streptomyces antibioticus	210-212.5	+136[m]	F-234
	$6\beta,11\beta,17\alpha,21$-tetrahydroxy-4-pregnene-3,20-dione	6β-OH	—	Mortierella sp.	—	—	F-239
		6β-OH; 11β-OH	—	Streptomyces sp.	—	—	C-112
	$6\beta,14\alpha,17\alpha,21$-tetrahydroxy-4-pregnene-3,20-dione	6β-OH	10	Curvularia lunata	—	—	K-469
		14α-OH; 6β-OH	5	Curvularia lunata	216-220d	+87[d]	K-469
			—	Curvularia sp.	—	—	K-469
	$7\alpha,11\beta,17\alpha,21$-tetrahydroxy-4-pregnene-3,20-dione	7α-OH	—	Diplodia natalensis	—	—	T-997
		7α-OH; 11β-OH	—	Curvularia lunata	—	—	K-443
	$7\alpha,14\alpha,17\alpha,21$-tetrahydroxy-4-pregnene-3,20-dione	7α-OH	40	Curvularia lunata	—	—	K-469
		7α-OH; 14α-OH	5	Curvularia lunata	231-234d	+146[d]	K-469
			—	Curvularia lunata	238-240d	+48[c]	S-879
			—	Curvularia sp.	—	—	K-469
	$11\alpha,16\alpha,17\alpha,21$-tetrahydroxy-4-pregnene-3,20-dione	16α-OH	—	Streptomyces roseochromogenus	—		G-297
	$11\beta,14\alpha,17\alpha,21$-tetrahydroxy-4-pregnene-3,20-dione	11β-OH; 14α-OH	—	Curvularia lunata	241-242	+183[e] +152[d]	A-2 S-877
			—	Curvularia lunata	232-233 solvate	+188[e]	S-877 S-879
			—	Curvularia lunata	—	—	K-443
	$11\alpha,15\beta,17\alpha,21$-tetrahydroxy-4-pregnene-3,20-dione	15β-OH	—	Bacillus megaterium	—	—	C-126

TABLE I

Transformations by Product

EMPIRICAL FORMULA	NAME OF REACTION PRODUCT	TRANSFORMATION	YIELD %	ORGANISM	CONSTANTS m.p.°	$[\alpha]_D$	REF
$C_{21}H_{30}O_6$	$11\beta,15\beta,17\alpha,21$-tetrahydroxy-4-pregnene-3,20-dione	11β-OH	—	Curvularia lunata	—	—	C-12
		15β-OH	—	Bacillus Megaterium	—	—	C-12 C-12
	$11\beta,16\alpha,17\alpha,21$-tetrahydroxy-4-pregnene-3,20-dione	16α-OH	30-70	Nocardia italica	—	—	S-91
			—	Streptomyces roseochromogenus	—	—	G-29 H-39
	$11\beta,17\alpha,19,21$-tetrahydroxy-4-pregnene-3,20-dione	19-OH	—	Hypochnus sasakii	—	—	S-87
	$X,11\beta,15\alpha,21$-tetrahydroxy-4-pregnene-3,20-dione (X is $8\beta,9\alpha$ or 14α)	X-OH; 15α-OH	—	Fusarium lycopersici	—	—	S-85
			29	Gibberella saubinetti	180-182	+216[m]	S-85
	Unknown	Substrate progesterone	2	Mucor corymbifer	225	—	C-82
$C_{21}H_{31}O_5F$	9α-fluoro-$11\beta,17\alpha,20\beta,21$-tetrahydroxy-4-pregnene-3-one	20-C=O → 20β-OH	—	Streptomyces roseochromogenus	—	—	S-90
		20-C=O → 20β-OH; 21-C=O → 21-OH	—	Streptomyces roseochromogenus	—	—	S-90
		20-C=O → 20β-OH; 21-OAc → 21-OH	—	Streptomyces olivochromogenus	—	—	M-56 S-94
$C_{21}H_{31}O_6F$	9α-fluoro-$11\beta,16\alpha,17\alpha,20\beta,21$-pentahydroxy-4-pregnen-3-one	$\overset{1}{\Delta}\to$H	—	Bacterium cyclooxydans	—	—	G-29
			—	Corynebacterium simplex	—	—	G-29
		20-C=O → 20β-OH	—	Bacterium cyclooxydans	—	—	G-29
			—	Corynebacterium simplex	—	—	G-29 S-90
			—	Mycobacterium rhodochorus	—	—	G-29
		$\overset{1}{\Delta}\to$H; 20-C=O → 20β-OH	—	Bacterium cyclooxydans	—	—	G-29
			—	Corynebacterium simplex	132-145; 227-231d (hydrate)	+49.5[m]	G-29 S-90
			—	Mycobacterium rhodochorus	—	—	G-29
		16α-OH; 20-C=O→20β-OH	—	Streptomyces roseochromogenus	—	—	S-90
$C_{21}H_{32}O_2$	5α-pregnane-3,20-dione	$\overset{4}{\Delta}\to 5\alpha$-H	—	Cortinarius evernius	—	—	S-82
			ca. 30	Mycobacterium smegmatis	197-200	—	S-82
			—	Ophiobolus herpotrichus	—	—	W-108

TABLE I

Transformations by Product

EMPIRICAL FORMULA	NAME OF REACTION PRODUCT	TRANSFORMATION	YIELD %	ORGANISM	CONSTANTS m. p.°	$[\alpha]_D$	REF.
$C_{21}H_{32}O_2$	5α-pregnane-3,20-dione	$\Delta^4 \rightarrow 5\alpha$-H	9	Penicillium urticae	185-198	—	M-602
			—	Streptomyces griseus	204-206	—	V-1059; W-1097
	5β-pregnane-3,20-dione	$\Delta^4 \rightarrow 5\beta$-H	—	Alternaria bataticola	120-122	+ 124	S-852
			87	Bacillus putrificus	119-120	—	M-545
	20α-hydroxy-4-pregnen-3-one	$\Delta^5 \rightarrow \Delta^4$; 3β-OH $\rightarrow$ 3-C=O	>39	Flavobacterium dehydrogenans	—	—	N-693
		20-C=O $\rightarrow$ 20α-OH	—	Rhodotorula longissima	—	—	C-122
	20β-hydroxy-4-pregnen-3-one	20-C=O $\rightarrow$ 20β-OH	2	Penicillium lilacinum	151-152	—	M-637; S-832
			—	Streptomyces lavendulae	170-172	+81[c]	F-284; F-271
$C_{21}H_{32}O_3$	17α-ethyl-17β,19-dihydroxy-4-androsten-3-one	19-OH	—	Hypochnus sasakii	—	—	S-869
	5-androstene-3β,17β-diol-3-acetate	17-C=O $\rightarrow$ 17β-OH	67	Saccharomyces cerevisiae	146	—	M-539
			71	Trichomonas gallinae	—	—	S-829; S-830
	3β,16α,20α-trihydroxy-17β-methyl-18-<u>nor</u>-17α-5,13-pregnadiene	16α,17α-oxide $\rightarrow$ 16α-OH; 13β-CH$_3$ $\rightarrow$ 17β-CH$_3$; 20-C=O $\rightarrow$ 20α-OH; Δ^{13}	20(cr.) -60	Saccharomyces cerevisiae	202-204	-189[e]	C-88; C-90
	11α-hydroxy-5α-pregnane-3,20-dione	11α-OH	26	Rhizopus nigricans	197-200	+82[c]	E-209; M-601
		11α-OH; $\Delta^4 \rightarrow 5\alpha$-H	tr.	Rhizopus nigricans	198-200	+84[c]	P-729
	11α-hydroxy-5β-pregnane-3,20-dione	11α-OH	—	Aspergillus niger	—	—	M-603
			40	Rhizopus nigricans	102-106	+83[c]	E-209; M-601
			—	Sporotrichum epigaeum	—	—	M-582
	11α-hydroxy-5β-pregnane-3,20-dione-12α-H³	11α-H³ $\rightarrow$ 11α-OH	—	Rhizopus nigricans	123-125	—	H-371
	15α-hydroxy-5α-pregnane-3,20-dione	15α-OH	—	Fusarium sulphureum	—	—	M-599
	15α-hydroxy-5ξ-pregnane-3,20-dione	15α-OH; $\Delta^4 \rightarrow 5\xi$-H	tr. -8	Fusarium lini	219-229	+84.5[c]	G-319; T-980
	16α-hydroxy-5β-pregnane-3,20-dione	16α-OH; $\Delta^4 \rightarrow 5\beta$-H	—	Streptomyces argenteolus	199-200	+90.5[c]	P-718; P-716; F-267

TABLE I

Transformations by Product

EMPIRICAL FORMULA	NAME OF REACTION PRODUCT	TRANSFORMATION	YIELD %	ORGANISM	CONSTANTS m.p.°	$[\alpha]_D$	REF.
$C_{21}H_{32}O_3$	21-hydroxy-5α-pregnane-3,20-dione	$\Delta^4 \to 5\alpha$-H	—	Streptomyces griseus	162-164	—	V-1059; W-1097
	21-hydroxy-5β-pregnane-3,20-dione	$\Delta^4 \to 5\beta$-H	—	Alternaria bataticola	—	—	S-852
	3α-hydroxy-5α-pregnane-11,20-dione	3-C=O → 3α-OH	40-44	Saccharomyces cerevisiae	160-165	+93[c]	C-83; C-89
	3α-hydroxy-5β-pregnane-11,20-dione	3-C=O → 3α-OH	60	Saccharomyces cerevisiae	169-171	+103[c]	C-83; C-89
	6β,11α-dihydroxy-3α,5α-<u>cyclo</u>pregnan-20-one	11α-OH	—	Aspergillus ochraceus	—	—	S-835
			16	Metarrhizium anisopliae	208-212	—	K-483
			82-85	Rhizopus nigricans	211.5-217	+92[c]	W-1069; W-1070
	6β,11β-dihydroxy-3α,5α-<u>cyclo</u>pregnan-20-one	11β-OH	2	Curvularia lunata	243.5-249.5	—	W-1070
	11α,20α-dihydroxy-4-pregnen-3-one	11α-OH	—	Rhizopus nigricans	—	—	S-832
		20-C=O → 20α-OH	—	Rhodotorula longissima	—	—	C-122
	11α,20β-dihydroxy-4-pregnen-3-one	11α-OH	—	Rhizopus nigricans	—	—	S-832
		20-C=O → 20β-OH	—	Penicillium lilacinum	178-179	+73[c]	S-832
	11β,20α-dihydroxy-4-pregnen-3-one	20-C=O → 20α-OH	—	Rhodotorula longissima	—	—	C-122
	16α,20β-dihydroxy-4-pregnen-3-one	20-C=O → 20β-OH	—	Streptomyces lavendulae	212-213	+44[c]	F-271; F-273; F-288
	17α,20α-dihydroxy-4-pregnen-3-one	20-C=O → 20α-OH	—	Rhodotorula longissima	—	—	C-122
	20β,21-dihydroxy-4-pregnen-3-one (revision of structure at 20 - see ref. S-832)	20-C=O → 20β-OH	—	Penicillium sp.	—	—	M-637
			—	Streptomyces sp.	—	—	E-202
		20-C=O → 20β-OH; 21-OAc → 21-OH	—	Penicillium sp.	—	—	M-637
	3β,7β-dihydroxy-5-pregnen-20-one	7β-OH	—	Rhizopus nigricans	—	—	E-202
	3β,11α-dihydroxy-5-pregnen-20-one	11α-OH	14	Metarrhizium anisopliae	181-183	—	K-483
	3β,21-dihydroxy-5-pregnen-20-one	21-OH	—	Aspergillus niger	—	—	R-783
	3β,16α-dihydroxy-5α-9(11)-pregnen-20-one	16α-OH; 3β-OAc → 3β-OH	—	Streptomyces sp.	—	—	W-1092

TABLE I

Transformations by Product

EMPIRICAL FORMULA	NAME OF REACTION PRODUCT	TRANSFORMATION	YIELD %	ORGANISM	m.p.°	$[\alpha]_D$	REF.
$C_{21}H_{32}O_3$	$16\alpha,20\alpha$-dihydroxy-17β-methyl-18-<u>nor</u>-$5\beta,17\alpha$-13-pregnen-3-one	$16\alpha,17\alpha$-oxido → 16α-OH; 13β-CH_3 → 17β-CH_3; 20-C=O → 20α-OH; Δ^{13}	20	Saccharomyces cerevisiae	223-225	-58[e]	C-88; C-90
$C_{21}H_{32}O_4$	$11\alpha,15\alpha$-dihydroxy-5α-pregnane-3,20-dione	15α-OH	60	Calonectria decora	208-210	+105[c]	S-816
	$11\alpha,15\alpha$-dihydroxy-5β-pregnane-3,20-dione	15α-OH	40	Calonectria decora	175-177	+108.5[c]	S-816
	$11\beta,21$-dihydroxy-5β-pregnane-3,20-dione	Δ^4 → 5β-H	—	Alternaria bataticola	—	—	S-852
	$12\beta,15\alpha$-dihydroxy-5α-pregnane-3,20-dione	12β-OH; 15α-OH	40	Calonectria decora	253-257	+70[m]	S-816
	$12\beta,15\alpha$-dihydroxy-5β-pregnane-3,20-dione	12β-OH; 15α-OH	40	Calonectria decora	225-231	+56[c]	S-816
	$15\alpha,21$-dihydroxy-5β-pregnane-3,20-dione	15α-OH; 21-OAc → 21-OH	—	Fusarium oxysporium	—	—	M-599
	$16\alpha,21$-dihydroxy-5β-pregnane-3,20-dione	16α-OH; 21-OAc → 21-OH; Δ^4 → 5β-H	—	Streptomyces argenteolus	215-217	+44[c]	F-267
	$17\alpha,21$-dihydroxy-5α-pregnane-3,20-dione	Δ^4 → 5α-H	—	Streptomyces griseus	—	—	V-1059
	$17\alpha,21$-dihydroxy-5β-pregnane-3,20-dione	Δ^4 → 5β-H	—	Alternaria bataticola	185-190	+40	S-852
	$3\beta,16\alpha$-dihydroxy-5α-pregnane-11,20-dione	16α-OH	—	Pestalotia funera	—	—	W-1092
	$6\beta,15\xi,20\xi$-trihydroxy-4-pregnen-3-one	6β-OH; 15ξ-OH; 20-C=O → 20ξ-OH	—	Rhizoctonia solani	237-240	+70[d]	G-312
	$11\beta,17\alpha,20\alpha$-trihydroxy-4-pregnen-3-one	20-C=O → 20α-OH	40	Rhodotorula glutinis	209-210	+94[c]	T-958
			—	Rhodotorula longissima	—	—	C-122
	$17\alpha,20\alpha,21$-trihydroxy-4-pregnen-3-one	20-C=O → 20α-OH	65(cr.)	Rhodotorula glutinis	220-222	+60[e]	T-958
			27(cr.)	Rhodotorula longissima	221-225	+55[d]	C-110
			—	Rhodotorula longissima	—	—	C-122
	$17\alpha,20\beta,21$-trihydroxy-4-pregnen-3-one	20-C=O → 20β-OH	—	Bacillus sp.	—	—	V-1045
			—	Bacillus subtilis	—	—	L-522
			62(cr.)	Candida pulcherrima	188-190	+77[c]	T-958
			—	Chlorella sp.	—	—	V-1045
			—	Corynebacterium simplex	—	—	L-522
			—	Dematiacea sp.	—	—	V-1045

TABLE I

Transformations by Product

EMPIRICAL FORMULA	NAME OF REACTION PRODUCT	TRANSFORMATION	YIELD %	ORGANISM	CONSTANTS m.p.°	$[\alpha]_D$	REF.
$C_{21}H_{32}O_4$	$17\alpha,20\beta,21$-trihydroxy-4-pregnen-3-one	$20\text{-C=O} \to 20\beta\text{-OH}$	5	Didymella lycopersici	—	—	V-1048; S-836; S-835
			—	Diplodia tubericola	189-190	—	A-28
			—	Epicoccum sp.	—	—	R-782
			—	Hydrogenomonas facilis	—	—	F-228
			32	Penicillium citrinum	172-177	+71[d]	S-846
			—	Penicillium lilacinum	—	—	M-637
			—	Pseudomonas fluorescens	—	—	N-652; T-960; U-1039
			—	Pythium ultimum	—	—	S-846
			54	Streptomyces albus	191-193	+65[d]	K-458
			64	Streptomyces diastaticus	188-189	+65.5[d]	K-470
			—	Streptomyces hydrogenans	183; 194	—	L-522
			—	Streptomyces lavendulae	—	—	S-835
			48	Streptomyces sp.	175; 190	+65[d]	C-110
			—	Streptomyces sp.	—	—	K-470
		$d,1\text{-}20\text{-C=O} \to d\text{-}20\beta\text{-OH} + 1$	—	Streptomyces coelicolor	193-194	+74[e]	W-1094
			—	Streptomyces lavendulae	—	—	W-1094
	$17\alpha,20\xi,21$-trihydroxy-4-pregnen-3-one	$20\text{-C=O} \to 20\xi\text{-OH}$	40-60	Rhizobium sp.	—	—	C-114
	$3\beta,7\beta,11\alpha$-trihydroxy-5-pregnen-20-one	$7\beta\text{-OH}$; $11\alpha\text{-OH}$	18	Rhizopus arrhizus	247-248	-41[m]	M-601; E-202
	Unknown	Substrate desoxycorticosterone or desoxycorticosterone acetate	6(cr.)	Mucor parasiticus	196-206	+121[c]	T-980
$C_{21}H_{32}O_5$	$11\alpha,17\alpha,21$-trihydroxy-5β-pregnane-3,20-dione	$11\alpha\text{-OH}$	12	Rhizopus nigricans	218-222	+57[c]	P-725
		$11\alpha\text{-OH}$; $\Delta^4 \to 5\beta\text{-H}$	8(cr.)	Rhizopus nigricans	190-196	—	P-725 M-606
	$11\beta,17\alpha,21$-trihydroxy-5β-pregnane-3,20-dione	$\Delta^4 \to 5\beta\text{-H}$	—	Alternaria bataticola	192-198	+94	S-852
	$3\beta,17\alpha,21$-trihydroxy-5α-pregnane-11,20-dione	$3\text{-C=O} \to 3\beta\text{-OH}$; $\Delta^4 \to 5\alpha\text{-H}$	17	Catenabacterium sp.	195-200	—	T-973

TABLE I

Transformations by Product

EMPIRICAL FORMULA	NAME OF REACTION PRODUCT	TRANSFORMATION	YIELD %	ORGANISM	CONSTANTS m.p.°	$[\alpha]_D$	REF.
$_{21}H_{32}O_5$	$3\alpha,17\alpha,21$-trihydroxy-5β-pregnane-11,20-dione	3-C=O $\rightarrow 3\alpha$-OH ; $\Delta^4 \rightarrow 5\beta$-H	—	Alternaria bataticola	188-191	+ 60	S-852
			56	Clostridium paraputrificum	187-189	+ 88[c]	S-823
			<1	Streptomyces sp.	186-190	+ 85.5[e]	B-41
	$11\alpha,17\alpha,20\alpha,21$-tetra-hydroxy-4-pregnen-3-one	20-C=O $\rightarrow 20\alpha$-OH	—	Rhodotorula longissima	—	—	C-122
	$11\alpha,17\alpha,20\beta,21$-tetra-hydroxy-4-pregnen-3-one	20-C=O $\rightarrow 20\beta$-OH	74	Streptomyces hydrogenans	205-206	+ 58[e]	L-522
	$11\beta,17\alpha,20\alpha,21$-tetra-hydroxy-4-pregnen-3-one	11β-OH	5	Pellicularia filamentosa	250-252	+ 73[c]	T-954
		20-C=O $\rightarrow 20\alpha$-OH	—	Rhodotorula longissima	—	—	C-122
	$11\beta,17\alpha,20\beta,21$-tetra-hydroxy-4-pregnen-3-one	20-C=O $\rightarrow 20\beta$-OH	—	Hydrogenomonas facilis	—	—	F-228
			—	Mycobacterium smegmatis	—	—	S-873
			—	Pellicularia filamentosa	—	—	T-954
			59	Streptomyces albus	124-126.5; 141-143; 177.5-179 (solvates)	+ 86[d]	K-459
			—	Streptomyces diastaticus	125-126	+ 92[d]	K-470
			16(cr.)	Streptomyces griseus	133-135	+ 85[d]	C-110
			80	Streptomyces hydrogenans	145	—	L-522
			—	Streptomyces sp.	—	—	K-470
	$11\beta,17\alpha,20\xi,21$-tetra-hydroxy-4-pregnen-3-one	20-C=O $\rightarrow 20\xi$-OH	40-60	Rhizobium sp.	—	—	C-114
	$17\alpha,19,20\alpha,21$-tetrahydroxy-4-pregnen-3-one	19-OH	10	Pellicularia filamentosa	217-220	+ 62[p]	T-954
		20-C=O $\rightarrow 20\alpha$-OH	—	Rhodotorula glutinis	—	—	T-958
	$X,17\alpha,21$-trihydroxy-5ξ-pregnane-3,20-dione (X probably is 11α-OH)	X-OH ; $\Delta^4 \rightarrow 5\xi$-H	—	Cercospora scirpicola	199-204	—	K-472
$_{21}H_{33}O_4 F$	9α-fluoro-$3\beta,11\beta,16\alpha$-trihydroxy-5α-pregnan-20-one	16α-OH	—	Streptomyces sp.	—	—	W-1092
$_{21}H_{34}O_2$	3α-hydroxy-5α-pregnan-20-one	3-C=O $\rightarrow 3\alpha$-OH ; $\Delta^4 \rightarrow 5\alpha$-H	—	Mycobacterium smegmatis	173-175	—	S-820
	3β-hydroxy-5α-pregnan-20-one	3-C=O $\rightarrow 3\beta$-OH	—	Streptomyces griseus	—	—	V-1059

TABLE I

Transformations by Product

EMPIRICAL FORMULA	NAME OF REACTION PRODUCT	TRANSFORMATION	YIELD %	ORGANISM	CONSTANTS m.p.°	[α]$_D$	REF
$C_{21}H_{34}O_2$	3β-hydroxy-5α-pregnan-20-one	3-C=O →3β-OH ; Δ^4→5α-H	8	Penicillium notatum	200	+ 94[c]	C-86
			—	Streptomyces griseus	192-195	—	V-105 W-10?
	3α-hydroxy-5β-pregnan-20-one	3-C=O →3α-OH ; Δ^4→5β-H	—	Alternaria bataticola	142	+ 96	S-852
			80	Clostridium paraputrificum	149-150	+108[c]	S-823
			—	Clostridium tertium	—	—	S-823
	3β-hydroxy-5β-pregnan-20-one	3-C=O →3β-OH ; Δ^4→5β-H	—	Alternaria bataticola	188-192	+ 90	S-852
$C_{21}H_{34}O_3$	3β,7β-dihydroxy-5α-pregnan-20-one	7β-OH	5	Rhizopus arrhizus	194-195	+ 78[c]	M-60? E-202
	3β,11α-dihydroxy-5α-pregnan-20-one	11α-OH	23	Rhizopus nigricans	178-181	+ 70[c]	M-60?
		3-C=O →3β-OH	60-70	Saccharomyces cerevisiae	179-181	+ 62[c]	C-83; C-89
	3β,16α-dihydroxy-5α-pregnan-20-one	16α-OH	—	Streptomyces sp.	258-260	—	N-653 W-10?
		16α-OH ; 3β-OAc→3β-OH	—	Streptomyces roseochromogenus	258-260	—	W-10?
		3-C=O →3β-OH ; Δ^4→5α-H	—	Streptomyces griseus	—	—	V-105
	3β,16α-dihydroxy-5β-pregnan-20-one	16α-OH	—	Streptomyces sp.	198-199	—	W-10?
	3β,21-dihydroxy-5α-pregnan-20-one	3-C=O →3β-OH	—	Streptomyces griseus	—	—	V-105
		3-C=O →3β-OH ; Δ^4→5α-H	—	Streptomyces griseus	168-174	—	V-105 W-10?
	3α,21-dihydroxy-5β-pregnan-20-one	3-C=O →3α-OH ; Δ^4→5β-H	—	Alternaria bataticola	139-145	—	S-852
			53	Clostridium paraputrificum	149-151	+ 99[c]	S-823
			—	Clostridium tertium	—	—	S-823
	3β,21-dihydroxy-5β-pregnan-20-one	3-C=O →3β-OH ; Δ^4→5β-H	—	Alternaria bataticola	—	—	S-852
	3β,16α,20α-trihydroxy-17β-methyl-18-nor-5α,17α-13-pregnene	16α,17α-oxide → 16α-OH ; 13β-CH$_3$→17β-CH$_3$; 20-C=O →20α-OH ; Δ^{13}	—	Saccharomyces cerevisiae	200-201	—	C-88
$C_{21}H_{34}O_4$	3β,4β,5α-trihydroxy-pregnan-20-one	4β,5β-oxide → 4β,5α-diOH ; 3-C=O →3β-OH	92	Saccharomyces cerevisiae	235-237	+ 79[c]	C-87; C-90
	3β,5α,6β-trihydroxy-pregnan-20-one	5α,6α-oxide → 5α,6β-diOH	40	Saccharomyces cerevisiae	248-251	—	C-87
	3α,6α,11α-trihydroxy-5β-pregnan-20-one	11α-OH	44	Calonectria decora	223-225	+ 61[m]	S-812

TABLE I

Transformations by Product

EMPIRICAL FORMULA	NAME OF REACTION PRODUCT	TRANSFORMATION	YIELD %	ORGANISM	CONSTANTS m.p.°	[α]$_D$	REF.
$C_{21}H_{34}O_4$	$3\beta,7\beta,11\alpha$-trihydroxy-5α-pregnan-20-one	7β-OH; 11α-OH	9.5	Rhizopus nigricans	268-270	+103[m]	M-601
	$3\beta,7\beta,21$-trihydroxy-5β-pregnan-20-one	7β-OH	—	Rhizopus sp.	205-213	+106[e]	K-433
	$3\beta,11\beta,16\alpha$-trihydroxy-5α-pregnan-20-one	16α-OH	—	Didymella vodakii	257-260	—	W-1092
	$3\beta,11\beta,21$-trihydroxy-5α-pregnan-20-one	3-C=O → 3β-OH; Δ^4 → 5α-H	—	Streptomyces griseus	—	—	V-1059
	$3\alpha,11\beta,21$-trihydroxy-5β-pregnan-20-one	3-C=O → 3α-OH; Δ^4 → 5β-H	—	Alternaria bataticola	196-197	+ 88	S-852
	$3\beta,17\alpha,21$-trihydroxy-5α-pregnan-20-one	3-C=O → 3β-OH	—	Streptomyces griseus	—	—	V-1059
		3-C=O → 3β-OH; Δ^4 → 5α-H	49	Streptomyces aureus	226-230d	+44.5[d]	K-471
			—	Streptomyces griseus	—	—	V-1059
	$3\alpha,17\alpha,21$-trihydroxy-5β-pregnan-20-one	3-C=O → 3α-OH; Δ^4 → 5β-H	—	Alternaria bataticola	203-205	+ 62	S-852
	$3\beta,17\alpha,21$-trihydroxy-5β-pregnan-20-one	3-C=O → 3β-OH; Δ^4 → 5β-H	—	Alternaria bataticola	215-225	+ 48	S-852
$C_{21}H_{34}O_5$	$3\beta,11\beta,17\alpha,21$-tetrahydroxy-$5\alpha$-pregnan-20-one	3-C=O → 3β-OH; Δ^4 → 5α-H	18	Catenabacterium sp.	184-186	—	T-973
	$3\alpha,11\beta,17\alpha,21$-tetrahydroxy-$5\beta$-pregnan-20-one	3-C=O → 3α-OH; Δ^4 → 5β-H	—	Alternaria bataticola	—	—	S-852
$C_{21}H_{36}O_4$	$3\beta,4\beta,5\alpha,20\beta$-tetrahydroxy-pregnane	$4\beta,5\beta$-oxide → $4\beta,5\alpha$-diOH	43	Saccharomyces cerevisiae	276-280	—	C-87
$C_{22}H_{24}O_2ClF$	17α-chlorethinyl-6-fluoro-17β-methoxy-1,4,6-androstatrien-3-one	Δ^1	—	Septomyxa affinis	—	—	O-694
$C_{22}H_{24}O_2Cl_2$	6-chloro-17α-chlorethinyl-17β-methoxy-1,4,6-androstatrien-3-one	Δ^1	—	Septomyxa affinis	—	—	O-694
$C_{22}H_{25}O_2Cl$	17α-chlorethinyl-17β-hydroxy-6-methyl-1,4,6-androstatrien-3-one	Δ^1	—	Septomyxa affinis	—	—	O-694
$C_{22}H_{25}O_3F$	17α-ethinyl-9α-fluoro-17β-hydroxy-16α-methyl-1,4-androstadiene-3,11-dione	Δ^1	—	Corynebacterium simplex	—	—	O-701
$C_{22}H_{25}O_4F_3$	$6\alpha,9\alpha,21$-trifluoro-17α-hydroxy-2-methyl-1,4-pregnadiene-3,11,20-trione	Δ^1 (2α-CH$_3$)	—	Septomyxa affinis	—	—	B-43
$C_{22}H_{25}O_5N$	7α-cyano-$17\alpha,21$-dihydroxy-1,4-pregnadiene-3,11,20-trione	Δ^1	—	Corynebacterium simplex	—	—	B-75

TABLE I

Transformations by Product

EMPIRICAL FORMULA	NAME OF REACTION PRODUCT	TRANSFORMATION	YIELD %	ORGANISM	CONSTANTS m.p.°	[α]$_D$	REF
$C_{22}H_{25}O_6N$	6α-cyano-16α,17α,21-tri-hydroxy-1,4-pregnadiene-3,11,20-trione	16α-OH	—	Streptomyces roseochromogenus	—	—	B-74
$C_{22}H_{26}O_2BrCl_2F$	17α-bromo-9α,11β-dichloro-21-fluoro-6α-methyl-1,4-pregnadiene-3,20-dione	Δ^1	—	Corynebacterium simplex	—	—	R-759
$C_{22}H_{26}O_2ClF$	17α-chlorethinyl-6α-fluoro-17β-methoxy-1,4-andro-stadien-3-one	Δ^1	—	Septomyxa affinis	—	—	O-694
$C_{22}H_{26}O_4$	3,14β-dihydroxy-1,3,5(10),20(22)-cardatetraenolide	Δ^1; enol.	—	Nocardia restrictus	—	—	K-481
		Δ^1; 10β-HC=O → 10β-H; enol.	—	Nocardia restrictus	—	—	K-481
		3β-OH →3-C=O; 5β-OH →Δ⁴; Δ¹; 10β-HC=O →10β-H; enol.	—	Nocardia restrictus	263-265d	+ 78[p]	K-481
$C_{22}H_{26}O_4F_2$	6α,9α-difluoro-17α-hydroxy-2-methyl-1,4-pregnadiene-3,11,20-trione	Δ^1 (2α-CH₃)	—	Septomyxa affinis	—	—	B-43
	6α,21-difluoro-17α-hydroxy-2-methyl-1,4-pregnadiene-3,11,20-trione	Δ^1 (2α-CH₃)	—	Septomyxa affinis	—	—	B-43
$C_{22}H_{26}O_5$	17α,21-dihydroxy-16-methylene-1,4-pregna-diene-3,11,20-trione	Δ^1	—	Corynebacterium simplex	218-219	+103[d]	M-558
	17α,21-dihydroxy-6-methyl-1,4,6-pregnatriene-3,11,20-trione	Δ^1	—	Septomyxa affinis	—	—	H-395
$C_{22}H_{26}O_5F_2$	6α,9α-difluoro-11β,17α,21-trihydroxy-16-methylene-1,4-pregnadiene-3,20-dione	Δ^1	—	Nocardia opaca	—	—	A-7
		Δ^1; 21-OPr→21-OH	—	Mycobacterium phlei	—	—	A-7
$C_{22}H_{26}O_6$	3,17α,21-trihydroxy-19-nor-1,3,5(10)-pregnatriene-11,20-dione 21-acetate	Δ^1; enol.	—	Corynebacterium simplex	—	—	H-386
$C_{22}H_{27}O_2Cl$	17α-chlorethinyl-17β-methoxy-1,4-androstadien-3-one	Δ^1	—	Septomyxa affinis	—	—	O-694
	17α-chlorethinyl-17β-hydroxy-6α-methyl-1,4-androstadien-3-one	Δ^1	—	Septomyxa affinis	—	—	O-694
$C_{22}H_{27}O_2Cl_2F$	9α,11β-dichloro-21-fluoro-6α-methyl-1,4-pregnadiene-3,20-dione	Δ^1	—	Corynebacterium simplex	—	—	R-755
$C_{22}H_{27}O_2Cl_2I$	9α,11β-dichloro-6α-methyl-21-iodo-1,4-pregnadiene-3,20-dione	Δ^1	—	Corynebacterium simplex	—	—	R-755
$C_{22}H_{27}O_2F$	21-fluoro-6α-methyl-1,4,9(11)-pregnatriene-3,20-dione	Δ^1	—	Corynebacterium simplex	—	—	R-755

TABLE I

Transformations by Product

EMPIRICAL FORMULA	NAME OF REACTION PRODUCT	TRANSFORMATION	YIELD %	ORGANISM	CONSTANTS m. p.°	$[\alpha]_D$	REF.
$C_{22}H_{27}O_2I$	21-iodo-6α-methyl-1,4, 9(11)-pregnatriene-3,20-dione	Δ^1	—	Corynebacterium simplex	—	—	R-755
$C_{22}H_{27}O_3Br$	9α-bromo-17α-ethinyl-11β, 17β-dihydroxy-16α-methyl-1,4-androstadien-3-one	Δ^1	—	Corynebacterium simplex	—	—	O-701
$C_{22}H_{27}O_3Cl$	9α-chloro-17α-ethinyl-11β, 17β-dihydroxy-16α-methyl-1,4-androstadien-3-one	Δ^1	—	Corynebacterium simplex	—	—	O-701
$C_{22}H_{27}O_3Cl_2F$	9α,11β-dichloro-21-fluoro-17α-hydroxy-6α-methyl-1,4-pregnadiene-3,20-dione	Δ^1	—	Corynebacterium simplex	—	—	R-759
$C_{22}H_{27}O_3Cl_2I$	9α,11β-dichloro-17α-hydroxy-21-iodo-6α-methyl-1,4-pregnadiene-3,20-dione	Δ^1	—	Corynebacterium simplex	—	—	R-759
$C_{22}H_{27}O_3F$	17α-ethinyl-9α-fluoro-11β, 17β-dihydroxy-16α-methyl-1,4-androstadien-3-one	Δ^1	—	Corynebacterium simplex	—	—	O-701
	6α-fluoro-17α-hydroxy-21-methyl-1,4,9(11)-pregnatriene-3,20-dione	Δ^1	—	Mycobacterium phlei	—	—	H-391
$C_{22}H_{27}O_3I$	17α-hydroxy-21-iodo-6α-methyl-1,4,9(11)-pregnatriene-3,20-dione	Δ^1	—	Corynebacterium simplex	—	—	R-759; R-756
$C_{22}H_{27}O_4F$	9α-fluoro-11β,17α-dihydroxy-16-methylene-1,4-pregnadiene-3,20-dione	Δ^1	—	Bacillus sphaericus	271-275	+30[e]	B-68
	6α-fluoro-17α-hydroxy-2-methyl-1,4-pregnadiene-3,11,20-trione	Δ^1 (2α - CH₃)	—	Septomyxa affinis	—	—	B-43
$C_{22}H_{27}O_4F_3$	6α,9α,21-trifluoro-11β,17α-dihydroxy-2-methyl-1,4-pregnadiene-3,20-dione	Δ^1 (2α - CH₃)	—	Septomyxa affinis	—	—	B-43
$C_{22}H_{27}O_5Br$	9α-bromo-17α,21-dihydroxy-16α-methyl-1,5-pregnadiene-3,11,20-trione	21-OAc → 21-OH	—	Flavobacterium dehydrogenans	—	—	N-690; N-692
	9α-bromo-17α,21-dihydroxy-16β-methyl-1,5-pregnadiene-3,11,20-trione	21-OAc → 21-OH	—	Flavobacterium dehydrogenans	—	—	N-690; N-692
$C_{22}H_{27}O_5Cl$	16-chloromethylene-11β,17α, 21-trihydroxy-1,4-pregnadiene-3,20-dione	Δ^1	48	Corynebacterium simplex	223-224	-34[d]	W-1084
$C_{22}H_{27}O_5F$	9α-fluoro-11β,17α,21-trihydroxy-16-methylene-1,4-pregnadiene-3,20-dione	Δ^1	—	Bacillus sphaericus	246-248	+27[d]	M-558
	16-fluoromethylene-11β,17α, 21-trihydroxy-1,4-pregnadiene-3,20-dione	Δ^1	67	Corynebacterium simplex	263-264	+25[d]	W-1084

TABLE I

Transformations by Product

EMPIRICAL FORMULA	NAME OF REACTION PRODUCT	TRANSFORMATION	YIELD %	ORGANISM	CONSTANTS m.p.°	$[\alpha]_D$	REF
$C_{22}H_{27}O_5F$	6α-fluoro-17α,21-dihydroxy-2-methyl-1,4-pregnadiene-3,11,20-trione	Δ^1 (2α - CH$_3$)	—	Septomyxa affinis	—	—	B-43
	6β-fluoro-17α,21-dihydroxy-2-methyl-1,4-pregnadiene-3,11,20-trione	Δ^1 (2α - CH$_3$)	—	Septomyxa affinis	—	—	B-43
	9α-fluoro-17α,21-dihydroxy-16α-methyl-1,5-pregna-diene-3,11,20-trione	21-OAc → 21-OH	—	Flavobacterium dehydrogenans	—	—	N-690 N-692
	9α-fluoro-17α,21-dihydroxy-16β-methyl-1,5-pregna-diene-3,11,20-trione	21-OAc → 21-OH	—	Flavobacterium dehydrogenans	—	—	N-690 N-692
	16-fluoromethyl-11β,17α,21-trihydroxy-1,4,15-pregna-triene-3,20-dione	Δ^1	68	Corynebacterium simplex	224-225	+23[d]	W-108
$C_{22}H_{27}O_5N$	7α-cyano-11β,17α,21-tri-hydroxy-1,4-pregnadiene-3,20-dione	Δ^1	—	Corynebacterium simplex	—	—	B-75
			—	Septomyxa affinis	—	—	B-75
	7β-cyano-11β,17α,21-tri-hydroxy-1,4-pregnadiene-3,20-dione	Δ^1	—	Corynebacterium simplex	—	—	B-75
			—	Septomyxa affinis	—	—	B-75
$C_{22}H_{27}O_6F$	9α-fluoro-15β,17α,21-tri-hydroxy-15α-methyl-1,4-pregnadiene-3,11,20-trione	Δ^1	—	Septomyxa affinis	—	—	B-44
$C_{22}H_{27}O_7N$	17α,21-dihydroxy-16α-nitromethyl-1,4-pregna-diene-3,11,20-trione	Δ^1	—	Bacillus sphaericus	—	—	R-751
$C_{22}H_{28}O_2$	6α-methyl-1,4,9(11)-pregnatriene-3,20-dione	Δ^1	—	Corynebacterium simplex	—	—	R-753
	6β-methyl-1,4,9(11)-pregnatriene-3,20-dione	Δ^1	—	Corynebacterium simplex	—	—	R-754
$C_{22}H_{28}O_2Cl_2$	6β-methyl-9α,11β-dichloro-1,4-pregnadiene-3,20-dione	Δ^1	—	Corynebacterium simplex	—	—	R-754
$C_{22}H_{28}O_3$	17α-[2'-carboxyethyl]-17β-hydroxy-1,4-androstadien-3-one lactone	Δ^1	—	Arthrobacter sp.	134-136; 179-180	—	C-121
	17α-hydroxy-16-methylene-1,4-pregnadiene-3,20-dione	Δ^1	—	Bacillus sphaericus	—	—	B-68
	17α-hydroxy-21-methyl-1,4,9(11)-pregnatriene-3,20-dione	Δ^1	—	Nocardia opaca	—	—	H-391
$C_{22}H_{28}O_3N_2$	11α-hydroxy-16α,17α,21-[3,1,1-(2-pyrazolino)]-4-pregnene-3,20-dione	11α-OH	67	Metarrhizium sp.	245-247	+392[c]	M-593
			—	Rhizopus nigricans	245-247	—	W-111

TABLE I

Transformations by Product

EMPIRICAL FORMULA	NAME OF REACTION PRODUCT	TRANSFORMATION	YIELD %	ORGANISM	CONSTANTS m.p.°	$[\alpha]_D$	REF.
$C_{22}H_{28}O_3N_2$	11β-hydroxy-16α,17α,21-[3,1,1-(2-pyrazolino)]-4-pregnene-3,20-dione	11β-OH	6	Cunninghamella sp.	255-258	+450[c]	M-593
			—	Curvularia lunata	255-258	—	W-1113
$C_{22}H_{28}O_4$	3,12-diketo-bisnor-4,6-choladienic acid	7α-OH→Δ^6; 3α-OH→3-C=O; Δ^4(5β-H); 17β-CH(CH$_3$)-(CH$_2$)$_2$-COOH→17β-CH(CH$_3$)-COOH	—	Streptomyces gelaticus	—	—	H-359
	11β,17α-dihydroxy-16-methylene-1,4-pregnadiene-3,20-dione	Δ^1	—	Bacillus sphaericus	238-241	-37.5[c]	B-68
		11β-OH	—	Curvularia lunata	—	—	B-68
	17α,21-dihydroxy-16-methylene-1,4-pregnadiene-3,20-dione	Δ^1	—	Bacillus sphaericus	222-226	-16[c]	M-558
	17α-hydroxy-16α-methyl-1,4-pregnadiene-3,11,20-trione	Δ^1	—	Bacillus lentus	219-220	—	R-750
	21-hydroxy-16α-methyl-1,4-pregnadiene-3,11,20-trione	Δ^1	—	Bacillus lentus	179-181	—	R-750
	21-hydroxy-17α-methyl-1,4-pregnadiene-3,11,20-trione	Δ^1; 21-OAc→21-OH	—	Didymella lycopersici	183-186d	+120[e]	V-1052; W-1096
$C_{22}H_{28}O_4Br_2$	9α,11β-dibromo-17α,21-dihydroxy-6-methyl-1,5-pregnadiene-3,20-dione	21-OAc→21-OH	—	Flavobacterium dehydrogenans	—	—	N-691
$C_{22}H_{28}O_4FI$	11β-fluoro-9α-iodo-16α-methyl-1,5-pregnadiene-3,20-dione	21-OAc→21-OH	—	Flavobacterium dehydrogenans	—	—	N-691
$C_{22}H_{28}O_4F_2$	6α,9α-difluoro-11β,17α-dihydroxy-2-methyl-1,4-pregnadiene-3,20-dione	Δ^1(2α-CH$_3$)	—	Septomyxa affinis	—	—	B-43
	6α,21-difluoro-11β,17α-dihydroxy-2-methyl-1,4-pregnadiene-3,20-dione	Δ^1(2α-CH$_3$)	—	Septomyxa affinis	—	—	B-43
$C_{22}H_{28}O_5$	11α,17α,21-trihydroxy-16-methylene-1,4-pregnadiene-3,20-dione	11α-OH	—	Penicillium sp.	—	—	M-558
	11β,17α,21-trihydroxy-16-methylene-1,4-pregnadiene-3,20-dione	Δ^1	—	Bacillus sphaericus	225-226	+22	M-558
			—	Bacillus sphaericus	210-211	—	T-981
	17α,21-dihydroxy-16β-methyl-9α,11α-oxido-1,4-pregnadiene-3,20-dione	$\Delta^{9(11)}$→9α,11α-oxide; Δ^1; Δ^4(5α-H); 21-OAc→21-OH	—	Corynebacterium simplex	196-198	+67[d]	C-138
	17α,21-dihydroxy-6α-methyl-1,4-pregnadiene-3,11,20-trione	Δ^1	—	Bacillus sphaericus	—	—	G-300
			—	Septomyxa affinis	230-232	—	L-512; S-833

TABLE I

Transformations by Product

EMPIRICAL FORMULA	NAME OF REACTION PRODUCT	TRANSFORMATION	YIELD %	ORGANISM	CONSTANTS m.p.°	[α]$_D$	REF
$C_{22}H_{28}O_5$	$17\alpha,21$-dihydroxy-6β-methyl-$1,4$-pregnadiene-$3,11,20$-trione	Δ^1	—	Septomyxa affinis	—	—	S-833
	$17\alpha,21$-dihydroxy-16α-methyl-$1,4$-pregnadiene-$3,11,20$-trione	Δ^1	—	Bacillus lentus	199-202	—	R-750
	$17\alpha,21$-dihydroxy-16β-methyl-$1,4$-pregnadiene-$3,11,20$-trione	Δ^1; $\Delta^4(5\alpha\text{-H})$	46	Corynebacterium simplex	200-205	+198[d]	K-451
		Δ^1; $\Delta^4(5\alpha\text{-H})$; 21-OAc→21-OH	—	Corynebacterium simplex	—	—	K-451
	$17\alpha,21$-dihydroxy-16α-methyl-$1,5$-pregnadiene-$3,11,20$-trione	21-OAc→21-OH	—	Flavobacterium dehydrogenans	—	—	N-690; N-692
	$17\alpha,21$-dihydroxy-16β-methyl-$1,5$-pregnadiene-$3,11,20$-trione	21-OAc→21-OH	—	Flavobacterium dehydrogenans	—	—	N-690; N-692
	$11\beta,17\alpha,21$-trihydroxy-6-methyl-$1,4,6$-pregnatriene-$3,20$-dione	Δ^1	—	Septomyxa affinis	221-222	—	H-395
	$11\beta,17\alpha,21$-trihydroxy-16-methyl-$1,4,15$-pregnatriene-$3,20$-dione	Δ^1	57	Corynebacterium simplex	250-251	+ 18[c]	W-108
$C_{22}H_{28}O_5FI$	11β-fluoro-$6\beta,17\alpha,21$-trihydroxy-9α-iodo-16α-methyl-$1,4$-pregnadiene-$3,20$-dione	6β-OH	—	Chaetomium funicolum	—	—	N-691
$C_{22}H_{28}O_6$	$6\beta,17\alpha,21$-trihydroxy-16α-methyl-$1,4$-pregnadiene-$3,11,20$-trione	6β-OH	—	Chaetomium funicolum	—	—	N-690; N-692
	$15\beta,17\alpha,21$-trihydroxy-15α-methyl-$1,4$-pregnadiene-$3,11,20$-trione	Δ^1	—	Septomyxa affinis	—	—	B-44
$C_{22}H_{28}O_6FN$	6α-cyano-9α-fluoro-$11\beta,16\alpha,17\alpha,21$-tetrahydroxy-$4$-pregnene-$3,20$-dione	16α-OH	—	Streptomyces roseochromogenus	—	—	B-74
$C_{22}H_{28}O_6F_2$	$6\alpha,9\alpha$-difluoro-$11\beta,16\alpha,17\alpha,21$-tetrahydroxy-$12\alpha$-methyl-$1,4$-pregnadiene-$3,20$-dione	Δ^1	—	Nocardia aurantia	—	—	F-260
$C_{22}H_{29}O_2F$	21-fluoro-17α-methyl-$1,4$-pregnadiene-$3,20$-dione	Δ^1	60	Septomyxa affinis	—	—	S-901
$C_{22}H_{29}O_3F$	6α-fluoro-17α-hydroxy-16α-methyl-$1,4$-pregnadiene-$3,20$-dione	Δ^1	—	Calonectria decora	—	—	W-109
	9α-fluoro-11β-hydroxy-6α-methyl-$1,4$-pregnadiene-$3,20$-dione	Δ^1	—	Septomyxa affinis	—	—	S-927; S-923
$C_{22}H_{29}O_4F$	6α-fluoro-$11\beta,17\alpha$-dihydroxy-2-methyl-$1,4$-pregnadiene-$3,20$-dione	$\Delta^1(2\alpha\text{-CH}_3)$	—	Septomyxa affinis	—	—	B-43

TABLE I

Transformations by Product

EMPIRICAL FORMULA	NAME OF REACTION PRODUCT	TRANSFORMATION	YIELD %	ORGANISM	CONSTANTS m. p.°	$[\alpha]_D$	REF.
$_{22}H_{29}O_4F$	6α-fluoro-17α,21-dihydroxy-16α-methyl-1,4-pregnadiene-3,20-dione	Δ^1	67	Actinoplanes missouriensis	177-179	—	M-536
	9α-fluoro-11β,17α-dihydroxy-6α-methyl-1,4-pregnadiene-3,20-dione	Δ^1	—	Septomyxa affinis	292-303	—	L-513
	9α-fluoro-15α-hydroxy-6α-methyl-4-pregnene-3,11,20-trione	15α-OH	—	Penicillium urticae	—	—	A-31
$_{22}H_{29}O_5Br$	9α-bromo-11β,17α,21-trihydroxy-16α-methyl-1,4-pregnadiene-3,20-dione	Δ^1	—	Corynebacterium simplex	—	—	R-752
	9α-bromo-11β,17α,21-trihydroxy-16α-methyl-1,5-pregnadiene-3,20-dione	21-OAc→21-OH	—	Flavobacterium dehydrogenans	—	—	N-690; N-692
	9α-bromo-11β,17α,21-trihydroxy-16β-methyl-1,5-pregnadiene-3,20-dione	21-OAc→21-OH	—	Flavobacterium dehydrogenans	—	—	N-690; N-692
$_{22}H_{29}O_5Cl$	9α-chloro-11β,17α,21-trihydroxy-16α-methyl-1,4-pregnadiene-3,20-dione	Δ^1	—	Corynebacterium simplex	—	—	R-752
	16-chloromethylene-11β,17α,21-trihydroxy-4-pregnene-3,20-dione	11β-OH	58(cr.)	Curvularia lunata	228	+ 40[d]	W-1084
	9α-chloro-11β,17α,21-trihydroxy-16α-methyl-1,5-pregnadiene-3,20-dione	21-OAc→21-OH	—	Flavobacterium dehydrogenans	—	—	N-690; N-692
	9α-chloro-11β,17α,21-trihydroxy-16β-methyl-1,5-pregnadiene-3,20-dione	21-OAc→21-OH	—	Flavobacterium dehydrogenans	—	—	N-690; N-692
$_{22}H_{29}O_5F$	6α-fluoro-11β,17α,21-trihydroxy-2-methyl-1,4-pregnadiene-3,20-dione	Δ^1(2α-CH₃)	—	Septomyxa affinis	—	—	B-43
	6α-fluoro-11β,17α,21-trihydroxy-16α-methyl-1,4-pregnadiene-3,20-dione	Δ^1	75-85	Corynebacterium simplex	—	—	U-1042
	6β-fluoro-11β,17α,21-trihydroxy-2-methyl-1,4-pregnadiene-3,20-dione	Δ^1(2α-CH₃)	—	Septomyxa affinis	—	—	B-43
	9α-fluoro-11β,17α,21-trihydroxy-6α-methyl-1,4-pregnadiene-3,20-dione	Δ^1	—	Bacillus sphaericus	—	—	G-300
			32	Septomyxa affinis	243-250	+ 93[a]	S-921
	9α-fluoro-11β,17α,21-trihydroxy-16α-methyl-1,4-pregnadiene-3,20-dione (dexamethasone)	Δ^1 21-OH	— —	Bacillus lentus Colletotrichum lindemuthianum	221-223 —	— —	R-750 M-598
	9α-fluoro-11β,17α,21-trihydroxy-16α-methyl-1,5-pregnadiene-3,20-dione	21-OAc→21-OH	—	Flavobacterium dehydrogenans	—	—	N-690; N-692

TABLE I

Transformations by Product

EMPIRICAL FORMULA	NAME OF REACTION PRODUCT	TRANSFORMATION	YIELD %	ORGANISM	CONSTANTS m. p.°	$[\alpha]_D$	REF.
$C_{22}H_{29}O_5F$	9α-fluoro-11β,17α,21-tri-hydroxy-16β-methyl-1,5-pregnadiene-3,20-dione	21-OAc →21-OH	—	Flavobacterium dehydrogenans	—	—	N-690; N-692
	16-fluoromethyl-11β,17α,21-trihydroxy-4,15-pregna-diene-3,20-dione	11β-OH; 21-OAc → 21-OH	19	Curvularia lunata	210-211	+ 70[d]	W-108
	6α-fluoro-11α,17α,21-tri-hydroxy-16-methylene-4-pregnene-3,20-dione	11α-OH	—	Rhizopus nigricans	—	—	A-7
	16-fluoromethylene-11β,17α,21-trihydroxy-4-pregnene-3,20-dione	11β-OH	48	Curvularia lunata	239-241	+ 85[d]	W-108
$C_{22}H_{29}O_6F$	6α-fluoro-9α-methyl-11β,16α,17α,21-tetra-hydroxy-1,4-pregnadiene-3,20-dione	Δ^1	—	Nocardia aurantia	—	—	F-260
	6α-fluoro-11β,14α,17α,21-tetrahydroxy-16α-methyl-1,4-pregnadiene-3,20-dione	Δ^1	80-85	Corynebacterium simplex	—	—	U-104
	9α-fluoro-11β,16α,17α,21-tetrahydroxy-2-methyl-1,4-pregnadiene-3,20-dione	16α-OH	—	Streptomyces argenteolus	—	—	H-380
	9α-fluoro-11β,16α,17α,21-tetrahydroxy-6α-methyl-1,4-pregnadiene-3,20-dione	16α-OH	—	Streptomyces roseochromogenus	—	—	F-257
$C_{22}H_{29}O_6N$	6α-cyano-16α,17α,21-tri-hydroxy-4-pregnene-3,11,20-trione	16α-OH	—	Streptomyces roseochromogenus	—	—	B-74
$C_{22}H_{29}O_7N$	11β,17α,21-trihydroxy-16α-nitromethyl-1,4-pregna-diene-3,20-dione	Δ^1	—	Bacillus sphaericus	—	—	R-751
$C_{22}H_{30}O_2$	17α-allyl-17β-hydroxy-1,4-androstadien-3-one	Δ^1	—	Didymella lycopersici	—	—	W-110
	17α-isopropenyl-17β-hydroxy-1,4-androstadien-3-one	Δ^1	—	Didymella lycopersici	—	—	W-110
	16α-methyl-1,4-pregnadiene-3,20-dione	Δ^1	—	Bacillus lentus	116-117	—	R-750
	17α-methyl-1,4-pregnadiene-3,20-dione	Δ^1	55	Septomyxa affinis	160	+ 38[c]	S-901
	20-methoxy-1,4,17(20)-pregnatrien-3-one	Δ^1	—	Septomyxa affinis	—	—	F-251
$C_{22}H_{30}O_3$	3-keto-bisnor-1,4-chola-dienic acid	3β-OH→3-C=O; $\Delta^5 \to \Delta^4$; Δ^1; 17β-[2'-isooctyl]→ 17β-[2'-propionic acid]	—	Nocardia sp.	—	—	W-111
	21-hydroxy-17α-methyl-1,4-pregnadiene-3,20-dione	Δ^1; 21-OAc→21-OH	62(cr.)	Septomyxa affinis	154.5-156.5	—	S-901

TABLE I

Transformations by Product

EMPIRICAL FORMULA	NAME OF REACTION PRODUCT	TRANSFORMATION	YIELD %	ORGANISM	CONSTANTS m.p.°	$[\alpha]_D$	REF.
$_2H_{30}O_3$	$11\beta,21$-dihydroxy-2-methyl-$1,4,17(20)$-pregnatrien-3-one	$\Delta^1 (2\alpha\text{-}CH_3)$	—	Septomyxa affinis	—	—	M-573; H-394
	$11\beta,21$-dihydroxy-6α-methyl-$1,4,17(20)$-pregnatrien-3-one	Δ^1	—	Septomyxa affinis	—	—	M-573; S-928
	16β-methyl-$16\alpha,17\alpha$-oxido-4-pregnene-3,20-dione	$3\beta\text{-}OH \rightarrow 3\text{-}C{=}O$; $\Delta^5 \rightarrow \Delta^4$	42	Flavobacterium dehydrogenans	164	—	S-837
$_2H_{30}O_4$	17β-hydroxy-$1\beta,11\beta$-oxido-5,9-cycloandrostan-3-one 17-propionate	$\Delta^1\text{-}11\beta\text{-}OAc \rightarrow 1\beta,11\beta$-oxide	—	Flavobacterium dehydrogenans	—	—	R-777
	17α-[2'-carboxyethyl]-7α,17β-dihydroxy-4-androsten-3-one spirolactone	$7\alpha\text{-}OH$	—	Gelasinospora tetraspora	268-270	+ 44	T-1035
	17α-[2'-carboxyethyl]-9α,17β-dihydroxy-4-androsten-3-one spirolactone	$9\alpha\text{-}OH$	—	Nocardia sp.	228-230	+ 76[c]	D-173
	$11\beta,17\alpha$-dihydroxy-16α-methyl-$1,4$-pregnadiene-3,20-dione	Δ^1	—	Bacillus lentus	212.5-213	—	R-750
	$11\beta,21$-dihydroxy-16α-methyl-$1,4$-pregnadiene-3,20-dione	Δ^1	—	Bacillus lentus	192-193.5	—	R-750
	$17\alpha,21$-dihydroxy-16α-methyl-$1,4$-pregnadiene-3,20-dione	Δ^1	—	Bacillus lentus	209-212	+ 46[d]	R-750
	$11\alpha,17\alpha$-dihydroxy-16-methylene-4-pregnene-3,20-dione	$11\alpha\text{-}OH$	—	Fusarium sp.	208-210	- 8[c]	B-68
	$11\beta,17\alpha$-dihydroxy-16-methylene-4-pregnene-3,20-dione	$11\beta\text{-}OH$	—	Curvularia lunata	216-217	+ 42[c]	B-68
	$17\alpha,21$-dihydroxy-16-methylene-4-pregnene-3,20-dione	$3\beta\text{-}OAc \rightarrow 3\text{-}C{=}O$; $21\text{-}OAc \rightarrow 21\text{-}OH$; $\Delta^5 \rightarrow \Delta^4$	—	Flavobacterium dehydrogenans	207	+ 47.5[c]	T-981; M-558
	15α-hydroxy-6α-methyl-4-pregnene-3,11,20-trione	$15\alpha\text{-}OH$	—	Penicillium urticae	—	—	A-31
	16α-hydroxy-6α-methyl-4-pregnene-3,11,20-trione	$16\alpha\text{-}OH$	—	Streptomyces roseochromogenus	—	—	S-834
	21-hydroxy-12α-methyl-4-pregnene-3,11,20-trione	$21\text{-}OH$	—	Cercosporella herpotrichoides	—	—	L-490
			49(cr.)	Kabatiella phoradendri	149-151	+207.5[c]	L-498
$_2H_{30}O_4ClF$	9α-chloro-11β-fluoro-$17\alpha,21$-dihydroxy-2α-methyl-5-pregnene-3,20-dione	$21\text{-}OAc \rightarrow 21\text{-}OH$	—	Flavobacterium dehydrogenans	—	—	N-691
$_2H_{30}O_4Cl_2$	$9\alpha,11\beta$-dichloro-$17\alpha,21$-dihydroxy-6-methyl-5-pregnene-3,20-dione	$21\text{-}OAc \rightarrow 21\text{-}OH$	—	Flavobacterium dehydrogenans	—	—	N-691

TABLE I

Transformations by Product

EMPIRICAL FORMULA	NAME OF REACTION PRODUCT	TRANSFORMATION	YIELD %	ORGANISM	CONSTANTS m. p.°	$[\alpha]_D$	REF.
$C_{22}H_{30}O_5$	7α-hydroxy-3,12-diketo-bisnor-4-cholenic acid	7-C=O → 7α-OH; Δ^4(5β-H); 17β-CH(CH$_3$)-(CH$_2$)$_2$-COOH→17β-CH(CH$_3$)-COOH	1	Streptomyces gelaticus	278-280	—	H-363
		3α-OH →3-C=O; 12α-OH→12-C=O; Δ^4(5β-H); 17β-CH(CH$_3$)-(CH$_2$)$_2$-COOH →17β-CH(CH$_3$)-COOH	—	Streptomyces gelaticus	280-282d	+ 77[e]	H-354
	11α,17α,21-trihydroxy-6ξ-methyl-1,4-pregnadiene-3,20-dione	Δ^1	—	Septomyxa affinis	—	—	S-833
	11α,17α,21-trihydroxy-16α-methyl-1,4-pregnadiene-3,20-dione	11α-OH	—	Beauveria sp.	—	—	I-421
			—	Glomerella cingulata	—	—	C-109
			—	Pestalotia foedans	236-238	+ 24[d]	O-702
			—	Phoma sp.	—	—	I-422
	11α,17α,21-trihydroxy-16β-methyl-1,4-pregnadiene-3,20-dione	11α-OH	—	Beauveria sp.	—	—	I-421
			—	Glomerella sp.	—	—	C-109
			—	Phoma sp.	—	—	I-422
		Δ^1	—	Corynebacterium simplex	—	—	I-421
	11β,17α,21-trihydroxy-2-methyl-1,4-pregnadiene-3,20-dione	Δ^1(2α-CH$_3$)	2	Septomyxa affinis	270-272	—	H-394; M-573
		Δ^1(2α-CH$_3$); 21-OAc→21-OH	—	Nocardia corallina	—	—	H-399
	11β,17α,21-trihydroxy-6α-methyl-1,4-pregnadiene-3,20-dione	Δ^1	—	Bacillus sphaericus	—	—	G-300
		Δ^1	46(cr.)	Septomyxa affinis	245-247	+ 83[d]	L-512; S-833; W-107; M-647; M-573; K-456
	11β,17α,21-trihydroxy-6β-methyl-1,4-pregnadiene-3,20-dione	Δ^1	—	Septomyxa affinis	—	—	L-512; S-833
	11β,17α,21-trihydroxy-16α-methyl-1,4-pregnadiene-3,20-dione	Δ^1	—	Bacillus lentus	219-220	—	R-750
			—	Bacillus sphaericus	—	—	H-392
		11β-OH	—	Phoma sp.	—	—	I-422
	11β,17α,21-trihydroxy-16β-methyl-1,4-pregnadiene-3,20-dione	Δ^1; 21-OAc →21-OH	—	Bacillus sphaericus	—	—	T-986
		11β-OH	—	Phoma sp.	—	—	I-422

TABLE I

Transformations by Product

EMPIRICAL FORMULA	NAME OF REACTION PRODUCT	TRANSFORMATION	YIELD %	ORGANISM	CONSTANTS m. p.°	$[\alpha]_D$	REF.
$_{22}H_{30}O_5$	$11\beta,17\alpha,21$-trihydroxy-16α-methyl-1,5-pregnadiene-3,20-dione	21-OAc→21-OH	—	Flavobacterium dehydrogenans	—	—	N-690; N-692
	$11\beta,17\alpha,21$-trihydroxy-16β-methyl-1,5-pregnadiene-3,20-dione	21-OAc→21-OH	—	Flavobacterium dehydrogenans	—	—	N-690; N-692
	$11\beta,17\alpha,21$-trihydroxy-16-methyl-4,15-pregnadiene-3,20-dione	11β-OH	27	Curvularia lunata	245-247	+ 53[c]	W-1084
	$17\alpha,21$-dihydroxy-16β-methyl-1-5α-pregnene-3,11,20-trione	Δ^1	—	Corynebacterium simplex	—	—	K-451
		Δ^1; 21-OAc→21-OH	—	Corynebacterium simplex	—	—	K-451
	$17\alpha,21$-dihydroxy-16α-methyl-1-5β-pregnene-3,11,20-trione	$\Delta^4 \rightarrow 5\beta$-H	4	Streptomyces sp.	206-212	+116[d]	G-314
	$11\alpha,17\alpha,21$-trihydroxy-16-methylene-4-pregnene-3,20-dione	11α-OH	—	Fusarium sp.	199-201	+ 42[d]	M-558
	$11\beta,17\alpha,21$-trihydroxy-16-methylene-4-pregnene-3,20-dione	11β-OH	—	Curvularia lunata	224-225	+ 69[d]	M-558; T-981
	$17\alpha,21$-dihydroxy-16β-methyl-$9\alpha,11\alpha$-oxido-4-pregnene-3,20-dione	$\Delta^{9(11)} \rightarrow 9\alpha,11\alpha$-oxide; $\Delta^4(5\alpha$-H); 21-OAc →21-OH	—	Corynebacterium simplex	—	—	C-138
$_{22}H_{30}O_6$	$11\beta,15\beta,17\alpha,21$-tetrahydroxy-$15\alpha$-methyl-1,4-pregnadiene-3,20-dione	Δ^1	—	Septomyxa affinis	—	—	B-44
	$11\beta,16\alpha,17\alpha,21$-tetrahydroxy-$6\alpha$-methyl-1,4-pregnadiene-3,20-dione	16α-OH	—	Streptomyces roseochromogenus	—	—	F-257
$_{22}H_{31}O_3Br$	17α-bromo-11β-hydroxy-6α-methyl-4-pregnene-3,20-dione	11β-OH	—	Curvularia lunata	—	—	R-756; R-759
$_{22}H_{31}O_3F$	6α-fluoro-11β-hydroxy-17α-methyl-4-pregnene-3,20-dione	11β-OH	—	Curvularia lunata	—	—	R-759
$_{22}H_{31}O_4F$	6β-fluoro-$11\alpha,17\alpha$-dihydroxy-21-methyl-4-pregnene-3,20-dione	11α-OH	—	Rhizopus nigricans	—	—	H-391
	6β-fluoro-$11\beta,17\alpha$-dihydroxy-21-methyl-4-pregnene-3,20-dione	11β-OH	—	Curvularia lunata	—	—	H-391
			—	Epicoccum oryzae	—	—	H-391
$_{22}H_{31}O_5F$	6α-fluoro-$11\alpha,17\alpha,21$-trihydroxy-16α-methyl-4-pregnene-3,20-dione	11α-OH	—	Aspergillus ochraceus	—	—	W-1098
		11α-OH; 21-OAc→21-OH	—	Aspergillus ochraceus	—	—	W-1098
	6α-fluoro-$11\beta,17\alpha,21$-trihydroxy-16α-methyl-4-pregnene-3,20-dione	11β-OH	70-75	Curvularia lunata	216.5-218.5	—	U-1042

TABLE I

Transformations by Product

EMPIRICAL FORMULA	NAME OF REACTION PRODUCT	TRANSFORMATION	YIELD %	ORGANISM	m. p.°	$[\alpha]_D$	REF.
$C_{22}H_{31}O_5F$	6α-fluoro-11β,17α,21-tri-hydroxy-21-methyl-4-pregnene-3,20-dione	11β-OH; 21-OAc→21-OH	—	Curvularia lunata	—	—	H-390
	6α-fluoro-14α,17α,21-tri-hydroxy-16α-methyl-4-pregnene-3,20-dione	14α-OH	0.5-2	Curvularia lunata	247-251	+124[d]	U-1042
	21-fluoro-11β,16α,17α-tri-hydroxy-6α-methyl-4-pregnene-3,20-dione	16α-OH	—	Streptomyces roseochromogenus	—	—	L-510
$C_{22}H_{31}O_6F$	6α-fluoro-11α,14α,17α,21-tetrahydroxy-16α-methyl-4-pregnene-3,20-dione	11α-OH	1	Cunninghamella elegans	—	—	U-1042
	6α-fluoro-11β,14α,17α,21-tetrahydroxy-16α-methyl-4-pregnene-3,20-dione	11β-OH	15-25	Cunninghamella elegans	—	—	U-1042
	6α-fluoro-11β,16α,17α,21-tetrahydroxy-9α-methyl-4-pregnene-3,20-dione	16α-OH	—	Streptomyces roseochromogenus	—	—	F-260
	9α-fluoro-11β,16α,17α,21-tetrahydroxy-2ξ-methyl-4-pregnene-3,20-dione	16α-OH	—	Streptomyces argenteolus	—	—	H-380
	9α-fluoro-11β,16α,17α,21-tetrahydroxy-12α-methyl-4-pregnene-3,20-dione	16α-OH	—	Streptomyces roseochromogenus	—	—	F-260
$C_{22}H_{32}O_2$	17β-hydroxy-4-androsten-3-one 17-propionate	3β-OH→3-C=O; $\Delta^5 \to \Delta^4$	—	Acetobacter pasteurianum	121	+ 87[e]	K-457
	3-keto-20-"iso"-bisnor-4-cholen-22-al	20-HC=O → 20-"iso"-HC=O*	9	Gliocladium catenulatum			W-106
$C_{22}H_{32}O_3$	15α-hydroxy-3-keto-bisnor-4-cholen-22-al	15α-OH	—	Fusarium solani	—	—	M-599
	3-keto-bisnor-4-cholenic acid	3β-OH→3-C=O; $\Delta^5 \to \Delta^4$; 17β-(2'-isooctyl)→ 17β-(2'-propionic acid)	—	Nocardia sp.	—	—	W-111
	7β-hydroxy-7α-methyl-4-pregnene-3,20-dione	3β-OH →3-C=O; $\Delta^5 \to \Delta^4$; 20β-OH→20-C=O	35	Flavobacterium dehydrogenans	154-157	+121[d]	R-776
	11α-hydroxy-16α-methyl-4-pregnene-3,20-dione	11α-OH	—	Rhizopus nigricans	161-163	+149[c]	S-804; L-515; L-517; C-141
	11α-hydroxy-17α-methyl-4-pregnene-3,20-dione	11α-OH	—	Aspergillus ochraceus	—	—	V-1048 S-835
	11β-hydroxy-6β-methyl-4-pregnene-3,20-dione	11β-OH	—	Cunninghamella blakesleeana	—	—	L-520
		—	Curvularia lunata	—	—	R-754; R-757; R-773	

*stereochemistry at 20- of starting material not defined

TABLE I

Transformations by Product

EMPIRICAL FORMULA	NAME OF REACTION PRODUCT	TRANSFORMATION	YIELD %	ORGANISM	CONSTANTS m. p.°	$[\alpha]_D$	REF.
$_{22}H_{32}O_4$	11α-hydroxy-3-keto-<u>bisnor</u>-4-cholenic acid	11α-OH	—	Sporotrichum sulfurescens	—	—	M-582
	11α,17α-dihydroxy-16α-methyl-4-pregnene-3,20-dione	11α-OH; 17α-OH	—	Dactylium dendroides	—	—	M-571
	11α,17α-dihydroxy-21-methyl-4-pregnene-3,20-dione	11α-OH	—	Rhizopus nigricans	—	—	H-391
	11β,16α-dihydroxy-6α-methyl-4-pregnene-3,20-dione	16α-OH	—	Streptomyces roseochromogenus	—	—	S-834
	11β,16α-dihydroxy-12α-methyl-4-pregnene-3,20-dione	16α-OH	—	Streptomyces roseochromogenus	—	—	F-257
	11β,17α-dihydroxy-21-methyl-4-pregnene-3,20-dione	11β-OH	—	Curvularia lunata	—	—	H-391
	17α,21-dihydroxy-16α-methyl-4-pregnene-3,20-dione	3β-OH→3-C=O; $\Delta^5 \to \Delta^4$; 21-OAc→21-OH	—	Flavobacterium dehydrogenans	—	—	C-109; I-421; I-422
	17α,21-dihydroxy-16β-methyl-4-pregnene-3,20-dione	3β-OAc→3-C=O; $\Delta^5 \to \Delta^4$; 21-OAc→21-OH	—	Flavobacterium dehydrogenans	219-220	+130[d]	C-109; I-421; I-422
$_{22}H_{32}O_5$	2β,17α,21-trihydroxy-16α-methyl-4-pregnene-3,20-dione	2β-OH	—	Gnomonia fragariae	196-198	- 61[c]	L-496
	11α,17α,21-trihydroxy-16α-methyl-4-pregnene-3,20-dione	11α-OH	—	Beauveria sp.	—	—	I-421
			—	Glomerella cingulata	—	—	C-109
			—	Phoma sp.	—	—	I-422
	11α,17α,21-trihydroxy-16β-methyl-4-pregnene-3,20-dione	11α-OH	—	Beauveria sp.	—	—	I-421
			—	Glomerella cingulata	—	—	C-109
			—	Phoma sp.	—	—	I-422
		11α-OH; 21-OAc→21-OH	—	Beauveria sp.	—	—	I-421
			—	Glomerella cingulata	—	—	C-109
	11β,16α,17α-trihydroxy-6α-methyl-4-pregnene-3,20-dione	16α-OH	—	Streptomyces roseochromogenus	—	—	L-511
	11β,17α,21-trihydroxy-2α-methyl-4-pregnene-3,20-dione	21-OAc→21-OH	—	Nocardia corallina	—	—	H-399
	11β,17α,21-trihydroxy-16α-methyl-4-pregnene-3,20-dione	11β-OH	55	Curvularia lunata	220-222	+110[d]	C-96
			—	Phoma sp.	—	—	I-422
	11β,17α,21-trihydroxy-16β-methyl-4-pregnene-3,20-dione	11β-OH	—	Phoma sp.	—	—	I-422

TABLE I

Transformations by Product

EMPIRICAL FORMULA	NAME OF REACTION PRODUCT	TRANSFORMATION	YIELD %	ORGANISM	CONSTANTS m. p.°	$[\alpha]_D$	REF
$C_{22}H_{32}O_5$	15α,17α,21-trihydroxy-16α-methyl-4-pregnene-3,20-dione	15α-OH	—	Curvularia lunata	—	—	C-96
$C_{22}H_{32}O_6$	11β,14α,17α,21-tetrahydroxy-16α-methyl-4-pregnene-3,20-dione	11β-OH; 14α-OH	—	Curvularia lunata	—	—	C-96
$C_{22}H_{33}ON$	4-conenin-3-one	3β-N(CH$_3$)$_2$→3-C=O; $\Delta^5 \to \Delta^4$	35	Gloeosporium cyclaminis	108-110	+160[d]	D-148
			—	Hypomyces haematococcus	—	—	D-148
$C_{22}H_{34}O_2$	22-hydroxy-bisnor-4-cholen-3-one	20-HC=O→20α-CH$_2$OH	20	Gliocladium catenulatum	133-146	—	W-106
	22-hydroxy-20β-bisnor-4-cholen-3-one	20-H-C=O→20β-CH$_2$OH	8	Penicillium lilacinum	143-145	+ 98[c]	W-106 E-202
$C_{22}H_{34}O_3$	17β,19-dihydroxy-17α-propyl-4-androsten-3-one	19-OH	—	Hypochnus sasakii	—	—	S-869
	11α,22-dihydroxy-bisnor-4-cholen-3-one	11α-OH	—	Sporotrichum sulfurescens	—	—	M-582
		11α-OH; 22-C=O→22-OH	15	Rhizopus nigricans	130-133	+ 78[c]	M-578 M-601
	15α,22-dihydroxy-bisnor-4-cholen-3-one	15α-OH; 22-C=O→22-OH	—	Rhizopus nigricans	—	—	E-202
$C_{22}H_{34}O_4$	6β,11α,22-trihydroxy-bisnor-4-cholen-3-one	6β-OH	4	Cunninghamella blakesleeana	222-228	—	M-578
		6β-OH; 11α-OH; 22-C=O→22-OH	30	Rhizopus arrhizus	238-240	+ 22[c]	M-578
			2-12	Rhizopus nigricans	232-238	—	M-578 M-601
$C_{22}H_{34}O_5$	3α,7α-dihydroxy-12-keto-bisnor-5β-cholanic acid	12α-OH→12α-C=O; 17β-CH(CH$_3$)-CH$_2$-CH$_2$-COOH→17β-CH(CH$_3$)-COOH	—	Streptomyces gelaticus	—	—	H-359
	11α,17α,21-trihydroxy-16α-methyl-5α-pregnane-3,20-dione	11α-OH	—	Beauveria sp.	—	—	I-421
			—	Glomerella cingulata	—	—	C-109
			—	Phoma sp.	—	—	I-422
	11α,17α,21-trihydroxy-16β-methyl-5α-pregnane-3,20-dione	11α-OH	—	Beauveria sp.	—	—	I-421
			—	Glomerella sp.	—	—	C-109
			—	Phoma sp.	—	—	I-422
	11β,17α,21-trihydroxy-16α-methyl-5α-pregnane-3,20-dione	11β-OH	—	Phoma sp.	—	—	I-422
	11β,17α,21-trihydroxy-16β-methyl-5α-pregnane-3,20-dione	11β-OH	—	Phoma sp.	—	—	I-422

TABLE III

Transformations by Product

EMPIRICAL FORMULA	NAME OF REACTION PRODUCT	TRANSFORMATION	YIELD %	ORGANISM	CONSTANTS m.p.°	$[\alpha]_D$	REF.
$_{23}H_{24}O_3ClF$	17α-chlorethinyl-6-fluoro-17β-hydroxy-1,4,6-androstatrien-3-one acetate	Δ^1	—	Corynebacterium simplex	—	—	O-694
$_{23}H_{24}O_3Cl_2$	6-chloro-17α-chlorethinyl-17β-hydroxy-1,4,6-androstatrien-3-one acetate	Δ^1	—	Corynebacterium simplex	—	—	O-694
$_{23}H_{26}O_3ClF$	17α-chlorethinyl-6α-fluoro-17β-hydroxy-1,4-androstadien-3-one acetate	Δ^1	—	Corynebacterium simplex	—	—	O-694
$_{23}H_{26}O_3Cl_2$	6α-chloro-17α-chlorethinyl-17β-hydroxy-1,4-androstadien-3-one acetate	Δ^1	—	Corynebacterium simplex	—	—	O-694
$_{23}H_{27}O_3Cl$	17α-chlorethinyl-17β-hydroxy-1,4-androstadien-3-one acetate	Δ^1	—	Corynebacterium simplex	—	—	O-694
$_{23}H_{27}O_3F$	17α-ethinyl-16α-ethyl-9α-fluoro-17β-hydroxy-1,4-androstadiene-3,11-dione	Δ^1	—	Corynebacterium simplex	—	—	O-701
$_{23}H_{27}O_4I$	17α-hydroxy-21-iodo-1,4,9(11)-pregnatriene-3,20-dione acetate	Δ^1	—	Corynebacterium simplex	—	—	R-756
$_{23}H_{27}O_9ClS$	12α-chloro-$11\beta,16\alpha,17\alpha,21$-tetrahydroxy-1,4-pregnadiene-3,20-dione 16,17-cyclosulfate 21-acetate	Δ^1	—	Bacterium cyclooxydans	—	—	F-262
$_{23}H_{28}O_3$	17α-ethinyl-16α-ethyl-17β-hydroxy-$9\beta,11\beta$-oxido-1,4-androstadien-3-one	Δ^1	—	Corynebacterium simplex	—	—	O-701
	17β-hydroxy-16α-methyl-17α-(1'-propinyl)-$9\beta,11\beta$-oxido-1,4-androstadien-3-one	Δ^1	—	Corynebacterium simplex	—	—	O-701
	17β-hydroxy-16α-methyl-17α-(1'-propinyl)-1,4-androstadien-3,11-dione	Δ^1	—	Corynebacterium simplex	—	—	O-701
$_{23}H_{28}O_4Cl_2$	$9\alpha,11\beta$-dichloro-17α-hydroxy-1,4-pregnadiene-3,20-dione acetate	Δ^1	—	Corynebacterium simplex	230-235	+129[c]	G-307
$_{23}H_{28}O_5$	14β-hydroxy-3,19-dioxo-4,20(22)-cardadienolide	19-OH→19-C=O	—	Penicillium thomii	—	—	S-892
		3β-OH→3-C=O; 5β-OH → Δ^4	8	Chaetomium globosum	222-224	—	S-891
			—	Nocardia restrictus	—	—	K-481
	21-hydroxy-$16\alpha,17\alpha$-oxido-1,4-pregnadiene-3,20-dione acetate	Δ^1	—	Bacterium havaniensis	—	—	F-233
$_{23}H_{28}O_6$	$17\alpha,21$-dihydroxy-1,4-pregnadiene-3,11,20-trione 21-acetate	Δ^1	11	Corynebacterium simplex	230-233d	—	N-665
	$17\alpha,21$-dihydroxy-1,4-pregnadiene-3,11,20-trione 21-acetate 4-C^{14}	Δ^1	6	Bacillus sphaericus	—	—	C-120

TABLE I

Transformations by Product

EMPIRICAL FORMULA	NAME OF REACTION PRODUCT	TRANSFORMATION	YIELD %	ORGANISM	CONSTANTS m. p.°	[α]$_D$	REF.
$C_{23}H_{29}O_2Cl_2I$	$9\alpha,11\beta$-dichloro-21-iodo-6α,17α-dimethyl-1,4-pregnadiene-3,20-dione	Δ^1	—	Corynebacterium simplex	—	—	R-759
$C_{23}H_{29}O_3F$	17α-ethinyl-16α-ethyl-9α-fluoro-11β,17β-dihydroxy-1,4-androstadien-3-one	Δ^1	—	Corynebacterium simplex	—	—	O-701
$C_{23}H_{29}O_5Br$	9α-bromo-16α-ethyl-17α,21-dihydroxy-1,5-pregnadiene-3,11,20-trione	21-OAc→21-OH	—	Flavobacterium dehydrogenans	—	—	N-692
$C_{23}H_{29}O_5F$	16α-ethyl-9α-fluoro-17α,21-dihydroxy-1,5-pregnadiene-3,11,20-trione	21-OAc→21-OH	—	Flavobacterium dehydrogenans	—	—	N-690; N-692
$C_{23}H_{29}O_6F$	9α-fluoro-11β,17α,21-trihydroxy-1,4-pregnadiene-3,20-dione 21-acetate	Δ^1	—	Bacterium havaniensis	—	—	F-233
			—	Bacterium mycoides	—	—	F-240
$C_{23}H_{30}O_2$	6,17α-dimethyl-1,4,6-pregnatriene-3,20-dione	Δ^1	79	Septomyxa affinis	121-121.5	+ 13[c]	S-901
$C_{23}H_{30}O_4$	14β-hydroxy-3-keto-4,20(22)-cardadienolide	5β-H →Δ^4 (via 5β-OH)	—	Absidia orchidis	—	—	N-682
			—	Mucor parasiticus	—	—	N-682
		3β-OH→3-C=O; 5β-H →Δ^4 (via 5β-OH)	—	Absidia orchidis	—	—	N-679
			<1	Mucor parasiticus	229-236	—	N-678
	21-hydroxy-1,4-pregnadiene-3,20-dione acetate	Δ^1	67(cr.)	Corynebacterium simplex	202-204	+143[c] +152[e]	H-389; N-671
$C_{23}H_{30}O_4Cl_2$	9α,11β-dichloro-6,16α-dimethyl-17α,21-dihydroxy-1,5-pregnadiene-3,20-dione	21-OAc→21-OH	—	Flavobacterium dehydrogenans	—	—	N-691
	9α,11β-dichloro-6,16β-dimethyl-17α,21-dihydroxy-1,5-pregnadiene-3,20-dione	21-OAc→21-OH	—	Flavobacterium dehydrogenans	—	—	N-691
$C_{23}H_{30}O_5$	14β,19-dihydroxy-3-keto-4,20(22)-cardadienolide	19-C=O →19-OH	55	Penicillium thomii	247-251	—	S-892
	14β-hydroxy-3,16-diketo-5β-20(22)-cardenolide (tentative)	3β-OH→3-C=O; 16β-OH→16-C=O	—	Gibberella fujikuroi	—	—	K-434
	11β,17α,21-trihydroxy-6α-methyl-16-methylene-1,4-pregnadiene-3,20-dione	Δ^1	—	Corynebacterium simplex	236-237	+ 5[d]	B-69
	17α,21-dihydroxy-6α,16α-dimethyl-1,4-pregnadiene-3,11,20-trione	Δ^1	—	Bacillus sphaericus	—	—	A-24; A-25
	16α-ethyl-17α,21-dihydroxy-1,5-pregnadiene-3,11,20-trione	21-OAc→21-OH	—	Flavobacterium dehydrogenans	—	—	N-690; N-692
	11β,17α,21-trihydroxy-6α,16-dimethyl-1,4,15-pregnatriene-3,20-dione	Δ^1	—	Corynebacterium simplex	246-248	+ 10[d]	B-69

TABLE I

Transformations by Product

EMPIRICAL FORMULA	NAME OF REACTION PRODUCT	TRANSFORMATION	YIELD %	ORGANISM	CONSTANTS m. p.°	$[\alpha]_D$	REF.
$_{23}H_{30}O_5$	$11\beta,16\alpha,21$-trihydroxy-$1,4,17(20)$-<u>cis</u>-pregnatrien-3-one 21-acetate	Δ^1	—	Septomyxa affinis	—	—	M-529
	21-hydroxy-$16\alpha,17\alpha$-oxido-4-pregnene-3,20-dione acetate	3β-OH$\rightarrow$3-C=O; $\Delta^5 \rightarrow \Delta^4$	—	Flavobacterium sp.	—	—	P-742
$_{23}H_{30}O_5NF$	21-(N-acetylamino)-9α-fluoro-$11\beta,17\alpha$-dihydroxy-1,4-pregnadiene-3,20-dione	Δ^1	—	Corynebacterium simplex	252-255 (ethanol solvate)	+107[m]	S-911
		21-OH$\rightarrow$21-AcNH	—	Streptomyces roseochromogenus	—	—	S-911
$_{23}H_{30}O_6$	$11\beta,17\alpha,21$-trihydroxy-1,4-pregnadiene-3,20-dione 21-acetate	Δ^1	—	Bacterium cyclooxydans	—	—	K-480
			13	Corynebacterium simplex	237-239d	—	N-665
	$11\beta,21$-dihydroxy-$16\alpha,17\alpha$-oxido-4-pregnene-3,20-dione 21-acetate	11β-OH	—	Curvularia lunata	—	—	A-3; A-5
	$14\alpha,21$-dihydroxy-$16\alpha,17\alpha$-oxido-4-pregnene-3,20-dione 21-acetate	14α-OH	—	Curvularia lunata	—	—	A-3; A-5
$C_{23}H_{30}O_7$	$11\beta,14\alpha,21$-trihydroxy-$16\alpha,17\alpha$-oxido-4-pregnene-3,20-dione	11β-OH; 14α-OH	—	Curvularia lunata	—	—	A-3; A-5
$C_{23}H_{31}O_5Br$	9α-bromo-16α-ethyl-$11\beta,17\alpha,21$-trihydroxy-1,5-pregnadiene-3,20-dione	21-OAc$\rightarrow$21-OH	—	Flavobacterium dehydrogenans	—	—	N-690; N-692
$C_{23}H_{31}O_5F$	9α-fluoro-$11\beta,17\alpha,21$-trihydroxy-$6\alpha,16\alpha$-dimethyl-1,4-pregnadiene-3,20-dione	Δ^1	—	Mycobacterium smegmatis	—	—	A-24; A-25
	16α-ethyl-9α-fluoro-$11\beta,17\alpha,21$-trihydroxy-1,5-pregnadiene-3,20-dione	21-OAc$\rightarrow$21-OH	—	Flavobacterium dehydrogenans	—	—	N-690; N-692
$C_{23}H_{32}O_2$	17α-ethyl-1,4-pregnadiene-3,20-dione	Δ^1	25	Septomyxa affinis	150-151	—	S-901
	$6\alpha,17\alpha$-dimethyl-1,4-pregnadiene-3,20-dione	Δ^1	27	Septomyxa affinis	118-119	+ 14[c]	S-901
$C_{23}H_{32}O_3$	1,4-pregnadiene-3,20-dione 20-cycloethylene ketal	Δ^1	—	Bacterium cyclooxydans	—	—	F-251
			—	Bacillus sphaericus	—	—	F-251
			—	Corynebacterium hoagii	—	—	F-251
			—	Cylindrocarpon radicicola	—	—	F-251
			—	Streptomyces lavendulae	—	—	F-251

TABLE I

Transformations by Product

EMPIRICAL FORMULA	NAME OF REACTION PRODUCT	TRANSFORMATION	YIELD %	ORGANISM	CONSTANTS m. p.°	[α]$_D$	REF
$C_{23}H_{32}O_3$	1,4-pregnadiene-3,20-dione 20-cycloethylene ketal	3β-OH →3-C=O; $\Delta^5 \to \Delta^4$; Δ^1	—	Septomyxa affinis	—	—	F-251
$C_{23}H_{32}O_4$	3β,14β-dihydroxy-5β-16,20(22)-cardadienolide (tentative)	Δ^{16}	1	Trichothecium roseum	—	—	T-1013
	3β-hydroxy-14α,15α-oxido-5β-20(22)-cardenolide	3β-OAc→3β-OH	93	Rhizopus shanghaiensis	—	—	M-576
	14β-hydroxy-3-keto-5β,17α-20(22)-cardenolide	3β-OH→3-C=O	—	Calonectria decora	—	—	N-681
			—	Mucor parasiticus	—	—	N-681
			4	Nigrospora sphaerica	219-223	—	N-681
			—	Rhizopus arrhizus	—	—	N-681
	14β-hydroxy-3-keto-5β-20(22)-cardenolide	3α-OH→3-C=O	—	Calonectria decora	—	—	N-681
			—	Mucor parasiticus	—	—	N-681
			10	Nigrospora sphaerica	198-204	—	N-681
			—	Rhizopus arrhizus	—	—	N-681
		3β-OH→3-C=O	—	Absidia sp.	—	—	N-682
			2	Aspergillus oryzae	—	—	J-432
			—	Cunninghamella sp.	—	—	N-682
			2	Mucor parasiticus	197-205	—	N-678
			—	Mucor sp.	—	—	N-682
			2	Psilocybe mexicana	205-207	—	W-1075
			—	Rhizopus sp.	—	—	N-682
			—	Trichothecium roseum	—	—	J-432
	5β-1-pregnene-3,11,20-trione 20-cycloethylene ketal	Δ^1	44	Septomyxa affinis	204-206	—	F-253; F-249; F-251
	21-hydroxy-4-pregnene-3,20-dione acetate	3β-OH→3-C=O; $\Delta^5 \to \Delta^4$	—	Flavobacterium sp.	—	—	P-742
$C_{23}H_{32}O_5$	7β,14β-dihydroxy-3-keto-5β-20(22)-cardenolide	7β-OH	—	Psilocybe mexicana	—	—	W-1075
			5	Rhizopus arrhizus	266-273	+ 56[c]	N-678
		3β-OH→3-C=O	—	Rhizopus arrhizus	—	—	N-678
		7β-OH; 3β-OH→3-C=O	1	Psilocybe mexicana	259-269	—	W-1075
			13	Rhizopus arrhizus	261-275	—	N-678
		7β-OH; 3β-OAc→3-C=O	—	Rhizopus arrhizus	—	—	N-678
	12β,14β-dihydroxy-3-keto-5β-20(22)-cardenolide	12β-OH	—	Calonectria decora	—	—	N-677

TABLE I

Transformations by Product

EMPIRICAL FORMULA	NAME OF REACTION PRODUCT	TRANSFORMATION	YIELD %	ORGANISM	CONSTANTS m. p.°	$[\alpha]_D$	REF.
$_3H_{32}O_5$	12β,14β-dihydroxy-3-keto-5β-20(22)-cardenolide	12β-OH	5	Fusarium lini	247-252 (hydrate)	+ 41[m]	G-320; T-978
			50	Gibberella saubinetti	251-254	+ 32 [1m: 1c]	O-699
		3β-OH→3-C=O	—	Calonectria decora	—	—	N-677
		12β-OH; 3α-OH→3-C=O	—	Calonectria decora	—	—	N-681
			13	Nigrospora sphaerica	243-248	—	N-681
		12β-OH; 3β-OH→3-C=O	10	Calonectria decora	242-253	—	N-677
			—	Nigrospora sphaerica	254-256	—	N-677
		12β-OH; 3β-OAc→3-C=O	—	Calonectria decora	—	—	N-677
	14β,16β-dihydroxy-3-keto-5β-20(22)-cardenolide	3β-OH→3-C=O	10	Calonectria decora	201-209	—	N-677
			—	Fusarium sp.	—	—	K-434
			10	Gibberella fujikuroi	199-202; 215-220	—	K-434
			—	Nigrospora sphaerica	—	—	N-677
		3β-OAc→3-C=O	8	Calonectria decora	195-198	—	N-677
			—	Nigrospora sphaerica	—	—	N-677
		3β-OAc→3-C=O; 16β-OAc→16β-OH	—	Calonectria decora	—	—	N-677
			—	Nigrospora sphaerica	—	—	N-677
	16α-ethyl-11α,17α,21-trihydroxy-1,4-pregnadiene-3,20-dione	11α-OH; 21-OAc→21-OH	—	Pestalotia foedans	221-222	+ 21[d]	O-703
	16β-ethyl-11α,17α,21-trihydroxy-1,4-pregnadiene-3,20-dione	11α-OH	—	Beauveria sp.	—	—	I-421
			—	Glomerella cingulata	—	—	C-109
			—	Phoma sp.	—	—	I-422
	16β-ethyl-11β,17α,21-trihydroxy-1,4-pregnadiene-3,20-dione	11β-OH	—	Phoma sp.	—	—	I-422
	11β,17α,21-trihydroxy-6α,16α-dimethyl-1,4-pregnadiene-3,20-dione	Δ^1	—	Nocardia asteroides	—	—	A-24; A-25
	16α-ethyl-11β,17α,21-trihydroxy-1,5-pregnadiene-3,20-dione	21-OAc→21-OH	—	Flavobacterium dehydrogenans	—	—	N-690; N-692
	11β,17α,21-trihydroxy-6α,16-dimethyl-4,15-pregnadiene-3,20-dione	11β-OH	—	Curvularia lunata	238-240	+ 51[d]	B-69
	11β,17α-dihydroxy-1-5α-pregnene-3,20-dione 17-acetate	11β-OH	—	Curvularia lunata	—	—	R-773

TABLE I

Transformations by Product

EMPIRICAL FORMULA	NAME OF REACTION PRODUCT	TRANSFORMATION	YIELD %	ORGANISM	CONSTANTS m.p.°	[α]$_D$	REF.
$C_{23}H_{32}O_5$	11β,17α,21-trihydroxy-6α-methyl-16-methylene-4-pregnene-3,20-dione	11β-OH; 21-OAc→21-OH	—	Curvularia lunata	218	+ 50[d]	B-69
	17α,21-dihydroxy-4-pregnene-3,20-dione 21-acetate	3β-OH→3-C=O; $\Delta^5 \to \Delta^4$	—	Flavobacterium sp.	—	—	P-742
		3β-OAc→3-C=O; $\Delta^5 \to \Delta^4$	3-11	Corynebacterium simplex	213-215	—	C-128; N-665
$C_{23}H_{32}O_5NF$	21-[N-acetylamino]-9α-fluoro-11β,17α-dihydroxy-4-pregnene-3,20-dione	21-NH$_2$→21-AcNH	—	Streptomyces roseochromogenus	—	—	S-911
		21-OH→21-AcNH	—	Streptomyces roseochromogenus	263-264	+132[m]	S-911
$C_{23}H_{32}O_6$	3β,5β,14β-trihydroxy-19-oxo-20(22)-cardenolide (strophanthidin)	3β-D-glucoside→3β-OH	51	Fusarium lini	135-140; 198-201	—	T-978
		3β-D-glucoside tetraacetate→3β-OH	57	Fusarium lini	133-135	—	T-978
$C_{23}H_{32}O_6NF$	21-[N-acetylamino]-9α-fluoro-2β,11β,17α-trihydroxy-4-pregnene-3,20-dione (tentative)	2β-OH	—	Streptomyces roseochromogenus	—	—	S-911
$C_{23}H_{34}O_2$	16,16-dimethyl-4-pregnene-3,20-dione	3β-OH→3-C=O; $\Delta^5 \to \Delta^4$	53	Flavobacterium dehydrogenans	168-169	+ 88[d] +104[c]	S-837
$C_{23}H_{34}O_3$	11α-hydroxy-6α,16α-dimethyl-4-pregnene-3,20-dione	11α-OH	—	Rhizopus nigricans	—	—	S-923
	11β-hydroxy-6α,16α-dimethyl-4-pregnene-3,20-dione	11β-OH	—	Cunninghamella blakesleeana	—	—	S-923
	11β-hydroxy-6α,17α-dimethyl-4-pregnene-3,20-dione	11β-OH	—	Curvularia lunata	—	—	R-759
$C_{23}H_{34}O_4$	3α,14β-dihydroxy-5β-20(22)-cardenolide	3-C=O→3α-OH	—	Absidia orchidis	—	—	N-682
			12-15	Fusarium lini	269-282	—	T-978; G-320
			4	Gibberella saubinetti	280-284	—	O-699
			—	Mucor parasiticus	—	—	N-678; N-682
	3β,14β-dihydroxy-5β-20(22)-cardenolide (digitoxigenin)	3-C=O→3β-OH	—	Mucor parasiticus	—	—	N-678
			—	Psilocybe semperviva	—	—	W-1075
	6β-hydroxy-4-pregnene-3,20-dione 20-cycloethylene ketal	6β-OH	—	Gliocladium catenulatum	—	—	F-251
	11α-hydroxy-4-pregnene-3,20-dione 20-cycloethylene ketal	11α-OH	—	Sporotrichum epigaeum	—	—	F-251
$C_{23}H_{34}O_5$	1β,3β,14β-trihydroxy-5β,17α-20(22)-cardenolide (tentative)	1β-OH	—	Absidia orchidis	—	—	N-681

TABLE I

Transformations by Product

EMPIRICAL FORMULA	NAME OF REACTION PRODUCT	TRANSFORMATION	YIELD %	ORGANISM	CONSTANTS m. p.°	$[\alpha]_D$	REF.
$_{23}H_{34}O_5$	$3\beta,5\beta,14\beta$-trihydroxy-17α-20(22)-cardenolide	5β-OH	3	Absidia orchidis	232-241d	+ 35[m]	N-681
			—	Mucor parasiticus	—	—	N-681
	$1\beta,3\beta,14\beta$-trihydroxy-5β-20(22)-cardenolide	1β-OH	17	Absidia orchidis	276-282d	+ 3[m]	N-679; N-680; I-426; N-683
			—	Absidia sp.	—	—	N-682
			—	Mucor sp.	—	—	N-682
			—	Rhizopus nigricans	—	—	N-683
			—	Rhizopus sp.	—	—	N-682
	$3\alpha,7\beta,14\beta$-trihydroxy-5β-20(22)-cardenolide	3-C=O →3α-OH; 7β-OH	4	Rhizopus arrhizus	255-259	+ 48[m]	N-678
	$3\alpha,12\beta,14\beta$-trihydroxy-5β-20(22)-cardenolide	3-C=O →3α-OH; 12β-OH	1	Fusarium lini	249-262	+ 27[m]	G-320; T-978
			—	Gibberella saubinetti	—	—	O-699
	$3\alpha,14\beta,16\beta$-trihydroxy-5β-20(22)-cardenolide	3-C=O →3α-OH	—	Fusarium lini	—	—	T-977
	$3\beta,5\beta,14\beta$-trihydroxy-20(22)-cardenolide	5β-OH	—	Absidia orchidis	—	—	N-679; N-680; N-683; I-426
			37-40	Mucor parasiticus	245-248	+ 25[c] + 28.5[m]	I-423; N-678; N-683; N-682
			—	Rhizopus arrhizus	—	—	N-678; N-682
	$3\beta,7\beta,14\beta$-trihydroxy-5β-20(22)-cardenolide	7β-OH	24	Absidia orchidis	266-275	+ 37[m]	N-680; N-679; I-426; N-683; N-681
			—	Absidia sp.	—	—	N-682
			22(cr.)	Aspergillus oryzae	275-280	+ 39[m]	J-432
			—	Cunninghamella sp.	—	—	N-682
			—	Mucor sp.	—	—	N-682; N-683
			4	Psilocybe mexicana	263-266	+ 39[m]	W-1075
			25	Rhizopus arrhizus	267-272	+ 34.5	N-678; I-425
			11(cr.)	Rhizopus arrhizus	275-280	+ 39[m]	J-432

TABLE I

Transformations by Product

EMPIRICAL FORMULA	NAME OF REACTION PRODUCT	TRANSFORMATION	YIELD %	ORGANISM	CONSTANTS m. p.°	$[\alpha]_D$	REF
$C_{23}H_{34}O_5$	$3\beta,7\beta,14\beta$-trihydroxy-5β-20(22)-cardenolide	7β-OH	11(cr.)	Rhizopus delemar	266-274d	—	N-682
			—	Rhizopus sp.	—	—	N-682; N-683
			—	Streptomyces aureofaciens	—	—	T-101:
			8	Trichothecium roseum	268-275	+ 37[m]	T-101:
			—	Trichothecium roseum	—	—	J-432
	$3\beta,11\alpha,14\beta$-trihydroxy-5β-20(22)-cardenolide (sarmentogenin)	11α-OH	4.5	Trichothecium roseum	—	—	T-101:
	$3\beta,12\beta,14\beta$-trihydroxy-5β-20(22)-cardenolide (digoxigenin)	12β-OH	—	Calonectria decora	—	—	N-677
			35	Fusarium lini	207-209	+ 22.5[m]	T-978; G-320; W-107
			—	Gibberella fujikuroi	—	—	N-651
			43	Gibberella saubinetti	206-209	—	O-699
			—	Helicostylum piriforme	—	—	N-651
			—	Nigrospora sphaerica	197-208	—	N-677
			2	Psilocybe mexicana	—	—	W-1075
			—	Psilocybe semperviva	—	—	W-1075
		12β-OH; 3β-OAc→3β-OH	25	Fusarium lini	210-213	—	T-978; G-320
		12β-OH; 3-C=O →3β-OH	—	Psilocybe semperviva	—	—	W-1075
	$3\beta,14\beta,16\beta$-trihydroxy-5β-20(22)-cardenolide (gitoxigenin)	16β-OH	—	Cunninghamella blakesleeana	—	—	N-651
			—	Helicostylum piriforme	—	—	N-651
		16β-OAc→16β-OH	—	Gibberella saubinetti	—	—	O-699
		3β-OAc→3β-OH; 16β-OAc→16β-OH	—	Calonectria decora	—	—	N-677
			—	Fusarium lini	—	—	T-977
			—	Nigrospora sphaerica	—	—	N-677
	$3\beta,14\beta,X$-trihydroxy-5β-20(22)-cardenolide	X-OH	9(cr.)	Rhizopus arrhizus	268-276	+ 18[m]	J-432
	17β-methyl-18-nor-17α-5,13-pregnadiene-$3\beta,16\alpha,20\alpha,21$-tetrol 21-acetate	20-C=O→20α-OH; 13β-CH$_3$-$16\alpha,17\alpha$-oxide→17β-CH$_3$-18-nor-16α-OH; Δ^{13}	40	Saccharomyces cerevisiae	205-210	—	C-90

TABLE I

Transformations by Product

EMPIRICAL FORMULA	NAME OF REACTION PRODUCT	TRANSFORMATION	YIELD %	ORGANISM	CONSTANTS m. p.°	$[\alpha]_D$	REF.
$_{23}H_{34}O_5$	$11\beta,17\alpha,21$-trihydroxy-6α,16α-dimethyl-4-pregnene-3,20-dione	11β-OH; 21-OAc$\rightarrow$21-OH	—	Curvularia lunata	—	—	S-805
$_{23}H_{34}O_6$	$1\beta,3\beta,7\beta,14\beta$-tetrahydroxy-$5\beta$-20(22)-cardenolide	1β-OH; 7β-OH	6-10	Absidia orchidis	244-254d	+ 19[m] + 22.5[m]	N-679; N-680; I-426; N-682
			—	Absidia sp.	—	—	N-682
			—	Mucor sp.	—	—	N-682
			—	Rhizopus sp.	—	—	N-682
	$3\beta,5\beta,7\beta,14\beta$-tetrahydroxy-20(22)-cardenolide	5β-OH; 7β-OH	4-7	Absidia orchidis	249-250	+ 49[m]	N-679; I-426; N-682
			—	Absidia sp.	—	—	N-682
			—	Mucor sp.	—	—	N-682
			—	Rhizopus sp.	—	—	N-682
	$3\beta,12\beta,14\beta,16\beta$-tetrahydroxy-$5\beta$-20(22)-cardenolide (diginatigenin)	12β-OH	—	Fusarium lini	155-156	—	T-977
			—	Fusarium sp.	—	—	K-434
			6	Gibberella saubinetti	154-156	+ 34[m]	O-699
		12β-OH; 16β-OAc$\rightarrow$16β-OH	2	Gibberella saubinetti	153-156	—	O-699
	$3\beta,5\beta,14\beta,19\beta$-tetrahydroxy-20(22)-cardenolide	19-C=O$\rightarrow$19-OH	—	Psilocybe semperviva	—	—	W-1075
	$3\alpha,17\alpha,21$-trihydroxy-5β-pregnane-11,20-dione 21-acetate	3-C=O$\rightarrow$3α-OH; $\Delta^4\rightarrow5\beta$-H	53	Clostridium paraputrificum	216	+ 73[a]	S-823
			—	Clostridium tertium	—	—	S-823
$_{23}H_{36}O_4$	$3\alpha,21$-dihydroxy-5β-pregnan-20-one 21-acetate	3-C=O$\rightarrow$3α-OH; $\Delta^4\rightarrow5\beta$-H	57	Clostridium paraputrificum	176-178	+100[c]	S-823
			—	Clostridium tertium	—	—	S-823
$_{23}H_{36}O_5$	16β-ethyl-$11\alpha,17\alpha,21$-trihydroxy-5α-pregnane-3,20-dione	11α-OH	—	Beauveria sp.	—	—	I-421
			—	Glomerella sp.	—	—	C-109
			—	Phoma sp.	—	—	I-422
	16β-ethyl-$11\beta,17\alpha,21$-trihydroxy-5α-pregnane-3,20-dione	11β-OH	—	Phoma sp.	—	—	I-422
$_{24}H_{29}O_4Cl_2F$	$9\alpha,11\beta$-dichloro-21-fluoro-17α-hydroxy-6α-methyl-1,4-pregnadiene-3,20-dione acetate	Δ^1	—	Corynebacterium simplex	—	—	R-759
	$9\alpha,11\beta$-dichloro-17α-hydroxy-21-iodo-6α-methyl-1,4-pregnadiene-3,20-dione acetate	Δ^1	—	Corynebacterium simplex	—	—	R-759

TABLE I

Transformations by Product

EMPIRICAL FORMULA	NAME OF REACTION PRODUCT	TRANSFORMATION	YIELD %	ORGANISM	CONSTANTS m.p.°	$[\alpha]_D$	REF
$C_{24}H_{30}O_4$	17α-hydroxy-16-methylene 1,4-pregnadiene-3,20-dione acetate	Δ^1	22	Bacillus sphaericus	222-223	-90[d]	S-837
$C_{24}H_{30}O_5BrF$	9α-bromo-11β-fluoro-16α,17α,21-trihydroxy-1,5-pregnadiene-3,20-dione 16,17-acetonide	21-OAc → 21-OH	—	Flavobacterium dehydrogenans	—	—	N-691
$C_{24}H_{30}O_6$	17α,21-dihydroxy-16α-methyl-1,4-pregnadiene-3,11,20-trione 21-acetate	$\Delta^{1,4}$ (5β-H); 3α-OH → 3-C=O	—	Nocardia blackwellii	—	—	S-902
	17α,21-dihydroxy-16β-methyl-1,4-pregnadiene 3,11,20-trione 21-acetate	$\Delta^{1,4}$ (5β-H); 3α-OH → 3-C=O	—	Nocardia blackwellii	—	—	S-905
$C_{24}H_{30}O_6ClF$	6α-chloro-12α-fluoro-11β,16α,17α,21-tetrahydroxy-1,4-pregnadiene-3,20-dione 16,17-acetonide	Δ^1	—	Nocardia aurantia	—	—	F-261
$C_{24}H_{30}O_6F_2$	2,9α-difluoro-11β,16α,17α,21-tetrahydroxy-1,4-pregnadiene-3,20-dione 16,17-acetonide	Δ^1(2α-F)	—	Nocardia corallina	—	—	H-401
$C_{24}H_{30}O_7$	3,11β,17α,21-tetrahydroxy-19-nor-1,3,5(10)-pregnatrien-20-one 11,21-diacetate	Δ^1; enol.	—	Corynebacterium simplex	—	—	H-386
$C_{24}H_{31}O_6F$	9α-fluoro-11β,16α,17α,21-tetrahydroxy-1,4-pregnadiene-3,20-dione 16,17-acetonide	Δ^1	—	Nocardia corallina	—	—	H-399
$C_{24}H_{31}O_7F$	9α-fluoro-2,11β,16α,17α,21-pentahydroxy-1,4-pregnadiene-3,20-dione 16,17-acetonide	2-OH	—	Streptomyces griseus	—	—	F-235; F-236
	9α-fluoro-6β,11β,16α,17α,21-pentahydroxy-1,4-pregnadiene-3,20-dione 16,17-acetonide	Δ^1	18	Nocardia corallina	277-282	+72[p]	H-400
	9α-fluoro-6β,16α,17α,21-tetrahydroxy-4-pregnene-3,11,20-trione 16,17-acetonide	6β-OH; 11β-OH → 11-C=O	6	Phycomyces sp.	243-245.5	+94[m]	H-400
$C_{24}H_{32}O_4$	3,12-diketo-4,6-choladienic acid	7-C=O → Δ^6	—	Corynebacterium sp.	—	—	T-975
		3α-OH → 3-C=O; 7α-OH → Δ^6; 12α-OH → 12-C=O; 5β-H → Δ^4	—	Streptomyces gelaticus	—	—	H-359
			1	Streptomyces rubescens	205-208	—	H-365
$C_{24}H_{32}O_5$	12β,14β-dihydroxy-3-keto-5β-20,22-bufadienolide	12β-OH	—	Fusarium lini	228-237	+1[m]	T-979

TABLE I

Transformations by Product

EMPIRICAL FORMULA	NAME OF REACTION PRODUCT	TRANSFORMATION	YIELD %	ORGANISM	CONSTANTS m.p.°	$[\alpha]_D$	REF.
$C_{24}H_{32}O_5$	21-hydroxy-16β-methyl-16α, 17α-oxido-4-pregnene-3,20-dione acetate	3β-OH →3-C=O; $\Delta^5 \to \Delta^4$	—	Flavobacterium sp.	—	—	P-742
$C_{24}H_{32}O_6$	11β,17α,21-trihydroxy-16α-methyl-1,4-pregnadiene-3,20-dione 21-acetate	11β-OH	—	Curvularia lunata	—	—	S-904
$C_{24}H_{32}O_7$	11β,17α,21-trihydroxy-16β-methoxy-1,4-pregnadiene-3,20-dione 21-acetate	Δ^1	—	Corynebacterium simplex	—	—	R-760
$C_{23}H_{32}O_7F_2$	6α,9α-difluoro-2β,11β,16α,17α,21-pentahydroxy-4-pregnene-3,20-dione 16,17-acetonide	2β-OH	—	Streptomyces griseus	—	—	F-235; F-236
$C_{24}H_{33}O_6F$	6α-fluoro-2β,16α,17α,21-tetrahydroxy-4-pregnene-3,20-dione 16,17-acetonide	2β-OH	14	Gnomonia fragariae	240-242	- 53[c]	L-496
	6α-fluoro-11α,16α,17α,21-tetrahydroxy-4-pregnene-3,20-dione 16,17-acetonide	11α-OH	24	Colletotrichum phomoides	—	—	D-159
			24	Trichothecium roseum	264-266	+102[c]	D-159
$C_{24}H_{33}O_7F$	9α-fluoro-2β,11β,16α,17α,21-pentahydroxy-4-pregnene-3,20-dione 16,17-acetonide	2β-OH	—	Streptomyces griseus	260-261	+ 13[m]	F-235; F-236
	9α-fluoro-6β,11β,16α,17α,21-pentahydroxy-4-pregnene-3,20-dione 16,17-acetonide	6β-OH	15	Phycomyces sp.	240.5-243.5	+ 72[m]	H-400
$C_{24}H_{34}O_4$	12α-hydroxy-3-keto-1,4-choladienic acid	3α-OH→3-C=O; 7α-OH→H; Δ^1; Δ^4(5β-H)	—	Corynebacterium simplex	—	—	H-358; H-367
	12α-hydroxy-3-keto-4,6-choladienic acid	3α-OH→3-C=O; 7α-OH→Δ^6; Δ^4(5β-H)	—	Corynebacterium simplex	—	—	H-367
			3	Corynebacterium sp.	249-252	—	T-974
			—	Streptomyces rubescens	—	—	H-362
$C_{24}H_{34}O_5$	3β,12β,14β-trihydroxy-5β-20,22-bufadienolide	12β-OH	50(cr.)	Fusarium lini	240-246	- 16[m]	T-979
	3,7,12-triketo-5β-cholanic acid	3α-OH→3-C=O; 7α-OH→7-C=O; 12α-OH→12-C=O	65-99	Alcaligenes faecalis	236-237	—	S-799; S-800; H-393
			—	Escherichia coli	—	—	S-799
	7α-hydroxy-3,12-diketo-4-cholenic acid	7-C=O →7α-OH; Δ^4(5β-H)	15	Corynebacterium sp.	246-249d	—	T-975
			2	Streptomyces gelaticus	224-226d	—	H-363
		3α-OH→3-C=O; 12α-OH→12-C=O; Δ^4(5β-H)	1	Streptomyces rubescens	248-252d	—	H-365
$C_{24}H_{33}O_6F$	6α-fluoro-11β,16α,17α,21-tetrahydroxy-4-pregnene-3,20-dione 16,17-acetonide	11β-OH	—	Cunninghamella bainieri	—	—	R-771

TABLE I

Transformations by Product

EMPIRICAL FORMULA	NAME OF REACTION PRODUCT	TRANSFORMATION	YIELD %	ORGANISM	CONSTANTS m.p.°	$[\alpha]_D$	REF.
$C_{24}H_{34}O_7$	2β,11β,16α,17α,21-pentahydroxy-4-pregnene-3,20-dione 16,17-acetonide	2β-OH	—	Streptomyces griseus	—	—	F-235
$C_{24}H_{36}O_3$	3-keto-4-cholenic acid	3β-OH→3-C=O; $\Delta^5 \to \Delta^4$	37	Proactinomyces erythropolis	185	—	T-1032
$C_{24}H_{36}O_4$	12α-hydroxy-3-keto-4-cholenic acid	3α-OH→3-C=O; 7α-OH→H; Δ^4(5β-H)	—	Corynebacterium simplex	—	—	H-367
$C_{24}H_{36}O_5$	3α-hydroxy-7,12-diketo-5β-cholanic acid	7α-OH→7-C=O; 12α-OH→12-C=O	—	Alcaligenes faecalis	—	—	H-393
	7α-hydroxy-3,12-diketo-5β-cholanic acid	7-C=O→7α-OH	10	Bacillus coli	195-196	+ 72[m]	F-289
		3α-OH→3-C=O; 12α-OH→12-C=O	—	Streptomyces gelaticus	—	—	H-366
	7α,12α-dihydroxy-3-keto-4-cholenic acid	3α-OH→3-C=O; Δ^4(5β-H)	—	Bacterium sp.*	—	—	E-194
			—	Corynebacterium simplex	—	—	H-367
			—	Corynebacterium sp.	—	—	T-974
			—	Streptomyces rubescens	—	—	H-365
$C_{24}H_{38}O_4$	3α-hydroxy-6-keto-5β-cholanic acid	3-C=O →3α-OH	—	Saccharomyces cerevisiae	—	—	E-221
	3α-hydroxy-7-keto-5β-cholanic acid	7α-OH→7-C=O	—	Escherichia coli	—	—	N-675
	3α-hydroxy-12-keto-5β-cholanic acid	3-C=O →3α-OH	60	Saccharomyces cerevisiae	165	—	M-543
			—	Saccharomyces cerevisiae	162	+111[e]	K-441
$C_{24}H_{38}O_5$	3α,7α-dihydroxy-12-keto-5β-cholanic acid	12α-OH→12-C=O	—	Streptomyces gelaticus	—	—	H-366
	3α,12α-dihydroxy-7-keto-5β-cholanic acid	7α-OH→7-C=O	—	Alcaligenes faecalis	—	—	H-393
			—	Clostridium perfringens	—	—	N-675
			—	Escherichia coli	—	—	N-675
	7α,12α-dihydroxy-3-keto-5β-cholanic acid	3α-OH→3-C=O	—	Corynebacterium simplex	—	—	H-367
			—	Streptomyces gelaticus	—	—	H-366
$C_{24}H_{40}O_4$	3α,7α-dihydroxy-5β-cholanic acid	3-C=O →3α-OH; 7-C=O →7α-OH	4	Bacillus coli	110-115	+ 12[e]	S-899
$C_{25}H_{30}O_5S$	21-hydroxy-16α-mercapto-1,4,9(11)-pregnatriene-3,20-dione 16,21-diacetate	Δ^1	—	Corynebacterium simplex	—	—	R-764

*unidentified gram-positive coccus

TABLE I

Transformations by Product

EMPIRICAL FORMULA	NAME OF REACTION PRODUCT	TRANSFORMATION	YIELD %	ORGANISM	CONSTANTS m. p.°	[α]$_D$	REF.
$_5H_{31}O_8F$	9α-fluoro-11β,16α,17α,21-tetrahydroxy-1,4-pregnadiene-3,20-dione 16,21-diacetate	Δ^1	—	Corynebacterium simplex	158-235 (solvate); 186-188; (solvate)	+ 22[c]	B-60; B-59
$_5H_{32}O_3$	16α-n-butyl-17α-ethinyl-17β-hydroxy-1,4-androstadiene-3,11-dione	Δ^1	—	Corynebacterium simplex	—	—	O-701
	16β-n-butyl-17α-ethinyl-17β-hydroxy-1,4-androstadiene-3,11-dione	Δ^1	—	Corynebacterium simplex	—	—	O-701
$_5H_{32}O_5$	17α,21-dihydroxy-6β,16α-dimethyl-1,4,9(11)-pregnatriene-3,20-dione 21-acetate	Δ^1	—	Corynebacterium simplex	—	—	N-691
$_5H_{32}O_5ClF$	9α-chloro-11β-fluoro-16α,17α,21-trihydroxy-6-methyl-1,5-pregnadiene-3,20-dione 16,17-acetonide	21-OAc→21-OH	—	Flavobacterium dehydrogenans	—	—	N-691
$_5H_{32}O_7$	11β,17α,21-trihydroxy-1,4-pregnadiene-3,20-dione 11,21-diacetate	Δ^1	59	Corynebacterium simplex	219-221	+152[c]	H-389
$_5H_{34}O_5$	16α-n-butyl-17α,21-dihydroxy-1,4-pregnadiene-3,11,20-trione	Δ^1	—	Corynebacterium simplex	—	—	N-692
	16β-n-butyl-17α,21-dihydroxy-1,4-pregnadiene-3,11,20-trione	Δ^1	—	Corynebacterium simplex	—	—	N-692
	16α-n-butyl-17α,21-dihydroxy-1,5-pregnadiene-3,11,20-trione	21-OAc→21-OH	—	Flavobacterium dehydrogenans	—	—	N-690; N-692
	16β-n-butyl-17α,21-dihydroxy-1,5-pregnadiene-3,11,20-trione	21-OAc→21-OH	—	Flavobacterium dehydrogenans	—	—	N-690; N-692
$_{25}H_{34}O_5ClF$	9α-chloro-11β-fluoro-16α,17α,21-trihydroxy-2α-methyl-5-pregnene-3,20-dione 16,17-acetonide	21-OAc→21-OH	—	Flavobacterium dehydrogenans	—	—	N-691
$_{25}H_{34}O_6$	14β,16β-dihydroxy-3-keto-5β-20(22)-cardenolide 16-acetate	3β-OH→3-C=O	2	Calonectria decora	242-249	—	N-677
			—	Nigrospora sphaerica	—	—	N-677
		3β-OAc→3-C=O	—	Calonectria decora	—	—	N-677
			—	Nigrospora sphaerica	—	—	N-677
$_{25}H_{36}O_5$	16α-t-butyl-11α,17α,21-trihydroxy-1,4-pregnadiene-3,20-dione	11α-OH	—	Beauveria sp.	—	—	I-421
			—	Glomerella sp.	—	—	C-109
			—	Phoma sp.	—	—	I-422
	16α-t-butyl-11β,17α,21-trihydroxy-1,4-pregnadiene-3,20-dione	11β-OH	—	Phoma sp.	—	—	I-422

TABLE I

Transformations by Product

EMPIRICAL FORMULA	NAME OF REACTION PRODUCT	TRANSFORMATION	YIELD %	ORGANISM	CONSTANTS m. p.°	[α]$_D$	REF
$C_{25}H_{36}O_6$	3β,14β,16β-trihydroxy-5β-20(22)-cardenolide 16-acetate (oleandrigenin)	3β-OAc →3β-OH	—	Calonectria decora	—	—	N-677
			—	Nigrospora sphaerica	—	—	N-677
$C_{25}H_{36}O_7$	3β,12β,14β,16β-tetrahydroxy-5β-20(22)-cardenolide 16-acetate	12β-OH	14	Gibberella saubinetti	233-238	+ 6[m]	O-699
$C_{25}H_{40}O_5$	16α-t-butyl-11α,17α,21-trihydroxy-5α-pregnane-3,20-dione	11α-OH	—	Beauveria sp.	—	—	I-421
			—	Glomerella sp.	—	—	C-109
			—	Phoma sp.	—	—	I-422
	16α-t-butyl-11β,17α,21-trihydroxy-5α-pregnane-3,20-dione	11β-OH	—	Phoma sp.	—	—	I-422
$C_{26}H_{34}O_7$	3β,6β,8β,14β-tetrahydroxy-4,20,22-bufatrienolide 6-acetate (scillirosidin)	3β-[1' ξ -glucoside] →3β-OH	15	Alternaria sp.	—	—	S-936
			5-100	Aspergillus sp.	—	—	S-936
			85-90	Claviceps purpurea	—	—	S-936
			90	Paecilomyces sp.	—	—	S-936
			60-90	Penicillium sp.	—	—	S-936
			50	Pullularia pullulans	—	—	S-936
			15	Rhizopus nigricans	—	—	S-936
			30	Stachybotrys sp.	—	—	S-936
			35	Stemphylium sp.	—	—	S-936
$C_{26}H_{35}O_7F$	9α-fluoro-11β,16α,17α,21-tetrahydroxy-4-pregnene-3,20-dione 16,17-acetonide 21-acetate	21-OH→21-OAc	70(cr.)	Trichoderma glauca	239-240	+136[m]	H-404
$C_{26}H_{36}O_6$	11β,17α,21-trihydroxy-1,4-pregnadiene-3,20-dione 21-trimethylacetate	d,1→d-Δ^1 +1	—	Didymella lycopersici	233-236	+103[c]	W-110
$C_{26}H_{40}O_2$	27-nor-4-cholestene-3,25-dione	3β-OH→3-C=O; Δ^5 → Δ^4	14	Micrococcus dehydrogenans	128	—	E-214
$C_{26}H_{42}O_5$	3α,12α-dihydroxy-5β-cholanic acid 12-acetate	3 -C=O →3α-OH	33(cr.)	Saccharomyces cerevisiae	174-175	—	K-442
$C_{26}H_{44}O_3$	A-nor-3,5-seco-5-keto-cholestan-3-oic acid	cholestenone → ring A cleavage	tr.	Proactinomyces erythropolis	150	—	T-103
		cholesterol → ring A cleavage	—	Mycobacterium sp.	—	—	S-930
$C_{27}H_{29}O_5P$	16α,17α-dihydroxy-1,4,6-pregnatriene-3,20-dione 16,17-cyclophenylphosphonate	Δ^1	—	Bacterium cyclooxydans	—	—	F-259
$C_{27}H_{30}O_5FP$	6α-fluoro-16α,17α-dihydroxy-1,4-pregnadiene-3,20-dione 16,17-cyclophenylphosphonate	Δ^1	—	Bacterium cyclooxydans	—	—	F-259

TABLE I

Transformations by Product

EMPIRICAL FORMULA	NAME OF REACTION PRODUCT	TRANSFORMATION	YIELD %	ORGANISM	CONSTANTS m.p.°	$[\alpha]_D$	REF.
H$_{37}$O$_6$F	6α-fluoro-11α,16α,17α,21-tetrahydroxy-4-pregnene-3,20-dione 16,17-cyclohexanonide	11α-OH	—	Colletotrichum phomoides	—	—	D-159
H$_{38}$O$_3$	1,4-diosgadien-3-one	3β-OH→3-C=O; $\Delta^5 \to \Delta^4$; Δ^1	—	Corynebacterium simplex	—	—	N-665
H$_{40}$O$_3$	4-diosgen-3-one	3β-OH→3-C=O; $\Delta^5 \to \Delta^4$	—	Corynebacterium simplex	—	—	N-665
		3β-glycoside (dioscin)→3β-OH; 3β-OH→3-C=O; $\Delta^5 \to \Delta^4$	2	Penicillium chrysogenum	180-181.5	- 7[c]	R-781
H$_{40}$O$_5$	9-dehydromanogenin	3β-glycoside (saponin)→3β-OH	—	Aspergillus sp.	—	—	K-479
			—	Penicillium sp.	—	—	K-479
	11α-hydroxy-7-ketodiosgenin	11α-OH; 7β-OH; 7β-OH→7-C=O	5-10	Helicostylum piriforme	221-225	-137[e]	H-368
H$_{42}$O$_2$	4-cholestene-3,6-dione	3β-OH→3-C=O; $\Delta^5 \to \Delta^4$; 6-C=O	—	Mycobacterium sp.	—	—	S-930
H$_{42}$O$_3$	22α,25D-5-spirosten-3β-ol (diosgenin)	3β-glycoside (dioscin)→3β-OH	5	Aspergillus terreus	205.5-208	-118[c]	R-781
H$_{42}$O$_4$	hecogenin	3β-glycoside (saponin)→3β-OH	—	Alternaria sp.	—	—	H-351
			—	Aspergillus sp.	—	—	K-479
			—	Corynespora casaiicola	—	—	H-351
			—	Penicillium sp.	—	—	K-479
H$_{42}$O$_5$	manogenin	3β-glycoside (saponin)→3β-OH	—	Aspergillus sp.	—	—	K-479
			—	Penicillium sp.	—	—	K-479
	7β,11α-dihydroxydiosgenin	7β-OH; 11α-OH	10-15	Helicostylum piriforme	263-266	- 47[e]	H-368
H$_{43}$O$_3$N	7β-hydroxysolasodine	7β-OH	1	Helicostylum piriforme	234-238	- 82[c]	S-791
	9α-hydroxysolasodine	9α-OH	27	Helicostylum piriforme	213-215	-138[c]	S-791
	11α-hydroxysolasodine	11α-OH	1	Helicostylum piriforme	200-203	-110[c]	S-791
H$_{44}$O	5,7-cholestadien-3β-ol	Δ^7	—	Azotobacter oxydans	141-143	—	H-406; H-407
	4-cholesten-3-one	3β-OH→3-C=O; $\Delta^5 \to \Delta^4$	—	Acetobacter xylinum	80-81	+ 87	K-457
			—	Azotobacter oxydans	—	—	H-406; H-407
			—	Bacterium cyclooxydans	—	—	T-1005
			—	Corynebacterium simplex	—	—	T-1005

TABLE I

Transformations by Product

EMPIRICAL FORMULA	NAME OF REACTION PRODUCT	TRANSFORMATION	YIELD %	ORGANISM	CONSTANTS		RE
					m. p. °	$[\alpha]_D$	
$C_{27}H_{44}O$	4-cholesten-3-one	3β-OH→3-C=O; $\Delta^5 \to \Delta^4$	16-44	Corynebacterium sp.	80	—	C-13
			11-23	Flavobacterium maris	80	—	A-21 A-19 A-22 B-50
			—	Mycobacterium rhodocrous	—	—	T-10
			—	Mycobacterium sp.	—	—	S-930
			—	Nocardia sp.	—	—	T-10
			34-45	Proactinomyces erythropolis	80	—	T-10 T-10
			—	Proactinomyces roseus	—	—	K-474
			—	Streptomyces sp.	—	—	T-10
$C_{27}H_{44}O_3$	tigogenin	3β-glycoside (saponin)→3β-OH	—	Aspergillus sp.	—	—	K-47
			—	Penicillium sp.	—	—	K-479
$C_{27}H_{44}O_4$	gitogenin	3β-glycoside (saponin)→3β-OH	—	Aspergillus sp.	—	—	K-479
			—	Penicillium sp.	—	—	K-479
$C_{27}H_{44}O_5$	digitogenin	3β-glycoside (saponin)→3β-OH	—	Bacillus macerans	—	—	S-794
			—	Flavobacterium sp.	—	—	S-795
$C_{27}H_{45}O_3N$	7α-hydroxytomatidine	7α-OH	5	Helicostylum piriforme	238-242d	- 3.5[c]	S-791
	9α-hydroxytomatidine	9α-OH	$<$ 1	Helicostylum piriforme	188-191	—	S-791
$C_{27}H_{45}O_4N$	$7\alpha,11\alpha$-dihydroxytomatidine	7α-OH; 11α-OH	20	Helicostylum piriforme	266-270d	+ 23[e]	S-791
$C_{27}H_{46}O$	5β-7-cholesten-3β-ol	$\Delta^5 \to 5\beta$-H	50	"rat feces anaerobes"	104-105	+ 54.5	C-133
	5β-cholestan-3-one	3β-OH→3-C=O	21	Proactinomyces erythropolis	61	—	T-103
$C_{27}H_{46}O_2$	5-cholestene-$3\beta,7\xi$-diol	7ξ-OH	—	Proactinomyces roseus	—	—	K-474
$C_{27}H_{48}O$	5α-cholestan-3β-ol	3-C=O→3β-OH	65	Saccharomyces cerevisiae	141-142	—	M-543
	5β-cholestan-3β-ol	$\Delta^5 \to 5\beta$-H	74	"rat feces anaerobes"	—	—	C-133
			—	fecal bacteria	99-101	—	S-914
$C_{28}H_{33}O_6P$	$16\alpha,17\alpha$-dihydroxy-6β-methyl-1,4-pregnadiene-3,20-dione 16,17-(phenyl cyclophosphate)	Δ^1	—	Bacterium cyclooxydans	—	—	F-259

TABLE I

Transformations by Product

EMPIRICAL FORMULA	NAME OF REACTION PRODUCT	TRANSFORMATION	YIELD %	ORGANISM	CONSTANTS m.p.°	$[\alpha]_D$	REF.
$C_{29}H_{35}O_6Cl$	6α-chloro-11α,16α,17α,21-tetrahydroxy-4-pregnene-3,20-dione 16,17-acetophenonide	11α-OH	—	Trichothecium roseum	—		D-159
$C_{29}H_{44}O_8$	3β,14β-dihydroxy-5β-20(22)-cardenolide 3-(L-rhamnoside)	2'-OAc→2'-OH; 3'-OAc→3'-OH; 4'-OAc→4'-OH	14	Fusarium lini	212-221	—	T-978
$C_{29}H_{46}O$	4,22-stigmastadien-3-one	3β-OH→3-C=O; $\Delta^5 \to \Delta^4$	19	Proactinomyces erythropolis	125	—	T-1032
$C_{29}H_{48}O$	4-stigmasten-3-one	3β-OH→3-C=O; $\Delta^5 \to \Delta^4$	36	Proactinomyces erythropolis	83	—	T-1032
$C_{29}H_{52}O$	5β-stigmastan-3β-ol	$\Delta^5 \to 5\beta$-H	66	"rat feces anaerobes"	126-127	+ 23	C-133
$C_{30}H_{34}O_7ClP$	12α-chloro-11β,16α,17α,21-tetrahydroxy-1,4-pregnadiene-3,20-dione 16,17-(benzyl cyclophosphonate) 21-acetate	Δ^1	—	Bacterium cyclooxydans	—	—	F-263
$C_{30}H_{46}O_7$	3β,14β-dihydroxy-5β-20(22)-cardenolide 3-[D-cymaroside]	4'-OAc→4'-OH	40	Fusarium lini	186-197	—	T-978
		digitoxigenin-3-[D-glucosyl-D-glucosyl-D-cymaroside]→digitoxigenin-3-[D-cymaroside]	28	Fusarium lini	188-200; 140-158	—	T-978
$C_{30}H_{44}O_9$	3β,5β,14β-trihydroxy-19-oxo-20(22)-cardenolide 3-[D-cymaroside]	strophanthidin-3-[heptaacetyl-D-glucosyl-D-glucosyl-D-cymaroside]→strophanthidin 3-[D-cymaroside]	52	Fusarium lini	131-133	—	T-978
$C_{30}H_{46}O_8$	3β,14β,16β-trihydroxy-5β-20(22)-cardenolide 3-[D-cymaroside]	4'-OAc→4-OH; 16β-OAc→16β-OH	3	Fusarium lini	154-195	—	T-978
$C_{32}H_{48}O_9$	3β,14β,16β-trihydroxy-5β-20(22)-cardenolide 3-[D-cymaroside] 16-acetate	4'-OAc→4'-OH	47	Fusarium lini	187-207	—	T-978
$C_{36}H_{54}O_{14}$	3β,5β,14β-trihydroxy-19-oxo-20(22)-cardenolide 3-[D-glucosyl-D-cymaroside]	D-glucosyl-D-cymaroside tetracetate→D-glucosyl-D-cymaroside	4	Fusarium lini	—	—	T-978
$C_{41}H_{64}O_{13}$	3β,14β-dihydroxy-5β-20(22)-cardenolide 3-[digitoxosyl-digitoxosyl-digitoxoside] (digitoxin)	digitoxosyl-digitoxosyl-digitoxoside tetraacetate→digitoxosyl-digitoxosyl-digitoxoside	18-100	Fusarium lini	247-250	—	T-978; G-320
		glucosyl-digitoxosyl-digitoxosyl-digitoxoside→digitoxosyl-digitoxosyl-digitoxoside	5-95	Aspergillus sp.	—	—	S-936a
			30-60	Claviceps purpurea	—	—	S-936a
			20	Paecilomyces sp.	—	—	S-936a
			5-95	Penicillium sp.	—	—	S-936a

CHAPTER IV

TAXONOMY

SYSTEM OF CLASSIFICATION

The system of classification used here is designed as an aid to determine the taxonomic position and relationships of the genera, active and inactive, that have been used for the transformations of steroids.

Generally, the same groupings or categories have been used for classifications of bacteria and fungi as have been used for plants. For example,

Kingdom: Plant

Phylum: Fungi (Eumycophyta); typically filamentous organisms lacking chlorophyll (depend for their food either directly or indirectly on green plants)

Class: Ascomycetes; ultimate reproductive spores produced *internally* in a saclike cell called ascus. Mycelium septate

Basidiomycetes; ultimate reproductive spores produced *externally* upon a special organ called basidium. Mycelium septate

Phycomycetes; mycelium usually aseptate and multinucleate

Fungi Imperfecti (Deuteromycetes); artificial grouping of fungi whose sexual stages are not known. They are the imperfect stages of the Ascomycetes and Basidiomycetes

Schizomycetes; true bacteria, single cell, reproduction by fission

Order: Subunit of Class

Family: Subunit of Order

Genus: Subunit of Family

Species: Subunit of Genus (may be further broken down into varieties, strains, and physiological or cultural races)

The classes, orders, families, genera, and species in the various tables are listed alphabetically for convenience and, therefore, may not be in the same sequence as would be found in various published systems of taxonomy.

Table II is a taxonomic listing for reference purposes containing all cultures reported in the literature and U.S. patents through January, 1964. This spectrum of genera encompasses all five classes of microorganisms, the Ascomycetes, Basidiomycetes, Fungi Imperfecti, Phycomycetes, and Schizomycetes, twenty-three out of 49 major orders, 292 different genera, and 1216 different species.

The most widely screened taxonomic class has been the Fungi Imperfecti. In fact, this is the only class in which all of the orders within a class (four) have been studied. One hundred eleven of the 292 genera listed in Table II and five hundred thirty-four of the 1216 species are members of the Fungi Imperfecti.

The tabulation entitled "Classes and Major Orders of Fungi and Bacteria" reported to transform steroids shows that this ability is rather widespread in the microbial world.

This is further emphasized in tabulations entitled "Hydroxylation — Taxonomic Distribution According to Order" and "Hydroxylation — Taxonomic Distribution According to Genus," as well as the distribution of cultures capable of Δ^1- dehydrogenation classified to taxonomic order and genus.

As a result, it is quite difficult to draw taxonomic inferences of major significance at the class or order level.

The differences observed at the genus, species, or strain levels are governed more by the nature of the substrates and the environmental conditions of growth than by taxonomic considerations. These differences can be selected readily by checking the species of the genus in question in Table III "Transformation by Genus."

Of the reported cultures, the group with the narrowest spectrum of activity appears to be the yeasts. Only two genera (of 19 tested), *Saccharomyces* and *Rhodotorula*, showed any activity and this was limited to their ability to reduce ketones to hydroxyl groups and to reduce double bonds.

An extensive discussion of the reactions listed in the aforementioned taxonomic tables is presented in the section on chemical transformations in Chapter II.

Classes and Major Orders of Fungi and Bacteria [*],[†]

Ascomycetes		Fungi Imperfecti (Deuteromycetes)	
Dothideales	0		
Endomycetales	+	Melanconiales	+
Erysiphales	0	Moniliales	+
Eurotiales	+	Mycelia Sterilia	+
Helotiales	+	Sphaeropsidales	+
Hemisphaeriales	0		
Hypocreales	+	Phycomycetes	
Hysteriales	0		
Laboulbeniales	0	Blastocladiales	0
Myriangiales	+	Chytridiales	0
Pezizales	+	Entomophthorales	+
Phacidiales	0	Hyphochytriales	0
Sphaeriales	+	Lagenidiales	0
Taphrinales	+	Leptomitales	0
Tuberales	+	Monoblepharidales	0
		Mucorales	+
Basidiomycetes		Peronosporales	+
		Plasmodiophorales	0
Agaricales	+	Saprolegniales	0
Hymenogastrales	0		
Lycoperdales	+	Schizomycetes	
Nidulariales	0		
Phallales	0	Actinomycetales	+
Sclerodermatales	0	Beggiatoales	0
Tremellales	+	Caryophanales	0
Uredinales	0	Chlamydobacteriales	0
Ustilaginales	+	Eubacteriales	+
		Hyphomicrobiales	0
		Mycoplasmatales	0
		Myxobacteriales	0
		Pseudomonadales	+
		Spirochaetales	0

[*] Arranged alphabetically. +, Reported to transform steroids; 0, not mentioned.

[†] Other taxonomic groups which have been reported to transform: algae (Chlorophyta), Order: Chlorococcales; plants (Spermatophyta), Orders: Liliiflorae, Rosales; protozoa (Mastigophora), Orders: Euglenoidina, Polymastigina.

Hydroxylation – Taxonomic Distribution According to Order

Class and Order	1 α	1 β	2 α	2 β	5 α	5 β	6 α	6 β	7 α	7 β	8 α	8 β	9 α	9 β	10 α	10 β	11 α	11 β	12 α	12 β	14 α	14 β	15 α	15 β	16 α	16 β	17 α	17 β	18	19	21
Ascomycetes																															
Eurotiales								*										*										*			*
Helotiales																		*						*		*	*				
Hypocreales								*	*								*			*				*		*		*			
Pezizales									*	*								*													
Sphaeriales		*		*				*	*	*			*					*				*	*	*	*		*				*
Basidiomycetes																															
Agaricales				*				*		*				*				*		*		*		*		*				*	
Fungi Imperfecti (Deuteromycetes)																															
Melanconiales	*							*	*				*				*		*		*		*		*				*		
Moniliales		*		*				*	*	*		*	*		*		*		*	*	*		*		*		*		*		
Mycelia Sterilia		*						*		*			*				*			*	*		*		*		*				
Sphaeropsidales		*						*	*	*			*				*			*	*		*		*						*
Phycomycetes																															
Entomophthorales				*				*	*				*				*		*												
Mucorales		*		*	*			*	*				*		*		*			*				*	*						
Peronosporales						*												*													
Schizomycetes																															
Actinomycetales	*		*					*		*			*				*				*		*		*						*
Eubacteriales		*		*	*			*					*				*					*		*		*					
Pseudomonadales														*				*													

Hydroxylation - Taxonomic Distribution According to Genus

Position and class	Order	Genus
1α-OH		
Ascomycetes	–	–
Basidiomycetes	–	–
Fungi Imperfecti (Deuteromycetes)	Moniliales	Penicillium
Phycomycetes	–	–
Schizomycetes	Actinomycetales	Nocardia
1β-OH		
Ascomycetes	Sphaeriales	Gnomonia Xylaria
Basidiomycetes	–	–
Fungi Imperfecti (Deuteromycetes)	Moniliales	Cladosporium
	Mycelia Sterilia	Rhizoctonia Sclerotium
	Sphaeropsidales	Haplosporella
Phycomycetes	Mucorales	Absidia Cunninghamella Mortierella
Schizomycetes	Actinomycetales	Streptomyces
	Eubacteriales	Corynebacterium
2α-OH		
Ascomycetes	–	–
Basidiomycetes	–	–
Fungi Imperfecti (Deuteromycetes)	–	–
Phycomycetes	–	–
Schizomycetes	Actinomycetales	Nocardia
2β-OH		
Ascomycetes	Sphaeriales	Diaporthe Gnomonia Pyrenophora Sclerotinia
Basidiomycetes	Agaricales	Corticium
Fungi Imperfecti (Deuteromycetes)	Moniliales	Botrytis Helminthosporium Macrosporium Penicillium Rhizoctonia Thyrospora
Phycomycetes	Entomophthorales	Conidiobolus
	Mucorales	Absidia
Schizomycetes	Actinomycetales	Streptomyces
	Eubacteriales	Bacillus Escherichia Serratia

Hydroxylation – Taxonomic Distribution According to Genus (continued)

Position and class	Order	Genus
5α-OH		
Ascomycetes	–	–
Basidiomycetes	–	–
Fungi Imperfecti (Deuteromycetes)	–	–
Phycomycetes	Mucorales	Cokeromyces
Schizomycetes	–	–
5β-OH		
Ascomycetes	–	–
Basidiomycetes	–	–
Fungi Imperfecti (Deuteromycetes)	–	–
Phycomycetes	Mucorales	Absidia Cunninghamella Mucor Rhizopus
Schizomycetes	–	–
6α-OH		
Ascomycetes	–	–
Basidiomycetes	–	–
Fungi Imperfecti (Deuteromycetes)	–	–
Phycomycetes	–	–
Schizomycetes	–	–
6β-OH		
Ascomycetes	Eurotiales Hypocreales Sphaeriales	Thielavia Cordyceps Gibberella Chaetomium Cochliobolus Daldinia Glomerella Ophiobolus Pyrenophora Xylaria
Basidiomycetes	Agaricales	Boletus Clavaria Coriolus Corticium Dermoloma Hydrophorus Irpex Lenzites Leucopaxillus Naematoloma Naucoria

Hydroxylation – Taxonomic Distribution According to Genus (continued)

Position and class	Order	Genus
6β-OH (continued)		
Basidiomycetes	Agaricales	Pellicularia
		Polyporus
		Polystictus
		Poria
Fungi Imperfecti (Deuteromycetes)	Melanconiales	Colletotrichum
		Gloesporium
	Moniliales	Acrostalagmus
		Arthrobotrys
		Aspergillus
		Botrytis
		Cephalothecium
		Curvularia
		Fusarium
		Gliocladium
		Helminthosporium
		Hyalopus
		Isaria
		Nigrospora
		Penicillium
		Piricularia
		Stysanus
		Tricoderma
		Tricophyton
		Tricothecium
		Virticillium
	Mycelia Sterilia	Rhizoctonia
		Sclerotium
	Sphaeropsidales	Coniothyrium
		Haplosporella
		Phoma
		Wojnowicia
Phycomycetes	Entomophthorales	Basidiobolus
	Mucorales	Absidia
		Blakeslea
		Chaetocladium
		Choanephora
		Circinella
		Cokeromyces
		Cunninghamella
		Helicostylum
		Mortierella
		Mucor
		Phycomycetes
		Rhizopus
		Syncephalastrum
		Thamnidium
		Zygorhynchus
Schizomycetes	Actinomycetales	Actinoplanes
		Streptomyces
	Eubacteriales	Achromobacter
		Bacillus

Hydroxylation – Taxonomic Distribution According to Genus (continued)

Position and class	Order	Genus
7α-OH		
Ascomycetes	Pezizales	Peziza
	Sphaeriales	Glasinospora
		Glomerella
		Neurospora
Basidiomycetes	–	–
Fungi Imperfecti	Moniliales	Aspergillus
(Deuteromycetes)		Curvularia
		Fusidium
		Helminthosporium
	Sphaeropsidales	Coniothyrium
		Diplodia
Phycomycetes	Mucorales	Helicostylum
		Mucor
		Phycomyces
		Rhizopus
Schizomycetes	–	–
7β-OH		
Ascomycetes	Sphaeriales	Xylaria
Basidiomycetes	Agaricales	Psilocybe
Fungi Imperfecti	Moniliales	Aspergillus
(Deuteromycetes)		Cephalosporium
		Cladosporium
		Penicillium
		Tricothecium
	Mycelia Sterilia	Rhizoctonia
	Sphaeropsidales	Diplodia
		Haplosporella
Phycomycetes	Mucorales	Absidia
		Cunninghamella
		Helicostylum
		Mucor
		Rhizopus
		Syncephalastrum
Schizomycetes	Actinomycetales	Proactinomyces
		(Nocardia)
		Streptomyces
8β-OH		
Ascomycetes	–	–
Basidiomycetes	–	–
Fungi Imperfecti	Moniliales	Cercospora
(Deuteromycetes)		
Phycomycetes	–	–
Schizomycetes	–	–
9α-OH		
Ascomycetes	Sphaeriales	Neurospora
Basidiomycetes	–	–

Hydroxylation –Taxonomic Distribution According to Genus (continued)

Position and class	Order	Genus
9α-OH (continued)		
Fungi Imperfecti (Deuteromycetes)	Moniliales	Cercospora
		Curvularia
		Cylindrocarpon
	Sphaeropsidales	Ascochyta
Phycomycetes	Mucorales	Absidia
		Circinella
		Cunninghamella
		Helicostylum
		Mucor
Schizomycetes	Actinomycetales	Mycobacterium
		Nocardia
		Streptomyces
	Eubacteriales	Arthrobacter
		Bacterium
		Corynebacterium
	Pseudomonadales	Pseudomonas
9β-OH		
Ascomycetes	–	–
Basidiomycetes	–	–
Fungi Imperfecti (Deuteromycetes)	–	–
Phycomycetes	–	–
Schizomycetes	–	–
10β-OH		
Ascomycetes	–	–
Basidiomycetes	–	–
Fungi Imperfecti (Deuteromycetes)	Moniliales	Botrytis
		Curvularia
		Helminthosporium
Phycomycetes	Mucorales	Rhizopus
Schizomycetes	–	–
11α-OH		
Ascomycetes	Eurotiales	Carpenteles
	Helotiales	Sclerotinia
	Hypocreales	Calonectria
		Cordyceps
	Pezizales	Pyrenema
	Sphaeriales	Chaetomium
		Cochliobolus
		Daldinia
		Didymella
		Glomerella
		Guignardia
		Ophiobolus
		Pyrenophora
		Xylaria

Hydroxylation—Taxonomic Distribution According to Genus (continued)

Position and class	Order	Genus
11α-OH (continued)		
Basidiomycetes	Agariales	Boletus
		Clavaria
		Conocybe
		Corticium
		Cortinellus
		Dermoloma
		Ganoderma
		Hygrophorus
		Leucopaxillus
		Pellicularia
		Polyporus
		Polystictus
		Psilocybe
		Stropharia
Fungi Imperfecti (Deuteromycetes)	Melanconiales	Colletotrichum
		Coryneum
		Gloesporium
		Pestalotia
	Moniliales	Acrostalagmus
		Arthrobotrys
		Aspergillus
		Beauvaria
		Botrytis
		Candelospora
		Cephalothecium
		Cercospora
		Cladosarum
		Dactylium
		Didymocladium
		Fusarium
		Helminthosporium
		Hyalopus
		Isaria
		Metarrhizium
		Mycogone
		Myrothecium
		Nigrospora
		Penicillium
		Piricularia
		Scopulariopsis
		Spicaria
		Sportrichum
		Stachylidium
		Stysanus
		Tricoderma
		Trichophton
		Trichothecium
		Verticillium
	Mycelia Sterilia	Rhacodium
		Rhizoctonia
		Sclerotium

Hydroxylation – Taxonomic Distribution According to Genus (continued)

Position and class	Order	Genus
11α-OH (continued)		
Fungi Imperfecti (Deuteromycetes)	Sphaeropsidales	Botryodiplodia
		Coniothyrium
		Diplodia
		Phoma
		Phomopsis
		Wojnowicia
Phycomycetes	Entomophthorales	Basidiobolus
		Conidiobolus
		Entomophthora
	Mucorales	Absidia
		Blakeslea
		Choanephora
		Circinella
		Cunninghamella
		Lichtheimia
		Mucor
		Mycocladus
		Phycomyces
		Rhizopus
		Syncephalastrum
		Thamnidium
		Tieghemella
		Zygorhynchus
Schizomycetes	Eubacteriales	Achromobacter
		Bacillus
		Escherichia
11β-OH		
Ascomycetes	Helotiales	Sclerotinia
Basidiomycetes	Agaricales	Corticium
		Omphalia
		Pellicularia
Fungi Imperfecti (Deuteromycetes)	Melanconiales	Colletotrichium
	Moniliales	Arthrobotrys
		Botrytis
		Cercospora
		Curvularia
		Epicoccum
		Isaria
		Penicillium
		Spicaria
		Spondylocladium
		Stachylidium
		Stigmina
		Tricophyton
		Tricothecium
		Verticillium
	Mycelia Sterilia	Rhizoctonia
		Sclerotium

Hydroxylation – Taxonomic Distribution According to Genus (continued)

Position and class	Order	Genus
11β-OH (continued)		
Fungi Imperfecti (Deuteromycetes)	Sphaeropsidales	Chaetomella
		Coniothyrium
		Dothichiza
		Phoma
		Pycnosporium
		Rhodoseptoria
Phycomycetes	Mucorales	Absidia
		Blakeslea
		Choanephora
		Circinella
		Cunninghamella
		Lichtheimia
		Rhizopus
		Syncephalastrum
		Thamnidium
		Tieghemella
	Peronosporales	Pythium
Schizomycetes	Actinomycetales	Streptomyces
	Eubacteriales	Bacillus
		Escherichia
		Proteus
	Pseudomonadales	Pseudomonas
12α-OH		
Ascomycetes	–	–
Basidiomycetes	–	–
Fungi Imperfecti (Deuteromycetes)	Melanconiales	Colletotrichum
	Moniliales	Aspergillus
		Cercospora
	Sphaeropsidales	Wojnowicia
Phycomycetes	Mucorales	Thamnidium
Schizomycetes	–	–
12β-OH		
Ascomycetes	Hypocreales	Calonectria
		Gibberella
Basidiomycetes	Agaricales	Psilocybe
Fungi Imperfecti (Deuteromycetes)	Melanconiales	Colletotrichum
	Moniliales	Fusarium
		Nigrospora
		Tricothecium
	Sphaeropsidales	Coniothyrium
Phycomycetes	Mucorales	Helicostylum
Schizomycetes	–	–
14α-OH		
Ascomycetes	Sphaeriales	Pleospora

Hydroxylation – Taxonomic Distribution According to Genus (continued)

Position	Order	Genus
14α-OH (continued)		
Basidiomycetes	Agaricales	Coriolus
		Naematoloma
		Pellicularia
		Polyporus
		Poria
Fungi Imperfecti (Deuteromycetes)	Moniliales	Cercospora
		Chrysosporium
		Curvularia
		Helminthosporium
		Stachylidium
		Stemphylium
		Tricothecium
	Sphaeropsidales	Wojnowicia
Phycomycetes	Mucorales	Absidia
		Circinella
		Cunninghamella
		Helicostylum
		Mucor
		Syncephalastrum
Schizomycetes	Actinomycetales	Mycobacterium
	Eubacteriales	Achromobacter
		Bacillus
15α-OH		
Ascomycetes	Hypocreales	Calonectria
		Gibberella
	Sphaeriales	Glomerella
Basidiomycetes	Agaricales	Hypholoma
Fungi Imperfecti (Deuteromycetes)	Melanconiales	Colletotrichum
	Moniliales	Aspergillus
		Curvularia
		Fusarium
		Helminthosporium
		Hormodendrum
		Nigrospora
		Penicillium
	Mycelia Sterilia	Rhizoctonia
Phycomycetes	Mucorales	Rhizopus
Schizomycetes	Actinomycetales	Streptomyces
15β-OH		
Ascomycetes	Helotiales	Sclerotinia
	Sphaeriales	Xylaria

Hydroxylation – Taxonomic Distribution According to Genus (continued)

Position	Order	Genus
15β-OH (continued)		
Basidiomycetes	Agaricales	Coriolus
		Lenzites
		Polyporus
		Poria
Fungi Imperfecti	Moniliales	Botrytis
(Deuteromycetes)		Cercospora
		Crinsporium
		Helminthosporium
		Penicillium
		Spicaria
	Mycelia Sterilia	Sclerotium
	Sphaeropsidales	Diplodia
		Phoma
Phycomycetes	Mucorales	Absidia
		Phycomyces
		Syncephalastrum
Schizomycetes	Eubacteriales	Bacillus
16α-OH		
Ascomycetes	Hypocreales	Hypomyces
	Sphaeriales	Didymella
		Gnomonia
		Mycosphaerella
Basidiomycetes	–	
Fungi Imperfecti	Melanconiales	Pestalotia
(Deuteromycetes)	Moniliales	Cephalosporium
		Sepedonium
	Sphaeropsidales	Staganospora
		Staurophoma
		Wojnowicia
Phycomycetes	–	–
Schizomycetes	Actinomycetales	Nocardia
		Streptomyces
	Eubacteriales	Bacillus
16β-OH		
Ascomycetes	Helotiales	Sclerotium
Basidiomycetes	Agaricales	Corticium
Fungi Imperfecti	Melanconiales	Colletotrichum
(Deuteromycetes)	Moniliales	Cephalosporium
		Curvularia
	Sphaeropsidales	Wojnowicia
Phycomycetes	Mucorales	Cunninghamella
		Helicostylum
Schizomycetes	Eubacteriales	Bacillus

Hydroxylation – Taxonomic Distribution According to Genus (continued)

Position	Order	Genus
<u>17α-OH</u>		
Ascomycetes	Eurotiales	Thielavia
	Hypocreales	Melanospora
	Sphaeriales	Cucurbitaria
		Leptosphaeria
		Lophotrichus
		Sporormia
Basidiomycetes	Agaricales	Naucoria
Fungi Imperfecti	Moniliales	Acrospeira
(Deuteromycetes)		Aspergillus
		Cephalothecium
		Dactylium
		Scopulariopsis
		Sepedonium
		Tricoderma
		Tricothecium
Phycomycetes	–	–
Schizomycetes	–	–
<u>18-OH</u>		
Ascomycetes	–	–
Basidiomycetes	–	–
Fungi Imperfecti	Moniliales	Cercospora
(Deuteromycetes)		
Phycomycetes	–	–
Schizomycetes	–	–
<u>19-OH</u>		
Ascomycetes	–	–
Basidiomycetes	Agaricales	Corticium
		Hypochnus
		Pellicularia
Fungi Imperfecti	–	–
(Deuteromycetes)		
Phycomycetes	–	–
Schizomycetes	–	–
<u>21-OH</u>		
Ascomycetes	Helotiales	Schlerotinia
	Sphaeriales	Ophiobolus
Basidiomycetes	Agaricales	Psilocybe

Hydroxylation – Taxonomic Distribution According to Genus (continued)

Position and class	Order	Genus
21-OH (continued)		
Fungi Imperfecti (Deuteromycetes)	Melanconiales	Colletotrichum
	Moniliales	Aspergillus
		Cercosporella
		Kabatiella
	Sphaeropsidales	Coniothyrium
		Hendersonia
		Wojnowicia
Phycomycetes	–	–
Schizomycetes	–	–

Δ^1-Dehydrogenation – Taxonomic Distribution According to Genus

Class	Order	Genus
Ascomycetes	Hypocreales	Calonectria Hypomyces
	Sphaeriales	Chaetomium Didymella Ophiobolus
Basidiomycetes	Agaricales	Corticium Stereum
	Ustilaginales	Graphicola
Fungi Imperfecti (Deuteromycetes)	Melanconiales	Gloeosporium Septomyxa
	Moniliales	Alternaria Cylindrocarpon Fusarium Gliocladium Helminthosporium Ramularia Volutella
	Mycelia Sterilia	Rhizoctonia
	Sphaeropsidales	Pycnodothis
Phycomycetes	Mucorales	Absidia
Schizomycetes	Actinomycetales	Actinoplanes Micromonospora Mycobacterium Mycococcus Nocardia
	Eubacteriales	Aerobacter Arthrobacter Azotobacter Bacillus Bacterium Corynebacterium Flavobacterium Micrococcus Serratia
	Pseudomonadales	Acetobacter Azotomonas Protaminobacter Pseudomonas Xanthomonas
Spermatophyta (plant)	Liliiflorae	Sansevieria
Zoomastigina (protozoa) [Mastigophora]	Polymastigina	Trichomonas

TABLE II

Taxonomy to Species

CLASS	ORDER	FAMILY	GENUS	SPECIES
scomycetes	Endomycetales	Endomycetaceae	Byssochlamys	nivea
			Debaryomyces	hansenii
			Dilplodasus	albidus
			Endomyces	lindneri
			Eremascus	albus
			Eremothecium	ashbyii
			Hansenula	anomala
			Nadsonia	fulvescens
			Pichia	membranaefaciens
			Saccharomycodes	ludwigii
			Schizosaccharomyces	octosporus
		Saccharomycetaceae	Histoplasma	capsulatum
			Saccharomyces	cerevisiae ellipsoideus fragilis lactis pastorianus
	Eurotiales	Eurotiaceae	Allescheria	boidii
			Thielavia	basicola terricola
		Gymnoscaceae	Carpenteles	javanicus
	Helotiales	Helotiaceae	Sclerotinia	allii fructicola fluctigena libertiana sclerotiorum
	Hypocreales	Hypocreaceae	Calonectria	decora
			Cordyceps	militaris
			Gibberella	baccata cyanea fujikuroi saubinetti zeae
			Hypomyces	aurantius haematococcus solani
			Melanospora	parasitica
			Neocosmospora	vasinfecta
	Myriangiales	Myriangiaceae	Elsinoe	ampelina fawcetti

238

TABLE II

Taxonomy to Species

CLASS	ORDER	FAMILY	GENUS	SPECIES
Ascomycetes	Pezizales	Hellvellaceae	Morchella	crassipes
		Pezizaceae	Peziza	species
			Pyronema	confluens
	Sphaeriales	Ceratostomaceae	Ceratostomella	fimbriate (fimbriata)
		Chaetomiaceae	Chaetomium	cochloides funicolum globosum species succineum
		Fimetariaceae	Neurospora	crassa sitophila species
		Sphaeriaceae	Cochliobolus	miyabeanus
			Cucurbitaria	laburni
			Daldinia	concentria (concentrica)
			Diaporthe	numurai
			Didymella	lycopersici vodakii
			Gelasinospora	tetraspora
			Glomerella	cingulata fluctigena fusaroides glycines gosypii (gossypii) lagenarium major mume phacidiomorpha rubicola
			Gnomonia	cingulata errabunda erythrostoma fimicola fragariae
			Guignardi	camelliae
			Leptosphaeria	maculans
			Lophotrichus	martini
			Mycosphaerella	horii latebrosa
			Ophiobolus	graminis herpotrichus heterostrophus

TABLE II

Taxonomy to Species

CLASS	ORDER	FAMILY	GENUS	SPECIES
Ascomycetes	Sphaeriales	Sphaeriaceae	Ophiobolus	miyabeanus sativus species
			Ophiostoma	catanianum
			Pleospora	gaeumanni
			Pyrenophora	greminea
			Rossellinia	necatrix
			Sordaria	species
			Spororrmia	fasciculata leporina minima montana pollaccii
			Venturia	pirma (pirina)
			Xylaria	polymorpha species
	Taphrinales	Taphrinaceae	Taphrina	deformans pruni
Basidiomycetes	Agaricales	Agaricaceae	Agaricus	campestris edulis rodmanii
			Agrocybe	acericola
			Amanita	muscaria porphyria
			Armillaria	mellae
			Cantharellus	cibarius
			Clitocybe	adirondackensis clavipes odora species
			Collybia	dryophila velutipes
			Conocybe	siligenoides
			Coprinus	atromentarius (atramentarius) sobiliferus
			Cortinarius	evernius
			Cortinellus	shiitake
			Dermoloma	species

TABLE II

Taxonomy to Species

CLASS	ORDER	FAMILY	GENUS	SPECIES
Basidiomycetes	Agaricales	Agaricaceae	Gymnopilus	junenius species
			Hebeloma	sinapizans
			Hygrophorus	conicus
			Hypholoma	species
			Lentinus	vulpinus
			Lentodium	squamosum
			Lepiota	molybdites naucina procera rachodes
			Leucopaxillus	paradoxus
			Lyophyllum	aggregatum
			Marasmius	siccus
			Mycena	strobilinoides
			Naematoloma	sublateratium
			Naucoria	confragosa
			Omphalia	tralucida
			Panaeolus	papilionaceus
			Panellus	stipticus
			Paxillus	involutus vernalis
			Pholiota	adiposa squarrosoides
			Pleurotus	japonicus ostreatus
			Pluteus	granularis
			Psilocybe	caerulescens caerulipes mexicana semperviva
			Russula	delicans
			Schizophyllum	commune
			Stropharia	cubensis normandii

TABLE II

Taxonomy to Species

CLASS	ORDER	FAMILY	GENUS	SPECIES
Basidiomycetes	Agaricales	Agaricaceae	Tricholoma	nudum species
			Tubaria	conspersa
			Xeromphalina	tenuipes
		Boletaceae	Boletinus	pictus
			Boletus	acidus americanus luteus
		Clavariaceae	Clavaria	mucida
		Hydnaceae	Echinodontium	tsugicola
			Irpex	consors lacteus
		Hypochnaceae	Hypochnus	centrifugum sasaki
		Polyporaceae	Coriolus	versicolor
			Fomes	pinicola robstus species
			Ganoderma	applam (applanatum)
			Lenzites	abietina bebulina (betulina) styracina
			Polyporus	abietinus brumalis caeruleoporus cinnabarinus conchifer frondosus pubescens radicata squamosus sulphureus tulipiferus
			Polystictus	cinnabarius hirstus polyzonus sanguineus versicola versicolorpus
			Poria	cocos species vaporaria
			Trametes	dickinsii pini

TABLE II

Taxonomy to Species

CLASS	ORDER	FAMILY	GENUS	SPECIES
Basidiomycetes	Agaricales	Thelephoraceae	Corticium	centrifugum centrifugus graminum microsclerotia practicola roefsii salmonicolar sasakii solani species vagium vagum
			Pellicularia	filamentosa
			Stereum	fasciatum induratum
			Tomentella	species
	Lycoperdales	Lycoperdaceae	Lycoperdon	umbrinum
	Tremellales	Auriculariaceae	Helicobasidium	mompa
	Ustilaginales	Graphiolaceae	Graphiola	cylindrica
		Ustilaginaceae	Ustilago	zeae
Fungi Imperfecti (Deuteromycetes)	Melanconiales	Melanconiaceae	Colletotrichum	antirrhini derridis gloeosporioides lindemuthianum phomoides pisi species
			Coryneum	cardinale
			Gloeosporium	cyclaminis foliicolum kaki laeticola olivarum
			Pestalotia	diospyri foedans funerea royenae
			Septomyxa	aesculi affinis corni salicina tulasuei
			Sphaceloma	species

TABLE II

Taxonomy to Species

CLASS	ORDER	FAMILY	GENUS	SPECIES
Fungi Imperfecti (Deuteromycetes)	Moniliales	Cryptococcaceae	Candida	guilliermondii krusei pulcherrima utilis
			Parendomyces	asteroides
			Pseudomycoderma	miso
			Tilletiopsis	lilacina
		Dematiaceae	Acrospeira	levis
			Alternaria	bataticola citri kikutiana passiflorae species
			Cercospora	apii baticola calotropidis canescens chenopodii cladosporioides cruenta diazu fusca hibsci-cannabini italica kaki kikuchii lagenarum macrospora malvacearum medicaginis melongenae melonis musae musarum nicotianae oryzae rosicola scirpicola sesami taiwanensis vaginae violae zebrina zinniae
			Chalara	mycoderma
			Cladosporium	cladosporiodes fulvam (fulvum) herbarum resinae species
			Corynespora	casaiicoli

TABLE II

Taxonomy to Species

CLASS	ORDER	FAMILY	GENUS	SPECIES
Fungi Imperfecti (Deuteromycetes)	Moniliales	Dematiaceae	Curvularia	brachyspora falcata fallax geniculata inaequalis lunata maculans oryzae pallescens species tetramera trifolii uncinata
			Cylindrocephalum	aureum
			Dematium	pullulans
			Fumago	species
			Fusicladium	diospiri
			Helicoceras	oryzae
			Helminthosporium	avenae brizae buchloes coices (coicis) gramineum irregulare kusanoi leersii leptochloae maydis nodulosum oryzae panici-meliacei (miliacei) sativum setariae sigmoideum species teres tritici-vulgaris turcicum velurinam (velutinum) zizaniae zonatum
			Hemispora	rogosa
			Hormodendrum	olivaceum pedrosoi viride
			Humicola	grisea (grisae)
			Macrosporium	bataticola
			Margarinomyces	species

TABLE II

Taxonomy to Species

CLASS	ORDER	FAMILY	GENUS	SPECIES
ungi Imperfecti (Deuteromycetes)	Moniliales	Dematiaceae	Nigrospora	oryzae species sphaerica
			Phialophora	verrucosa
			Pullularia	pullulans species
			Spondylocladium	australe xylogenum
			Stachybotrys	species
			Stachylidium	bicolor theobromae
			Stemphylium	botryosum species
			Stigmina	platani
			Thyrospora	astragali
		"Dermatophytes"	Epidermophyton	floccasum
		Moniliaceae	Acremonium	potronii
			Acrostalagmus	albus
			Arthrobotrys	conoides dactyloides musiformis superba
			Aspergillus	aculeatus alliaceus amstelodami asperescens astianus atropurpureus aureus auricomus avenaceus awamori batatae brevipes butyracea caesiellus caespitosus candidus carbonarius carneus chevalieri cinnamomeus citri citrisporus clavatus conicus echinulatus effusus elegans fischeri

246

TABLE II

Taxonomy to Species

CLASS	ORDER	FAMILY	GENUS	SPECIES
Fungi Imperfecti (Deuteromycetes)	Moniliales	Moniliaceae	Aspergillus	flavipes flavus fonsecaeus fumigatus giganteus glaucus gracilis gymnosardae herbariorum inuii itaconicus janus japonicus kanagaw-aensis kawachii luchuensis mangini melleus minimus (minutus) miyakoensis mollis montevidensis nakazawai nidulans niger niveo-glaucus niveus ochraceus oryzae ostianus panamensis parasiticus penicilloides phoenicis proliferans pseudoglaucus pulverulentus quadrilineatus rehmii repens restrictus ruber rugulosus saitoi sclerotiorum sojae sparsus species sulphureus sydowi tamarii terreus terricola unguis usamii ustus varians variecolor versicolor violaceo-fuscus wentii

TABLE II

Taxonomy to Species

CLASS	ORDER	FAMILY	GENUS	SPECIES
ungi Imperfecti Deuteromycetes)	Moniliales	Moniliaceae	Beauveria	bassiana species
			Botrytis	cinerea fabae paeoniae reptons spectabilis species
			Candelospora	penicilloides
			Cephalosporium	acremonium asperum species subverticillatum
			Cephalothecium	roseum
			Cercosporella	herpotrichoides
			Chrysosporium	luteium
			Cladosarum	olivaceus (olivaceum)
			Corethropsis	hominis
			Crinsporium	panorum
			Dactylium	dendroides
			Didymocladium	ternatum
			Fusidium	species
			Geotrichum	lactis
			Gliocladium	catenulatum deliquescens luteolum roseum species
			Hyalopus	nopporoensis
			Metarrhizium	anisopliae species
			Monilia	species
			Monosporium	apiospermum
			Mycogone	jaepii
			Oidium	species
			Oospora	aurantii lactis
			Paecilomyces	species varitoi

TABLE II

Taxonomy to Species

CLASS	ORDER	FAMILY	GENUS	SPECIES
Fungi Imperfecti (Deuteromycetes)	Moniliales	Moniliaceae	Penicillium	aculeatum adametzi albidum asperum atramentosum aurantio-violaceum aurantio-virens avellaneum biforme brefeldianum brevi-compactum camemberti canescens casei caseicolum charlesii chermesinum chrysogenum citreo-viride citrinum claviforme clavigerum commune corylophilum corymbiferum crustosum cyaneofulvum cyaneum cyclopium daleae decumbens digitatum diversum duponti egyptaceum ehrlichii expansum fellutanum frequentans funiculosum fuscum gladioli godlewskii granulatum helicum herquei humuli implicatum islandicum italicum janthinellum javanicum jensenii kapuscinskii lanoso-coeruleum lanoso-griseum lanoso-viridi lanosum lavendulum levitum lilacinum lividum luteum

TABLE II

Taxonomy to Species

CLASS	ORDER	FAMILY	GENUS	SPECIES
Fungi Imperfecti (Deuteromycetes)	Moniliales	Moniliaceae	Penicillium (continued)	martensii
				melearginum
				melinii
				miczynskii
				multicolor
				nalgiovensis
				namyslowskii
				nigricans
				notatum
				novae-zeelandii
				ochraceum
				ochro-chlorum
				olivino-viride
				oxalicum
				palitans
				pallidum
				parvum
				patulum
				phoenicum
				piscarium
				psittacinum
				puberulum
				pulvillorum
				purpurescens
				purpurogenum
				pusillum
				raciborskii
				raistrickii
				restrictum
				restriculosum
				rolfsii
				roqueforti
				roseo-purpureum
				rubrum
				rugulosum
				sclerotiorum
				simplicissimum
				solitum
				soppi
				species
				spiculisporum
				spinulosum
				steckii
				stoloniferum
				striatum
				subalteritium
				tardum
				terlikowski
				terrestre
				thomii
				trzebinskii
				turbatum
				urticae
				variabile
				vermiculatum
				verruculosum
				vinaceum
				viridicatum
				waksmanni
				wortmanni
			Piricularia	oryzae

TABLE II

Taxonomy to Species

CLASS	ORDER	FAMILY	GENUS	SPECIES
Fungi Imperfecti (Deuteromycetes)	Moniliales	Moniliaceae	Ramularia	robusta
			Sarcinomyces	crustaceum
			Scopulariopsis	americana brevicaulis
			Sepedonium	ampullosporum chrysospermum
			Spicaria	simplicissima species violacea viridans
			Sporotrichum	asteroides bombycinum epigaeum gougeroti sulfurescens
			Sterigmatocystis	japonica
			Trichoderma	album glaucum koningi lignorum nigrovirens species viride
			Trichophyton	concentricum
			Tricothecium	arrhenopum candidum cystosporium domesticum luteum plasmoparae polybrochum roseum
			Tritirachium	purureum
			Verticillium	albo-atrum dahliae malthousii nieveostratosum species theobromae
		Rhodotorulaceae	Rhodotorula	glutinis gracilis longissima
		Sporobolomycetaceae	Sporobolomyces	roseum
		Stilbaceae	Isaria	farinosa
			Stysanus	medius
		Torulopsidaceae	Kloeckera	apiculata

TABLE II

Taxonomy to Species

CLASS	ORDER	FAMILY	GENUS	SPECIES
ungi Imperfecti ⠠euteromycetes)	Moniliales	Torulopsidaceae	Torula	species
			Torulopsis	aeria candida
		Tuberculariaceae	Cylindrocarpon	radicicola
			Epicoccum	humicola neglectum oryzae purpurascens species yuccae
			Fusarium	aquaeductum arthoceras aspidioti avenaceum batatatis bulbigenum buxicola caucasicum cocophilum coeruleum concolor culmorum dimerum diversisporum equiseti expansum gibosum gigas graminearum herberum heterosporum javanicum lateritium lini lycopersici macroceras merismoides microcrea moniliforme nivale niveum niveus orthoceras oxysporum poae pruni redolens roseum sambucinum sarcochroum semitectum solani species sphaeriae sporotrichella sporotrichioides sulphureum udum vasinfectum

TABLE II

Taxonomy to Species

CLASS	ORDER	FAMILY	GENUS	SPECIES
Fungi Imperfecti (Deuteromycetes)	Moniliales	Tuberculariaceae	Kabatiella	phoradendri
			Myrothecium	roridum species
			Volutella	ciliata
	Mycelia Sterilia	No Family	Rhacodium	cellare
			Rhizoctonia	ferrugena solani species
			Sclerotium	coffeicolum hydrophilum oryzae rolfsii
	Sphaeropsidales	Sphaerioidaceae	Ascochyta	favae linicola pinadella vicial
			Botryodiplodia	theobromae
			Chaetomella	oblonga raphigera
			Coniothyrium	diplodiella hellebori helleborine species
			Diplodia	natalensis tubericola
			Dothichiza	ferruginosa
			Haplosporella	species
			Hendersonia	aberrans acicola herpotricha phragmitis rubi
			Phoma	species
			Phomopsis	citri
			Pycnodothis	species
			Pycnosporium	species
			Rhodoseptoria	species
			Stagonospora	curtisii
			Staurophoma	species
			Wojnowicia	graminis

TABLE II

Taxonomy to Species

CLASS	ORDER	FAMILY	GENUS	SPECIES
Phycomycetes	Entomophthorales	Basidiobolaceae	Basidiobolus	ranarum
		Empusaceae	Entomophthora	coronata
		Entomophthoraceae	Conidiobolus	species
	Mucorales	Choanephoraceae	Choanephora	cucurbitarum
		Cunninghameoaceae	Cunninghamella	africana albidia bainieri blakesleeana echinata echinulata elegans homothallica ramosa species verticillata
		Mortieriellaceae	Mortierella	alpina bainieri candelabrum isabellina marburgensis oligospora polycephala pusilla tuberosa zonata
		Mucoraceae	Absidia	coerulea cylindrospora glauca hyalospora orchidis ramosa regnieri repens species
			Actinomucor	corymbosus repens
			Blakeslea	trispora
			Circinella	muscae simplex species syndowi umbellata
			Cokeromyces	recurvatus
			Lichtheimia	corymbifera ramosa

TABLE II

Taxonomy to Species

CLASS	ORDER	FAMILY	GENUS	SPECIES
Phycomycetes	Mucorales	Mucoraceae	Mucor	adriaticus
				adventitius
				angulisporus
				berolinensis
				buntingii
				christianensis
				circinelloides
				corymbifer
				dimorphosporus
				dispersus
				dubius
				erectus
				genevensis
				globosus
				glomerula
				griseocyanus
				guilliermondii
				hiemalis
				humicola
				(humicolus)
				humilis
				hypochninus
				javanicus
				mandshuricus
				microsporus
				mucedo
				murorum
				parasiticus
				piriformis
				plumbeus
				pusillus
				racemosus
				ramannianus
				rouxianus
				rouxii
				simplex
				solani
				species
				sphaerospora
				spinosus
				stolonifer
				varians
				vuillemini
			Mycocladus	hyalinus
			Parasitella	simplex
			Phycomyces	blakesleeanus
				nitens
				pirottianus
				species
				theobromatus
			Rhizopus	arrhizus
				cambodjae
				chinensis
				chiuniang
				cohnii
				delemar
				formosensis
				(formosaensis)
				japonicus

TABLE II

Taxonomy to Species

CLASS	ORDER	FAMILY	GENUS	SPECIES
Phycomycetes	Mucorales	Mucoraceae	Rhizopus (continued)	javanicus kansho kasanensis nigricans niveus nodosus oryzae pseudochinensis pygmaeus reflexus shangaiensis (shanghaiensis) species stolonifer suinus tonkinensis tritici
			Syncephalastrum	cincereum (cinereum) racemosum species
			Syncephalis	nodosa reflexa
			Thamnidium	elegans
			Tieghemella	coerulea cylindrospora hyalospora orchidis repens spinosa tieghemii turkestanica
			Zygorhynchus	heterogamus moelleri
		Pilobolaceae	Pilaira	anomala
		Thamnidaceae	Chaetocladium	brefeldii
			Helicostylum	piriforme species
	Peronosporales	Pythiaceae	Phytophthora	citrophthora parasitica
			Pythium	ultimum
Schizomycetes	Actinomycetales	Actinomycetaceae	Nocardia	asteroides aurantia blackwellii braziliensis coeliaca convoluta corallina erythropolis farcinica formica

TABLE II

Taxonomy to Species

CLASS	ORDER	FAMILY	GENUS	SPECIES
Schizomycetes	Actinomycetales	Actinomycetaceae	Nocardia (continued)	gardneri globerula italica leishmanii maculata madurae mexicanus minima opaca paraffinae polychromogenes restrictus rubra salmonicolor species
			Proactinomyces	actinomorphus agrestis aquosus coeliacus crystallophagus erythropolis globerulus minimus paraffinae polychromogenes restrictus roseus rubropertinctus species
		Actinoplanaceae	Actinoplanes	missouriensis species
		Mycobacteriaceae	Mycobacterium	album berolinense butyricum chelonei cholesterolicum flavum fortuitum friedmannii hyalinum lacticola luteum phlei ranae rhodochrous rubropertinctum rubrum salmonicolor smegmatis species thamnopheos tuberculosis
			Mycococcus	species
		Streptomycetaceae	Streptomyces	albidoflavus albidus albosporeus albus annulatus

TABLE II

Taxonomy to Species

CLASS	ORDER	FAMILY	GENUS	SPECIES
hizomycetes	Actinomycetales	Streptomycetaceae	Streptomyces	antibioticus argenteolus aureofaciens aureus bikiniensis bobilae californicus celluloflavus chartreusis chrysomallus coelicolor diastaticus diastatochromogenes endus erythreus exfoliatus fimicarius flaveolus flavogriseus fradiae fulvissimus gelaticus globisporus globosus griseocarneus griseolus griseus halstedii hydrogenans hygroscopius lavendulae lipmanii mediocidicus microflavus nitrosporeus olivaceus olivochromogenus parvus purpureochromogenus rimosus roseochromogenus ruber rubescens rubrireticuli rubroocyanodiastaticus rutgersensis scabies setonii species tanashiensis tendae thioluteus vinaceus viridans viridifaciens viridis viridochromogenus willmorei
			Micromonospora	chalcea species

TABLE II

Taxonomy to Species

CLASS	ORDER	FAMILY	GENUS	SPECIES
Schizomycetes	Eubacteriales	Achromobacteriaceae	Achromobacter	cyclocoastes (cycloclastes) kashiwasakiensis liquidum species
			Alcaligenes	faecalis species
			Flavobacterium	androstenedionicum aquatile aurantiacum buccalis carbonilicum dehydrogenans flavescens flavotennae fulvum helvoium maris sewanense species
		Azotobacteriaceae	Azotobacter	agilis chroococcum indicus oxydans species vinlandii
		Bacillaceae	Bacillus	alvei brevis cereus circulans closteroides coagulans coli firmus lentus macerans megaterium mycoides polymyxa proteus pulvifaciens pumilus putrificus pymilus roseus species sphaericus subtilis thiaminolyticus tumescens
			Clostridium	bifermentans paraputrificum perfringens sporogenes tertium welchii
		Bacteriaceae	Bacterium	bifidum cyclo-oxydans

TABLE II

Taxonomy to Species

CLASS	ORDER	FAMILY	GENUS	SPECIES
hizomycetes	Eubacteriales	Bacteriaceae	Bacterium	havaniensis mycoides species steroidiclasium
		Corynebacteriaceae	Arthrobacter	simplex species
			Cellulomonas	biazotea
			Corynebacterium	equi fascians helvolum hoagii mediolanum pseudodiphtheriticum simplex species xerose
		Enterobacteriaceae	Aerobacter	aerogenes cloacae
			Erwinia	aroideae carotovora
			Escherichia	coli freundii
			Proteus	species vulgaris
			Serratia	marcescens plymuthica
		Lactobacillaceae	Catenabacterium	catenaforme species
			Lactobacillus	brevis buchneri bulgaricus
			Streptococcus	pyogenes
		Micrococcaceae	Micrococcus	candidus citreus congloneratus dehydrogenans flava flavus luteus lysodeiktius piltonensis pyogenus-aureus roseus species subflavus ureae varians
			Sarcina	albida albiden

TABLE II

Taxonomy to Species

CLASS	ORDER	FAMILY	GENUS	SPECIES
Schizomycetes	Eubacteriales	Micrococcaceae	Sarcina	aurentiace marginata variabilis
			Staphylococcus	albus aureus
		Rhizobiaceae	Agrobacterium	ethanicus radiobacter tumefaciens
			Chromobacterium	violaceum
			Rhizobium	leguminosarum meliloti phaseoli trifolii
	Pseudomonadales	Methanomonadaceae	Hydrogenomonas	facilis
		Pseudomonadaceae	Acetobacter	aceti pasteurianum suboxydans xylinum
			Azotomonas	fluorescens
			Mycoplana	bullata dimorpha
			Phytomonas	citri eicobatryae malvacearum
			Protaminobacter	alboflavum rubrum
			Pseudomonas	aeruginosa aureofaciens azoformicans boreopolis caudata chlororaphis cohaerens cruciviae dacunhae desmolytica fluorescens fragi gaegeri gelidicola graveolens indoloxidans inertia jaegeri lacunogenes melanogenes myxogenes nitroreductans ochracea oleovorans ovalis

TABLE II

Taxonomy to Species

CLASS	ORDER	FAMILY	GENUS	SPECIES
Schizomycetes	Pseudomonadales	Pseudomonadaceae	Pseudomonas (continued)	pavonacea perlurida pictorum putida pyocyanea rathonis riboflavinus roseum schuylkill schuylkilliensis species striafaciens stutzeri synxantha taetrolens testosteroni trifoli xanthe
			Xanthomonas	citri malvacerum
		Spirillaceae	Vibrio	cyclosites metschnikovu percolans tyrogenes
OTHER TAXONOMIC GROUPS				
Algae - Chlorophyta	Chlorococcales	Chlorellaceae	Chlorella	species
		Scenedesmaceae	Scenedesmus	species
Plants - Spermatophyta Angiosperme Monocotyledonae	Liliiflorae	Liliaceae	Sansevieria	zeylanica
Dicotyledonae	Rosales	Leguminosae	Medicago	sativa
Protozoa - Mastigophora				
Subclass: Phytomastigina	Euglenoidina	Euglenidae	Euglena	gracilis
Subclass: Zoomastigina	Polymastigina	Trichomonadidae	Trichomonas	foetus gallinae vaginalis
			Pentatrichomonas	gallinarum hominis

CHAPTER V

THE CONSTRUCTION AND USE OF TABLE III — TRANSFORMATIONS BY GENUS

ORDER OF THE TABLE

The entries in Table III include all the genera, species, sources, substrates, and reactions reported in the cited references. These include both inactive genera and assignments for reactions based solely on chromatographic evidence.

Transformations that are documented with specific experimental details are cross-indexed with the product table. The references for those entries are under-lined.

The table entries are recorded in an order determined by the following rules which are applied sequentially.

(a) According to genus (alphabetically)
(b) According to species (alphabetically)
(c) According to source (alphabetically)
(d) According to substrate (using the following systematic stem names sequentially):

estrane
androstane
pregnane
cardanolide
bufanolide
cholanic acid
cholestane
stigmastane
sapogenins (common stem name)

Taxonomic names and identifying culture collection numbers, as well as the spellings of the genera, species, and varieties are as given in the cited references. Occasional changes in spelling were made to conform to standard reference texts or culture collection catalogs. In a few instances, to avoid misinterpretation, the prob-able correct spelling is given parenthetically.

SPECIFIC NOTES ON DIVISIONS OF THE TABLE

Genera

The taxonomic position by class and order are given for each genus the first time is appears in the table. A complete list of related families and genera can be found in Table II ("Taxonomy to Species"). Where more than one genus is tabulated on a page, the genus, in capital letters is repeated in the species column and under-lined.

Species

An asterisk indicates that the corresponding entry in Table I ("Transformation by Product") is recorded by the generic description (e.g. *Aspergillus* sp. for a list of species which perform the same transformation on a given substrate).

Occasionally, to better identify a species lacking a culture collection number, additional data are supplied, e.g., *Absidia orchidis* (Vuill.) hagem.

Transformations performed with one or more cultures (mixed or sequential) are recorded at the end of the list of substrates for the given species. Only the reaction carried out by the primary culture is cited in the reaction column.

Transformations carried out by the second or third culture of the mixed group are listed parenthetically in the species column giving the full name of the culture and the particular reaction. The original references should be consulted for the experimental details.

When an organism has simply been identified as species in early work, but fully characterized in later reports, the final assignment is used giving the appropriate reference for the change. For example, *Streptomyces argenteolus* [Species ATCC-11009 (F-265, H-380, P-716, P-719; identified as *argenteolus* in F-267)].

Sources

The source, with rare exceptions, is not related to the source from which the culture was originally isolated but, wherever possible, to the major culture collection where it can be obtained. The sources are coded and listed alphabetically (including the addresses) at the end of this chapter.

If the culture is not provided with an identifying number, the source is listed as either the name of the laboratory where the work was done or NG (not given).

All accession or identifying numbers for strains of a species are listed in numerical sequence. All identifying numbers for strains other than those available from the American Type Culture Collection or from the United States Department of Agriculture are enclosed in parentheses.

Different sources for the same species are listed alphabetically.

Substrates

Systematic organic chemical nomenclature has been used, in most entries, excepting for sapogenins and steroidal alkaloids. No more than one class of suffix designation for substituents is affixed to any stem. All remaining substituents are expressed in prefixes, arranged alphabetically.

In general, following the systematic stem name, the order of precedence, once the degree of substitution is established, is as follows.

> (a)   ____ane, ene, diene, triene
> (b)   ____ol, diol, triol
> (c)   ____one, dione, trione

For example,

> 5α-pregnane-3,20-dione
> 3β-hydroxy-5-pregnen-20-one
> 4-pregnene-3,20-dione
> 6β-hydroxy-4-pregnene-3,20-dione
> 17α,21-dihydroxy-4-pregnene-3,20-dione
> 9α-fluoro-17α,21-dihydroxy-4-pregnene-3,20-dione
> 11β,17α,21-trihydroxy-4-pregnene-3,20-dione

4-pregnene-3,11,20-trione
3β-hydroxy-5,16-pregnadien-20-one

For the definition of terms such as nor, homo, and other notations with regard to nomenclature, see the explanations in the section on nomenclature in Chapter III.

Reactions

The shorthand notation used to describe the reaction is identical with the notation used in Table I (cf. Chapter III). Reactions accomplished with cellfree enzymes and enzyme systems or those concerned with special effects of nutrients or environmental conditions are carried as notes in the substrate column under the appropriate culture.

A dash (−) in the reaction column indicates generally that no reaction took place or that the reaction was not characterized. Positive, though otherwise unspecified reactions are recorded as "oxidation − products not identified" or equivalent nonspecific terminology.

Two categories of entries are recorded in Table III. (a) Those for which the reference is underlined correspond to equivalent entries in Table I "Transformation by Product." To determine the structure of the product, thereby gaining access to Table I, the following rules apply.

Rule 1:   For those entries wherein no more than one hydroxylation appears in the reaction column, the product is determined by the sum of all the recorded changes applied to the substrate.

Rule 2:   For those entries wherein more than one hydroxylation is recorded, each hydroxylation determines a separate transformation product from the given substrate. Exception: A polyhydroxylation expressed as di-OH is read as a single, combined transformation of the substrate.

Examples: Substrate   3β-hydroxy-5-pregnene-20-one
          +
          Reactions   3β-OH ⟶ 3-C=O; Δ⁵ ⟶ Δ⁴; 12β-OH
          ↓
          Product   12β-hydroxy-4-pregnene-3,20-dione

          Substrate   3β-hydroxy-5-pregnen-20-one
          +
          Reactions   3β-OH ⟶ 3-C=O; Δ⁵ ⟶ Δ⁴; 12β,15α-diOH
          ↓
          Product   12β,15α-dihydroxy-4-pregnene-3,20-dione

          Substrate   4-pregnene-3,20-dione
          +
          Reactions   6β-OH; 11α-OH; 15β-OH
          ↓
          Products   6β-hydroxy-4-pregnene-3,20-dione
                             11α-hydroxy-4-pregnene-3,20-dione
                             15β-hydroxy-4-pregnene-3,20-dione

          Substrate   4-pregnene-3,20-dione
          +
          Reactions   6β-OH; 11α-OH; 6β,11α-diOH
          ↓
          Products   6β-hydroxy-4-pregnene-3,20-dione
                             11α-hydroxy-4-pregnene-3,20-dione
                             6β,11α-dihydroxy-4-pregnene-3,20-dione

(b) Entries which do not bear underlined reference citations have no equivalents in Table I. The reactions for these entries merely record the variety of transformations which may occur with the indicated substrate. For those instances in which multiple transformations are recorded, these may occur either in concert (to give a single product) or individually (and in combinations) to give multiple products.

References

The references for each entry are given by coded citation in the reference column. These citations are arranged alphabetically in the Bibliography (Chapter VI).

Those transformations for which there are data listed in Table I are identified by underlined references.

SOURCE OF CULTURES

Code Used to Identify Source in Transformation by Genus (Table III)

Code	Source
AL	Department of Biochemistry, Research Division, Abbott Laboratories, North Chicago, Ill.
AMCY	American Cyanamid Co. (see also under LED), Lederle Division, Pearl River, N. Y.
ARMOUR	Armour and Co., Chicago, Ill.
ASRI	Akimov State Research Institute (see under IPB)
ATCC *	American Type Culture Collection, 12301 Parklawn Drive, Rockeville, Md.
AY	Ayerst Research Laboratories, Montreal, Canada
BEN MAY LAB	Ben May Laboratory for Cancer Research, University of Chicago, Chicago, Ill.
C	Ciba Pharmaceutical Products, Inc., Summit, N. J. and Basle, Switzerland
CBS *	Centraalbureau Voor Schimmelcultures, Baarn, Netherlands
CHARLES	Microbiological Institute of Charles Univ., Czechoslovakia
CMI *	Commonwealth Mycological Institute, Kew, Surrey, England
CORNELL	Department of Plant Pathology, Cornell University, Ithaca, N. Y.
CZAA	Czechoslovak Academy of Agricultural Sciences, Prague, Czechoslovakia
CZAS	Czechoslovak Academy of Sciences, Prague, Czechoslovakia
EM	E. Merck A. G., Darmstadt, West Germany
FAHU	Faculty of Agriculture, Hokkaido University, Sapporo, Japan
FAKU	Faculty of Agriculture, Kyushu University, Fukuoka, Japan
FARMIT	Research Laboratories, Farmitalia, Milan, Italy

*Asterisk indicates major collections.

Code	Source
FCUTS	Department of Fermentation Chemistry, University of Technical Science, Prague, Czechoslovakia
FRI	Fermentation Research Institute, Agency of Industrial Science and Technology, Japan
HOECHST	Hoechst A. G., Frankfurt, West Germany
IAM	Institute of Applied Microbiology, University of Tokyo, Japan
IFO	Institute for Fermentation, 4-54, Juso-Nishinocho, Higashiyodogawa-Ku, Osaka, Japan
IMJ	Institut für Microbiologie und Experimentelle Therapie, Jena, W. Germany
IPB	Research Institute for Pharmacy and Biochemistry, Kourimska 17, Prague, Czechoslovakia
K	Laboratory of Food Science, Kyoto University, Japan
KAG	Kagawa University, Japan
KSC	Department of Botany, Kansas State College, Manhattan, Kans.
LED	Lederle Laboratories Division, American Cyanamid Co., Pearl River, N. Y. (see AMCY)
LEO	Leo Pharmaceutical Products, Copenhagen, Denmark
LEPETIT	Research Laboratories, Lepetit, S.p.A., Milan, Italy
LRL	Lilly Research Laboratories, Eli Lilly and Co., Indianapolis, Ind.
MCC	Merck Culture Collection, Merck and Co., Rahway, N. J.
NAGAS	Nagas Laboratories, 380 Mi-Shuka-Cho, Setagayaku, Tokyo, Japan
NARI	National Agricultural Research Institute, Japan
NCIB*	National Collection of Industrial Bacteria, Chemical Research Laboratory, Teddington, Middlesex, England
NCTC*	National Collection of Type Cultures, Central Public Health Laboratory, London N.W. 9, England
NG	Source not given
NI	Nagao Institute, Tokyo, Japan
NIH	National Institutes of Health, Bethesda, Md.
NIHJ	National Institute of Health, Japan
NRRL*	Northern Regional Research Laboratories, Northern Utilization Branch, Agricultural Research Service, U.S. Department of Agriculture, Peoria, Ill.
OIAB	Ohara Institute for Agricultural Biology, Kurashiki, Japan
OKAYAMA	Department of Biochemistry, Okayama Medical School, Okayama, Japan
OR	Research Laboratories, N. V. Organon, Netherlands
PD	Research Laboratories, Park, Davis and Co., Ann Arbor, Mich.
PF	Charles Pfizer and Co., New York, N. Y.

Code	Source
PH	N. V. Philips Duphar, Apollolaan 151, Amsterdam, Netherlands
PIRI	Research Institute for the Pharmaceutical Industry, Budapest, Hungary
QM *	Quartermaster Culture Collection, Quartermaster Research and Engineering Command, United States Army, Natick, Mass.
RIDPI	Research Institute of the Distillers and Preservation Industry, Prague, Czechoslovakia
RIND	Research Institute for Natural Drugs, Prague, Czechoslovakia
RUTGERS	Department of Plant Pathology and Mycology, Rutgers University, New Brunswick, N. J.
S	Sankyo Co., Ltd., Japan
SAG	Schering A. G., Berlin, Germany
SANDOZ	Sandoz, Basle, Switzerland
SCH	Research Laboratories, Schering Corporation, Bloomfield, N. J.
SEARLE	G. D. Searle and Co., Chicago, Ill.
SHIONOGI	Shionogi Research Laboratory, Shionogi and Co., Ltd., Fukushima-Ku, Osaka, Japan
SP-WISC	School of Pharmacy, University of Wisconsin, Madison, Wisc.
SQ	Squibb Institute for Medical Research, E. R. Squibb and Son, New Brunswick, N. J. (Division of Olin Mathieson Chemical Corporation, New York, N. Y.)
SSSR	Soviet Union. Includes Institute of Microbiology of the Academy of Sciences of the USSR, Institute of the Chemistry of Natural Products of the Academy of Science of the USSR; S. Ordzhonikidze, All-Union Scientific Research Chemical - Pharmaceutical Institute
SY	Research Laboratories, Syntex, S. A., Mexico, D. F.
TAKEDA	Research Laboratories, Takeda Chemical Industries, Ltd., Juso-Nishino-Cho, Higashiyodogawa-Ku, Osaka, Japan
TBRI	Tokyo Biochemical Research Institute 2-593, Takadaminami-Cho, Toshima-Ku, Tokyo, Japan
TNAES	Tokai-Kinki National Agricultural Experiment Station, Japan
TSURUMI	Tsurumi Chemical Research Laboratories, Yokohama, Japan
UB	Institute of Organic Chemistry, University of Basle, Switzerland
UC	Upjohn Co., Kalamazoo, Mich.
UCT	Department of Fermentation, University of Chemical Technology, Prague, Czechoslovakia
UM	University of Minnesota, Minneapolis, Minn.
VEB	Research Laboratories, VEB Jena Pharm., Jena, Germany
WC *	Waksman Collection, Institute of Microbiology, Rutgers University, New Brunswick, N. J.

Code	Source
WFEB	Worcester Foundation for Experimental Biology, Shrewsbury, Mass.
WISC	Wisconsin Strain, University of Wisconsin, Madison, Wis.
WURB	Western Utilization Research Branch, Agricultural Research Service, U. S. Department of Agriculture, Albany, Calif.

TABLE III

ansformations by Genus: ABSIDIA   (Phyco. - Mucorales)

SPECIES		SOURCE	SUBSTRATE	REACTION	REF.
oerulea		ATCC-1359b	19-nor-4-pregnene-3,20-dione	unidentified monohydroxylation	B-71
		RIDPI	4-pregnene-3,20-dione	11α-OH; 11β-OH	C-98
			17α,21-dihydroxy-4-pregnene-3,20-dione 21-acetate	11α-OH; 11β-OH; 11-C=O (via 11β-OH); 21-OAc→21-OH	C-98
ylindrospora	*	NI	4-pregnene-3,20-dione	11α-OH; 14α-OH; 6β,11α-diOH	N-682
			17α,21-dihydroxy-4-pregnene-3,20-dione	6β-OH; 11α-OH	N-682
	*		14β-hydroxy-3-keto-5β-20(22)-cardenolide	7β-OH	N-682
	*		3β,14β-dihydroxy-5β-20(22)-cardenolide	3β-OH→3-C=O; 1β-OH; 7β-OH; 1β,7β-diOH; 5β,7β-diOH	N-682
lauca	*	IPB	4-pregnene-3,20-dione	11α-OH	C-98
	*			11β-OH	C-98
			17α,21-dihydroxy-4-pregnene-3,20-dione	6β-OH; 11α-OH	C-98
	*			11β-OH	C-98
				11-C=O (via 11β-OH)	C-98
			17α,21-dihydroxy-4-pregnene-3,20-dione 21-acetate	21-OAc→21-OH	C-98
	*	OIAB	4-pregnene-3,20-dione	11α-OH	N-682
	*			14α-OH; 6β,11α-diOH	N-682
			17α,21-dihydroxy-4-pregnene-3,20-dione	11α-OH; 11β-OH	N-682
	*			6β-OH	N-682
	*		14β-hydroxy-3-keto-5β-20(22)-cardenolide	7β-OH	N-682
	*		3β,14β-dihydroxy-5β-20(22)-cardenolide	3β-OH→3-C=O; 1β-OH; 5β-OH; 7β-OH	N-682
				1β,7β-diOH; 5β,7β-diOH	N-682
	*	UCT	4-pregnene-3,20-dione	11α-OH	C-98
	*			11β-OH	C-98

TABLE III

Transformations by Genus: ABSIDIA

SPECIES		SOURCE	SUBSTRATE	REACTION	REF.
glauca		UCT	$17\alpha,21$-dihydroxy-4-pregnene-3,20-dione	6β-OH; 11α-OH	C-98
	*			11β-OH	C-98
				11-C=O(via 11β-OH)	C-98
			$17\alpha,21$-dihydroxy-4-pregnene-3,20-dione 21-acetate	21-OAc→21-OH	C-98
	*	VEB	4-pregnene-3,20-dione	11α-OH	C-98
	*			11β-OH	C-98
hyalospora	*	NI	4-pregnene-3,20-dione	11α-OH; 14α-OH; $6\beta,11\alpha$-diOH	N-682
			$17\alpha,21$-dihydroxy-4-pregnene-3,20-dione	6β-OH; 11α-OH; 14α-OH	N-682
	*		14β-hydroxy-3-keto-5β-20(22)-cardenolide	7β-OH	N-682
	*		$3\beta,14\beta$-dihydroxy-5β-20(22)-cardenolide	3β-OH→3-C=O; 7β-OH; $1\beta,7\beta$-diOH; $5\beta,7\beta$-diOH	N-682
orchidis (-)		CZAA	B-nor-4-androstene-3,17-dione	6ξ-OH; 11α-OH	P-741
orchidis		NG	$17\alpha,21$-dihydroxy-4-pregnene-3,20-dione	1β-OH	S-825a
				11α-OH	S-825a
				11β-OH	S-825a
				11-C=O (via 11β-OH	S-825a
	*	OIAB	4-pregnene-3,20-dione	11α-OH	N-682
	*			14α-OH; $6\beta,11\alpha$-diOH	N-682
			$17\alpha,21$-dihydroxy-4-pregnene-3,20-dione	6β-OH; 11α-OH	N-682
	*			11β-OH	C-98; H-334; N-682
			14β-hydroxy-3-keto-5β-20(22)-cardenolide	3-C=O→3α-OH	N-682
				5β-H → Δ^4	N-682
	*	PIRI	4-pregnene-3,20-dione	11α-OH	C-98
	*		$17\alpha,21$-dihydroxy-4-pregnene-3,20-dione	11α-OH	C-98
	*			11β-OH	C-98
				11-C=O (via 11β-OH)	

TABLE III

ansformations by Genus: ABSIDIA

SPECIES	SOURCE	SUBSTRATE	REACTION	REF.
rchidis	PIRI	17α, 21-dihydroxy-4-pregnene-3, 20-dione 21-acetate	21-OAc→21-OH	C-98
*	RIDPI	17α, 21-dihydroxy-4-pregnene-3, 20-dione 21-acetate	11α-OH	C-98
*			11β-OH	C-98
*			11-C=O (via 11β-OH)	C-98
			21-OAc→21-OH	C-98
*	UCT (310)	4-pregnene-3, 20-dione	11α-OH	C-98
*		17α, 21-dihydroxy-4-pregnene-3, 20-dione 21-acetate	11α-OH	C-98; H-334
*			11-C=O (via 11β-OH)	C-98; H-334
			21-OAc→21-OH	C-98
*	VEB	4-pregnene-3, 20-dione	11α-OH	C-98
*		17α, 21-dihydroxy-4-pregnene-3, 20-dione 21-acetate	11α-OH	C-98
			11β-OH	C-98
			11-C=O (via 11β-OH)	C-98
			21-OAc→21-OH	C-98
rchidis (Vuill.) Hagem	OIAB	3β, 14β-dihydroxy-5β, 17α-20(22)-cardenolide	1β-OH; 5β-OH; 7β-OH; 3β-OH→ 3-C=O; 5β-H→ Δ^4	N-679; N-681
		3β, 14β-dihydroxy-5β-20(22)-cardenolide	1β-OH	I-426; N-679; N-680; N-682; N-683; N-684
			5β-OH	I-426; N-679; N-680; N-682; N-683; N-684
			7β-OH	I-426; N-679; N-680; N-681; N-682; N-683; N-684
*				

TABLE III

Transformations by Genus: ABSIDIA

SPECIES	SOURCE	SUBSTRATE	REACTION	REF.
orchidis (Vuill.) Hagem	OIAB	$3\beta,14\beta$-dihydroxy-5β-20(22)-cardenolide	$1\beta,7\beta$-diOH	I-426; N-679; N-680; N-682
			$5\beta,7\beta$-diOH	I-426; N-679; N-682
ramosa	NRRL	Sarsasapogenin	—	M-587
		Diosgenin	—	M-587
		4-dehydrotigogenone	—	M-587
regnieri	IAM	4-pregnene-3,20-dione	14α-OH	S-849
			15β-OH	S-849
			$6\beta,14\alpha$-diOH	S-849
			$7\beta,14\alpha$-diOH (revised structure)	S-849
			$9\alpha,14\alpha$-diOH (assignment of structure - doubtful)	S-849
		17α-hydroxy-4-pregnene-3,20-dione	11α-OH	S-849
		21-hydroxy-4-pregnene-3,20-dione	14α-OH	S-849
		$11\beta,21$-dihydroxy-4-pregnene-3,20-dione	14α-OH	S-849
			11β-OH→11-C=O	S-849
		$17\alpha,21$-dihydroxy-4-pregnene-3,20-dione	2β-OH	S-849
			11α-OH	S-849
	NG	4-pregnene-3,20-dione	14α-OH	S-120; S-859; T-982
			$6\beta,14\alpha$-diOH	S-844; S-859; T-982
			$7\beta,14\alpha$-diOH (revised structure)	S-844; T-982; T-1037
			$9\alpha,14\alpha$-diOH (assignment of structure - doubtful)	T-982

TABLE III

Transformations by Genus: ABSIDIA

SPECIES	SOURCE	SUBSTRATE	REACTION	REF.
egnieri	NG	4-pregnene-3,20-dione	$7\beta,14\alpha,15\beta$-tri-OH (revised structure)	S-844; T-982; T-1037
		17α-hydroxy-4-pregnene-3,20-dione	—	S-859
			11α-OH	S-841
		21-hydroxy-4-pregnene-3,20-dione	14α-OH	S-841
		21-hydroxy-4-pregnene-3,20-dione acetate	21-OAc→21-OH; 14α-OH	S-841
		$11\beta,21$-dihydroxy-4-pregnene-3,20-dione	14α-OH	S-851
			11β-OH→11-C=O	S-841
			14α-OH; 11β-OH →11-C=O	S-841; S-851
		$11\alpha,21$-dihydroxy-4-pregnene-3,20-dione	—	S-851
		21-hydroxy-4-pregnene-3,11,20-trione	14α-OH	S-841; S-851
		$17\alpha,21$-dihydroxy-4-pregnene-3,20-dione	11α-OH	S-841; S-844; S-859
			14α-OH	S-841; S-844; S-859
		$11\beta,17\alpha,21$-trihydroxy-4-pregnene-3,20-dione	—	S-851
repens	UCT	4-pregnene-3,20-dione	11α-OH; 11β-OH	C-98
*		$17\alpha,21$-dihydroxy-4-pregnene-3,20-dione	11α-OH; 11β-OH; 11-C=O (via 11β-OH)	C-98
		$17\alpha,21$-dihydroxy-4-pregnene-3,20-dione acetate	21-OAc→21-OH	C-98
species	NG	$17\alpha,21$-dihydroxy-4-pregnene-3,20-dione	11α-OH	C-98; N-682; S-801
			11β-OH	C-98; S-801
		Saponins (sapogenin glycosides)	—	K-478

TABLE III

Transformations by Genus: ACETOBACTER (Schizo. - Pseudomonadales)
ACHROMOBACTER (Schizo. - Eubacteriales)

SPECIES	SOURCE	SUBSTRATE	REACTION	REF.
aceti	IFO (3169)	$11\beta,17\alpha,21$-trihydroxy-4-pregnene-3,20-dione	—	I-428
	NRRL	Sarsasapogenin	—	M-587
		Diosgenin	—	M-587
		4-dehydrotigogenone	—	M-587
(in mixed culture with Mycococcus sp.)	IFO (A$_1$)	$11\beta,17\alpha,21$-trihydroxy-4-pregnene-3,20-dione	—	I-428
pasteurianum	NG	5-androstene-3β,17β-diol	3β-OH→3-C=O; Δ^5→Δ^4	K-457
		5-androstene-3β,17β-diol 17-propionate	3β-OH→3-C=O; Δ^5→Δ^4	K-457
		3β-hydroxy-5-androsten-17-one	3β-OH→3-C=O; Δ^5→Δ^4	K-457
suboxydans	NG	5-pregnene-3β,17α,20β,21-tetrol	3β-OH→3-C=O; Δ^5→Δ^4; 20β-OH→20-C=O	L-523
	NRRL	Sarsasapogenin	—	M-587
		Diosgenin	—	M-587
		4-dehydrotigogenone	—	M-587
xylinum	IFO (3174)	$11\beta,17\alpha,21$-trihydroxy-4-pregnene-3,20-dione	—	I-428
	NG	5-cholesten-3β-ol	3β-OH→3-C=O; Δ^5→Δ^4	K-457
(in mixed culture with Mycococcus sp.)	IFO (A$_1$)	$11\beta,17\alpha,21$-trihydroxy-4-pregnene-3,20-dione	—	I-428
ACHROMOBACTER				
cyclocoastes (cycloclastes)	IAM	$17\alpha,21$-dihydroxy-4-pregnene-3,20-dione	11α-OH	S-849
kashiwasakiensis	IAM	4-pregnene-3,20-dione	$6\beta,14\alpha$-diOH	T-1026
		$17\alpha,21$-dihydroxy-4-pregnene-3,20-dione	6β-OH	T-1026
liquidum	IFO (3084)	$11\beta,17\alpha,21$-trihydroxy-4-pregnene-3,20-dione	—	I-428
(in mixed culture with Mycococcus sp.)	IFO (A$_1$)		Δ^1	I-428

TABLE III

Transformations by Genus:

ACREMONIUM	(Imperf. - Moniliales)
ACROSPEIRA	(Imperf. - Moniliales)
ACROSTALAGMUS	(Imperf. - Moniliales)
ACTINOMUCOR	(Phyco. - Mucorales)
ACTINOMYCES	(Schizo. - Actinomycetales)
ACTINOPLANES	(Schizo. - Actinomycetales)

SPECIES	SOURCE	SUBSTRATE	REACTION	REF.
species	IAM (K-40-5)	4-pregnene-3,20-dione	$6\beta,14\alpha$-diOH	I-418
		$17\alpha,21$-dihydroxy-4-pregnene-3,20-dione	6β-OH	I-418
ACREMONIUM				
potronii	FRI	$17\alpha,21$-dihydroxy-4-pregnene-3,20-dione	—	S-849
ACROSPEIRA				
levis	NG	not given	17α-OH	W-1106; W-1107
ACROSTALAGMUS				
albus	FRI	$17\alpha,21$-dihydroxy-4-pregnene-3,20-dione	6β-OH; 11α-OH	S-849
ACTINOMUCOR				
corymbosus	NG	$17\alpha,21$-dihydroxy-4-pregnene-3,20-dione	—	E-224
repens	NRRL	Sarsasapogenin	—	M-587
		Diosgenin	—	M-587
		4-dehydrotigogenone	—	M-587
ACTINOMYCES				
(See Streptomyces)				
ACTINOPLANES				
missouriensis	ATCC-14538	17β-hydroxy-17α-methyl-5α-androstan-3-one	Δ^1	M-536
		3β-hydroxy-5-androsten-17-one	3β-OH$\rightarrow$3-C=O; $\Delta^5 \rightarrow \Delta^4$; Δ^1	M-536; M-537
			3β-OH$\rightarrow$3-C=O; $\Delta^5 \rightarrow \Delta^4$; Δ^1	M-536; M-537
			3β-OH$\rightarrow$3-C=O; $\Delta^5 \rightarrow \Delta^4$; Δ^1; 6β-OH	M-536; M-537

TABLE III

TAXONOMY

Transformations by Genus: ACTINOPLANES
AEROBACTER   (Schizo. - Eubacteriales)

SPECIES	SOURCE	SUBSTRATE	REACTION	REF.
missouriensis	ATCC-14538	11α,17β-dihydroxy-4-androsten-3-one	Δ^1; 17β-OH → 17-C=O	M-536
		17β-hydroxy-17α-methyl-4-androsten-3-one	Δ^1	M-536
		17β-hydroxy-4-estren-3-one	Δ^1; enol.	M-536
		4-androstene-3,17-dione	Δ^1	M-537
		4-pregnene-3,20-dione	Δ^1	M-536
(in sequential fermentation with Curvularia lunata [11β-OH])			Δ^1	M-536
		4-pregnene-3,11,20-trione	Δ^1	M-536
		21-hydroxy-4-pregnene-3,20-dione	Δ^1	M-536
		17α,21-dihydroxy-4-pregnene-3,11,20-trione 21 acetate	Δ^1; 21-OAc→ 21-OH	M-536
		6α-fluoro-17α,21-dihydroxy-16α-methyl-4-pregnene-3,20-dione	Δ^1	M-536
(in sequential fermentation with Curvularia lunata [11β-OH])			Δ^1	M-536
species	LRL-431	3β-hydroxy-5-androsten-17-one	3β-OH→3-C=O; $\Delta^5 \to \Delta^4$; Δ^1	M-537
			3β-OH→3-C=O; $\Delta^5 \to \Delta^4$; Δ^1	M-537
			3β-OH→3-C=O; $\Delta^5 \to \Delta^4$; Δ^1; 6β-OH	M-537
		17β-hydroxy-4-androsten-3-one	Δ^1; 17β-OH → 17-C=O	M-537
		4-androstene-3,17-dione	Δ^1	M-537
AEROBACTER				
aerogenes	NCTC	5-cholesten-3β-ol	—	T-1030
	NG	5-cholesten-3β-ol	—	S-914; W-1062
		3α,7α,12α-trihydroxy-5β-cholanic acid	—	N-675

TABLE III

nsformations by Genus: AEROBACTER
AGARICUS   (Basidio. - Agaricales)
AGROBACTERIUM   (Schizo. - Eubacteriales)

SPECIES	SOURCE	SUBSTRATE	REACTION	REF.
rogenes (Izaki)	ATCC-7256	$3\alpha,7\alpha,12\alpha$-trihydroxy-5β-cholanic acid	—	S-849
	ATCC-8308		—	S-849
	ATCC-8329		—	S-849
	ATCC-8724		—	S-849
	IFO(3321)	$11\beta,17\alpha,21$-trihydroxy-4-pregnene-3,20-dione	—	I-428
oacae	IAM(1-1)	$17\alpha,21$-dihydroxy-4-pregnene-3,20-dione	—	I-428
	IAM(A1-2)		—	I-428
	IAM (K-5)		Δ^1	S-849
GARICUS				
ampestris	FRI	$17\alpha,21$-dihydroxy-4-pregnene-3,20-dione	—	S-849
	NRRL-2334	4-pregnene-3,20-dione	—	R-778
dulis	AL(698)	4-pregnene-3,20-dione	—	S-825
odmanii	WURB	4-pregnene-3,20-dione	—	R-778
GROBACTERIUM				
thanicus	NG	5-cholesten-3β-ol	degradation	T-1015; T-1016
(in mixed culture with Aspergillus wentii)		5-cholesten-3β-ol acetate	degradation	T-1015; T-1016
		24β-methyl-5,7,22-cholestatrien-3β-ol	degradation	T-1015; T-1016
		$4,4,14\alpha$-trimethyl-5α-8,24-cholestadien-3β-ol	degradation	T-1015; T-1016
		24-ethyl-5,22-cholestadien-3β-ol	degradation	T-1015; T-1016
adiobacter	NRRL	Sarsasapogenin	—	M-587
		Diosgenin	—	M-587
		4-dehydrotigogenone	—	M-587
umefaciens	IFO (3058)	$17\alpha,21$-dihydroxy-4-pregnene-3,20-dione	—	S-849

TABLE III

TAXONOMY

Transformations by Genus: AGROBACTERIUM, AGROCYBE (Basidio. - Agaricales), ALCALIGENES (Schizo. - Eubacteriales)

SPECIES	SOURCE	SUBSTRATE	REACTION	REF.
tumefaciens	IFO (3058)	11β, 17α, 21-trihydroxy-4-pregnene-3, 20-dione	—	I-428
(in mixed culture with Mycococcus sp.)	IFO (Δ_1)		Δ^1	I-428
AGROCYBE				
acericola	AL(SS-14)	4-pregnene-3, 20-dione	—	S-825
ALCALIGENES				
faecalis	IAM (ACC 101)	17α, 21-dihydroxy-4-pregnene-3, 20-dione	—	S-849
	IAM (ACC 107)		—	S-849
	NG	1, 3, 5(10)-estratriene-3, 17β-diol	—	H-411
		1, 3, 5(10)-estratriene-3, 16α, 17β-triol	—	H-411
		3β-hydroxy-5-androsten-17-one	keto derivative	H-411
		3α, 7α, 12α-trihydroxy-5β-cholanic acid	3α-OH→3-C=O	S-799
			7α-OH→7-C=O	H-393; S-799
			12α-OH→12-C=O	S-799
			3α-OH→3-C=O; 7α-OH→7-C=O	S-799
			3α-OH→3-C=O; 12α-OH→12-C=O	S-799
			7α-OH→7-C=O; 12α-OH→12-C=O	H-393; S-799
			3α-OH→3-C=O; 7α-OH→7-C=O; 12α-OH→12-C=O	H-393; S-799; S-800
		3α, 12α-dihydroxy-5β-cholanic acid	keto derivative	H-411
		3α, 6α-dihydroxy-5β-cholanic acid	keto derivative	H-411
		3α-hydroxy-5β-cholanic acid	keto derivative	H-411
		5-cholesten-3β-ol	degradation	T-1030

TABLE III

nsformations by Genus: ALLESCHERIA   (Asco. - Eurotiales)
                         ALTERNARIA   (Imperf. - Moniliales)

SPECIES	SOURCE	SUBSTRATE	REACTION	REF.
ecies	SCH (ON-1-42)	17α, 21-dihydroxy-4-pregnene-3,20-dione	Δ^1; 20-C=O → 20β-OH	S-945
LLESCHERIA				
odii	FRI	17α, 21-dihydroxy-4-pregnene-3,20-dione	—	S-849
LTERNARIA				
taticola	FAKU	17α, 21-dihydroxy-4-pregnene-3,20-dione	Δ^1	S-849
	S	17α, 21-dihydroxy-5β-pregnane-3,20-dione	3-C=O→3β-OH	S-845
		4-pregnene-3,20-dione	$\Delta^4 \to 5\beta$-H	S-845; S-849; S-852
			$\Delta^4 \to 5\beta$-H; 3-C=O→3α-OH	S-845; S-849; S-852
			$\Delta^4 \to 5\beta$-H; 3-C=O→3β-OH	S-845; S-849; S-852
		11α-hydroxy-4-pregnene-3,20-dione	$\Delta^4 \to 5\beta$-H	S-852
			$\Delta^4 \to 5\beta$-H; 3-C=O→3α-OH	S-845
		17α-hydroxy-4-pregnene-3,20-dione	$\Delta^4 \to 5\beta$-H	S-852
			$\Delta^4 \to 5\beta$-H; 3-C=O→3α-OH	S-845; S-849
		21-hydroxy-4-pregnene-3,20-dione	$\Delta^4 \to 5\beta$-H	S-845; S-849; S-852
			$\Delta^4 \to 5\beta$-H; 3-C=O→3α-OH	S-845; S-849; S-852
			$\Delta^4 \to 5\beta$-H; 3-C=O→3β-OH	S-845; S-849; S-852
		11β, 21-dihydroxy-4-pregnene-3,20-dione	$\Delta^4 \to 5\beta$-H	S-852
			$\Delta^4 \to 5\beta$-H; 3-C=O→3α-OH	S-845; S-849; S-852

TABLE III

Transformations by Genus: ALTERNARIA

SPECIES	SOURCE	SUBSTRATE	REACTION	REF.
bataticola	S	$17\alpha,21$-dihydroxy-4-pregnene-3,20-dione	$\Delta^4 \to 5\beta$-H	S-845; S-849; S-852
			$\Delta^4 \to 5\beta$-H; 3-C=O$\to 3\alpha$-OH	S-845; S-849; S-852
			$\Delta^4 \to 5\beta$-H; 3-C=O$\to 3\beta$-OH	S-845; S-849; S-852
		$17\alpha,21$-dihydroxy-4-pregnene-3,11,20-trione	$\Delta^4 \to 5\beta$-H	S-845; S-849; S-852
			$\Delta^4 \to 5\beta$-H; 3-C=O$\to 3\alpha$-OH	S-845; S-849; S-852
		$11\beta,17\alpha,21$-trihydroxy-4-pregnene-3,20-dione	$\Delta^4 \to 5\beta$-H	S-845; S-849; S-852
			$\Delta^4 \to 5\beta$-H; 3-C=O$\to 3\alpha$-OH	S-845; S-849; S-852
citri	FRI	$17\alpha,21$-dihydroxy-4-pregnene-3,20-dione	—	S-849
	TNAES	$17\alpha,21$-dihydroxy-4-pregnene-3,20-dione	—	S-849
kikutiana	TNAES	$17\alpha,21$-dihydroxy-4-pregnene-3,20-dione	—	S-849
passiflorae	NG	3β-hydroxy-5-androsten-17-one	Δ^1	W-1105
		4-androstene-3,17-dione	Δ^1	W-1105
		3β-hydroxy-5-pregnen-20-one	Δ^1	W-1105
		$3\beta,21$-dihydroxy-5-pregnen-20-one	Δ^1	W-1105
		4-pregnene-3,20-dione	Δ^1	W-1105
		21-hydroxy-4-pregnene-3,20-dione	Δ^1	W-1105
		$17\alpha,21$-dihydroxy-4-pregnene-3,20-dione	Δ^1	W-1105
		$11\alpha,21$-dihydroxy-4-pregnene-3,20-dione	Δ^1	W-1105
		$11\beta,21$-dihydroxy-4-pregnene-3,20-dione	Δ^1	W-1105

TABLE III

ansformations by Genus: ALTERNARIA
AMANITA   (Basidio. - Agaricales)

SPECIES	SOURCE	SUBSTRATE	REACTION	REF.
assiflorae	NG	$11\alpha,17\alpha,21$-trihydroxy-4-pregnene-3,20-dione	Δ^1	W-1105
		$17\alpha,21$-dihydroxy-4-pregnene-3,11,20-trione	Δ^1	W-1105
		$11\beta,21$-dihydroxy-3,20-diketo-4-pregnen-18-al	Δ^1	W-1105
		$11\beta,17\alpha,21$-trihydroxy-3,20-diketo-4-pregnen-18-al	Δ^1	W-1105
(in sequential fermentation with Curvularia lunata [11β], Ophiobolus herpotrichus [21-OH] and Leptosphaeria maculans [17-OH])		4-pregnene-3,20-dione	Δ^1	W-1107
species	CMI	Hecogenin glycoside	3β - glycoside (saponin) $\rightarrow$ 3β-OH	H-351
	NG	4-pregnene-3,20-dione	Δ^1; 17β-Ac $\rightarrow$ 17-C=O	V-1053
		21-hydroxy-4-pregnene-3,20-dione	Δ^1	V-1053
		$11\beta,21$-dihydroxy-4-pregnene-3,20-dione	Δ^1	V-1053
		$17\alpha,21$-dihydroxy-4-pregnene-3,20-dione	Δ^1	V-1053
		$17\alpha,21$-dihydroxy-4-pregnene-3,11,20-trione	Δ^1	V-1053
		$3\beta,6\beta,8\beta,14\beta$-tetrahydroxy-4,20,22 -bufatrienolide 6-acetate 3-glucoside	3β-[$1^1\xi$-glucoside] $\rightarrow 3\beta$-OH	S-936a
	NRRL	Sarsasapogenin	—	M-587
		Diosgenin	—	M-587
		4-dehydrotigogenone	—	M-587
AMANITA				
mucaria	AL(H-26) AL(F-6)	4-pregnene-3,20-dione	—	S-825
porphyria	AL(H-104)	4-pregnene-3,20-dione	—	S-825

TABLE III

Transformations by Genus: ARMILLARIA   (Basidio. - Agaricales)
ARTHROBACTER   (Schizo. - Eubacteriales)
(See Corynebacterium)

SPECIES	SOURCE	SUBSTRATE	REACTION	REF.
ARMILLARIA				
mellea	WURB (M-6a)	4-pregnene-3,20-dione	—	R-778
ARTHROBACTER				
(See Corynebacterium)				
simplex	ATCC-6946	17β-hydroxy-4-estren-3-one	Δ^1; enol.	K-463
			Δ^1; enol.; 17β-OH $\rightarrow$ 17-C=O	C-116
		4-pregnene-3,20-dione	Δ^1	K-463
		5-pregnene-3β,17α,21-triol-20-one 3,21-diacetate	Δ^1; $\Delta^5 \rightarrow \Delta^4$; 3$\beta$-OH $\rightarrow$3-C=O; 20-C=O $\rightarrow$ 20β-OH; 3,21-diOAc $\rightarrow$3,21-diOH; degradation	C-115
		17α,21-dihydroxy-4-pregnene-3,20-dione	Δ^1	K-463
		17α,21-dihydroxy-4-pregnene-3,11,20-trione	Δ^1	K-463
		11β,17α,21-trihydroxy-4-pregnene-3,20-dione	Δ^1 - high concentration, 50 gm substrate per 100 ml broth	K-463; K-467
		3,20-dioxo-11β-hydroxy-4-pregnen-18-oic acid (18 $\rightarrow$11) lactone	Δ^1	U-1044
	UV(mutant)	17β-hydroxy-4-estren-3-one	Δ^1; enol.; 17β-OH $\rightarrow$ 17-C=O	C-116
		5-pregnene-3β,17α,21-triol-20-one 3,21-diacetate	Δ^1; $\Delta^5 \rightarrow \Delta^4$; 3$\beta$-OH$\rightarrow$3-C=O; 3,21-diOAc $\rightarrow$ 3,21-diOH no degradation	C-115
	(enzyme preparation)	4-androstene-3,17-dione	Δ^1	K-463

TABLE III

ansformations by Genus: ARTHROBACTER
(See Corynebacterium)
ARTHROBOTRYS   (Imperf. - Moniliales)

SPECIES	SOURCE	SUBSTRATE	REACTION	REF.
simplex	ATCC-13260 (Searle B-22-8)	4-androstene-3,17-dione	Δ^1	D-171; M-597
			9α-OH; Δ^1 reverse aldol	D-171; M-597
		19-hydroxy-4-androstene-3,17-dione	Δ^1; reverse aldol (Formaldehyde ↑) enol.	M-597
	NG	9α-fluoro-11β,16α,17α,21-tetrahydroxy-4-pregnene-3,20-dione	Δ^1	T-1007
(Jensen)Lochhead	NG	6α-fluoro-11β,17α,21-trihydroxy-16α-methyl-4-pregnene-3,20-dione	Δ^1	U-1042
		6α-fluoro-11β,14α,17α,21-tetrahydroxy-16α-methyl-4-pregnene-3,20-dione	Δ^1	U-1042
species	ATCC-14560	3β-hydroxy-12a-aza-C-homo-5α-pregnane-12,20-dione acetate	3β-OAc → 3-C=O; Δ^1	M-563
	Searle (20-178)	4-androstene-3,17-dione	Δ^1	D-170
		9α-hydroxy-4-androstene-3,17-dione	Δ^1; reverse aldol; enol.	D-170
		17α[2^1-carboxyethyl]-17β-hydroxy-4-androsten-3-one lactone	Δ^1	C-121
	Searle (B-20-27)	9α-hydroxy-4-pregnene-3,20-dione	17β-Ac→17-C=O	D-172
	Searle (B-22-9)	9α-hydroxy-4-androstene-3,17-dione	Δ^1; reverse aldol; enol.	D-172
RTHROBOTRYS				
onoides	NG	17α,21-dihydroxy-4-pregnene-3,20-dione	—	E-226
actyloides	NG	17α,21-dihydroxy-4-pregnene-3,20-dione	—	E-226
usiformis	NG	17α,21-dihydroxy-4-pregnene-3,20-dione	—	E-226
uperba var. oligospora	NG	17α,21-dihydroxy-4-pregnene 3,20-dione	6β-OH	E-226
			11α-OH	E-226; E-227
			11β-OH	E-226; E-227

TABLE III

Transformations by Genus: ASCOCHYTA (Imperf. - Sphaeropsidales)
ASPERGILLUS (Imperf. - Moniliales)

SPECIES	SOURCE	SUBSTRATE	REACTION	REF.
ASCOCHYTA				
favae	FAKU	17α, 21-dihydroxy-4-pregnene-3,20-dione	—	S-849
linicola	NRRL-2923	17β-hydroxy-4-androsten-3-one	9α-OH	S-828
			9α-OH; 17β-OH $\rightarrow$ 17-C=O	S-828
		17β-hydroxy-17α-methyl-4-androsten-3-one	9α-OH	S-828
		4-pregnene-3,20-dione	9α-OH	S-828
		4-pregnene-3,11,20-trione	9α-OH	S-828
		17α,21-dihydroxy-4-pregnene-3,20-dione	9α-OH	S-828
		21-hydroxy-4-pregnene-3,20-dione acetate	9α-OH; 21-OAc $\rightarrow$ 21-OH	S-828
		11β,21-dihydroxy-4-pregnene-3,20-dione	9α-OH	S-828
pinadella	FAKU	17α,21-dihydroxy-4-pregnene-3,20-dione	—	S-849
vicial	FRI	17α,21-dihydroxy-4-pregnene-3,20-dione	—	S-849
ASPERGILLUS				
aculeatus	IAM	4-pregnene-3,20-dione	—	I-416; I-417
alliaceus	CZAA	4-androstene-3,17-dione	17-C=O$\rightarrow$17a-oxa-17-C=O	C-104
*		3β-hydroxy-5-pregnen-20-one	$\Delta^5\rightarrow\Delta^4$; 3β-OH $\rightarrow$ 3-C=O	C-104
*		4-pregnene-3,20-dione	17β-Ac$\rightarrow$17a-oxa-17-C=O	C-104
	IAM	4-pregnene-3,20-dione	11α-OH	I-416; I-417
amstelodami	CZAA	4-androstene-3,17-dione	—	C-104
*		3β-hydroxy-5-pregnen-20-one	$\Delta^5\rightarrow\Delta^4$; 3β-OH $\rightarrow$3-C=O	C-104
		4-pregnene-3,20-dione	11α-OH; metabolite-X	C-104
	IAM	4-pregnene-3,20-dione	—	I-416; I-417

TABLE III

ransformations by Genus: ASPERGILLUS

SPECIES	SOURCE	SUBSTRATE	REACTION	REF.
amstelodami *	MCC	4-pregnene-3,20-dione	11α-OH; 6β,11α-diOH	D-190
asperescens	IAM	4-pregnene-3,20-dione	11α-OH	I-416; I-417
astianus	IAM	4-pregnene-3,20-dione	6β,11α-diOH	I-416
atropurpureus	CZAA	4-androstene-3,17-dione	metabolite - X	C-104
*		3β-hydroxy-5-pregnen-20-one	$\Delta^5 \to \Delta^4$; 3β-OH → 3-C=O	C-104
		4-pregnene-3,20-dione	metabolite - X	C-104
aureus *	IAM	4-pregnene-3,20-dione	11α-OH; 6β, 11α-diOH	I-416; I-417
auricomus	IAM	4-pregnene-3,20-dione	—	I-416; I-417
avenaceus	IAM	4-pregnene-3,20-dione	—	I-416; I-417
awamori (Nakazawa) *	NRRL (An-S)	Saponins (sapogenin glycoside)	3β-glycoside (saponin) → 3β-OH	K-478; K-479
awamori	CZAA	4-androstene-3,17-dione	—	C-104
*		3β-hydroxy-5-pregnen-20-one	$\Delta^5 \to \Delta^4$; 3β-OH → 3-C=O	C-104
		4-pregnene-3,20-dione	11α-OH	C-104
	IAM (K-0625, K-0924, K-3532, K-5112)	4-pregnene-3,20-dione	11α-OH	I-416; I-417
	NG	4-pregnene-3,20-dione	11α-OH; 6β, 11α-diOH	S-859
		17α-hydroxy-4-pregnene-3,20-dione	—	S-859
		17α,21-dihydroxy-4-pregnene-3,20-dione	—	S-859
patatae	IAM	4-pregnene-3,20-dione	—	I-416; I-417
brevipes	IAM	4-pregnene-3,20-dione	—	I-416; I-417
butyracea	IAM	4-pregnene-3,20-dione	—	I-416; I-417
caesiellus	IAM	4-pregnene-3,20-dione	—	I-416; I-417

TABLE III

Transformations by Genus: ASPERGILLUS

SPECIES	SOURCE	SUBSTRATE	REACTION	REF.
caespitosus	IAM	4-pregnene-3,20-dione	—	I-416; I-417
*	MCC	4-pregnene-3,20-dione	11α-OH	D-190
candidus	CZAA	4-androstene-3,17-dione	metabolite - X	C-104
*		3β-hydroxy-5-pregnen-20-one	$\Delta^5 \rightarrow \Delta^4$; 3β-OH $\rightarrow$ 3-C=O	C-104
		4-pregnene-3,20-dione	metabolite - X	C-104
	FRI	17α,21-dihydroxy-4-pregnene-3,20-dione	—	S-849
	IAM	4-pregnene-3,20-dione	11α-OH	I-416; I-417
*	MCC	4-pregnene-3,20-dione	11α-OH	D-190
	SSSR (28)	4-pregnene-3,20-dione	11α-OH; 6β, 11α-diOH	T-1010
		4-pregnene-3,11,20-trione	—	T-1010
carbonarius	IAM	4-pregnene-3,20-dione	—	I-416; I-417
	MCC	4-pregnene-3,20-dione	—	D-190
carneus	CBS	3-hydroxy-1,3,5(10)-estratrien-17-one	7α-OH	L-495; L-497
			15α-OH	L-495; L-497
			7α-OH; 17-C=O $\rightarrow 17\beta$-OH	L-495; L-497
			15α-OH; 17-C=O $\rightarrow 17\beta$-OH	L-495; L-497
		1,3,5(10)-estratriene-3,17β-diol	7α-OH	L-495; L-497
			15α-OH	L-495; L-497
			7α-OH; 17β-OH $\rightarrow$ 17-C=O	L-495; L-497
			15α-OH; 17β-OH $\rightarrow$ 17-C=O	L-495; L-497
*	IAM	4-pregnene-3,20-dione	11α-OH; 6β, 11α-diOH	I-416; I-417
chevalieri	CZAA	4-androstene-3,17-dione	17-C=O $\rightarrow$17a-oxa-17-C=O	C-104
*		3β-hydroxy-5-pregnen-20-one	$\Delta^5 \rightarrow \Delta^4$; 3β-OH $\rightarrow$ 3-C=O	C-104

TABLE III

ansformations by Genus: ASPERGILLUS

SPECIES		SOURCE	SUBSTRATE	REACTION	REF.
chevalieri		IAM	4-pregnene-3,20-dione	—	I-416; I-417
	*	MCC	4-pregnene-3,20-dione	11α-OH; 6β, 11α-diOH	D-190
		NG	4-pregnene-3,20-dione	17β-Ac→ 17-C=O	C-102
				17β-Ac →17a- oxa-17-C=O	C-102
	*	NRRL (CZ-43)	Saponins (sapogenin glycosides)	3β-glycoside (saponin) → 3β-OH	K-478; K-479
cinnamomeus		CZAA	4-androstene-3,17-dione	metabolite - X	C-104
	*		3β-hydroxy-5-pregnen-20-one	$\Delta^5 \to \Delta^4$; 3β- OH →3-C=O	C-104
			4-pregnene-3,20-dione	metabolite - X	C-104
	*	IAM	4-pregnene-3,20-dione	11α-OH; 6β, 11α-diOH	I-416; I-417
citri		FRI	17α,21-dihydroxy-4-pregnene- 3,20-dione	—	S-849
citrisporus	*	IAM	4-pregnene-3,20-dione	11α-OH; 6β, 11α-diOH	I-416; I-417
clavatus		ATCC-9598	21-hydroxy-4-pregnene-3,20- dione acetate	11α-OH; 21- OAc → 21-OH	M-603
		ATCC-10058	4-pregnene-3,20-dione	11α-OH	M-603
		CZAA	4-androstene-3,17-dione	—	C-104
	*		3β-hydroxy-5-pregnen-20-one	$\Delta^5 \to \Delta^4$; 3β-OH → 3-C=O	C-104
			4-pregnene-3,20-dione	11α-OH	C-104
		IAM	4-pregnene-3,20-dione	11α-OH; 6β, 11α-diOH	I-416; I-417
	*	MCC	4-pregnene-3,20-dione	11α-OH	D-190
conicus	*	MCC	4-pregnene-3,20-dione	11α-OH	D-190
echinulatus	*	IAM	4-pregnene-3,20-dione	11α-OH; 6β, 11α-diOH	I-416; I-417
	*	MCC	4-pregnene-3,20-dione	11α-OH	D-190
effusus		CZAA	4-androstene-3,17-dione	—	C-104
	*		3β-hydroxy-5-pregnen-20-one	$\Delta^5 \to \Delta^4$; 3β-OH → 3-C=O	C-104

TABLE III

Transformations by Genus: ASPERGILLUS

SPECIES	SOURCE	SUBSTRATE	REACTION	REF.
effusus	CZAA	4-pregnene-3,20-dione	11α-OH	C-104
elegans	CZAA	4-androstene-3,17-dione	metabolite - X	C-104
*		3β-hydroxy-5-pregnen-20-one	$\Delta^5 \rightarrow \Delta^4$; 3β-OH $\rightarrow 3$-C=O	C-104
		4-pregnene-3,20-dione	metabolite - X	C-104
	IAM	4-pregnene-3,20-dione	11α-OH; 6β, 11α-diOH	I-416; I-417
fischeri	ATCC-1020	21-hydroxy-4-pregnene-3,20-dione acetate	21-OAc→21-OH; 11α-OH	M-603
	CZAA	4-androstene-3,17-dione	17-C=O → 17a-oxa-17-C=O	C-104
		3β-hydroxy-5-pregnen-20-one	no oxidation at 3-C	C-104
		4-pregnene-3,20-dione	17β-Ac→17a-oxa-17-C=O	C-104
	IAM	4-pregnene-3,20-dione	11α-OH; 6β, 11α-diOH	I-416; I-417
*	MCC	4-pregnene-3,20-dione	11α-OH	D-190
flavipes	ATCC-11013	4-androstene-3,17-dione	17-C=O→13,17-seco-13α-OH-16-COOH	H-398
		17α-oxa-D-homo-4-androstene-3,17-dione	17a-oxa-17-C=O →13,17-seco-13α-OH-16-COOH	H-398
		4-pregnene-3,20-dione	17β-Ac→17a-oxa-17-C=O	F-270
			17β-Ac→13,17-seco-13α-OH-16-COOH	H-398
	CZAA	4-androstene-3,17-dione	17-C=O → 17a-oxa-17-C=O	C-104
*		3β-hydroxy-5-pregnene-20-one	$\Delta^5 \rightarrow \Delta^4$; 3β-OH $\rightarrow 3$-C=O	C-104
*		4-pregnene-3,20-dione	17β-Ac → 17a-oxa-17-C=O	C-104
	IAM	4-pregnene-3,20-dione	11α-OH; 6β, 11α-diOH	I-416; I-417
*	MCC	4-pregnene-3,20-dione	11α-OH; 6β, 11α-diOH	D-190

TABLE III

Transformations by Genus: ASPERGILLUS

SPECIES	SOURCE	SUBSTRATE	REACTION	REF.
flavus	ATCC-9170	4-pregnene-3,20-dione	11α-OH	M-603
	ATCC-9807	Saponins (sapogenin glycosides)	hydrolysis of glycosides to aglycones (sapogenins)	K-478
	CZAA	4-androstene-3,17-dione	17-C=O→17a-oxa-17-C=O	C-104
*		3β-hydroxy-5-pregnen-20-one	Δ^5→Δ^4; 3β-OH →3-C=O	C-104
*		4-pregnene-3,20-dione	17β-Ac→17a-oxa-17-C=O	C-104
	FRI	17α,21-dihydroxy-4-pregnene-3,20-dione	—	S-849
*	IAM	4-pregnene-3,20-dione	11α-OH; 6β, 11α-diOH	I-416; I-417
	IPB	5-androstene-3β,17α-diol	3β-OH→3-C=O; Δ^5→Δ^4	H-337
		5-androstene-3β,17β-diol	3β-OH→3-C=O; Δ^5→Δ^4	H-337
*	MCC	4-pregnene-3,20-dione	11α-OH	D-190
	NG	4-pregnene-3,20-dione	17β-Ac → 17-C=O	P-726
			17β-Ac→17a-oxa-17-C=O	P-726
		17α-hydroxy-4-pregnene-3,20-dione	17α-OH-17β-Ac →17a-oxa-17-C=O	P-726
		21-hydroxy-4-pregnene-3,20-dione	17β-(20-C=O-21-OH) → 17-C=O	P-726
			17β-(20-C=O-21-OH)→17a-oxa-17-C=O	P-726
		17α,21-dihydroxy-4-pregnene-3,20-dione	17α-OH-17β-(20-C=O-21-OH)→17-C=O	P-726
			17α-OH-17β-(20-C=O-21-OH)→17a-oxa-17-C=O	P-726
	NRRL	Sarsasapogenin	—	M-587
		Diosgenin	—	M-587

TABLE III

Transformations by Genus: ASPERGILLUS

SPECIES		SOURCE	SUBSTRATE	REACTION	REF.
flavus		NRRL	4-dehydrotigogenone	—	M-587
	*	SSSR (27)	4-pregnene-3,20-dione	$6\beta,11\alpha$-diOH	T-1010
			4-pregnene-3,11,20-trione	—	T-1010
fonsecaeus		IAM	4-pregnene-3,20-dione	—	I-416; I-417
fumigatus		CZAA	4-androstene-3,17-dione	metabolite - X	C-104
	*		3β-hydroxy-5-pregnen-20-one	$\Delta^5 \to \Delta^4$; 3β-OH $\to$ 3-C=O	C-104
			4-pregnene-3,20-dione	metabolite - X	C-104
	*	IAM	4-pregnene-3,20-dione	11α-OH; 6β, 11α-diOH	I-416; I-417
		IAM (mutant)		—	I-416; I-417
	*	MCC	4-pregnene-3,20-dione	11α-OH	D-190
			21-hydroxy-4-pregnene-3,20-dione	11β-OH	H-328
		NRRL	Sarsasapogenin	—	M-587
			Diosgenin	—	M-587
			4-dehydrotigogenone	—	M-587
	*	SSSR (12)	4-pregnene-3,20-dione	$6\beta,11\alpha$-diOH	T-1010
	*	SSSR (14)	4-pregnene-3,20-dione	$6\beta,11\alpha$-diOH	T-1010
			4-pregnene-3,11,20-trione	—	T-1010
fumigatus Fres.		NG	$3\beta,6\beta,8\beta,14$-tetrahydroxy-4,20,22 -bufatrienolide 6-acetate 3-glucoside	3β-$[1^1 \xi$-glucoside] $\to 3\beta$-OH	S-936a
giganteus		ATCC-10059	4-pregnene-3,20-dione	$11\alpha,15\beta$-diOH	D-179; D-180
	*	IAM	4-pregnene-3,20-dione	11α-OH; 6β, 11α-diOH	I-416; I-417
		IAM (mutant)		—	D-190
glaucus		IAM	4-pregnene-3,20-dione	—	I-416; I-417
	*	NRRL (CZ-5)	Saponins (sapogenin glycosides)	3β-glycoside (saponin) $\to$ 3β-OH	K-478; K-479
		SSSR	4-pregnene-3,11,20-trione	—	T-1010

TABLE III

Transformations by Genus: ASPERGILLUS

SPECIES		SOURCE	SUBSTRATE	REACTION	REF.
gracilis	*	IAM	4-pregnene-3,20-dione	11α-OH; 6β, 11α-diOH	I-416; I-417
		MCC	4-pregnene-3,20-dione	—	D-190
gymnosardae		IAM	4-pregnene-3,20-dione	—	I-416; I-417
herbariorum		IAM	4-pregnene-3,20-dione	—	I-416; I-417
inuii	*	IAM	4-pregnene-3,20-dione	11α-OH; 6β, 11α-diOH	I-416; I-417
itaconicus		ATCC-10021	4-pregnene-3,20-dione	11α-OH	M-603
		IAM	4-pregnene-3,20-dione	11α-OH; 6β, 11α-diOH	I-416; I-417
janus		IAM	4-pregnene-3,20-dione	—	I-416; I-417
japonicus	*	IAM	4-pregnene-3,20-dione	11α-OH; 6β, 11α-diOH	I-416; I-417
kanagaw-aensis		IAM	4-pregnene-3,20-dione	—	I-416; I-417
kawachii		IAM	4-pregnene-3,20-dione	—	I-416; I-417
luchuensis		ATCC-10061	4-pregnene-3,20-dione	11α-OH	M-603
		CZAA	4-androstene-3,17-dione	—	C-104
	*		3β-hydroxy-5-pregnen-20-one	$\Delta^5 \rightarrow \Delta^4$; 3β-OH → 3-C=O	C-104
			4-pregnene-3,20-dione	11α-OH	C-104
	*	MCC	4-pregnene-3,20-dione	11α-OH	D-190
mangini	*	MCC	4-pregnene-3,20-dione	11α-OH	D-190
melleus		CZAA	4-androstene-3,17-dione	—	C-104
	*		3β-hydroxy-5-pregnen-20-one	$\Delta^5 \rightarrow \Delta^4$; 3β-OH →3-C=O	C-104
			4-pregnene-3,20-dione	11α-OH	C-104
		IAM	4-pregnene-3,20-dione	—	I-416; I-417
minimus (minutus)	*	IAM	4-pregnene-3,20-dione	11α-OH; 6β, 11α-diOH	I-416; I-417
miyakoensis	*	IAM	4-pregnene-3,20-dione	11α-OH; 6β, 11α-diOH	I-416; I-417

TABLE III

Transformations by Genus: ASPERGILLUS

SPECIES		SOURCE	SUBSTRATE	REACTION	REF.
mollis	*	IAM	4-pregnene-3,20-dione	11α-OH; 6β, 11α-diOH	I-416; I-417
montevidensis	*	MCC	4-pregnene-3,20-dione	11α-OH	D-190
nakazawai	*	IAM (K-2024)	4-pregnene-3,20-dione	11α-OH; 6β, 11α-diOH	I-416; I-417
nidulans		ATCC-10074	4-pregnene-3,20-dione	11α-OH	M-603
			16α-hydroxy-4-pregnene-3,20-dione	6β-OH	F-265; F-267; F-288
			21-hydroxy-4-pregnene-3,20-dione acetate	11α-OH; 21-OAc $\rightarrow$ 21-OH	M-603
			$17\alpha,21$-dihydroxy-4-pregnene-3,20-dione	11α-OH	F-288
		ATCC-11267	4,9(11)-pregnadiene-3,20-dione	$6\beta,12\alpha$-diOH	F-277; F-279
			A-nor-3-pregnene-2,20-dione	6β-OH	T-1006; W-1076
				11α-OH	T-1006; W-1076
			6α-fluoro-17α-hydroxy-4-pregnene-3,20-dione	11α-OH	F-268
			6α-chloro-17α-hydroxy-4-pregnene-3,20-dione	11α-OH	F-268
			6α-chloro-$17\alpha,21$-dihydroxy-4-pregnene-3,20-dione	11α-OH	F-268
			6α-fluoro-$17\alpha,21$-dihydroxy-4-pregnene-3,20-dione	11α-OH	F-268
				15β-OH	F-268
		CZAA	4-androstene-3,17-dione	—	C-104
	*		3β-hydroxy-5-pregnen-20-one	$\Delta^5 \rightarrow \Delta^4$; 3β-OH $\rightarrow$ 3-C=O	C-104
			4-pregnene-3,20-dione	11α-OH	C-104
	*	IAM	4-pregnene-3,20-dione	11α-OH; 6β, 11α-diOH	I-416; I-417
	*	MCC	4-pregnene-3,20-dione	11α-OH	D-190
		NRRL	Sarsasapogenin	—	M-587
			Diosgenin	—	M-587
			4-dehydrotigogenone	—	M-587

TABLE III

ansformations by Genus: ASPERGILLUS

SPECIES	SOURCE	SUBSTRATE	REACTION	REF.
hidulans	SSSR	11α-hydroxy-4-pregnene-3,20-dione	—	T-1010
	SSSR (13)	4-pregnene-3,20-dione	11α-OH; 6β,11α-diOH	T-1010
*		4-pregnene-3,11,20-trione	17α-OH	T-1010
	SSSR (23)	4-pregnene-3,20-dione	11α-OH; 6β,11α-diOH	T-1010
*		4-pregnene-3,11,20-trione	17α-OH	T-1010
higer	ATCC-6257	4-pregnene-3,20-dione	11α-OH	M-603
	ATCC-9142	A-nor-3-pregnene-2,20-dione	21-OH	W-1077
		19-nor-4-pregnene-3,20-dione	21-OH	Z-1123; Z-1124
		4-pregnene-3,20-dione	21-OH	Z-1123; Z-1124
		6β-hydroxy-4-pregnene-3,20-dione	21-OH	Z-1123; Z-1124
		11α-hydroxy-4-pregnene-3,20-dione	21-OH	Z-1123; Z-1124
		11β-hydroxy-4-pregnene-3,20-dione	21-OH	Z-1123; Z-1124
		14α-hydroxy-4-pregnene-3,20-dione	21-OH	Z-1123
		17α-hydroxy-4-pregnene-3,20-dione	21-OH	Z-1124
		4-pregnene-3,11,20-trione	21-OH	Z-1123; Z-1124
	ATCC-9145	19-nor-4-pregnene-3,20-dione	21-OH	R-783
		3β-hydroxy-5-pregnen-20-one	21-OH	R-783
		4-pregnene-3,20-dione	21-OH	R-783
		6β-hydroxy-4-pregnene-3,20-dione	21-OH	R-783
		11β-hydroxy-4-pregnene-3,20-dione	21-OH	R-783
		17α-hydroxy-4-pregnene-3,20-dione	21-OH	R-783
		4-pregnene-3,11,20-trione	21-OH	R-783

TABLE III

Transformations by Genus: ASPERGILLUS

SPECIES	SOURCE	SUBSTRATE	REACTION	REF.
niger	ATCC-10549	4-pregnene-3,20-dione	11α-OH	M-603
	ATCC-10577	5β-pregnane-3,20-dione	11α-OH	M-603
		4-pregnene-3,20-dione	11α-OH	M-603
		17α-hydroxy-4-pregnene-3,20-dione	11α-OH	M-603
		21-hydroxy-4-pregnene-3,20-dione	11α-OH	M-603
		$17\alpha,21$-dihydroxy-4-pregnene-3,20-dione	11α-OH	M-603
		4,16-pregnadiene-3,20-dione	11α-OH; Δ^{16}-17-Ac$\rightarrow$17α-Ac	M-603
	CZAA	4-androstene-3,17-dione	—	C-104
*		3β-hydroxy-5-pregnen-20-one	3β-OH$\rightarrow$3-C=O; $\Delta^5\rightarrow\Delta^4$	C-104
		4-pregnene-3,20-dione	11α-OH	C-104
	FRI	$17\alpha,21$-dihydroxy-4-pregnene-3,20-dione	—	S-849
*	IAM	4-pregnene-3,20-dione	11α-OH; 6β, 11α-diOH	I-416; I-417
*	MCC	4-pregnene-3,20-dione	11α-OH; 6β, 11α-diOH	D-190
	NG	4-androstene-3,17-dione	6β-OH	F-288
		A-nor-3-pregnene-2,20-dione	21-OH	L-502
		d,l-3β-hydroxy-5-pregnen-20-one	d,l-3β-OH $\rightarrow$ d-3-C=O + l-3β-OH	W-1102
*		3β-hydroxy-5-pregnen-20-one	3β-OH$\rightarrow$3-C=O; $\Delta^5\rightarrow\Delta^4$	P-710
			3β-OH$\rightarrow$3-C=O; $\Delta^5\rightarrow\Delta^4$; 11α-OH	F-288
			3β-OH$\rightarrow$3-C=O; $\Delta^5\rightarrow\Delta^4$; 6β, 11α-diOH	F-288
		4-pregnene-3,20-dione	11α-OH	M-566
		16α-hydroxy-4-pregnene-3,20-dione	11α-OH	F-265; F-267; F-283
		(20S)-20-hydroxy-18,20-cyclo-4-pregnen-3-one	—	W-1071

TABLE III

ansformations by Genus: ASPERGILLUS

SPECIES		SOURCE	SUBSTRATE	REACTION	REF.
iger		Sandoz NG	$3\beta,6\beta,8\beta,14\beta$-tetrahydroxy-4, 20,22 -bufatrienolide 6- acetate 3-glucoside	3β-[1^1_ξ-glucoside] $\rightarrow 3\beta$-OH	S-936a
	*	NRRL-3,328, 330,334,1292 ALCA(5 TC-251-4247)	Saponins (agave)	3β-glycoside (saponin) $\rightarrow$ 3β-OH	K-479
		PIRI(47)	4-pregnene-3,20-dione	11α-OH	W-1120
				$11\alpha,21$-diOH	W-1081; W-1120; W-1121
		PIRI (mutant)	4-pregnene-3,20-dione	11α-OH (only)	W-1120
		SSSR(3, 10, 25)	4-pregnene-3,20-dione	11α-OH	T-1010
		SSSR(21, 22,24,29, 30,31,33)	4-pregnene-3,20-dione	11α-OH; 6β, 11α-diOH	T-1010
	*	SSSR(2, 7,10,29,31)	4-pregnene-3,11,20-trione	17α-OH	T-1010
		SSSR(3, 4,5,6,8,21, 22,24,25,30, 33)	4-pregnene-3,11,20-trione	—	T-1010
		WISC (72-2)	4-pregnene-3,20-dione	11α-OH	F-283
				$6\beta,11\alpha$-diOH	F-283
			17α-hydroxy-4-pregnene-3,20- dione	11α-OH	F-283
				11α-OH; 17α- OH-17β-Ac $\rightarrow$ D-homo-17a ξ- OH-$17a\xi$-Me- 17-C=O	F-283
			21-hydroxy-4-pregnene-3,20- dione	11α-OH	F-283
			$17\alpha,21$-dihydroxy-4-pregnene- 3,20-dione	11α-OH	F-283
			6α-fluoro-$17\alpha,21$-dihydroxy-4- pregnene-3,20-dione	11α-OH	F-268
iveo-glaucus	*	MCC	4-pregnene-3,20-dione	11α-OH; 6β, 11α-diOH	D-190
iveus	*	MCC	4-pregnene-3,20-dione	11α-OH	D-190

TABLE III

Transformations by Genus: ASPERGILLUS

SPECIES	SOURCE	SUBSTRATE	REACTION	REF.
ochraceus	ATCC-1009	4-pregnene-3,20-dione	11α-OH	M-603
ochraceus (Wilhelm)	C	20S-hydroxy-18,20-cyclo-4-pregnen-3-one	11α-OH	W-1071
	C (924)	18-hydroxy-4-pregnene-3,20-dione	11α-OH	W-1110
		6α-fluoro-17α,21-dihydroxy-16α-methyl-4-pregnene-3,20-dione	11α-OH	W-1098
		6α-fluoro-17α,21-dihydroxy-16α-methyl-4-pregnene-3,20-dione 21-acetate	11α-OH; 21-OAc →21-OH	W-1098
	CZAA	4-androstene-3,17-dione	—	C-104
*		3β-hydroxy-5-pregnen-20-one	$\Delta^5 \rightarrow \Delta^4$; 3β-OH $\rightarrow$ 3-C=O	C-104
		4-pregnene-3,20-dione	11α-OH	C-104
*	IAM	4-pregnene-3,20-dione	11α-OH; 6β,11α-diOH	I-416; I-417
	IAM (mutant)	4-pregnene-3,20-dione	11α-OH (only)	I-416; I-417
	MCC	16α,17α-oxido-5α-pregnane-3,20-dione	11α-OH	K-439; K-440
		4-pregnene-3,20-dione	11α-OH; 6β,11α-diOH	D-190
			11α-OH (High concentration 30 - 50 grams per liter)	W-1067
	NRRL-405	4-estrene-3,17-dione	11α-OH	D-150
		17β-hydroxy-4-estren-3-one	11α-OH; 17β-OH $\rightarrow$ 17-C=O	D-150
		17β-hydroxy-4-androsten-3-one	11α-OH	S-835; V-1048
		6β-hydroxy-3α,5α-cyclo-pregnan-20-one	11α-OH	S-835
		16α,17α-oxido-5β-pregnane-3,20-dione	11α-OH	K-440; W-1066

TABLE III

ansformations by Genus: ASPERGILLUS

SPECIES	SOURCE	SUBSTRATE	REACTION	REF.
ɔchraceus	NRRL-405	4-pregnene-3,20-dione	11α-OH; (suppression of 6β-OH - effect of zinc)	D-181
			11α-OH	D-182; D-193; K-435; K-436; S-835; S-900; V-1048; W-1065; W-1066
			11α-OH (with conidia)	K-454; S-797
			11α-OH (continuous fermentation)	M-562
			6β,11α-diOH	D-181; D-182; D-193; K-435; K-436; M-562; S-900; V-1048
			6β,11α-diOH (with conidia)	S-797
		4,16-pregnadiene-3,20-dione	11α-OH; 17β-Ac→17-C=O	V-1048
			11α-OH; 17β-Ac→17-C=O (with conidia)	S-835
		6α-fluoro-4-pregnene-3,20-dione	11α-OH	S-835; V-1048
		11α-hydroxy-4-pregnene-3,20-dione	6β-OH	V-1048
		17α-hydroxy-4-pregnene-3,20-dione	11α-OH	S-835; V-1048
		17α-bromo-4-pregnene-3,20-dione	11α-OH	S-835; V-1048
		17α-methyl-4-pregnene-3,20-dione	11α-OH	S-835; V-1048
		21-hydroxy-4-pregnene-3,20-dione	11α-OH	D-182; D-193; S-835; V-1048

TABLE III

Transformations by Genus: ASPERGILLUS

SPECIES	SOURCE	SUBSTRATE	REACTION	REF.
ochraceus	NRRL-405	17α,21-dihydroxy-4-pregnene-3,20-dione	11α-OH	D-182; D-193; K-435; K-436; S-835; V-1048
		17α,21-dihydroxy-1,4-pregna-diene-3,20-dione	11α-OH	S-835; V-1048
	SSSR(26)	4-pregnene-3,20-dione	11α-OH; 6β, 11α-diOH	T-1010
oryzae	CBS	3β,14β-dihydroxy-5β-20(22)-cardenolide	3β-OH→3-C=O	J-432
			7β-OH	J-432
	CZAA	4-androstene-3,17-dione	17-C=O →17a-oxa-17-C=O	C-104
*		3β-hydroxy-5-pregnen-20-one	Δ⁵→Δ⁴; 3β-OH → 3-C=O	C-104
*		4-pregnene-3,20-dione	17β-Ac→17a-oxa-17-C=O	C-104
*	IAM	4-pregnene-3,20-dione	11α-OH; 6β, 11α-diOH	I-416; I-417
	IAM (mutant)	4-pregnene-3,20-dione	—	I-416; I-417
	IAM(24,31)	4-pregnene-3,20-dione	17β-Ac→17a-oxa-17-C=O	K-461
	IAM(1,2,3, 11,15,82)	4-pregnene-3,20-dione	17β-Ac→17a-oxa-17-C=O	K-461
	IAM(24,31)	3β,21-dihydroxy-5-pregnen-20-one 21 acetate	3β-OH→3-C=O; Δ⁵→Δ⁴; 17β-(20-C=O-21-OAc)→17a-oxa-17-C=O	K-461
		21-hydroxy-4-pregnene-3,20-dione	17β-(20-C=O-21-OH)→17a-oxa-17-C=O	K-461
	IAM(24)	17α,21-dihydroxy-4-pregnene-3,20-dione	—	K-461
	IPB	4-androstene-3,17-dione	17-C=O →17β-OH	C-102
			17-C=O→17a-oxa-17-C=O	C-102
		17β-hydroxy-4-androsten-3-one	17β-OH→17-C=O	C-102; H-332

TABLE III

ansformations by Genus: ASPERGILLUS

SPECIES	SOURCE	SUBSTRATE	REACTION	REF.
ryzae	IPB	17β-hydroxy-4-androsten-3-one	17β-OH$\rightarrow$17a-oxa-17-C=O	C-102
		4-pregnene-3,20-dione	17β-Ac$\rightarrow$17β-OH	C-102
			17β-Ac$\rightarrow$17-C=O	C-102
			17β-Ac$\rightarrow$17a-oxa-17-C=O	C-102; H-332
		11α-hydroxy-4-pregnene-3,20-dione	17β-Ac$\rightarrow$17-C=O	C-102; H-332
			17β-Ac$\rightarrow$17β-OH	C-102; H-332
		17α-hydroxy-4-pregnene-3,20-dione	17α-OH-17β-Ac$\rightarrow$17-C=O	C-102
			17α-OH-17β-Ac$\rightarrow$17β-OH	C-102
			17α-OH-17β-Ac$\rightarrow$17a-oxa-17-C=O	C-102; H-332
		4-pregnene-3,11,20-trione	17β-Ac$\rightarrow$17-C=O	C-102
			17β-Ac$\rightarrow$17β-OH	C-102
*	MCC	4-pregnene-3,20-dione	11α-OH	D-190
	Sandoz NG	3β,6β,8β,14β-tetrahydroxy-4,20,22-bufatrienolide 6-acetate 3-glucoside	3β-[1ξ-glucoside]$\rightarrow$3β-OH	S-936a
		3β,14β-dihydroxy-5β-20(22)-cardenolide 3-[glucosyl-digitoxosyl-digitoxosyl-digitoxoside]	glucosyl-digitoxosyl-digitoxosyl-digitoxoside$\rightarrow$digitoxosyl-digitoxosyl-digitoxoside	S-936a
	NI	17β-hydroxy-4-androsten-3-one	17β-OH$\rightarrow$17-C=O	K-482
	SSSR	4-pregnene-3,20-dione	11α-OH; 6β,11α-diOH	T-1010
	SSSR(17)	4-pregnene-3,11,20-trione	—	T-1010
stianus	CZAA	4-androstene-3,17-dione	metabolite - X	C-104
*		3β-hydroxy-5-pregnen-20-one	$\Delta^5\rightarrow\Delta^4$; 3$\beta$-OH$\rightarrow$3-C=O	C-104

TABLE III

Transformations by Genus: ASPERGILLUS

SPECIES		SOURCE	SUBSTRATE	REACTION	REF.
ostianus		CZAA	4-pregnene-3,20-dione	metabolite - X	C-104
	*	IAM	4-pregnene-3,20-dione	11α-OH; 6β, 11α-diOH	I-416; I-417
panamensis		IAM	4-pregnene-3,20-dione	—	I-416; I-417
parasiticus		CZAA	4-androstene-3,17-dione	metabolite - X	C-104
	*		3β-hydroxy-5-pregnen-20-one	$\Delta^5 \to \Delta^4$; 3β-OH $\to$ 3-C=O	C-104
			4-pregnene-3,20-dione	metabolite - X	C-104
	*	IAM	4-pregnene-3,20-dione	11α-OH; 6β, 11α-diOH	I-416; I-417
		MCC	4-pregnene-3,20-dione	—	D-190
penicilloides		CZAA	4-androstene-3,17-dione	17-C=O $\to$ 17a-oxa-17-C=O	C-104
	*		3β-hydroxy-5-pregnen-20-one	$\Delta^5 \to \Delta^4$; 3β-OH $\to$ 3-C=O	C-104
	*		4-pregnene-3,20-dione	17β-Ac $\to$ 17a-oxa-17-C=O	C-104
phoenicis		IAM	4-pregnene-3,20-dione	—	I-416; I-417
		NRRL-1956	plant saponins	3β-glycoside (saponin) $\to$ 3β-OH	K-478
	*			3β-glycoside (saponin) $\to$ 3β-OH	K-479
proliferans		IAM	4-pregnene-3,20-dione	—	I-416; I-417
pseudoglaucus		IAM	4-pregnene-3,20-dione	—	I-416; I-417
	*	MCC	4-pregnene-3,20-dione	11α-OH; 6β, 11α-diOH	D-190
pulverulentus		IAM	4-pregnene-3,20-dione	—	I-416; I-417
quadrilineatus		IAM	4-pregnene-3,20-dione	11α-OH; 6β, 11α-diOH	I-416; I-417
	*	MCC	4-pregnene-3,20-dione	11α-OH; 6β, 11α-diOH	D-190
rehmii		CZAA	4-androstene-3,17-dione	metabolite - X	C-104

TABLE III

ansformations by Genus: ASPERGILLUS

SPECIES		SOURCE	SUBSTRATE	REACTION	REF.
ehmii	*	CZAA	3β-hydroxy-5-pregnen-20-one	$\Delta^5 \to \Delta^4$; 3β-OH $\to$ 3-C=O	C-104
			4-pregnene-3,20-dione	metabolite - X	C-104
epens	*	IAM	4-pregnene-3,20-dione	11α-OH; 6β, 11α-diOH	D-190; I-416; I-417
estrictus		CZAA	4-androstene-3,17-dione	metabolite - X	C-104
			3β-hydroxy-5-pregnen-20-one	$\Delta^5 \to \Delta^4$; 3β-OH $\to$ 3-C=O	C-104
			4-pregnene-3,20-dione	metabolite - X	C-104
		MCC	4-pregnene-3,20-dione	11α-OH	D-190
uber		CZAA	4-androstene-3,17-dione	17-C=O $\to$ 17a-oxa-17-C=O	C-104
			3β-hydroxy-5-pregnen-20-one	—	C-104
	*		4-pregnene-3,20-dione	17β-Ac$\to$17a-oxa-17-C=O	C-104
		IAM	4-pregnene-3,20-dione	11α-OH; 6β, 11α-diOH	I-416; I-417
	*	MCC	4-pregnene-3,20-dione	11α-OH; 6β, 11α-diOH	D-190
ugulosus		IAM	4-pregnene-3,20-dione	11α-OH; 6β, 11α-diOH	I-416; I-417
		MCC	4-pregnene-3,20-dione	11α-OH	D-190
aitoi		IAM (R-1216) (H-0756)	4-pregnene-3,20-dione	11α-OH	I-416; I-417
				6β-OH; 11α-OH	I-416; I-417
clerotiorum		CZAA	4-androstene-3,17-dione	17-C=O $\to$ 17a-oxa-17-C=O	C-104
	*		3β-hydroxy-5-pregnen-20-one	$\Delta^5 \to \Delta^4$; 3β-OH $\to$ 3-C=O	C-104
	*		4-pregnene-3,20-dione	17β-Ac$\to$17a-oxa-17-C=O	C-104
		IAM	4-pregnene-3,20-dione	—	I-416; I-417
ojae	*	IAM	4-pregnene-3,20-dione	6β,11α-diOH	I-416; I-417
		IAM mutant	4-pregnene-3,20-dione	11α-OH	I-416; I-417

TABLE III

Transformations by Genus: ASPERGILLUS

SPECIES		SOURCE	SUBSTRATE	REACTION	REF.
sparsus		IAM	4-pregnene-3,20-dione	—	I-416; I-417
species	*	MCC	4-pregnene-3,20-dione	$11\alpha,17\alpha$-diOH	D-180
		NG	1,3,5(10)-estratriene-3β,17β-diol (sole carbon source)	—	T-1033
			3-hydroxy-1,3,5(10)-estratrien-17-one (sole carbon source)	—	T-1033
		Sandoz NG (811,882, 883,888,895, 906)	$3\beta,6\beta,8\beta,14\beta$-tetrahydroxy-4-20,22-bufatrienolide 6-acetate 3-glucoside	3β-[$1^1\xi$-gluco-side] $\rightarrow 3\beta$-OH	S-936a
			$3\beta,14\beta$-dihydroxy-5β-20(22)-cardenolide 3-[glucosyl-digitoxosyl-digitoxosyl-digitoxoside]	glucosyl-digitoxosyl-digitoxosyl-digitoxoside $\rightarrow$ digitoxosyl-digitoxosyl-digitoxoside	S-936a
		NG	3-hydroxy-4-cholenic acid (sole carbon source)	—	T-1033
			$3\alpha,7\alpha,12\alpha$-trihydroxy-5β-cholanic acid (sole carbon source)	—	T-1033
			3β-chloro-5-cholestene (sole carbon source)	—	T-1033
			$5\alpha,6\beta$-dibromocholestan-3β-ol acetate (sole carbon source)	—	T-1033
		PIRI	4-pregnene-3,20-dione	11α-OH; $11\alpha,21$-diOH	W-1081
sulphureus	*	IAM	4-pregnene-3,20-dione	11α-OH; $6\beta,11\alpha$-diOH	I-416; I-417
sydowi		CZAA	4-androstene-3,17-dione	—	C-104
	*		3β-hydroxy-5-pregnen-20-one	$\Delta^5 \rightarrow \Delta^4$; 3β-OH$\rightarrow$ 3-C=O	C-104
			4-pregnene-3,20-dione	11α-OH; metabolite - X	C-104
		IAM	4-pregnene-3,20-dione	11α-OH; $6\beta,11\alpha$-diOH	I-416; I-417
	*	MCC	4-pregnene-3,20-dione	11α-OH	D-190
tamarii		CZAA	4-androstene-3,17-dione	—	C-104

TABLE III

Transformations by Genus: ASPERGILLUS

SPECIES		SOURCE	SUBSTRATE	REACTION	REF.
marii	*	CZAA	3β-hydroxy-5-pregnen-20-one	$\Delta^5 \to \Delta^4$; 3β-OH → 3-C=O	C-104
			4-pregnene-3,20-dione	11α-OH	C-104
	*	IAM (mutant)	4-pregnene-3,20-dione	11α-OH; 6β, 11α-diOH	I-416; I-417
	*	MCC	4-pregnene-3,20-dione	11α-OH	D-190
		NRRL (RBI)	Saponins (agave)	3β-glycoside (saponin) → 3β-OH	K-479
erreus		CZAA	4-androstene-3,17-dione	17-C=O→17a- oxa-17-C=O	C-104
	*		3β-hydroxy-5-pregnen-20-one	$\Delta^5 \to \Delta^4$; 3β-OH → 3-C=O	C-104
	*		4-pregnene-3,20-dione	17β-Ac→17a- oxa-17-C=O	C-104
	*	IAM (mutant)	4-pregnene-3,20-dione	11α-OH; 6β, 11α-diOH	I-416; I-417
	*	MCC	4-pregnene-3,20-dione	11α-OH; 6β, 11α-diOH	D-190
		MCC (MF-181)	Dioscin	3β-glycoside → 3β-OH	R-781
		NRRL	Sarsasapogenin	—	M-587
			Diosgenin	—	M-587
			4-dehydrotigogenone	—	M-587
erricola		CZAA	4-androstene-3,17-dione	17-C=O → 17a- oxa-17-C=O	C-104
	*		3β-hydroxy-5-pregnen-20-one	$\Delta^5 \to \Delta^4$; 3β-OH →3-C=O	C-104
	*		4-pregnene-3,20-dione	17β-Ac→17a- oxa-17-C=O	C-104
	*	IAM	4-pregnene-3,20-dione	11α-OH; 6β, 11α-diOH	I-416; I-417
	*	MCC	4-pregnene-3,20-dione	11α-OH	D-190
nguis		IAM	4-pregnene-3,20-dione	—	I-416; I-417
	*	MCC	4-pregnene-3,20-dione	11α-OH; 6β, 11α-diOH	D-190
		NRRL	Sarsasapogenin	—	M-587

304

TABLE III

Transformations by Genus: ASPERGILLUS

SPECIES		SOURCE	SUBSTRATE	REACTION	REF.
unguis		NRRL	Diosgenin	—	M-587
			4-dehydrotigogenone	—	M-587
usamii		IAM (B-407)	4-pregnene-3,20-dione	11α-OH	I-416; I-417
	*	IAM (R-0635)	4-pregnene-3,20-dione	11α-OH; $6\beta,11\alpha$-diOH	I-416; I-417
	*	IAM (mutant) (59-1)	4-pregnene-3,20-dione	11α-OH; $6\beta,11\alpha$-diOH	I-416; I-417
ustus		ATCC-10032	4-pregnene-3,20-dione	11α-OH	M-603
			21-hydroxy-4-pregnene-3,20-dione acetate	11α-OH; 21-OAc→21-OH	M-603
		CZAA	4-androstene-3,17-dione	—	C-104
	*		3β-hydroxy-5-pregnen-20-one	$\Delta^5\to\Delta^4$; 3β-OH → 3-C=O	C-104
			4-pregnene-3,20-dione	11α-OH	C-104
	*	IAM	4-pregnene-3,20-dione	11α-OH; $6\beta,11\alpha$-diOH	I-416; I-417
	*	MCC	4-pregnene-3,20-dione	11α-OH	D-190
varians	*	IAM	4-pregnene-3,20-dione	11α-OH; $6\beta,11\alpha$-diOH	I-416; I-417
variecolor		CZAA	4-androstene-3,17-dione	—	C-104
	*		3β-hydroxy-5-pregnen-20-one	$\Delta^5\to\Delta^4$; 3β-OH → 3-C=O	C-104
			4-pregnene-3,20-dione	11α-OH	C-104
		IAM	4-pregnene-3,20-dione	—	I-416; I-417
	*	MCC	4-pregnene-3,20-dione	11α-OH; $6\beta,11\alpha$-diOH	D-190
versicolor		CZAA	4-androstene-3,17-dione	—	C-104
	*		3β-hydroxy-5-pregnen-20-one	$\Delta^5\to\Delta^4$; 3β-OH →3-C=O	C-104
			4-pregnene-3,20-dione	11α-OH; metabolite - X	C-104
		IAM	4-pregnene-3,20-dione	11α-OH; $6\beta,11\alpha$-diOH	I-416
	*	MCC	4-pregnene-3,20-dione	11α-OH	D-190

TABLE III

ansformations by Genus: ASPERGILLUS
                          AZOTOBACTER   (Schizo. - Eubacteriales)

SPECIES	SOURCE	SUBSTRATE	REACTION	REF.
ersicolor	SSSR (16)	4-pregnene-3,20-dione	$6\beta,11\alpha$-diOH	T-1010
		4-pregnene-3,11,20-trione	—	T-1010
iolaceo-fuscus *	IAM	4-pregnene-3,20-dione	11α-OH; 6β, 11α-diOH	I-416; I-417
entii	ATCC-10583	4-pregnene-3,20-dione	11α-OH	M-603
*	IAM	4-pregnene-3,20-dione	11α-OH; 6β, 11α-diOH	I-416; I-417
	IAM (mutant)	4-pregnene-3,20-dione	—	I-416; I-417
*	MCC	4-pregnene-3,20-dione	11α-OH	D-190
	NRRL	Sarsasapogenin	—	M-587
		Diosgenin	—	M-587
		4-dehydrotigogenone	—	M-587
(in mixed culture with Agrobacterium ethanicus)	NG	5-cholesten-3β-ol	degradation	T-1015; T-1016
		5-cholesten-3β-ol acetate	degradation	T-1015; T-1016
		24β-methyl-5,7,22-cholesta-trien-3β-ol	degradation	T-1015; T-1016
		4,4,14α-trimethyl-5α,8,24-cholestadien-3β-ol	degradation	T-1015; T-1016
		24-ethyl-5,22-cholestadien-3β-ol	degradation	T-1015; T-1016
AZOTOBACTER				
agilis	ATCC-9042	11β,17α,21-trihydroxy-4-pregnene-3,20-dione	Δ^1	T-989
chroococcum	NG	5-cholesten-3β-ol	degradation	M-595
indicus	ATCC-9037	11β,17α,21-trihydroxy-4-pregnene-3,20-dione	Δ^1	T-989
	ATCC-9540	11β,17α,21-trihydroxy-4-pregnene-3,20-dione	Δ^1	T-989
oxydans	NG	5-cholesten-3β-ol	3β-OH →3-C=O; $\Delta^5 \to \Delta^4$; degradation	H-406; H-407
			Δ^7	H-406; H-407

TABLE III

Transformations by Genus: AZOTOBACTER
                             AZOTOMONAS   (Schizo. - Pseudomonadales)
                             BACILLUS   (Schizo. - Eubacteriales)

SPECIES	SOURCE	SUBSTRATE	REACTION	REF.
species	NG	5-cholesten-3β-ol	Δ^7; 3β-OH $\rightarrow$ 3-C=O; $\Delta^5 \rightarrow \Delta^4$; degradation	H-406
vinlandii	NG	5-cholesten-3β-ol	degradation	M-595
AZOTOMONAS				
fluorescens	ATCC-13544	17α,21-dihydroxy-4-pregnene-3,20-dione	Δ^1	T-989
		11β,17α,21-trihydroxy-4-pregnene-3,20-dione	Δ^1	T-989
BACILLUS				
alvei	IFO(3343)	17α,21-dihydroxy-4-pregnene-3,20-dione	11α-OH	S-849
brevis	IFO(3331)	17α,21-dihydroxy-4-pregnene-3,20-dione	—	S-849
cereus	IAM(B-204-1)	17α,21-dihydroxy-4-pregnene-3,20-dione	6β-OH	S-944
			11α-OH	S-944
	IFO	21-hydroxy-4-pregnene-3,20-dione	6β-OH; 11α-OH; 14α-OH	S-849
		11β,21-dihydroxy-4-pregnene-3,20-dione	14α-OH; 11β-OH $\rightarrow$11-C=O	S-849
		17α,21-dihydroxy-4-pregnene-3,20-dione	Δ^1; 6β-OH; 11α-OH; 11β-OH	S-849
			6β-OH; 11α-OH	S-849
	IFO (murao)		Δ^1; 6β-OH; 11α-OH; 11β-OH	S-849
	IFO (DC-3)	17α,21-dihydroxy-4-pregnene-3,20-dione	11α-OH	S-849
	IFO(3001)	17α,21-dihydroxy-4-pregnene-3,20-dione	11α-OH	S-849
	IFO(3015)	17α,21-dihydroxy-4-pregnene-3,20-dione	11α-OH	S-849
	IFO(3039)	17α,21-dihydroxy-4-pregnene-3,20-dione	—	S-849
	IFO(3131)	17α,21-dihydroxy-4-pregnene-3,20-dione	Δ^1	S-849

TABLE III

nsformations by Genus: BACILLUS

SPECIES	SOURCE	SUBSTRATE	REACTION	REF.
ereus	IFO (3466)	11β,17α,21-trihydroxy-4-preg-nene-3,20-dione	—	I-428
(in mixed culture with Myococcus sp. A₁)			Δ^1	I-428
	MCC (MB-718)	4-pregnene-3,20-dione	11α-OH	M-568
	NRRL B-1666	4-pregnene-3,20-dione	11α-OH	M-568
	NG	4-pregnene-3,20-dione	14α-OH	F-288
			6β-OH; 11α-OH	S-859
		17α-hydroxy-4-pregnene-3,20-dione	—	S-859
		17α,21-dihydroxy-4-pregnene-3,20-dione	—	S-859
irculans	IFO(3029)	11β,17α,21-trihydroxy-4-preg-nene-3,20-dione	—	I-428
(in mixed culture with Myococcus sp. A₁)			—	I-428
	IFO (3329)	17α,21-dihydroxy-4-pregnene-3,20-dione	—	S-849
	IFO(3342)	17α,21-dihydroxy-4-pregnene-3,20-dione	—	S-849
losteroides	NG	5-cholesten-3β-ol (sole carbon source)	—	T-1030
oagulans	ATCC-7050	17α,21-dihydroxy-4-pregnene-3,20-dione	—	S-849
	IFO (P-22)	17α,21-dihydroxy-4-pregnene-3,20-dione	—	S-849
	IFO (P-33)	17α,21-dihydroxy-4-pregnene-3,20-dione	—	S-849
	IFO (P-55)	17α,21-dihydroxy-4-pregnene-3,20-dione	—	S-849
oli (communis)	Feces	3,7,12-triketo-5β-cholanic acid	7-C=O→7α-OH	F-289
Taxonomy - now considered in genus - Escherichia		3,7-diketo-5β-cholanic acid	3-C=O→3α-OH; 7-C=O→7α-OH	S-899
irmus	IFO (3330)	17α,21-dihydroxy-4-pregnene-3,20-dione	—	S-849

TABLE III

Transformations by Genus: BACILLUS

SPECIES	SOURCE	SUBSTRATE	REACTION	REF
lentus	ATCC-13805 (mutant)	3β-hydroxy-5-androsten-17-one	Δ^1; 3β-OH $\rightarrow$ 3-C=O; $\Delta^5 \rightarrow \Delta^4$	R-750
		3β-hydroxy-5-androsten-17-one acetate	Δ^1; 3β-OAc $\rightarrow$ 3β-OH; 3β-OH$\rightarrow$ 3-C=O; $\Delta^5 \rightarrow \Delta^4$	R-750
		4-androstene-3,17-dione	Δ^1	R-750
		D-homo-17a-oxa-4-androstene-3,17-dione	Δ^1	R-750
		17β-hydroxy-17α-methyl-4-androsten-3-one	Δ^1	R-750
		3,21-dihydroxy-16α,17α-oxido-5-pregnen-20-one	3β-OH$\rightarrow$3-C=O; $\Delta^5 \rightarrow \Delta^4$; Δ^1	R-750
		17α,21-dihydroxy-4-pregnene-3,20-dione	Δ^1	R-750
		17α,21-dihydroxy-4-pregnene-3,11,20-trione	Δ^1	R-750
		6β,17α,21-trihydroxy-4-pregnene-3,20-dione	Δ^1	R-750
		11β,17α,21-trihydroxy-4-pregnene-3,20-dione	Δ^1	R-750
		12β,17α,21-trihydroxy-4-pregnene-3,20-dione	Δ^1	R-750
		14α,17α,21-trihydroxy-4-pregnene-3,20-dione	Δ^1	R-750
		9α-fluoro-11β,17α,21-trihydroxy-4-pregnene-3,20-dione	Δ^1	R-750
		16α-methyl-4-pregnene-3,20-dione	Δ^1	R-750
		17α-hydroxy-16α-methyl-4-pregnene-3,11,20-trione	Δ^1	R-750
		21-hydroxy-16α-methyl-4-pregnene-3,11,20-trione	Δ^1	R-750
		17α,21-dihydroxy-16α-methyl-4-pregnene-3,11,20-trione	Δ^1	R-750
		9α-fluoro-11β,17α,21-trihydroxy-16α-methyl-4-pregnene-3,20-dione	Δ^1	R-750
		11β,17α-dihydroxy-16α-methyl-4-pregnene-3,20-dione	Δ^1	R-750
		11β,21-dihydroxy-16α-methyl-4-pregnene-3,20-dione	Δ^1	R-750

TABLE III

nsformations by Genus: BACILLUS

SPECIES	SOURCE	SUBSTRATE	REACTION	REF.
ntus	ATCC-13805 (mutant)	17α,21-dihydroxy-16α-methyl-4-pregnene-3,20-dione	Δ¹	R-750
		11β,17α,21-trihydroxy-16α-methyl-4-pregnene-3,20-dione	Δ¹	R-750
acerans (Schardinger) (from leaves of Digitalis purpurea)	NG	Digitonin	3β-glycoside (saponin) → 3β-OH	S-794
	IFO(3483)	17α,21-dihydroxy-4-pregnene-3,20-dione	—	S-849
	IFO(3490)	17α,21-dihydroxy-4-pregnene-3,20-dione	—	S-849
egaterium	ATCC-13368 (SCH-41) (WC-41)	4-pregnene-3,20-dione	15β-OH	H-382
		17α,21-dihydroxy-4-pregnene-3,20-dione	15β-OH	C-126; C-127; H-382
		17α,21-dihydroxy-4-pregnene-3,11,20-trione	15β-OH	C-126
		11α,17α,21-trihydroxy-4-pregnene-3,20-dione	15β-OH	C-126
		11β,17α,21-trihydroxy-4-pregnene-3,20-dione	15β-OH	C-126; C-127
		17α,21-dihydroxy-1,4-pregnadiene-3,11,20-trione	Δ¹ → H	H-382
		11β,17α,21-trihydroxy-1,4-pregnadiene-3,20-dione	Δ¹ → H	H-382
		9α-fluoro-11β,16α,21-trihydroxy-4-pregnene-3,20-dione	15β-OH	N-669
		9α-fluoro-11β,17α,21-trihydroxy-4-pregnene-3,20-dione	15β-OH	N-669
	IFO(6-1)	17α,21-dihydroxy-4-pregnene-3,20-dione	11β-OH; 2β-OH	S-849
	IFO(12-1)	17α,21-dihydroxy-4-pregnene-3,20-dione	11α-OH; 6β-OH	S-849
	IFO(37-1)	17α,21-dihydroxy-4-pregnene-3,20-dione	—	S-849
	IFO(899-1)	17α,21-dihydroxy-4-pregnene-3,20-dione	11α-OH	S-849
	IFO(EC-34)	17α,21-dihydroxy-4-pregnene-3,20-dione	2β-OH	S-849

TABLE III

Transformations by Genus: BACILLUS

SPECIES	SOURCE	SUBSTRATE	REACTION	REF.
megaterium	NG	5-cholesten-3β-ol	—	T-1030
	NRRL	Sarsasapogenin	—	M-587
		Diosgenin	—	M-587
		4-dehydrotigogenone	—	M-587
	NRRL B-938	4-estren-3-one	16α-OH	S-793a
			16β-OH	S-793a
			16-C=O; (via 16α-OH and 16β-OH)	S-793a
		16α-hydroxy-4-estren-3-one	16α-OH → 16-C=O	S-793a
			16α-OH → 16β-OH (via 16-C=O)	S-793a
		16β-hydroxy-4-estren-3-one	16β-OH → 16-C=O	S-793a
		4-estrene-3,16-dione	16-C=O → 16β-OH	S-793a
		4-pregnene-3,20-dione	15β-OH	D-191; M-568
	SSSR	21-hydroxy-4-pregnene-3,20-dione acetate	21-OAc →21-OH	S-948
		17α,21-dihydroxy-4-pregnene-3,20-dione 21-acetate	21-OAc→21-OH	S-948
		17α,21-dihydroxy-4-pregnene-3,11,20-trione 21-acetate	21-OAc→21-OH	S-948
		17α,21-dihydroxy-1,4-pregna-diene-3,11,20-trione 21-acetate	21-OAc→21-OH	S-948
		17α,21-dihydroxy-5β-pregnane-3,11,20-trione 21-acetate	21-OAc→21-OH	S-948
(in mixed culture with Mycobacterium sp.)		17α,20β,21-trihydroxy-4-pregnene-3,11-dione-20,21-diacetate	20β-OAc→20β-OH; 21-OAc → 21-OH; Δ¹	S-917
		16α,17α-oxido-4-pregnene-3,20-dione	20-C=O → 20α-OH	S-947
mycoides	NG	5-cholesten-3β-ol (sole carbon source)	—	T-1018
		24-methyl-5,7,22-cholesta-trien-3β-ol	—	T-1018

TABLE III

nsformations by Genus: BACILLUS

SPECIES	SOURCE	SUBSTRATE	REACTION	REF.
lymyxa	IFO-3020	17α, 21-dihydroxy-4-pregnene-3,20-dione	—	S-849
	NRRL B-694	17α, 21-dihydroxy-4-pregnene-3,20-dione	—	S-849
oteus (ee Genus - Proteus)				
lvifaciens	IAM (N-19-2)	3β-hydroxy-5-androsten-17-one (or acetate)	3β-OH→3-C=O; Δ^5→Δ^4	I-419; I-420; T-1027
			Δ^1; 3β-OH → 3-C=O; Δ^5→Δ^4	I-419; I-420; T-1027
			Δ^1; 3β-OAc → 3β-OH; 3β-OH→ 3-C=O; Δ^5→Δ^4	I-419; I-420
			3β-OH→3-C=O; Δ^5→Δ^4; 6β-OH	I-419; I-420; T-1027
			14α-OH; 3β-OH →3-C=O; Δ^5→Δ^4	I-419; I-420; S-792; T-1027
			6β-OH; X-OH; 3β-OH→3-C=O; Δ^5→Δ^4	S-792; T-1027
			Δ^1; Δ^5→Δ^4; 3β-OH→3-C=O; 14α-OH	I-419; I-420; S-792
			6-C=O; 3β-OH →3-C=O; Δ^5→ 5α-H	I-419; I-420; T-1027
		17β-hydroxy-4-androsten-3-one	17β-OH → 17-C=O	I-419; I-420
			17β-OH → 17-C=O; Δ^1	I-419; I-420
		6β-hydroxy-4-androstene-3,17-dione	Δ^4→Δ^5; ketoniz.	I-419; I-420
		14α-hydroxy-4-androstene-3,17-dione	Δ^1	I-419; I-420
		3β-hydroxy-5-pregnen-20-one	3β-OH→3-C=O; Δ^5→Δ^4	I-419; I-420; T-1027

TABLE III

Transformations by Genus: BACILLUS

SPECIES	SOURCE	SUBSTRATE	REACTION	REF
pulvifaciens	IAM (N-19-2)	3β-hydroxy-5-pregnen-20-one	3β-OH$\rightarrow$3-C=O; $\Delta^5\rightarrow\Delta^4$; Δ^1	I-419; I-420; T-1027
		3β-hydroxy-5-pregnen-20-one acetate	3β-OAc$\rightarrow$3-C=O; $\Delta^5\rightarrow\Delta^4$	I-419; I-420; T-1027
			3β-OAc$\rightarrow$3-C=O; $\Delta^5\rightarrow\Delta^4$; Δ^1	I-419; I-420; T-1027
		$17\alpha,21$-dihydroxy-4-pregnene-3,20-dione	Δ^1	I-419; I-420 T-1027
		$11\beta,21$-dihydroxy-4-pregnene-3,20-dione	Δ^1	I-419; I-420
		$11\beta,17\alpha,21$-trihydroxy-4-pregnene-3,20-dione	Δ^1	I-419; I-420; T-1019 T-1027
		$17\alpha,21$-dihydroxy-4-pregnene-3,11,20-trione	Δ^1	I-419; I-420
pumilus	IAM	$17\alpha,21$-dihydroxy-4-pregnene-3,20-dione	—	S-849
putrificus	NG	4-androstene-3,17-dione	$\Delta^4\rightarrow5\beta$-H	M-545
		17β-hydroxy-4-androsten-3-one	$\Delta^4\rightarrow5\beta$-H	M-545
		4-pregnene-3,20-dione	$\Delta^4\rightarrow5\beta$-H	M-545
pymilus	IFO(3020)	$11\beta,17\alpha,21$-trihydroxy-4-pregnene-3,20-dione	—	I-428
(in mixed culture with Mycococcus sp. A_1)			Δ^1	I-428
roseus	IFO(3041)	$17\alpha,21$-dihydroxy-4-pregnene-3,20-dione	Δ^1	S-849
species	IAM (B-A)	21-hydroxy-4-pregnene-3,20-dione	Δ^1	S-848; S-849
		$11\beta,21$-dihydroxy-4-pregnene-3,20-dione	Δ^1	S-848; S-849
		$17\alpha,21$-dihydroxy-4-pregnene-3,20-dione	Δ^1	S-848; S-849
		$17\alpha,21$-dihydroxy-4-pregnene-3,11,20-trione	Δ^1	S-848; S-849
		$11\beta,17\alpha,21$-trihydroxy-4-pregnene-3,20-dione	Δ^1	S-848; S-849

TABLE III

nsformations by Genus: BACILLUS

SPECIES	SOURCE	SUBSTRATE	REACTION	REF.
ecies	NG	3β-hydroxy-5-androsten-17-one	$\Delta^5 \rightarrow \Delta^4$; 3β-OH→ 3-C=O; 17-C=O →17β-OH (anaerobic conditions)	S-822
		4-androstene-3,17-dione	17-C=O→17β-OH (anaerobic conditions)	S-822
		4-pregnene-3,20-dione	—	S-859
		17α-hydroxy-4-pregnene-3,20-dione	—	S-859
		17α,21-dihydroxy-4-pregnene-3,20-dione	Δ^1	S-859
			20-C=O → 20β-OH	V-1045
haericus	ATCC-245	12α-chloro-21-hydroxy-4-pregnene-3,11,20-trione acetate	Δ^1; 21-OAc → 21-OH	W-1083
		17α,21-dihydroxy-6α,16α-dimethyl-4-pregnene-3,11,20-trione	Δ^1	A-24; A-25
		11β,17α,21-trihydroxy-16α-methyl-4-pregnene-3,20-dione	Δ^1	H-392
	ATCC-7054	12α-fluoro-21-hydroxy-4-pregnene-3,11,20-trione 21-acetate	Δ^1; 21-OAc → 21-OH	W-1083
		12α-fluoro-11β,21-dihydroxy-4-pregnene-3,20-dione acetate	Δ^1; 21-OAc → 21-OH	W-1083
	ATCC-7055	5α-androstane-3,17-dione	Δ^1	H-373; S-933
		5α-androstane-3,17-dione-1α-H^3	Δ^1-(1α-H^3)	B-75a; G-323
		5α-androstane-3,17-dione-1α-H^2	Δ^1-(1α-H^2)	R-768; R-769
		5β-androstane-3,17-dione	—	S-933
		17β-hydroxy-5α-androstan-3-one	Δ^1; 17β-OH → 17-C=O	H-373
		17β-hydroxy-1β-methyl-5α-androstan-3-one	Δ^1; 17β-OH → 17-C=O	H-373
		5α,10α-estrane-3,17-dione	—	S-933

TABLE III

Transformations by Genus: BACILLUS

SPECIES	SOURCE	SUBSTRATE	REACTION	REF.
sphaericus	ATCC-7055	5α-estrane-3,17-dione	Δ^1	S-933
		4-androstene-3,17-dione	Δ^1	H-373; H-399; S-933
		4-androstene-3,17-dione-1α-H^3	Δ^1(from 1α-H^3, 2β-H)	B-75a; G-323
		4-androstene-3,17-dione-1β-H^3	Δ^1 .	B-75a
		4-androstene-3,17-dione-1α-H^2	Δ^1	R-469
		4-androstene-3,17-dione-1β-H^2	Δ^1	R-469
		4-androstene-3,17-dione-2-H^2	Δ^1	R-469
		1α-hydroxy-4-androstene-3,17-dione	—	H-373
		2β-hydroxy-4-androstene-3,17-dione	Δ^1	H-373
		9α-hydroxy-4-androstene-3,17-dione	Δ^1; reverse aldol; enol.	K-473
		9α,18-dihydroxy-4-androstene-3,17-dione	Δ^1; reverse aldol; enol.	K-473
		17β-hydroxy-4-androstene-3-one	Δ^1; 17β-OH $\rightarrow$ 17-C=O	H-373
		17β-hydroxy-4-estren-3-one	Δ^1; enol; 17β-OH $\rightarrow$ 17-C=O	G-317; S-933
		2α,17β-dihydroxy-4-androsten-3-one	Δ^1; 17β-OH $\rightarrow$ 17-C=O	G-318; H-373
		2α,17β-dihydroxy-4-androsten-3-one diacetate	2α-OAc $\rightarrow$ 2α-OH; 17β-OAc $\rightarrow$ 17-C=O	H-399
			Δ^1; 2α-OAc $\rightarrow$ 2α-OH; 17β-OAc $\rightarrow$ 17-C=O	H-399
			2α-OAc $\rightarrow$ 2α-OH; 17β-OAc $\rightarrow$ 17β-OH	H-399
		2β,17β-dihydroxy-4-androsten-3-one diacetate	2β-OAc $\rightarrow$ 2β-OH; 17β-OAc $\rightarrow$ 17-C=O	H-399

TABLE III

nsformations by Genus: BACILLUS

SPECIES	SOURCE	SUBSTRATE	REACTION	REF.
haericus	ATCC-7055	$2\beta,17\beta$-dihydroxy-4-androsten-3-one diacetate	2β-OAc$\rightarrow$2β-OH; 17β-OAc$\rightarrow$ 17β-OH	H-399
		17β-hydroxy-1α-methyl-19-nor-4-androsten-3-one	—	H-373
		17β-hydroxy-2α-methyl-4-androsten-3-one	Δ^1; 17β-OH$\rightarrow$ 17-C=O	H-373
		17α-ethinyl-9α-fluoro-11β,17β-dihydroxy-4-androsten-3-one	Δ^1	N-667
		$11\beta,17\beta$-dihydroxy-17α-methyl-4-androsten-3-one	Δ^1	G-305
		17α-ethinyl-17β-hydroxy-4-androstene-3,11-dione	Δ^1	G-304
		17α-ethinyl-11β,17β-dihydroxy-4,6-androstadien-3-one	Δ^1	G-304
		17α-ethinyl-17β-hydroxy-4,6-androstadiene-3,11-dione	Δ^1	G-304
		17β-hydroxy-17α-methyl-4,9(11)-androstadien-3-one	Δ^1	R-775
		4-pregnene-3,20-dione	Δ^1	H-399
		D-nor-4-pregnene-3,20-dione	Δ^1	R-763
		21-hydroxy-4-pregnene-3,20-dione acetate	Δ^1; 21-OAc $\rightarrow$ 21-OH	S-933
		$11\alpha,21$-dihydroxy-4-pregnene-3,20-dione	Δ^1	S-933
		$17\alpha,21$-dihydroxy-4-pregnene-3,20-dione	Δ^1	H-399; S-942
(in mixed culture with Curvularia lunata - [11β-OH])			Δ^1	K-444
(in mixed culture with Curvularia lunata -[11β-OH])			Δ^1	K-466
(in mixed culture with Cunninghamella blakesleeana-Lendner No. 1[11β-OH])			—	K-466
(in mixed culture with Cunninghamella echinulata -[11α-OH])			Δ^1	K-466

TABLE III

Transformations by Genus: BACILLUS

SPECIES	SOURCE	SUBSTRATE	REACTION	REF.
sphaericus (in mixed culture with Stachylidium biocolor - [11α-OH, 11β-OH])	ATCC-7055	17α,21-dihydroxy-4-pregnene-3,20-dione	Δ^1	K-468
in mixed culture with Verticillium theobromae - [11α-OH,11β-OH])			Δ^1	K-468
		15β,17α,21-trihydroxy-4-pregnene-3,20-dione	Δ^1	C-126; C-127
		11β,17α,21-trihydroxy-4-pregnene-3,20-dione	Δ^1	H-399; S-942
		11α,15β,17α,21-tetrahydroxy-4-pregnene-3,20-dione	Δ^1	C-126; C-127
		11β,15β,17α,21-tetrahydroxy-4-pregnene-3,20-dione	Δ^1	C-126; C-127
		17α-hydroxy-16-methylene-4-pregnene-3,20-dione acetate	Δ^1	S-837
		12α-fluoro-11β,21-dihydroxy-4-pregnene-3,20-dione 21-acetate	Δ^1; 21-OAc → 21-OH	W-1083
		12α-fluoro-21-hydroxy-4-pregnene-3,11,20-trione	Δ^1	W-1083
		17α,21-dihydroxy-4-pregnene-3,11,20-trione	Δ^1	C-127
		17α,21-dihydroxy-4-pregnene-3,11,20-trione 21-acetate	Δ^1	C-120
			Δ^1; 17α-OH-17β-(20-C=O-21-OAc) → 17-C=O	C-120
		15β,17α,21-trihydroxy-4-pregnene-3,11,20-trione	Δ^1	C-126
		7α,17α,21-trihydroxy-4-pregnene-3,11,20-trione 21-acetate	Δ^1; 21-OAc → 21-OH	N-687
		17α,21-dihydroxy-16α-methoxy-4-pregnene-3,11,20-trione	Δ^1	S-838
		17α,21-dihydroxy-6α-methyl-4-pregnene-3,11,20-trione	Δ^1	G-300
		17α,21-dihydroxy-16-methylene-4-pregnene-3,20-dione	Δ^1	M-558
		17α,21-dihydroxy-16α-nitro-methyl-4-pregnene-3,11,20-trione	Δ^1	R-751

TABLE III

Transformations by Genus: BACILLUS

SPECIES	SOURCE	SUBSTRATE	REACTION	REF.
sphaericus	ATCC-7055	6α-fluoro-17α,21-dihydroxy-6α,16α-dimethyl-4-pregnene-3,11,20-trione 21-acetate	Δ^1; 21-OAc $\rightarrow$ 21-OH	A-24
		9α-fluoro-17α,21-dihydroxy-6α,16α-dimethyl-4-pregnene-3,11,20-trione 21-acetate	Δ^1; 21-OAc $\rightarrow$ 21-OH	A-25
		2α-fluoro-17α,21-dihydroxy-4-pregnene-3,11,20-trione	Δ^1	H-401
		11β,17α,21-trihydroxy-16-methylene-4-pregnene-3,20-dione	Δ^1	T-981
		11β,17α,21-trihydroxy-16α-methoxy-4-pregnene-3,20-dione	Δ^1	S-838
		11β,17α,21-trihydroxy-6α-methyl-4-pregnene-3,20-dione	Δ^1	G-300
		9α-fluoro-11β,17α,21-trihydroxy-6α-methyl-4-pregnene-3,20-dione	Δ^1	G-300
		11β,17α,21-trihydroxy-16α-nitromethyl-4-pregnene-3,20-dione	Δ^1	R-751
		9α-fluoro-11β,17α,21-trihydroxy-4-pregnene-3,20-dione	Δ^1	N-669; S-942
		12α-fluoro-11β,17α,21-tri-hydroxy-4-pregnene-3,20-dione	Δ^1	H-380
		9α-fluoro-11β,15β,17α,21-tetrahydroxy-4-pregnene-3,20-dione	Δ^1	N-669
		9α-fluoro-11β,15α,16α,21-tetrahydroxy-4-pregnene-3,20-dione	Δ^1	N-669
		9α-fluoro-11β,16α,17α,21-tetrahydroxy-4-pregnene-3,20-dione	Δ^1	H-399
		9α-fluoro-11β,14α,15β,17α,21-pentahydroxy-4-pregnene-3,20-dione	Δ^1	N-669
		17β,20α-oxido-16-oximino-4-pregnen-3-one	Δ^1	N-686

318

TABLE III

Transformations by Genus: BACILLUS

SPECIES	SOURCE	SUBSTRATE	REACTION	REF.
sphaericus	ATCC-7055	17β,20α-oxido-16-oximino-5-pregnen-3β-ol	$\Delta^5 \to \Delta^4$; 3β-OH→ 3-C=O; Δ^1	N-686
		21-hydroxy-17β,20α-oxido-16-oximino-4-pregnene-3,11-dione	Δ^1	N-686
		17α,21-dihydroxy-4,6-pregnadiene-3,11,20-trione	Δ^1	G-310
		17α,21-dihydroxy-4,6-pregnadiene-3,11,20-trione 21-acetate	Δ^1; 21-OAc → 21-OH	G-310
		11β,17α,21-trihydroxy-4,6-pregnadiene-3,20-dione	Δ^1	G-310
	ATCC-7063	9α-fluoro-11β,17α,21-trihydroxy-6α,16α-dimethyl-4-pregnene-3,20-dione 21-acetate	Δ^1; 21-OAc → 21-OH	A-24; A-25
	ATCC-12488	17α-bromethinyl-17β-methoxy-4-androsten-3-one	Δ^1	O-694; O-695
		17α-chlorethinyl-17β-methoxy-4-androsten-3-one	Δ^1	O-694; O-695
		17α-bromethinyl-6α-fluoro-17β-methoxy-4-androsten-3-one	Δ^1	O-694; O-695
		17α-bromethinyl-17β-hydroxy-6α-methyl-4-androsten-3-one	Δ^1	O-694; O-695
		17α-chlorethinyl-6α-fluoro-17β-methoxy-4-androsten-3-one	Δ^1	O-694; O-695
		17α-chlorethinyl-17β-hydroxy-6α-methyl-4-androsten-3-one	Δ^1	O-694; O-695
		17α-bromethinyl-6-chloro-17β-methoxy-4,6-androstadien-3-one	Δ^1	O-694; O-695
		17α-bromethinyl-6-fluoro-17β-methoxy-4,6-androstadien-3-one	Δ^1	O-694; O-695
		17α-bromethinyl-17β-hydroxy-6-methyl-4,6-androstadien-3-one	Δ^1	O-694; O-695
		6-chloro-17α-chlorethinyl-17β-methoxy-4,6-androstadien-3-one	Δ^1	O-694; O-695

TABLE III

Transformations by Genus: BACILLUS

SPECIES	SOURCE	SUBSTRATE	REACTION	REF.
sphaericus	ATCC-12488	17α-chlorethinyl-6-fluoro-17β-methoxy-4,6-androstadien-3-one	Δ^1	O-694; O-695
		17α-chlorethinyl-17β-hydroxy-6-methyl-4,6-androstadien-3-one	Δ^1	O-694; O-695
		11β,17α,21-trihydroxy-6-methylene-4-pregnene-3,20-dione	Δ^1	F-264
		11β,17α,21-trihydroxy-16α-methyl-6-methylene-4-pregnene-3,20-dione	Δ^1	F-264
	EM	17α,21-dihydroxy-16-methylene-4-pregnene-3,20-dione	Δ^1	M-558
		11β,17α,21-trihydroxy-16-methylene-4-pregnene-3,20-dione	Δ^1	M-558
		9α-fluoro-11β,17α,21-trihydroxy-16-methylene-4-pregnene-3,20-dione	Δ^1	M-558
	EM(1001)	17α-hydroxy-16-methylene-4-pregnene-3,20-dione	Δ^1	B-68
		11β,17α-dihydroxy-16-methylene-4-pregnene-3,20-dione	Δ^1	B-68
		9α-fluoro-11β,17α-dihydroxy-16-methylene-4-pregnene-3,20-dione	Δ^1	B-68
	IFO	14α-hydroxy-4-androstene-3,11,17-trione	Δ^1	T-955
		17α,21-dihydroxy-4-pregnene-3,20-dione	—	S-849
	MCC	4-androstene-3,17-dione	Δ^1	S-942
		4-pregnene-3,20-dione	Δ^1	S-942
		11β-hydroxy-4-pregnene-3,20-dione	Δ^1	S-942
		21-hydroxy-4-pregnene-3,20-dione	Δ^1	S-942
		21-hydroxy-4-pregnene-3,11,20-trione	Δ^1	S-942
		11β,21-dihydroxy-4-pregnene-3,20-dione	Δ^1	S-942

TABLE III

Transformations by Genus: BACILLUS

SPECIES	SOURCE	SUBSTRATE	REACTION	REF.
sphaericus	MCC	$17\alpha,21$-dihydroxy-4-pregnene-3,20-dione	Δ^1	S-942
		$11\beta,17\alpha,21$-trihydroxy-4-pregnene-3,20-dione	Δ^1	S-942
		9α-fluoro-$11\beta,17\alpha,21$-trihydroxy-4-pregnene-3,20-dione	Δ^1	S-942
		12α-fluoro-$11\beta,21$-dihydroxy-4-pregnene-3,20-dione	Δ^1	T-984
		12α-fluoro-$11\beta,21$-dihydroxy-4-pregnene-3,20-dione 21-acetate	Δ^1; 21-OAc → 21-OH	T-985
		$17\alpha,21$-dihydroxy-16-methylene-4-pregnene-3,11,20-trione 21-acetate	Δ^1; 21-OAc → 21-OH	W-1083a
		$11\beta,17\alpha,21$-trihydroxy-16-methylene-4-pregnene-3,20-dione 21-acetate	Δ^1; 21-OAc → 21-OH	W-1083a
		$11\beta,17\alpha,21$-trihydroxy-16β-methyl-4-pregnene-3,20-dione 21-acetate	Δ^1; 21-OAc → 21-OH	T-986; T-987
		9α-fluoro-$11\beta,17\alpha,21$-trihydroxy-16β-methyl-4-pregnene-3,20-dione 21-acetate	Δ^1; 21-OAc → 21-OH	T-986
		9α-fluoro-$11\beta,17\alpha,21$-trihydroxy-16-methylene-4-pregnene-3,20-dione 21-acetate	Δ^1; 21-OAc → 21-OH	W-1083a
	MCC MB(431)	12α-fluoro-21-hydroxy-4-pregnene-3,11,20-trione acetate	Δ^1; 21-OAc → 21-OH	W-1083
		12α-fluoro-$11\beta,21$-dihydroxy-4-pregnene-3,20-dione 21-acetate	Δ^1; 21-OAc → 21-OH	W-1083
		$11\beta,17\alpha,21$-trihydroxy-4-pregnene-3,20-dione	Δ^1 (vitamin K_2 (35) identified as co-factor)	G-291
	NG	5α-androstane-3,17-dione	Δ^1	H-375
		5α-androstane-3,17-dione-1α-H^3	Δ^1-(1α-H^3)	G-323
		4-androstene-3,17-dione	Δ^1	H-375
		4-androstene-3,17-dione-1α-H^3	Δ^1-(from 1α-H^3, 2β-H)	G-323
		deuterioandrostene-3,17-dione	Δ^1 (cell free)	M-535
		4-androstene-3,17-dione-6β-H^2	Δ^1 (cell free)	M-535

TABLE III

ansformations by Genus: BACILLUS

SPECIES	SOURCE	SUBSTRATE	REACTION	REF.
sphaericus	NG	4-pregnene-3,20-dione-7α-H^3	Δ^1	G-323
		4-pregnene-3,20-dione-16α-H^3	Δ^1	G-323
		4-pregnene-3,20-dione-11α-H^3, 12α-H^3	Δ^1	G-323
		4-pregnene-3,20-dione 20-cycloethyleneketal	Δ^1	F-251
		11β,17α,21-trihydroxy-12β-methyl-4-pregnene-3,20-dione 21-acetate	Δ^1; 21-OAc → 21-OH	C-131
subtilis	IAM (ACTU-B-3-3)	17α,21-dihydroxy-4-pregnene-3,20-dione	2β-OH	S-849
	(ACTU-B-3-4)	17α,21-dihydroxy-4-pregnene-3,20-dione	2β-OH	S-849
	(ACTU-B-3-5)	17α,21-dihydroxy-4-pregnene-3,20-dione	2β-OH	S-849
	(ACTU-B-5-6)	17α,21-dihydroxy-4-pregnene-3,20-dione	2β-OH	S-849
	(Hay-1)	17α,21-dihydroxy-4-pregnene-3,20-dione	2β-OH; 11α-OH	S-849
	(Hay-2)	17α,21-dihydroxy-4-pregnene-3,20-dione	2β-OH	S-849
	(Hay-3)	17α,21-dihydroxy-4-pregnene-3,20-dione	2β-OH	S-849
	(Hay-4)	17α,21-dihydroxy-4-pregnene-3,20-dione	2β-OH	S-849
	(Hay-5)	17α,21-dihydroxy-4-pregnene-3,20-dione	2β-OH	S-849
	(Hay-6)	17α,21-dihydroxy-4-pregnene-3,20-dione	2β-OH	S-849
	(Hay-8)	17α,21-dihydroxy-4-pregnene-3,20-dione	2β-OH; 11α-OH	S-849
	IFO(3026)	17α,21-dihydroxy-4-pregnene-3,20-dione	2β-OH	S-849
	IFO(3027)	17α,21-dihydroxy-4-pregnene-3,20-dione	—	S-849
	IFO(3033)	17α,21-dihydroxy-4-pregnene-3,20-dione	Δ^1; 11α-OH	S-849
	IFO(3035)	17α,21-dihydroxy-4-pregnene-3,20-dione	—	S-849
	IFO(3036)	17α,21-dihydroxy-4-pregnene-3,20-dione	2β-OH; 11α-OH	S-849

TABLE III

Transformations by Genus: BACILLUS

SPECIES	SOURCE	SUBSTRATE	REACTION	REF.
subtilis	IAM (Natto-1-2)	$17\alpha,21$-dihydroxy-4-pregnene-3,20-dione	—	S-849
	(Natto-1-3)	$17\alpha,21$-dihydroxy-4-pregnene-3,20-dione	—	S-849
	(Natto-1-4)	$17\alpha,21$-dihydroxy-4-pregnene-3,20-dione	2β-OH	S-849
	(Natto-1-5)	$17\alpha,21$-dihydroxy-4-pregnene-3,20-dione	2β-OH	S-849
	(Natto-1-6)	$17\alpha,21$-dihydroxy-4-pregnene-3,20-dione	—	S-849
	(Natto-1-7)	$17\alpha,21$-dihydroxy-4-pregnene-3,20-dione	—	S-849
	(Natto-1-8)	$17\alpha,21$-dihydroxy-4-pregnene-3,20-dione	2β-OH	S-849
	(Natto-1-9)	$17\alpha,21$-dihydroxy-4-pregnene-3,20-dione	11α-OH	S-849
	(Natto-1-10)	$17\alpha,21$-dihydroxy-4-pregnene-3,20-dione	11α-OH	S-849
	(Natto-II-1)	$17\alpha,21$-dihydroxy-4-pregnene-3,20-dione	—	S-849
	NRRL-B-558	$17\alpha,21$-dihydroxy-4-pregnene-3,20-dione	Δ^1	S-849
	(PCI-219)	$17\alpha,21$-dihydroxy-4-pregnene-3,20-dione	Δ^1	S-849
	(PCI-220)	$17\alpha,21$-dihydroxy-4-pregnene-3,20-dione	2β-OH	S-849
	NC	$17\alpha,21$-dihydroxy-4-pregnene-3,20-dione	Δ^1 (yield of Δ^1 increased if grown in mixed culture with Rhizopus nigricans)	L-521; L-522
			20-C=O $\rightarrow$ 20β-OH	L-522
		$11\beta,17\alpha,21$-trihydroxy-4-pregnene-3,20-dione	Δ^1	L-521; S-801
		$17\alpha,21$-dihydroxy-4-pregnene-3,11,20-trione	Δ^1	L-521; S-801
			Δ^1; 20-C=O $\rightarrow$ 20β-OH	L-522

TABLE III

ransformations by Genus: BACILLUS
BACTERIUM (Schizo. - Eubacteriales)

SPECIES	SOURCE	SUBSTRATE	REACTION	REF.
subtilis	NG	$3\alpha,7\alpha,12\alpha$-trihydroxy-5β-cholanic acid (sole carbon source)	—	N-675
		5-cholesten-3β-ol (sole carbon source)	—	T-1018; T-1030
		24-methyl-5,7,22-cholesta-trien-3β-ol (sole carbon source)	—	T-1018
	NRRL	Sarsasapogenin	—	M-587
		Diosgenin	—	M-587
		4-dehydrotigogenone	—	M-587
hiaminolyticus	IAM	$17\alpha,21$-dihydroxy-4-pregnene-3,20-dione	—	S-849
umescens	NG	5-cholesten-3β-ol (sole carbon source)	—	T-1030

BACTERIUM

SPECIES	SOURCE	SUBSTRATE	REACTION	REF.
bifidum (genus and species changed to Lacto-bacillus parabifidus)	NG	5-cholesten-3β-ol	—	S-914
cyclo-oxydans	ATCC-12673	17β-hydroxy-4-androsten-3-one	Δ^1	S-890
			9α-OH	P-740
			9α-OH (use of inhibitors for Δ^1)	S-898
		A-nor-17β-hydroxy-3-androsten-2-one	9α-OH; 17β-OH $\rightarrow$ 17-C=O	S-885
		3β-hydroxy-9,10-seco-1,3,5(10)-androstatriene-9,17-dione	degradation (product - $3a\alpha$-H-4α-$7a\beta$-methyl-hexa-hydro-1,5-indane-dione)	S-985
		4-pregnene-3,20-dione	Δ^1; 20-C=O $\rightarrow$ 20β-OH	F-251
			Δ^1	S-980; T-1005
			9α-OH	S-885
		4-pregnene-3,20-dione 20-cycloethyleneketal	Δ^1	F-251

TABLE III

Transformations by Genus: BACTERIUM

SPECIES	SOURCE	SUBSTRATE	REACTION	REF.
cyclo-oxydans	ATCC-12673	11α-hydroxy-4-pregnene-3,20-dione	Δ^1	K-480
			Δ^1; 20-C=O $\rightarrow$ 20β-OH	K-480
		16α,17α-dihydroxy-4-pregnene-3,20-dione	Δ^1	F-258; F-259
		17α,21-dihydroxy-4-pregnene-3,20-dione	Δ^1	K-480
		17α,21-dihydroxy-4-pregnene-3,11,20-trione	Δ^1	K-480
		6α-fluoro-16α,17α-dihydroxy-4-pregnene-3,20-dione 16,17-phenylcyclophosphate	Δ^1	F-259
		16α,17α-dihydroxy-6β-methyl-4-pregnene-3,20-dione 16,17-phenylcyclophosphate	Δ^1	F-259
		16α,17α-dihydroxy-4,6-pregnadiene-3,20-dione 16,17-phenylcyclophosphate	Δ^1	F-259
		11β,17α,21-trihydroxy-4-pregnene-3,20-dione (Ref. F-231 refers to use of dry cell material rather than free growing cells)	Δ^1	F-231; F-232; K-480; R-779
		11β,17α,21-trihydroxy-4-pregnene-3,20-dione 21-acetate	Δ^1	K-480
		9α-fluoro-11β,17α,21-trihydroxy-4-pregnene-3,20-dione	Δ^1	K-480
		12α-chloro-11β,16α,17α,21-tetrahydroxy-4-pregnene-3,20-dione 16,17-cyclosulfate 21-acetate	Δ^1	F-262
		9α-fluoro-11β,16α,17α,21-tetrahydroxy-4-pregnene-3,20-dione	Δ^1	G-296; G-297; L-505; R-779; S-890; S-908
			Δ^1; 16α,17α,21-triOH-20-C=O $\rightarrow$ 16α,17aα-dihydroxy-17aβ-hydroxymethyl-D-homo-17-C=O	G-297

TABLE III

ansformations by Genus: BACTERIUM

SPECIES	SOURCE	SUBSTRATE	REACTION	REF.
yclo-oxydans	ATCC-12673	9α-fluoro-$11\beta,16\alpha,17\alpha,21$-tetrahydroxy-4-pregnene-3,20-dione	20-C=O → 20β-OH	G-296
			Δ^1; 20-C=O → 20β-OH	S-908
		6α-fluoro-$11\alpha,16\alpha,17\alpha,21$-tetrahydroxy-4-pregnene-3,20-dione 16,17-acetonide	Δ^1	D-159
		12α-chloro-$11\beta,16\alpha,17\alpha,21$-tetrahydroxy-4-pregnene-3,20-dione 16,17-cyclobenzylphosphonate 21-acetate	Δ^1	F-263
		9α-fluoro-$11\beta,16\alpha,17\alpha,20\beta,21$-pentahydroxy-4-pregnen-3-one	Δ^1	G-294; G-296
			Δ^1; 20β-OH → 20-C=O	G-294; G-296
		9α-fluoro-$11\beta,16\alpha,17\alpha,21$-tetrahydroxy-1,4-pregnadiene-3,20-dione	Δ^1 → H	G-296
			20-C=O → 20β-OH	G-296; S-908
			Δ^1→H; 20-C=O →20β-OH	G-296
		9α-fluoro-$11\beta,16\alpha,17\alpha,20\beta,21$-pentahydroxy-1,4-pregnadien-3-one	Δ^1→H	G-296
			20β-OH → 20-C=O	G-294; G-296
		5-cholesten-3β-ol	Δ^5→Δ^4; 3β-OH →3-C=O	T-1005
avaniensis	ATCC-4001	4-pregnene-3,20-dione	Δ^1	F-233
		11α-hydroxy-4-pregnene-3,20-dione	Δ^1	F-233
		21-hydroxy-4-pregnene-3,20-dione	Δ^1	F-233
		11α-hydroxy-$16\alpha,17\alpha$-oxido-4-pregnene-3,20-dione	Δ^1	F-233
		21-hydroxy-$16\alpha,17\alpha$-oxido-4-pregnene-3,20-dione acetate	Δ^1	F-233
		$16\alpha,21$-dihydroxy-4-pregnene-3,20-dione	Δ^1	F-233
		$17\alpha,21$-dihydroxy-4-pregnene-3,20-dione	Δ^1	F-233

TABLE III

Transformations by Genus: BACTERIUM

SPECIES	SOURCE	SUBSTRATE	REACTION	REF.
havaniensis	ATCC-1004	$11\beta,17\alpha,21$-trihydroxy-4-preg-nene-3,20-dione	Δ^1	F-233
		$16\alpha,17\alpha,21$-trihydroxy-4-preg-nene-3,20-dione	Δ^1	F-233
		9α-fluoro-$11\beta,16\alpha,17\alpha$-tri-hydroxy-4-pregnene-3,20-dione	Δ^1	F-238
		9α-fluoro-$11\beta,17\alpha,21$-trihydroxy-4-pregnene-3,20-dione	Δ^1	F-233
		9α-fluoro-$11\beta,17\alpha,21$-trihydroxy-4-pregnene-3,20-dione 21-acetate	Δ^1; 21-OAc → 21-OH	F-233
			Δ^1	F-233
		$3\beta,16\alpha,17\alpha,21$-tetrahydroxy-9(11)-$5\alpha$-pregnen-20-one 3$\beta$,21-diacetate	3β-OAc→3-C=O; $\Delta^{1,4}$; 21-OAc → 21-OH	O-705
		$11\beta,16\alpha,17\alpha,21$-tetrahydroxy-4-pregnene-3,20-dione	Δ^1	F-233
		9α-fluoro-$11\beta,16\alpha,17\alpha,21$-tetrahydroxy-4-pregnene-3,20-dione	Δ^1	F-233
mycoides	ATCC-4004	4-pregnene-3,20-dione	Δ^1	F-240
		11α-hydroxy-4-pregnene-3,20-dione	Δ^1	F-240
		11α-hydroxy-$16\alpha,17\alpha$-oxido-4-pregnene-3,20-dione	Δ^1	F-240
		$16\alpha,21$-dihydroxy-4-pregnene-3,20-dione	Δ^1	F-240
		$17\alpha,21$-dihydroxy-4-pregnene-3,20-dione	Δ^1	F-240
		$11\beta,17\alpha,21$-trihydroxy-4-pregnene-3,20-dione	Δ^1	F-240
		$16\alpha,17\alpha,21$-trihydroxy-4-preg-nene-3,20-dione	Δ^1	F-240
		9α-fluoro-$11\beta,16\alpha,17\alpha$-tri-hydroxy-4-pregnene-3,20-dione	Δ^1	F-238
		9α-fluoro-$11\beta,17\alpha,21$-tri-hydroxy-4-pregnene-3,20-dione	Δ^1	F-240
		9α-fluoro-$11\beta,17\alpha,21$-tri-hydroxy-4-pregnene-3,20-dione 21-acetate	Δ^1; 21-OAc → 21-OH	F-240

TABLE III

Transformations by Genus:　　BACTERIUM

BASIDIOBOLUS　　(Phyco. - Entomophthorales)

BEAUVERIA　　(Imperf. - Moniliales)

SPECIES	SOURCE	SUBSTRATE	REACTION	REF.
mycoides	ATCC-4004	9α-fluoro-$11\beta,17\alpha,21$-trihydroxy-4-pregnene-3,20-dione 21-acetate	Δ^1	F-240
		$11\beta,16\alpha,17\alpha,21$-tetrahydroxy-4-pregnene-3,20-dione	Δ^1	F-240
		9α-fluoro-$11\beta,16\alpha,17\alpha,21$-tetrahydroxy-4-pregnene-3,20-dione	Δ^1	F-240
	IFO(3040)	$11\beta,17\alpha,21$-trihydroxy-4-pregnene-3,20-dione	—	I-428
(in mixed culture with Mycococcus sp.)			Δ^1	I-428
	LED	$11\beta,17\alpha,21$-trihydroxy-4-pregnene-3,20-dione	Δ^1 (dry thalli)	F-231
			Δ^1	F-232
	NG	5-cholesten-3β-ol	—	T-1030
species (Schatz) 303	NG	5-cholesten-3β-ol (sole carbon source)	utilization	M-595
genus incorrect * (gram positive coccus)		SEE UNIDENTIFIED GENUS		E-194
steroidiclasium	NG	1,3,5(10)-estratriene-3,17β-diol	17β-OH → 17-C=O	A-23
		3β-hydroxy-5-androstene-17-one	degradation	A-23
		4-androstene-3,17-dione	degradation	A-23
		5-cholesten-3β-ol	—	A-23
BASIDIOBOLUS				
ranarum (Eidam)	CBS	$17\alpha,21$-dihydroxy-4-pregnene-3,20-dione	6-OH; 11α-OH	W-1073
BEAUVERIA				
bassiana	FRI	$17\alpha,21$-dihydroxy-4-pregnene-3,20-dione	11α-OH	S-849
species	ATCC-13144	$17\alpha,21$-dihydroxy-4-pregnene-3,20-dione	11α-OH	I-421

TABLE III

TAXONOMY

Transformations by Genus:

BEAUVERIA
BLAKESLEA
BOLETINUS
BOLETUS

(Phyco. - Mucorales)
(Basidio. - Agaricales)
(Basidio. - Agaricales)

SPECIES	SOURCE	SUBSTRATE	REACTION	REF.
species	ATCC-13144	16α-t-butyl-17α,21-dihydroxy-5α-pregnane-3,20-dione	11α-OH	I-421
		17α,21-dihydroxy-16α-methyl-5α-pregnane-3,20-dione	11α-OH	I-421
		16β-ethyl-17α,21-dihydroxy-5α-pregnane-3,20-dione	11α-OH	I-421
		17α,21-dihydroxy-16β-methyl-5α-pregnane-3,20-dione	11α-OH	I-421
		17α,21-dihydroxy-16α-methyl-4-pregnene-3,20-dione	11α-OH	I-421
		17α,21-dihydroxy-16β-methyl-4-pregnene-3,20-dione	11α-OH	I-421
		17α,21-dihydroxy-16β-methyl-4-pregnene-3,20-dione 21-acetate	11α-OH; 21-OAc→21-OH	I-421
		17α,21-dihydroxy-1,4-pregnadiene-3,20-dione	11α-OH	I-421
		16α-t-butyl-17α,21-dihydroxy-1,4-pregnadiene-3,20-dione	11α-OH	I-421
		17α,21-dihydroxy-16α-methyl-1,4-pregnadiene-3,20-dione	11α-OH	I-421
		16β-ethyl-17α,21-dihydroxy-1,4-pregnadiene-3,20-dione	11α-OH	I-421
BLAKESLEA				
trispora	SSSR	17α,21-dihydroxy-4-pregnene-3,20-dione	11α-OH; 11β-OH; 6β-OH	E-224
BOLETINUS				
pictus	AL (F-12)	4-pregnene-3,20-dione	—	S-825
BOLETUS				
acidus	AL (H-35)	4-pregnene-3,20-dione	—	S-825
americanus	AL (G-119)	4-pregnene-3,20-dione	—	S-825

TABLE III

ransformations by Genus:
BOLETUS
BOTRYODIPLODIA (Imperf. - Sphaeropsidales)
BOTRYTIS (Imperf. - Moniliales)

SPECIES	SOURCE	SUBSTRATE	REACTION	REF.
luteus	AL (H-11)	4-pregnene-3,20-dione	$6\beta,11\alpha$-diOH	S-825
BOTRYODIPLODIA				
theobromae	AMCY	$16\alpha,17\alpha$-oxido-4-pregnene-3,20-dione	11α-OH	P-746
BOTRYTIS				
cinerea	ATCC-12481	$17\alpha,21$-dihydroxy-4-pregnene-3,20-dione	11β-OH	F-229
		$17\alpha,21$-dihydroxy-4-pregnene-3,20-dione 21-acetate	11β-OH; 21-OAc →21-OH	F-229
	ATCC	4-pregnene-3,20-dione	11α-OH	C-98
			11β-OH	C-98
		$17\alpha,21$-dihydroxy-4-pregnene-3,20-dione	11α-OH	C-98
			11β-OH	C-98
			11β-OH; 11-C=O (via 11β-OH)	C-98
		$17\alpha,21$-dihydroxy-4-pregnene-3,20-dione 21-acetate	11β-OH; 11-C =O(via 11β-OH); 21-OAc→21-OH	C-98
			11β-OH; 11-C=O (via 11β-OH)	C-98
	S	17α-hydroxy-4-pregnene-3,20-dione	6β-OH	S-842
		21-hydroxy-4-pregnene-3,20-dione	6β-OH	S-842
			15β-OH	S-842
		$11\beta,21$-dihydroxy-4-pregnene-3,20-dione	15β-OH	S-842
			15β-OH; 11β-OH→11-C=O	S-842
		17,21-dihydroxy-4-pregnene-3,20-dione	6β-OH	S-842
			11β-OH	S-842
	TNAES	17α-hydroxy-4-pregnene-3,20-dione	6β-OH	S-849

TABLE III

Transformations by Genus: BOTRYTIS

SPECIES	SOURCE	SUBSTRATE	REACTION	REF.
cinerea	TNAES	21-hydroxy-4-pregnene-3,20-dione	6β-OH; 11β-OH	S-849
		11β,21-dihydroxy-4-pregnene-3,20-dione	11β-OH →11-C=O; 15β-OH	S-849
		17α,21-dihydroxy-4-pregnene-3,20-dione	2β-OH; 6β-OH; 11β-OH	S-849
	TNAES (CI-17)		6β-OH; 11β-OH	S-849
	UCT	4-pregnene-3,20-dione	11α-OH	C-98
			11β-OH	C-98
		17α,21-dihydroxy-4-pregnene-3,20-dione	11α-OH	C-98
			11β-OH	C-98
			11β-OH; 11-C=O (via 11β-OH)	C-98
		17α,21-dihydroxy-4-pregnene-3,20-dione 21-acetate	11β-OH; 21-OAc →21-OH	C-98
			11β-OH; 11-C=O (via 11β-OH); 21-OAc→21-OH	C-98
fabae	S	4-pregnene-3,20-dione	—	S-859
		17α-hydroxy-4-pregnene-3,20-dione	—	S-859
		17α,21-dihydroxy-4-pregnene-3,20-dione	11α-OH	S-859
			11β-OH	S-859
	TNAES (PI-1)	17α,21-dihydroxy-4-pregnene-3,20-dione	2β-OH	S-849
paeoniae	ATCC-12482	17β-hydroxy-4-estren-3-one	10β-OH	D-150
		17α,21-dihydroxy-4-pregnene-3,20-dione	11β-OH	F-229
reptons	FRI	17α,21-dihydroxy-4-pregnene-3,20-dione	6β-OH; 11α-OH	S-849
species	NRRL	plant saponins	—	K-478
spectabilis	NRRL	Sarsasapogenin	—	M-587
		Diosgenin	—	M-587
		4-dehydrotigogenone	—	M-587

TABLE III

TAXONOMY

ansformations by Genus: BYSSOCHLAMYS   (Asco. - Endomycetales)
CALONECTRIA   (Asco. - Hypocreales)

SPECIES	SOURCE	SUBSTRATE	REACTION	REF.
BYSSOCHLAMYS				
nivea	FRI	$17\alpha,21$-dihydroxy-4-pregnene-3, 20-dione	—	S-849
CALONECTRIA				
decora	C	5α-androstane-3,17-dione	$\Delta^{1,4}$	W-1096
		3β-hydroxy-5-androsten-17-one	—	W-1096
		4-androstene-3,17-dione	Δ^{1}	W-1096
		$11\beta,17\alpha,21$-trihydroxy-5α-pregnane-3,20-dione	$\Delta^{1,4}$	W-1096
		$17\alpha,21$-dihydroxy-5α-pregnane-3,11,20-trione	$\Delta^{1,4}$	W-1096
		$17\alpha,21$-dihydroxy-5β-pregnane-3,11,20-trione	$\Delta^{1,4}$	W-1096
		3β-hydroxy-5-pregnen-20-one	—	W-1096
		$3\beta,21$-dihydroxy-5-pregnen-20-one	—	W-1096
		4-pregnene-3,20-dione	Δ^{1}	W-1096; V-1053
			Δ^{1}; 17β-Ac → 17-C=O	V-1053
(in sequential fermentation with one or more of the following cultures: Curvularia lunata, Cunninghamella blakesleeana, Curvularia brachyspora and Tricothecium roseum)			Δ^{1}	W-1107
(in sequential fermentation with one or more of the following cultures: Curvularia lunata, Cunninghamella blakesleeana, Curvularia brachyspora and Tricothecium roseum)		11β-hydroxy-4-pregnene-3,20-dione	Δ^{1}	W-1107

TABLE III

Transformations by Genus: CALONECTRIA

SPECIES	SOURCE	SUBSTRATE	REACTION	REF.
decora	C	21-hydroxy-4-pregnene-3,20-dione	Δ^1	V-1053; W-1096
(in sequential fermentation with one or more of the following cultures: Curvularia lunata, Cunninghamella blakesleeana, Curvularia brachyspora and Tricothecium roseum)			Δ^1	W-1107
		11α,21-dihydroxy-4-pregnene-3,20-dione	Δ^1	W-1096
		11β,21-dihydroxy-4-pregnene-3,20-dione	Δ^1	V-1053; W-1096
		17α,21-dihydroxy-4-pregnene-3,20-dione	Δ^1	V-1053; W-1096
		21-hydroxy-4-pregnene-3,11,20-trione	Δ^1	W-1096
		17α,21-dihydroxy-4-pregnene-3,11,20-trione	Δ^1	V-1053; W-1096
		11α,17α,21-trihydroxy-4-pregnene-3,20-dione	Δ^1	W-1096
		11β,17α,21-trihydroxy-4-pregnene-3,20-dione	Δ^1	W-1096
		6α-fluoro-17α-hydroxy-16α-methyl-4-pregnene-3,20-dione	Δ^1	W-1090a
		11β,21-dihydroxy-3,20-diketo-4-pregnen-18-al (18→11) hemiacetal	Δ^1	W-1096; W-1104
		11β,17α,21-trihydroxy-3,20-diketo-4-pregnen-18-al (18→11) hemiacetal	Δ^1	W-1096
	CBS	17β-hydroxy-7α-methyl-thio-4-androsten-3-one acetate	7α-SCH$_3$ → 7α-S(O)CH$_3$; 17β-OAc → 17β-OH	H-405
		14β-hydroxy-3-keto-5β-20(22)-cardenolide	12β-OH	N-677
		3α,14β-dihydroxy-5β-20(22)-cardenolide	3α-OH→3-C=O	N-681
			3α-OH→3-C=O; 12β-OH	N-681

TABLE III

nsformations by Genus: CALONECTRIA

SPECIES	SOURCE	SUBSTRATE	REACTION	REF.
ecora	CBS	$3\beta,14\beta$-dihydroxy-5β-20(22)-cardenolide	3β-OH→3-C=O	N-677
			12β-OH	N-677
			3β-OH→3-C=O; 12β-OH	N-677
		$3\beta,14\beta$-dihydroxy-5β-20(22)-cardenolide 3-acetate	3β-OAc→3-C=O; 12β-OH	N-677
		$3\beta,14\beta$-dihydroxy-5β,17α-20(22)-cardenolide	3β-OH→3-C=O	N-681
		$3\beta,12\beta,14\beta$-trihydroxy-5β-20(22)-cardenolide	3β-OH→3-C=O	N-677
		$3\beta,14\beta,16\beta$-trihydroxy-5β-20(22)-cardenolide	3β-OH→3-C=O	N-677
		$3\beta,14\beta,16\beta$-trihydroxy 5β-20(22)-cardenolide 3-acetate	3β-OAc→3-C=O	N-677
		$3\beta,14\beta,16\beta$-trihydroxy-5β-20(22)-cardenolide 16-acetate	3β-OH→3-C=O	N-677
		$3\beta,14\beta,16\beta$-trihydroxy-5β-20(22)-cardenolide 3,16-diacetate	3β-OAc→3β-OH; 16β-OAc→16β-OH	N-677
			3β-OAc→3-C=O; 16β-OAc→16β-OH	N-677
			3β-OAc→3-C=O	N-677
			3β-OAc→3β-OH	N-677
	OR	$17\alpha,20\beta,21$-trihydroxy-4-pregnene-3,11-dione	Δ^1	S-951
		$17\alpha,21$-dihydroxy-4-pregnene-3,11,20-trione	20-C=O→20β-OH (limited oxygen)	S-951
			Δ^1	S-951
			Δ^1; 20-C=O → 20β-OH (normal aeration)	S-951
		$17\alpha,21$-dihydroxy-1,4-pregnadiene-3,11,20-trione	20-C=O → 20β-OH	S-951
	VEB	5α-pregnane-3,20-dione	$12\beta,15\alpha$-diOH	S-816
		5β-pregnane-3,20-dione	$12\beta,15\alpha$-diOH	S-816
		11α-hydroxy-5α-pregnane-3,20-dione	15α-OH	S-816

TABLE III

Transformations by Genus: CALONECTRIA
CANDELOSPORA (Imperf. - Moniliales)
CANDIDA (Imperf. - Moniliales)

SPECIES	SOURCE	SUBSTRATE	REACTION	REF.
decora	VEB	11α-hydroxy-5β-pregnane-3,20-dione	15α-OH	S-816
		$3\alpha,6\alpha$-dihydroxy-5β-pregnan-20-one	11α-OH	S-812
		3β-hydroxy-5-pregnene-3,20-dione	3β-OH$\rightarrow$3-C=O; $\Delta^5\rightarrow\Delta^4$; $12\beta,15\alpha$-diOH	S-816
		4-pregnene-3,20-dione	$12\beta,15\alpha$-diOH	S-814
			$12\beta,15\alpha$-diOH (O_2^{18})	K-485
		4-pregnene-3,20-dione ($11\alpha,12\alpha$-$^3H_2$)	$12\beta,15\alpha$-diOH	H-370
		9α-hydroxy-4-pregnene-3,20-dione	15α-OH	S-810
		11α-hydroxy-4-pregnene-3,20-dione	15α-OH	S-814
		11β-hydroxy-4-pregnene-3,20-dione	15α-OH	S-817
		12α-hydroxy-4-pregnene-3,20-dione	15α-OH; 12α-OH $\rightarrow$12-C=O	S-810
		14α-hydroxy-4-pregnene-3,20-dione	12β-OH	S-810
		15β-hydroxy-4-pregnene-3,20-dione	12β-OH	S-814
		$17\alpha,21$-dihydroxy-4-pregnene-3,20-dione	15α-OH	S-810
		4-pregnene-3,11,20-trione	15α-OH	S-810
CANDELOSPORA				
penicilloides	FRI	$17\alpha,21$-dihydroxy-4-pregnene-3,20-dione	11α-OH	S-849
CANDIDA				
guilliermondii	NRRL	Sarsasapogenin	—	M-587
		Diosgenin	—	M-587
		4-dehydrotigogenone	—	M-587

TABLE III

TAXONOMY

ansformations by Genus:

CANDIDA
CANTHARELLUS (Basidio. - Agaricales)
CARPENTELES (Asco. - Eurotiales)
CATENABACTERIUM (Schizo. - Eubacteriales)

SPECIES	SOURCE	SUBSTRATE	REACTION	REF.
.rusei	NRRL	Sarsasapogenin	—	M-587
		Diosgenin	—	M-587
		4-dehydrotigogenone	—	M-587
ulcherrima	IFO(C964)	17α,21-dihydroxy-4-pregnene-3,20-dione	20-C=O → 20β-OH	T-958
		17α,21-dihydroxy-1,4-pregnadiene-3,20-dione	20-C=O → 20β-OH	T-958
tilis	NRRL	Sarsasapogenin	—	M-587
		Diosgenin	—	M-587
		4-dehydrotigogenone	—	M-587
ANTHARELLUS				
ibarius	NRRL	4-pregnene-3,20-dione	—	R-778
ARPENTELES				
avanicus	FRI	17α,21-dihydroxy-4-pregnene-3,20-dione	11α-OH	S-849
CATENABACTERIUM				
catenaforme	NC	5-cholesten-3β-ol	— (anaerobic)	T-973
		4-cholesten-3-one	— (anaerobic)	T-973
		3β-hydroxy-5-pregnen-20-one	— (anaerobic)	T-973
		3β,17α-dihydroxy-5-pregnen-20-one	— (anaerobic)	T-973
		21-hydroxy-4-pregnene-3,20-dione	— (anaerobic)	T-973
	*	11β,17α,21-trihydroxy-4-pregnene-3,20-dione	3-C=O→3β-OH; Δ^4→5α-H (anaerobic)	P-739; T-973
	*	17α,21-dihydroxy-4-pregnene-3,11,20-trione	3-C=O→3β-OH; Δ^4→5α-H (anaerobic)	P-739; T-973
		17α,21-dihydroxy-4-pregnene-3,11,20-trione 21-acetate	— (anaerobic)	T-973

TABLE III

Transformations by Genus: CELLULOMONAS (Schizo. - Eubacteriales)
CEPHALOSPORIUM (Imperf. - Moniliales)

SPECIES	SOURCE	SUBSTRATE	REACTION	REF.
CELLULOMONAS				
biazotea	NRRL	Sarsasapogenin	—	M-587
		Diosgenin	—	M-587
		4-dehydrotigogenone	—	M-587
CEPHALOSPORIUM				
acremonium	NRRL-3092	4-estren-3-one	16-C=O; (via 16α-OH and 16β-OH)	S-793a
			16α-OH → 16-C=O	S-793a
			16β-OH → 16-C=O	S-793a
			16α-OH	S-793a
			16β-OH	S-793a
			16-C=O → 16β-OH	S-793a
			16α-OH → 16β-OH (via 16-C=O)	S-793a
		4-androstene-3,17-dione	17-C=O → 13,17-seco-13α-OH-16-COOH	H-398
			17-C=O→17a-oxa-17-C=O	H-398
		17a-oxa-D-homo-1,4-androsta-diene-3,17-dione	17a-oxa-17-C=O →17,17a-seco-13α-OH-16-COOH	H-398
		4-pregnene-3,20-dione (with and without 4-C^{14})	17β-Ac→17β-OH	H-398
			17β-Ac→13,17-seco-13α-OH-16-COOH	H-398
			17β-Ac→17-C=O	H-398
			17β-Ac→17a-oxa-17-C=O	H-398

TABLE III

ransformations by Genus: CEPHALOSPORIUM
CEPHALOTHECIUM   (Imperf. - Moniliales)

SPECIES	SOURCE	SUBSTRATE	REACTION	REF.
asperum	LED	17α,21-dihydroxy-4-pregnene-3,20-dione	7β-OH	B-56
species	LED (Z-164)	17α,21-dihydroxy-4-pregnene-3,20-dione	7β-OH	B-55
	NRRL-1866	4-pregnene-3,20-dione	7β-OH	B-56
		21-hydroxy-4-pregnene-3,20-dione	7β-OH	B-56
		9α-fluoro-11β-hydroxy-4-pregnene-3,20-dione	7β-OH	B-56
		11β,21-dihydroxy-4-pregnene-3,20-dione	7β-OH	B-56
		17α,21-dihydroxy-4-pregnene-3,20-dione	7β-OH	B-56
		17α,21-dihydroxy-9β,11β-oxido-4-pregnene-3,20-dione	7β-OH	B-56
		9α-fluoro-11β,21-dihydroxy-4-pregnene-3,20-dione	7β-OH	B-56
subverticillatum	PIRI	4-pregnene-3,20-dione	17β-Ac→17-C=O	B-67
			17β-Ac→17a-oxa-17-C=O	B-67
CEPHALOTHECIUM (See Trichothecium)				
roseum (Trichothecium roseum - NRRL-1665)	ATCC-8685	4-pregnene-3,20-dione	17α-OH (O_2^{18})	H-374
			17α-OH; 11α,17α-diOH	M-581; M-600
		11β-hydroxy-4-pregnene-3,20-dione	17α-OH	M-600
		21-hydroxy-4-pregnene-3,20-dione	6β,17α-diOH	M-581
			11α,17α-diOH	M-581
		21-hydroxy-4-pregnene-3,20-dione acetate	6β,17α-diOH; 21-OAc→21-OH	M-600
			11α,17α-diOH; 21-OAc→21-OH	M-600
		11β,21-dihydroxy-4-pregnene-3,20-dione	17α-OH; 11β-OH →11-C=O	M-581; M-600
			17α-OH	M-600

TABLE III

Transformations by Genus: CEPHALOTHECIUM
CERATOSTOMELLA   (Asco. - Sphaeriales)
CERCOSPORA   (Imperf. - Moniliales)

SPECIES	SOURCE	SUBSTRATE	REACTION	REF.
roseum	ATCC-8685	$17\alpha,21$-dihydroxy-4-pregnene-3,20-dione	11α-OH	M-600
		4-pregnene-3,11,20-trione	17α-OH	M-600
		21-hydroxy-4-pregnene-3,11,20-trione	17α-OH	M-581; M-600
CERATOSTOMELLA				
fimbriate (fimbriata)	FAHU	$17\alpha,21$-dihydroxy-4-pregnene-3,20-dione	—	S-849
CERCOSPORA (See genus Cercosporina)				
apii	IFO (6161)	$17\alpha,21$-dihydroxy-4-pregnene-3,20-dione	oxidation - products not identified	K-472
baticola	FAKU	$17\alpha,21$-dihydroxy-4-pregnene-3,20-dione	—	S-849
beticola	IFO (6162)	$17\alpha,21$-dihydroxy-4-pregnene-3,20-dione	—	K-472
	KAG (C-32)	$17\alpha,21$-dihydroxy-4-pregnene-3,20-dione	—	K-472
	KAG (C-33)	$17\alpha,21$-dihydroxy-4-pregnene-3,20-dione	—	K-472
calotropidis	CBS	$17\alpha,21$-dihydroxy-4-pregnene-3,20-dione	oxidation - products not identified	K-472
canescens	IFO (6163)	$17\alpha,21$-dihydroxy-4-pregnene-3,20-dione	oxidation - products not identified	K-472
chenopodii	CBS	$17\alpha,21$-dihydroxy-4-pregnene-3,20-dione	oxidation - products not identified	K-472
cladosporioides	CBS	$17\alpha,21$-dihydroxy-4-pregnene-3,20-dione	oxidation - products not identified	K-472
cruenta	IFO (6164)	$17\alpha,21$-dihydroxy-4-pregnene-3,20-dione	oxidation - products not identified	K-472
diazu	CBS	$17\alpha,21$-dihydroxy-4-pregnene-3,20-dione	oxidation - products not identified	K-472

TABLE III

ansformations by Genus: CERCOSPORA

SPECIES	SOURCE	SUBSTRATE	REACTION	REF.
fusca	CBS	17α,21-dihydroxy-4-pregnene-3,20-dione	oxidation-products not identified	K-472
hibsci-cannabini	KAC	17α,21-dihydroxy-4-pregnene-3,20-dione	oxidation-products not identified	K-472
italica	CBS	17α,21-dihydroxy-4-pregnene-3,20-dione	oxidation-products not identified	K-472
kaki	CBS	17α,21-dihydroxy-4-pregnene-3,20-dione	oxidation-products not identified	K-472
kikuchii (see genus Cercospor-ina)	FRI	17α,21-dihydroxy-4-pregnene-3,20-dione	—	S-849
	NARI	17α,21-dihydroxy-4-pregnene-3,20-dione	—	S-849
lagenarium	TNAES	17α,21-dihydroxy-4-pregnene-3,20-dione	—	S-849
macrospora	CBS	17α,21-dihydroxy-4-pregnene-3,20-dione	oxidation-products not identified	K-472
malvacearum	CBS	17α,21-dihydroxy-4-pregnene-3,20-dione	oxidation-products not identified	K-472
medicaginis	CBS	17α,21-dihydroxy-4-pregnene-3,20-dione	—	K-472
melongenae	KAG(C-36)	17α,21-dihydroxy-4-pregnene-3,20-dione	11α-OH	K-472
melonis	CBS	4-androstene-3,17-dione	9α,12α-diOH	K-473
			9α,14α-diOH	K-473
			9α,15β-diOH	K-473
			9α,18-diOH	K-473
		9α-hydroxy-4-androstene-3,17-dione	12α-OH	K-473
			14α-OH	K-473
			15β-OH	K-473
			18-OH	K-473
		12α-hydroxy-4-androstene-3,17-dione	9α-OH	K-473
		14α-hydroxy-4-androstene-3,17-dione	9α-OH	K-473

TABLE III

Transformations by Genus: CERCOSPORA.

SPECIES	SOURCE	SUBSTRATE	REACTION	REF.
melonis	CBS	15β-hydroxy-4-androstene-3,17-dione	9α-OH	K-473
		$17\alpha,21$-dihydroxy-4-pregnene-3,20-dione	8β-OH; 15β-OH	K-472; K-473
musae	CBS	$17\alpha,21$-dihydroxy-4-pregnene-3,20-dione	—	K-472
musarum	CBS	$17\alpha,21$-dihydroxy-4-pregnene-3,20-dione	—	K-472
nicotianae	CBS	$17\alpha,21$-dihydroxy-4-pregnene-3,20-dione	oxidation-products not identified	K-472
oryzae	CBS	$17\alpha,21$-dihydroxy-4-pregnene-3,20-dione	—	K-472
	FRI	$17\alpha,21$-dihydroxy-4-pregnene-3,20-dione	11α-OH	S-849
	NAH	$17\alpha,21$-dihydroxy-4-pregnene-3,20-dione	—	S-849
rosicola	CBS	$17\alpha,21$-dihydroxy-4-pregnene-3,20-dione	—	K-472
scirpicola	CBS	$17\alpha,21$-dihydroxy-4-pregnene-3,20-dione	11α-OH	K-472
			X-OH; $\Delta^4 \rightarrow 5\xi$-H	K-472
sesami	IFO(6165)	$17\alpha,21$-dihydroxy-4-pregnene-3,20-dione	—	K-472
taiwanensis	CBS	$17\alpha,21$-dihydroxy-4-pregnene-3,20-dione	oxidation-products not identified	K-472
vaginae	CBS	$17\alpha,21$-dihydroxy-4-pregnene-3,20-dione	oxidation-products not identified	K-472
violae	CBS	$17\alpha,21$-dihydroxy-4-pregnene-3,20-dione	—	K-472
zebrina	CBS	$17\alpha,21$-dihydroxy-4-pregnene-3,20-dione	—	K-472
zinniae	KAG	$17\alpha,21$-dihydroxy-4-pregnene-3,20-dione	11α-OH	K-472
			11β-OH	K-472

TABLE III   TAXONOMY

	CERCOSPORELLA	(Imperf. - Moniliales)
nsformations by Genus:	CERCOSPORINA	(Imperf. - Moniliales)
	CHAETOCLADIUM	(Phyco. - Mucorales)
	CHAETOMELLA	(Imperf. - Sphaeropsidales)

SPECIES	SOURCE	SUBSTRATE	REACTION	REF.
ERCOSPORELLA rpotrichoides	ATCC-12083	4-pregnene-3,20-dione	21-OH	L-490
		11β,12β-oxido-4-pregnene-3,20-dione	21-OH	L-490
		9α-fluoro-4-pregnene-3,11,20-trione	21-OH	L-490
		12α-methyl-4-pregnene-3,11,20-trione	21-OH	L-490
		4,16-pregnadiene-3,20-dione	21-OH	L-490
ERCOSPORINA ee genus Cercospora)				
kuchii	FRI	17α,21-dihydroxy-4-pregnene-3,20-dione	—	S-849
HAETOCLADIUM				
refeldii	SSSR	17α,21-dihydroxy-4-pregnene-3,20-dione	6β-OH	E-224
HAETOMELLA				
olonga	ATCC-12718	4-androstene-3,17-dione	11β-OH	S-789
		17β-hydroxy-4-androsten-3-one	11β-OH	S-789
		20-hydroxy-5α-pregnan-3-one	11β-OH	S-789
		20-hydroxy-5β-pregnan-3-one	11β-OH	S-789
		4-pregnene-3,20-dione	11β-OH	S-789
		17α-hydroxy-4-pregnene-3,20-dione	11β-OH	S-789
		21-hydroxy-4-pregnene-3,20-dione	11β-OH	S-789
		17α,21-dihydroxy-4-pregnene-3,20-dione	11β-OH	S-789
		6β-fluoro-17α-hydroxy-4-pregnene-3,20-dione	11β-OH	H-391
		6α-fluoro-17α,21-dihydroxy-16-methylene-4-pregnene-3,20-dione	11β-OH	A-7

TABLE III

Transformations by Genus: CHAETOMELLA
                                CHAETOMIUM   (Asco. - Sphaeriales)

SPECIES	SOURCE	SUBSTRATE	REACTION	REF.
oblonga	ATCC-12718	$17\alpha,21$-dihydroxy-1,4-pregna-diene-3,20-dione	11β-OH	S-789
		4,6-pregnadiene-3,20-dione	11β-OH	S-789
raphigera	ATCC-12719	4-androstene-3,17-dione	11β-OH	S-789
		17β-hydroxy-4-androsten-3-one	11β-OH	S-789
		20-hydroxy-5α-pregnan-3-one	11β-OH	S-789
		20-hydroxy-5β-pregnan-3-one	11β-OH	S-789
		4-pregnene-3,20-dione	11β-OH	S-789
		17α-hydroxy-4-pregnene-3,20-dione	11β-OH	S-789
		$17\alpha,21$-dihydroxy-4-pregnene-3,20-dione	11β-OH	S-789
		$17\alpha,21$-dihydroxy-1,4-pregna-diene-3,20-dione	11β-OH	S-789
		4,6-pregnadiene-3,20-dione	11β-OH	S-789
CHAETOMIUM				
cochloides	NG	5-cholesten-3β-ol (sole carbon source)	utilization	S-793c
		24-methyl-5,7,22-cholestatrien-3β-ol (sole carbon source)	utilization	S-793c
	QM-624	$11\beta,17\alpha,21$-trihydroxy-1,4-pregnadiene-3,20-dione	6β-OH	C-108
funicolum	QM-33C	17α-hydroxy-1,4-pregnadiene-20-one	6β-OH	C-108
		$17\alpha,21$-dihydroxy-1,4-pregna-diene-3,20-dione	6β-OH	C-108
		11β-fluoro-$17\alpha,21$-dihydroxy-9α-iodo-16α-methyl-1,4-pregnadiene-3,20-dione	6β-OH	N-691
		11β-fluoro-$17\alpha,21$-dihydroxy-9α-iodo-16β-methyl-1,4-pregna-diene-3,20-dione	6β-OH	N-691
		$17\alpha,21$-dihydroxy-1,4-pregna-diene-3,11,20-triene	6β-OH	C-108
		$17\alpha,21$-dihydroxy-16α-methyl-1,4-pregnadiene-3,11,20-trione	6β-OH	N-690; N-692

TABLE III   <u>TAXONOMY</u>

<u>ransformations by Genus:</u>

CHAETOMIUM
CHALARA   (Imperf. - Moniliales)
CHLORELLA   (Chlorophyta - Chlorococcales)
CHOANEPHORA (Phyco. - Mucorales)
CHROMOBACTERIUM (Schizo. - Eubacteriales)

SPECIES	SOURCE	SUBSTRATE	REACTION	REF.
globosum	FRI	$17\alpha,21$-dihydroxy-4-pregnene-3,20-dione	Δ^1; 11α-OH	S-849
	WISC	$3\beta,5\beta,14\beta$-trihydroxy-19-oxo-20(22)-cardenolide	3β-OH$\rightarrow$3-C=O; 5β-OH$\rightarrow\Delta^4$	S-891
species	NRRL	plant saponins	—	K-478
succineum	QM(1044)	17α-hydroxy-1,4-pregnadiene-3,20-dione	6β-OH	C-108
CHALARA				
mycoderma	FRI	$17\alpha,21$-dihydroxy-4-pregnene-3,20-dione	—	S-849
CHLORELLA (Algae)				
pyrenoidosa	UM(C-37-2)	3β-hydroxy-5-androsten-17-one	reduction to 4 products	G-321
		4-androstene-3,17-dione	17-C=O $\rightarrow$ 17β-OH	G-321
		4-pregnene-3,20-dione	toxic (but culture could be adapted to substrate)	G-321; G-322
		5-cholesten-3β-ol	—	G-321
species	NG	$17\alpha,21$-dihydroxy-4-pregnene-3,20-dione	20-C=O $\rightarrow$ 20β-OH	V-1045
CHOANEPHORA				
cucurbitarum	SSSR	$17\alpha,21$-dihydroxy-4-pregnene-3,20-dione	11α-OH; 11β-OH; 6β-OH	E-224
CHROMOBACTERIUM				
violaceum	NG	5-cholesten-3β-ol (sole carbon source)	—	T-1030

TABLE III

Transformations by Genus: CIRCINELLA   (Phyco. - Mucorales)
                           CLADOSARUM   (Imperf. - Moniliales)
                           CLADOSPORIUM   (Imperf. - Moniliales)

SPECIES	SOURCE	SUBSTRATE	REACTION	REF.
muscae	VEB	17β-hydroxy-4-androsten-3-one	9α-OH	R-748
			9α-OH; 17β-OH $\rightarrow$ 17-C=O	R-748
		$9\alpha,17\beta$-dihydroxy-4-androsten-3-one	17β-OH $\rightarrow$ 17-C=O	R-748
simplex	SSSR	$17\alpha,21$-dihydroxy-4-pregnene-3,20-dione	6β-OH; 11α-OH; 11β-OH	E-224
species	NRRL	Saponins (sapogenin - glycosides)	—	K-478
	VEB	4-pregnene-3,20-dione	9α-OH	S-815
			14α-OH	S-815
			$9\alpha,14\alpha$-diOH	S-815
		9α-hydroxy-4-pregnene-3,20-dione	14α-OH	S-815
		14α-hydroxy-4-pregnene-3,20-dione	9α-OH	S-815
sydowi	FRI	$17\alpha,21$-dihydroxy-4-pregnene-3,20-dione	6β-OH	S-849
umbellata	NRRL	Sarsasapogenin	—	M-587
		Diosgenin	—	M-587
		4-dehydrotigogenone	—	M-587
CLADOSARUM				
olivaceus (olivaceum)	FRI	$17\alpha,21$-dihydroxy-4-pregnene-3,20-dione	11α-OH	S-849
CLADOSPORIUM				
cladosporiodes	NRRL	Saponins (sapogenin - glycosides)	hydrolysis of glycosides to aglycones	K-478
fulvam (fulvum)	TNAES (S-10-1)	$17\alpha,21$-dihydroxy-4-pregnene-3,20-dione	—	S-849
herbarum	FRI	$17\alpha,21$-dihydroxy-4-pregnene-3,20-dione	—	S-849

TABLE III

ansformations by Genus: CLADOSPORIUM

SPECIES	SOURCE	SUBSTRATE	REACTION	REF.
erbarum	NRRL	Sarsasapogenin	—	M-587
		Diosgenin	—	M-587
		4-dehydrotigogenone	—	M-587
esinae	CBS	17β-hydroxy-4-androsten-3-one	17β-OH → 17-C=O	F-254
		4-pregnene-3,20-dione	17β-Ac → 17-C=O	F-254
			17β-Ac → 17β-OH	F-254
			17β-Ac → 17β-OAc	F-254
	NRRL 2778	4-pregnene-3,20-dione	17β-Ac → 17β-OAc	F-250
		6α-fluoro-4-pregnene-3,20-dione	17β-Ac → 17β-OAc	F-250
		6β-fluoro-4-pregnene-3,20-dione	17β-Ac → 17β-OAc	F-250
		11α-hydroxy-4-pregnene-3,20-dione	17β-Ac → 17β-OAc	F-250
		11β-hydroxy-4-pregnene-3,20-dione	17β-Ac → 17β-OAc	F-250
		6α-methyl-4-pregnene-3,20-dione	17β-Ac → 17β-OAc	F-250
		6β-methyl-4-pregnene-3,20-dione	17β-Ac → 17β-OAc	F-250
		6α-fluoro-11α-hydroxy-4-pregnene-3,20-dione	17β-Ac → 17β-OAc	F-250
		6β-fluoro-11α-hydroxy-4-pregnene-3,20-dione	17β-Ac → 17β-OAc	F-250
		6α-fluoro-11β-hydroxy-4-pregnene-3,20-dione	17β-Ac → 17β-OAc	F-250
		6β-fluoro-11β-hydroxy-4-pregnene-3,20-dione	17β-Ac → 17β-OAc	F-250
		6α-methyl-11α-hydroxy-4-pregnene-3,20-dione	17β-Ac → 17β-OAc	F-250
		6β-methyl-11α-hydroxy-4-pregnene-3,20-dione	17β-Ac → 17β-OAc	F-250
		6α-methyl-11β-hydroxy-4-pregnene-3,20-dione	17β-Ac → 17β-OAc	F-250

346

TABLE III

TAXONOMY

Transformations by Genus:

CLADOSPORIUM
CLAVARIA   (Basidio. - Agaricales)
CLAVICEPS   (Asco. - Hypocreales)
CLITOCYBE   (Basidio. - Agaricales)

SPECIES	SOURCE	SUBSTRATE	REACTION	REF.
resinae	NRRL-2778	6β-methyl-11β-hydroxy-4-pregnene-3,20-dione	17β-Ac→ 17β-OAc	F-250
		4-pregnene-3,11,20-trione	17β-Ac→ 17β-OAc	F-250
		6α-fluoro-4-pregnene-3,11,20-trione	17β-Ac→ 17β-OAc	F-250
		6β-fluoro-4-pregnene-3,11,20-trione	17β-Ac→ 17β-OAc	F-250
		6α-methyl-4-pregnene-3,11,20-trione	17β-Ac→ 17β-OAc	F-250
		6β-methyl-4-pregnene-3,11,20-trione	17β-Ac→ 17β-OAc	F-250
species	ATCC-13026	4-pregnene-3,20-dione	1ξ-OH	S-941
			7β-OH	S-941
	MCC(SF-523)	4-pregnene-3,20-dione	7β-OH	M-570
		21-hydroxy-4-pregnene-3,20-dione	7β-OH	M-570
CLAVARIA				
mucida	FRI	17α,21-dihydroxy-4-pregnene-3,20-dione	6β-OH; 11α-OH	S-849
CLAVICEPS				
purpurea	NG	$3\beta,6\beta,8\beta,14\beta$-tetrahydroxy-4,20,22-bufatrienolide 6-acetate 3-glucoside	3β-[$1'\xi$-glucoside] → 3β-OH	S-936a
		$3\beta,14\beta$-dihydroxy-5β-20(22)-cardenolide-3-[glucosyl-digitoxosyl-digitoxosyl-digitoxoside]	glucosyl-digitoxosyl-digitoxosyl-digitoxoside → digitoxosyl-digitoxosyl-digitoxoside	S-936a
CLITOCYBE				
adirondackensis	AL(SS-43)	4-pregnene-3,20-dione	—	S-825
clavipes	AL(G-107)	4-pregnene-3,20-dione	—	S-825
odora	AL(H-21)	4-pregnene-3,20-dione	—	S-825
species "C"	AL(G-8)	4-pregnene-3,20-dione	—	S-825

TABLE III

TAXONOMY

ansformations by Genus: CLOSTRIDIUM   (Schizo.- Eubacteriales)

SPECIES	SOURCE	SUBSTRATE	REACTION	REF.
difermentans	IMJ	3β-hydroxy-5-androsten-17-one	—	S-822
		4-androstene-3,17-dione	—	S-822
paraputrificum	IMJ	3α-hydroxy-5α-androstan-17-one	—	S-822
		3β-hydroxy-5-androsten-17-one	—	S-822
		17β-hydroxy-4-androsten-3-one	$\Delta^4 \to 5\beta$-H; 3-C=O$\to$3α-OH	S-823
		4-androstene-3,17-dione	$\Delta^4 \to 5\beta$-H; 3-C=O$\to$3α-OH	S-822
		1,4-androstadiene-3,17-dione	$\Delta^4 \to 5\beta$-H	S-824
			$\Delta^1 \to$ H; $\Delta^4 \to 5\beta$-H	S-824
			$\Delta^1 \to$ H; $\Delta^4 \to 5\beta$-H; 3-C=O $\to$3α-OH	S-824
		4-pregnene-3,20-dione	3-C=O $\to$ 3α-OH; $\Delta^4 \to 5\beta$-H	S-823
		21-hydroxy-4-pregnene-3,20-dione	3-C=O $\to$3α-OH; $\Delta^4\to5\beta$-H	S-823
		21-hydroxy-4-pregnene-3,20-dione acetate	3-C=O$\to$3α-OH; $\Delta^4\to5\beta$-H	S-823
		17α,21-dihydroxy-4-pregnene-3,11,20-trione	3-C=O$\to$3α-OH; $\Delta^4\to5\beta$-H	S-823
		17α,21-dihydroxy-4-pregnene-3,11,20-trione 21-acetate	3-C=O$\to$3α-OH; $\Delta^4\to5\beta$-H	S-823
erfringens	NG	3α,7α,12α-trihydroxy-5β-cholanic acid	7α-OH $\to$7-C=O	N-675
porogenes	IMJ	3β-hydroxy-4-androsten-17-one	—	S-822
		4-androstene-3,17-dione	—	S-822
	NG	5-cholesten-3β-ol	—	S-914
ertium	IMJ	17β-hydroxy-4-androsten-3-one	$\Delta^4\to5\beta$; 3-C=O$\to$3α-OH	S-823
		4-pregnene-3,20-dione	3-C=O$\to$3α-OH; $\Delta^4\to5\beta$-H	S-823
		21-hydroxy-4-pregnene-3,20-dione	3-C=O$\to$3α-OH; $\Delta^4\to5\beta$-H	S-823
		21-hydroxy-4-pregnene-3,20-dione acetate	3-C=O$\to$3α-OH; $\Delta^4\to5\beta$-H	S-823

TABLE III

Transformations by Genus: CLOSTRIDIUM
COCHLIOBOLUS   (Asco. - Sphaeriales)
COKEROMYCES   (Phyco. - Mucorales)
COLLETOTRICHUM (Imperf. - Melanconiales)

SPECIES	SOURCE	SUBSTRATE	REACTION	REF.
tertium	IMJ	17α,21-dihydroxy-4-pregnene-3,11,20-trione	3-C=O→3α-OH; Δ^4→5β-H	S-823
		17α,21-dihydroxy-4-pregnene-3,11,20-trione 21-acetate	3-C=O→3α-OH; Δ^4→5β-H	S-823
welchii	NG	5-cholesten-3β-ol	—	S-914
COCHLIOBOLUS				
miyabeanus	FAKU	17α,21-dihydroxy-4-pregnene-3,20-dione	—	S-849
	FRI	17α,21-dihydroxy-4-pregnene-3,20-dione	6β-OH; 11α-OH	S-849
COKEROMYCES				
recurvatus	CBS	20β-hydroxy-A-nor-5α-pregnan-2-one	17β-Ac→17β-OH; 5α-H → 5α-OH	P-706a
		A-nor-5α-pregnane-2,20-dione	5α-H → 5α-OH	P-706a
		A-nor-3-pregnene-2,20-dione	6β-OH	L-503a
COLLETOTRICHUM				
antirrhini	Cornell (Plant Pathology Dept.)	4-pregnene-3,20-dione	15α-OH	F-285; F-287; F-288
derridis	CBS	17β-hydroxy-4-estren-3-one	12β-OH	D-152
			12β-OH; 17β-OH →17-C=O	D-152
gloeosporioides	TNAES	17α,21-dihydroxy-4-pregnene-3,20-dione	11α-OH	S-849
lindemuthianum	ATCC-12611	pregnane-3,20-dione	21-OH unspecified products	H-324
		4-pregnene-3,20-dione	21-OH unspecified products	H-324
		11β,17α-dihydroxy-18-nor-4-pregnene-3,20-dione	21-OH	A-12
		9α-fluoro-11β,17α-dihydroxy-16α-methyl-1,4-pregnadiene-3,20-dione	21-OH	M-598

TABLE III

ransformations by Genus: COLLETOTRICHUM
                           COLLYBIA   (Basidio. - Agaricales)

SPECIES	SOURCE	SUBSTRATE	REACTION	REF.
lindemothianum	ATCC-12611	17α-hydroxy-1,4-pregnadiene-3,11,20-trione	21-OH	H-324
		17α-hydroxy-18-nor-4-pregnene-3,11,20-trione	21-OH	A-10; A-13
		17α-hydroxy-16α-methyl-18-nor-4-pregnene-3,11,20-trione	21-OH	A-11
	IAM	17α,21-dihydroxy-4-pregnene-3,20-dione	—	S-849
phomoides *	ATCC-12521	21-hydroxy-4-pregnene-3,20-dione	11β-OH	T-1003
*		17α,21-dihydroxy-4-pregnene-3,20-dione	11β-OH; 11α-OH	T-1003
		4,9(11)-pregnadiene-3,20-dione	6β,12α-diOH	F-277; F-279
			6β,X-diOH	F-277; F-279
			$\Delta^{9(11)} \rightarrow 9\beta,11\beta$-oxide; 6β,12α-diOH	F-277; F-279; F-280
	NARI	17α,21-dihydroxy-4-pregnene-3,20-dione	11α-OH	S-849
	NG	6α-fluoro-16α,17α,21-trihydroxy-4-pregnene-3,20-dione 16,17-acetonide	11α-OH	D-159
		6α-fluoro-16α,17α,21-trihydroxy-4-pregnene-3,20-dione 16,17-cyclohexanonide	11α-OH	D-159
	OR	17α-allyl-17β-hydroxy-4-estren-3-one	16β-OH	S-950
pisi	ATCC-12520	21-hydroxy-4-pregnene-3,20-dione	11β-OH	T-1004
		17α,21-dihydroxy-4-pregnene-3,20-dione	11α-OH; 11β-OH	T-1004
species	IAM	17α,21-dihydroxy-4-pregnene-3,20-dione	—	S-849
COLLYBIA				
dryophila	AL	4-pregnene-3,20-dione	17β-Ac→17a-oxa-17-C=O	S-825

TABLE III

TAXONOMY

Transformations by Genus: COLLYBIA
CONIDIOBOLUS (Phyco. - Entomophthorales)
CONIOTHYRIUM (Imperf. - Sphaeropsidales)

SPECIES	SOURCE	SUBSTRATE	REACTION	REF.
velutipes	FRI	17α,21-dihydroxy-4-pregnene-3,20-dione	—	S-849
CONIDIOBOLUS				
species	NRRL	Sarsasapogenin	—	M-587
		Diosgenin	—	M-587
		4-dehydrotigogenone	—	M-587
	NRRL-1612	17α,21-dihydroxy-4-pregnene-3,20-dione	2β-OH	W-1073
			11α-OH	W-1073
CONIOTHYRIUM				
diplodiella	TNAES	17α,21-dihydroxy-4-pregnene-3,20-dione	11α-OH	S-849
hellebori	SAG(078)	4-pregnene-3,20-dione	11β-OH	R-749
			12β-OH	R-749
		17α,21-dihydroxy-4-pregnene-3,20-dione	6β-OH	R-749
			11β-OH	R-749
			12β-OH	R-749
	SQ (mutant)	17α,21-dihydroxy-4-pregnene-3,20-dione	11β-OH	T-993
helleborine	ATCC-12522	17a-oxa-D-homo-4-androstene-3,17-dione	6β-OH	F-281; F-282; T-994
			7α-OH	F-281; F-282; T-994
		21-hydroxy-4-pregnene-3,20-dione	11α-OH	T-1003; T-1004
			11β-OH	T-1003; T-1004
		17α,21-dihydroxy-4-pregnene-3,20-dione	11α-OH	T-1003; T-1004
			11β-OH	F-288; R-749; T-993; T-1003; T-1004

TABLE III

ansformations by Genus:

CONIOTHYRIUM	
CONOCYBE	(Basidio. - Agaricales)
COPRINUS	(Basidio. - Agaricales)
CORDYCEPS	(Asco. - Hypocreales)
CORETHROPSIS	(Imperf. - Moniliales)
CORIOLUS	(Basidio. - Agaricales)

SPECIES	SOURCE	SUBSTRATE	REACTION	REF.
elleborine	ATCC-12522	17α,21-dihydroxy-1,4-pregna-diene-3,20-dione	11β-OH	T-1004
species	NRRL-2476	4-pregnene-3,20-dione	21-OH	D-186
		11β-hydroxy-4-pregnene-3,20-dione	21-OH	D-186
		17α-hydroxy-4-pregnene-3,20-dione	21-OH	D-186
		11β,17α-dihydroxy-4-pregnene-3,20-dione	21-OH	D-186
CONOCYBE				
iligenoides	NG	17α,21-dihydroxy-4-pregnene-3,20-dione	11α-OH	C-113
COPRINUS				
atromentarius (atramentarius)	AL(G-75)	4-pregnene-3,20-dione	—	S-825
obiliferus	AL(G-63)	4-pregnene-3,20-dione	—	S-825
CORDYCEPS				
militaris	FRI	17α,21-dihydroxy-4-pregnene-3,20-dione	6β-OH; 11α-OH	S-849
CORETHROPSIS				
hominis	FRI	17α,21-dihydroxy-4-pregnene-3,20-dione	—	S-849
CORIOLUS				
ersicolor	ATCC-13488	17α,21-dihydroxy-4-pregnene-3,20-dione	6β-OH	B-63
			14α-OH	B-63
			15β-OH	B-63

TABLE III

Transformations by Genus: CORTICIUM   (Basidio. - Agaricales)
(See Rhizoctonia)

Other Synonyms - Hypochnus and Pellicularia

SPECIES	SOURCE	SUBSTRATE	REACTION	REF.
centrifugum	ATCC-11908	4-androstene-3,17-dione	16-C=O; 17-C=O → 17β-OH	D-166
			16β-OH; 17-C=O → 17β-OH	D-166
centrifugus	FAHU	17α,21-dihydroxy-4-pregnene-3,20-dione	—	S-849
	FRI	17α,21-dihydroxy-4-pregnene-3,20-dione	2β-OH; 6β-OH; 11α-OH	S-849
graminum	NARI	17α,21-dihydroxy-4-pregnene-3,20-dione	—	S-849
microsclerotia	CMI	4-pregnene-3,20-dione	11-OH	H-349
		21-hydroxy-4-pregnene-3,20-dione	11-OH	H-349
		17α,21-dihydroxy-4-pregnene-3,20-dione	11α-OH; 11β-OH	H-349
		17α,21-dihydroxy-1,4-pregnadiene-3,20-dione	11-OH	H-349
	NRRL-2727	4-androstene-3,17-dione	19-OH	H-350
		4-pregnene-3,20-dione	19-OH	H-350
		21-hydroxy-4-pregnene-3,20-dione	19-OH	H-350
		17α,21-dihydroxy-4-pregnene-3,20-dione	11β-OH	H-350
		17α,21-dihydroxy-4-pregnene-3,20-dione 21-acetate	11β-OH;21-OAc →21-OH	H-350
		17α,21-dihydroxy-4-pregnene-3,20-dione	19-OH	H-350
		17α,21-dihydroxy-4-pregnene-3,20-dione 21-acetate	19-OH; 21-OAc →21-OH	H-350
practicola	CMI	4-pregnene-3,20-dione	11-OH	H-349
		21-hydroxy-4-pregnene-3,20-dione	11-OH	H-349
		17α,21-dihydroxy-4-pregnene-3,20-dione	11α-OH; 11β-OH	H-349
		17α,21-dihydroxy-1,4-pregnadiene-3,20-dione	11-OH	H-349

TABLE III

Transformations by Genus: CORTICIUM

SPECIES	SOURCE	SUBSTRATE	REACTION	REF.
practicola	NRRL-2724	17α,21-dihydroxy-4-pregnene-3,20-dione	11β-OH	H-350
roefsii	FAKU	17α,21-dihydroxy-4-pregnene-3,20-dione	—	S-849
salmonicolar	FAKU	17α,21-dihydroxy-4-pregnene-3,20-dione	—	S-849
sasakii	ATCC-13269	21-hydroxy-4-pregnene-3,20-dione	11β-OH	H-350
		17α,21-dihydroxy-4-pregnene-3,20-dione	11β-OH	H-350
		17α,21-dihydroxy-1,4-pregna-diene-3,20-dione	11β-OH	H-350
			11-C=O (via 11β-OH)	H-350
	CMI	4-pregnene-3,20-dione	11-OH	H-349
		21-hydroxy-4-pregnene-3,20-dione	11-OH	H-349
		17α,21-dihydroxy-4-pregnene-3,20-dione	11α-OH; 11β-OH	H-349
		17α,21-dihydroxy-1,4-pregna-diene-3,20-dione	11-OH	H-349
	IFO	17α,21-dihydroxy-4-pregnene-3,20-dione	11α-OH	H-347
			11β-OH	H-347
			19-OH	H-347; N-660
	IFO(5254)	17α,21-dihydroxy-4-pregnene-3,20-dione	6β-OH	H-327
			11α-OH	H-325; T-954
			11β-OH	H-325; T-954
			11β-OH;11-C=O (via 11β-OH)	H-327
			Δ^1; 11β-OH	H-327
			19-OH	H-325; H-326; T-954
	NG	17α,21-dihydroxy-4-pregnene-3,20-dione	19-OH	N-672

TABLE III

Transformations by Genus:

CORTICIUM
CORTINARIUS
CORTINELLUS
CORYNEBACTERIUM

<u>TAXONOMY</u>

(Basidio. - Agaricales)
(Basidio. - Agaricales)
(Schizo. - Eubacteriales)

SPECIES	SOURCE	SUBSTRATE	REACTION	REF.
solani (see vagum)	IFO (6251)	$17\alpha,21$-dihydroxy-4-pregnene-3,20-dione	Δ^1; 6β-OH	H-348
species	IAM (B-57, B-60, B-64)	$17\alpha,21$-dihydroxy-4-pregnene-3,20-dione	—	S-849
vagium	S	$17\alpha,21$-dihydroxy-4-pregnene-3,20-dione	11α-OH	S-849
vagum (see solani)	IAM	$17\alpha,21$-dihydroxy-4-pregnene-3,20-dione	11α-OH	S-840
	IFO (6192)	$17\alpha,21$-dihydroxy-4-pregnene-3,20-dione	11α-OH	H-350
			11β-OH	H-350
			19-OH	H-350
<u>CORTINARIUS</u>				
evernius	AL (C-351)	4-pregnene-3,20-dione	$\Delta^4 \rightarrow 5\alpha$-H	S-825
<u>CORTINELLUS</u>				
shiitake	FAKU	$17\alpha,21$-dihydroxy-4-pregnene-3,20-dione	11α-OH	S-849
<u>CORYNEBACTERIUM</u>				
equi (in mixed culture with Trichomonas foetus)	ATCC-10146	11β-hydroxy-4-estrene-3,17-dione	Δ^1; enol.	S-830
(in mixed culture with Trichomonas foetus)		4-estrene-3,11,17-trione	Δ^1; enol.	S-830
(in mixed culture with Trichomonas foetus)		4-androstene-3,17-dione	Δ^1	S-830
	IAM	$17\alpha,21$-dihydroxy-4-pregnene-3,20-dione	—	S-849
fascians	IAM	$17\alpha,21$-dihydroxy-4-pregnene-3,20-dione	—	S-849
helvolum (<u>nomen confusum</u> - see mediolanum and Flavobacterium helvolum)	NG	3β-hydroxy-5-androsten-17-one	3β-OH$\rightarrow$3-C=O; $\Delta^5 \rightarrow \Delta^4$	M-546
		17α-methyl-4-androstene-$3\beta,17\beta$-diol	3β-OH$\rightarrow$3-C=O; $\Delta^5 \rightarrow \Delta^4$	M-546

TABLE III

ansformations by Genus: CORYNEBACTERIUM

SPECIES	SOURCE	SUBSTRATE	REACTION	REF.
elvolum (nomen confusum - see mediolanum and Flavobacterium helvolum)	NG	3β-hydroxy-5-pregnen-20-one	3β-OH$\rightarrow$3-C=O; $\Delta^5\rightarrow\Delta^4$	M-546
oagii	ATCC-7005	11β-hydroxy-19-nor-4-pregnene- 3,20-dione	Δ^1; enol.	H-386
		$11\beta,17\alpha$-dihydroxy-19-nor-4- pregnene-3,20-dione	Δ^1; enol.	H-386
		$11\beta,21$-dihydroxy-19-nor-4- pregnene-3,20-dione	Δ^1; enol.	H-386
		19-nor-4-pregnene-3,11,20- trione	Δ^1; enol.	H-386
		17α-hydroxy-19-nor-4-pregnene- 3,11,20-trione	Δ^1; enol.	H-386
		4-pregnene-3,20-dione	Δ^1	F-251
		9α-chloro-11β-hydroxy-4- pregnene-3,20-dione	Δ^1	H-379
		9α-bromo-$11\beta,21$-dihydroxy- 4-pregnene-3,20-dione 21-acetate	Δ^1; 21-OAc $\rightarrow$ 21-OH	N-668
		9α-chloro-$11\beta,17\alpha$-dihydroxy- 4-pregnene-3,20-dione	Δ^1	H-379
		9α-chloro-$11\beta,21$-dihydroxy-4- pregnene-3,20-dione	Δ^1	N-668
		$11\beta,17\alpha,21$-trihydroxy-4-preg- nene-3,20-dione	Δ^1	N-665; N-670
		9α-fluoro-$11\beta,17\alpha,21$-trihydroxy- 4-pregnene-3,20-dione	Δ^1	N-669
		9α-fluoro-$11\beta,14\alpha,15\beta,17\alpha,21$- pentahydroxy-4-pregnene- 3,20-dione	Δ^1	N-669
		4-pregnene-3,20-dione 20- cycloethyleneketal	Δ^1	F-251
		9α-bromo-4-pregnene-3,11,20- trione	Δ^1	H-379
		9α-chloro-4-pregnene-3,11,20- trione	Δ^1	H-379
	IAM	$17\alpha,21$-dihydroxy-4-pregnene- 3,20-dione	—	S-849

TABLE III

Transformations by Genus: CORYNEBACTERIUM

SPECIES	SOURCE	SUBSTRATE	REACTION	REF.
mediolanum	NG	3β-hydroxy-5-androsten-17-one	3β-OH$\rightarrow$3-C=O; $\Delta^5\rightarrow\Delta^4$	M-591
		5-androstene-$3\beta,17\beta$-diol	3β-OH$\rightarrow$3-C=O; $\Delta^5\rightarrow\Delta^4$	M-591
		5-androstene-$3\beta,16\alpha,17\beta$-triol	3β-OH$\rightarrow$3-C=O; $\Delta^5\rightarrow\Delta^4$	A-1
		$1\beta,3\beta$-dihydroxy-5-pregnen-20-one	3β-OH$\rightarrow$3-C=O; $\Delta^5\rightarrow\Delta^4$	B-77
		$3\beta,21$-dihydroxy-5-pregnen-20-one 21-acetate	3β-OH$\rightarrow$3-C=O; $\Delta^5\rightarrow\Delta^4$; 21-OAc $\rightarrow$21-OH	M-541; M-544
(in mixed culture with Cunninghamella blakesleeana[11β-OH])		$3\beta,17\alpha,21$-trihydroxy-5-pregnen-20-one	$\Delta^5\rightarrow\Delta^4$; 3β-OH $\rightarrow$3-C=O	S-920
		$3\beta,17\alpha,21$-trihydroxy-5-pregnen-20-one 21-acetate	$\Delta^5\rightarrow\Delta^4$; 3β-OH $\rightarrow$3-C=O; 21-OAc$\rightarrow$21-OH	S-920
		$3\beta,17\alpha,21$-trihydroxy-5-pregnen-20-one 3,21-diacetate	$\Delta^5\rightarrow\Delta^4$; 3β-OAc $\rightarrow$3-C=O; 21-OAc$\rightarrow$21-OH	S-920
pseudodiphtheriticum *	NG	1,3,5(10)-estratriene-3,17β-diol	17β-OH$\rightarrow$17-C=O	Z-1133
*		5-androstene-$3\beta,17\beta$-diol	$\Delta^5\rightarrow\Delta^4$; 3β-OH $\rightarrow$3-C=O	Z-1133
*			$\Delta^5\rightarrow\Delta^4$; 3β-OH $\rightarrow$3-C=O; 17β-OH$\rightarrow$17-C=O	Z-1133
		5-cholesten-3β-ol (sole carbon source)	—	T-1033
simplex (see genus - Arthrobacter)	ATCC-6946	A-nor-17β-hydroxy-3-androsten-2-one	9α-OH; 17β-OH $\rightarrow$17-C=O	S-885
		17β-hydroxy-4-estren-3-one	Δ^1; enol.	C-128; K-487; K-488
			Δ^1; enol. 17β-OH $\rightarrow$ 17-C=O	K-487; K-488
			17β-OH $\rightarrow$ 17-C=O	K-487; K-488
		17β-hydroxy-4-estren-3-one acetate	Δ^1; enol	G-315; K-487; K-488
			1ξ-OH	G-315; K-487

TABLE III

ansformations by Genus: CORYNEBACTERIUM

SPECIES	SOURCE	SUBSTRATE	REACTION	REF.
simplex (see genus - Arthrobacter)	ATCC-6946	$10\beta,17\beta$-dihydroxy-4-estren-3-one	Δ^1; enol.	D-150
		$9\beta,11\beta$-oxido-4-estrene-3,17-dione	Δ^1; enol.	R-762
		9α-bromo-4-estrene-3,11,17-trione	Δ^1; enol.	R-762
		4,7-estradiene-3,17-dione	Δ^1; enol.	B-72; Z-1126; Z-1127
		4,6-estradiene-3,17-dione	Δ^1; enol.	Z-1127
		5-androstene-$3\beta,17\beta$-diol	Δ^1; $\Delta^5 \to \Delta^4$; 3β-OH$\to$3-C=O	C-128; N-665; N-670
			3β-OH$\to$3-C=O; $\Delta^5 \to \Delta^4$; 17β-OH $\to$17-C=O	C-128
			Δ^1; 3β-OH $\to$ 3-C=O; 17β-OH $\to$17-C=O; $\Delta^5 \to \Delta^4$	C-128; N-665
		17α-methyl-16-methylene-5-androstene-$3\beta,17\beta$-diol	Δ^1; $\Delta^5 \to \Delta^4$; 3β-OH$\to$3-C=O	B-76
		3β-hydroxy-5-androsten-17-one	3β-OH$\to$3-C=O; $\Delta^5 \to \Delta^4$	C-128; N-665; N-670
		17β-hydroxy-4-androsten-3-one	Δ^1	C-128; N-665; N-670; S-890
			17β-OH $\to$ 17-C=O	C-128
			Δ^1; 17β-OH $\to$ 17-C=O	C-128; N-665
		17α-bromethinyl-17β-hydroxy-4-androsten-3-one acetate	Δ^1	O-694; O-695
		17α-chlorethinyl-17β-hydroxy-4-androsten-3-one acetate	Δ^1	O-694; O-695
		17α-ethinyl-17β-hydroxy-4-androsten-3-one	Δ^1	N-665; N-670
		17α-ethyl-17β-hydroxy-4-androsten-3-one	Δ^1	N-677a

TABLE III

Transformations by Genus: CORYNEBACTERIUM

SPECIES	SOURCE	SUBSTRATE	REACTION	REF.
simplex (See genus - Arthrobacter)	ATCC-6946	$2\beta,17\beta$-dihydroxy-4-androsten-3-one diacetate	2β-OAc$\rightarrow 2\beta$-OH; 17β-OAc $\rightarrow$ 17-C=O	H-399
		17β-hydroxy-17α-methyl-4 androsten-3-one	Δ^1	N-665; N-667a; N-670
		17α-bromethinyl-6α-chloro-17β-hydroxy-4-androsten-3-one acetate	Δ^1	O-694; O-695
		17α-bromethinyl-6α-fluoro-17β-hydroxy-4-androsten-3-one acetate	Δ^1	O-694; O-695
		6α-chloro-17α-chlorethinyl-17β-hydroxy-4-androsten-3-one acetate	Δ^1	O-694; O-695
		17α-chlorethinyl-6α-fluoro-17β-hydroxy-4-androsten-3-one acetate	Δ^1	O-694; O-695
		17α-ethyl-$11\beta,17\beta$-dihydroxy-4-androsten-3-one	Δ^1	N-667a
		12α-fluoro-$11\beta,17\beta$-dihydroxy-4-androsten-3-one	Δ^1; 17β-OH $\rightarrow$ 17-C=O	R-772
			Δ^1	R-772
		$11\beta,17\beta$-dihydroxy-17α-methyl-4-androsten-3-one	Δ^1	N-667a
		17β-hydroxy-17α-methyl-16-methylene-4-androsten-3-one	Δ^1	B-76
		$9\alpha,11\beta$-dichloro-17β-hydroxy-17α-methyl-4-androsten-3-one	Δ^1	G-308
		9α-bromo-17α-ethinyl-$11\beta,17\beta$-dihydroxy-16α-methyl-4-androsten-3-one	Δ^1	O-701
		9α-chloro-17α-ethinyl-$11\beta,17\beta$-dihydroxy-16α-methyl-4-androsten-3-one	Δ^1	O-701
		17α-ethinyl-16α-ethyl-9α-fluoro-$11\beta,17\beta$-dihydroxy-4-androsten-3-one	Δ^1	O-701
		17α-ethinyl-9α-fluoro-$11\beta,17\beta$-dihydroxy-16α-methyl-4-androsten-3-one	Δ^1	O-701
		17α-ethinyl-16α-ethyl-17β-hydroxy-$9\beta,11\beta$-oxido-4-androsten-3-one	Δ^1	O-701

TABLE III

Transformations by Genus: CORYNEBACTERIUM

SPECIES	SOURCE	SUBSTRATE	REACTION	REF.
simplex	ATCC-6946	17β-hydroxy-16α-methyl-17α-(1'-propinyl)-9β,11β-oxido-4-androsten-3-one	Δ^1	O-701
		17β-hydroxy-17α-methyl-4,9(11)-androstadien-3-one	Δ^1	G-308
		17α-bromethinyl-6-chloro-17β-hydroxy-4,6-androstadien-3-one acetate	Δ^1	O-694; O-695
		17α-bromethinyl-6-fluoro-17β-hydroxy-4,6-androstadien-3-one acetate	Δ^1	O-694; O-695
		6-chloro-17α-chlorethinyl-17β-hydroxy-4,6-androstadien-3-one	Δ^1	O-694; O-695
		17α-chlorethinyl-6-fluoro-17β-hydroxy-4,6-androstadien-3-one acetate	Δ^1	O-694; O-695
		6α-fluoro-17β-hydroxy-17α-methyl-4,9(11)-androstadien-3-one	Δ^1	G-308
		11β-hydroxy-4-androstene-3,17-dione	Δ^1	C-128; N-666; N-667
(in mixed culture with Trichomonas gallinae)			Δ^1	S-830
		9α,11β-dichloro-4-androstene-3,17-dione	Δ^1	G-308
		11α-hydroxy-16α-methyl-4-androstene-3,17-dione	Δ^1	R-752
		16α-n-butyl-17α-ethinyl-17β-hydroxy-4-androstene-3,11-dione	Δ^1	O-701
		16β-n-butyl-17α-ethinyl-17β-hydroxy-4-androstene-3,11-dione	Δ^1	O-701
		17β-hydroxy-16α-methyl-17α-(1'-propinyl)-4-androstene-3,11-dione	Δ^1	O-701
		17α-ethinyl-9α-fluoro-17β-hydroxy-16α-methyl-4-androstene-3,11-dione	Δ^1	O-701
		17α-ethinyl-16α-ethyl-9α-fluoro-17β-hydroxy-4-androstene-3,11-dione	Δ^1	O-701

TABLE III

Transformations by Genus: CORYNEBACTERIUM

SPECIES	SOURCE	SUBSTRATE	REACTION	REF.
simplex (in mixed culture with Trichomonas gallinae)	ATCC-6946	4-androstene-3,11,17-trione	Δ^1	S-830
		16β-methyl-4-androstene-3,11, 17-trione	Δ^1	R-752
		19-nor-4-pregnene-3,20-dione	Δ^1; enol.	B-71; B-73
		19-nor-4-pregnene-3,11,20-trione	Δ^1; enol.	B-73
		11β,21-dihydroxy-19-nor-4-pregnene-3,20-dione	Δ^1; enol.	H-386
		11β,17α,21-trihydroxy-19-nor-4-pregnene-3,20-dione	Δ^1; enol.	H-386
		11β,17α,21-trihydroxy-19-nor-4-pregnene-3,20-dione 11, 21-diacetate	Δ^1; enol.	H-386
		21-hydroxy-19-nor-4-pregnene-3,11,20-trione	Δ^1; enol.	H-386
		17α,21-dihydroxy-19-nor-4-pregnene-3,11,20-trione	Δ^1; enol.	H-386
		17α,21-dihydroxy-19-nor-4-pregnene-3,11,20-trione 21-acetate	Δ^1; enol.	H-386
		3α,17α,21-trihydroxy-5α-pregnane-11,20-dione	—	C-128
		17α,21-dihydroxy-5α-pregnane-3,11,20-trione	—	C-128
		17α,21-dihydroxy-16β-methyl-5α-pregnane-3,11,20-trione	Δ^1; Δ^4	K-451
			Δ^1	K-451
		17α,21-dihydroxy-16β-methyl-5α-pregnane-3,11,20-trione 21-acetate	Δ^1; 21-OAc → 21-OH	K-451
			Δ^1; Δ^4; 21-OAc→21-OH	K-451
		5-pregnene-3β,20β-diol	$\Delta^5 \rightarrow \Delta^4$; Δ^1; 3β-OH→3-C=O; 20β-OH→ 20-C=O	C-128; N-665; N-670
		3β,17α,21-trihydroxy-5-pregnene-20-one 3,21-diacetate	Δ^1; $\Delta^5 \rightarrow \Delta^4$; 3$\beta$-OAc→3-C=O; 21-OAc → 21-OH	C-115; C-128; N-665; N-670

TABLE III

Transformations by Genus: CORYNEBACTERIUM

SPECIES	SOURCE	SUBSTRATE	REACTION	REF.
simplex	ATCC-6946	$3\beta,17\alpha,21$-trihydroxy-5-pregnen-20-one 3,21-diacetate	3β-OAc$\rightarrow$3-C=O; $\Delta^5\rightarrow\Delta^4$	C-128; N-665
			3β-OAc$\rightarrow$3-C=O; $\Delta^5\rightarrow\Delta^4$; Δ^1; 21-OAc$\rightarrow$21-OH	C-115; C-128; N-665
			3β-OAc$\rightarrow$3-C=O; $\Delta^5\rightarrow\Delta^4$; Δ^1; 20-C=O$\rightarrow$20β-OH; 21-OAc$\rightarrow$ 21-OH	C-115
		3β-hydroxy-4-pregnen-20-one	Δ^1; 3β-OH $\rightarrow$ 3-C=O	N-665; N-670
		4-pregnene-3,20-dione	Δ^1	F-251; H-399; T-1005
			9α-OH	P-740; S-885
		4-pregnene-3,20-dione 20-cycloethyleneketal	Δ^1 (ketal prevents degradation)	F-251
		11α-hydroxy-4-pregnene-3,20-dione	Δ^1	T-995; T-1001
			Δ^1; 20-C=O $\rightarrow$ 20β-OH	T-995
		21-hydroxy-4-pregnene-3,20-dione	Δ^1	N-665; N-670
		21-hydroxy-4-pregnene-3,20-dione acetate	Δ^1	H-389; N-671
		$9\alpha,11\beta$-dibromo-4-pregnene-3,20-dione	Δ^1	R-754
		9α-bromo-11β-chloro-4-pregnene-3,20-dione	Δ^1	R-754
		9α-bromo-11β-fluoro-4-pregnene-3,20-dione	Δ^1	R-754
		9α-bromo-11β-hydroxy-4-pregnene-3,20-dione	Δ^1	H-379
		9α-chloro-11β-fluoro-4-pregnene-3,20-dione	Δ^1	R-754
		11β-chloro-9α-iodo-4-pregnene-3,20-dione	Δ^1	R-754

TABLE III

Transformations by Genus: CORYNEBACTERIUM

SPECIES	SOURCE	SUBSTRATE	REACTION	REF.
simplex	ATCC-6946	$9\alpha,11\beta$-dichloro-4-pregnene-3,20-dione	Δ^1	R-754
		9α-fluoro-11β-hydroxy-4-pregnene-3,20-dione	Δ^1	H-379
		11β-fluoro-9α-iodo-4-pregnene-3,20-dione	Δ^1	R-754
		$11\beta,21$-dihydroxy-4-pregnene-3,20-dione	Δ^1	H-389; N-665; N-670; N-671
		$16\alpha,21$-dihydroxy-4-pregnene-3,20-dione	Δ^1	H-376
		$17\alpha,21$-dihydroxy-4-pregnene-3,20-dione	Δ^1	H-389; H-399; L-522; N-665; N-671
			20-C=O → 20β-OH	L-522
			20-C=O → 20β-OH; Δ^1	H-389; N-665; N-670; L-522
		11β-hydroxy-3,20-diketo-4-pregnen-18-oic acid (18 → 11) lactone	Δ^1	U-1044
		9α-bromo-$11\beta,17\alpha$-dichloro-4-pregnene-3,20-dione	Δ^1	R-761
		17α-bromo-$9\alpha,11\beta$-dichloro-4-pregnene-3,20-dione	Δ^1	R-761
		9α-bromo-17α-chloro-11β-fluoro-4-pregnene-3,20-dione	Δ^1	R-761
		9α-bromo-11β-chloro-17α-hydroxy-4-pregnene-3,20-dione acetate	Δ^1	R-761
		9α-bromo-11β-fluoro-17α-hydroxy-4-pregnene-3,20-dione acetate	Δ^1	R-761
		9α-bromo-11β-fluoro-6α-methyl-4-pregnene-3,20-dione	Δ^1	R-754
		$9\alpha,17\alpha$-dibromo-11β-chloro-4-pregnene-3,20-dione	Δ^1	R-761

TABLE III

ansformations by Genus: CORYNEBACTERIUM

SPECIES	SOURCE	SUBSTRATE	REACTION	REF.
simplex	ATCC-6946	9α,11β-dibromo-17α-hydroxy-4-pregnene-3,20-dione acetate	Δ^1	R-761
		11β,17α-dibromo-9α-iodo-4-pregnene-3,20-dione	Δ^1	R-761
		9α,11β-dibromo-6α-methyl-4-pregnene-3,20-dione	Δ^1	R-754
		9α-chloro-11β-fluoro-17α-hydroxy-4-pregnene-3,20-dione acetate	Δ^1	R-761
		9α-chloro-11β-fluoro-6α-methyl-4-pregnene-3,20-dione	Δ^1	R-754
		9α-chloro-11β-fluoro-6β-methyl-4-pregnene-3,20-dione	Δ^1	R-754
		11β-chloro-17α-hydroxy-9α-iodo-4-pregnene-3,20-dione acetate	Δ^1	R-761
		11β-chloro-9α-iodo-6α-methyl-4-pregnene-3,20-dione	Δ^1	R-754
		11β-chloro-9α-iodo-6β-methyl-4-pregnene-3,20-dione	Δ^1	R-754
		11β-chloro-9α-iodo-17α-hydroxy-4-pregnene-3,20-dione	Δ^1	R-761
		9α,17α-dichloro-11β-fluoro-4-pregnene-3,20-dione	Δ^1	R-761
		9α,11β-dichloro-17α-hydroxy-4-pregnene-3,20-dione	Δ^1	G-307
		9α,11β-dichloro-17α-hydroxy-4-pregnene-3,20-dione acetate	Δ^1	R-761
		9α,11β-dichloro-17α-hydroxy-4-pregnene-3,20-dione caproate	Δ^1	R-761
		9α,11β-dichloro-6α-methyl-4-pregnene-3,20-dione	Δ^1	R-754
		9α,11β-dichloro-6β-methyl-4-pregnene-3,20-dione	Δ^1	R-754
		9α,11β,17α-trichloro-4-pregnene-3,20-dione	Δ^1	R-761
		9α-fluoro-11β,17α-dihydroxy-4-pregnene-3,20-dione	Δ^1	H-379; N-668
		9α-fluoro-11β,21-dihydroxy-4-pregnene-3,20-dione	Δ^1	N-668

TABLE III

Transformations by Genus: CORYNEBACTERIUM

SPECIES	SOURCE	SUBSTRATE	REACTION	REF.
simplex	ATCC-6946	$11\alpha,21$-dihydroxy-17α-methyl-4-pregnene-3,20-dione 21-acetate	Δ^1	H-377
		$11\alpha,17\alpha,21$-trihydroxy-4-pregnene-3,20-dione	Δ^1	H-384; H-389; N-665; N-671
		$11\beta,17\alpha,21$-trihydroxy-4-pregnene-3,20-dione (effect of antibiotics-Ref. B-37) (use of dried thalli-Ref. F-231)	Δ^1	B-37; F-231; F-232; H-389; H-399; K-467; N-665; N-670; N-671
		$11\beta,17\alpha,21$-trihydroxy-4-pregnene-3,20-dione 21-acetate	Δ^1	N-665; N-670
		$11\beta,17\alpha,21$-trihydroxy-4-pregnene-3,20-dione 11,21-diacetate	Δ^1	H-389
		$12\beta,17\alpha,21$-trihydroxy-4-pregnene-3,20-dione	Δ^1	R-749
			Δ^1; 20-C=O → 20β-OH	R-749
		21-(N-acetyl amino)-9α-fluoro-$11\beta,17\alpha$-dihydroxy-4-pregnene-3,20-dione	Δ^1	S-911
		17α-bromo-$9\alpha,11\beta$-dichloro-21-fluoro-4-pregnene-3,20-dione	Δ^1	R-756
		9α-bromo-11β-chloro-21-fluoro-17α-hydroxy-4-pregnene-3,20-dione	Δ^1	R-756
		9α-bromo-11β-chloro-21-fluoro-6α-methyl-4-pregnene-3,20-dione	Δ^1	R-755
		9α-bromo-$6\alpha,11\beta,21$-trifluoro-4-pregnene-3,20-dione	Δ^1	R-758
		9α-bromo-$11\beta,21$-difluoro-17α-hydroxy-4-pregnene-3,20-dione	Δ^1	R-756
		9α-bromo-$11\beta,21$-difluoro-17α-hydroxy-4-pregnene-3,20-dione caproate	Δ^1	R-756
		9α-bromo-$11\beta,17\alpha,21$-trihydroxy-4-pregnene-3,20-dione	Δ^1	N-668

TABLE III

ansformations by Genus: CORYNEBACTERIUM

SPECIES	SOURCE	SUBSTRATE	REACTION	REF.
simplex	ATCC-6946	$9\alpha,17\alpha$-dibromo-$11\beta,21$-difluoro-4-pregnene-3,20-dione	Δ^1	R-756
		$9\alpha,11\beta$-dibromo-21-fluoro-6α-methyl-4-pregnene-3,20-dione	Δ^1	R-755
		9α-chloro-$11\beta,21$-difluoro-17α-hydroxy-4-pregnene-3,20-dione	Δ^1	R-756
		9α-chloro-$11\beta,21$-difluoro-6α-methyl-4-pregnene-3,20-dione	Δ^1	R-755
		11β-chloro-21-fluoro-17α-hydroxy-9α-iodo-4-pregnene-3,20-dione	Δ^1	R-756
		11β-chloro-21-fluoro-9α-iodo-6α-methyl-4-pregnene-3,20-dione	Δ^1	R-755
		9α-chloro-$11\beta,17\alpha,21$-trihydroxy-4-pregnene-3,20-dione	Δ^1	N-668
		7α-cyano-$11\beta,17\alpha,21$-trihydroxy-4-pregnene-3,20-dione	Δ^1	B-75
		7β-cyano-$11\beta,17\alpha,21$-trihydroxy-4-pregnene-3,20-dione	Δ^1	B-75
		16-chlormethylene-$11\beta,17\alpha,21$-trihydroxy-4-pregnene-3,20-dione	Δ^1	W-1084
		$9\alpha,11\beta$-dichloro-$6\alpha,21$-difluoro-4-pregnene-3,20-dione	Δ^1	R-758
		$9\alpha,11\beta$-dichloro-21-fluoro-17α-hydroxy-4-pregnene-3,20-dione	Δ^1	R-756
		$9\alpha,11\beta$-dichloro-21-fluoro-17α-hydroxy-4-pregnene-3,20-dione acetate	Δ^1	R-756
		$9\alpha,11\beta$-dichloro-6α-fluoro-21-iodo-4-pregnene-3,20-dione	Δ^1	R-758
		$9\alpha,11\beta$-dichloro-21-fluoro-6α-methyl-4-pregnene-3,20-dione	Δ^1	R-755
		$9\alpha,11\beta$-dichloro-17α-hydroxy-21-iodo-4-pregnene-3,20-dione	Δ^1	R-756

TABLE III

Transformations by Genus: CORYNEBACTERIUM

SPECIES	SOURCE	SUBSTRATE	REACTION	REF.
simplex	ATCC-6946	9α,11β-dichloro-21-iodo-6α-methyl-4-pregnene-3,20-dione	Δ^1	R-755
		9α-fluoro-11β,17α,21-trihydroxy-4-pregnene-3,20-dione	Δ^1	H-389; N-665; N-668; N-669; N-670; N-671
		16-fluormethylene-11β,17α,21-trihydroxy-4-pregnene-3,20-dione	Δ^1	W-1084
		6α,11β,21-trifluoro-9α-iodo-4-pregnene-3,20-dione	Δ^1	R-758
		11α,17α,21-trihydroxy-16β-methyl-4-pregnene-3,20-dione	Δ^1	C-109; I-421
		11β,17α,21-trihydroxy-16β-methoxy-4-pregnene-3,20-dione 21-acetate	Δ^1	R-760
		11β,17α,21-trihydroxy-6-methylene-4-pregne..e-3,20-dione 21-acetate	Δ^1	F-264
		11β,15β,17α,21-tetrahydroxy-4-pregnene-3,20-dione	Δ^1	C-127
		11β,16α,17α,21-tetrahydroxy-4-pregnene-3,20-dione	Δ^1	B-54; B-59; B-61
		17α-bromo-9α,11β-dichloro-21-fluoro-6α-methyl-4-pregnene-3,20-dione	Δ^1	R-759
		9α-bromo-11β-chloro-6α,21-difluoro-17α-methyl-4-pregnene-3,20-dione	Δ^1	R-759
		9α-bromo-11β-chloro-21-fluoro-17α-hydroxy-6α-methyl-4-pregnene-3,20-dione	Δ^1	R-759
		9α-bromo-11β-chloro-21-fluoro-17α-hydroxy-6α-methyl-4-pregnene-3,20-dione acetate	Δ^1	R-759

TABLE III

ansformations by Genus: CORYNEBACTERIUM

SPECIES	SOURCE	SUBSTRATE	REACTION	REF.
implex	ATCC-6946	17α-bromo-9α,21-dichloro-6α, 21-difluoro-4-pregnene-3, 20-dione	Δ^1	R-759
		9α-bromo-11β,21-difluoro-17α-hydroxy-6α-methyl-4-pregnene-3,20-dione	Δ^1	R-759
		9α-bromo-11β,21-difluoro-17α-hydroxy-6α-methyl-4-pregnene-3,20-dione acetate	Δ^1	R-759
		9α-bromo-11β,21-difluoro-17α-hydroxy-6α-methyl-4-pregnene-3,20-dione caproate	Δ^1	R-759
		9α-bromo-6α,11β,21-trifluoro-17α-hydroxy-4-pregnene-3,20-dione	Δ^1	R-759
		9α-bromo-6α,11β,21-trifluoro-17α-hydroxy-4-pregnene-3,20-dione acetate	Δ^1	R-759
		9α-bromo-11β,17α,21-trihydroxy-16α-methyl-4-pregnene-3,20-dione	Δ^1	R-752
		9α,17α-dibromo-11β-chloro-21-fluoro-6α-methyl-4-pregnene-3,20-dione	Δ^1	R-759
		9α,11β-dibromo-21-fluoro-6α,17α-dimethyl-4-pregnene-3,20-dione	Δ^1	R-759
		11β-chloro-6α,21-difluoro-17α-hydroxy-9α-iodo-4-pregnene-3,20-dione	Δ^1	R-759
		11β-chloro-6α,21-difluoro-17α-hydroxy-9α-iodo-4-pregnene-3,20-dione	Δ^1	R-759
		9α-chloro-11β,21-difluoro-6α,17α-dimethyl-4-pregnene-3,20-dione	Δ^1	R-759
		9α-chloro-11β-fluoro-17α,21-dihydroxy-2α-methyl-4-pregnene-3,20-dione 21-acetate	Δ^1	N-691
		11β-chloro-21-fluoro-17α-hydroxy-9α-iodo-6α-methyl-4-pregnene-3,20-dione	Δ^1	R-759
		11β-chloro-21-fluoro-17α-hydroxy-9α-iodo-6α-methyl-4-pregnene-3,20-dione acetate	Δ^1	R-759

TABLE III

Transformations by Genus: CORYNEBACTERIUM

SPECIES	SOURCE	SUBSTRATE	REACTION	REF.
simplex	ATCC-6946	9α-chloro-11β,17α,21-trihydroxy-16α-methyl-4-pregnene-3,20-dione	Δ^1	R-752
		9α,11β-dichloro-6α,21-difluoro-17α-hydroxy-4-pregnene-3,20-dione	Δ^1	R-759
		9α,11β-dichloro-6α,21-difluoro-17α-hydroxv-4-pregnene-3,20-dione acetate	Δ^1	R-759
		9α,11β-dichloro-6α,21-difluoro-17α-hydroxy-4-pregnene-3,20-dione caproate	Δ^1	R-759
		9α,11β-dichloro-6α,21-difluoro-17α-methyl-4-pregnene-3,20-dione	Δ^1	R-759
		9α,11β-dichloro-6α-fluoro-17α-hydroxy-21-iodo-4-pregnene-3,20-dione	Δ^1	R-759
		9α,11β-dichloro-6α-fluoro-17α-hydroxy-21-iodo-4-pregnene-3,20-dione acetate	Δ^1	R-759
		9α,11β-dichloro-21-fluoro-17α-hydroxy-6α-methyl-4-pregnene-3,20-dione	Δ^1	R-759
		9α,11β-dichloro-21-fluoro-17α-hydroxy-6α-methyl-4-pregnene-3,20-dione acetate	Δ^1	R-759
		9α,11β-dichloro-21-fluoro-17α-hydroxy-6α-methyl-4-pregnene-3,20-dione caproate	Δ^1	R-759
		9α,11β-dichloro-6α-fluoro-21-iodo-17α-methyl-4-pregnene-3,20-dione	Δ^1	R-759
		9α,11β-dichloro-21-fluoro-6α,17α-dimethyl-4-pregnene-3,20-dione	Δ^1	R-759
		9α,11β-dichloro-17α,21-dihydroxy-2α-methyl-4-pregnene-3,20-dione 21-acetate	Δ^1	N-691
		9α,11β-dichloro-17α-hydroxy-21-iodo-6α-methyl-4-pregnene-3,20-dione	Δ^1	R-759
		9α,11β-dichloro-17α-hydroxy-21-iodo-6α-methyl-4-pregnene-3,20-dione acetate	Δ^1	R-759

TABLE III

ansformations by Genus: CORYNEBACTERIUM

SPECIES	SOURCE	SUBSTRATE	REACTION	REF.
simplex	ATCC-6946	$9\alpha,11\beta$-dichloro-21-iodo-6α, 17α-dimethyl-4-pregnene-3,20-dione	Δ^1	R-759
		9α-fluoro-$11\beta,16\alpha,17\alpha,21$-tetrahydroxy-4-pregnene-3,20-dione	Δ^1	B-61; G-296; H-399; S-908
		9α-fluoro-$11\beta,16\alpha,17\alpha,21$-tetrahydroxy-4-pregnene-3,20-dione	Δ^1; 20-C=O → 20β-OH	S-908
			20-C=O→20β-OH	G-296; S-908
		9α-fluoro-$11\beta,16\alpha,17\alpha,21$-tetrahydroxy-4-pregnene-3,20-dione 16,21-diacetate	Δ^1	B-57; B-59; B-60
		6α-fluoro-$11\beta,17\alpha,21$-trihydroxy-16α-methyl-4-pregnene-3,20-dione	Δ^1	U-1042
		$9\alpha,11\beta$-difluoro-$17\alpha,21$-dihydroxy-2α-methyl-4-pregnene-3,20-dione 21-acetate	Δ^1	N-691
		$11\beta,17\alpha,21$-trihydroxy-6α-methyl-16-methylene-4-pregnene-3,20-dione	Δ^1	B-69
		$11\beta,17\alpha,21$-trihydroxy-16α-methyl-6-methylene-4-pregnene-3,20-dione	Δ^1	F-264
		9α-chloro-11β-fluoro-$16\alpha,17\alpha$, 21-trihydroxy-2α-methyl-4-pregnene-3,20-dione 21-acetate	Δ^1	N-691
		9α-chloro-11β-fluoro-21-hydroxy-2α-methyl-$16\alpha,17\alpha$-isopropylidenedioxy-4-pregnene-3,20-dione acetate	Δ^1	N-691
		6α-fluoro-$11\beta,14\alpha,17\alpha,21$-tetrahydroxy-$16\alpha$-methyl-4-pregnene-3,20-dione	Δ^1	U-1042
		$17\alpha,21$-dihydroxy-16β-methyl-5α-9(11)-pregnene-3,20-dione 21-acetate	$\Delta^{9(11)}$→$9\alpha,11\alpha$-oxide; Δ^1; Δ^4; 21-OAc →→21-OH	C-138
			$\Delta^{9(11)}$→$9\alpha,11\alpha$-oxide; Δ^4; 21-OAc→21-OH	C-138

TABLE III

Transformations by Genus: CORYNEBACTERIUM

SPECIES	SOURCE	SUBSTRATE	REACTION	REF.
simplex	ATCC -6946	9α-fluoro-4-pregnene-3,11,20-trione	Δ^1	H-379
		21-hydroxy-4-pregnene-3,11,20-trione	Δ^1	N-665; N-670
		9α-fluoro-17α-hydroxy-4-pregnene-3,11,20-trione	Δ^1	H-379
		9α-fluoro-21-hydroxy-4-pregnene-3,11,20-trione	Δ^1	N-668
		17α,21-dihydroxy-4-pregnene-3,11,20-trione	Δ^1	H-389; N-665; N-670; N-671
			Δ^1; 20-C=O → 20β-OH	H-389
		17α,21-dihydroxy-4-pregnene-3,11,20-trione 4-C^{14}	Δ^1	C-120
		17α,21-dihydroxy-4-pregnene-3,11,20-trione 21-acetate	Δ^1	N-665; N-670
		9α-bromo-17α,21-dihydroxy-4-pregnene-3,11,20-trione	Δ^1	N-668
		16α-n-butyl-17α,21-dihydroxy-4-pregnene-3,11,20-trione	Δ^1	N-690; N-692
		16α-n-butyl-17α,21-dihydroxy-4-pregnene-3,11,20-trione 21-acetate	Δ^1	N-690; N-692
		17α,21-dihydroxy-16-methylene-4-pregnene-3,11,20-trione	Δ^1	M-558
		9α-chloro-17α,21-dihydroxy-4-pregnene-3,11,20-trione	Δ^1	N-668
		7α-cyano-17α,21-dihydroxy-4-pregnene-3,11,20-trione	Δ^1	B-75
		2α-fluoro-17α,21-dihydroxy-4-pregnene-3,11,20-trione	Δ^1	H-401
		9α-fluoro-17α,21-dihydroxy-4-pregnene-3,11,20-trione	Δ^1	H-379; N-668; N-669
		7β-cyano-9α-fluoro-17α,21-dihydroxy-4-pregnene-3,11,20-trione	Δ^1	B-75
		9α-fluoro-11β,16α,17α,20β,21-pentahydroxy-1,4-pregnadien-3-one	20β-OH → 20-C=O	G-294; G-296

TABLE III

ansformations by Genus: CORYNEBACTERIUM

SPECIES	SOURCE	SUBSTRATE	REACTION	REF.
implex	ATCC-6946	9α-fluoro-$11\beta,16\alpha,17\alpha,20\beta,21$-pentahydroxy-$1,4$-pregnadien-$3$-one	$\Delta^1 \rightarrow$ H	G-296
		$3\beta,21$-dihydroxy-$5,16$-pregnadien-20-one diacetate	Δ^1; $\Delta^5 \rightarrow \Delta^4$; 3β-OAc$\rightarrow$ 3-C=O; 21-OAc $\rightarrow 21$-OH	H-388; O-700
		9α-fluoro-$11\beta,16\alpha,17\alpha,21$-tetrahydroxy-$1,4$-pregnadiene-$3,20$-dione	$\Delta^1 \rightarrow$ H	G-296
		9α-bromo-$11\beta,17\alpha,21$-trihydroxy-$4,6$-pregnadiene-$3,20$-dione	Δ^1	A-7
		$6\alpha,9\alpha$-difluoro-$11\beta,17\alpha,21$-trihydroxy-$4,6$-pregnadiene-$3,20$-dione	Δ^1	A-7
		$4,9(11)$-pregnadiene-$3,20$-dione	Δ^1	R-754; R-773
		17α-bromo-$4,9(11)$-pregnadiene-$3,20$-dione	Δ^1	R-761
		17α-chloro-$4,9(11)$-pregnadiene-$3,20$-dione	Δ^1	R-761
		6β-fluoro-$4,9(11)$-pregnadiene-$3,20$-dione	Δ^1	R-757
		21-fluoro-$4,9(11)$-pregnadiene-$3,20$-dione	Δ^1	R-773
		17α-hydroxy-$4,9(11)$-pregnadiene-$3,20$-dione	Δ^1	R-773
		17α-hydroxy-$4,9(11)$-pregnadiene-$3,20$-dione caproate	Δ^1	R-761
		21-hydroxy-$4,9(11)$-pregnadiene-$3,20$-dione	Δ^1	R-755
		6α-methyl-$4,9(11)$-pregnadiene-$3,20$-dione	Δ^1	R-754; R-755
		6β-methyl-$4,9(11)$-pregnadiene-$3,20$-dione	Δ^1	R-754
		17α-methyl-$4,9(11)$-pregnadiene-$3,20$-dione	Δ^1	R-761
		17α-bromo-6α-fluoro-$4,9(11)$-pregnadiene-$3,20$-dione	Δ^1	R-759
		17α-bromo-6α-methyl-$4,9(11)$-pregnadiene-$3,20$-dione	Δ^1	R-759

TABLE III

Transformations by Genus: CORYNEBACTERIUM

SPECIES	SOURCE	SUBSTRATE	REACTION	REF
simplex	ATCC-6946	6α-fluoro-17α-hydroxy-4,9(11)-pregnadiene-3,20-dione	Δ^1	H-391
		6α-fluoro-21-iodo-4,9(11)-pregnadiene-3,20-dione	Δ^1	R-758
		21-fluoro-6α-methyl-4,9(11)-pregnadiene-3,20-dione	Δ^1	R-755
		6α,21-difluoro-4,9(11)-pregnadiene-3,20-dione	Δ^1	R-758
		17α-hydroxy-4,9(11)-pregnadiene-3,20-dione cyclopentylpropionate	Δ^1	R-761
		17α-hydroxy-21-iodo-4,9(11)-pregnadiene-3,20-dione	Δ^1	R-756
		17α-hydroxy-21-iodo-4,9(11)-pregnadiene-3,20-dione acetate	Δ^1	R-756
		21-hydroxy-16α-mercapto-4,9(11)-pregnadiene-3,20-dione 16,21-diacetate	Δ^1	R-764
		21-iodo-6α-methyl-4,9(11)-pregnadiene-3,20-dione	Δ^1	R-755
		6α,17α-dimethyl-4,9(11)-pregnadiene-3,20-dione	Δ^1	R-759
		17α-bromo-6α,21-difluoro-4,9(11)-pregnadiene-3,20-dione	Δ^1	R-759
		17α-bromo-6α-fluoro-21-iodo-4,9(11)-pregnadiene-3,20-dione	Δ^1	R-759
		17α-bromo-21-fluoro-6α-methyl-4,9(11)-pregnadiene-3,20-dione	Δ^1	R-759
		17α-bromo-21-iodo-6α-methyl-4,9(11)-pregnadiene-3,20-dione	Δ^1	R-759
		9α,11β-dichloro-17α-hydroxy-4,9(11)-pregnadiene-3,20-dione cyclopentylpropionate	Δ^1	R-761
		6α-fluoro-17α-hydroxy-21-iodo-4,9(11)-pregnadiene-3,20-dione	Δ^1	R-759
		6α-fluoro-17α-hydroxy-21-iodo-4,9(11)-pregnadiene-3,20-dione acetate	Δ^1	R-759

TABLE III

nsformations by Genus: CORYNEBACTERIUM

SPECIES	SOURCE	SUBSTRATE	REACTION	REF.
mplex	ATCC - 6946	21-fluoro-17α-hydroxy-6α-methyl-4,9(11)-pregnadiene-3,20-dione	Δ^1	R-759
		21-fluoro-17α-hydroxy-6α-methyl-4,9(11)-pregnadiene-3,20-dione caproate	Δ^1	R-759
		6α-fluoro-21-iodo-17α-methyl-4,9(11)-pregnadiene-3,20-dione	Δ^1	R-759
		21-fluoro-6α,17α-dimethyl-4,9(11)-pregnadiene-3,20-dione	Δ^1	R-759
		6α,21-difluoro-17α-hydroxy-4,9(11)-pregnadiene-3,20-dione	Δ^1	R-759
		6α,21-difluoro-17α-hydroxy-4,9(11)-pregnadiene-3,20-dione acetate	Δ^1	R-759
		6α,21-difluoro-17α-hydroxy-4,9(11)-pregnadiene-3,20-dione caproate	Δ^1	R-759
		6α,21-difluoro-17α-methyl-4,9(11)-pregnadiene-3,20-dione	Δ^1	R-759
		17α-hydroxy-21-iodo-6α-methyl-4,9(11)-pregnadiene-3,20-dione	Δ^1	R-756
		21-iodo-6α,17α-dimethyl-4,9(11)-pregnadiene-3,20-dione	Δ^1	R-759
		17α,21-dihydroxy-6β,16α-dimethyl-4,9(11)-pregnadiene-3,20-dione 21-acetate	Δ^1	N-691
		17α,21-dihydroxy-6β,16β-dimethyl-4,9(11)-pregnadiene-3,20-dione 21-acetate	Δ^1	N-691
		16-fluormethyl-11β,17α,21-trihydroxy-4,15-pregnadiene-3,20-dione	Δ^1	W-1084
		11β,17α,21-trihydroxy-16-methyl-4,15-pregnadiene-3,20-dione	Δ^1	W-1084
		11β,17α,21-trihydroxy-6α,16-dimethyl-4,15-pregnadiene-3,20-dione	Δ^1	B-69
		4,16-pregnadiene-3,20-dione	Δ^1	H-388; O-700
		17α-hydroxy-9β,11β-oxido-1,4,6-pregnatriene-3,20-dione	20-C=O → 20β-OH	G-303

TABLE III

Transformations by Genus: CORYNEBACTERIUM
CORYNESPORA
CORYNEUM

TAXONOMY

(Imperf. - Moniliales)
(Imperf. - Melanconiales)

SPECIES	SOURCE	SUBSTRATE	REACTION	REF.
simplex	ATCC-6946	$17\alpha,21$-dihydroxy-$9\beta,11\beta$-oxido-$1,4,6$-pregnatriene-$3,20$-dione	20-C=O → 20β-OH	G-303
		5-cholesten-3β-ol	3β-OH→3-C=O; Δ^5→Δ^4	T-1005
		Diosgenin	3β-OH→3-C=O; Δ^5→Δ^4	N-665; N-670
			3β-OH→3-C=O; Δ^5→Δ^4; Δ^1	N-665; N-670
	IFO (3530)	$3\alpha,7\alpha,12\alpha$-trihydroxy-5β-cholanic acid	3α-OH→3-C=O; 7α-OH→H; Δ^1; Δ^4	H-358; H-367
			3α-OH-3-C=O; 7α-OH → Δ^6; Δ^4	H-367
			3α-OH→3-C=O; 7α-OH →H; Δ^4	H-367
			3α-OH→3-C=O; Δ^4	H-367
			3α-OH→3-C=O	H-367
species	soil	$3\alpha,7\alpha,12\alpha$-trihydroxy-5β-cholanic acid	3α-OH→3-C=O; 7α-OH→Δ^6; Δ^4	T-974
			3α-OH→3-C=O; Δ^4	T-974
		$3,7,12$-triketo-5β-cholanic acid	7-C=O→7α-OH; Δ^4	T-975
			7-C=O →Δ^6	T-975
		5-cholesten-3β-ol	3β-OH→3-C=O; Δ^5→Δ^4	C-136
xerose	NG	5-cholesten-3β-ol	—	T-1030
CORYNESPORA				
casaiicoli	CMI(6302)	Saponins (agave)	3β-glycoside (saponin) → 3β-OH	H-351
CORYNEUM				
cardinale	ATCC-13063t	$17\alpha,21$-dihydroxy-4-pregnene-$3,20$-dione	11α-OH	T-991

TABLE III

TAXONOMY

nsformations by Genus:

CORYNEUM
CRINSPORIUM
CUCURBITARIA
CUNNINGHAMELLA

(Imperf. - Moniliales)
(Asco. - Sphaeriales)
(Phyco. - Mucorales)

SPECIES	SOURCE	SUBSTRATE	REACTION	REF.
ardinale	ATCC-13063t	17α,21-dihydroxy-4-pregnene-3,20-dione 21-acetate	11α-OH; 21-OAc →21-OH	T-991
RINSPORIUM				
anorum	NAGAS	4-pregnene-3,20-dione	15β-OH	K-486
UCURBITARIA				
burni	C	not given	17α-OH	W-1106; W-1107
UNNINGHAMELLA				
ricana	SSSR	17α,21-dihydroxy-4-pregnene-3,20-dione	11α-OH; 11β-OH; 11-C=O(via11β-OH)	E-224
bida	SSSR	17α,21-dihydroxy-4-pregnene-3,20-dione	6β-OH; 11β-OH; 11-C=O(via 11β-OH)	E-224
ainieri	ATCC-9244	6α-chloro-17α,21-dihydroxy-4-pregnene-3,20-dione 21-acetate	11β-OH; 21-OAc →21-OH	R-770
		6α-chloro-17α,21-dihydroxy-1,4-pregnadiene-3,20-dione	11β-OH	R-770
		6α-fluoro-16α,17α,21-trihydroxy-1,4-pregnadiene-3,20-dione	11β-OH	R-771
		6α-fluoro-21-hydroxy-16α,17α-isopropylidenedioxy-4-pregnene-3,20-dione	11β-OH	R-771
lakesleeana	ATCC-8688a (Upjohn H-334)	3α,11β,17α-trihydroxy-pregnan-20-one	9α-OH; 11β-OH →11-C=O	H-342
		3β,11β,17α-trihydroxy-pregnan-20-one	9α-OH; 11β-OH →11-C=O	H-342
		11β-hydroxy-pregnane-3,20-dione	9α-OH; 11β-OH →11-C=O	H-342
		11β,17α-dihydroxy-5α-pregnane-3,20-dione	9α-OH; 11β-OH →11-C=O	H-342
		11β,21-dihydroxy-5α-pregnane-3,20-dione	9α-OH; 11β-OH →11-C=O	H-342
		3α,11β,21-trihydroxy-5α-pregnane-3,20-dione	9α-OH; 11β-OH →11-C=O	H-342
		11β,17α,21-trihydroxy-5α-pregnane-3,20-dione	9α-OH; 11β-OH →11-C=O	H-342
		4-pregnene-3,20-dione	11β-OH;11-C=O (via 11β-OH)	O-696

TABLE III

Transformations by Genus: CUNNINGHAMELLA

SPECIES	SOURCE	SUBSTRATE	REACTION	REF
blakesleeana	ATCC-8688a (Upjohn-H-334)	11α-hydroxy-4-pregnene-3,20-dione	9α-OH; 11α-OH →11-C=O	H-342
		21-hydroxy-4-pregnene-3,20-dione	11β-OH	M-555
			14α-OH	M-555
			11β-OH(O_2^{18})	H-374
		11β,17α-dihydroxy-4-pregnene-3,20-dione	9α-OH; 11β-OH →11-C=O	H-342
		17α,21-dihydroxy-4-pregnene-3,20-dione	6β-OH	H-339; S-919
		(effect of nutrients - Ref. O-696 and S-919)	11β-OH	M-556; N-659; O-696; S-919; S-920
		(use of vitamin K to inhibit by-products - Ref. S-920)		
		(effect of ethanol and phenols - Ref. M-556)		
		(effect of enzyme inhibitors - Ref. M-555)	11β-OH; 11-C=O (via 11β-OH)	H-339; M-555; M-556; S-919
		(effect of ethanol and phenols - Ref. M-556)		
		(effect of environment and nutrients)	11-C=O (via 11β-OH); 6β-OH; 14α-OH	S-919
(in mixed culture with Bacillus sphaericus - ATCC-7055 [Δ¹])			—	K-466
		19,21-dihydroxy-4-pregnene-3,20-dione	11β-OH	B-40
		11β,17α,21-trihydroxy-4-pregnene-3,20-dione	9α-OH	H-344
			11β-OH→11-C=O	H-344
			9α-OH; 11β-OH →11-C=O	H-342
		11α,21-dihydroxy-4,17(20)-pregnadien-3-one	9α-OH	H-342
		11β,21-dihydroxy-4,17(20)-pregnadien-3-one	9α-OH; 11β-OH →11-C=O	H-342; H-344
		11α,22-dihydroxy-bisnor-4-cholen-3-one	6β-OH	M-578

TABLE III

nsformations by Genus: CUNNINGHAMELLA

SPECIES	SOURCE	SUBSTRATE	REACTION	REF.
kesleeana	ATCC-8688b	6α,16α-dimethyl-4-pregnene-3,20-dione	11β-OH	S-923
		16α,17α-methylene-4-pregnene-3,20-dione	11β-OH	C-92
		6α-chloro-16α,17α-methylene-4-pregnene-3,20-dione	11β-OH	C-92
		6α-fluoro-16α,17α-methylene-4-pregnene-3,20-dione	11β-OH	C-92
		6β-fluoro-16α,17α-methylene-4-pregnene-3,20-dione	11β-OH	C-92
		6α-methyl-16α,17α-methylene-4-pregnene-3,20-dione	11β-OH	C-92
		16α,17α-methylene-1,4-pregnadiene-3,20-dione	11β-OH	C-92
		6α-fluoro-16α,17α-methylene-1,4-pregnadiene-3,20-dione	11β-OH	C-92
		6β-fluoro-16α,17α-methylene-1,4-pregnadiene-3,20-dione	11β-OH	C-92
		6α-methyl-16α,17α-methylene-1,4-pregnadiene-3,20-dione	11β-OH	C-92
		16α,17α-methylene-4,6-pregnadiene-3,20-dione	11β-OH	C-92
		6-chloro-16α,17α-methylene-4,6-pregnadiene-3,20-dione	11β-OH	C-92
		6-fluoro-16α,17α-methylene-4,6-pregnadiene-3,20-dione	11β-OH	C-92
		6-methyl-16α,17α-methylene-4,6-pregnadiene-3,20-dione	11β-OH	C-92
		16α,17α-methylene-1,4,6-pregnatriene-3,20-dione	11β-OH	C-92
		6-fluoro-16α,17α-methylene-1,4,6-pregnatriene-3,20-dione	11β-OH	C-92
		6-methyl-16α,17α-methylene-1,4,6-pregnatriene-3,20-dione	11β-OH	C-92
(ATCC number reported as elegans in catalog)	ATCC-9245	17α,21-dihydroxy-4-pregnene-3,20-dione	11β-OH	M-641; M-645
		17α,21-dihydroxy-7-methyl-4-pregnene-3,20-dione 21-acetate	11β-OH	B-33

TABLE III

Transformations by Genus: CUNNINGHAMELLA

SPECIES	SOURCE	SUBSTRATE	REACTION	REF.
blakesleeana (ATCC number reported as elegans in catalog)	ATCC-9245	17α,21-dihydroxy-4,14-pregna-diene-3,20-dione	Δ^{14}→14α,15α-oxide	B-66; S-865
			11β-OH; Δ^{14}→14α,15α-oxide	S-865
		17α,21-dihydroxy-4,9(11)-pregna-diene-3,20-dione	$\Delta^{9(11)}$→9β,11β-oxide	B-66
(in sequential fermentation with Ophiobolus herpotri-chus [21-OH] and Tricothecium roseum [17α-OH])	C	4-pregnene-3,20-dione	11β-OH; 11β-OH→11-C=O	W-1106
(in sequential fermentation with Tricothecium roseum [17α-OH])		21-hydroxy-4-pregnene-3,20-dione	11β-OH; 11β-OH→11-C=O	W-1106
(in sequential fermentation with Tricothecium roseum [17α-OH] and Calonectria decora [Δ¹])		21-hydroxy-4-pregnene-3,20-dione	11β-OH; 11β-OH→11-C=O	W-1107
(in sequential fermentation with Tricothecium roseum [17α-OH])		d,1-21-hydroxy-4-pregnene-3,20-dione	d,1→d-11β-OH; 11-C=O (via 11β-OH) + 1	W-1102
		18,21-dihydroxy-4-pregnene-3,20-dione	11β-OH	W-1100
		21-hydroxy-3,20-diketo-4-preg-nen-18-al	11β-OH	W-1100
		21-hydroxy-3,20-diketo-4-preg-nene-18-al acetate	11β-OH	W-1100
(in sequential fermentation with Ophiobolus herpotri-chus [21-OH] and Tricothecium roseum [17α-OH])		1,4-pregnadiene-3,20-dione	11β-OH	W-1106
*	CBS	4-pregnene-3,20-dione	11α-OH	C-98
*			11β-OH	C-98
*		17α,21-dihydroxy-4-pregnene-3,20-dione	11β-OH;11-C=O (via 11β-OH)	C-98
*			6β-OH	C-98
*			11β-OH	C-98

TABLE III

ansformations by Genus: CUNNINGHAMELLA

SPECIES	SOURCE	SUBSTRATE	REACTION	REF.
lakesleeana	CZAS	4-pregnene-3,20-dione	11β-OH	T-1028
(Lendner)	IFO	3β,14β-dihydroxy-5β-20(22)-cardenolide	16β-OH	N-651
(in sequential fermentation with Trichoderma glaucum [17α-OH] and Wojnowicia graminis - NRRL-2472 [21-OH])	MCC	4-pregnene-3,20-dione	11β-OH	M-566
	NG	4-pregnene-3,20-dione	14α-OH	N-661
		(mechanism of hydroxylation)	11β-OH	B-64
	OIAB(1)	4-pregnene-3,20-dione	11α-OH; 14α-OH; 6β,11α-diOH	N-682
*		17α,21-dihydroxy-4-pregnene-3,20-dione	11α-OH	N-682
*		3β,14β-dihydroxy-5β-20(22)-cardenolide	7β-OH	N-682
			1β,7β-diOH; 5β,7β-diOH	N-682
*			3β-OH→3-C=O	N-682
	OIAB(2)	4-pregnene-3,20-dione	11α-OH; 14α-OH; 6β,11α-diOH	N-682
		17α,21-dihydroxy-4-pregnene-3,20-dione	6β-OH	N-682
*		3β,14β-dihydroxy-5β-20(22)-cardenolide	7β-OH	N-682
			1β,7β-diOH; 5β,7β-diOH	N-682
*			3β-OH→3-C=O	N-682
*	PIRI	4-pregnene-3,20-dione	11α-OH	C-98
*			11β-OH	C-98
*		17α,21-dihydroxy-4-pregnene-3,20-dione	11β-OH:11-C=O (via 11β-OH)	C-98
*			6β-OH	C-98
*			11β-OH	C-98
	QM-631	4-pregnene-3,20-dione (method to obtain higher yields-dilution culture)	11-OH	W-1066

TABLE III

Transformations by Genus: CUNNINGHAMELLA

SPECIES	SOURCE	SUBSTRATE	REACTION	REF.
blakesleeana	SSSR	17α,21-dihydroxy-4-pregnene-3,20-dione	11β-OH; 11-C=O (via 11β-OH	E-224
	UC	4-pregnene-3,20-dione	11β-OH	E-202
		11α-hydroxy-4-pregnene-3,20-dione	6β-OH	E-202
		6β-methyl-4-pregnene-3,20-dione	11β-OH	L-520
		17α,21-dihydroxy-4-pregnene-3,20-dione	11β-OH	M-601
			11β-OH; 11-C=O (via 11β-OH)	M-601; M-636; M-641
	VEB	4-pregnene-3,20-dione	6β,14α-diOH	S-811
echinata	SSSR	17α,21-dihydroxy-4-pregnene-3,20-dione	11α-OH	E-224
echinulata	ATCC-1387	4-pregnene-3,20-dione	11α-OH	Z-1125
		17α-hydroxy-4-pregnene-3,20-dione	11α-OH	Z-1125
		21-hydroxy-4-pregnene-3,20-dione	11α-OH	Z-1125
		17α,21-dihydroxy-4-pregnene-3,20-dione	11α-OH	Z-1125
	FRI	17α,21-dihydroxy-4-pregnene-3,20-dione	6β-OH; 11α-OH	S-849
*	IPB	4-pregnene-3,20-dione	11α-OH	C-98
*			11β-OH	C-98
*		17α,21-dihydroxy-4-pregnene-3,20-dione	11β-OH; 11-C=O (via 11β-OH)	C-98
*			6β-OH	C-98
*			11β-OH	C-98
(Thaxter - 7) (In mixed culture with Bacillus sphaericus - ATCC-7055 [Δ^1])	NG	17α,21-dihydroxy-4-pregnene-3,20-dione	11α-OH	K-466
	NRRL	Sarsasapogenin	—	M-587
		Diosgenin	—	M-587
		4-dehydrotigogenone	—	M-587

TABLE III

ansformations by Genus: CUNNINGHAMELLA

SPECIES	SOURCE	SUBSTRATE	REACTION	REF.
egans (Lendner)	C	15α-hydroxy-4-androstene-3,17-dione	11β-OH	U-1043
		6α-fluoro-14α,17α,21-trihydroxy-16α-methyl-4-pregnene-3,20-dione	11α-OH	U-1042
			11β-OH	U-1042
*	CZAS	4-pregnene-3,20-dione	11α-OH	C-98
*			11β-OH	C-98
*		17α,21-dihydroxy-4-pregnene-3,20-dione	11β-OH; 11-C=O (via 11β-OH)	C-98
*			6β-OH	C-98
*			11β-OH	C-98
	OIAB	4-pregnene-3,20-dione	11α-OH; 14α-OH; 6β,11α-diOH	N-682
		17α,21-dihydroxy-4-pregnene-3,20-dione	6β-OH; 11α-OH	N-682
		14β-hydroxy-3-keto-5β-20(22)-cardenolide	7β-OH	N-682
*		3β,14β-dihydroxy-5β-20(22)-cardenolide	7β-OH	N-682
	SSSR	17α,21-dihydroxy-4-pregnene-3,20-dione	11α-OH; 11β-OH; 11-C=O (via 11β-OH)	E-224; E-225
		11α,17α,21-trihydroxy-4-pregnene-3,20-dione	—	E-225
		11β,17α,21-trihydroxy-4-pregnene-3,20-dione	11-C=O (via 11β-OH)	E-225
		11β,17α,21-trihydroxy-4-pregnene-3,20-dione 21-acetate	21-OAc → 21-OH	E-225
			11β-OH→ 11-C=O; 21-OAc →21-OH	E-225
		11β,17α,21-trihydroxy-1,4-pregnadiene-3,20-dione	—	E-225
	VEB	4-pregnene-3,20-dione	6β,14α-diOH	S-811
mothallica	SSSR	17α,21-dihydroxy-4-pregnene-3,20-dione	6β-OH; 11β-OH; 11-C=O (via 11β-OH)	E-224
mosa	CZAS	17α,21-dihydroxy-4-pregnene-3,20-dione	6β-OH; 11α-OH; 11β-OH; 11-C=O (via 11β-OH)	C-98

TABLE III

Transformations by Genus: CUNNINGHAMELLA
CURVULARIA

<u>TAXONOMY</u>

(Imperf. - Moniliales)

SPECIES	SOURCE	SUBSTRATE	REACTION	REF.
ramosa	SSSR	$17\alpha,21$-dihydroxy-4-pregnene-3,20-dione	6β-OH; 11β-OH; 11-C=O (via 11β-OH)	E-224
species	NRRL	plant saponins	—	K-478
	Parke-Davis (M-2047)	$16\alpha,17\alpha,21$-[3,1,1-2-pyrazolino] 4-pregnene-3,20-dione	11β-OH	<u>M-593</u>
verticillata	SSSR	$17\alpha,21$-dihydroxy-4-pregnene-3,20-dione	11α-OH; 11β-OH	E-224
<u>CURVULARIA</u>				
brachyspora (in sequential fermentation with Ophiobolus herpotrichus [21-OH])	C	4-pregnene-3,20-dione	11β-OH	W-1106; W-1107
		18-oxo-4-pregnene 3,20-dione	11β-OH	W-1107
(in mixed culture with Mycobacterium)	PF	$17\alpha,21$-dihydroxy-4-pregnene-3,20-dione	11β-OH	S-868
		$17\alpha,21$-dihydroxy-4,9(11)-pregnadiene-3,20-dione	$\Delta^{9(11)}\rightarrow 9\beta,11\beta$-oxide	<u>S-865</u>
falcata *	C	21-hydroxy-4-pregnene-3,20-dione	7α-OH	<u>M-585</u>
	QM-102H	21-hydroxy-4-pregnene-3,20-dione	11β-OH	S-878
		$17\alpha,21$-dihydroxy-4-pregnene-3,20 dione	11β-OH	<u>S-878</u>
(in sequential fermentation with Mycobacterium sp. [Δ^1])		$17\alpha,21$-dihydroxy-4-pregnene-3,20-dione	11β-OH	S-868
	VEB	4-pregnene-3,20-dione	11β-OH; 14α-OH; $7\alpha,11\beta$-diOH; $7\alpha,14\alpha$-diOH; $11\beta,14\alpha$-diOH; $6\beta,14\alpha$-diOH	Z-1132
fallax *	C	21-hydroxy-4-pregnene-3,20-dione	7α-OH	<u>M-585</u>
	VEB	4-pregnene-3,20-dione	11β-OH; 14α-OH; $7\alpha,14\alpha$-diOH; $11\beta,14\alpha$-diOH	Z-1132
geniculata	IFO(6284)	$17\alpha,21$-dihydroxy-4-pregnene-3,20-dione	6β-OH; 11β-OH; 14α-OH	K-469

TABLE III

ansformations by Genus: CURVULARIA

SPECIES	SOURCE	SUBSTRATE	REACTION	REF.
eniculata	VEB (C)	4-pregnene-3,20-dione	11β-OH; 14α-OH; $7\alpha,14\alpha$-diOH; $6\beta,14\alpha$-diOH; $11\beta,14\alpha$-diOH	Z-1132
	VEB(XCI)	4-pregnene-3,20-dione	11β-OH; $11\beta,14\alpha$-diOH	Z-1132
	VEB-(XCXXXIII)	4-pregnene-3,20-dione	14α-OH; $6\beta,14\alpha$-diOH; $7\alpha,14\alpha$-diOH	Z-1132
aequalis	VEB-(XCIV)	4-pregnene-3,20-dione	11β-OH; $11\beta,14\alpha$-diOH	Z-1132
nata	ATCC	4-pregnene-3,20-dione	11β-OH	C-98
		$17\alpha,21$-dihydroxy-4-pregnene-3,20-dione	11β-OH	C-98
			11β-OH; 11-C=O (via 11β-OH)	C-98
			11α-OH: metabolite - X	C-98
	ATCC-12017	6β-hydroxy-$3\alpha,5\alpha$-cyclopregnan-20-one	11β-OH	W-1070
		$17\alpha,21$-dihydroxy-$6\alpha,16\alpha$-di-methyl-4-pregnene-3,20-dione 21-acetate	11β-OH; 21-OAc $\rightarrow$ 21-OH	S-805
(in mixed culture with one or more of the following: Alternaria passiflorae [Δ^1] Calonectria decora[Δ^1] Didymella lycopersici [Δ^1], Leptosphaeria maculans [17α-OH], Ophiobolus herpotri-chus [21-OH], Tricothecium roseum [17α-OH])	C	4-pregnene-3,20-dione	11β-OH	W-1106; W-1107
*		21-hydroxy-4-pregnene-3,20-dione	7α-OH	M-585
(in mixed culture with Leptosphaeria maculans [17α-OH])		21-hydroxy-4-pregnene-3,20-dione	11β-OH	W-1106
		d,1-21-hydroxy-4-pregnene-3,20-dione	d,1$\rightarrow$d-11β-OH + 1	W-1106
		$6\beta,21$-dihydroxy-4-pregnene-3,20-dione	11β-OH	N-654
		d,1-$17\alpha,21$-dihydroxy-4-pregnene-3,20-dione	d,1 $\rightarrow$ d-11β-OH + 1	W-1102

TABLE III

Transformations by Genus: CURVULARIA

SPECIES	SOURCE	SUBSTRATE	REACTION	REF.
lunata	C	19,21-dihydroxy-4-pregnene-3,20-dione	11β-OH	N-654
		6α-fluoro-17α,21-dihydroxy-16α-methyl-4-pregnene-3,20-dione	11β-OH	U-1042
			14α-OH	U-1042
		21-hydroxy-1,4-pregnadiene-3,20-dione	11β-OH	W-1106
	EM	17α-hydroxy-16-methylene-4-pregnene-3,20-dione	11β-OH	B-68
		17α,21-dihydroxy-16-methylene-4-pregnene-3,20-dione	11β-OH	M-558
	IFO (6286)	17α,21-dihydroxy-4-pregnene-3,20-dione	9α-OH	K-469
*			11α-OH	K-469
			11β-OH	K-469
*			14α-OH	K-469
*	KAG(49)	17α,21-dihydroxy-4-pregnene-3,20-dione	6β-OH	K-469
			11α-OH; 14α-OH	K-469
			6β,14α-diOH	K-469
*			7α,14α-diOH	K-469
		14α,17α,21-trihydroxy-4-pregnene-3,20-dione	7α-OH	K-469
			6β-OH	K-469
(in sequential fermentation with Actinoplanes missouriensis - ATCC-1538 [Δ^1])	LRL	4-pregnene-3,20-dione	11β-OH	M-536
		6α-fluoro-17α,21-dihydroxy-16α-methyl-4-pregnene-3,20-dione	11β-OH	M-536
	MCC	17α,21-dihydroxy-4-pregnene-3,20-dione (effect of nutrients - trace elements)	11β-OH	D-192
	NRRL-2380	17β-hydroxy-4-estren-3-one	10β-OH	D-150
			11β-OH	D-150
			14α-OH	D-150
			10β,11β-diOH	D-150

TABLE III

ansformations by Genus: CURVULARIA

SPECIES	SOURCE	SUBSTRATE	REACTION	REF.
ınata	NRRL-2380	17α-ethyl-17β-hydroxy-1,4-androstadien-3-one	11β-OH	N-677a
		17α-hydroxy-1-5α-pregnene-3,20-dione acetate	11β-OH	R-761; R-773
		17α-methyl-1-5α-pregnene-3,20-dione	11β-OH	R-761
		21-fluoro-19-nor-4-pregnene-3,20-dione	11β-OH	R-755
		17α-hydroxy-19-nor-4-pregnene-3,20-dione	11β-OH	R-761; R-773
		4-pregnene-3,20-dione	14α-OH	D-187
			7α,14α-diOH	D-187
			11β-OH	S-871
			11β,14α-diOH	D-187
		17α-bromo-4-pregnene-3,20-dione	11β-OH	R-756; R-773
		17α-chloro-4-pregnene-3,20-dione	11β-OH	R-761
		17α-hydroxy-4-pregnene-3,20-dione	11β-OH	S-871
			11β,14α-diOH	S-876
		21-hydroxy-4-pregnene-3,20-dione	11β-OH	S-871; S-875
		6β-methyl-4-pregnene-3,20-dione	11β-OH	R-754; R-757; R-773
		17α-bromo-6α-fluoro-4-pregnene-3,20-dione	11β-OH	R-759
		17α-bromo-6α-methyl-4-pregnene-3,20-dione	11β-OH	R-756; R-759
		6α-fluoro-17α-methyl-4-pregnene-3,20-dione	11β-OH	R-759
		17α,21-dihydroxy-4-pregnene-3,20-dione (compare reaction with C. lunata - IFO-6286-Ref. K-469)	11α-OH	K-443; K-469
		(effect of antibiotics - Ref. B-37. In mixed culture with Bacillus sphaericus - ATCC-7055 - Ref. K-444)	11β-OH	B-37; K-443; K-444

TABLE III

Transformations by Genus: CURVULARIA

SPECIES	SOURCE	SUBSTRATE	REACTION	REF.
lunata	NRRL-2380	17α,21-dihydroxy-4-pregnene-3,20-dione (compare reaction with C. lunata - IFO-6286 - Ref. K-469)	11β-OH	K-466; K-469
		(in mixed culture with M. phlei - Ref. S-868)	11β-OH	S-868; S-871; S-875; S-879
		(with cell free enzyme)	11β-OH	Z-1134
		(compare reaction with IFO-6286 - Ref. K-469)	14α-OH	K-443; K-469; Z-1134
		(compare reaction with IFO-6286 - Ref. K-469)	6β,14α-diOH	K-469
		(effect of trace elements - solvents)	7α,11β-diOH	K-443
		(compare reaction with IFO-6286 - Ref. K-469)	7α,14α-diOH	K-469; S-879
		(effect of trace elements - solvents; compare reaction with IFO-6286 - Ref. -K-469)	11β,14α-diOH	A-2; K-443; K-469; S-879; S-877
		(enzyme preparation)	20-C=O → 20β-OH	T-1017; Z-1134
		17α-hydroxy-21-methyl-4-pregnene-3,20-dione	11β-OH	H-391
		21-hydroxy-17α-methyl-4-pregnene-3,20-dione acetate	11β-OH	H-377
		17α-hydroxy-16-methylene-4-pregnene-3,20-dione	11β-OH	B-68
		6α,17α-dimethyl-4-pregnene-3,20-dione	11β-OH	R-759
		6β-fluoro-17α-hydroxy-21-methyl-4-pregnene-3,20-dione	11β-OH	H-391
		21-hydroxy-16α,17α-oxido-4-pregnene-3,20-dione acetate	11β-OH; 21-OAc → 21-OH	A-3
			14α-OH; 21-OAc → 21-OH	A-3
			11β-OH; 14α-OH; 21-OAc→21-OH	A-4; A-5
			11β,14α-diOH; 21-OAc→21-OH	A-3

TABLE III

ransformations by Genus: CURVULARIA

SPECIES	SOURCE	SUBSTRATE	REACTION	REF.
lunata	NRRL-2380	$17\alpha,21$-dihydroxy-16α-methyl-4-pregnene-3,20-dione	11β-OH	C-96
			15α-OH	C-96
			$11\beta,14\alpha$-diOH	C-96
		$17\alpha,21$-dihydroxy-16-methylene-4-pregnene-3,20-dione	11β-OH	T-981
		$15\beta,17\alpha,21$-trihydroxy-4-pregnene-3,20-dione	11β-OH	C-126
		$16\alpha,17\alpha,21$-[3,1,1-2-pyrazolino] 4-pregnene-3,20-dione	11β-OH	W-1113
		16-chlormethylene-17α,21-dihydroxy-4-pregnene-3,20-dione	11β-OH	W-1084
		6α-fluoro-17α,21-dihydroxy-21-methyl-4-pregnene-3,20-dione 21-acetate	11β-OH; 21-OAc $\to$ 21-OH	H-390
		6α-fluoro-17α,21-dihydroxy-16-methylene-4-pregnene-3,20-dione	11β-OH	A-7
		16-fluoromethylene-17α,21-dihydroxy-4-pregnene-3,20-dione	11β-OH	W-1084
		$17\alpha,21$-dihydroxy-6α-methyl-16-methylene-4-pregnene-3,20-dione 21-acetate	11β-OH; 21-OAc $\to$ 21-OH	B-69
		17α-hydroxy-16-methylene-1,4-pregnadiene-3,20-dione	11β-OH	B-68
		$17\alpha,21$-dihydroxy-4,9(11)-pregnadiene-3,20-dione	$\Delta^{9(11)} \to 9\beta,11\beta$-oxide	B-65; B-66; S-865
			14α-OH	B-65
			14α-OH; $\Delta^{9(11)} \to 9\beta,11\beta$-oxide	B-65
		$17\alpha,21$-dihydroxy-4,9(11)-pregnadiene-3,20-dione [11,12α-H^3] 21-acetate	$\Delta^{9(11)} \to 9\beta,11\beta$-oxide; 21-OAc $\to$ 21-OH	K-484
			21-OAc$\to$21-OH	K-484
		4,11-pregnadiene-3,20-dione	$\Delta^{11} \to 11\beta,12\beta$-oxide	K-484

TABLE III

Transformations by Genus: CURVULARIA

SPECIES	SOURCE	SUBSTRATE	REACTION	REF.
lunata	NRRL-2380	$17\alpha,21$-dihydroxy-$4,14$-pregnadiene-$3,20$-dione	$\Delta^{14} \to 14\alpha,\ 15\alpha$-oxide	B-66; S-865
			11β-OH; $\Delta^{14} \to$ $14\alpha,15\alpha$-oxide	S-865
		$17\alpha,21$-dihydroxy-16-methyl-$4,15$-pregnadiene-$3,20$-dione	11β-OH	W-1084
		16-fluormethyl-$17\alpha,21$-dihydroxy-$4,15$-pregnadiene-$3,20$-dione 21-acetate	11β-OH; 21-OAc $\to 21$-OH	W-1084
		$17\alpha,21$-dihydroxy-$6\alpha,16$-dimethyl-$4,15$-pregnadiene-$3,20$-dione	11β-OH	B-69
		$17\alpha,21$-dihydroxy-$4,6$-pregnadiene-$3,11,20$-trione	20-C=O $\to$ 20β-OH	G-306
		$1,4,16$-pregnatriene-$3,20$-dione	11β-OH	H-388; O-700
		9α-bromo-$11\beta,17\alpha,21$-trihydroxy-$1,4,6$-pregnatriene-$3,20$-dione	14α-OH	G-301; G-302
		9α-chloro-$17\alpha,21$-dihydroxy-$1,4,6$-pregnatriene-$3,11,20$-trione	14α-OH	G-301; G-302
		9α-fluoro-$17\alpha,21$-dihydroxy-$1,4,6$-pregnatriene-$3,11,20$-trione	14α-OH	G-301; G-302
	NRRL-2434	$17\alpha,21$-dihydroxy-$6\alpha,16\alpha$-dimethyl-4-pregnene-$3,20$-dione	11β-OH	S-903
		$17\alpha,21$-dihydroxy-16α-methyl-$1,4$-pregnadiene-$3,20$-dione 21-acetate	11β-OH	S-904
	OR	17β-hydroxy-17α-methyl-4-androstene-3-one	16β-OH	S-950
			16β-OH; 16β-OH $\to 16$-C=O	S-950
	SAG	$17\alpha,21$-dihydroxy-1α-methyl-4-pregnene-$3,20$-dione	11β-OH	W-1112
	SY(192)	19-nor-4-pregnene-$3,20$-dione	11β-OH	B-71; B-73
	SY(961-29E)	4-pregnene-$3,20$-dione	$11\beta,21$-diOH	R-783
	Takeda	4-pregnene-$3,20$-dione	14α-OH	N-661
	UC	$17\alpha,21$-dihydroxy-7-methyl-4-pregnene-$3,20$-dione 21-acetate	11β-OH; 21-OAc $\to 21$-OH	B-33

TABLE III

ansformations by Genus: CURVULARIA

SPECIES	SOURCE	SUBSTRATE	REACTION	REF.
unata	VEB	4-pregnene-3,20-dione (effect of inhibitors and Fe - Ref. Z-1130)	11β-OH	Z-1130
			$6\beta,14\alpha$-diOH	S-811
			$7\alpha,14\alpha$-diOH	Z-1130
			$11\beta,14\alpha$-diOH	Z-1130
		$17\alpha,21$-dihydroxy-4-pregnene-3,20-dione 21-acetate	11β-OH; 21-OAc $\rightarrow$ 21-OH	Z-1131
	VEB (XCIII)	4-pregnene-3,20-dione (comparison of different species and strains-effect of nutrients-trace elements -pH-inhibitors-cofactors- substrate specificity-Ref. Z-1132)	11β-OH; 14α-OH	Z-1132
*			$7\alpha,14\alpha$-diOH	Z-1132
			$6\beta,14\alpha$-diOH	Z-1132
			$11\beta,14\alpha$-diOH	Z-1132
*	VEB(XCV)	4-pregnene-3,20-dione	$7\alpha,14\alpha$-diOH	Z-1132
*			$11\beta,14\alpha$-diOH	Z-1132
	VEB (CII)	4-pregnene-3,20-dione	$7\alpha,14\alpha$-diOH	Z-1132
*			$11\beta,14\alpha$-diOH	Z-1132
	VEB CIII	4-pregnene-3,20-dione	$7\alpha,14\alpha$-diOH	Z-1132
*			$11\beta,14\alpha$-diOH	Z-1132
		(plus other substrates- products of which are un- known or questionable structure-See page 262 of Ref. Z-1132)		
naculans	IFO (6292)	$17\alpha,21$-dihydroxy-4-pregnene-3,20-dione (comparison of different strains - Ref. K-469)	6β-OH; 11α-OH; 14α-OH; $6\beta,$ 14α-diOH; $7\alpha,$ 14α-diOH	K-469
ryzae	VEB(CXXXI)	4-pregnene-3,20-dione	11β-OH; $11\beta,$ 14α-diOH	Z-1132
allescens *	C	21-hydroxy-4-pregnene-3,20-dione	7α-OH	M-585
		12α-fluoro-11β-hydroxy-4-pregnene-3,20-dione	14α-OH	W-1103
		9α-fluoro-$11\beta,17\alpha,21$-trihydroxy-4-pregnene-3,20-dione	14α-OH	W-1108a
		$11\beta,21$-dihydroxy-3,20-diketo-4-pregnen-18-al	14α-OH	W-1108

TABLE III

Transformations by Genus: CURVULARIA

SPECIES	SOURCE	SUBSTRATE	REACTION	REF.
pallescens	NRRL-2381 (QM-371-D)	17α,21-dihydroxy-4-pregnene-3,20-dione	11β-OH	S-875
(in mixed culture with Mycobacterium sp. - [Δ¹])	PF	17α,21-dihydroxy-4-pregnene-3,20-dione	11β-OH	S-868
*	VEB(XCVI)	4-pregnene-3,20-dione	11β-OH	Z-1132
*			14α-OH	Z-1132
*			6β,14α-diOH	Z-1132
			7α,14α-diOH	Z-1132
*			11β,14α-diOH	Z-1132
	CI	4-pregnene-3,20-dione	14α-OH	Z-1132
			7α,14α-diOH	Z-1132
species	PF	17α,21-dihydroxy-4,9(11)-pregnadiene-3,20-dione [11,12α-H³] 21-acetate	$\Delta^{9(11)}$→9β,11β-oxide; 21-OAc → 21-OH	K-484
*	VEB	4-pregnene-3,20-dione	7α,14α-diOH	S-813
*		14α-hydroxy-4-pregnene-3,20-dione	7α-OH	S-813
tetramera	FRI	17α,21-dihydroxy-4-pregnene-3,20-dione	—	S-849
*	VEB (CIX)	4-pregnene-3,20-dione	11β-OH	Z-1132
*			14α-OH	Z-1132
*			6β,14α-diOH	Z-1132
			7α,14α-diOH	Z-1132
*			11β,14α-diOH	Z-1132
trifolii *	IFO (6241)	17α,21-dihydroxy-4-pregnene-3,20-dione	6β-OH	K-469
*		(compare with other species- Ref. K-469)	11α-OH	K-469
			14α-OH	K-469
			6β,14α-diOH	K-469
*			7α,14α-diOH	K-469
uncinata *	VEB(CXXXIV)	4-pregnene-3,20-dione	11β-OH	Z-1132
*			14α-OH	Z-1132
*			6β,14α-diOH	Z-1132
			7α,14α-diOH	Z-1132
*			11β,14α-diOH	Z-1132

TABLE III

TAXONOMY

ansformations by Genus: CYLINDROCARPON   (Imperf. - Moniliales)

SPECIES	SOURCE	SUBSTRATE	REACTION	REF.
adicicola	ATCC-11011	17β-hydroxy-4-androsten-3-one	Δ^1; 17β-OH $\rightarrow$ 17a-oxa-17-C=O	F-269; F-274; F-284
		(with cell free enzyme)	Δ^1	S-890
		4-androstene-3,17-dione (with KCN to inhibit Δ^1 - Ref. S-898)	9α-OH	P-740; S-898
			Δ^1; 17-C=O $\rightarrow$ 17a-oxa-17-C=O	H-398
		D-homo-17a-oxa-4-androstene-3,17-dione	Δ^1	H-398
		1,4-androstadiene-3,17-dione	17-C=O $\rightarrow$ 17a-oxa-17-C=O	P-733
		17β-hydroxy-1,4-androstadien-3-one	17β-OH $\rightarrow$ 17-C=O	P-733
			17β-OH $\rightarrow$ 17a-oxa-17-C=O	P-733
		5α-pregnane-3,20-dione (with cell free enzymes)	$\Delta^{1,4}$	S-890
		5β-pregnane-3,20-dione (with cell free enzymes)	Δ^4; $\Delta^{1,4}$	S-890
		19-nor-4-pregnene-3,20-dione	9α-OH	P-740; S-898
		4-pregnene-3,20-dione (with cell free enzymes - see Ref. S-890)	Δ^1	P-733; S-890
			Δ^1; 17β-Ac$\rightarrow$ 17a-oxa-17-C=O	F-251; F-269; F-274; F-284; H-398; P-733
			Δ^1; 17β-Ac $\rightarrow$ 17β-OH	P-733
			Δ^1; 17β-Ac $\rightarrow$ 17-C=O	P-733
		4-pregnene-3,20-dione 20-cycloethyleneketal	Δ^1	F-251
		17α,21-dihydroxy-4-pregnene-3,20-dione	Δ^1	F-275
			Δ^1; 17α-OH-17β-(20-C=O-21-OH) $\rightarrow$17a-oxa-17-C=O	F-269; F-275; F-284

TABLE III

Transformations by Genus: CYLINDROCARPON   <u>TAXONOMY</u>

CYLINDROCEPHALUM   (Imperf. - Moniliales)

SPECIES	SOURCE	SUBSTRATE	REACTION	REF.
radicicola	ATCC-11011	17α,21-dihydroxy-4-pregnene-3,20-dione 21-acetate	Δ^1; 21-OAc → 21-OH	<u>F-275</u>
		16α,17α-oxido-4-pregnene-3,20-dione	16α,17α-oxido-17β-Ac → 16α-OH-17a-oxa-17-C=O	<u>E-195</u>
		9α-bromo-11β-hydroxy-4-pregnene-3,20-dione	17β-Ac→17-C=O	T-996
		9α-chloro-11β-hydroxy-4-pregnene-3,20-dione	17β-Ac→17-C=O	T-996
		9α-fluoro-11β-hydroxy-4-pregnene-3,20-dione	17β-Ac→17-C=O	<u>T-996</u>
		9α-fluoro-11β,16α-dihydroxy-4-pregnene-3,20-dione (use of cell free enzyme)	Δ^1	S-890
		6α,9α-difluoro-11β,16α-dihydroxy-4-pregnene-3,20-dione (with cell free enzymes)	Δ^1	S-890
		4-pregnene-3,11,20-trione	Δ^1; 17β-Ac → 17a-oxa-17-C=O	L-492
		9α-bromo-4-pregnene-3,11,20-trione	9α-Br→H; Δ^1; 17β-Ac → 17a-oxa-17-C=O	L-492
			17β-Ac→17-C=O	T-996
		9α-chloro-4-pregnene-3,11,20-trione	Δ^1; 17β-Ac → 17a-oxa-17-C=O	T-996
		9α-fluoro-4-pregnene-3,11,20-trione	Δ^1; 17β-Ac → 17a-oxa-17-C=O	L-492; T-996
		5-cholesten-3β-ol	—	T-1005
<u>CYLINDROCEPHALUM</u>				
aureum	ATCC-12720 (QM-610)	4-pregnene-3,20-dione	17β-Ac→17-C=O	<u>S-880</u>
			17β-Ac→17β-OH	<u>S-880</u>
		21-hydroxy-4-pregnene-3,20-dione	17β-(20-C=O-21-OH)→17-C=O	<u>S-880</u>
			17β-(20-C=O-21-OH)→17β-OH	<u>S-880</u>

TABLE III

TAXONOMY

CYLINDROCEPHALUM
DACTYLIUM   (Imperf. - Moniliales)
DALDINIA   (Asco. - Sphaeriales)
DEBARYOMYCES   (Asco. - Endomycetales)

SPECIES	SOURCE	SUBSTRATE	REACTION	REF.
aureum	ATCC-12720 (QM-610)	21-hydroxy-4-pregnene-3,20-dione propionate	17β-(20-C=O-21-OPr) $\rightarrow$ 17-C=O	S-880
			17β-(20-C=O-21-OPr) $\rightarrow$ 17β-OH	S-880
DACTYLIUM				
endroides	NRRL-2574 (QM-508)	4-pregnene-3,20-dione	$11\alpha,17\alpha$-diOH	D-188
		21-hydroxy-4-pregnene-3,20-dione	$11\alpha,17\alpha$-diOH	D-188
		16α-methyl-4-pregnene-3,20-dione	$11\alpha,17\alpha$-diOH	M-571
	NRRL-2575 (QM-513)	4-pregnene-3,20-dione	$11\alpha,17\alpha$-diOH	D-188
	QM	4-pregnene-3,20-dione	11α-OH	D-189
			17α-OH	D-189
			$11\alpha,17\alpha$-diOH	D-189
		11α-hydroxy-4-pregnene-3,20-dione	17α-OH	D-189
		17α-hydroxy-4-pregnene-3,20-dione	11α-OH	D-189
		21-hydroxy-4-pregnene-3,20-dione	11α-OH	D-189
			$11\alpha,17\alpha$-diOH	D-189
		$17\alpha,21$-dihydroxy-4-pregnene-3,20-dione	11α-OH	D-189
ALDINIA				
oncentria (concentrica)	FRI	$17\alpha,21$-dihydroxy-4-pregnene-3,20-dione	6β-OH; 11α-OH	S-849
EBARYOMYCES				
ansenii	NRRL	Sarsasapogenin	—	M-587
		Diosgenin	—	M-587
		4-dehydrotigogenone	—	M-587

TABLE III

Transformations by Genus:

DEMATIACEAE (Family)	(Imperf. - Moniliales)
DEMATIUM	(Imperf. - Moniliales)
DERMOLOMA	(Basidio. - Agaricales)
DIAPORTHE	(Asco. - Sphaeriales)
DIDYMELLA	(Asco. - Sphaeriales)

SPECIES	SOURCE	SUBSTRATE	REACTION	REF.
species	NG	$17\alpha,21$-dihydroxy-4-pregnene-3,20-dione	20-C=O → 20β-OH	V-1045
DEMATIUM				
pullulans	NRRL	Sarsasapogenin	—	M-587
		Diosgenin	—	M-587
		4-dehydrotigogenone	—	M-587
DERMOLOMA				
species	AL(F-27)	4-pregnene-3,20-dione	$6\beta,11\alpha$-diOH	S-825
DIAPORTHE				
numurai	FRI	$17\alpha,21$-dihydroxy-4-pregnene-3,20-dione	—	S-849
	IAM	$17\alpha,21$-dihydroxy-4-pregnene-3,20-dione	—	S-849
	(A-47)		2β-OH	S-849
DIDYMELLA				
lycopersici	AMCY	$11\beta,17\alpha,21$-trihydroxy-4-pregnene-3,20-dione (use of dried thalli)	Δ^1	F-231
	ATCC-11847	$17\alpha,21$-dihydroxy-4-pregnene-3,20-dione	17α-OH-17β-(20-C=O-21-OH) → 17-C=O	V-1048
		(use of spores - Ref. S-835, S-836)	11α-OH	S-835; S-836; V-1048
			20-C=O → 20β-OH	S-835; S-836; V-1048
		2α-fluoro-$17\alpha,21$-dihydroxy-4-pregnene-3,11,20-trione	Δ^1	H-401
	C	17β-hydroxy-4-androsten-3-one	Δ^1	W-1105
		17α-ethinyl-17β-hydroxy-4-androsten-3-one	Δ^1	V-1052; W-1096; W-1104

TABLE III

ansformations by Genus: DIDYMELLA

SPECIES	SOURCE	SUBSTRATE	REACTION	REF.
lycopersici	C	17β-hydroxy-17α-methyl-4-andro-sten-3-one	Δ^1	V-1052; W-1096; W-1104
		17β-hydroxy-17α-vinyl-4-andro-sten-3-one	Δ^1	W-1109
		1-androstene-3,17-dione	Δ^4	W-1096
		4-androstene-3,17-dione	Δ^1	W-1096
		pregnane-3,20-dione	$\Delta^{1,4}$	W-1096
		17α,21-dihydroxy-5α-pregnane-3,11,20-trione	$\Delta^{1,4}$	W-1096
		5α-1-pregnene-3,20-dione	Δ^4	W-1096
		4-pregnene-3,20-dione	Δ^1	W-1096
		21-hydroxy-4-pregnene-3,20-dione	Δ^1	W-1096
		17α,21-dihydroxy-4-pregnene-3,20-dione	Δ^1	V-1052; W-1096
		11β,17α,21-trihydroxy-4-preg-nene-3,20-dione	Δ^1	V-1052; W-1096
		d,l-11β,17α,21-trihydroxy-4-pregnene-3,20-dione	d,l→d-Δ^1 + l	W-1102
		9α-fluoro-11β,17α,21-trihydroxy-4-pregnene-3,20-dione	Δ^1	W-1096
		9α-fluoro-11β,17α,21-trihydroxy-4-pregnene-3,20-dione 21-acetate	Δ^1; 21-OAc → 21-OH	V-1052
		17α,21-dihydroxy-9β,11β-oxido-4-pregnene-3,20-dione 21-acetate	Δ^1; 21-OAc → 21-OH	W-1096
		d,l-11β,17α,21-trihydroxy-4-pregnene-3,20-dione 21-trimethylacetate	d,l →d-Δ^1 + l	W-1102
		d,l-11β,21-dihydroxy-3,20-di-keto-4-pregnen-18-al (18 → 11) hemiacetal	d,l → d-Δ^1 + l	V-1055; W-1102
		21-hydroxy-4-pregnene-3,11,20-trione	Δ^1	W-1096
		17α,21-dihydroxy-4-pregnene-3,11,20-trione	Δ^1	V-1052; W-1096
		d,l-17α,21-dihydroxy-4-preg-nene-3,11,20-trione	d,l → d-Δ^1 + l	V-1055; W-1102

TABLE III

TAXONOMY

Transformations by Genus: DIDYMELLA
DIDYMOCLADIUM (Imperf. - Moniliales)
DIPLODIA (Imperf. - Sphaeropsidales)

SPECIES	SOURCE	SUBSTRATE	REACTION	REF.
lycopersici	C	17α-methyl-21-hydroxy-4-pregnene-3,11,20-trione 21-acetate	Δ^1	V-1052; W-1096
		21-hydroxy-4,6-pregnadiene-3,20-dione 21-acetate	Δ^1; 21-OAc $\rightarrow$ 21-OH	V-1052; W-1096
		4,11-pregnadiene-3,20-dione	Δ^1	V-1052; W-1096
	CBS	17α,21-dihydroxy-4-pregnene-3,20-dione	20-C=O $\rightarrow$ 20β-OH	S-836
vodakii	C	3β,11β-dihydroxy-5α-pregnan-20-one	16α-OH	W-1092
		3β-hydroxy-19-_nor_-4-pregnen-20-one	16α-OH	W-1093
DIDYMOCLADIUM				
ternatum	AMCY	16α,17α-oxido-4-pregnene-3,20-dione	11α-OH	P-746
DIPLODIA				
natalensis	ATCC-9055	4-androstene-3,17-dione	7α-OH	T-997
		A-_nor_-3-pregnene-2,20-dione	7α-OH	L-502; L-506; W-1078
		4-pregnene-3,20-dione	7α-OH	T-997
		21-hydroxy-4-pregnene-3,20-dione	7α-OH	T-997
		17α,21-dihydroxy-4-pregnene-3,20-dione	7α-OH	T-997; T-998; T-999
		11β,17α,21-trihydroxy-4-pregnene-3,20-dione	7α-OH	T-997
		9α-fluoro-11β,17α,21-trihydroxy-4-pregnene-3,20-dione	7α-OH	T-997
		17α,21-dihydroxy-4-pregnene-3,11,20-trione	7α-OH	T-997
		17α,21-dihydroxy-1,4-pregnadiene-3,20-dione	7α-OH	T-997
		11β,17α,21-trihydroxy-1,4-pregnadiene-3,20-dione	7α-OH	T-997

TABLE III

Transformations by Genus:

| DIPLODIA |
| DIPLODASCUS |
| DOTHICHIZA |

TAXONOMY

(Asco. - Endomycetales)
(Imperf. - Sphaeropsidales)

SPECIES	SOURCE	SUBSTRATE	REACTION	REF.
natalensis	FRI	$17\alpha,21$-dihydroxy-4-pregnene-3,20-dione	11α-OH	S-849
tubericola	IAM	3β-hydroxy-5-pregnen-20-one	$\Delta^5 \to \Delta^4$; 3β-OH $\to$ 3-C=O; 7β-OH	A-28; T-1025
			$\Delta^5 \to \Delta^4$; 3β-OH $\to$ 3-C=O; $7\beta,15\beta$-diOH	A-28; T-1025
		4-pregnene-3,20-dione	7β-OH	A-28; T-1023; T-1025
			$7\beta,15\beta$-diOH	A-28; T-1025
		7β-hydroxy-4-pregnene-3,20-dione	15β-OH	A-28; T-1025
		$17\alpha,21$-dihydroxy-4-pregnene-3,20-dione	7α-OH	A-28; T-1023
			20-C=O $\to$ 20β-OH	A-28
DIPLODASCUS				
albidus	FRI	$17\alpha,21$-dihydroxy-4-pregnene-3,20-dione	—	S-849
DOTHICHIZA				
ferruginosa	ATCC-11918	3-hydroxy-1,3,5(10)-estratrien-17-one	11β-OH	K-449
		17β-hydroxy-4-androsten-3-one	11β-OH	K-449
		4-androstene-3,17-dione	11β-OH	K-449
		4-pregnene-3,20-dione	11β-OH	K-449
		17α-hydroxy-4-pregnene-3,20-dione	11β-OH	K-449
		21-hydroxy-4-pregnene-3,20-dione	11β-OH	K-449
		$17\alpha,21$-dihydroxy-4-pregnene-3,20-dione	11β-OH	K-449

398

TABLE III

TAXONOMY

Transformations by Genus:

ECHINODONTIUM (Basidio. - Agaricales)
ELSINOE (Asco. - Myriangiales)
ENDOMYCES (Asco. - Endomycetales)
ENDOTINIA (Taxonomy Unclear - Prob. ENDOTHIA)
(Asco.-Sphaeriales)
ENTOMOPHTHORA (Phyco. - Entomophthorales)
EPICOCCUM (Imperf. - Moniliales)

SPECIES	SOURCE	SUBSTRATE	REACTION	REF.
tsugicola	IAM (2-2)	17α,21-dihydroxy-4-pregnene-3,20-dione	—	S-849
	IAM (2-3)	17α,21-dihydroxy-4-pregnene-3,20-dione	—	S-849
ELSINOE				
ampelina	FRI	17α,21-dihydroxy-4-pregnene-3,20-dione	—	S-849
	TNAES	17α,21-dihydroxy-4-pregnene-3,20-dione	—	S-849
fawcetti	TNAES	17α,21-dihydroxy-4-pregnene-3,20-dione	—	S-849
ENDOMYCES				
lindneri	FRI	17α,21-dihydroxy-4-pregnene-3,20-dione	—	S-849
ENDOTINIA (probably ENDOTHIA)				
parasitica	TNAES	17α,21-dihydroxy-4-pregnene-3,20-dione	—	S-849
ENTOMOPHTHORA				
coronata	ATCC-10151	4-pregnene-3,20-dione	oxidation - products not identified	W-1073
		17α,21-dihydroxy-4-pregnene-3,20-dione	6-OH; 11α-OH	W-1073
EPICOCCUM				
humicola	ATCC-12722 (QM-1049)	17β-hydroxy-4-androsten-3-one	11β-OH	R-782
		4-androstene-3,17-dione	11β-OH	R-782
		20-hydroxy-5β-pregnan-3-one	11β-OH	R-782
		20-hydroxy-5α-pregnan-3-one	11β-OH	R-782
		3β-hydroxy-5-pregnen-20-one	11β-OH	R-782

TABLE III

ansformations by Genus: EPICOCCUM

SPECIES	SOURCE	SUBSTRATE	REACTION	REF.
umicola	ATCC-12722 (QM-1049)	4-pregnene-3,20-dione	11β-OH	R-782
		17α-hydroxy-4-pregnene-3,20-dione	11β-OH	R-782
*		17α,21-dihydroxy-4-pregnene-3,20-dione	11β-OH	R-782
*			20-C=O → 20β-OH	R-782
		17α,21-dihydroxy-1,4-pregnadiene-3,20-dione	11β-OH	R-782
		4,6-pregnadiene-3,20-dione	11β-OH	R-782
eglectum	ATCC-12723 (QM-1070)	17β-hydroxy-4-androsten-3-one	11β-OH	R-782
		4-androstene-3,17-dione	11β-OH	R-782
		20-hydroxy-5β-pregnan-3-one	11β-OH	R-782
		20-hydroxy-5α-pregnan-3-one	11β-OH	R-782
		3β-hydroxy-5-pregnen-20-one	11β-OH	R-782
		4-pregnene-3,20-dione	11β-OH	R-782
		17α-hydroxy-4-pregnene-3,20-dione	11β-OH	R-782
*		17α,21-dihydroxy-4-pregnene-3,20-dione	11β-OH	R-782
		17α,21-dihydroxy-1,4-pregnadiene-3,20-dione	11β-OH	R-782
		4,6-pregnadiene-3,20-dione	11β-OH	R-782
oryzae	ATCC-12724 (QM-1053)	17β-hydroxy-4-androsten-3-one	11β-OH	R-782
		4-androstene-3,17-dione	11β-OH	R-782
		20-hydroxy-5α-pregnan-3-one	11β-OH	R-782
		20-hydroxy-5β-pregnan-3-one	11β-OH	R-782
		3β-hydroxy-5-pregnen-20-one	11β-OH	R-782
		4-pregnene-3,20-dione	11β-OH	R-782
		17α-hydroxy-4-pregnene-3,20-dione	11β-OH	R-782
*		17α,21-dihydroxy-4-pregnene-3,20-dione	11β-OH	R-782
		6β-fluoro-17α-hydroxy-21-methyl-4-pregnene-3,20-dione	11β-OH	H-391

TABLE III

Transformations by Genus: EPICOCCUM

SPECIES	SOURCE	SUBSTRATE	REACTION	REF.
oryzae	ATCC-12724 (QM-1053)	6α-fluoro-17α,21-dihydroxy-16-methylene-4-pregnene-3,20-dione	11β-OH	A-7
		17α,21-dihydroxy-1,4-pregnadiene-3,20-dione	11β-OH	R-782
		4,6-pregnadiene-3,20-dione	11β-OH	R-782
purpurascens	FRI	17α,21-dihydroxy-4-pregnene-3,20-dione	—	S-849
species	QM-649	17β-hydroxy-4-androsten-3-one	11β-OH	R-782
		4-androstene-3,17-dione	11β-OH	R-782
		20-hydroxy-5α-pregnan-3-one	11β-OH	R-782
		20-hydroxy-5β-pregnan-3-one	11β-OH	R-782
		3β-hydroxy-5-pregnen-20-one	11β-OH	R-782
		4-pregnene-3,20-dione	11β-OH	R-782
		17α-hydroxy-4-pregnene-3,20-dione	11β-OH	R-782
		17α,21-dihydroxy-4-pregnene-3,20-dione	11β-OH	R-782
		17α,21-dihydroxy-1,4-pregnadiene-3,20-dione	11β-OH	R-782
		4,6-pregnadiene-3,20-dione	11β-OH	R-782
yuccae	ATCC-12725 (QM-284e)	17β-hydroxy-4-androsten-3-one	11β-OH	R-782
		4-androstene-3,17-dione	11β-OH	R-782
		20-hydroxy-5α-pregnan-3-one	11β-OH	R-782
		20-hydroxy-5β-pregnan-3-one	11β-OH	R-782
		3β-hydroxy-5-pregnen-20-one	11β-OH	R-782
		4-pregnene-3,20-dione	11β-OH	R-782
		17α-hydroxy-4-pregnene-3,20-dione	11β-OH	R-782
		17α,21-dihydroxy-4-pregnene-3,20-dione	11β-OH	R-782
		17α,21-dihydroxy-1,4-pregnadiene-3,20-dione	11β-OH	R-782
		4,6-pregnadiene-3,20-dione	11β-OH	R-782

TABLE III

ansformations by Genus:

EPIDERMOPHYTON	(Imperf. - Moniliales)
EREMASCUS	(Asco. - Endomycetales)
EREMOTHECIUM	(Asco. - Endomycetales)
ERWINIA	(Schizo. - Eubacteriales)
ESCHERICHIA	(Schizo. - Eubacteriales)

SPECIES	SOURCE	SUBSTRATE	REACTION	REF.
floccasum	FRI	$17\alpha,21$-dihydroxy-4-pregnene-3,20-dione	—	S-849
EREMASCUS				
albus	NRRL	Sarsasapogenin	—	M-587
		Diosgenin	—	M-587
		4-dehydrotigogenone	—	M-587
EREMOTHECIUM				
ashbyii	SQ	3β-hydroxy-5-pregnen-20-one	$\Delta^5 \to \Delta^4$; 3β-OH $\to 3$-C=O	P-710
ERWINIA				
aroideae	FAKU	$17\alpha,21$-dihydroxy-4-pregnene-3,20-dione	—	S-849
carotovora	IFO (3380)	$11\beta,17\alpha,21$-trihydroxy-4-pregnene-3,20-dione	—	I-428
(in mixed culture with Mycococcus sp. A_1)			Δ^1	I-428
ESCHERICHIA				
coli	IAM (strain 2,6-Bordet, Najiar ATCC-3635)	$17\alpha,21$-dihydroxy-4-pregnene-3,20-dione	—	S-849
	(strain 7)	$17\alpha,21$-dihydroxy-4-pregnene-3,20-dione	2β-OH	S-849
	(strain 8)	$17\alpha,21$-dihydroxy-4-pregnene-3,20-dione	11α-OH; 11β-OH	S-849
	(ML-3)	$17\alpha,21$-dihydroxy-4-pregnene-3,20-dione	2β-OH	S-849
	IFO (3O43)	$11\beta,17\alpha,21$-dihydroxy-4-pregnene-3,20-dione	—	I-428
(in mixed culture with Mycococcus sp. A_1)			Δ^1	I-428

TABLE III

TAXONOMY

Transformations by Genus: ESCHERICHIA
EUGLENA (Phytomastigina - Euglenoidina)
FLAVOBACTERIUM (Schizo. - Eubacteriales)

SPECIES	SOURCE	SUBSTRATE	REACTION	REF.
coli	IMJ	3β-hydroxy-5-androsten-17-one	$\Delta^5 \to \Delta^4$; 3β-OH $\to$ 3-C=O	S-822
	NG	$3\alpha,7\alpha$-dihydroxy-5β-cholanic acid	7α-OH$\to$7-C=O	N-675
		$3\alpha,7\alpha,12\alpha$-trihydroxy-5β-cholanic acid	3α-OH$\to$3-C=O; 7α-OH$\to$7-C=O; 12α-OH $\to$ 12-C=O	S-799
			7α-OH$\to$7-C=O	N-675
		5-cholesten-3β-ol (sole carbon source)	—	S-914; T-1030
			utilization	C-140; M-595; S-793c
		24β-methyl-5,7,22-cholesta-triene-3β-ol	utilization	S-793c
freundii	NIH	3α-hydroxy-5β-cholanic acid (preparation of 3-hydroxy bile acid dehydrogenase - grown in presence of cholic acid.)	3α-OH $\to$3-C=O	H-352; H-353
EUGLENA (Protozoa)				
gracilis var. bacillaris	NG	4-androstene-3,17-dione	6-C=O	G-322
			17-C=O $\to$ 17β-OH	G-322
			$\Delta^4 \to 5\alpha$-H; 3-C=O$\to$3α-OH	G-322
			$\Delta^4 \to 5\alpha$-H; 3-C=O$\to$3α-OH; 17-C=O$\to$17β-OH	G-322
FLAVOBACTERIUM				
androstenedionicum	NG	5-androstene-3β,17β-diol	$\Delta^5 \to \Delta^4$; 3β-OH $\to$3-C=O; 17β-OH $\to$ 17-C=O	E-219
		3β-hydroxy-5-androsten-17-one	$\Delta^5 \to \Delta^4$; 3β-OH $\to$ 3-C=O	E-219

TABLE III

ansformations by Genus: FLAVOBACTERIUM

SPECIES	SOURCE	SUBSTRATE	REACTION	REF.
ndrostenedionicum	NG	$3\beta,17\alpha$-dihydroxy-5-pregnen-20-one	$\Delta^5 \to \Delta^4$; 3β-OH $\to$ 3-C=O	E-222
(variant i)		5-androstene-$3\beta,17\beta$-diol	$\Delta^5 \to \Delta^4$; 3β-OH $\to$ 3-C=O; 17β-OH $\to$ 17-C=O	E-220
quatile	RIND (36-1)	$3\beta,17\alpha,21$-trihydroxy-5-pregnen-20-one	—	P-744
		$3\beta,17\alpha,21$-trihydroxy-5-pregnen-20-one 21-acetate	21-OAc$\to$21-OH	P-744
		$3\beta,17\alpha,21$-trihydroxy-5-pregnen-20-one 3,21-diacetate	—	P-744
		$3\beta,17\alpha,21$-trihydroxy-5-pregnen-20-one 3-formate 21-acetate	3-formate $\to$ 3β-OH	P-744
urantiacum	NRRL	Sarsasapogenin	—	M-587
		Diosgenin	—	M-587
		4-dehydrotigogenone	—	M-587
uccalis	RIND (38-3)	$3\beta,17\alpha,21$-trihydroxy-5-pregnen-20-one	$\Delta^5 \to \Delta^4$; 3β-OH $\to$3-C=O	P-744
		$3\beta,17\alpha,21$-trihydroxy-5-pregnen-20-one 21-acetate	$\Delta^5 \to \Delta^4$; 3β-OH $\to$3-C=O; 21-OAc$\to$21-OH	P-744
		$3\beta,17\alpha,21$-trihydroxy-5-pregnen-20-one 3,21-diacetate	$\Delta^5 \to \Delta^4$; 3β-OAc $\to$3-C=O	P-744
		$3\beta,17\alpha,21$-trihydroxy-5-pregnen-20-one 3-formate 21-acetate	—	P-744
arbonilicum	NG	5β-androstene-$3\beta,17\beta$-diol	$\Delta^5 \to \Delta^4$; 3β-OH $\to$3-C=O; 17β-OH $\to$17-C=O	M-592
			$\Delta^5 \to \Delta^4$; 3β-OH $\to$ 3-C=O	M-592
ehydrogenans var. hydrolyticum	ATCC-13930 (WC-130)	5,9-cyclo-1-androstene-$11\beta,17\beta$-diol-3-one 11-acetate 17-propionate	Δ^1 -11β-OAc $\to$ $1\beta,11\beta$-oxide	R-777
		16,16-difluoro-5-androsten-3β-ol-17-one	17-C=O $\to$ 17α-OH; 3β-OH $\to$3-C=O; $\Delta^5 \to \Delta^4$	R-774
		16,16-difluoro-3-hydroxy-1,3,5(10)-estratrien-17-one 3-methyl ether	17-C=O $\to$ 17α-OH	R-774

TABLE III

Transformations by Genus: FLAVOBACTERIUM

SPECIES	SOURCE	SUBSTRATE	REACTION	REF.
dehydrogenans var. hydrolyticum	ATCC-13930 (WC-130)	16-diazo-3β-hydroxy-5-androsten-17-one	3β-OH→3-C=O; Δ^5→Δ^4	R-763
		17α-ethinyl-11β,17β-dihydroxy-4,6-androstadien-3-one diacetate	11β,17β-diOAc →11β,17β-diOH	G-304
		17α-ethinyl-11β,17β-dihydroxy-1,4,6-androstatrien-3-one diacetate	11β-OAc → 11β-OH; 17β-OAc→17β-OH	G-304
		11β,17β-dihydroxy-17α-methyl-1,4,6-androstatrien-3-one diacetate	11β-OAc→11β-OH; 17β-OAc →17β-OH	G-305
		3β-hydroxy-16-methylene-5-androsten-17-one	3β-OH →3-C=O; Δ^5→Δ^4	B-76
		5-pregnene-3β,20α-diol	Δ^5→Δ^4; 3β-OH →3-C=O	N-693
		5-pregnene-3β,20β-diol	Δ^5→Δ^4; 3β-OH →3-C=O; 20β-OH →20-C=O	N-693
		7α-methyl-5-pregnene-3β,7β,20β-triol	Δ^5→Δ^4; 3β-OH→3-C=O; 20β-OH →20-C=O	R-776
		3β-hydroxy-D-<u>nor</u>-5-pregnen-20-one	Δ^5→Δ^4; 3β-OH →3-C=O	R-763
		17α-chloro-3β-hydroxy-5-pregnen-20-one acetate	Δ^5→Δ^4; 3β-OAc → 3-C=O	R-761
		1β,3β-dihydroxy-5-pregnen-20-one	Δ^5→Δ^4; 3β-OH →3-C=O	N-688; N-689
		3β,17α,21-trihydroxy-5-pregnen-20-one 21-acetate	3β-OH→3-C=O; Δ^5→Δ^4; 21-OAc →21-OH	H-378
		3β,17α,21-trihydroxy-5-pregnen-20-one 3,21-diacetate	3β-OAc→3-C=O; Δ^5→Δ^4; 21-OAc →21-OH	H-378
		3β-hydroxy-16,16-dimethyl-5-pregnen-20-one	3β-OH→3-C=O; Δ^5→Δ^4	S-837
		3β-hydroxy-16β-methyl-16α,17α-oxido-5-pregnen-20-one	3β-OH→3-C=O; Δ^5→Δ^4	S-837
		3β,17α,21-trihydroxy-16α-methyl-5-pregnen-20-one 21-acetate	3β-OH→3-C=O; Δ^5→Δ^4; 21-OAc →21-OH	C-109; I-421; I-422
		3β,17α,21-trihydroxy-16β-methyl-5-pregnen-20-one 3,21-diacetate	3β-OAc→3-C=O; Δ^5→Δ^4; 21-OAc →21-OH	C-109; I-421; I-422

TABLE III

ansformations by Genus: FLAVOBACTERIUM

SPECIES	SOURCE	SUBSTRATE	REACTION	REF.
lehydrogenans	ATCC-13930 (WC-130)	$3\beta,17\alpha,21$-trihydroxy-16-methylene-5-pregnen-20-one 3,21-diacetate	$\Delta^5 \to \Delta^4$; 3β-OAc $\to$3-C=O; 21-OAc$\to$21-OH	T-981
		$1\beta,3\beta,17\alpha,21$-tetrahydroxy-5-pregnen-20-one 1,3,21-triacetate	1β-OAc$\to$1β-OH; 21-OAc$\to$21-OH; 3β-OAc$\to$3-C=O; $\Delta^5 \to \Delta^4$	N-689
		$11\beta,17\alpha,21$-trihydroxy-5,9-cyclo-1-pregnene-3,20-dione $11\beta,21$-diacetate	$11\beta,21$-diOAc$\to$ $11\beta,21$-diOH; Δ^1-11β-OH $\to$ $1\beta,11\beta$-oxide	G-292; R-777
		$11\beta,17\alpha,21$-trihydroxy-4-pregnene-3,20-dione $11\beta,21$-diacetate	11β-OAc$\to$11β-OH; 21-OAc $\to$ 21-OH	C-129
		21-hydroxy-17$\beta,20\alpha$-oxido-16-oximino-4-pregnene-3,11-dione acetate	21-OAc $\to$ 21-OH	N-686
		9α-bromo-11β-chloro-17$\alpha,21$-dihydroxy-5-pregnene-3,20-dione 21-acetate	21-OAc$\to$21-OH	N-691
		9α-bromo-11β-fluoro-17$\alpha,21$-dihydroxy-5-pregnene-3,20-dione 21-acetate	21-OAc$\to$21-OH	N-691
		11β-bromo-9α-fluoro-17$\alpha,21$-dihydroxy-5-pregnene-3,20-dione 21-acetate	21-OAc$\to$21-OH	N-691
		11β-chloro-9α-fluoro-17$\alpha,21$-dihydroxy-5-pregnene-3,20-dione 21-acetate	21-OAc$\to$21-OH	N-691
		$9\alpha,11\beta$-dichloro-17$\alpha,21$-dihydroxy-5-pregnene-3,20-dione 21-acetate	21-OAc$\to$21-OH	N-691
		$9\alpha,11\beta$-difluoro-17$\alpha,21$-dihydroxy-5-pregnene-3,20-dione 21-acetate	21-OAc$\to$21-OH	N-691
		9α-chloro-11β-fluoro-17$\alpha,21$-dihydroxy-2α-methyl-5-pregnene-3,20-dione 21-acetate	21-OAc$\to$21-OH	N-691
		$9\alpha,11\beta$-dichloro-16α-ethyl-17$\alpha,21$-dihydroxy-5-pregnene-3,20-dione 21-acetate	21-OAc$\to$21-OH	N-691
		$9\alpha,11\beta$-dichloro-17$\alpha,21$-dihydroxy-6-methyl-5-pregnene-3,20-dione 21-acetate	21-OAc$\to$21-OH	N-691

TABLE III

Transformations by Genus: FLAVOBACTERIUM

SPECIES	SOURCE	SUBSTRATE	REACTION	REF.
dehydrogenans	ATCC-13930 (WC-130)	$9\alpha,11\beta$-dichloro-$17\alpha,21$-dihydroxy-2α-methyl-5-pregnene-3,20-dione 21-acetate	21-OAc→21-OH	N-691
		$9\alpha,11\beta$-dichloro-$16\alpha,17\alpha,21$-trihydroxy-5-pregnene-3,20-dione 21-acetate	21-OAc→21-OH	N-691
		$9\alpha,11\beta$-dichloro-21-hydroxy-$16\alpha,17\alpha$-isopropylidenedioxy-5-pregnene-3,20-dione acetate	21-OAc→21-OH	N-691
		$9\alpha,11\beta$-difluoro-$17\alpha,21$-dihydroxy-2α-methyl-5-pregnene-3,20-dione 21-acetate	21-OAc→21-OH	N-691
		9α-chloro-11β-fluoro-21-hydroxy-2α-methyl-$16\alpha,17\alpha$-iso-propylidenedioxy-5-pregnene-3,20-dione acetate	21-OAc→21-OH	N-691
		9α-chloro-11β-fluoro-$16\alpha,17\alpha,21$-trihydroxy-2α-methyl-5-pregnene-3,20-dione 21-acetate	21-OAc→21-OH	N-691
		$3\beta,16\alpha$-dihydroxy-17β-methyl-18-<u>nor</u>-5,13-17α-pregnadien-20-one	3β-OH→3-C=O; Δ^5→Δ^4	S-839
			3β-OH→3-C=O; Δ^5→5ξ-H	S-839
		$3\beta,16\beta$-dihydroxy-17β-methyl-18-<u>nor</u>-5,13-17α-pregnadien-20-one	3β-OH→3-C=O; Δ^5→Δ^4	S-839
			3β-OH→3-C=O; Δ^5→5ξ-H	S-839
		21-hydroxy-17α-methyl-1,4-pregnadiene-3,20-dione acetate	21-OAc→21-OH	H-377
		$11\beta,17\alpha$-dihydroxy-21-mercapto-1,4-pregnadiene-3,20-dione 21-acetate	21-SAc→21-SH	N-685
		$11\beta,21$-dihydroxy-17α-methyl-1,4-pregnadiene-3,20-dione 21-acetate	21-OAc→21-OH	H-377
		9α-fluoro-$11\beta,17\alpha$-dihydroxy-21-mercapto-1,4-pregnadiene-3,20-dione 21-acetate	21-SAc→21-SH	N-685
		6β-bromo-$11\beta,17\alpha,21$-trihydroxy-1,4-pregnadiene-3,20-dione triacetate	$11\beta,17\alpha,21$-triOAc →$11\beta,17\alpha,21$-triOH	N-690

TABLE III

ansformations by Genus: FLAVOBACTERIUM

SPECIES	SOURCE	SUBSTRATE	REACTION	REF.
ehydrogenans	ATCC-13930 (WC-130)	9α-fluoro-6ξ,11β,17α,21-tetra-hydroxy-1,4-pregnadiene-3,20-dione tetraacetate	6ξ,11β,17α,21-tetraOAc → 6ξ, 11β,17α,21-tetraOH	G-309
		17α-hydroxy-21-mercapto-1,4-pregnadiene-3,11,20-trione 21-acetate	21-SAc→21-SH	N-685
		9α-fluoro-17α-hydroxy-21-mercapto-1,4-pregnadiene-3,11,20-trione 21-acetate	21-SAc→21-SH	N-685
		9α-fluoro-6ξ,17α,21-trihydroxy-1,4-pregnadiene-3,11,20-trione 6,21-diacetate	6ξ-OAc→6ξ-OH; 21-OAc→21-OH	G-309
		11β,17α,21-trihydroxy-1,5-pregnadiene-3,20-dione 21-acetate	21-OAc→21-OH	N-690
		11β,17α,21-trihydroxy-1,5-pregnadiene-3,20-dione triacetate	11β,17α,21-triOAc→11β,17α,21-triOH	N-690
		9α-bromo-11β-chloro-17α,21-dihydroxy-1,5-pregnadiene-3,20-dione 21-acetate	21-OAc→21-OH	N-691
		11β-bromo-9α-chloro-17α,21-dihydroxy-1,5-pregnadiene-3,20-dione 21-acetate	21-OAc→21-OH	N-691
		9α-bromo-11β-fluoro-17α,21-dihydroxy-1,5-pregnadiene-3,20-dione 21-acetate	21-OAc→21-OH	N-691
		11β-bromo-9α-fluoro-17α,21-dihydroxy-1,5-pregnadiene-3,20-dione 21-acetate	21-OAc→21-OH	N-691
		9α,11β-dibromo-17α,21-dihydroxy-1,5-pregnadiene-3,20-dione 21-acetate	21-OAc→21-OH	N-691
		9α-chloro-11β-fluoro-17α,21-dihydroxy-1,5-pregnadiene-3,20-dione 21-acetate	21-OAc→21-OH	N-691
		11β-chloro-9α-fluoro-17α,21-dihydroxy-1,5-pregnadiene-3,20-dione 21-acetate	21-OAc→21-OH	N-691
		11β-chloro-9α-iodo-17α,21-dihydroxy-1,5-pregnadiene-3,20-dione 21-acetate	21-OAc→21-OH	N-691

TABLE III

Transformations by Genus: FLAVOBACTERIUM

SPECIES	SOURCE	SUBSTRATE	REACTION	REF.
dehydrogenans	ATCC-13930 (WC-130)	$9\alpha,11\beta$-dichloro-$17\alpha,21$-di-hydroxy-1,5-pregnadiene-3,20-dione 21-acetate	21-OAc→21-OH	N-691
		16α-ethyl-$11\beta,17\alpha,21$-trihydroxy-1,5-pregnadiene-3,20-dione 21-acetate	21-OAc→21-OH	N-690; N-692
		11β-fluoro-$17\alpha,21$-dihydroxy-9α-iodo-1,5-pregnadiene-3,20-dione 21-acetate	21-OAc→21-OH	N-691
		9α-fluoro-$11\beta,17\alpha,21$-trihydroxy-1,5-pregnadiene-3,20-dione triacetate	$11\beta,17\alpha,21$-tri-OAc→$11\beta,17\alpha$, 21-triOH	N-690
		$9\alpha,11\beta$-difluoro-$17\alpha,21$-dihydroxy-1,5-pregnadiene-3,20-dione 21-acetate	21-OAc→21-OH	N-691
		$11\beta,17\alpha,21$-trihydroxy-16α-methyl-1,5-pregnadiene-3,20-dione 21-acetate	21-OAc→21-OH	N-690; N-692
		$11\beta,17\alpha,21$-trihydroxy-16β-methyl-1,5-pregnadiene-3,20-dione 21-acetate	21-OAc→21-OH	N-690; N-692
		9α-bromo-11β-chloro-16α-ethyl-$17\alpha,21$-dihydroxy-1,5-pregnadiene-3,20-dione 21-acetate	21-OAc→21-OH	N-691
		9α-bromo-11β-chloro-21-hydroxy-$16\alpha,17\alpha$-isopropylidenedioxy-1,5-pregnadiene-3,20-dione 21-acetate	21-OAc→21-OH	N-691
		9α-bromo-16α-ethyl-$11\beta,17\alpha,21$-trihydroxy-1,5-pregnadiene-3,20-dione 21-acetate	21-OAc→21-OH	N-690; N-692
		9α-bromo-11β-fluoro-$17\alpha,21$-dihydroxy-1,5-pregnadiene-3,20-dione 21-acetate	21-OAc→21-OH	N-691
		9α-bromo-11β-fluoro-21-hydroxy-$16\alpha,17\alpha$-isopropylidenedioxy-1,5-pregnadiene-3,20-dione 21-acetate	21-OAc→21-OH	N-691
		9α-bromo-$11\beta,17\alpha,21$-trihydroxy-16α-methyl-1,5-pregnadiene-3,20-dione 21-acetate	21-OAc→21-OH	N-690; N-692
		9α-bromo-$11\beta,17\alpha,21$-trihydroxy-16β-methyl-1,5-pregnadiene-3,20-dione 21-acetate	21-OAc→21-OH	N-690; N-692
		$6,9\alpha$-dibromo-11β-fluoro-$17\alpha,21$-dihydroxy-1,5-pregnadiene-3,20-dione 21-acetate	21-OAc→21-OH	N-691

TABLE III

Transformations by Genus: FLAVOBACTERIUM

SPECIES	SOURCE	SUBSTRATE	REACTION	REF.
dehydrogenans	ATCC-13930 (WC-130)	$9\alpha,11\beta$-dibromo-$17\alpha,21$-di-hydroxy-6-methyl-1,5-pregna-diene-3,20-dione 21-acetate	21-OAc→21-OH	N-691
		$9\alpha,11\beta$-dibromo-$17\alpha,21$-di-hydroxy-16β-methyl-1,5-pregnadiene-3,20-dione 21-acetate	21-OAc→21-OH	N-691
		$9\alpha,11\beta$-dibromo-$17\alpha,21$-di-hydroxy-16α-methyl-1,5-pregnadiene-3,20-dione 21-acetate	21-OAc→21-OH	N-691
		9α-chloro-11β-fluoro-$16\alpha,17\alpha,$21-trihydroxy-1,5-pregna-diene-3,20-dione 21-acetate	21-OAc→21-OH	N-691
		9α-chloro-11β-fluoro-$17\alpha,21$-dihydroxy-16β-methyl-1,5-pregnadiene-3,20-dione 21-acetate	21-OAc→21-OH	N-691
		9α-chloro-11β-fluoro-$17\alpha,21$-dihydroxy-6-methyl-1,5-pregnadiene-3,20-dione 21-acetate	21-OAc→21-OH	N-691
		9α-chloro-11β-fluoro-21-hydroxy-$16\alpha,17\alpha$-isopropylidenedioxy-1,5-pregnadiene-3,20-dione acetate	21-OAc→21-OH	N-691
		9α-chloro-$11\beta,17\alpha,21$-trihydroxy-16α-methyl-1,5-pregnadiene-3,20-dione 21-acetate	21-OAc→21-OH	N-690; N-692
		9α-chloro-$11\beta,17\alpha,21$-trihydroxy-16β-methyl-1,5-pregnadiene-3,20-dione 21-acetate	21-OAc→21-OH	N-690; N-692
		$9\alpha,11\beta$-dichloro-$16\alpha,17\alpha,21$-tri-hydroxy-1,5-pregnadiene-3,20-dione 21-acetate	21-OAc→21-OH	N-691
		$9\alpha,11\beta$-dichloro-$17\alpha,21$-dihydroxy-16α-methyl-1,5-pregnadiene-3,20-dione 21-acetate	21-OAc→21-OH	N-691
		$9\alpha,11\beta$-dichloro-21-hydroxy-$16\alpha,17\alpha$-isopropylidenedioxy-1,5-pregnadiene-3,20-dione acetate	21-OAc→21-OH	N-691
		$9\alpha,11\beta$-dichloro-$17\alpha,21$-dihydroxy-16β-methyl-1,5-pregnadiene-3,20-dione 21-acetate	21-OAc→21-OH	N-691

TABLE III

Transformations by Genus: FLAVOBACTERIUM

SPECIES	SOURCE	SUBSTRATE	REACTION	REF.
dehydrogenans	ATCC-13930 (WC-130)	$9\alpha,11\beta$-dichloro-$17\alpha,21$-dihydroxy-6-methyl-$1,5$-pregnadiene-$3,20$-dione 21-acetate	21-OAc→21-OH	N-691
		16α-ethyl-9α-fluoro-$11\beta,17\alpha,21$-trihydroxy-$1,5$-pregnadiene-$3,20$-dione 21-acetate	21-OAc→21-OH	N-690; N-692
		11β-fluoro-21-hydroxy-9α-iodo-$16\alpha,17\alpha$-isopropylidenedioxy-$1,5$-pregnadiene-$3,20$-dione 21-acetate	21-OAc→21-OH	N-691
		11β-fluoro-$17\alpha,21$-dihydroxy-9α-iodo-6-methyl-$1,5$-pregnadiene-$3,20$-dione 21-acetate	21-OAc→21-OH	N-691
		11β-fluoro-$17\alpha,21$-dihydroxy-9α-iodo-16α-methyl-$1,5$-pregnadiene-$3,20$-dione 21-acetate	21-OAc→21-OH	N-691
		11β-fluoro-$17\alpha,21$-dihydroxy-9α-iodo-16β-methyl-$1,5$-pregnadiene-$3,20$-dione 21-acetate	21-OAc→21-OH	N-691
		9α-fluoro-$11\beta,17\alpha,21$-trihydroxy-16α-methyl-$1,5$-pregnadiene-$3,20$-dione 21-acetate	21-OAc→21-OH	N-690; N-692
		9α-fluoro-$11\beta,17\alpha,21$-trihydroxy-16β-methyl-$1,5$-pregnadiene-$3,20$-dione 21-acetate	21-OAc→21-OH	N-690; N-692
		$9\alpha,11\beta$-difluoro-$17\alpha,21$-dihydroxy-16α-methyl-$1,5$-pregnadiene-$3,20$-dione 21-acetate	21-OAc→21-OH	N-691
		$9\alpha,11\beta$-difluoro-$17\alpha,21$-dihydroxy-16β-methyl-$1,5$-pregnadiene $3,20$-dione 21-acetate	21-OAc→21-OH	N-691
		9α-bromo-11β-fluoro-$17\alpha,21$-di-hydroxy-$6,16\alpha$-dimethyl-$1,5$-pregnadiene-$3,20$-dione 21-acetate	21-OAc→21-OH	N-691
		9α-bromo-11β-fluoro-$17\alpha,21$-di-hydroxy-$6,16\beta$-dimethyl-$1,5$-pregnadiene-$3,20$-dione 21-acetate	21-OAc→21-OH	N-691
		$9\alpha,11\beta$-dibromo-$17\alpha,21$-dihydroxy-$6,16\alpha$-dimethyl-$1,5$-pregnadiene-$3,20$-dione 21-acetate	21-OAc→21-OH	N-691
		$9\alpha,11\beta$-dibromo-$17\alpha,21$-dihydroxy-$6,16\beta$-dimethyl-$1,5$-pregnadiene-$3,20$-dione 21-acetate	21-OAc→21-OH	N-691

TABLE III

ransformations by Genus: FLAVOBACTERIUM

SPECIES	SOURCE	SUBSTRATE	REACTION	REF.
dehydrogenans	ATCC-13930 (WC-130)	$9\alpha,11\beta$-dichloro-$16\alpha,17\alpha,21$-tri-hydroxy-6-methyl-1,5-pregna-diene-3,20-dione 21-acetate	21-OAc→21-OH	N-691
		$9\alpha,11\beta$-dichloro-$17\alpha,21$-di-hydroxy-6,16α-dimethyl-1,5-pregnadiene-3,20-dione 21-acetate	21-OAc→21-OH	N-691
		$9\alpha,11\beta$-dichloro-$17\alpha,21$-dihydroxy-6,16β-dimethyl-1,5-pregna-diene-3,20-dione 21-acetate	21-OAc→21-OH	N-691
		9α-chloro-11β-fluoro-$16\alpha,17\alpha$,21-trihydroxy-6-methyl-1,5-pregnadiene-3,20-dione 21-acetate	21-OAc→21-OH	N-691
		9α-chloro-11β-fluoro-21-hydroxy-$16\alpha,17\alpha$-isopropylidenedioxy-6-methyl-1,5-pregnadiene-3,20-dione acetate	21-OAc→21-OH	N-691
		$9\alpha,11\beta$-difluoro-$17\alpha,21$-dihydroxy-6,16α-dimethyl-1,5-pregna-diene-3,20-dione 21-acetate	21-OAc→21-OH	N-691
		$9\alpha,11\beta$-difluoro-$17\alpha,21$-dihydroxy-6,16β-dimethyl-1,5-pregna-diene-3,20-dione 21-acetate	21-OAc→21-OH	N-691
		$17\alpha,21$-dihydroxy-1,5-pregna-diene-3,11,20-trione 21-acetate	21-OAc→21-OH	N-690
		$17\alpha,21$-dihydroxy-1,5-pregna-diene-3,11,20-trione 21-isobutyrate	21-O-i-Bu → 21-OH	N-690
		9α-bromo-$17\alpha,21$-dihydroxy-1,5-pregnadiene-3,11,20-trione 21-acetate	21-OAc→21-OH	N-690
		16α-n-butyl-$17\alpha,21$-dihydroxy-1,5-pregnadiene-3,11,20-trione 21-acetate	21-OAc→21-OH	N-690; N-692
		16β-n-butyl-$17\alpha,21$-dihydroxy-1,5-pregnadiene-3,11,20-trione 21-acetate	21-OAc→21-OH	N-690; N-692
		9α-chloro-$17\alpha,21$-dihydroxy-1,5-pregnadiene-3,11,20-trione 21-acetate	21-OAc→21-OH	N-690
		16α-ethyl-$17\alpha,21$-dihydroxy-1,5-pregnadiene-3,11,20-trione 21-acetate	21-OAc→21-OH	N-690; N-692

TABLE III

Transformations by Genus: FLAVOBACTERIUM

SPECIES	SOURCE	SUBSTRATE	REACTION	REF.
dehydrogenans	ATCC-13930 (WC-130)	9α-fluoro-17α,21-dihydroxy-1,5-pregnadiene-3,11,20-trione 21-acetate	21-OAc→21-OH	N-690
		17α,21-dihydroxy-16α-methyl-1,5-pregnadiene-3,11,20-trione 21-acetate	21-OAc→21-OH	N-690; N-692
		17α,21-dihydroxy-16β-methyl-1,5-pregnadiene-3,11,20-trione 21-acetate	21-OAc→21-OH	N-690; N-692
		9α-bromo-16α-ethyl-17α,21-dihydroxy-1,5-pregnadiene-3,11,20-trione 21-acetate	21-OAc→21-OH	N-690; N-692
		9α-bromo-17α,21-dihydroxy-16α-methyl-1,5-pregnadiene-3,11,20-trione 21-acetate	21-OAc→21-OH	N-690; N-692
		9α-bromo-17α,21-dihydroxy-16β-methyl-1,5-pregnadiene-3,11,20-trione 21-acetate	21-OAc→21-OH	N-690; N-692
		16α-ethyl-9α-fluoro-17α,21-dihydroxy-1,5-pregnadiene-3,11,20-trione 21-acetate	21-OAc→21-OH	N-690; N-692
		9α-fluoro-17α,21-dihydroxy-16α-methyl-1,5-pregnadiene-3,11,20-trione 21-acetate	21-OAc→21-OH	N-690; N-692
		9α-fluoro-17α,21-dihydroxy-16β-methyl-1,5-pregnadiene-3,11,20-trione 21-acetate	21-OAc→21-OH	N-690; N-692
		9α-fluoro-11β,16α,17α,21-tetra-hydroxy-1,4,6-pregnatriene-3,20-dione 16,21-diacetate	16α-OAc → 16α-OH; 21-OAc→21-OH	G-299
		11β,17α,21-trihydroxy-1,4,6-pregnatriene-3,20-dione 11-formate 21-acetate	11-formate → 11β-OH; 21-OAc →21-OH	G-302
	EM	3β-hydroxy-16-methylene-5-androsten-17-one	3β-OH →3-C=O; Δ^5→Δ^4	B-76
		3β,17β-dihydroxy-17α-methyl-16-methylene-5-androstene	3β-OH→3-C=O; Δ^5→Δ^4	B-76
		3β-hydroxy-pyrazolo-[4^1.3^1: 16.17]-5-androstene	3β-OH→3-C=O; Δ^5→Δ^4	B-76
		3β,17β-dihydroxy-Δ^{2^1}-isoxazolino-[4^1.5^1:16.17]-5-androstene	3β-OH→3-C=O; Δ^5→Δ^4	B-76
		3β,17α,21-trihydroxy-16-methylene-5-pregnen-20-one 3,21-diacetate	3β-OAc→3-C=O; 21-OAc→21-OH; Δ^5→Δ^4	M-558

TABLE III

ansformations by Genus: FLAVOBACTERIUM

SPECIES	SOURCE	SUBSTRATE	REACTION	REF.
dehydrogenans	NG (see genus Micrococcus)	1,3,5(10)-estratriene-3,17β-diol	17β-OH $\rightarrow$ 17-C=O	A-15; A-16; E-216
		5α-androstane-3β,17β-diol	3β-OH$\rightarrow$3-C=O; 17β-OH $\rightarrow$ 17-C=O	A-15; A-16
		5-androstene-3β,17β-diol	3β-OH$\rightarrow$3-C=O; $\Delta^5\rightarrow\Delta^4$	A-15; A-16; E-217
		17α-ethinyl-5-androstene-3β, 17β-diol	3β-OH$\rightarrow$3-C=O; $\Delta^5\rightarrow\Delta^4$	A-15; A-16; E-215
		3β-hydroxy-5-androsten-17-one	3β-OH$\rightarrow$3-C=O; $\Delta^5\rightarrow\Delta^4$	A-15; A-16; A-17; E-214
		3β-hydroxy-5-pregnen-20-one	3β-OH$\rightarrow$3-C=O; $\Delta^5\rightarrow\Delta^4$	A-15; A-16; E-214
		5-cholesten-3β-ol	—	E-214
			utilization	M-595
		3β-hydroxy-27-<u>nor</u>-5-cholesten- 25-one	3β-OH$\rightarrow$3-C=O; $\Delta^5\rightarrow\Delta^4$	A-15; A-16; E-214
flavescens	IFO (3085)	11β,17α,21-trihydroxy-4-preg- nene-3,20-dione	—	I-428
(in mixed culture with Mycococcus sp. A$_1$)			Δ^1	I-428
	RIND (37-3)	3β,17α,21-trihydroxy-5-pregnen- 20-one	—	P-744
		3β,17α,21-trihydroxy-5-pregnen- 20-one 21-acetate	21-OAc$\rightarrow$21-OH	P-744
		3β,17α,21-trihydroxy-5-pregnen- 20-one 3-formate 21-acetate	3-OFo$\rightarrow$3-OH	P-744
		3β,17α,21-trihydroxy-5-pregnen- 20-one 3,21-diacetate	—	P-744
flavotennae	NG	5-cholesten-3β-ol (effect of nutrients)	degradation	A-19
ulvum	RIND (39-2)	3β,17α,21-trihydroxy-5-pregnen- 20-one	$\Delta^5\rightarrow\Delta^4$; 3$\beta$-OH$\rightarrow$ 3-C=O	P-744
		3β,17α,21-trihydroxy-5-pregnen- 20-one 21-acetate	$\Delta^5\rightarrow\Delta^4$; 3$\beta$-OH$\rightarrow$ 3-C=O	P-744

TABLE III

Transformations by Genus: FLAVOBACTERIUM

SPECIES	SOURCE	SUBSTRATE	REACTION	REF.
fulvum	RIND (39-2)	$3\beta,17\alpha,21$-trihydroxy-5-pregnen-20-one 3-formate 21-acetate	$\Delta^5 \to \Delta^4$; 3-OFo→ 3-C=O; 21-OAc →21-OH	P-744
		$3\beta,17\alpha,21$-trihydroxy-5-pregnen-20-one 3,21-diacetate	—	P-744
helvolum (Nomen confusum - see Corynebacterium helvolum and C. mediolanum)	SCH	$3\beta,21$-dihydroxy-5-pregnen-20-one 21-acetate	$\Delta^5 \to \Delta^4$; 21-OAc →21-OH; 3β-OH→3-C=O	M-544
maris	NG	5-cholesten-3β-ol	3β-OH→3-C=O; $\Delta^5 \to \Delta^4$	A-19; A-21; A-22; B-50
sewanense *	NG	Digitonin	3β-glycoside (saponin) → 3β-OH	S-795
species	ATCC-13552	17β-hydroxy-17α-methyl-4-androsten-3-one	Δ^1	I-430
		4-pregnene-3,20-dione	Δ^1	I-430
		21-hydroxy-4-pregnene-3,20-dione	Δ^1	I-430
		$17\alpha,21$-dihydroxy-4-pregnene-3,20-dione	Δ^1	I-430
		$11\beta,17\alpha,21$-trihydroxy-4-pregnene-3,20-dione	Δ^1	I-430
		9α-fluoro-$11\beta,17\alpha,21$-trihydroxy-4-pregnene-3,20-dione	Δ^1	I-430
		$17\alpha,21$-dihydroxy-4-pregnene-3,11,20-trione	Δ^1	I-430
	NG (AC-5)	5-cholesten-3β-ol (sole carbon source - effect of nutrients)	(with asparagine - no reaction) (without aspara-gine - degrada-tion)	A-19
			utilization	M-595
	RIND (35-1)	$3\beta,17\alpha,21$-trihydroxy-5-pregnen-20-one	$\Delta^5 \to \Delta^4$; 3β-OH→ 3-C=O	P-744
		$3\beta,17\alpha,21$-trihydroxy-5-pregnen-20-one 21-acetate	$\Delta^5 \to \Delta^4$; 3β-OH→ 3-C=O; 21-OAc →21-OH	P-744
		$3\beta,17\alpha,21$-trihydroxy-5-pregnen-20-one 3-formate 21-acetate	$\Delta^5 \to \Delta^4$; 3β-OFo →3-C=O; 21-OAc →21-OH	P-744

TABLE III

Transformations by Genus:

FLAVOBACTERIUM	
FOMES	(Basidio. - Agaricales)
FRAMETES	(Taxonomy Unclear - Probably TRAMETES)
FUMAGO	(Imperf. - Moniliales)
FUSARIUM	(Imperf. - Moniliales)

SPECIES	SOURCE	SUBSTRATE	REACTION	REF.
species	RIND (35-1)	$3\beta,17\alpha,21$-trihydroxy-5-pregnen-20-one 3,21-diacetate	—	P-744
	RIND (38-3) (39-2)	$3\beta,21$-dihydroxy-5-pregnen-20-one	3β-OH→3-C=O; $\Delta^5 \to \Delta^4$	P-742
		$3\beta,21$-dihydroxy-5-pregnen-20-one 21-acetate	3β-OH→3-C=O; $\Delta^5 \to \Delta^4$	P-742
		$3\beta,17\alpha,21$-trihydroxy-5-pregnen-20-one	3β-OH→3-C=O; $\Delta^5 \to \Delta^4$	P-742
		$3\beta,17\alpha,21$-trihydroxy-5-pregnen-20-one 21-acetate	3β-OH→3-C=O; $\Delta^5 \to \Delta^4$	P-742
		$3\beta,21$-dihydroxy-$16\alpha,17\alpha$-oxido-5-pregnen-20-one 21-acetate	3β-OH→3-C=O; $\Delta^5 \to \Delta^4$	P-742
FOMES				
pinicola	FRI	$17\alpha,21$-dihydroxy-4-pregnene-3,20-dione	—	S-849
robstus	IAM	$17\alpha,21$-dihydroxy-4-pregnene-3,20-dione	—	S-849
species	IAM	$17\alpha,21$-dihydroxy-4-pregnene-3,20-dione	—	S-849
FRAMETES (see **TRAMETES**)				
pini	IAM	$17\alpha,21$-dihydroxy-4-pregnene-3,20-dione	—	S-849
FUMAGO				
species	FRI	$17\alpha,21$-dihydroxy-4-pregnene-3,20-dione	—	S-849
FUSARIUM				
aquaeductum	CZAS	4-androstene-3,17-dione	6β-OH; 15α-OH	C-97
		4-pregnene-3,20-dione	—	C-97
(var. dimerum)	CZAS	4-androstene-3,17-dione	6β-OH; 15α-OH	C-97
		4-pregnene-3,20-dione	—	C-97

TABLE III

Transformations by Genus: FUSARIUM

SPECIES	SOURCE	SUBSTRATE	REACTION	REF.
arthoceras	OIAB (F-75)	$17\alpha,21$-dihydroxy-4-pregnene-3,20-dione	–	K-462
aspidioti	OIAB (F-61)	$17\alpha,21$-dihydroxy-4-pregnene-3,20-dione	oxidation - products not identified	K-462
avenaceum	CZAS	4-androstene-3,17-dione	6β-OH; 15α-OH	C-97
		4-pregnene-3,20-dione	—	C-97
(var. herbarum)	CZAS	4-androstene-3,17-dione	6β-OH; 15α-OH	C-97
		4-pregnene-3,20-dione	—	C-97
batatatis	OIAB (F-68)	$17\alpha,21$-dihydroxy-4-pregnene-3,20-dione	oxidation - products not identified	K-462
bulbigenum	ATCC-7618	$17\alpha,21$-dihydroxy-4-pregnene-3,11,20-trione	Δ^1	C-125
	OIAB (F-59)	$17\alpha,21$-dihydroxy-4-pregnene-3,20-dione	oxidation - products not identified	K-462
(var. plum)	OIAB (F-76)	$17\alpha,21$-dihydroxy-4-pregnene-3,20-dione	—	K-462
buxicola	CZAS	4-androstene-3,17-dione	6β-OH; 15α-OH	C-97
		4-pregnene-3,20-dione	—	C-97
caucasicum (poss. synonym for solani)	C	5α-androstane-3,17-dione	$\Delta^{1,4}$	V-1056
		3β-hydroxy-5-androsten-17-one	Δ^1; 3β-OH $\rightarrow$ 3-C=O; $\Delta^5 \rightarrow \Delta^4$	V-1056
		4-androstene-3,17-dione	Δ^1	V-1056; W-1095
			Δ^1; 17-C=O $\rightarrow$ 17a-oxa-17-C=O	W-1095
		1,4-androstadiene-3,17-dione	17-C=O $\rightarrow$ 17a-oxa-17-C=O	W-1095
		3β-hydroxy-5α-pregnan-20-one acetate	$\Delta^{1,4}$; 3β-OAc$\rightarrow$3-C=O; 17β-OAc $\rightarrow$ 17-C=O	V-1056
			17β-Ac$\rightarrow$17-C=O 3β-OAc$\rightarrow$3-C=O	V-1056
		5α-pregnane-3,20-dione	$\Delta^{1,4}$; 17β-Ac$\rightarrow$ 17-C=O	V-1056
			17β-Ac$\rightarrow$17-C=O	V-1056

TABLE III

Transformations by Genus: FUSARIUM

SPECIES	SOURCE	SUBSTRATE	REACTION	REF.
caucasicum	C	3β-hydroxy-5-pregnen-20-one	Δ^1; $\Delta^5 \to \Delta^4$; 17β-Ac→17-C=O; 3β-OH→3-C=O	V-1056; W-1095
			17β-Ac → 17-C=O	V-1056
		4-pregnene-3,20-dione	17β-Ac → 17-C=O; Δ^1	V-1056; W-1095
		21-hydroxy-4-pregnene-3,20-dione	Δ^1; 17β-(20-C=O-21-OH) → 17-C=O	V-1056; W-1095
(For Ref. W-1116, 1117 and 1118 - interaction of unsaturated and saturated steroids.)	CBS	androstane-3,17-dione	$\Delta^{1,4}$	W-1116
		3β-hydroxy-5-androsten-17-one	Δ^1; 3β-OH → 3-C=O; $\Delta^5 \to \Delta^4$	W-1118
		17β-hydroxy-4-androsten-3-one	Δ^1; 17β-OH → 17-C=O	W-1118
		4-androstene-3,17-dione	Δ^1	W-1116; W-1117; W-1118
		3β-hydroxy-5α-pregnan-20-one	$\Delta^{1,4}$; 3β-OH→3-C=O; 17β-Ac→17-C=O	W-1118
		3β-hydroxy-5α-pregnan-20-one acetate	Δ^1; 3β-OAc→3-C=O; 17β-Ac→17-C=O	V-1056
		5α-pregnane-3,20-dione	$\Delta^{1,4}$; 17β-Ac→17-C=O	W-1116; W-1118
			$\Delta^{1,4}$; 17β-Ac →17a-oxa-17-C=O	W-1116
			17β-Ac → 17-C=O; Δ^4	W-1116
		5β-pregnane-3,20-dione	—	W-1116
		5α-16-pregnene-3,20-dione	$\Delta^{1,4}$; Δ^{16}-17-Ac → 17-C=O	W-1118
		3β-hydroxy-5-pregnen-20-one	Δ^1; $\Delta^5 \to \Delta^4$; 17β-Ac→17-C=O; 3β-OH→3-C=O	W-1118
		4-pregnene-3,20-dione	Δ^1; 17β-Ac→17a-oxa-17-C=O	W-1116
			Δ^1; 17β-Ac → 17-C=O	W-1116; W-1117; W-1118

TABLE III

Transformations by Genus: FUSARIUM

SPECIES	SOURCE	SUBSTRATE	REACTION	REF.
caucasicum	CBS	4-pregnene-3,20-dione	17β-Ac$\rightarrow$ 17-C=O	W-1116
		21-hydroxy-4-pregnene-3,20-dione	Δ^1; 17β-(20-C=O-21-OH) $\rightarrow$ 17-C=O	W-1118
		16α,17α-oxido-4-pregnene-3,20-dione	Δ^1; 16α,17α-oxido-17β-Ac$\rightarrow$ 17-C=O	W-1118
		3β-hydroxy-5,16-pregnadien-20-one	Δ^1; $\Delta^5 \rightarrow \Delta^4$; Δ^{16}-17-Ac$\rightarrow$17-C=O; 3β-OH$\rightarrow$3-C=O	W-1118
		4,16-pregnadiene-3,20-dione	Δ^1; Δ^{16}-17-Ac $\rightarrow$17-C=O	W-1118
	CZAS	17β-hydroxy-4-androsten-3-one acetate	Δ^1; 17β-OAc$\rightarrow$ 17-C=O	C-97
			Δ^1; 17β-OAc$\rightarrow$ 17a-oxa-17-C=O	C-97
		17β-hydroxy-4-androsten-3-one benzoate	—	C-97
		17β-hydroxy-4-androsten-3-one isobutyrate	—	C-97
		17β-hydroxy-4-androsten-3-one formate	Δ^1; 17β-OFo$\rightarrow$ 17a-oxa-17-C=O	C-97
			Δ^1; 17β-OFo $\rightarrow$ 17-C=O	C-97
		17β-hydroxy-4-androsten-3-one propionate	Δ^1; 17β-OPr $\rightarrow$ 17a-oxa-17-C=O	C-97
			Δ^1; 17β-OPr $\rightarrow$ 17-C=O	C-97
		4-androstene-3,17-dione	6β-OH	C-97
			15α-OH	C-97
			Δ^1	C-97; H-399
			Δ^1; 17-C=O $\rightarrow$ 17β-OH	C-97
			17-C=O $\rightarrow$17a-oxa-17-C=O	C-97

TABLE III

Transformations by Genus: FUSARIUM

SPECIES	SOURCE	SUBSTRATE	REACTION	REF.
caucasicum	CZAS	4-androstene-3,17-dione	Δ^1; 17-C=O → 17a-oxa-17-C=O	C-97
		17β-hydroxy-4-androsten-3-one	Δ^1	C-97
			17β-OH → 17-C=O	C-97
			17β-OH→17a-oxa-17-C=O	C-97
			Δ^1; 17β-OH → 17-C=O	C-97
			Δ^1; 17β-OH→17a-oxa-17-C=O	C-97
		4-pregnene-3,20-dione	Δ^1; 17β-Ac → 17-C=O	C-97
			Δ^1; 17β-Ac → 17β-OH	C-97
			17β-Ac→ 17-C=O	C-97
			Δ^1; 17β-Ac → 17a-oxa-17-C=O	C-97
	PIRI	4-pregnene-3,20-dione	Δ^1; 17β-Ac→17a-oxa-17-C=O	M-588
cocophilum	CZAS	4-androstene-3,17-dione	6β-OH; 15α-OH	C-97
		4-pregnene-3,20-dione	—	C-97
coeruieum	OIAB (F-83)	17α,21-dihydroxy-4-pregnene-3,20-dione	—	K-462
concolor	CBS	4-pregnene-3,11,20-trione	15α-OH	M-599
culmorum	CZAS	4-androstene-3,17-dione	6β-OH; 15α-OH	C-97
		4-pregnene-3,20-dione	—	C-97
	EM (2092)	17α,21-dihydroxy-4-pregnene-3,20-dione	11α-OH	M-557
	VEB	4-pregnene-3,20-dione	15α-OH	K-452
limerum	OIAB (F-39)	17α,21-dihydroxy-4-pregnene-3,20-dione	6β-OH	K-462
			11α-OH	K-462
diversisporum	OIAB (F-43)	17α,21-dihydroxy-4-pregnene-3,20-dione	oxidation - products not identified	K-462

TABLE III

Transformations by Genus: FUSARIUM

SPECIES	SOURCE	SUBSTRATE	REACTION	REF.
equiseti	EM (2083)	$17\alpha,21$-dihydroxy-4-pregnene-3,20-dione 21-acetate	11α-OH	M-557
			11α-OH; 21-OAc →21-OH	M-577
		$17\alpha,21$-dihydroxy-1,4-pregnadiene-3,20-dione	11α-OH	M-557
		$17\alpha,21$-dihydroxy-4,6-pregnadiene-3,20-dione	11α-OH	M-557
		$17\alpha,21$-dihydroxy-1,4,6-pregnatriene-3,20-dione	11α-OH	M-557
expansum	CZAS	4-androstene-3,17-dione	6β-OH; 15α-OH	C-97
		4-pregnene-3,20-dione	—	C-97
gibosum	CZAS	4-androstene-3,17-dione	6β-OH; 15α-OH	C-97
		4-pregnene-3,20-dione	—	C-97
(var. acuminatum)		4-androstene-3,17-dione	6β-OH; 15α-OH	C-97
		4-pregnene-3,20-dione	—	C-97
gigas	CZAS	4-androstene-3,17-dione	6β-OH; 15α-OH	C-97
		4-pregnene-3,20-dione	—	C-97
graminearum	CZAS	4-androstene-3,17-dione	6β-OH; 15α-OH	C-97
		4-pregnene-3,20-dione	—	C-97
herberum	OIAB (F-55)	$17\alpha,21$-dihydroxy-4-pregnene-3,20-dione	oxidation - products not identified	K-462
heterosporum	CZAS	4-androstene-3,17-dione	6β-OH; 15α-OH	C-97
		4-pregnene-3,20-dione	—	C-97
javanicum	ATCC-12575	4-pregnene-3,20-dione	17β-Ac→17-C=O; Δ^1; 11α-OH	F-274
			Δ^1; 17β-Ac → 17a-oxa-17-C=O	F-274
			Δ^1; 17β-Ac → 17β-OH; 11α-OH	F-274
		11α-hydroxy-4-pregnene-3,20-dione	Δ^1; 17β-Ac → 17a-oxa-17-C=O	F-274
		4-pregnene-3,20-dione 20-cyclo-ethyleneketal	Δ^1	F-251
		4-pregnene-3,11,20-trione	Δ^1; 17β-Ac→ 17a-oxa-17-C=O	F-274

TABLE III

ansformations by Genus: FUSARIUM

SPECIES	SOURCE	SUBSTRATE	REACTION	REF.
avanicum	CZAS	4-androstene-3,17-dione	6β-OH; 15α-OH	C-97
		4-pregnene-3,20-dione	—	C-97
			Δ^1; 17β-Ac→ 17a-oxa-17-C=O	F-274; F-278
	QM-524	4-pregnene-3,20-dione	Δ^1; 11α-OH; 17β-Ac→17-C=O	F-278
			Δ^1; 17β-Ac→17a-oxa-17-C=O	F-287
			Δ^1; 17β-Ac→17β-OH; 11α-OH	F-287
		11α-hydroxy-4-pregnene-3,20-dione	Δ^1; 17β-Ac → 17-C=O	F-276
		17α,21-dihydroxy-4-pregnene-3,20-dione	Δ^1	F-275
			Δ^1; 20-C=O → 20β-OH	F-275
iteritium	CZAS	17β-hydroxy-4-androsten-3-one acetate	Δ^1; 17β-OAc→ 17-C=O	C-97
			Δ^1; 17β-OAc→17a-oxa-17-C=O	C-97
		17β-hydroxy-4-androsten-3-one benzoate	—	C-97
		17β-hydroxy-4-androsten-3-one isobutyrate	—	C-97
		17β-hydroxy-4-androsten-3-one formate	Δ^1; 17β-OFo→ 17a-oxa-17-C=O	C-97
			Δ^1; 17β-OFo→ 17-C=O	C-97
		17β-hydroxy-4-androsten-3-one propionate	Δ^1; 17β-OPr→ 17a-oxa-17-C=O	C-97
			Δ^1; 17β-OPr→ 17-C=O	C-97
		4-androstene-3,17-dione	6β-OH	C-97
			15α-OH	C-97
			Δ^1; 17-C=O → 17β-OH	C-97
			17-C=O →17a-oxa-17-C=O	C-97
			Δ^1; 17-C=O → 17a-oxa-17-C=O	C-97

TABLE III

Transformations by Genus: FUSARIUM

SPECIES	SOURCE	SUBSTRATE	REACTION	REF.
lateritium	CZAS	17β-hydroxy-4-androsten-3-one	Δ^1	C-97
			17β-OH → 17-C=O	C-97
			17β-OH→17a-oxa-17-C=O	C-97
			Δ^1; 17β-OH → 17-C=O	C-97
			Δ^1; 17β-OH → 17a-oxa-17-C=O	C-97
		4-pregnene-3,20-dione	Δ^1; 17β-Ac → 17-C=O	C-97
			Δ^1; 17β-Ac→ 17β-OH	C-97
			17β-Ac→ 17-C=O	C-97
			Δ^1; 17β-Ac→17a-oxa-17-C=O	C-97
	OIAB (F-52)	17α,21-dihydroxy-4-pregnene-3,20-dione	oxidation - products not identified	K-462
(var. fructigenum)	OIAB (F-1)	17α,21-dihydroxy-4-pregnene-3,20-dione	oxidation - products not identified	K-462
lini	ATCC-9593	4-pregnene-3,20-dione	15α-OH	M-599
	CBS	17β-hydroxy-4-androsten-3-one	15α-OH	T-980
		4-androstene-3,17-dione	15α-OH	T-980
		4-pregnene-3,20-dione	15α-OH	T-980
		(6β,15α-diOH - corrected to 12β,15α-diOH; Dodson, R.M., Helv. 48: 1933, 1965)	6β,15α-diOH	T-980
			15α-OH; Δ^4 → 5ξ-H	T-980
		21-hydroxy-4-pregnene-3,20-dione	15α-OH	T-980; W-1074
		14α,21-dihydroxy-4-pregnene-3,20-dione	15α-OH	T-980
		17α,21-dihydroxy-4-pregnene-3,20-dione 21-acetate	15α-OH; 21-OAc → 21-OH	T-980

TABLE III

Transformations by Genus: FUSARIUM

SPECIES	SOURCE	SUBSTRATE	REACTION	REF.
lini	CBS	$3\beta,14\beta$-dihydroxy-5β-20(22)-cardenolide	12β-OH	W-1074
	FAHU	$17\alpha,21$-dihydroxy-4-pregnene-3,20-dione	—	S-849
	NARI	$17\alpha,21$-dihydroxy-4-pregnene-3,20-dione	11α-OH	S-849
	OIAB (F-85)	$17\alpha,21$-dihydroxy-4-pregnene-3,20-dione	oxidation - products not identified	K-462
	UB	17β-hydroxy-4-androsten-3-one	15α-OH	G-319
			15α-OH; 17β-OH $\rightarrow$17-C=O	G-319
		4-androstene-3,17-dione	15α-OH	G-319
		4-pregnene-3,20-dione	15α-OH	G-319
		[$6\beta,15\alpha$-OH - corrected to $12\beta,15\alpha$-diOH - Dodson, R. M. Helv. 48: 1933 (1965)]	$6\beta,15\alpha$-diOH	G-319
			15α-OH; $\Delta^4 \rightarrow$ 5ξ-H	G-319
		21-hydroxy-4-pregnene-3,20-dione	15α-OH	G-319
		14β-hydroxy-3-keto-5β-20(22)-cardenolide	12β-OH	G-320; T-978
			3-C=O$\rightarrow3\alpha$-OH	G-320; T-978
			3-C=O$\rightarrow3\alpha$-OH; 12β-OH	G-320; T-978
		$3\beta,14\beta$-dihydroxy-5β-20(22)-cardenolide	12β-OH	G-320; T-978
		$3\beta,14\beta$-dihydroxy-5β-20(22)-cardenolide 3-acetate	12β-OH; 3β-OAc $\rightarrow3\beta$-OH	G-320; T-978
		$3\beta,14\beta$-dihydroxy-5β-20(22)-cardenolide-3-(L-rhamnoside $2^1,3^1,4^1$-triacetate)	2^1-OAc$\rightarrow2^1$-OH; 3^1-OAc$\rightarrow3^1$-OH; 4^1-OAc$\rightarrow4^1$-OH	T-978
		$3\beta,14\beta$-dihydroxy-5β-20(22)-cardenolide-3-(D-cymaroside 4^1-acetate)	4^1-OAc$\rightarrow4^1$-OH	T-978

TABLE III

Transformations by Genus: FUSARIUM

SPECIES	SOURCE	SUBSTRATE	REACTION	REF.
lini	UB	$3\beta,14\beta$-dihydroxy-5β-20(22)-cardenolide 3-[D-glucosyl-D-glucosyl-D-cymaroside]	digitoxigenin-3-[D-glucosyl-D-glucosyl-D-cymaroside]→ digitoxigenin-3-[D-cymaroside]	T-978
		$3\beta,14\beta$-dihydroxy-5β-20(22)-cardenolide 3-[digitoxosyl-digitoxosyl-digitoxoside-tetraacetate]	digitoxosyl-digitoxosyl-digitoxoside-tetraacetate → digitoxosyl-digitoxosyl-digitoxoside	G-320; T-978
		$3\beta,14\beta$-dihydroxy-5β-20(22)-cardenolide 3-[digitoxosyl-digitoxosyl-digitoxoside]	—	G-320; T-978
		$3\beta,14\beta$-dihydroxy-5β-20(22)-cardenolide 3-[D-cymaroside]	—	G-320; T-978
		$3\beta,14\beta$-dihydroxy-5β-20(22)-cardenolide 3-[D-rhamnoside]	—	G-320; T-978
		3-O-acetyl-14-anhydro-digitoxigenin	—	T-978
		$3\beta,5\beta,14\beta$-trihydroxy-19-oxo-20(22)-cardenolide 3β-D-glucoside	3β-D-glucoside → 3β-OH	T-978
		$3\beta,5\beta,14\beta$-trihydroxy-19-oxo-20(22)-cardenolide 3β-D-glucoside tetraacetate	3β-D-glucoside tetraacetate → 3β-OH	T-978
		$3\beta,5\beta,14\beta$-trihydroxy-19-oxo-20(22)-cardenolide 3-[D-glucosyl-D-glucosyl-D-cymaroside heptaacetate]	strophanthidin-3-[D-hepta-acetyl-D-gluco-syl-D-glucosyl-D-cymaroside]→ strophanthidin-3-[D-cymaroside]	T-978
		$3\beta,5\beta,14\beta$-trihydroxy-19-oxo-20(22)-cardenolide 3-[D-glucosyl-D-cymaroside tetraacetate]	D-glucosyl-D-cymaroside-tetraacetate → D-glucosyl-D-cymaroside	T-978
		$3\beta,5\beta,14\beta,19$-tetrahydroxy-20(22)-cardenolide	—	T-978
		$14\beta,16\beta$-dihydroxy-3-keto-5β-20(22)-cardenolide	3-C=O→3α-OH	T-977

TABLE III

ransformations by Genus: FUSARIUM

SPECIES	SOURCE	SUBSTRATE	REACTION	REF.
lini	UB	$3\beta,14\beta,16\beta$-trihydroxy-5β-20(22)-cardenolide	12β-OH	T-977
		$3\beta,14\beta,16\beta$-trihydroxy-5β-20(22)-cardenolide 3-D-cymaroside 4^1,16-diacetate	4^1-OAc$\rightarrow 4^1$-OH	T-978
		$3\beta,14\beta,16\beta$-trihydroxy-5β-20(22)-cardenoiide 3-D-cymaroside 4^1,16-diacetate	4^1-OAc$\rightarrow 4^1$-OH; 16-OAc$\rightarrow$ 16-OH	T-978
		$3\beta,14\beta,19$-trihydroxy-5α-20(22)-cardenolide	—	T-978
		$3\beta,11\alpha,14\beta$-trihydroxy-5β-20(22)-cardenolide	—	T-978
		3-keto-$11\alpha,14\beta$-dihydroxy-5β-20(22)-cardenolide	—	T-978
		3,11-diketo-14β-hydroxy-5β-20(22)-cardenolide	—	T-978
		3-keto-$14\beta,19$-dihydroxy-4,20(22)-cardadienolide	—	T-978
		$3\beta,14\beta$-dihydroxy-5β-16,20(22)-cardadienolide	—	T-978
		14β-hydroxy-3-keto-5β-20,22-bufadienolide	12β-OH	T-979
		$3\beta,14\beta$-dihydroxy-5β-20,22-bufadienolide	12β-OH	T-979
lycopersici	NRRL	Sarsasapogenin	—	M-587
		Diosgenin	—	M-587
		4-dehydrotigogenone	—	M-587
	S	4-pregnene-3,20-dione	15α-OH	S-849; S-858; S-859
		17α-hydroxy-4-pregnene-3,20-dione	6β-OH	S-849; S-858
		21-hydroxy-4-pregnene-3,20-dione	15α-OH	S-849; S-858
		$17\alpha,21$-dihydroxy-4-pregnene-3,20-dione	6β-OH	S-849; S-858
		$11\beta,21$-dihydroxy-4-pregnene-3,20-dione	X-OH; 15α-OH	S-849; S-858
	TNAES	$17\alpha,21$-dihydroxy-4-pregnene-3,20-dione	—	S-849

TABLE III

Transformations by Genus: FUSARIUM

SPECIES	SOURCE	SUBSTRATE	REACTION	REF.
lycopersici	VEB	4-pregnene-3,20-dione	15α-OH	K-452
macroceras	CZAS	4-androstene-3,17-dione	6β-OH; 15α-OH	C-97
		4-pregnene-3,20-dione	—	C-97
merismoides	CZAS	4-androstene-3,17-dione	6β-OH; 15α-OH	C-97
		4-pregnene-3,20-dione	—	C-97
microcrea	CZAS	4-androstene-3,17-dione	6β-OH; 15α-OH	C-97
		4-pregnene-3,20-dione	—	C-97
moniliforme (imperfect stage of Gibberella fujikuroi)	ATCC-10052	11β,21-dihydroxy-4-pregnene-3,20-dione	15α-OH	M-599
	CZAS	4-androstene-3,17-dione	6β-OH; 15α-OH	C-97
		4-pregnene-3,20-dione	—	C-97
(var. lactis)		4-androstene-3,17-dione	6β-OH; 15α-OH	C-97
		4-pregnene-3,20-dione	—	C-97
(var. subglutinans)		4-androstene-3,17-dione	6β-OH; 15α-OH	C-97
		4-pregnene-3,20-dione	—	C-97
	OIAB (F-7)	17α,21-dihydroxy-4-pregnene-3,20-dione	oxidation - products not identified	K-462
(var. majus)	(F-5)	17α,21-dihydroxy-4-pregnene-3,20-dione	oxidation - products not identified	K-462
	SY	1,3,5(10)-estratriene-3,17β-diol	15α-OH	C-139
		1,3,5(10)-estratriene-3,17β-diol 3-methylether	6β-OH	C-139
		1,3,5(10)-estratrien-3-ol-17-one	15α-OH	C-139
nivale	CZAS	4-androstene-3,17-dione	6β-OH; 15α-OH	C-97
		4-pregnene-3,20-dione	—	C-97
niveum	OIAB	17α,21-dihydroxy-4-pregnene-3,20-dione	oxidation - products not identified	K-462
niveus	S	4-pregnene-3,20-dione	—	S-859
		17α-hydroxy-4-pregnene-3,20-dione	—	S-859
		17α,21-dihydroxy-4-pregnene-3,20-dione	11α-OH	S-859

TABLE III

ansformations by Genus: FUSARIUM

SPECIES	SOURCE	SUBSTRATE	REACTION	REF.
iiveus	TNAES	$17\alpha,21$-dihydroxy-4-pregnene-3,20-dione	6β-OH	S-849
rthoceras	ATCC-10082	17β-hydroxy-4-estren-3-one	15α-OH	M-599
	CBS	17β-hydroxy-4-estren-3-one	15α-OH	D-151
			15α-OH; 17β-OH →17-C=O	D-151
oxysporum	ATCC-7601	$17\alpha,21$-dihydroxy-4-pregnene-3,11,20-trione	Δ^1	C-125
	ATCC-9991	4-androstene-3,17-dione	15α-OH	M-599
		21-hydroxy-5β-pregnane-3,20-dione acetate	15α-OH; 21-OAc →21-OH	M-599
		6β-hydroxy-4-pregnene-3,20-dione	15α-OH	M-599
		21-hydroxy-4-pregnene-3,20-dione	15α-OH	M-599
		$17\alpha,21$-dihydroxy-4-pregnene-3,11,20-trione 21-acetate	15α-OH; 21-OAc →21-OH	M-599
	CZAS	4-androstene-3,17-dione	6β-OH; 15α-OH	C-97
		4-pregnene-3,20-dione	—	C-97
(var. orthoceras)		4-androstene-3,17-dione	6β-OH; 15α-OH	C-97
		4-pregnene-3,20-dione	—	C-97
	FRI	$17\alpha,21$-dihydroxy-4-pregnene-3,20-dione	—	S-849
	OIAB (F-3)	$17\alpha,21$-dihydroxy-4-pregnene-3,20-dione	—	K-462
(var. aurantiacum)	OIAB (F-4)	$17\alpha,21$-dihydroxy-4-pregnene-3,20-dione	—	K-462
poae	OIAB (F-40)	$17\alpha,21$-dihydroxy-4-pregnene-3,20-dione	oxidation - products not identified	K-462
pruni	OIAB (F-69)	$17\alpha,21$-dihydroxy-4-pregnene-3,20-dione	oxidation - products not identified	K-462
redolens	EM(2087)	$17\alpha,21$-dihydroxy-4-pregnene-3,20-dione	11α-OH	M-557
roseum	VEB	17β-hydroxy-4-androsten-3-one	6β-OH	R-747
		4-pregnene-3,20-dione	15α-OH	R-747
			$6\beta,15\alpha$-diOH	R-747

TABLE III

Transformations by Genus: FUSARIUM

SPECIES	SOURCE	SUBSTRATE	REACTION	REF.
roseum	VEB	$17\alpha,21$-dihydroxy-4-pregnene-3,20-dione	6β-OH	R-747
			15α-OH	R-747
sambucinum	CZAS	4-androstene-3,17-dione	6β-OH; 15α-OH	C-97
		4-pregnene-3,20-dione	—	C-97
sarcochroum	CZAS	4-androstene-3,17-dione	6β-OH; 15α-OH	C-97
		4-pregnene-3,20-dione	—	C-97
semitectum	CZAS	4-androstene-3,17-dione	6β-OH; 15α-OH	**C**-97
		4-pregnene-3,20-dione	—	C-97
	OIAB (F-42)	$17\alpha,21$-dihydroxy-4-pregnene-3,20-dione	oxidation - products not identified	K-462
solani	AMCY	3β-hydroxy-$16\alpha,17\alpha$-oxido-5-pregnen-20-one	11α-OH	P-746
	ATCC-12823	2α-fluoro-$17\alpha,21$-dihydroxy-4-pregnene-3,11,20-trione	Δ^1	H-401
	AY	4-pregnene-3,20-dione (use of spores)	Δ^1	S-835
		$17\alpha,21$-dihydroxy-4-pregnene-3,20-dione (use of spores)	Δ^1	S-835; V-1048
		$11\alpha,17\alpha,21$-trihydroxy-4-pregnene-3,20-dione (use of spores)	Δ^1	S-835; V-1048
	C	5α-androstane-3,17-dione	$\Delta^{1,4}$	V-1056; W-1095
		4-androstene-3,17-dione	Δ^1	V-1056; W-1095
		3β-hydroxy-5-androsten-17-one	$\Delta^5\rightarrow\Delta^4$; 3β-OH$\rightarrow$3-C=O; Δ^1	V-1056
		1,4-androstadiene-3,17-dione	—	V-1056
		3β-hydroxy-5α-pregnan-20-one acetate	$\Delta^{1,4}$; 3β-OAc$\rightarrow$3-C=O; 17β-Ac$\rightarrow$17-C=O	V-1056; W-1095
			17β-Ac$\rightarrow$17-C=O; 3β-OAc$\rightarrow$3-C=O	V-1056
		5α-pregnan-3,20-dione	$\Delta^{1,4}$; 17β-Ac$\rightarrow$17-C=O	V-1056; W-1095
			17β-Ac$\rightarrow$17-C=O	V-1056; W-1095

TABLE III

ansformations by Genus: FUSARIUM

SPECIES	SOURCE	SUBSTRATE	REACTION	REF.
solani	C	3β-hydroxy-5-pregnen-20-one	17β-Ac→17-C=O	V-1056; W-1095
			Δ^1; $\Delta^5\to\Delta^4$; 17β-Ac→17-C=O; 3β-OH→3-C=O	V-1056; W-1095
		4-pregnene-3,20-dione	Δ^1; 17β-Ac → 17-C=O	V-1056; W-1095
		$17\alpha,21$-dihydroxy-4-pregnene-3,20-dione	(weitere substanz)	V-1056
			Δ^1	V-1053
		21-hydroxy-4-pregnene-3,20-dione	Δ^1; 17β-(20-C =O-21-OH) → 17-C=O	V-1056; W-1095
		$17\alpha,21$-dihydroxy-4-pregnene-3,11,20-trione	(weitere substanz)	V-1056
			Δ^1	V-1053
		11β-hydroxy-3,20-diketo-4-pregnen-18-oic acid (18→11) lactone	17β-Ac→17-C=O	U-1044
			17β-Ac→17-C=O; 13β-COOH → 13β-H; Δ^1	U-1044
			17β-Ac→17-C=O; 13β-COOH → 13α-H; Δ^1	U-1044
			Δ^1; 17β-Ac → 17β-OH	U-1044
		11β-hydroxy-3,20-diketo-1,4-pregnadien-18-oic acid (18 → 11) lactone	17β-Ac → 17-C=O; Δ^1	U-1044
			17β-Ac→17β-OH	U-1044
	CZAS	17β-hydroxy-4-androsten-3-one acetate	Δ^1; 17β-OAc → 17-C=O	C-97
			Δ^1; 17β-OAc → 17a-oxa-17-C=O	C-97
		17β-hydroxy-4-androsten-3-one benzoate	—	C-97
		17β-hydroxy-4-androsten-3-one isobutyrate	—	C-97
*		17β-hydroxy-4-androsten-3-one formate	Δ^1; 17β-OFo→17a-oxa-17-C=O	C-97
		17β-hydroxy-4-androsten-3-one propionate	Δ^1; 17β-OPr → 17-C=O	C-97

TABLE III

Transformations by Genus: FUSARIUM

SPECIES	SOURCE	SUBSTRATE	REACTION	REF.
solani	CZAS	17β-hydroxy-4-androsten-3-one propionate	Δ^1; 17β-OPr→ 17a-oxa-17-C=O	C-97
		4-androstene-3,17-dione	6β-OH	C-97
			15α-OH	C-97
			Δ^1; 17-C=O → 17β-OH	C-97
			17-C=O →17a-oxa-17-C=O	C-97
			Δ^1; 17-C=O→17a-oxa-17-C=O	C-97
		17β-hydroxy-4-androsten-3-one	Δ^1	C-97
			17β-OH→17-C=O	C-97
			17β-OH→17a-oxa-17-C=O	C-97
			Δ^1; 17β-OH→ 17-C=O	C-97
			Δ^1; 17β-OH→17a-oxa-17-C=O	C-97
		4-pregnene-3,20-dione	Δ^1; 17β-Ac → 17-C=O	C-97
			Δ^1; 17β-Ac → 17β-OH	C-97
			17β-Ac→17-C=O	C-97
			Δ^1; 17β-Ac→17a-oxa-17-C=O	C-97
(var. aduncisporum)		4-androstene-3,17-dione	6β-OH; 15α-OH	C-97
		4-pregnene-3,20-dione	—	C-97
(var. argilaceum)		4-androstene-3,17-dione	6β-OH; 15α-OH	C-97
		4-pregnene-3,20-dione	—	C-97
(var. coeruleum)		4-androstene-3,17-dione	6β-OH; 15α-OH	C-97
		4-pregnene-3,20-dione	—	C-97
(var. redolens)		4-androstene-3,17-dione	6β-OH; 15α-OH	C-97
		4-pregnene-3,20-dione	—	C-97
	IFO	4-pregnene-3,20-dione	Δ^1	N-663; N-664
			Δ^1; 17β-Ac → 17β-OH	N-663; N-664

TABLE III

ansformations by Genus: FUSARIUM

SPECIES	SOURCE	SUBSTRATE	REACTION	REF.
solani	IFO	4-pregnene-3,20-dione	Δ^1; 17β-Ac → 17-C=O	N-663; N-664
			Δ^1; 17β-Ac→17a-oxa-17-C=O	N-663; N-664
	(K-101)	3β,21-dihydroxy-5-pregnen-20-one 21-acetate	Δ^5→Δ^4; Δ^1; 3β-OH→3-C=O; 17β-(20-C=O-21-OAc)→17a-oxa-17-C=O	K-462
		4-pregnene-3,20-dione	Δ^1; 17β-Ac→17a-oxa-17-C=O	K-462
		21-hydroxy-4-pregnene-3,20-dione	Δ^1; 17β-(20-C=O-21-OH) → 17a-oxa-17-C=O	K-462
		17α,21-dihydroxy-4-pregnene-3,20-dione	Δ^1	K-462
		11β,17α,21-trihydroxy-4-pregnene-3,20-dione	—	K-462
		17α,21-dihydroxy-4-pregnene-3,11,20-trione	Δ^1	K-462
	(K-102)	17α,21-dihydroxy-4-pregnene-3,20-dione	Δ^1	K-462
(var. eumartii)	OR	4-pregnene-3,20-dione	Δ^1; 17β-Ac→17a-oxa-17-C=O	S-949
			17β-Ac→17-C=O	S-949
			Δ^1; 17β-Ac → 17-C=O	S-949
		17α,20β,21-trihydroxy-4-pregnene-3,11-dione	Δ^1	S-949
		17α,21-dihydroxy-4-pregnene-3,11,20-trione	20-C=O→20β-OH	S-949
	UC	17α-hydroxy-4-pregnene-3,20-dione acetate	Δ^1	B-36
		3-ketobisnor-4-cholen-22-al	15α-OH	M-599
	VEB	4-pregnene-3,20-dione	15α-OH	K-452
species	EM (2070)	17α,21-dihydroxy-4-pregnene-3,20-dione	11α-OH	M-557
	EM (2083)	17α-hydroxy-16-methylene-4-pregnene-3,20-dione	11α-OH	B-68
		17α,21-dihydroxy-16-methylene-4-pregnene-3,20-dione	11α-OH	M-558

TABLE III

Transformations by Genus: FUSARIUM
FUSICLADIUM (Imperf. - Moniliales)

SPECIES	SOURCE	SUBSTRATE	REACTION	REF.
species	NRRL	Saponins (sapogenin glycosides)	hydrolysis of glycosides to aglycones (sapogenins)	K-478
	OIAB (F-8,32,34)	$17\alpha,21$-dihydroxy-4-pregnene-3,20-dione	oxidation - products not identified	K-462
	OIAB (36)	$17\alpha,21$-dihydroxy-4-pregnene-3,20-dione	—	K-462
	OR	$17\alpha,21$-dihydroxy-4-pregnene-3,11,20-trione (virtually anaerobic)	20-C=O → 20β-OH	S-951
			Δ^1; 20-C=O → 20β-OH	S-951
		$17\alpha,20\beta,21$-trihydroxy-4-pregnene-3,11-dione	Δ^1	S-951
		$17\alpha,21$-dihydroxy-1,4-pregnadiene-3,11,20-trione	20-C=O → 20β-OH	S-951
	Takeda	$3\beta,14\beta,16\beta$-trihydroxy-5β-20(22)-cardenolide	3β-OH→3-C=O	K-434
			12β-OH	K-434
sphaeriae	CZAS	4-androstene-3,17-dione	6β-OH; 15α-OH	C-97
		4-pregnene-3,20-dione	—	C-97
sporotrichella	CZAS	4-androstene-3,17-dione	6β-OH; 15α-OH	C-97
		4-pregnene-3,20-dione	—	C-97
(var. poae)		4-androstene-3,17-dione	6β-OH; 15α-OH	C-97
		4-pregnene-3,20-dione	—	C-97
sporotrichioides	OIAB (F-41)	$17\alpha,21$-dihydroxy-4-pregnene-3,20-dione	oxidation - products not identified	K-462
sulphureum	ATCC-7642	5α-pregnane-3,20-dione	15α-OH	M-599
udum	ATCC-10084	17β-hydroxy-4-androsten-3-one	15α-OH	M-599
vasinfectum	ATCC-7808	5β-pregnane-3,11,20-trione	15α-OH	M-599
FUSICLADUM				
diospiri	TNAES (B-1)	$17\alpha,21$-dihydroxy-4-pregnene-3,20-dione	—	S-849

TABLE III

ransformations by Genus:

FUSIDIUM	(Imperf. - Moniliales)
GANODERMA	(Basidio. - Agaricales)
GELASINOSPORA	(Asco. - Sphaeriales)
GEOTRICHUM	(Imperf. - Moniliales)
GIBBERELLA	(Asco. - Hypocreales)

SPECIES	SOURCE	SUBSTRATE	REACTION	REF.
species	Searle (M-61-1)	3β-hydroxy-5-androsten-17-one	7α-OH	D-175
			17-C=O → 17β-OH	D-175
GANODERMA				
applam (applanatum)	FRI	17α,21-dihydroxy-4-pregnene-3,20-dione	11α-OH	S-849
GELASINOSPORA				
tetraspora	ATCC-14512	17α-(2^1-carboxyethyl)-17β-hydroxy-4-androsten-3-one gamma lactone	7α-OH	T-1035
GEOTRICHUM				
lactis	FRI	17α,21-dihydroxy-4-pregnene-3,20-dione	—	S-849
GIBBERELLA				
baccata	C	4-androstene-3,17-dione	15α-OH	U-1043
		21-hydroxy-4-pregnene-3,20-dione	15α-OH	M-585; U-1043
		17α,21-dihydroxy-4-pregnene-3,20-dione	15α-OH	U-1043
	CBS	21-hydroxy-4-pregnene-3,20-dione	15-OH	M-599
		d,1-21-hydroxy-4-pregnene-3,20-dione	d,1→d-15α-OH + 1	W-1102
cyanea	CBS	24-ethyl-5,22-cholestadien-3β-ol	15-OH	M-599
fujikuroi	CBS	21-hydroxy-4-pregnene-3,20-dione	15α-OH	M-599
	FAKU	17α,21-dihydroxy-4-pregnene-3,20-dione	—	S-849
	IFO	3β,14β-dihydroxy-5β-20(22)-cardenolide	12β-OH	N-651
	Takeda	3β,14β,16β-trihydroxy-5β-20(22)-cardenolide	3β-OH→3-C=O	K-434
			3β-OH→3-C=O; 16β-OH → 16-C=O	K-434

TABLE III

Transformations by Genus: GIBBERELLA

SPECIES	SOURCE	SUBSTRATE	REACTION	REF.
saubinetti	C	17β-hydroxy-17α-methyl-4-androsten-3-one	6β-OH	U-1043
		4-androstene-3,17-dione	6β-OH	U-1043
			15α-OH	U-1043
		11β-hydroxy-4-androstene-3,17-dione	6β-OH	U-1043
			15α-OH	U-1043
			11-C=O (via 11β-OH)	U-1043
		21-hydroxy-4-pregnene-3,20-dione	6β-OH	U-1043
			15α-OH	U-1043
		17α,21-dihydroxy-4-pregnene-3,20-dione	6β-OH	U-1043
			15α-OH	U-1043
	CBS	4,9(11)-pregnadiene-3,20-dione	15α-OH	M-599
	FRI	17α,21-dihydroxy-4-pregnene-3,20-dione	6β-OH; 11α-OH	S-849
	S	4-pregnene-3,20-dione	15α-OH	S-849; S-858; S-859
		17α-hydroxy-4-pregnene-3,20-dione	6β-OH	S-849; S-858
			—	S-859
		21-hydroxy-4-pregnene-3,20-dione	15α-OH	S-849; S-858
		11β,21-dihydroxy-4-pregnene-3,20-dione	X-OH; 15α-OH	S-858
			15α-OH	S-849
		17α,21-dihydroxy-4-pregnene-3,20-dione	6β-OH	S-849; S-858
			15α-OH	S-858
			—	S-859
	TBRI	14β-hydroxy-3-keto-5β-20(22)-cardenolide	12β-OH	O-699
			3-C=O$\rightarrow$3α-OH	O-699
			3-C=O$\rightarrow$3α-OH; 12β-OH	O-699
		3β,14β-dihydroxy-5β-20(22)-cardenolide	12β-OH	O-699

TABLE III

ansformations by Genus: GIBBERELLA
GLIOCLADIUM   (Imperf. - Moniliales)

SPECIES	SOURCE	SUBSTRATE	REACTION	REF.
aubinetti	TBRI	$3\beta,14\beta,16\beta$-trihydroxy-5β-20(22)-cardenolide	12β-OH	O-699
		$3\beta,14\beta,16\beta$-trihydroxy-5β-20(22)-cardenolide 16-acetate	12β-OH	O-699
			16β-OAc $\rightarrow$ 16β-OH	O-699
			12β-OH; 16β-OAc $\rightarrow$ 16β-OH	O-699
eae	ATCC-10910	11α-hydroxy-4-pregnene-3,20-dione	15α-OH	M-599
		21-hydroxy-4-pregnene-3,20-dione	15α-OH	M-599
LIOCLADIUM				
atenulatum	ATCC-10523	5α-pregnane-3,11,20-trione	17β-Ac$\rightarrow$17-C=O	M-633
		5β-pregnane-3,20-dione	17β-Ac$\rightarrow$17-C=O	M-633
		5β-pregnane-3,6,20-trione	17β-Ac$\rightarrow$17-C=O	M-633
		3β-hydroxy-21-ethyl-5-pregnen-20-one	17β-Bu$\rightarrow$17-C=O	M-633
		4-pregnene-3,20-dione	17β-Ac$\rightarrow$17-C=O	M-633; P-726
			17β-Ac $\rightarrow$ 17-C=O; 6β-OH	M-633; P-726
		4-pregnene-3,20-dione 20-cyclo-ethyleneketal	6β-OH	F-251
		6β-hydroxy-4-pregnene-3,20-dione	17β-Ac$\rightarrow$17-C=O	M-633
		21-hydroxy-4-pregnene-3,20-dione	17β-(20-C=O-21-OH) $\rightarrow$ 17-C=O	M-633
			17β-(20-C=O-21-OH)$\rightarrow$ 17-C=O; 6β-OH	M-633
		21-methyl-4-pregnene-3,20-dione	17β-Pr$\rightarrow$17-C=O	M-633
		17α,21-dihydroxy-4-pregnene-3,20-dione	17α-OH-17β-(20-C=O-21-OH) $\rightarrow$17-C=O	M-633
			17α-OH-17β-(20-C=O-21-OH) $\rightarrow$17-C=O;6β-OH	M-633

TABLE III

Transformations by Genus: GLIOCLADIUM

SPECIES	SOURCE	SUBSTRATE	REACTION	REF.
catenulatum	ATCC-10523	11α,17α,21-trihydroxy-4-pregnene-3,20-dione	17α-OH-17β-(20-C=O-21-OH) → 17-C=O	M-633; M-637
		4-pregnene-3,11,20-trione	17β-Ac→17-C=O	M-633
		17α,21-dihydroxy-4-pregnene-3,11,20-trione	17α-OH-17β-(20-C=O-21-OH) → 17-C=O	M-633
		17α,21-dihydroxy-4-pregnene-3,11,20-trione 21-acetate	17α-OH-17β-(20-C=O-21-OAc)→ 17-C=O	M-633
		3-keto<u>bisnor</u>-4-cholen-22-al	20α-HC=O → 20β-HC=O	W-1068
			22-C=O →22-OH	W-1068
	NRRL	Sarsasapogenin	—	M-587
		Diosgenin	—	M-587
		4-dehydrotigogenone	—	M-587
deliquescens	CBS	21-hydroxy-4-pregnene-3,20-dione acetate	17β-(20-C=O-21-OAc)→17-C=O	M-633
			17β-(20-C=O-21-OAc)→ 17-C=O; 6β-OH	M-633
luteolum	CBS	21-hydroxy-4-pregnene-3,20-dione acetate	17β-(20-C=O-21-OAc)→17-C=O	M-633
			17β-(20-C=O-21-OAc)→17-C=O; 6β-OH	M-633
roseum	ATCC-10521	3β,17α,20α-trihydroxy-5α-pregnane	17α-OH-17β-(20α-OH-21-H) → 17-C=O	M-633
		21-hydroxy-4-pregnene-3,20-dione acetate	17β-(20-C=O-21-OAc)→17-C=O	M-633
			17β-(20-C=O-21-OAc)→17-C=O; 6β-OH	M-633
	FRI	17α,21-dihydroxy-4-pregnene-3,20-dione	—	S-859
	S	21-hydroxy-4-pregnene-3,20-dione	Δ[1]	S-857; S-859
		11β,21-dihydroxy-4-pregnene-3,20-dione	Δ[1]	S-857; S-859

TABLE III

ansformations by Genus: GLIOCLADIUM
GLOEOSPORIUM   (Imperf. - Moniliales)

SPECIES	SOURCE	SUBSTRATE	REACTION	REF.
roseum	S	$17\alpha,21$-dihydroxy-4-pregnene-3,20-dione	Δ^1	S-857; S-859
		$11\beta,17\alpha,21$-trihydroxy-4-preg-nene-3,20-dione	—	S-857; S-859
		$17\alpha,21$-dihydroxy-4-pregnene-3,11,20-trione	Δ^1	S-857; S-859
species	NG	5-cholesten-3β-ol (sole carbon source)	utilization	S-793c
		24β-methyl-5,7,22-cholesta-trien-3β-ol (sole carbon source)	utilization	S-793c
	NRRL	plant saponins	—	K-478
GLOEOSPORIUM				
cyclaminis	OR	3β-(N,N-dimethylamino)-5-conenine	3β-N-$(CH_3)_2 \rightarrow$ 3-C=O; $\Delta^5 \rightarrow \Delta^4$	D-148
foliicolum	KAG	$17\alpha,21$-dihydroxy-4-pregnene-3,20-dione	6β-OH	K-464
			11α-OH	K-464
kaki	FAKU (438)	$17\alpha,21$-dihydroxy-4-pregnene-3,20-dione	—	S-849
	KAG	$17\alpha,21$-dihydroxy-4-pregnene-3,20-dione	—	K-464
	S	4-pregnene-3,20-dione	11α-OH	S-849; S-855
			$6\beta,11\alpha$-diOH	S-849; S-855
		17α-hydroxy-4-pregnene-3,20-dione	11α-OH	S-849; S-855
		21-hydroxy-4-pregnene-3,20-dione	11α-OH	S-849; S-855
		$11\beta,21$-dihydroxy-4-pregnene-3,20-dione	—	S-849; S-855
		$17\alpha,21$-dihydroxy-4-pregnene-3,20-dione	11α-OH	S-849; S-855; S-859
	TNAES	$17\alpha,21$-dihydroxy-4-pregnene-3,20-dione	11α-OH	S-849
laeticola	S	$17\alpha,21$-dihydroxy-4-pregnene-3,20-dione	11α-OH	S-849

TABLE III

TAXONOMY

Transformations by Genus: GLOEOSPORIUM
GLOMERELLA   (Asco. - Sphaeriales)

SPECIES	SOURCE	SUBSTRATE	REACTION	REF.
laeticola	TNAES	$17\alpha,21$-dihydroxy-4-pregnene-3,20-dione	11α-OH	S-849
olivarum (taxonomically - perfect stage of Glomerella cingulata)	KAG	$17\alpha,21$-dihydroxy-4-pregnene-3,20-dione	Δ^1	K-464
			20-C=O → 20β-OH	K-464
	NI	4-pregnene-3,20-dione	Δ^1	K-465
		$17\alpha,21$-dihydroxy-4-pregnene-3,20-dione	Δ^1	K-465
		$11\beta,17\alpha,21$-trihydroxy-4-pregnene-3,20-dione	Δ^1	K-465
		$17\alpha,21$-dihydroxy-4-pregnene-3,11,20-trione	Δ^1	K-465
			20-C=O → 20β-OH	K-465
			Δ^1; 20-C=O → 20β-OH	K-465
	TNAES	$17\alpha,21$-dihydroxy-4-pregnene-3,20-dione	11α-OH	S-859
GLOMERELLA				
cingulata	ATCC-10529	$17\alpha,21$-dihydroxy-16α-methyl-5α-pregnane-3,20-dione	11α-OH	C-109
		$17\alpha,21$-dihydroxy-1,4-pregnadiene-3,20-dione	11α-OH	C-109
	ATCC-10530	$17\alpha,21$-dihydroxy-4-pregnene-3,20-dione	11α-OH	C-109
	ATCC-10531	$17\alpha,21$-dihydroxy-4-pregnene-3,20-dione	11α-OH	C-109
		16β-ethyl-17$\alpha,21$-dihydroxy-1,4-pregnadiene-3,20-dione	11α-OH	C-109
	ATCC-10532	$17\alpha,21$-dihydroxy-4-pregnene-3,20-dione	11α-OH	C-109
	ATCC-10533	$17\alpha,21$-dihydroxy-16α-methyl-1,4-pregnadiene-3,20-dione	11α-OH	C-109
*	ATCC-10534	16α-tert-butyl-17$\alpha,21$-dihydroxy-5α-pregnane-3,20-dione	11α-OH	C-109
*		16β-ethyl-17$\alpha,21$-dihydroxy-5α-pregnane-3,20-dione	11α-OH	C-109

TABLE III

nsformations by Genus: GLOMERELLA

SPECIES	SOURCE	SUBSTRATE	REACTION	REF.
ingulata	ATCC-10534	$17\alpha,21$-dihydroxy-16α-methyl-5α-pregnane-3,20-dione	11α-OH	C-109
*		$17\alpha,21$-dihydroxy-16β-methyl-5α-pregnane-3,20-dione	11α-OH	C-109
		$17\alpha,21$-dihydroxy-4-pregnene-3,20-dione	11α-OH	C-109
		$17\alpha,21$-dihydroxy-16α-methyl-4-pregnene-3,20-dione	11α-OH	C-109
		$17\alpha,21$-dihydroxy-16β-methyl-4-pregnene-3,20-dione	11α-OH	C-109
		$17\alpha,21$-dihydroxy-16β-methyl-4-pregnene-3,20-dione 21-acetate	11α-OH; 21-OAc → 21-OH	C-109
		D-nor-1,4-pregnadiene-3,20-dione	11α-OH	R-763
		$17\alpha,21$-dihydroxy-1,4-pregnadiene-3,20-dione	11α-OH	C-109
		$17\alpha,21$-dihydroxy-1,4-pregnadiene-3,20-dione 21-acetate	11α-OH; 21-OAc → 21-OH	C-109
		16β-ethyl-$17\alpha,21$-dihydroxy-1,4-pregnadiene-3,20-dione	11α-OH	C-109
		$17\alpha,21$-dihydroxy-16α-methyl-1,4-pregnadiene-3,20-dione	11α-OH	C-109
*		$17\alpha,21$-dihydroxy-16β-methyl-1,4-pregnadiene-3,20-dione	11α-OH	C-109
	ATCC-12097	3-hydroxy-1,3,5(10)-estratrien-17-one	7α-OH	L-494
			15α-OH	L-494
	FRI	$17\alpha,21$-dihydroxy-4-pregnene-3,20-dione	11α-OH	S-849
*	KA G	$17\alpha,21$-dihydroxy-4-pregnene-3,20-dione	6β-OH	K-464
*			11α-OH	K-464
	QM-1407	$17\alpha,21$-dihydroxy-16β-methyl-4-pregnene-3,20-dione 21-acetate	11α-OH; 21-OAc → 21-OH	C-109
luctigena	TNAES	$17\alpha,21$-dihydroxy-4-pregnene-3,20-dione	11α-OH	S-849

TABLE III

Transformations by Genus: GLOMERELLA

SPECIES	SOURCE	SUBSTRATE	REACTION	REF.
fusaroides	ATCC-9552	1,3,5(10)-estratrien-3,17β-diol	7α-OH	L-495; L-497
			15α-OH	L-495; L-497
			7α-OH; 17β-OH → 17-C=O	L-497
			15α-OH; 17β-OH → 17-C=O	L-497
		3-hydroxy-1,3,5(10)-estratrien-17-one	7α-OH	L-494; L-495; L-497
			15α-OH	L-494; L-495; L-497
			7α-OH; 17-C=O → 17β-OH	L-497
			15α-OH; 17-C=O → 17β-OH	L-494; L-497
*		17α,21-dihydroxy-16β-methyl-5α-pregnane-3,20-dione	11α-OH	C-109
*		17α,21-dihydroxy-4-pregnene-3,20-dione	11α-OH	C-109
glycines	ATCC-3422	1,3,5(10)-estratriene-3,17β-diol	7α-OH	L-495; L-497
			15α-OH	L-495; L-497
			7α-OH; 17β-OH → 17-C=O	L-497
		3-hydroxy-1,3,5(10)-estratrien-17-one	7α-OH	L-495; L-497
			15α-OH	L-495; L-497
			7α-OH; 17-C=O → 17β-OH	L-497
			15α-OH; 17-C=O → 17β-OH	L-497

TABLE III

ansformations by Genus: GLOMERELLA

SPECIES		SOURCE	SUBSTRATE	REACTION	REF.
lycines		ATCC-11871	3-hydroxy-1,3,5(10)-estratrien-17-one	7α-OH	L-494
				15α-OH	L-494
				15α-OH; 17-C=O → 17β-OH	L-494
		CBS	16α-tert-butyl-17α,21-dihydroxy-5α-pregnane-3,20-dione	11α-OH	C-109
osypii (gossypii)		IAM	17α,21-dihydroxy-4-pregnene-3,20-dione	—	S-849
agenarium	*	CBS	16β-ethyl-17α,21-dihydroxy-5α-pregnane-3,20-dione	11α-OH	C-109
	*		17α,21-dihydroxy-4-pregnene-3,20-dione	11α-OH	C-109
			17α,21-dihydroxy-1,4-pregnadiene-3,20-dione	11α-OH	C-109
			17α,21-dihydroxy-1,4-pregnadiene-3,20-dione 21-acetate	11α-OH; 21-OAc → 21-OH	C-109
			16α-tert-butyl-17α,21-dihydroxy-1,4-pregnadiene-3,20-dione	11α-OH	C-109
		S	4-pregnene-3,20-dione	11α-OH	S-849; S-855
				6β,11α-diOH	S-849; S-855
			17α-hydroxy-4-pregnene-3,20-dione	11α-OH	S-849; S-855
			21-hydroxy-4-pregnene-3,20-dione	11α-OH	S-849; S-855
			17α,21-dihydroxy-4-pregnene-3,20-dione	11α-OH	S-849; S-855
		TNAES	17α,21-dihydroxy-4-pregnene-3,20-dione	11α-OH	S-849
najor	*	CBS	17α,21-dihydroxy-4-pregnene-3,20-dione	11α-OH	C-109
	*		17α,21-dihydroxy-16β-methyl-1,4-pregnadiene-3,20-dione	11α-OH	C-109
nume	*	KAG	17α,21-dihydroxy-4-pregnene-3,20-dione	11α-OH	K-464

442

TABLE III

Transformations by Genus:

GIOMERELLA
GNOMONIA

TAXONOMY

(Asco. - Sphaeriales)

SPECIES	SOURCE	SUBSTRATE	REACTION	REF.
phacidiomorpha *	CBS	17α,21-dihydroxy-4-pregnene-3,20-dione	11α-OH	C-109
		16α-tert-butyl-17α,21-dihydroxy-1,4-pregnadiene-3,20-dione	11α-OH	C-109
rubicola *	CBS	17α,21-dihydroxy-4-pregnene-3,20-dione	11α-OH	C-109
GNOMONIA				
cingulata	SQ	4-pregnene-3,20-dione	2β-OH	L-496
		17α,21-dihydroxy-16α-methyl-4-pregnene-3,20-dione	2β-OH	L-496
errabunda	SQ	4-pregnene-3,20-dione	2β-OH	L-496
		17α,21-dihydroxy-16α-methyl-4-pregnene-3,20-dione	2β-OH	L-496
erythrostoma	SQ	4-pregnene-3,20-dione	2β-OH	L-496
		17α,21-dihydroxy-16α-methyl-4-pregnene-3,20-dione	2β-OH	L-496
fimicola	SQ	4-pregnene-3,20-dione	2β-OH	L-496
		17α,21-dihydroxy-16-methyl-4-pregnene-3,20-dione	2β-OH	L-496
fragariae	ATCC-11430	17β-hydroxy-A-nor-3-androsten-2-one	1β-OH	L-496
		17β-hydroxy-4-androsten-3-one	2β-OH	L-496
		17β-hydroxy-17α-methyl-4-androsten-3-one	2β-OH	L-496
		17α-oxa-D-homo-4-androstene-3,17-dione	2β-OH	L-496
		4-pregnene-3,20-dione	2β-OH; 16α-OH	L-499
		16α-hydroxy-4-pregnene-3,20-dione	2β-OH	L-496; L-499
		21-hydroxy-4-pregnene-3,20-dione	2β-OH	L-496
		9α-fluoro-11β-hydroxy-4-pregnene-3,20-dione	2β-OH	L-496
		17α,21-dihydroxy-4-pregnene-3,20-dione	2β-OH	L-496

TABLE III

ansformations by Genus:

GNOMONIA	
GRAPHIOLA	(Basidio. - Ustilaginales)
GUIGNARDIA	(Asco. - Sphaeriales)
GYMNOPILUS	(Basidio. - Agaricales)
HANSENULA	(Asco. - Endomycetales)

SPECIES	SOURCE	SUBSTRATE	REACTION	REF.
fragariae	ATCC-11430	6α-fluoro-17α,21-dihydroxy 4-pregnene-3,20-dione	2β-OH	L-496
		21-hydroxy-16α,17α-oxido-4-pregnene-3,20-dione	2β-OH	L-496
		17α,21-dihydroxy-16α-methyl-4-pregnene-3,20-dione	2β-OH	L-496
		6α-fluoro-16α,17α,21-trihydroxy-4-pregnene-3,20-dione 16,17-acetonide	2β-OH	L-496
GRAPHIOLA				
cylindrica	NI	4-pregnene-3,20-dione	Δ^1	K-465
		17α,21-dihydroxy-4-pregnene-3,20-dione	Δ^1	K-465
		11β,17α,21-trihydroxy-4-pregnene-3,20-dione	Δ^1	K-465
		17α,21-dihydroxy-4-pregnene-3,11,20-trione	Δ^1	K-465
GUIGNARDIA				
camelliae	FRI	17α,21-dihydroxy-4-pregnene-3,20-dione	11α-OH	S-849
GYMNOPILUS				
junenius	AL (C-142)	4-pregnene-3,20-dione	——	S-825
species	AL (2-6-69)	4-pregnene-3,20-dione	——	S-825
HANSENULA				
anomala	NRRL	Sarsasapogenin	——	M-587
		Diosgenin	——	M-587
		4-dehydrotigogenone	——	M-587

TABLE III

Transformations by Genus:

HAPLOSPORELLA	(Imperf. - Sphaeropsidales)
HEBELOMA	(Basidio. - Agaricales)
HELICOBASIDIUM	(Basidio. - Tremellales)
HELICOCERAS	(Imperf. - Moniliales)
HELICOSTYLUM	(Phyco. - Mucorales)

SPECIES	SOURCE	SUBSTRATE	REACTION	REF.
HAPLOSPORELLA				
species	Searle (M-1086)	4-androstene-3,17-dione	1β-OH	D-165
			6β-OH	D-165
			7β-OH	D-165
HEBELOMA				
sinapizans	WURB (M-84)	4-pregnene-3,20-dione	reaction not identified	R-778
HELICOBASIDIUM				
mompa	FAKU	17α,21-dihydroxy-4-pregnene-3,20-dione	——	S-849
	NARI	17α,21-dihydroxy-4-pregnene-3,20-dione	——	S-849
HELICOCERAS				
oryzae	FRI	17α,21-dihydroxy-4-pregnene-3,20-dione	——	S-849
HELICOSTYLUM				
piriforme	ATCC 8686	21-hydroxy-4-pregnene-3,20-dione	8-OH(later shown to be 9α-OH)	M-640
		17α,21-dihydroxy-4,14-pregnadiene-3,20-dione	$\Delta^{14} \rightarrow 14\alpha$, 15α-oxide	B-66
	ATCC 8992	11β,17α-dihydroxy-5α-pregnane-3,20-dione	9α-OH; 11β-OH → 11-C=O	H-342
		11β,21-dihydroxy-5α-pregnane-3,20-dione	9α-OH; 11β-OH → 11-C=O	H-342
		3α,11β,21-trihydroxy-5α-pregnane-3,20-dione	9α-OH; 11β-OH → 11-C=O	H-342
		11β,17α,21-trihydroxy-5α-pregnane-3,20-dione	9α-OH; 11β-OH → 11-C=O	H-342
		3α,11β,17α-trihydroxy-5β-pregnan-20-one	9α-OH; 11β-OH → 11-C=O	H-342

TABLE III

Transformations by Genus: HELICOSTYLUM

SPECIES	SOURCE	SUBSTRATE	REACTION	REF.
piriforme	ATCC-8992	$3\beta,11\beta,17\alpha$-trihydroxy-5β-pregnan-20-one	9α-OH; 11β-OH $\rightarrow$11-C=O	H-342
		11β-hydroxy-5β-pregnane-3,20-dione	9α-OH; 11β-OH $\rightarrow$11-C=O	H-342
		19-nor-4-pregnene-3,20-dione	14α-OH	B-73
			oxidation - products not identified	M-636
		4-pregnene-3,20-dione	14α-OH	E-204; M-614
			14-OH	M-636
		11α-hydroxy-4-pregnene-3,20-dione	9α-OH	H-342
		21-hydroxy-4-pregnene-3,20-dione	8-OH (later shown to be 9α-OH)	M-640
		21-hydroxy-4-pregnene-3,20-dione acetate	14α-OH; 21-OAc $\rightarrow$21-OH	E-204
			9α-OH; 21-OAc $\rightarrow$21-OH	E-204
		$11\beta,17\alpha$-dihydroxy-4-pregnene-3,20-dione	9α-OH; 11β-OH $\rightarrow$11-C=O	H-342
		$11\beta,21$-dihydroxy-4-pregnene-3,20-dione 21-acetate	9α-OH; 11β-OH $\rightarrow$11-C=O; 21-OAc$\rightarrow$21-OH	H-342
		$17\alpha,21$-dihydroxy-4-pregnene-3,20-dione	6β-OH	E-204; M-601; M-636
			9α-OH	E-204; M-601; M-609; M-632; M-636
			11α-OH	E-204; M-601; M-636
			14α-OH	E-204; M-601; M-617; M-636
		$11\beta,17\alpha,21$-trihydroxy-4-pregnene-3,20-dione 21-acetate	9α-OH; 11β-OH $\rightarrow$11-C=O; 21-OAc$\rightarrow$21-OH	H-342

TABLE III

Transformations by Genus: HELICOSTYLUM

SPECIES	SOURCE	SUBSTRATE	REACTION	REF.
piriforme	ATCC-8992	9α-fluoro-$11\beta,15\beta,17\alpha,21$-tetra-hydroxy-4-pregnene-3,20-dione	14α-OH	N-669
		9α-fluoro-$11\beta,17\alpha,21$-trihydroxy-1,4-pregnadiene-3,20-dione	14α-OH	N-669
		9α-fluoro-$17\alpha,21$-dihydroxy-1,4-pregnadiene-3,11,20-trione	14α-OH	N-669
		$11\alpha,21$-dihydroxy-4,17(20)-pregnadien-3-one	9α-OH; 11α-OH $\rightarrow 11$-C=O	H-342
		$11\beta,21$-dihydroxy-4,17(20)-pregnadien-3-one	9α-OH; 11β-OH $\rightarrow 11$-C=O	H-342; H-344
		$17\alpha,21$-dihydroxy-4,14-pregnadiene-3,20-dione	$\Delta^{14} \rightarrow 14\alpha,15\alpha$-oxide	B-66; S-865
		$11\beta,17\alpha,21$-trihydroxy-1,4,6-pregnatriene-3,20-dione	9α-OH	G-301; G-302
			14α-OH	G-301; G-302
		$17\alpha,21$-dihydroxy-1,4,6-pregnatriene-3,11,20-trione	9α-OH	G-301; G-302
			14α-OH	G-301; G-302
		Diosgenin	$7\beta,11\alpha$-diOH	H-368
			$7\beta,11\alpha$-diOH; 7β-OH$\rightarrow 7$-C=O	H-368; H-369
		Solasodine	7β-OH	S-791
			9α-OH	S-791
			11α-OH	S-791
		Tomatidine	7α-OH	S-791
			9α-OH	S-791
			$7\alpha,11\alpha$-diOH	S-791
	IFO	$3\beta,14\beta$-dihydroxy-5β-20(22)-cardenolide	12β-OH	N-651
			16β-OH	N-651
species	NRRL	Saponins (sapogenin glycosides)	—	K-478

TABLE III

TAXONOMY

ransformations by Genus: HELMINTHOSPORIUM   (Imperf. - Moniliales)

SPECIES	SOURCE	SUBSTRATE	REACTION	REF.
avenae	FRI	$17\alpha,21$-dihydroxy-4-pregnene-3,20-dione	—	S-849
	NI	$17\alpha,21$-dihydroxy-4-pregnene-3,20-dione	—	S-849
	NIHJ	$17\alpha,21$-dihydroxy-4-pregnene-3,20-dione	—	S-849
	OIAB (H-9)	$17\alpha,21$-dihydroxy-4-pregnene-3,20-dione	14α-OH	K-460
brizae	NI	$17\alpha,21$-dihydroxy-4-pregnene-3,20-dione	—	S-849
	OIAB (H-10)	$17\alpha,21$-dihydroxy-4-pregnene-3,20-dione	oxidation - products not identified	K-460
buchloes	CBS	17β-hydroxy-4-estren-3-one	10β-OH	D-153
			14α-OH	D-153
coices (coicis)	NI	$17\alpha,21$-dihydroxy-4-pregnene-3,20-dione	6β-OH; 11α-OH	S-849
gramineum	NI	4-pregnene-3,20-dione	possible side chain degradation	K-465
		$17\alpha,21$-dihydroxy-4-pregnene-3,20-dione	—	S-849
*			Δ^1	K-460; K-465
		$11\beta,17\alpha,21$-trihydroxy-4-pregnene-3,20-dione	—	K-465
		$17\alpha,21$-dihydroxy-4-pregnene-3,11,20-trione	Δ^1	K-465
irregulare	NARI	$17\alpha,21$-dihydroxy-4-pregnene-3,20-dione	—	S-849
kusanoi	CBS	17β-hydroxy-4-estren-3-one	6β-OH	D-153
	NI	$17\alpha,21$-dihydroxy-4-pregnene-3,20-dione	6β-OH	S-849
	OIAB	$17\alpha,21$-dihydroxy-4-pregnene-3,20-dione	oxidation - products not identified	K-460
leersii	NI	$17\alpha,21$-dihydroxy-4-pregnene-3,20-dione	6β-OH; 11α-OH	S-849
	OIAB (H-20)	$17\alpha,21$-dihydroxy-4-pregnene-3,20-dione	6β-OH	K-460

TABLE III

Transformations by Genus: HELMINTHOSPORIUM

SPECIES	SOURCE	SUBSTRATE	REACTION	REF.
lepochloae	NI	$17\alpha,21$-dihydroxy-4-pregnene-3,20-dione	11α-OH	S-849
	OIAB (H-5)	$17\alpha,21$-dihydroxy-4-pregnene-3,20-dione	oxidation - products not identified	K-460
	OIAB (H-6)	$17\alpha,21$-dihydroxy-4-pregnene-3,20-dione	oxidation - products not identified	K-460
	OIAB (H-19)	$17\alpha,21$-dihydroxy-4-pregnene-3,20-dione	11α-OH	K-460
maydis	NI	$17\alpha,21$-dihydroxy-4-pregnene-3,20-dione	—	S-849
	OIAB (H-18)	$17\alpha,21$-dihydroxy-4-pregnene-3,20-dione	oxidation - products not identified	K-460
nodulosum	S	$17\alpha,21$-dihydroxy-4-pregnene-3,20-dione	—	S-849
oryzae	NI	$17\alpha,21$-dihydroxy-4-pregnene-3,20-dione	—	S-849
	OIAB (H-2)	$17\alpha,21$-dihydroxy-4-pregnene-3,20-dione	6β-OH	K-460
panici-meliacei (panici-miliacei)	OIAB (H-3)	$17\alpha,21$-dihydroxy-4-pregnene-3,20-dione	—	K-460
sativum	IAM	4-pregnene-3,20-dione	15α-OH	T-1022
			15β-OH	T-1022
			$7\alpha,15\beta$-diOH	T-1022
			$7\beta,15\beta$-diOH	T-1022
			$14\alpha,15\beta$-diOH	T-1022
		$17\alpha,21$-dihydroxy-4-pregnene-3,20-dione	15α-OH	T-1024
	NIHJ (F-1-40)	$17\alpha,21$-dihydroxy-4-pregnene-3,20-dione	—	S-849
	OIAB (H-15)	$17\alpha,21$-dihydroxy-4-pregnene-3,20-dione	oxidation - products not identified	K-460

TABLE III

Transformations by Genus: HELMINTHOSPORIUM

SPECIES	SOURCE	SUBSTRATE	REACTION	REF.
setariae	NI	$17\alpha,21$-dihydroxy-4-pregnene-3,20-dione	11α-OH	S-849
	OIAB (H-8)	$17\alpha,21$-dihydroxy-4-pregnene-3,20-dione	11α-OH	K-460
	NIHJ (B-15)	$17\alpha,21$-dihydroxy-4-pregnene-3,20-dione	—	S-849
sigmoideum	NARI	$17\alpha,21$-dihydroxy-4-pregnene-3,20-dione	—	S-849
	OIAB (H-37)	$17\alpha,21$-dihydroxy-4-pregnene-3,20-dione	11α-OH	K-460
	OIAB (H-39)	$17\alpha,21$-dihydroxy-4-pregnene-3,20-dione	11α-OH	K-460
	OIAB (H-40)	$17\alpha,21$-dihydroxy-4-pregnene-3,20-dione	6β-OH; 11α-OH	K-460
			11β-OH	K-460
	OIAB (H-42)	$17\alpha,21$-dihydroxy-4-pregnene-3,20-dione	6β-OH; 11α-OH	K-460
species	MCC (I-39)	4-pregnene-3,20-dione	7α-OH	M-570
		21-hydroxy-4-pregnene-3,20-dione	7α-OH	M-570
	NIHJ (B-8)	$17\alpha,21$-dihydroxy-4-pregnene-3,20-dione	—	S-849
	NIHJ (B-36)	$17\alpha,21$-dihydroxy-4-pregnene-3,20-dione	Δ^1	S-849
	NIHJ (B-37)	$17\alpha,21$-dihydroxy-4-pregnene-3,20-dione	Δ^1	S-849
	NIHJ (B-66)	$17\alpha,21$-dihydroxy-4-pregnene-3,20-dione	11α-OH	S-849
	NIHJ (B-69)	$17\alpha,21$-dihydroxy-4-pregnene-3,20-dione	—	S-849
	NIHJ (B-70)	$17\alpha,21$-dihydroxy-4-pregnene-3,20-dione	—	S-849
	NIHJ (B-74)	$17\alpha,21$-dihydroxy-4-pregnene-3,20-dione	11α-OH	S-849
	OIAB (H-12)	$17\alpha,21$-dihydroxy-4-pregnene-3,20-dione	—	K-460
	OIAB (H-13)	$17\alpha,21$-dihydroxy-4-pregnene-3,20-dione	—	K-460

TABLE III

Transformations by Genus: HELMINTHOSPORIUM

SPECIES	SOURCE	SUBSTRATE	REACTION	REF.
species	OIAB (H-16)	17α,21-dihydroxy-4-pregnene-3,20-dione	—	K-460
	OIAB (H-27)	17α,21-dihydroxy-4-pregnene-3,20-dione	6β,11α-diOH	K-460
	S	17α,21-dihydroxy-4-pregnene-3,20-dione	Δ^{1}	S-857
teres	OIAB (H-43)	17α,21-dihydroxy-4-pregnene-3,20-dione	6β-OH; 14α-OH	K-460
tritici-vulgaris	NI	17α,21-dihydroxy-4-pregnene-3,20-dione	6β-OH	S-849
	OIAB(H-25)	17α,21-dihydroxy-4-pregnene-3,20-dione	2β-OH	K-460
			$\Delta^{4} \rightarrow 5\beta$-H	K-460
turcicum	NIHJ	17α,21-dihydroxy-4-pregnene-3,20-dione	—	S-849
	NIHJ (B-34)	17α,21-dihydroxy-4-pregnene-3,20-dione	—	S-849
	NIHJ (B-51)	17α,21-dihydroxy-4-pregnene-3,20-dione	—	S-849
	NIHJ (F-1-73)	17α,21-dihydroxy-4-pregnene-3,20-dione	—	S-849
	OIAB (H-11)	17α,21-dihydroxy-4-pregnene-3,20-dione	—	K-460
	S (4068)	17α,21-dihydroxy-4-pregnene-3,20-dione	—	S-849
	S	21-hydroxy-4-pregnene-3,20-dione	Δ^{1}	S-849; S-857
		11β,21-dihydroxy-4-pregnene-3,20-dione	Δ^{1}	S-849; S-857
		17α,21-dihydroxy-4-pregnene-3,20-dione	Δ^{1}	S-849; S-857
		11β,17α,21-trihydroxy-4-pregnene-3,20-dione	—	S-849; S-857
		17α,21-dihydroxy-4-pregnene-3,11,20-trione	Δ^{1}	S-849; S-857
velurinum (velutinum)	OIAB (H-30)	17α,21-dihydroxy-4-pregnene-3,20-dione	14α-OH	K-460
zonatum	NARI	17α,21-dihydroxy-4-pregnene-3,20-dione	—	S-849
	NIHJ	17α,21-dihydroxy-4-pregnene-3,20-dione	—	S-849

TABLE III

Transformations by Genus:

	HELMINTHOSPORIUM	TAXONOMY
	HEMISPORA	(Imperf. - Moniliales)
	HENDERSONIA	(Imperf. - Sphaeropsidales)

SPECIES	SOURCE	SUBSTRATE	REACTION	REF.
zizaniae	NI	4-pregnene-3,20-dione	oxidation - products not identified	K-465
		17α,21-dihydroxy-4-pregnene-3,20-dione	Δ^1	K-465
		11β,17α,21-trihydroxy-4-pregnene-3,20-dione	—	K-465
		17α,21-dihydroxy-4-pregnene-3,11,20-trione	Δ^1	K-465
	OIAB (H-4)	17α,21-dihydroxy-4-pregnene-3,20-dione	Δ^1	K-460
HEMISPORA				
rogosa	FRI	17α,21-dihydroxy-4-pregnene-3,20-dione	—	S-849
HENDERSONIA				
aberrans	MCC	11α-hydroxy-4-pregnene-3,20-dione	21-OH	D-183
cicola	ATCC-2585	4-pregnene-3,20-dione	21-OH	M-566
(in mixed culture with Aspergillus niger [11α-OH])			21-OH	M-566
(in mixed culture with Trichoderma album [17α-OH])			21-OH	M-566
	NRRL-2595	11β-hydroxy-4-pregnene-3,20-dione	21-OH	D-183
erpotricha	NRRL-2594	11β,17α-dihydroxy-4-pregnene-3,20-dione	21-OH	D-183
hragmitis	MCC	17α-hydroxy-4-pregnene-3,20-dione	21-OH	D-183
ubi	NRRL-2593	4-pregnene-3,20-dione	21-OH	D-183; M-566
(in mixed culture with Trichoderma nigrovirens [17α-OH])			21-OH	M-566
(in mixed culture with Stigmina platani [11β-OH])			21-OH	M-566

TABLE III   <u>TAXONOMY</u>

Transformations by Genus:

HISTOPLASMA	(Asco. - Endomycetales)
HORMODENDRUM	(Imperf. - Moniliales)
HUMICOLA	(Imperf. - Moniliales)
HURODAKE	(Taxonomy Unclear)
HYALOPUS	(Imperf. - Moniliales)
HYDROGENOMONAS	(Schizo. - Pseudomonadales)

SPECIES	SOURCE	SUBSTRATE	REACTION	REF.
HISTOPLASMA				
capsulatum	FRI	17α,21-dihydroxy-4-pregnene-3,20-dione	—	S-849
HORMODENDRUM				
olivaceum	ATCC-13596	17α,21-dihydroxy-4-pregnene-3,20-dione	15α-OH	<u>A-9</u>; <u>B-58</u>
pedrosoi	FRI	17α,21-dihydroxy-4-pregnene-3,20-dione	—	S-849
viride	LED(Z-10)	17α,21-dihydroxy-4-pregnene-3,20-dione	15α-OH	B-56
HUMICOLA				
grisea (grisae)	FRI	17α,21-dihydroxy-4-pregnene-3,20-dione	—	S-849
HURODAKE				
(Taxonomy Unclear)	S (15)	17α,21-dihydroxy-4-pregnene-3,20-dione	6β-OH; 11α-OH	S-849
HYALOPUS				
nopporoensis	FRI	17α,21-dihydroxy-4-pregnene-3,20-dione	6β-OH; 11α-OH	S-849
HYDROGENOMONAS				
facilis	ATCC-11228	4-androstene-3,17-dione (autotrophic)	17-C=O → 17β-OH	<u>F-228</u>
		17α,21-dihydroxy-4-pregnene-3,20-dione (autotrophic and heterotrophic)	20-C=O → 20β-OH	<u>F-228</u>
		11β,17α,21-trihydroxy-4-pregnene-3,20-dione	20-C=O → 20β-OH	<u>F-228</u>
		17α,21-dihydroxy-4-pregnene-3,11,20-trione (heterotrophic)	20-C=O → 20β-OH	<u>F-228</u>

TABLE III

ansformations by Genus:

HYGROPHORUS	(Basidio. - Agaricales)
HYPHOLOMA	(Basidio. - Agaricales)
HYPOCHNUS	(Basidio. - Agaricales)
HYPOMYCES	(Asco. - Hypocreales)

SPECIES	SOURCE	SUBSTRATE	REACTION	REF.
HYGROPHORUS				
conicus	AL(C-219)	4-pregnene-3,20-dione	$6\beta,11\alpha$-diOH	S-825
HYPHOLOMA				
species	NRRL-2471	4-pregnene-3,20-dione	15α-OH	D-191; M-568
HYPOCHNUS				
centrifugum	S	$17\alpha,21$-dihydroxy-4-pregnene-3,20-dione	11α-OH	S-849
centrifugus	TNAES	$17\alpha,21$-dihydroxy-4-pregnene-3,20-dione	—	S-849
sasakii	CBS	3ξ-hydroxy-4-androsten-17-one	19-OH	S-869
		17α-ethyl-17β-hydroxy-4-androsten-3-one	19-OH	S-869
		17β-hydroxy-17α-propyl-4-androsten-3-one	19-OH	S-869
		$17\alpha,21$-dihydroxy-4-pregnene-3,20-dione	19-OH	S-869
		$11\beta,17\alpha,21$-trihydroxy-4-pregnene-3,20-dione	19-OH	S-870
	FAHU	$17\alpha,21$-dihydroxy-4-pregnene-3,20-dione	—	S-849
	IAM	$17\alpha,21$-dihydroxy-4-pregnene-3,20-dione	11α-OH	S-849
HYPOMYCES				
aurantius	CBS	17β-hydroxy-4-estren-3-one	16α-OH	D-149
haematococcus (var. cancri - Ref. M-574)	OR	3β-(N,N-dimethylamino)-5-conenine	3β-N(CH$_3$)$_2$ → 3-C=O; $\Delta^5 \rightarrow \Delta^4$	D-148
	UC	5α-pregnane-3,11,20-trione	$\Delta^{1,4}$; 17β-Ac→17β-OH	M-574
		4-pregnene-3,20-dione	Δ^1	F-251

TABLE III

Transformations by Genus:

HYPOMYCES
INTESTINAL MICROORGANISMS -   (Schizo. -   )
(Genera not Identified)
IRPEX   (Basidio. - Agaricales)
ISARIA   (Imperf. - Moniliales)

SPECIES	SOURCE	SUBSTRATE	REACTION	REF.
solani	NG	17β-hydroxy-4-androsten-3-one	Δ^1; 17β-OH $\rightarrow$ 17a-oxa-17-C=O	L-525
		17β-hydroxy-17α-methyl-4-androsten-3-one	Δ^1	L-525
		17α,21-dihydroxy-4-pregnene-3,20-dione	Δ^1	L-525
		17α,21-dihydroxy-4-pregnene-3,11,20-trione	Δ^1	L-525
INTESTINAL MICROORGANISMS				
unidentified	human feces	5-cholesten-3β-ol (anaerobic)	$\Delta^5 \rightarrow 5\beta$-H	S-914
	rat feces	5-cholesten-3β-ol	$\Delta^5 \rightarrow 5\beta$-H	C-133
		7-cholestenol	—	C-133
		5,7-cholestadien-3β-ol	$\Delta^5 \rightarrow 5\beta$-H	C-133
		5-stigmasten-3β-ol	$\Delta^5 \rightarrow 5\beta$-H	C-133
IRPEX				
consors	IAM	17α,21-dihydroxy-4-pregnene-3,20-dione	—	S-849
lacteus	FRI	17α,21-dihydroxy-4-pregnene-3,20-dione	11α-OH	S-849
	IAM	17α,21-dihydroxy-4-pregnene-3,20-dione	6β-OH; 11α-OH	S-849
ISARIA				
farinosa	FRI	17α,21-dihydroxy-4-pregnene-3,20-dione	6β-OH; 11α-OH; 11β-OH	S-849

TABLE III

TAXONOMY

nsformations by Genus:

KABATIELLA	(Imperf. - Moniliales)
KAIGARADAKE	(Taxonomy Unclear)
KAWARADAKE	(Taxonomy Unclear)
KLOECKERA	(Imperf. - Moniliales)
LACTOBACILLUS	(Schizo. - Eubacteriales)

SPECIES	SOURCE	SUBSTRATE	REACTION	REF.
ABATIELLA				
noradendri	ATCC-11129	4-pregnene-3,20-dione	21-OH	L-498
		12α-methyl-4-pregnene-3,11,20-trione	21-OH	L-498
		4,16-pregnadiene-3,20-dione	21-OH	L-498
AIGARADAKE				
xonomy unclear)	S(27)	17α,21-dihydroxy-4-pregnene-3,20-dione	6β-OH; 11α-OH	S-849
AWARADAKE				
xonomy unclear)	S(16)	17α,21-dihydroxy-4-pregnene-3,20-dione	6β-OH	S-849
LOECKERA				
iculata	NRRL	Sarsasapogenin	—	M-587
		Diosgenin	—	M-587
		4-dehydrotigogenone	—	M-587
CTARIUS				
sorrheus	AL(F-31)	4-pregnene-3,20-dione	oxidation - products not identified	S-825
lemus	AL(SS-15)	4-pregnene-3,20-dione	oxidation - products not identified	S-825
CTOBACILLUS				
vis	IFO(3345)	11β,17α,21-trihydroxy-4-pregnene-3,20-dione	—	I-428
(in mixed culture with Mycococcus sp. Δ¹)			Δ^1	I-428

TABLE III

Transformations by Genus: LACTOBACILLUS
                            LENITZITES   (Taxonomy Unclear)
                            LENTINUS   (Basidio. - Agaricales)
                            LENTODIUM   (Basidio. - Agaricales)
                            LENZITES   (Basidio. - Agaricales)

SPECIES	SOURCE	SUBSTRATE	REACTION	REF.
buchneri	IFO(3230)	$11\beta,17\alpha,21$-trihydroxy-4-pregnene-3,20-dione	—	I-428
(in mixed culture with Mycococcus sp. Δ^1)			Δ^1	I-428
bulgaricus	IFO(3492)	$11\beta,17\alpha,21$-trihydroxy-4-pregnene-3,20-dione	—	I-428
(in mixed culture with Mycococcus sp. Δ^1)			—	I-428
LENITZITES				
betulina	IAM	$17\alpha,21$-dihydroxy-4-pregnene-3,20-dione	6β-OH; 11α-OH	S-849
sepiaria	IAM	$17\alpha,21$-dihydroxy-4-pregnene-3,20-dione	—	S-849
styracina	IAM	$17\alpha,21$-dihydroxy-4-pregnene-3,20-dione	—	S-849
tennis	IAM	$17\alpha,21$-dihydroxy-4-pregnene-3,20-dione	—	S-849
LENTINUS				
vulpinus	AL (C-137)	4-pregnene-3,20-dione	oxidation - products not identified	S-825
LENTODIUM				
squamosum	AL (G-17)	4-pregnene-3,20-dione	oxidation - products not identified	S-825
LENZITES				
abietina	C	d,l-21-hydroxy-4-pregnene-3,20-dione	d,l→d-15β-OH +1	W-1102
		21-hydroxy-4-pregnene-3,20-dione	6β-OH	M-585
			15β-OH	M-585

TABLE III

ansformations by Genus:

	LENZITES	
	LEPIOTA	(Basidio. - Agaricales)
	LEPTOSPHAERIA	(Asco. - Sphaeriales)
	LEUCOPAXILLUS	(Basidio. - Agaricales)

SPECIES	SOURCE	SUBSTRATE	REACTION	REF.
ebulina	S	4-pregnene-3,20-dione	—	S-859
(betulina)		17α-hydroxy-4-pregnene-3,20-dione	—	S-859
		17α,21-dihydroxy-4-pregnene-3,20-dione	6β-OH	S-859
tyracina	FRI	17α,21-dihydroxy-4-pregnene-3,20-dione	—	S-849
EPIOTA				
nolybdites	AL (G-19)	4-pregnene-3,20-dione	oxidation - products not identified	S-825
aucina	AL (G-59)	4-pregnene-3,20-dione	oxidation - products not identified	S-825
	NRRL-2368	4-pregnene-3,20-dione	oxidation - products not identified	R-778
rocera	FRI	17α,21-dihydroxy-4-pregnene-3,20-dione	oxidation - products not identified	S-849
	WURB (M-44)	4-pregnene-3,20-dione	oxidation - products not identified	R-778
achodes	WURB (M-76)	4-pregnene-3,20-dione	oxidation - products not identified	R-778
EPTOSPHAERIA				
aculans	C	4-pregnene-3,20-dione	17α-OH	W-1107
(in mixed culture with Curvularia lunata -[11β-OH])		21-hydroxy-4-pregnene-3,20-dione	17α-OH	W-1106
(in mixed culture with Curvularia lunata -[11β-OH - 11β-OH→11-C=O])		21-hydroxy-1,4-pregnadiene-3,20-dione	17α-OH	W-1106
EUCOPAXILLUS				
aradoxus	AL (F-55)	4-pregnene-3,20-dione	6β,11α-diOH	S-825

Transformations by Genus:

TABLE III

			TAXONOMY
LICHTHEIMIA			(Phyco. - Mucorales)
LOPHOTRICHUS			(Asco. - Sphaeriales)
LYCOPERDON			(Basidio. - Lycoperdales)
LYOPHYLLUM			(Basidio. - Agaricales)
MACROSPORIUM			(Imperf. - Moniliales)
MARASMIUS			(Basidio. - Agaricales)
MARGARINOMYCES			(Imperf. - Moniliales)

SPECIES	SOURCE	SUBSTRATE	REACTION	REF.
LICHTHEIMIA				
corymbifera	SSSR	$17\alpha,21$-dihydroxy-4-pregnene-3,20-dione	11α-OH; 11β-OH	E-224
ramosa	SSSR	$17\alpha,21$-dihydroxy-4-pregnene-3,20-dione	11α-OH; 11β-OH	E-224
LOPHOTRICHUS				
martini (used in mixed culture)	C	not given	17α-OH	W-1106 W-1107
LYCOPERDON				
umbrinum	NRRL-2372	4-pregnene-3,20-dione	oxidation - products not identified	R-778
LYOPHYLLUM				
aggregatum	AL(SS-60)	4-pregnene-3,20-dione	oxidation - products not identified	S-825
MACROSPORIUM				
bataticola	FRI	$17\alpha,21$-dihydroxy-4-pregnene-3,20-dione	2β-OH	S-849
MARASMIUS				
siccus	AL(SS-21)	4-pregnene-3,20-dione	oxidation - products not identified	S-825
MARGARINOMYCES				
species	FRI	$17\alpha,21$-dihydroxy-4-pregnene-3,20-dione	—	S-849

TABLE III

TAXONOMY

Transformations by Genus:

	TAXONOMY
MEDICAGO	(Spermatophyta - Rosales)
MELANCONIALES	(Imperf. - Melanconiales)
MELANOSPORA	(Asco. - Hypocreales)
METARRHIZIUM	(Imperf. - Moniliales)
MICROCOCCUS	(Schizo. - Eubacteriales)

SPECIES	SOURCE	SUBSTRATE	REACTION	REF.
MEDICAGO (Plant-Alfalfa)				
sativa	—	$17\alpha,21$-dihydroxy-1,4-pregna-diene-3,11,20-trione	20-C=O $\rightarrow$ 20α-OH	L-526
TAXONOMIC ORDER MELANCONIALES				
(genus not given)	Lepetit (L-952)	$17\alpha,21$-dihydroxy-1,4-pregna-diene-3,20-dione	11α-OH	T-990
MELANOSPORA				
parasitica (used in mixed culture)	C	not given	17α-OH	W-1106; W-1107
METARRHIZIUM				
anisopliae	NI	6β-hydroxy-$3\alpha,5\alpha$-cyclopregnan-20-one	11α-OH	K-483
		3β-hydroxy-5-pregnen-20-one	11α-OH	K-483
species	PD (M-2313)	$16\alpha,17\alpha,21$-[3,1,1-2-pyrazolino]-4-pregnene-3,20-dione	11α-OH	M-593
MICROCOCCUS				
candidus	IAM	4-pregnene-3,20-dione	oxidation	I-414; I-415
		$17\alpha,21$-dihydroxy-4-pregnene-3,20-dione	—	I-414; I-415
citreus	IFO (3332)	$11\beta,17\alpha,21$-trihydroxy-4-pregnene-3,20-dione	—	I-428
(in mixed culture with Mycococcus sp. A_1)			—	I-428
congloneratus	IAM	4-pregnene-3,20-dione	oxidation	I-414; I-415
		$17\alpha,21$-dihydroxy-4-pregnene-3,20-dione	—	I-414; I-415

TABLE III

Transformations by Genus: MICROCOCCUS

SPECIES	SOURCE	SUBSTRATE	REACTION	REF.
dehydrogenans (see also under genus - Flavobacterium)	NG	1,3,5(10)-estratriene-3,17β-diol	17β-OH → 17-C=O	M-546
		5-androstene-3β,17β-diol	$\Delta^5 \to \Delta^4$; 3β-OH →3-C=O	E-212; E-217
			$\Delta^5 \to \Delta^4$; 3β-OH →3-C=O; 17β-OH → 17-C=O	E-217
		17α-ethinyl-5-androstene-3β, 17β-diol	3β-OH→3-C=O; $\Delta^5 \to \Delta^4$	C-84
		3β-hydroxy-5-androsten-17-one	$\Delta^5 \to \Delta^4$; 3β-OH → 3-C=O	A-14; E-213; E-214
		3β-hydroxy-5-pregnen-20-one	3β-OH→3-C=O; $\Delta^5 \to \Delta^4$	E-214
		3β-hydroxy-27-nor-5-cholesten-25-one	$\Delta^5 \to \Delta^4$; 3β-OH → 3-C=O	E-214
flava	IAM	4-pregnene-3,20-dione	—	I-414; I-415
		17α,21-dihydroxy-4-pregnene-3,20-dione	—	I-414; I-415
flavus	IFO (3242)	11β,17α,21-trihydroxy-4-pregnene-3,20-dione	—	I-428
(in mixed culture with Mycococcus sp. A₁)			—	I-428
luteus	IAM	4-pregnene-3,20-dione	oxidation	I-414; I-415
	(19-2)	17α,21-dihydroxy-4-pregnene-3,20-dione	—	I-414; I-415; S-849
lysodeikticus	IAM	4-pregnene-3,20-dione	oxidation	I-414; I-415
		17α,21-dihydroxy-4-pregnene-3,20-dione	—	I-414; I-415; S-849
piltonensis	NG	5-cholesten-3β-ol (sole carbon source)	—	T-1030
pyogenus aureus	IFO (3061)	11β,17α,21-trihydroxy-4-pregnene-3,20-dione	—	I-428
(in mixed culture with Mycococcus sp. A₁)			—	I-428

TABLE III

ransformations by Genus: MICROCOCCUS
MICROMONOSPORA   (Schizo. - Actinomycetales)

SPECIES	SOURCE	SUBSTRATE	REACTION	REF.
roseus	Takeda	$11\beta,17\alpha,21$-trihydroxy-4-pregnene-3,20-dione	Δ^1	I-431
species	ATCC-13553 (IFO-3769)	$11\beta,17\alpha,21$-trihydroxy-4-pregnene-3,20-dione	Δ^1	I-431
	ATCC-13554	$11\beta,17\alpha,21$-trihydroxy-4-pregnene-3,20-dione	Δ^1	I-431
	ATCC-13555	$11\beta,17\alpha,21$-trihydroxy-4-pregnene-3,20-dione	Δ^1	I-431
	IAM	$17\alpha,21$-dihydroxy-4-pregnene-3,20-dione	—	S-849
subflavus	IFO (3062)	$11\beta,17\alpha,21$-trihydroxy-4-pregnene-3,20-dione	—	I-428
(in mixed culture with Mycococcus sp. - A_1)			Δ^1	I-428
ureae	IAM	4-pregnene-3,20-dione	—	I-414; I-415
	(S-4)	$17\alpha,21$-dihydroxy-4-pregnene-3,20-dione	—	I-414; I-415; S-849
varians	IAM	4-pregnene-3,20-dione	oxidation	I-414; I-415
	(P-93)	$17\alpha,21$-dihydroxy-4-pregnene-3,20-dione	—	I-414; I-415; S-849
MICROMONOSPORA				
chalcea	ATCC-10026	estran-3-one	$\Delta^{1,4}$; enol.	S-867
		5α-androstan-3-one	$\Delta^{1,4}$	S-867
		17α-hydroxy-5α-androstan-3-one	$\Delta^{1,4}$	S-867
		5α-androstane-3,17-dione	$\Delta^{1,4}$	S-867
		11β-hydroxy-4-estren-3-one	Δ^1; enol.	S-864
		4-androstene-3,17-dione	Δ^1	S-864
		4,6-androstadiene-3,17-dione	Δ^1	S-864
		5α-pregnan-3-one	$\Delta^{1,4}$	S-867
		5α-pregnane-3,11-dione	$\Delta^{1,4}$	S-867
		5α-pregnane-3,20-dione	$\Delta^{1,4}$	S-867

TABLE III

Transformations by Genus: MICROMONOSPORA

SPECIES	SOURCE	SUBSTRATE	REACTION	REF.
chalcea	ATCC-10026	5α-pregnane-3,11,20-trione	$\Delta^{1,4}$	S-867
		5β-pregnan-3-one	$\Delta^{1,4}$	S-867
		11β-hydroxy-5β-pregnan-3-one	$\Delta^{1,4}$	S-867
		14α-hydroxy-5β-pregnan-3-one	$\Delta^{1,4}$	S-867
		17α-hydroxy-5β-pregnan-3-one	$\Delta^{1,4}$	S-867
		20-hydroxy-5β-pregnan-3-one	$\Delta^{1,4}$	S-867
		5β-pregnane-3,11-dione	$\Delta^{1,4}$	S-867
		5β-pregnane-3,20-dione	$\Delta^{1,4}$	S-867
		11β-hydroxy-5β-pregnane-3,20-dione	$\Delta^{1,4}$	S-867
		14α-hydroxy-5β-pregnane-3,20-dione	$\Delta^{1,4}$	S-867
		17α-hydroxy-5β-pregnane-3,20-dione	$\Delta^{1,4}$	S-867
		21-hydroxy-5β-pregnane-3,20-dione	Δ^{4}; $\Delta^{1,4}$	S-867
		11β,21-dihydroxy-5β-pregnane-3,20-dione	$\Delta^{1,4}$	S-867
		11β,14α,17α,21-tetrahydroxy-5β-pregnane-3,20-dione	$\Delta^{1,4}$	S-867
		5β-pregnane-3,11,20-trione	$\Delta^{1,4}$	S-867
		17α-hydroxy-4-pregnene-3,20-dione	Δ^{1}	S-864
		21-hydroxy-4-pregnene-3,20-dione	Δ^{1}	S-867
		11β,21-dihydroxy-4-pregnene-3,20-dione	Δ^{1}	S-867
		17α,21-dihydroxy-4-pregnene-3,20-dione	Δ^{1}	S-864
		11β,17α,21-trihydroxy-4-pregnene-3,20-dione	Δ^{1}	S-864; S-867
		9α-fluoro-11β,17α,21-trihydroxy-4-pregnene-3,20-dione	Δ^{1}	S-864
		11β,14α,17α,21-tetrahydroxy-4-pregnene-3,20-dione	Δ^{1}	S-864
		17α,21-dihydroxy-14α,15α-oxido-4-pregnene-3,20-dione	Δ^{1}	S-864

TABLE III

Transformations by Genus: MICROMONOSPORA

SPECIES	SOURCE	SUBSTRATE	REACTION	REF.
chalcea	ATCC-10026	$11\beta,17\alpha,21$-trihydroxy-$14\alpha,15\alpha$-oxido-4-pregnene-3,20-dione	Δ^1	S-864
		4-pregnene-3,11,20-trione	Δ^1	S-864
		$17\alpha,21$-dihydroxy-4-pregnene-3,11,20-trione	Δ^1	S-864; S-867
		$14\alpha,17\alpha,21$-trihydroxy-4-pregnene-3,11,20-trione	Δ^1	S-864
		$17\alpha,21$-dihydroxy-4,9(11)-pregnadiene-3,20-dione	Δ^1	S-864
		$17\alpha,21$-dihydroxy-4,14-pregnadiene-3,20-dione	Δ^1	S-864
		4,16-pregnadiene-3,20-dione	Δ^1	S-864
		5β-bisnor-cholan-3-one	$\Delta^{1,4}$	S-867
	ATCC-12452	estran-3-one	$\Delta^{1,4}$; enol.	S-867
		5α-androstan-3-one	$\Delta^{1,4}$	S-867
		17α-hydroxy-5α-androstan-3-one	$\Delta^{1,4}$	S-867
		5α-androstan-3,17-dione	$\Delta^{1,4}$	S-867
		17β-hydroxy-4-estren-3-one	Δ^1; enol.	S-864
		4-androstene-3,17-dione	Δ^1	S-864
		4,6-androstadiene-3,17-dione	Δ^1	S-864
		5α-pregnan-3-one	$\Delta^{1,4}$	S-867
		5α-pregnan-3,11-dione	$\Delta^{1,4}$	S-867
		5α-pregnane-3,20-dione	$\Delta^{1,4}$	S-867
		5α-pregnane-3,11,20-trione	$\Delta^{1,4}$	S-867
		5β-pregnan-3-one	$\Delta^{1,4}$	S-867
		11β-hydroxy-5β-pregnan-3-one	$\Delta^{1,4}$	S-867
		14α-hydroxy-5β-pregnan-3-one	$\Delta^{1,4}$	S-867
		17α-hydroxy-5β-pregnan-3-one	$\Delta^{1,4}$	S-867
		20-hydroxy-5β-pregnan-3-one	$\Delta^{1,4}$	S-867
		5β-pregnane-3,11-dione	$\Delta^{1,4}$	S-867
		5β-pregnane-3,20-dione	$\Delta^{1,4}$	S-867
		11β-hydroxy-5β-pregnane-3,20-dione	$\Delta^{1,4}$	S-867

TABLE III

Transformations by Genus: MICROMONOSPORA

SPECIES	SOURCE	SUBSTRATE	REACTION	REF.
chalcea	ATCC-12452	14α-hydroxy-5β-pregnane-3,20-dione	$\Delta^{1,4}$	S-867
		17α-hydroxy-5β-pregnane-3,20-dione	$\Delta^{1,4}$	S-867
		21-hydroxy-5β-pregnane-3,20-dione	$\Delta^{4}; \Delta^{1,4}$	S-867
		11β,21-dihydroxy-5β-pregnane-3,20-dione	$\Delta^{1,4}$	S-867
		11β,17α,21-trihydroxy-5β-pregnane-3,20-dione	$\Delta^{1,4}$	S-867
		11β,14α,17α,21-tetrahydroxy-5β-pregnane-3,20-dione	$\Delta^{1,4}$	S-867
		5β-pregnane-3,11,20-trione	$\Delta^{1,4}$	S-867
		17α,21-dihydroxy-5β-pregnane-3,11,20-trione	$\Delta^{1,4}$	S-867
		17α-hydroxy-4-pregnene-3,20-dione	Δ^{1}	S-864
		17α,21-dihydroxy-4-pregnene-3,20-dione	Δ^{1}	S-864
		11β,17α,21-trihydroxy-4-pregnene-3,20-dione	Δ^{1}	S-864; S-867
		9α-fluoro-11β,17α,21-trihydroxy-4-pregnene-3,20-dione	Δ^{1}	S-864
		11β,14α,17α,21-tetrahydroxy-4-pregnene-3,20-dione	Δ^{1}	S-864
		17α,21-dihydroxy-14α,15α-oxido-4-pregnene-3,20-dione	Δ^{1}	S-864
		11β,17α,21-trihydroxy-14α,15α-oxido-4-pregnene-3,20-dione	Δ^{1}	S-864
		4-pregnene-3,11,20-trione	Δ^{1}	S-864
		17α,21-dihydroxy-4-pregnene-3,11,20-trione	Δ^{1}	S-864; S-867
		14α,17α,21-trihydroxy-4-pregnene-3,11,20-trione	Δ^{1}	S-864
		17α,21-dihydroxy-4,9(11)-pregnadiene-3,20-dione	Δ^{1}	S-864
		17α,21-dihydroxy-4,14-pregnadiene-3,20-dione	Δ^{1}	S-864

TABLE III

ransformations by Genus:

MICROMONOSPORA
MILAN YEAST
MONILIA
MONILIALES
MONOSPORIUM
MORCHELLA
MORTIELLA

TAXONOMY

(Imperf. - Moniliales)
(Imperf. - Moniliales)
(Imperf. - Moniliales)
(Asco. - Pezizales)
(Taxonomy Unclear)

SPECIES	SOURCE	SUBSTRATE	REACTION	REF.
chalcea	ATCC-12452	4,16-pregnadiene-3,20-dione	Δ^1	S-864
		5β-bisnor-cholan-3-one	$\Delta^{1,4}$	S-867
species	NG	5-cholesten-3β-ol (sole carbon source)	utilization	S-793c
		24β-methyl-5,7,22-cholestatrien-3β-ol (sole carbon source)	utilization	S-793c
MILAN YEAST (See under genus Saccharomyces)	NG	3β-hydroxy-5-androsten-17-one	3β-OH$\rightarrow$3-C=O; $\Delta^5\rightarrow\Delta^4$	M-552
MONILIA				
species	NRRL	plant saponins	—	K-478
TAXONOMIC ORDER MONILIALES				
(genus not given)	Lepetit (L-1465)	$17\alpha,21$-dihydroxy-1,4-pregna-diene-3,20-dione	11α-OH; 14α-OH	T-990
MONOSPORIUM				
apiospermum	FRI	$17\alpha,21$-dihydroxy-4-pregnene-3,20-dione	—	S-849
MORCHELLA				
crassipes	NRRL-2369	4-pregnene-3,20-dione	oxidation - products not identified	R-778
MORTIELLA (Taxonomy Unclear)				
pusilla	FRI	$17\alpha,21$-dihydroxy-4-pregnene-3,20-dione	6β-OH	S-849

466

TABLE III

TAXONOMY

Transformations by Genus: MORTIERELLA   (Phyco. - Mucorales)

SPECIES	SOURCE	SUBSTRATE	REACTION	REF.
MORTIERELLA				
alpina	ATCC-8979	1,3,5(10)-estratriene-3,17β-ol	6β-OH	L-493; L-497
		3-hydroxy-1,3,5(10)-estratrien-17-one	6β-OH; 17-C=O →17β-OH	L-493
			6β-OH	L-495
	CBS	4-pregnene-3,20-dione	6β-OH	F-239
		9α-fluoro-11β,17α,21-trihydroxy-4-pregnene-3,20-dione	1ξ-OH	F-237
bainieri	CBS	4-pregnene-3,20-dione	6β-OH	F-239
*		9α-fluoro-11β,17α,21-trihydroxy-4-pregnene-3,20-dione	1ξ-OH	F-237
candelabrum *	CBS	9α-fluoro-11β,17α,21-trihydroxy-4-pregnene-3,20-dione	1ξ-OH	F-237
isabellina	NRRL	Sarsasapogenin	—	M-587
		Diosgenin	—	M-587
		4-dehydrotigogenone	—	M-587
marburgensis	CBS	4-pregnene-3,20-dione	6β-OH	F-239
*		9α-fluoro-11β,17α,21-trihydroxy-4-pregnene-3,20-dione	1ξ-OH	F-237
oligospora	NRRL	Sarsasapogenin	—	M-587
		Diosgenin	—	M-587
		4-dehydrotigogenone	—	M-587
polycephala *	CBS	11β,17α,21-trihydroxy-4-pregnene-3,20-dione	6β-OH	F-239
*		9α-fluoro-11β,17α,21-trihydroxy-4-pregnene-3,20-dione	1ξ-OH	F-237
pusilla	CBS	4-pregnene-3,20-dione	6β-OH	F-239
		11α-hydroxy-4-pregnene-3,20-dione	6β-OH	F-239
*		9α-fluoro-11β,17α,21-trihydroxy-4-pregnene-3,20-dione	1ξ-OH	F-237
tuberosa	CBS	4-pregnene-3,20-dione	6β-OH	F-239
*		9α-fluoro-11β,17α,21-trihydroxy-4-pregnene-3,20-dione	1ξ-OH	F-237

TABLE III

Transformations by Genus: MORTIERELLA <u>TAXONOMY</u>
MUCOR (Phyco. - Mucorales)

SPECIES	SOURCE	SUBSTRATE	REACTION	REF.
zonata	ATCC-13309	4-pregnene-3,20-dione	6β-OH	F-239
		11α-hydroxy-4-pregnene-3,20-dione	6β-OH	F-239
		$17\alpha,21$-dihydroxy-4-pregnene-3,20-dione	6β-OH	F-239
*		$11\beta,17\alpha,21$-trihydroxy-4-pregnene-3,20-dione	6β-OH	<u>F-239</u>
*		9α-fluoro-$11\beta,17\alpha,21$-trihydroxy-4-pregnene-3,20-dione	1ξ-OH	<u>F-237</u>
		9α-fluoro-$11\beta,16\alpha,17\alpha,21$-tetra-hydroxy-4-pregnene-3,20-dione	1ξ-OH	<u>F-237</u>
MUCOR				
adriaticus	SSSR	$17\alpha,21$-dihydroxy-4-pregnene-3,20-dione	6β-OH; 11α-OH	E-224
adventitius	UC	4-pregnene-3,20-dione	11-OH	M-601; M-636
		17α-hydroxy-4-pregnene-3,20-dione	11-OH	M-601; M-636
		21-hydroxy-4-pregnene-3,20-dione	11-OH	M-601; M-636
		$17\alpha,21$-dihydroxy-4-pregnene-3,20-dione	11-OH	M-601; M-636
angulisporus	SSSR	$17\alpha,21$-dihydroxy-4-pregnene-3,20-dione	6β-OH; 11α-OH	E-224
berolinensis	SSSR	$17\alpha,21$-dihydroxy-4-pregnene-3,20-dione	6β-OH	E-224
buntingii	SSSR	$17\alpha,21$-dihydroxy-4-pregnene-3,20-dione	6β-OH	E-224
christianensis	UC	21-hydroxy-4-pregnene-3,20-dione	(8-OH) revised 9α-OH	M-640
circinelloides	SSSR	$17\alpha,21$-dihydroxy-4-pregnene-3,20-dione	6β-OH	E-224
corymbifer	FARMIT	4-pregnene-3,20-dione	$6\beta,14\alpha$-diOH	<u>C-82</u>
			products of un-known or questionable structure	<u>C-82</u>
			unknown	<u>C-82</u>

TABLE III

Transformations by Genus: MUCOR

SPECIES	SOURCE	SUBSTRATE	REACTION	REF.
dimorphosporus	SSSR	$17\alpha,21$-dihydroxy-4-pregnene-3,20-dione	6β-OH	E-224
dispersus	UC	21-hydroxy-4-pregnene-3,20-dione	(8-OH) revised 9α-OH	M-640
dubius	UC	4-pregnene-3,20-dione	oxidation	M-601; M-636
		17α-hydroxy-4-pregnene-3,20-dione	oxidation	M-601; M-636
		21-hydroxy-4-pregnene-3,20-dione	oxidation	M-601; M-636
		$17\alpha,21$-dihydroxy-4-pregnene-3,20-dione	oxidation	M-601; M-636
erectus	SSSR	$17\alpha,21$-dihydroxy-4-pregnene-3,20-dione	6β-OH; 11α-OH	E-224
genevensis	SSSR	$17\alpha,21$-dihydroxy-4-pregnene-3,20-dione	6β-OH; 11α-OH; 11β-OH	E-224
	UC	4-pregnene-3,20-dione	11-OH	M-601; M-636
		17α-hydroxy-4-pregnene-3,20-dione	11-OH	M-601; M-636
		21-hydroxy-4-pregnene-3,20-dione	11-OH	M-601; M-636
			(8-OH) revised 9α-OH	M-640
		$17\alpha,21$-dihydroxy-4-pregnene-3,20-dione	11-OH	M-601; M-636
globosus	SSSR	$17\alpha,21$-dihydroxy-4-pregnene-3,20-dione	6β-OH; 11α-OH; 11β-OH	E-224
glomerula	UC	21-hydroxy-4-pregnene-3,20-dione	(8-OH) revised 9α-OH	M-640
griseo cyanus	ATCC-1027	17β-hydroxy-4-androsten-3-one	14α-OH	E-204
		4-pregnene-3,20-dione	14α-OH	E-204
		21-hydroxy-4-pregnene-3,20-dione acetate	14α-OH; 21-OAc $\rightarrow$21-OH	E-204
			21-OAc$\rightarrow$21-OH	E-204
griseo cyanus (+)	ATCC-1207a	17β-hydroxy-4-estren-3-one	14α-OH	M-610; M-634
		17β-hydroxy-4-androsten-3-one	14α-OH	M-610; M-634

TABLE III

Transformations by Genus: MUCOR

SPECIES	SOURCE	SUBSTRATE	REACTION	REF.
griseo-cyanus (+)	ATCC-1207a	19-<u>nor</u>-4-pregnene-3,20-dione	oxidation	M-601; M-636
		4-pregnene-3,20-dione	11-OH	M-601; M-636
			14α-OH	M-601; M-636; <u>M-614</u>
		21-hydroxy-4-pregnene-3,20-dione	11-OH	M-601; M-636
			(8-OH) revised 9α-OH	M-640
			7α-OH	<u>C-94</u>
			7α,14α-diOH	<u>C-94</u>
		21-hydroxy-4-pregnene-3,20-dione acetate	14α-OH	M-601; <u>M-635</u>; M-636
			14α-OH; 21-OAc →21-OH	<u>M-635</u>
		17α,21-dihydroxy-4,14-pregnadiene-3,20-dione	Δ^{14}→14α,15α-oxide	<u>β-66</u>; <u>S-865</u>
		3β-hydroxy-14α-5,20(22)-cardadienolide acetate	7α-OH; 3β-OAc →3β-OH	C-95
griseo-cyanus (-)	ATCC-1207b	4-pregnene-3,20-dione	11-OH	M-601; M-636
		21-hydroxy-4-pregnene-3,20-dione	11-OH	M-601; M-636
	AY	4-pregnene-3,20-dione (using spores)	14α-OH	<u>S-835</u>; <u>V-1048</u>
		6α-fluoro-17α,21-dihydroxy-16α-methyl-4-pregnene-3,20-dione	11β-OH	V-1042a
guilliermondii	SSSR	17α,21-dihydroxy-4-pregnene-3,20-dione	6β-OH	E-224
hiemalis	ATCC-8690	4-pregnene-3,20-dione	11-OH	M-601; M-636
(var. albus)	ATCC-6800	4-pregnene-3,20-dione	11-OH	M-601; M-636
	NRRL-2684	4-pregnene-3,20-dione	6β,14α-diOH	<u>D-177</u>
			7α,14α-diOH	<u>D-177</u>
	SSSR	17α,21-dihydroxy-4-pregnene-3,20-dione	6β-OH	E-224

TABLE III

Transformations by Genus: MUCOR

SPECIES	SOURCE	SUBSTRATE	REACTION	REF.
hiemalis	UC	21-hydroxy-4-pregnene-3,20-dione	(8-OH) revised 9α-OH	M-640
humicola (humicolus)	SSSR	17α,21-dihydroxy-4-pregnene-3,20-dione	6β-OH	E-224
humilis	SSSR	17α,21-dihydroxy-4-pregnene-3,20-dione	6β-OH	E-224
hypochninus	SSSR	17α,21-dihydroxy-4-pregnene-3,20-dione	6β-OH	E-224
javanicus	NI	4-pregnene-3,20-dione	6β,11α-diOH	N-682
		17α,21-dihydroxy-4-pregnene-3,20-dione	6β-OH; 11α-OH; 14α-OH	N-682
		3β,14β-dihydroxy-5β-20(22)-cardenolide	3β-OH→3-C=O; 1β-OH; 7β-OH; 1β,7β-diOH; 5β,7β-diOH	N-682
		14β-hydroxy-3-keto-5β-20(22)-cardenolide	7β-OH	N-682
	SSSR	17α,21-dihydroxy-4-pregnene-3,20-dione	6β-OH	E-224
	UC	21-hydroxy-4-pregnene-3,20-dione	(8-OH) revised 9α-OH	M-640
mandshuricus	SSSR	17α,21-dihydroxy-4-pregnene-3,20-dione	6β-OH; 11α-OH	E-224
microsporus	UC	4-pregnene-3,20-dione	oxidation	M-601; M-636
		17α-hydroxy-4-pregnene-3,20-dione	oxidation	M-601; M-636
		21-hydroxy-4-pregnene-3,20-dione	oxidation	M-601; M-636
		17α,21-dihydroxy-4-pregnene-3,20-dione	oxidation	M-601; M-636
mucedo	ATCC-7941	4-pregnene-3,20-dione	11-OH	M-601; M-636
	ATCC-9635	4-pregnene-3,20-dione	11-OH	M-601; M-636
	ATCC-9836	4-pregnene-3,20-dione	11-OH	M-601; M-636
	FRI	4-pregnene-3,20-dione	6β-OH; 11α-OH	S-849
	NI	4-pregnene-3,20-dione	6β,11α-diOH	N-682

TABLE III

ansformations by Genus: MUCOR

SPECIES	SOURCE	SUBSTRATE	REACTION	REF.
nucedo	NI	$17\alpha,21$-dihydroxy-4-pregnene-3,20-dione	6β-OH; 11α-OH	N-682
		$3\beta,14\beta$-dihydroxy-5β-20(22)-cardenolide	7β-OH	N-682
		14β-hydroxy-3-keto-5β-20(22)-cardenolide	7β-OH	N-682
	SSSR	$17\alpha,21$-dihydroxy-4-pregnene-3,20-dione	6β-OH; 11α-OH	E-224
	UC	21-hydroxy-4-pregnene-3,20-dione	(8-OH) revised 9α-OH	M-640
	VEB	4-pregnene-3,20-dione	$6\beta,14\alpha$-diOH	S-811
iurorum	SSSR	$17\alpha,21$-dihydroxy-4-pregnene-3,20-dione	6β-OH	E-224
arasiticus	ATCC-6476	4-pregnene-3,20-dione	11α-OH	M-601
			14α-OH	E-204; I-424; M-601; M-614; N-682
		19-nor-4-pregnene-3,20-dione	oxidation	M-636
		17α-hydroxy-4-pregnene-3,20-dione	11-OH	M-601
		21-hydroxy-4-pregnene-3,20-dione	11-OH	M-601
			unknown	T-980
		21-hydroxy-4-pregnene-3,20-dione acetate	9α-OH; 21-OAc →21-OH	M-640
			14α-OH	T-980
			products of unknown or questionable structure	T-980
			unknown	T-980
		$17\alpha,21$-dihydroxy-4-pregnene-3,20-dione	6β-OH	N-682
			11α-OH	M-601; N-682
*			14α-OH	N-682
		$17\alpha,21$-dihydroxy-4,14-pregnadiene-3,20-dione	Δ^{14} —$14\alpha,15\alpha$-oxide	B-66; S-865

TABLE III

Transformations by Genus: MUCOR

SPECIES	SOURCE	SUBSTRATE	REACTION	REF
parasiticus	ATCC-6476	14β-hydroxy-3-keto-5β-20(22)-cardenolide	3-C=O→ 3α-OH	N-682 N-678
			3-C=O→ 3β-OH	N-678
			5β-H→Δ^4 (via 5β-OH)	N-682
		$3\alpha,14\beta$-dihydroxy-5β-20(22)-cardenolide	3α-OH→ 3-C=O	N-681
*		$3\beta,14\beta$-dihydroxy-5β-20(22)-cardenolide	1β-OH	N-682
		(Ref. N-683-acceleration of hydroxylation by preincubation with 4-pregnene-3,20-dione)	5β-OH	I-423; N-678; N-682; N-683
* *			7β-OH	N-678; N-682; N-683
*			$1\beta,7\beta$-diOH	N-682
*			$5\beta,7\beta$-diOH	N-682
*			3β-OH → 3-C=O	N-678; N-682
			3β-OH→ 3-C=O; 5β-H→Δ^4	N-678
		$3\beta,14\beta$-dihydroxy-17α-20(22)-cardenolide	5β-OH	N-681
			3β-OH→ 3-C=O	N-681
piriformis	SSSR	21-hydroxy-4-pregnene-3,20-dione	(8-OH) revised 9α-OH	M-640
		$17\alpha,21$-dihydroxy-4-pregnene-3,20-dione	6β-OH; 11α-OH	E-224
plumbeus	NRRL	Sarsasapogenin	——	M-587
		Diosgenin	——	M-587
		4-dehydrotigogenone	——	M-587
	SSSR	$17\alpha,21$-dihydroxy-4-pregnene-3,20-dione	6β-OH	E-224
	UC	4-pregnene-3,20-dione	oxidation	M-601; M-636

TABLE III

nsformations by Genus: MUCOR

SPECIES	SOURCE	SUBSTRATE	REACTION	REF.
umbeus	UC	17α-hydroxy-4-pregnene-3,20-dione	oxidation	M-601; M-636
		21-hydroxy-4-pregnene-3,20-dione	oxidation	M-601; M-636
		17α,21-dihydroxy-4-pregnene-3,20-dione	oxidation	M-601; M-636
ısilius	SSSR	17α,21-dihydroxy-4-pregnene-3,20-dione	6β-OH; 11α-OH	E-224
cemosus	NI	4-pregnene-3,20-dione	11α-OH; 14α-OH; 6β,11α-diOH	N-682
		17α,21-dihydroxy-4-pregnene-3,20-dione	6β-OH; 11α-OH; 14α-OH	N-682
		14β-hydroxy-3-keto-5β-20(22)-cardenolide	7β-OH	N-682
		3β,14β-dihydroxy-5β-20(22)-cardenolide	7β-OH; 1β,7β-diOH; 5β,7β-diOH; 3β-OH→3-C=O	N-682
	SSSR	17α,21-dihydroxy-4-pregnene-3,20-dione	6β-OH	E-224
	UC	4-pregnene-3,20-dione	oxidation	M-601; M-636
		17α-hydroxy-4-pregnene-3,20-dione	oxidation	M-601; M-636
		21-hydroxy-4-pregnene-3,20-dione	oxidation	M-601; M-636
			(8-OH) revised 9α-OH	M-640
		17α,21-dihydroxy-4-pregnene-3,20-dione	oxidation	M-601; M-636
mannianus	SSSR	17α,21-dihydroxy-4-pregnene-3,20-dione	6β-OH; 11α-OH	E-224
	UC	21-hydroxy-4-pregnene-3,20-dione	(8-OH) revised 9α-OH	M-640
ıxii	ATCC-4857	4-pregnene-3,20-dione	11-OH	M-601; M-636
		21-hydroxy-4-pregnene-3,20-dione	11-OH	M-601; M-636
ıxianus	SSSR	17α,21-dihydroxy-4-pregnene-3,20-dione	11α-OH	E-224

TABLE III

Transformations by Genus: MUCOR
MYCENA   (Basidio. - Agaricales)
MYCOBACTERIUM   (Schizo. - Actinomycetales)

SPECIES	SOURCE	SUBSTRATE	REACTION	REF.
rouxianus	UC	4-pregnene-3,20-dione	oxidation	M-601; M-636
		17α-hydroxy-4-pregnene-3,20-dione	oxidation	M-601; M-636
		21-hydroxy-4-pregnene-3,20-dione	oxidation	M-601; M-636
		17α,21-dihydroxy-4-pregnene-3,20-dione	oxidation	M-601; M-636
simplex	UC	21-hydroxy-4-pregnene-3,20-dione	(8-OH) revised 9α-OH	M-640
solani	UC	21-hydroxy-4-pregnene-3,20-dione	(8-OH) revised 9α-OH	M-640
species	NRRL	plant saponins	——	K-478
sphaerosporoa	UC	21-hydroxy-4-pregnene-3,20-dione	(8-OH) revised 9α-OH	M-640
spinosus	UC	21-hydroxy-4-pregnene-3,20-dione	(8-OH) revised 9α-OH	M-640
stolonifer	UC	21-hydroxy-4-pregnene-3,20-dione	(8-OH) revised 9α-OH	M-640
varians	SSSR	17α,21-dihydroxy-4-pregnene-3,20-dione	——	E-224
vuillemini	SSSR	17α,21-dihydroxy-4-pregnene-3,20-dione	6β-OH	E-224
MYCENA				
strobilinoides	AL (SS-75)	4-pregnene-3,20-dione	oxidation - products not identified	S-825
MYCOBACTERIUM				
album	NG	5-cholesten-3β-ol	utilization	S-916
berolinense	NG	5-cholesten-3β-ol	utilization	M-594; M-595
			degradation	T-952
	PF	17β-hydroxy-4-estren-3-one	Δ^1	S-873
		4-androstene-3,17-dione	Δ^1	S-873
		4,6-androstadiene-3,17-dione	Δ^1	S-873
		17α-hydroxy-4-pregnene-3,20-dione	Δ^1	S-873

TABLE III

ansformations by Genus: MYCOBACTERIUM

SPECIES	SOURCE	SUBSTRATE	REACTION	REF.
ɔerolinense	PF	11β,17α-dihydroxy-4-pregnene-3,20-dione	Δ^1	S-873
		17α,21-dihydroxy-4-pregnene-3,20-dione	Δ^1	S-873
		9α-fluoro-11β,17α,21-tri-hydroxy-4-pregnene-3,20-dione	Δ^1	S-873
		11β,14α,17α,21-tetrahydroxy-4-pregnene-3,20-dione	Δ^1	S-874
		17α,21-dihydroxy-14α,15α-oxido-4-pregnene-3,20-dione	Δ^1	S-873
		11β,17α,21-trihydroxy-14α,15α-oxido-4-pregnene-3,20-dione	Δ^1	S-873
		4,6-pregnadiene-3,20-dione	Δ^1	S-873
		17α,21-dihydroxy-4,9(11)-pregnadiene-3,20-dione	Δ^1	S-873
		4-pregnene-3,11,20-trione	Δ^1	S-873
		14α,17α,21-trihydroxy-4-pregnene-3,11,20-trione	Δ^1	S-874
(In sequential fermentation with Curvularia sp. -[11β-OH])		17α,21-dihydroxy-4-pregnene 3,20-dione	Δ^1	S-868
ɹtyricum	PF	17β-hydroxy-4-estren-3-one	Δ^1; enol.	S-873
		4-androstene-3,17-dione	Δ^1	S-873
		4,6-androstadiene-3,17-dione	Δ^1	S-873
		17α-hydroxy-4-pregnene-3,20-dione	Δ^1	S-873
		11β,17α-dihydroxy-4-pregnene-3,20-dione	Δ^1	S-873
		17α,21-dihydroxy-4-pregnene-3,20-dione	Δ^1	S-873
		9α-fluoro-11β,17α,21-tri-hydroxy-4-pregnene-3,20-dione	Δ^1	S-873
		11β,14α,17α,21-tetrahydroxy-4-pregnene-3,20-dione	Δ^1	S-874
		17α,21-dihydroxy-14α,15α-oxido-4-pregnene-3,20-dione	Δ^1	S-873

TABLE III

Transformations by Genus: MYCOBACTERIUM

SPECIES	SOURCE	SUBSTRATE	REACTION	REF.
butyricum	PF	$11\beta,17\alpha,21$-trihydroxy-$14\alpha,15\alpha$-oxido-4-pregnene-3,20-dione	Δ^1	S-873
		4,6-pregnadiene-3,20-dione	Δ^1	S-873
		$17\alpha,21$-dihydroxy-4,9(11)-pregnadiene-3,20-dione	Δ^1	S-873
		4-pregnene-3,11,20-trione	Δ^1	S-873
		$14\alpha,17\alpha,21$-trihydroxy-4-pregnene-3,11,20-trione	Δ^1	S-874
(in mixed culture with Curvularia sp. - [11β-OH])		$17\alpha,21$-dihydroxy-4-pregnene-3,20-dione	Δ^1	S-868
	U	4-pregnene-3,20-dione 20-cycloethyleneketal	Δ^1	F-251
chelonei	NG	5-cholesten-3β-ol (sole carbon source)	utilization	M-594
cholesterolicum	NG	5-cholesten-3β-ol (sole carbon source)	utilization	M-594; M-595; T-952
flavum	IPB-390	17β-hydroxy-4-androsten-3-one	Δ^1; 17β-OH $\rightarrow$ 17-C=O	C-100
		4-androstene-3,17-dione	Δ^1	C-100
			Δ^1; 17-C=O $\rightarrow$ 17β-OH	C-100
		20β-hydroxy-4-pregnen-3-one	Δ^1; 17β-(20β-OH-21-H) $\rightarrow$ 17-C=O	C-100
			Δ^1; 17β-(20β-OH-21-H) $\rightarrow$ 17β-OH	C-100
		4-pregnene-3,20-dione	Δ^1; 17β-Ac $\rightarrow$ 17-C=O	C-100
			Δ^1; 17β-Ac $\rightarrow$ 17β-OH	C-100
		21-hydroxy-4-pregnene-3,20-dione	Δ^1; 17β-(20-C=O-21-OH) $\rightarrow$ 17-C=O	C-100
		$17\alpha,21$-dihydroxy-4-pregnene-3,20-dione	Δ^1	C-100
			Δ^1; 20-C=O $\rightarrow$ 20β-OH	C-100

TABLE III

ansformations by Genus: MYCOBACTERIUM

SPECIES	SOURCE	SUBSTRATE	REACTION	REF.
flavum	IPB (390)	$17\alpha,21$-dihydroxy-4-pregnene-3,11,20-trione	Δ^1	C-100; C-101
			Δ^1; 20-C=O→ 20β-OH	C-100; C-101
		$17\alpha,21$-dihydroxy-1,4-pregna-diene-3,11,20-trione	20-C=O → 20β-OH	C-100
fortuitum	IMJ (SG-988)	3α-hydroxy-5α-androstan-17-one	3α-OH→3-C=O, Δ^4	S-818
			3α-OH→3-C=O, $\Delta^{1,4}$	S-818
			3α-OH→3-C=O; $\Delta^{1,4}$; 9α-OH; rev. aldol.; enol.; 9-C=O→9ξ-OH	S-818
		3α-hydroxy-5β-androstan-17-one	3α-OH→3-C=O; Δ^4	S-818
			3α-OH→3-C=O; $\Delta^{1,4}$	S-818
			3α-OH→3-C=O; $\Delta^{1,4}$; 9α-OH; rev. aldol.; enol.; 9-C=O→9ξ-OH	S-818
		3β-hydroxy-5-androsten-17-one	Δ^1; Δ^5→Δ^4; 3β-OH→3-C=O	S-818
			Δ^5→Δ^4; 3β-OH →3-C=O	S-818
			Δ^1; Δ^5→Δ^4; 3β-OH→3-C=O; 9α-OH; rev. aldol.; enol.; 9-C=O→9ξ-OH	S-818
riedmannii	PF	17β-hydroxy-4-estren-3-one	Δ^1; enol.	S-873
		4-androstene-3,17-dione	Δ^1	S-873
		4,6-androstadiene-3,17-dione	Δ^1	S-873
		17α-hydroxy-4-pregnene-3,20-dione	Δ^1	S-873
		$11\beta,17\alpha$-dihydroxy-4-pregnene-3,20-dione	Δ^1	S-873
		$17\alpha,21$-dihydroxy-4-pregnene-3,20-dione	Δ^1	S-873

TABLE III

Transformations by Genus: MYCOBACTERIUM

SPECIES	SOURCE	SUBSTRATE	REACTION	REF.
friedmannii	PF	9α-fluoro-11β,17α,21-trihydroxy-4-pregnene-3,20-dione	Δ^1	S-873
		11β,14α,17α,21-tetrahydroxy-4-pregnene-3,20-dione	Δ^1	S-874
		17α,21-dihydroxy-14α,15α-oxido-4-pregnene-3,20-dione	Δ^1	S-873
		11β,17α,21-trihydroxy-14α,15α-oxido-4-pregnene-3,20-dione	Δ^1	S-873
		4,6-pregnadiene-3,20-dione	Δ^1	S-873
		17α,21-dihydroxy-4,9(11)-pregnadiene-3,20-dione	Δ^1	S-873
		4-pregnene-3,11,20-trione	Δ^1	S-873
		14α,17α,21-trihydroxy-4-pregnene-3,11,20-trione	Δ^1	S-874
(in mixed culture with Curvularia sp. -[11β-OH])		17α,21-dihydroxy-4-pregnene-3,20-dione	Δ^1	S-868
hyalinum	NG	5-cholesten-3β-ol	utilization	S-916
lacticola	ATCC-9626	17α,21-dihydroxy-4-pregnene-3,20-dione	Δ^1; 20-C=O → 20β-OH	S-945
		9α-fluoro-11β,17α,21-trihydroxy-4-pregnene-3,20-dione	Δ^1	T-1005
	ATCC-12297	17α,21-dihydroxy-6α,16α-dimethyl-4-pregnene-3,11,20-trione	Δ^1	A-24; A-25
	NG	5-cholesten-3β-ol (Ref. T-952, T-1030 - sole carbon source)	utilization	M-595; S-916; T-952; T-1030
	PF	17β-hydroxy-4-estren-3-one	Δ^1; enol.	S-873
		4-androstene-3,17-dione	Δ^1	S-873
		4,6-androstadiene-3,17-dione	Δ^1	S-873
		17α-hydroxy-4-pregnene-3,20-dione	Δ^1	S-873
		11β,17α-dihydroxy-4-pregnene-3,20-dione	Δ^1	S-873
		17α,21-dihydroxy-4-pregnene-3,20-dione	Δ^1	S-873

TABLE III

ansformations by Genus: MYCOBACTERIUM

SPECIES	SOURCE	SUBSTRATE	REACTION	REF.
acticola	PF	9α-fluoro-11β,17α,21-trihydroxy-4-pregnene-3,20-dione	Δ^1	S-873
		11β,14α,17α,21-tetrahydroxy-4-pregnene-3,20-dione	Δ^1	S-874
		17α,21-dihydroxy-14α,15α-oxido-4-pregnene-3,20-dione	Δ^1	S-873
		11β,17α,21-trihydroxy-14α,15α-oxido-4-pregnene-3,20-dione	Δ^1	S-873
		4,6-pregnadiene-3,20-dione	Δ^1	S-873
		17α,21-dihydroxy-4,9(11)-pregnadiene-3,20-dione	Δ^1	S-873
		4-pregnene-3,11,20-trione	Δ^1	S-873
		14α,17α,21-trihydroxy-4-pregnene-3,11,20-trione	Δ^1	S-874
(in mixed culture with Curvularia sp. - [11β-OH])		17α,21-dihydroxy-4-pregnene-3,20-dione	Δ^1	S-868
uteum	NG	5-cholesten-3β-ol	utilization	S-916
hlei	AMCY	11β,17α,21-trihydroxy-4-pregnene-3,20-dione	Δ^1	F-231
	ATCC-354	11β,21-dihydroxy-4-pregnene-3,20-dione	Δ^1	S-873
		6α,9α-dibromo-11β,17α,21-trihydroxy-16-methylene-4-pregnene-3,20-dione	Δ^1	A-7
		6α,9α-difluoro-11β,17α,21-trihydroxy-16-methylene-4-pregnene-3,20-dione 21-propionate	Δ^1; 21-OPr→ 21-OH	A-7
		6α-fluoro-17α-hydroxy-21-methyl-4,9(11)-pregnadiene-3,20-dione	Δ^1	H-391
		2α-fluoro-17α,21-dihydroxy-4-pregnene-3,11,20-trione	Δ^1	H-401
(in mixed culture with Curvularia lunata -NRRL-2380-[11β-OH]		17α,21-dihydroxy-4-pregnene-3,20-dione	Δ^1; 14α-OH	S-868
	ATCC-10142	17β-hydroxy-4-estren-3-one	Δ^1; enol.	S-873
		4-androstene-3,17-dione	Δ^1	S-873
		4,6-androstadiene-3,17-dione	Δ^1	S-873

TABLE III

Transformations by Genus: MYCOBACTERIUM

SPECIES	SOURCE	SUBSTRATE	REACTION	REF.
phlei	ATCC-10142	17α-hydroxy-4-pregnene-3,20-dione	Δ^1	S-873
		11β,17α-dihydroxy-4-pregnene-3,20-dione	Δ^1	S-873
		17α,21-dihydroxy-4-pregnene-3,20-dione	Δ^1	S-873
		9α-fluoro-11β,17α,21-trihydroxy-4-pregnene-3,20-dione	Δ^1	S-873
		17α,21-dihydroxy-14α,15α-oxido-4-pregnene-3,20-dione	Δ^1	S-873
		11β,17α,21-trihydroxy-14α,15α-oxido-4-pregnene-3,20-dione	Δ^1	S-873
		4,6-pregnadiene-3,20-dione	Δ^1	S-873
		17α,21-dihydroxy-4,9(11)-pregnadiene-3,20-dione	Δ^1	S-873
		4-pregnene-3,11,20-trione	Δ^1	S-873
	ATCC-12298	11β,17α,21-trihydroxy-6α,16α-dimethyl-4-pregnene-3,20-dione	Δ^1	A-24; A-25
	NG	5-cholesten-3β-ol (Ref. T-952, T-1030 - sole carbon source)	utilization	M-594; M-595; S-916; T-952; T-1030
	PF	11β,14α,17α,21-tetrahydroxy-4-pregnene-3,20-dione	Δ^1	S-874
		14α,17α,21-trihydroxy-4-pregnene-3,11,20-trione	Δ^1	S-874
ranae	ATCC-110	17β-hydroxy-4-estren-3-one	Δ^1; enol.	S-873
		4-androstene-3,17-dione	Δ^1	S-873
		4,6-androstadiene-3,17-dione	Δ^1	S-873
		17α-hydroxy-4-pregnene-3,20-dione	Δ^1	S-873
		11β,17α-dihydroxy-4-pregnene-3,20-dione	Δ^1	S-873
		17α,21-dihydroxy-4-pregnene-3,20-dione	Δ^1	S-873
		9α-fluoro-11β,17α,21-trihydroxy-4-pregnene-3,20-dione	Δ^1	S-873

TABLE III

Transformations by Genus: MYCOBACTERIUM

SPECIES	SOURCE	SUBSTRATE	REACTION	REF.
ranae	ATCC-110	$11\beta,14\alpha,17\alpha,21$-tetrahydroxy-4-pregnene-3,20-dione	Δ^1	S-874
		$17\alpha,21$-dihydroxy-$14\alpha,15\alpha$-oxido-4-pregnene-3,20-dione	Δ^1	S-873
		$11\beta,17\alpha,21$-trihydroxy-$14\alpha,15\alpha$-oxido-4-pregnene-3,20-dione	Δ^1	S-873
		4,6-pregnadiene-3,20-dione	Δ^1	S-873
		$17\alpha,21$-dihydroxy-4,9(11)-pregnadiene-3,20-dione	Δ^1	S-873
		4-pregnene-3,11,20-trione	Δ^1	S-873
	NC	5-cholesten-3β-ol	utilization	M-594
	PF	$14\alpha,17\alpha,21$-trihydroxy-4-pregnene-3,11,20-trione	Δ^1	S-874
(in mixed culture with Curvularia sp. - [11β-OH])		$17\alpha,21$-dihydroxy-4-pregnene-3,20-dione	Δ^1	S-868
rhodochrous	ATCC-12674	$11\beta,17\alpha,21$-trihydroxy-4-pregnene-3,20-dione	Δ^1	F-232
	SQ (SC-2318)	17β-hydroxy-4-androsten-3-one	Δ^1	S-890
		5α-pregnane-3,20-dione	$\Delta^{1,4}$	S-890
		5β-pregnane-3,20-dione	Δ^4; $\Delta^{1,4}$	S-890
		4-pregnene-3,20-dione	Δ^1	S-890
		9α-fluoro-$11\beta,17\alpha,21$-trihydroxy-4-pregnene-3,20-dione	Δ^1	T-1002
		9α-fluoro-$11\beta,16\alpha,17\alpha,21$-tetrahydroxy-4-pregnene-3,20-dione	Δ^1	G-296; S-890; T-1002
			20-C=O→20β-OH	G-296
		$6\alpha,9\alpha$-difluoro-$11\beta,16\alpha,17\alpha,21$-tetrahydroxy-4-pregnene-3,20-dione	Δ^1	S-890
		9α-fluoro-$11\beta,16\alpha,17\alpha,21$-tetrahydroxy-1,4-pregnadiene-3,20-dione	20-C=O→20β-OH	G-296
			Δ^1→H; 20-C=O→20β-OH	G-296
		9α-fluoro-$11\beta,17\alpha,20\beta,21$-tetrahydroxy-1,4-pregnadiene-3,20-dione	20β-OH→20-C=O	G-294

TABLE III

Transformations by Genus: MYCOBACTERIUM

SPECIES	SOURCE	SUBSTRATE	REACTION	REF.
rhodochrous	SQ (SC-2318)	9α-fluoro-$11\beta,16\alpha,17\alpha,20\beta,21$-pentahydroxy-1,4-pregnadiene-3,20-dione	20β-OH → 20-C=O	G-294; G-296
	SQ (SC-2921)	5-cholesten-3β-ol	$\Delta^5 \to \Delta^4$; 3β-OH→ 3-C=O	T-1005
		4-pregnene-3,20-dione	Δ^1	T-1005
		9α-fluoro-$11\beta,17\alpha,21$-trihydroxy-4-pregnene-3,20-dione	Δ^1	T-1005
	WISC	17β-hydroxy-A-<u>nor</u>-3-androsten-2-one	9α-OH; 17β-OH →17-C=O	S-885
		4-pregnene-3,20-dione	9α-OH	S-885
rubropertinctum [rhodochrous - J. Bact. <u>73</u>:, 15 (1957)]	SQ (SC-2753)	9α-fluoro-$11\beta,17\alpha,21$-trihydroxy-4-pregnene-3,20-dione	Δ^1	T-1005
rubrum	NC	5-cholesten-3β-ol (Ref. T-952 - sole carbon source)	utilization	S-916; T-952
salmonicolor	NC	5-cholesten-3β-ol (sole carbon source)	utilization	T-952
smegmatis	ATCC-278	4-pregnene-3,20-dione	Δ^1	S-873
	ATCC-361	$14\alpha,17\alpha,21$-trihydroxy-4-pregnene-3,20-dione	Δ^1	S-872; S-873
	ATCC-12051	$11\beta,17\alpha,21$-trihydroxy-4-pregnene-3,20-dione	Δ^1	S-873
			20-C=O → 20β-OH	S-873
		$11\beta,14\alpha,17\alpha,21$-tetrahydroxy-4-pregnene-3,20-dione	Δ^1	S-873; S-874
		$17\alpha,21$-dihydroxy-4-pregnene-3,11,20-trione	Δ^1	S-873
		$14\alpha,17\alpha,21$-trihydroxy-4-pregnene-3,11,20-trione	Δ^1	S-873; S-874
	ATCC-12549	17β-hydroxy-4-androsten-3-one	Δ^1	S-873
		21-hydroxy-4-pregnene-3,20-dione acetate	Δ^1; 21-O Ac → 21-OH	S-873
			14α-OH; 21-OAc →21-OH	S-873
		$17\alpha,21$-dihydroxy-4-pregnene-3,20-dione 21-acetate	Δ^1; 21-OAc → 21-OH	S-873
			14α-OH; 21-OAc → 21-OH	S-873

TABLE III

ansformations by Genus: MYCOBACTERIUM

SPECIES	SOURCE	SUBSTRATE	REACTION	REF.
smegmatis	IMJ (SC-98)	3α-hydroxy-5α-androstan-17-one	3α-OH →3-C=O; Δ^4	S-818
			3α-OH →3-C=O; $\Delta^{1,4}$	S-818
*			9α-OH; 3α-OH →3-C=O; $\Delta^{1,4}$; rev. aldol.; enol.	S-818
			3α-OH →3-C=O; $\Delta^{1,4}$; 9α-OH; rev. aldol.; enol.; 9-C=O→9ξ-OH	S-818
		3α-hydroxy-5β-androstan-17-one	3α-OH →3-C=O; Δ^4	S-818
			3α-OH —3-C=O; $\Delta^{1,4}$	S-818
*			9α-OH; 3α-OH →3-C=O; $\Delta^{1,4}$; rev. aldol., enol.	S-818
			3α-OH →3-C=O; $\Delta^{1,4}$; 9α-OH; rev. aldol.; enol.; 9-C=O→9ξ-OH	S-818
		3β-hydroxy-5-androsten-17-one	Δ^5→Δ^4; 3β-OH →3-C=O	S-818
			Δ^1; Δ^5→Δ^4; 3β-OH →3-C=O	S-818
*			9α-OH; Δ^1; Δ^5→Δ^4; 3β-OH →3-C=O; rev. aldol.; enol.	S-818
			Δ^1; Δ^5→Δ^4; 3β-OH →3-C=O; 9α-OH; rev. aldol.; enol.; 9-C=O→9ξ-OH	S-818
		4-pregnene-3,20-dione	Δ^4→5α-H	S-820
			3-C=O→3α-OH; Δ^4→5α-H	S-820
			Δ^1	S-820
			Δ^1; 9α-OH; rev. aldol.; enol.	S-820

TABLE III

Transformations by Genus: MYCOBACTERIUM

SPECIES	SOURCE	SUBSTRATE	REACTION	REF.
smegmatis	IMJ (SG-98)	4-pregnene-3,20-dione	Δ^1; 9α-OH; rev. aldol.; enol.; 9-C=O $\rightarrow 9\xi$-OH	S-820
			Δ^1; 17β-Ac $\rightarrow$17-C=O	S-820
			9α-OH; Δ^1; rev. aldol.; enol.; 17β-Ac $\rightarrow$17-C=O	S-820
			17β-Ac $\rightarrow$17-C=O; Δ^1; 9α-OH; rev. aldol.; enol.; 9-C=O $\rightarrow 9\xi$-OH	S-820
			degradation [A,B] to $C_{13}H_{20}O_3$	S-821
			degradation [A,B] to $C_{15}H_{22}O_4$	S-819
			degradation [A,B] to $C_{15}H_{24}O_3$	S-821
	NG	3β-hydroxy-5-androsten-17-one	—	S-915
		4-pregnene-3,20-dione	—	S-915
		$3\alpha,12\alpha$-dihydroxy-5β-cholanic acid	—	S-915
		$3\alpha,7\alpha,12\alpha$-trihydroxy-5β-cholanic acid	—	S-915
		5-cholesten-3β-ol (Ref. S-793c sole carbon source)	utilization	S-793c; S-915
		5-cholesten-3β-ol succinate	partial utilization	S-915
		24β-methyl-5,7,22-cholestatriene-3β-ol	utilization	S-793c
	NRRL-B-1667	9α-fluoro-$11\beta,17\alpha,21$-trihydroxy-$6\alpha,16\alpha$-dimethyl-4-pregnene-3,20-dione	Δ^1	A-24; A-25
(in mixed culture with Curvularia sp. -[11β-OH])	PF	$17\alpha,21$-dihydroxy-4-pregnene-3,20-dione	Δ^1	S-868

TABLE III

ransformations by Genus: MYCOBACTERIUM

SPECIES	SOURCE	SUBSTRATE	REACTION	REF.
smegmatis	SQ(SC-1684)	9α-fluoro-11β,17α,21-tri-hydroxy-4-pregnene-3,20-dione	Δ^1	T-1005
species	NG	5-cholesten-3β-ol	3β-OH$\rightarrow$3-C=O; $\Delta^5\rightarrow\Delta^4$	S-930; L-524
			3β-OH$\rightarrow$3-C=O; $\Delta^5\rightarrow\Delta^4$; 6-C=O	S-930
			cholesterol$\rightarrow$ ring A cleavage to $C_{26}H_{44}O_3$	S-930
	SSSR (193)	11β,17α,21-trihydroxy-4-pregnene-3,20-dione	Δ^1	K-476
		17α,21-dihydroxy-4-pregnene-3,11,20-trione	Δ^1	K-477
(in mixed culture with Bacillus megatherium (Δ^1))		17α,20β,21-trihydroxy-4-pregnene-3,11-dione 20β,21-diacetate	20β-OAc$\rightarrow$20β-OH; 21-OAc$\rightarrow$21-OH	S-917
*	SSSR(B-5)	17α,21-dihydroxy-4-pregnene-3,11,20-trione	20-C=O$\rightarrow$20β-OH	S-917
thamnopheos	NG	5-cholesten-3β-ol	utilization	M-594
	PF	17β-hydroxy-4-estren-3-one	Δ^1; enol.	S-873
		4-androstene-3,17-dione	Δ^1	S-873
		4,6-androstadiene-3,17-dione	Δ^1	S-873
		17α-hydroxy-4-pregnene-3,20-dione	Δ^1	S-873
		11β,17α-dihydroxy-4-pregnene-3,20-dione	Δ^1	S-873
		17α,21-dihydroxy-4-pregnene-3,20-dione	Δ^1	S-873
		9α-fluoro-11β,17α,21-tri-hydroxy-4-pregnene-3,20-dione	Δ^1	S-873
		11β,14α,17α,21-tetrahydroxy-4-pregnene-3,20-dione	Δ^1	S-874
		17α,21-dihydroxy-14α,15α-oxido-4-pregnene-3,20-dione	Δ^1	S-873
		11β,17α,21-trihydroxy-14α,15α-oxido-4-pregnene-3,20-dione	Δ^1	S-873
		4,6-pregnadiene-3,20-dione	Δ^1	S-873

TABLE III

Transformations by Genus: MYCOBACTERIUM

SPECIES	SOURCE	SUBSTRATE	REACTION	REF.
thamnopheos	PF	17α,21-dihydroxy-4,9(11)-pregnadiene-3,20-dione	Δ^1	S-873
		4-pregnene-3,11,20-trione	Δ^1	S-873
		14α,17α,21-trihydroxy-4-pregnene-3,11,20-trione	Δ^1	S-874
(in sequential fermentation with Curvularia sp. [11β-OH])		17α,21-dihydroxy-4-pregnene-3,20-dione	Δ^1	S-868
tuberculosis (BCG-strain)	IMJ	3α-hydroxy-5α-androstan-17-one	3α-OH→3-C=O; Δ^4	S-818
			3α-OH→3-C=O; $\Delta^{1,4}$	S-818
			3α-OH→3-C=O; $\Delta^{1,4}$; 9α-OH; rev. aldol.; enoliz.; 9-C=O→9ξ-OH	S-818
		3α-hydroxy-5β-androstan-17-one	3α-OH→3-C=O; Δ^4	S-818
			3α-OH→3-C=O; $\Delta^{1,4}$	S-818
			3α-OH→3-C=O; $\Delta^{1,4}$; 9α-OH; rev. aldol.; enol.; 9-C=O→9ξ-OH	S-818
		3β-hydroxy-5-androsten-17-one	Δ^1; Δ^5→Δ^4; 3β-OH→3-C=O	S-818
			Δ^5→Δ^4; 3β-OH→3-C=O	S-818
			Δ^1; Δ^5→Δ^4; 3β-OH→3-C=O; 9α-OH; rev. aldol.; enol.; 9-C=O→9ξ-OH	S-818
	PF	17β-hydroxy-4-estren-3-one	Δ^1; enol.	S-873
		4-androstene-3,17-dione	Δ^1	S-873
		4,6-androstadiene-3,17-dione	Δ^1	S-873
		17α-hydroxy-4-pregnene-3,20-dione	Δ^1	S-873
		11β,17α-dihydroxy-4-pregnene-3,20-dione	Δ^1	S-873
		17α,21-dihydroxy-4-pregnene-3,20-dione	Δ^1	S-873

TABLE III

TAXONOMY

ansformations by Genus: MYCOBACTERIUM
MYCOCLADUS   (Phyco. - Mucorales)
MYCOCOCCUS   (Schizo. - Actinomycetales)

SPECIES	SOURCE	SUBSTRATE	REACTION	REF.
tuberculosis	PF	9α-fluoro-11β,17α,21-tri-hydroxy-4-pregnene-3,20-dione	Δ^1	S-873
		11β,14α,17α,21-tetrahydroxy-4-pregnene-3,20-dione	Δ^1	S-874
		17α,21-dihydroxy-14α,15α-oxido-4-pregnene-3,20-dione	Δ^1	S-873
		11β,17α,21-trihydroxy-14α,15α-oxido-4-pregnene-3,20-dione	Δ^1	S-873
		4,6-pregnadiene-3,20-dione	Δ^1	S-873
		17α,21-dihydroxy-4,9(11)-pregnadiene-3,20-dione	Δ^1	S-873
		4-pregnene-3,11,20-trione	Δ^1	S-873
		14α,17α,21-trihydroxy-4-pregnene-3,11,20-trione	Δ^1	S-874
,in sequential fermenta-:ion with Curvularia sp. 11β-OH])		17α,21-dihydroxy-4-pregnene-3,20-dione	Δ^1	S-868
MYCOCLADUS				
hyalinus	SSSR	17α,21-dihydroxy-4-pregnene-3,20-dione	11α-OH	E-224
MYCOCOCCUS				
species	ATCC-13556 (IFO-3574)	4-pregnene-3,20-dione	Δ^1	I-429
		11β,21-dihydroxy-4-pregnene-3,20-dione	Δ^1	I-429
		17α,21-dihydroxy-4-pregnene-3,20-dione	Δ^1	I-429
		11β,17α,21-trihydroxy-4-pregnene-3,20-dione	Δ^1	I-429
		9α-fluoro-11β,17α,21-tri-hydroxy-4-pregnene-3,20-dione	Δ^1	I-429
		17α,21-dihydroxy-4-pregnene-3,11,20-trione	Δ^1	I-429

488

TABLE III

Transformations by Genus: MYCOCOCCUS

SPECIES	SOURCE	SUBSTRATE	REACTION	REF.
species	ATCC-13557 (IFO-3588)	11β,17α,21-trihydroxy-4-pregnene-3,20-dione	Δ^1	I-429
(in mixed culture with: Acetobacter aceti IFO-3169	IFO (A$_1$)		—	I-428
Acetobacter xylinum IFO-3174			—	I-428
Achromobacter liquidum IFO-3084			Δ^1	I-428
Aerobacter arogenus IFO-3321			Δ^1	I-428
Agrobacterium tumefaciens IFO-3058			Δ^1	I-428
Bacillus cereus IFO-3466			Δ^1	I-428
Bacillus circulans IFO-3029			—	I-428
Bacillus pymilus IFO-3020			Δ^1	I-428
Bacterium mycoides IFO-3040			Δ^1	I-428
Erwinia carotovora IFO-3380			Δ^1	I-428
Escherichia coli IFO-3043			Δ^1	I-428
Flavobacterium flavescens IFO-3058			Δ^1	I-428
Lactobacillus brevis IFO-3345			Δ^1	I-428
Lactobacillus buchneri IFO-3230			Δ^1	I-428
Lactobacillus bulgaricus IFO-3492			—	I-428
Micrococcus citreus IFO-3332)			—	I-428

TABLE III

Transformations by Genus: MYCOCOCCUS

SPECIES	SOURCE	SUBSTRATE	REACTION	REF.
species (in mixed culture with Micrococcus flavus - IFO-3242	IFO	$11\beta,17\alpha,21$-trihydroxy-4-preg- nene-3,20-dione	—	I-428
Micrococcus pyogenus - IFO-3061			—	I-428
Micrococcus sub- flavus- IFO-3062			Δ^1	I-428
Pseudomonas aeruglnosa-IFO-3505			Δ^1	I-428
Pseudomonas fragi - IFO-3458			Δ^1	I-428
Pseudomonas fluor- escens - IFO-3459			Δ^1	I-428
Pseudomonas grav- eolens - IFO-3460			Δ^1	I-428
Pseudomonas sp. - TAKEDA - B-1, B-6, B-7, B-9, B-24, B-29, B-34, B-36, B-38, B-39, B-44, B-49			Δ^1	I-428
Pseudomonas stria- faciens - IFO-3309			—	I-428
Sarcina albida - IFO-3063			—	I-428
Sarcina lutea - IFO-3232			—	I-428
Serratia marcescens- IFO-3046			—	I-428
Vibrio percolans - IFO-3348			—	I-428
Xanthomonas malvacerum - IFO- 3383)			--	I-428

490

TABLE III

Transformations by Genus:

	TAXONOMY
MYCOCONE	(Imperf. - Moniliales)
MYCOPLANA	(Schizo. - Pseudomonadales)
MYCOSPHAERELLA	(Asco. - Sphaericales)
MYROTHECIUM	(Imperf. - Moniliales)
NADSONIA	(Asco. - Endomycetales)

SPECIES	SOURCE	SUBSTRATE	REACTION	REF.
MYCOCONE				
jaepii	FRI	17α,21-dihydroxy-4-pregnene-3,20-dione	11α-OH	S-849
MYCOPLANA				
bullata	NG	5-cholesten-3β-ol (sole carbon source)	—	T-1030
dimorpha	NRRL	Sarsasapogenin	—	M-587
		Diosgenin	—	M-587
		4-dehydrotigogenone	—	M-587
MYCOSPHAERELLA				
horii	TNAES	17α,21-dihydroxy-4-pregnene-3,20-dione	—	S-849
latebrosa	CBS	17β-hydroxy-4-estren-3-one	16β-OH	D-149
			16-C=O (via-16β-OH)	D-149
	OR	17β-hydroxy-4-estren-3-one	16β-OH	S-950
		17α-ethyl-17β-hydroxy-4-estren-3-one	16β-OH	S-950
MYROTHECIUM				
roridum	AMCY	3β-hydroxy-16α,17α-oxido-5-pregnen-20-one	11α-OH	P-746
species	NRRL	plant saponins	—	K-478
NADSONIA				
fulvescens	NRRL	Sarsasapogenin	—	M-587
		Diosgenin	—	M-587
		4-dehydrotigogenone	—	M-587

TABLE III

TAXONOMY

ransformations by Genus:

NAEMATOLOMA	(Basidio. - Agaricales)
NAUCORIA	(Basidio. - Agaricales)
NEOCOSMOSPORA	(Asco. - Hypocreales)
NEUROSPORA	(Asco. - Sphaeriales)

SPECIES	SOURCE	SUBSTRATE	REACTION	REF.
NAEMATOLOMA				
sublateratium	AL(H-6)	4-pregnene-3,20-dione	oxidation- products not identified	S-825
	VEB	4-pregnene-3,20-dione	$6\beta,14\alpha$-diOH	S-811
		14α-hydroxy-4-pregnene-3,20- dione	6β-OH	S-811
NAUCORIA				
confragosa	AL(C-172)	4-pregnene-3,20-dione	$6\beta,17\alpha$-diOH	S-825
NEOCOSMOSPORA				
vasinfecta	ATCC-12717	5β-pregnane-3,20-dione	17β-Ac → 17β-OH	S-881
		4-pregnene-3,20-dione	17β-Ac → 17β-OH	S-881
		14α-hydroxy-4-pregnene-3,20- dione	17β-Ac → 17β-OH	S-881
		21-hydroxy-4-pregnene-3,20- dione	17β-(20-C=O- 21-OH) →17β- OH	S-881
		21-hydroxy-4-pregnene-3,20- dione acetate	17β-(20-C=O- 21-OAc) →17β- OH	S-881
		4-pregnene-3,11,20-trione	17β-Ac → 17β-OH	S-881
NEUROSPORA				
crassa	ATCC-10336	4-pregnene-3,20-dione	X-OH	M-601; M-624; M-636
	NG	5-cholesten-3β-ol (sole carbon source)	utilization	S-793c
		24β-methyl-5,7,22-cholesta- triene-3β-ol (sole carbon source)	utilization	S-793c
	WFEB(74)	21-hydroxy-4-pregnene-3,20- dione	9α-OH	S-937

TABLE III

Transformations by Genus: NEUROSPORA
                              NIGROSPORA   (Imperf. - Moniliales)

SPECIES	SOURCE	SUBSTRATE	REACTION	REF.
sitophila	ATCC-9278	5β-pregnane-3,20-dione	X-OH	M-601; M-624
		4-pregnene-3,20-dione	X-OH	M-601; M-624
		17α-hydroxy-4-pregnene-3,20-dione	X-OH	M-601; M-624
		21-hydroxy-4-pregnene-3,20-dione	X-OH	M-601; M-624
		17α,21-dihydroxy-4-pregnene-3,20-dione	X-OH	M-601; M-624
		4,16-pregnadiene-3,20-dione	X-OH	M-601; M-624
	FRI	17α,21-dihydroxy-4-pregnene-3,20-dione	——	S-849
species	Searle (M-714)	4-androstene-3,17-dione	7α-OH	T-1037
NIGROSPORA				
oryzae	ATCC-8667	17β-hydroxy-4-androsten-3-one	X-OH	M-596
		4-androstene-3,17-dione	X-OH	M-596
		4-pregnene-3,20-dione	15α-OH	M-596
			12β,15α-diOH	M-596
		21-hydroxy-4-pregnene-3,20-dione	X-OH	M-596
		17α,21-dihydroxy-4-pregnene-3,20-dione	X-OH	M-596
		16α,17α-oxido-4-pregnene-3,20-dione	X-OH	M-596
	ATCC-12771	17α-hydroxy-4-pregnene-3,20-dione	15β-OH	M-596
		21-hydroxy-4-pregnene-3,20-dione acetate	15α-OH; 21-OAc$\rightarrow$21-OH	M-596
	FRI	17α,21-dihydroxy-4-pregnene-3,20-dione	6β-OH; 11α-OH	S-849
species	ATCC-12773	4-pregnene-3,20-dione	X-OH	M-596

TABLE III

ansformations by Genus: NIGROSPORA
NOCARDIA (Schizo. - Actinomycetales)

SPECIES	SOURCE	SUBSTRATE	REACTION	REF.
species	ATCC-12774	4-pregnene-3,20-dione	15α-OH	M-596
sphaerica	ATCC-12772	4-pregnene-3,20-dione	X-OH	M-596
	NI	3α,14β-dihydroxy-5β-20(22)-cardenolide	3α-OH→3-C=O	N-681
			3α-OH→3-C=O; 12β-OH	N-681
		3β,14β-dihydroxy-5β-17α-20(22)-cardenolide	3β-OH→3-C=O	N-681
		3β,14β-dihydroxy-5β-20(22)-cardenolide	12β-OH; 3β-OH→3-C=O	N-677
			12β-OH	N-677
		3β,14β,16β-trihydroxy-5β-20(22)-cardenolide	3β-OH→3-C=O	N-677
		3β,14β,16β-trihydroxy-5β-20(22)-cardenolide 3-acetate	3β-OAc→3β-OH	N-677
		3β,14β,16β-trihydroxy-5β-20(22)-cardenolide 16-acetate	3β-OH→3-C=O	N-677
		3β,14β,16β-trihydroxy-5β-20(22)-cardenolide 3,16-diacetate	3β-OAc→3-C=O; 16β-OAc→16β-OH	N-677
			3β-OAc→3β-OH; 16β-OAc→16β-OH	N-677
			3β-OAc→3-C=O	N-677
			3β-OAc→3β-OH	N-677
NOCARDIA (synonym - proactino-mycetes)				
asteroides (synonym for species blackwellii)	ATCC-3308	2α-fluoro-17α,21-dihydroxy-4-pregnene-3,11-20-trione	Δ^1	H-401
	ATCC-9970	11β,17α,21-trihydroxy-5β-pregnane-3,20-dione	Δ^4	S-939
*		11β,17α,21-trihydroxy-4-pregnene-3,20-dione	Δ^1	S-939

TABLE III

Transformations by Genus: NOCARDIA

SPECIES	SOURCE	SUBSTRATE	REACTION	REF.
asteroides (synonum for species blackwellii)	ATCC-9970	$11\beta,17\alpha,21$-trihydroxy-16α-methyl -4-pregnene-3,20-dione	Δ^1	H-392
		$11\beta,17\alpha,21$-trihydroxy-$6\alpha,16\alpha$- dimethyl-4-pregnene-3,20- dione	Δ^1	A-24; A-25
	ATCC-10904	$11\beta,17\alpha,21$-trihydroxy-4-preg- nene-3,20-dione	Δ^1	S-939
	LED	5-cholesten-3β-ol	utilization	M-595
*	SQ (SC-2626)	9α-fluoro-$11\beta,17\alpha,21$-trihydroxy- 4-pregnene-3,20-dione	Δ^1	T-1005
aurantia	AMCY	$11\beta,17\alpha,21$-trihydroxy-4-preg- nene-3,20-dione (use of dried thalli)	Δ^1	F-231
	ATCC-12674	4-pregnene-3,20-dione	Δ^1	S-890; T-1005
		$17\alpha,21$-dihydroxy-4-pregnene- 3,20-dione	9α-OH	P-740; S-898
		6α-fluoro-$11\beta,16\alpha,17\alpha,21$-tetra- hydroxy-$9\alpha$-methyl-4-preg- nene-3,20-dione	Δ^1	F-260
		9α-fluoro-$11\beta,17\alpha,21$-trihydroxy- 4-pregnene-3,20-dione	Δ^1	T-1005
		$6\alpha,9\alpha$-difluoro-$11\beta,16\alpha,17\alpha,21$- tetrahydroxy-$12\alpha$-methyl-4- pregnene-3,20-dione	Δ^1	F-260
		$6\alpha,12\alpha$-difluoro-$11\beta,16\alpha,17\alpha,21$- tetrahydroxy-4-pregnene- 3,20-dione	Δ^1	F-261
*		5-cholesten-3β-ol	$\Delta^5 \to \Delta^4$; 3β-OH $\to$3-C=O	T-1005
		4-cholesten-3-one (use of cell free enzymes)	Δ^1	S-890
	SQ	6α-chloro-12α-fluoro-$11\beta,16\alpha,17\alpha,$ 21-tetrahydroxy-4-pregnene- 3,20-dione	Δ^1	F-261
		6α-chloro-12α-fluoro-$11\beta,16\alpha,17\alpha,$ 21-tetrahydroxy-4-pregnene- 3,20-dione 16,17-acetonide	Δ^1	F-261
		12α-chloro-6α-fluoro-$16\alpha,17\alpha,21$- trihydroxy-4-pregnene-3,11, 20-trione	Δ^1	F-261

TABLE III

Transformations by Genus: NOCARDIA

SPECIES	SOURCE	SUBSTRATE	REACTION	REF.
aurantia	SQ(SC-2316)	4-pregnene-3,20-dione	Δ^1	T-1005
*		9α-fluoro-11β,17α,21-tri-hydroxy-4-pregnene-3,20-dione	Δ^1	T-1005
*		5-cholesten-3β-ol	$\Delta^5 \to \Delta^4$; 3β-OH $\to$ 3-C=O	T-1005
	SQ(SC-2317)	4-pregnene-3,20-dione	Δ^1	T-1005
*		9α-fluoro-11β,17α,21-tri-hydroxy-4-pregnene-3,20-dione	Δ^1	T-1005
*		5-cholesten-3β-ol	$\Delta^5 \to \Delta^4$: 3β-OH $\to$ 3-C=O	T-1005
blackwellii (see asteroides)	ATCC-6846 (Squibb-SC-1584)	17α,21-dihydroxy-5α-pregnane-3,20-dione	$\Delta^{1,4}$	S-939; S-943
		17α,21-dihydroxy-5α-pregnane-3,11,20-trione	$\Delta^{1,4}$	S-943
		3α,11β,17α,21-tetrahydroxy-5β-pregnan-20-one	$\Delta^{1,4}$; 3α-OH $\to$ 3-C=O	S-943
		17α,21-dihydroxy-5β-pregnane-3,20-dione	$\Delta^{1,4}$	S-939; S-943
		11β,17α,21-trihydroxy-5β-pregnane-3,20-dione	$\Delta^{1,4}$	S-939; S-943
		3α,17α,21-trihydroxy-5β-pregnane-11,20-dione	$\Delta^{1,4}$; 3α-OH $\to$ 3-C=O	S-943
		3α,17α,21-trihydroxy-5β-pregnane-11,20-dione 21-acetate	$\Delta^{1,4}$; 3α-OH $\to$ 3-C=O 21-OAc $\to$ 21-OH	S-939
		3α,17α,21-trihydroxy-16α-methyl-5β-pregnane-11,20-dione 21-acetate	$\Delta^{1,4}$; 3α-OH $\to$ 3-C=O	S-902
		3α,17α,21-trihydroxy-16β-methyl-5β-pregnane-11,20-dione 21-acetate	$\Delta^{1,4}$; 3α-OH $\to$ 3-C=O	S-905
		17α,21-dihydroxy-5β-pregnane-3,11,20-trione 21-acetate	$\Delta^{1,4}$; 21-OAc $\to$ 21-OH	S-939; S-943
		9α-fluoro-11β,17α,21-tri-hydroxy-4-pregnene-3,20-dione	Δ^1	T-1005
		2α-fluoro-17α,21-dihydroxy-4-pregnene-3,11,20-trione	Δ^1	H-401
	UC	4-pregnene-3,20-dione 20-cycloethyleneketal	Δ^1	F-251

TABLE III

Transformations by Genus: NOCARDIA

SPECIES		SOURCE	SUBSTRATE	REACTION	REF.
braziliensis	*	SQ(SC-2627)	9α-fluoro-$11\beta,17\alpha,21$-trihydroxy-4-pregnene-3,20-dione	Δ^1	T-1005
coeliaca	*	SQ(SC-2751) (WC-704)	9α-fluoro-$11\beta,17\alpha,21$-trihydroxy-4-pregnene-3,20-dione	Δ^1	T-1005
convoluta	*	ATCC-4275	$11\beta,17\alpha,21$-trihydroxy-4-pregnene-3,20-dione	Δ^1	S-939
corallina		ATCC-999	17β-hydroxy-4-estren-3-one (possible synonym -Mycobacterium rhodochrous -Ref. F-231 - use of dried thalii) (Ref., F-232 and H-399 - use of inhibitors)	Δ^1; enol.; 17β-OH$\rightarrow$ 17-C=O	F-231 H-399
			4-estrene-3,16-dione	Δ^1; enol.	S-793a
			16α-hydroxy-4-estren-3-one	Δ^1; enol.; 16α-OH$\rightarrow$ 16-C=O	S-793a
			16β-hydroxy-4-estren-3-one	Δ^1; enol., 16β-OH$\rightarrow$ 16-C=O	S-793a
			17β-hydroxy-4-androsten-3-one	Δ^1	F-231; H-399
				17β-OH$\rightarrow$ 17-C=O	F-231; H-399
				Δ^1; 17β-OH$\rightarrow$ 17-C=O	F-231; H-399
			$2\alpha,17\beta$-dihydroxy-4-androsten-3-one	Δ^1; 17β-OH$\rightarrow$ 17-C=O	H-399
			$2\alpha,17\beta$-dihydroxy-4-androsten-3-one diacetate	Δ^1; 2α-OAc$\rightarrow$ 2α-OH; 17β-OAc$\rightarrow$17-C=O	F-231; H-399
				2α-OAc$\rightarrow2\alpha$-OH; 17β-OAc$\rightarrow$ 17-C=O	H-399
			$2\beta,17\beta$-dihydroxy-4-androsten-3-one diacetate	Δ^1; 2β-OAc$\rightarrow$ 2β-OH; 17β-OAc$\rightarrow$17-C=O	H-399
				2β-OAc$\rightarrow$ 2β-OH; 17β-OAc$\rightarrow$17-C=O	H-399

TABLE III

Transformations by Genus: NOCARDIA

SPECIES	SOURCE	SUBSTRATE	REACTION	REF.
corallina	ATCC-999	4-androstene-3,17-dione	Δ^1	F-231; F-232; H-399
		9α-fluoro-11β,16α,17aα-tri-hydroxy-17aβ-hydroxymethyl-D-<u>homo</u>-4-androstene-3,17-dione	Δ^1	<u>S-910</u>
		4-pregnene-3,20-dione	Δ^1	F-231; F-232; H-399
		11β,21-dihydroxy-4-pregnene-3,20-dione	Δ^1	F-231; <u>H-399</u>
		17α,21-dihydroxy-4-pregnene-3,20-dione	Δ^1	F-231; F-232; H-399
		9α-chloro-11β,21-dihydroxy-4-pregnene-3,20-dione	Δ^1	<u>H-399</u>
		9α-fluoro-7α,11β-dihydroxy-4-pregnene-3,20-dione	Δ^1	B-56
		9α-fluoro-11β,21-dihydroxy-4-pregnene-3,20-dione	Δ^1	F-231; <u>H-399</u>
		7α,11β,21-trihydroxy-4-pregnene-3,20-dione	Δ^1	B-56
		11β,17α,21-trihydroxy-4-pregnene-3,20-dione	Δ^1	F-230; F-231; F-232; H-399
		2α-fluoro-11β,17α,21-trihydroxy-4-pregnene-3,20-dione	Δ^1	F-231; <u>H-401</u>
		9α-fluoro-7α,11β,21-trihydroxy-4-pregnene-3,20-dione	Δ^1	B-56
		9α-fluoro-11β,16α,21-trihydroxy-4-pregnene-3,20-dione	Δ^1	H-403
		9α-fluoro-11β,17α,21-trihydroxy-4-pregnene-3,20-dione	Δ^1	F-231; <u>H-399</u>; <u>H-403</u>
		11β,17α,21-trihydroxy-2α-methyl-4-pregnene-3,20-dione 21-acetate	Δ^1; 21-OAc→21-OH	F-231; <u>H-399</u>
			21-OAc→21-OH	<u>H-399</u>
		11β,16α,17α,21-tetrahydroxy-4-pregnene-3,20-dione	Δ^1	<u>B-61</u>; <u>F-231</u>; <u>H-399</u>

TABLE III

Transformations by Genus: NOCARDIA

SPECIES	SOURCE	SUBSTRATE	REACTION	REF.
corallina	ATCC-999	9α-chloro-11β,16α,17α,21-tetra-hydroxy-4-pregnene-3,20-dione	Δ^1	H-399
		9α-fluoro-1ξ,11β,17α,21-tetra-hydroxy-4-pregnene-3,20-dione	—	H-399
		9α-fluoro-6β,11β,17α,21-tetra-hydroxy-4-pregnene-3,20-dione	Δ^1	F-231
		9α-fluoro-11β,16α,17α,21-tetra-hydroxy-4-pregnene-3,20-dione	Δ^1	B-61; F-231; H-399; O-704
		9α-fluoro-11β,16α,17α,21-tetra-hydroxy-4-pregnene-3,20-dione 16,21-diacetate	Δ^1; 16α-OAc→ 16α-OH; 21-OAc → 21-OH	B-61; F-255; O-704
		9α-fluoro-11β,16α,17α,21-tetra-hydroxy-4-pregnene-3,20-dione 16,17-acetonide	Δ^1	F-231; H-399
		2α,9α-difluoro-11β,16α,17α,21-tetrahydroxy-4-pregnene-3,20-dione 16,17-acetonide	Δ^1	H-401
		9α-fluoro-6β,11β,16α,17α,21-pentahydroxy-4-pregnene-3,20-dione 16,17-acetonide	Δ^1	H-400
		17α,21-dihydroxy-4-pregnene-3,11,20-trione	Δ^1	F-231; H-399
		2α-fluoro-17α,21-dihydroxy-4-pregnene-3,11,20-trione	Δ^1	H-401; H-402
*	ATCC-4273	11β,17α,21-trihydroxy-4-pregnene-3,20-dione	Δ^1	S-939
	ATCC-4275	4-pregnene-3,20-dione	Δ^1	T-1005
*		9α-fluoro-11β,17α,21-trihydroxy-4-pregnene-3,20-dione	Δ^1	T-1005
*		5-cholesten-3β-ol	$\Delta^5 \rightarrow \Delta^4$; 3β-OH →3-C=O	T-1005
	ATCC-13258	4-androstene-3,17-dione	9α-OH; Δ^1; rev. aldol.; enol.	M-597
		19-hydroxy-4-androstene-3,17-dione	Δ^1; reverse aldol; (Formaldehyde ↑) enol.	M-597

NOTE: For source ATCC-4273 above - possibly Mycobacterium agreste and Mycobacterium rhodochrous - J. Gen. Microbiol., 21: 139 (1959)

TABLE III

Transformations by Genus: NOCARDIA

SPECIES	SOURCE	SUBSTRATE	REACTION	REF.
corallina	ATCC-13258	17α,21-dihydroxy-4-pregnene-3,20-dione	9α-OH	D-173
	ATCC-13259	4-androstene-3,17-dione	9α-OH; Δ^1; rev. aldol.; enol.	D-172; M-597
*			9α-OH	D-172; M-597
		19-hydroxy-4-androstene-3,17-dione	Δ^1; rev. aldol; (Formaldehyde ↑) enol.	M-597
		4-pregnene-3,20-dione	9α-OH	D-173
			9α-OH; 17β-Ac →17β-OH	D-172
	NG	5-cholesten-3β-ol (sole carbon source)	utilization	S-793c
		24β-methyl-5,7,22-cholestatrien-3β-ol (sole carbon source)	utilization	S-793c
erythropolis (Mycobacterium rhodochrous, J. Bact. 73: 23, 1957)	ATCC-4277 (Squibb SC-2820)	11β,17α,21-trihydroxy-4-pregnene-3,20-dione	Δ^1	T-1005
	NCTC-2569	5-cholesten-3β-ol (sole carbon source)	utilization	M-595; S-793c
	NG	1,3,5(10)-estratrien-3,17β-diol	—	S-793c
		1,3,5(10)-estratrien-3,16α,17β-triol	—	S-793c
		17β-hydroxy-4-androsten-3-one	utilization	S-793c
		3-hydroxy-5-androsten-17-one	utilization	S-793c
		4-pregnene-3,20-dione	utilization	S-793c
		3α-hydroxy-5β-cholanic acid	—	S-793c
		3α,7α-dihydroxy-5β-cholanic acid	—	S-793c
		3α,12α-dihydroxy-5β-cholanic acid	utilization	S-793c
		3α,7α,12α-trihydroxy-5β-cholanic acid	utilization	S-793c
		5-cholesten-3β-ol acetate	—	S-793c
		5-cholesten-3β-ol palmitate	utilization	S-793c
		24β-methyl-5,7,22-cholestatrien-3β-ol (sole carbon source)	utilization	S-793c

TABLE III

Transformations by Genus: NOCARDIA

SPECIES	SOURCE	SUBSTRATE	REACTION	REF.
farcinica	NG (No. 1, 2)	5-cholesten-3β-ol (sole carbon source)	utilization	S-793c
		24β-methyl-5,7,22-cholestatrien-3β-ol (sole carbon source)	utilization	S-793c
formica	NRRL-2470	11β,17α,21-trihydroxy-5β-pregnane-3,20-dione	Δ^4	S-939
*		11β,17α,21-trihydroxy-4-pregnene-3,20-dione	Δ^1	S-939
		9α-fluoro-11β,17α,21-trihydroxy-6α,16α-dimethyl-4-pregnene-3,20-dione	Δ^1	A-24; A-25
gardneri * (see asteroides)	ATCC-9604 (Squibb-SC-1940)	9α-fluoro-11β,17α,21-trihydroxy-4-pregnene-3,20-dione	Δ^1	T-1005
*	NCTC-6531 (Squibb-SC-6531)	9α-fluoro-11β,17α,21-trihydroxy-4-pregnene-3,20-dione	Δ^1	T-1005
	NG	5-cholesten-3β-ol (sole carbon source)	utilization	S-793c
		24β-methyl-5,7,22-cholestatrien-3β-ol (sole carbon source)	utilization	S-793c
globerula (Mycobacterium rhodochrous-J. Bact. 73: 24, 1957)	ATCC-9356	11β,17α,21-trihydroxy-5β-pregnane-3,20-dione	Δ^4	S-939
*		11β,17α,21-trihydroxy-4-pregnene-3,20-dione (Ref. B-37 - use of antibiotics)	Δ^1	B-37 S-939
*		9α-fluoro-11β,17α,21-trihydroxy-4-pregnene-3,20-dione	Δ^1	T-1005
italica n.s.	FARMIT	17α,21-dihydroxy-4-pregnene-3,20-dione	16α-OH	S-918
		11β,17α,21-trihydroxy-4-pregnene-3,20-dione	16α-OH	S-918
		9α-fluoro-11β,17α,21-trihydroxy-4-pregnene-3,20-dione	16α-OH	S-918
		9α-fluoro-11β,17α,21-trihydroxy-1,4-pregnadiene-3,20-dione	16α-OH	S-918
leishmanii	ATCC-6855	11β,17α,21-trihydroxy-5β-pregnane-3,20-dione	Δ^4	S-939
*		11β,17α,21-trihydroxy-4-pregnene-3,20-dione	Δ^1	S-939
		9α-fluoro-17α,21-dihydroxy-6α,16α-dimethyl-4-pregnene-3,11,20-trione	Δ^1	A-24; A-25

TABLE III

nsformations by Genus: NOCARDIA

SPECIES	SOURCE	SUBSTRATE	REACTION	REF.
aculata	NG	5-cholesten-3β-ol (sole carbon source)	utilization	S-793c
		24β-methyl-5,7,22-cholestatrien-3β-ol (sole carbon source)	utilization	S-793c
adurae *	SQ(SC-2628)	9α-fluoro-11β,17α,21-trihydroxy-4-pregnene-3,20-dione	Δ^1	T-1005
exicanus	NG	5-cholesten-3β-ol (sole carbon source)	utilization	S-793c
		24β-methyl-5,7,22-cholestatrien-3β-ol (sole carbon source)	utilization	S-793c
inima	ATCC-8674	11β,17α,21-trihydroxy-5β-pregnane-3,20-dione	Δ^4	S-939
*		11β,17α,21-trihydroxy-4-pregnene-3,20-dione	Δ^1	S-939
paca	ATCC-4276	17β-hydroxy-4-estren-3-one	Δ^1; enol.	B-37
		4-androstene-3,17-dione	Δ^1	B-37
		4,6-androstadiene-3,17-dione	Δ^1	B-37
		17α-hydroxy-4-pregnene-3,20-dione	Δ^1	B-37
		11β,17α-dihydroxy-4-pregnene-3,20-dione	Δ^1	B-37
		17α,21-dihydroxy-4-pregnene-3,20-dione	Δ^1	B-37
		9α-fluoro-17α,21-dihydroxy-4-pregnene-3,20-dione	Δ^1	B-37
		11β,17α,21-trihydroxy-4-pregnene-3,20-dione (use of antibiotics)	Δ^1	B-37
		17α,21-dihydroxy-14α,15α-oxido-4-pregnene-3,20-dione	Δ^1	B-37
		11β,17α,21-trihydroxy-14α,15α-oxido-4-pregnene-3,20-dione	Δ^1	B-37
		11β,14α,17α,21-tetrahydroxy-4-pregnene-3,20-dione	Δ^1	B-37
		6α,9α-difluoro-11β,17α,21-trihydroxy-16-methylene-4-pregnene-3,20-dione	Δ^1	A-7
		4-pregnene-3,11,20-trione	Δ^1	B-37
		2α-fluoro-17α,21-dihydroxy-4-pregnene-3,20-dione	Δ^1	H-401

TABLE III

Transformations by Genus: NOCARDIA

SPECIES	SOURCE	SUBSTRATE	REACTION	REF.
opaca	ATCC-4276	$14\alpha,17\alpha,21$-trihydroxy-4-pregnene-3,11,20-trione	Δ^1	B-37
		4,16-pregnadiene-3,20-dione	Δ^1	B-37
		$17\alpha,21$-dihydroxy-4,9(11)-pregnadiene-3,20-trione	Δ^1	B-37
		$17\alpha,21$-dihydroxy-4,14-pregnadiene-3,20-dione	Δ^1	B-37
		17α-hydroxy-21-methyl-4,9(11)-pregnadiene-3,20-dione	Δ^1	H-391
	SQ (SC-2812) (WC-560)	9α-fluoro-$11\beta,17\alpha,21$-trihydroxy-4-pregnene-3,20-dione	Δ^1	T-1005
paraffinae	NG	5-cholesten-3β-ol (sole carbon source)	utilization	S-793c
		24β-methyl-5,7-22-cholestatrien-3β-ol (sole carbon source)	utilization	S-793c
polychromogenes	NG	5-cholesten-3β-ol (sole carbon source)	utilization	S-793c
		24β-methyl-5,7-22-cholestatrien-3β-ol (sole carbon source)	utilization	S-793c
restrictus	AY	19-hydroxy-4,7-androstadiene-3,17-dione	Δ^1; rev. aldol; enol.	B-38
		19-methoxy-4,7-androstadiene-3,17-dione	Δ^1; rev. aldol; enol.	B-38
	NCTC-6846	5-cholesten-3β-ol	utilization	M-595
	Sp-WISC	17β-hydroxy-A-nor-3-androsten-2-one	9α-OH; 17β-OH → 17-C=O	S-885
		9α-hydroxy-4-androstene-3,17-dione (enzyme preparation)	Δ^1; rev. aldol; enol.	S-885
		17β-hydroxy-5-androsten-3-one cycloethyleneketal	17β-OH → 17-C=O	S-885
		3,4-dihydroxy-9,10-seco-1,3,5(10)-androstene-9,17-dione (cell free extract)	degradation [A,B]	S-896
		4-pregnene-3,20-dione	Δ^1	S-885
			9α-OH	S-885

TABLE III

ansformations by Genus: NOCARDIA

SPECIES	SOURCE	SUBSTRATE	REACTION	REF.
restrictus	Sp-WISC	4-pregnene-3,20-dione (with KCN)	9α-OH; 17β-Ac $\rightarrow$ 17-C$=$O	S-885
		9α-fluoro-11β,17α,21-tri-hydroxy-4-pregnene-3,20-dione	Δ^1	S-885
		3β,5β,14β-trihydroxy-19-oxo-20(22)-cardenolide	3β-OH $\rightarrow$ 3-C$=$O; 5β-OH $\rightarrow\Delta^4$	K-481
			3β-OH $\rightarrow$ 3-C$=$O; 5β-OH $\rightarrow\Delta^4$; Δ^1; 10β-HC$=$O $\rightarrow$ 10β-H; enol.	K-481
		14β-hydroxy-3,19-dioxo-4,20 (22)-cardadienolide	Δ^1; 10β-HC$=$O $\rightarrow$ 10β-H; enol.	K-481
		14β-hydroxy-3-keto-19-nor-4,20(22)-cardadienolide	Δ^1; enol.	K-481
	SQ	17β-hydroxy-4-estren-3-one	Δ^1; enol.	S-889
		17β-hydroxy-4-androsten-3-one	Δ^1	S-889
		17α,21-dihydroxy-4-pregnene-3,20-dione	Δ^1	S-889
		11β,17α,21-trihydroxy-4-pregnene-3,20-dione	Δ^1	S-889
	SQ(SC-2914 SC-2915 SC-2917 SC-2919)	4-pregnene-3,20-dione	Δ^1	T-1005
*		9α-fluoro-11β,17α,21-trihydroxy-4-pregnene-3,20-dione	Δ^1	T-1005
*		5-cholesten-3β-ol	$\Delta^5\rightarrow\Delta^4$; 3β-OH $\rightarrow$ 3-C$=$O	T-1005
	WC (545)	17β-hydroxy-A-nor-3-androsten-2-one	9α-OH; 17β-OH $\rightarrow$ 17-C$=$O	W-1080
		17β-hydroxy-17α-methyl-A-nor-3-androsten-2-one	9α-OH	W-1080
		A,19-bisnor-3-androstene-2,17-dione	9α-OH	W-1080

TABLE III

Transformations by Genus: NOCARDIA

SPECIES	SOURCE	SUBSTRATE	REACTION	REF.
restrictus	WC(545)	17β-hydroxy-4-androsten-3-one	Δ^1	S-883
			9α-OH; Δ^1; rev. aldol; enol.; 17β-OH →17-C=O	W-1063
			9α-OH; Δ^1; rev. aldol; enol.; 9-C=O →9β-OH 17β-OH → 17-C=O	W-1063
			9α-OH; Δ^1 rev. aldol; enol.; 9-C=O →9α-OH 17β-OH → 17-C=O	W-1063
			17-C=O → 17β-OH; 9α-OH; Δ^1; rev. aldol; enol.; 9-C=O →9β-OH	W-1063
			17β-OH → 17-C=O degradation; [A,B]	W-1063
		4-androstene-3,17-dione (cell free extract-Ref. S-883)	Δ^1	S-883; S-884; S-894
			9α-OH	S-884; S-894
			9α-OH; Δ^1; rev. aldol; enol.	S-884; S-894; S-895
		9α-hydroxy-4-androstene-3,17-dione (cell-free extract)	Δ^1; rev. aldol; enol.	S-884; S-894
		19-hydroxy-4-androstene-3,17-dione	Δ^1; rev. aldol; enol.	S-884; S-894
		4-androstene-3,17-dione	degradation; [A,B]	S-895
		A-nor-3-pregnene-2,20-dione	9α-OH	W-1079
		4-pregnene-3,20-dione (cell free extract - Ref. S-883)	Δ^1	S-883; T-1005

TABLE III

nsformations by Genus: NOCARDIA

SPECIES	SOURCE	SUBSTRATE	REACTION	REF.
estrictus	WC (545)	4-pregnene-3,20-dione (use of inhibitors-Ref. S-898)	9α-OH	P-740; S-897; S-898
			17β-Ac $\rightarrow$ 17-C=O	S-898
		$17\alpha,21$-dihydroxy-4-pregnene- 3,20-dione (cell-free extract)	Δ^1	S-883
			9α-OH	P-740
		$11\beta,17\alpha,21$-trihydroxy-4- pregnene-3,20-dione (cell-free extract)	Δ^1	S-883
*		9α-fluoro-$11\beta,17\alpha,21$-trihy- droxy-4-pregnene-3,20-dione (cell-free extract-Ref. S-883)	Δ^1	S-883; S-884; S-894; T-1005
*		9α-fluoro-$11\beta,16\alpha,17\alpha,21$- tetrahydroxy-4-pregnene- 3,20-dione (cell-free extract)	Δ^1	S-883; T-1005
		$17\alpha,21$-dihydroxy-4-pregnene- 3,11,20-trione (cell-free extract)	Δ^1	S-883
		5-cholesten-3β-ol	$\Delta^5 \rightarrow \Delta^4$; 3β-OH $\rightarrow$ 3-C=O	T-1005
ubra * Mycobacterium rhodo- hrous-J. Bact. 73:15, 957)	SQ (SC-2823) (WC-546)	9α-fluoro-$11\beta,17\alpha,21$-tri- hydroxy-4-pregnene-3,20- dione	Δ^1	T-1005
almonicolor	NG	5-cholesten-3β-ol (sole carbon source)	utilization	S-793c
	NG	24β-methyl-5,7,22-cholesta- trien-3β-ol (sole carbon source)	utilization	S-793c
*	SQ (SC-2750) (WC-647)	9α-fluoro-$11\beta,17\alpha,21$-tri- hydroxy-4-pregnene-3,20- dione	Δ^1	T-1005
pecies	ATCC-13259	4-androstene-3,17-dione	9α-OH; Δ^1; rev. aldol; enol.	D-171
	ATCC-13934	4,9(11)-androstadiene-3,17-dione	$\Delta^{9(11)} \rightarrow$ $9\alpha,11\alpha$-oxide	S-886
		17α-$(2^1$-carboxyethyl)-17β- hydroxy-4-androsten-3-one spirolactone	9α-OH	D-173

506

TABLE III

Transformations by Genus: NOCARDIA

SPECIES	SOURCE	SUBSTRATE	REACTION	REF.
species	ATCC-13934	4-pregnene-3,20-dione	9α-OH; 17β-Ac $\rightarrow$17-C=O	D-172
			9α-OH	D-172
			9α-OH; 17β-Ac $\rightarrow$17β-OH	D-172
			17β-Ac$\rightarrow$17-C=O	D-172
		17α-hydroxy-4-pregnene-3,20-dione	9α-OH	D-173
		21-hydroxy-4-pregnene-3,20-dione	9α-OH	D-173
		17α,21-dihydroxy-4,9(11)-pregnadiene-3,20-dione	$\Delta^{9(11)}\rightarrow9\alpha,11\alpha$-oxide	S-886
	ATCC-14558	12a-aza-3β-hydroxy-C-homo-5α-pregnane-12,20-dione	3β-OH$\rightarrow$3-C=O; $\Delta^{1,4}$ (5α-H)	M-563
	ATCC-14559	12a-aza-3β,17α-dihydroxy-C-homo-5α-pregnane-12,20-dione	3β-OAc $\rightarrow$ 3-C=O; $\Delta^{1,4}$	M-563
	Searle (A-20-10)	4-androstene-3,17-dione	9α-OH	D-170
			9α-OH; Δ^1; rev. aldol; enol.	
	NG	21-hydroxy-4-pregnene-3,20-dione	9α-OH	S-796
		$3\alpha,7\alpha,12\alpha$-trihydroxy-5β-cholanic acid	degradation	H-330
		5-cholesten-3β-ol (sole carbon source - Ref. S-793c)	$\Delta^5\rightarrow\Delta^4$; 3β-OH $\rightarrow$3-C=O	L-501; S-793c
			3β-OH$\rightarrow$3-C=O; $\Delta^5\rightarrow\Delta^4$; 17β-(2^1-isooctyl) $\rightarrow$ 17-C=O	W-1111
			$\Delta^5\rightarrow\Delta^4$; Δ^1; 3β-OH$\rightarrow$3-C=O; 17β-(2^1-isooctyl) $\rightarrow$17-C=O	W-1111
			3β-OH$\rightarrow$3-C=O; $\Delta^5\rightarrow\Delta^4$; 17β-(2^1-isooctyl)$\rightarrow$17β-(2^1-propionic acid)	W-1111

TABLE III

ransformations by Genus:

NOCARDIA
OIDIUM
OMPHALIA
OOSPORA

TAXONOMY

(Imperf. - Moniliales)
(Basidio. - Agaricales)
(Imperf. - Moniliales)

SPECIES	SOURCE	SUBSTRATE	REACTION	REF.
species	NG	5-cholesten-3β-ol (sole carbon source)	3β-OH→3-C=O; Δ^5→Δ^4; Δ^1; 17β- (2^1-isooctyl)→ 17β-(2^1-prop- ionic acid)	W-1111
		24β-methyl-5,7,22-cholesta- trien-3β-ol (sole carbon source)	utilization	S-793c
		digitonin	decomposition	S-794
	SQ	5α-pregnane-3,20-dione	$\Delta^{1,4}$	S-887; S-888
		5β-pregnane-3,20-dione	$\Delta^{1,4}$	S-887; S-888
		4-pregnene-3,20-dione	Δ^1	S-887; S-888; S-897
		(use of inhibitors)	9α-OH	S-897
OIDIUM				
species	NRRL	plant saponins	—	K-478
OMPHALIA				
tralucida (in mixed culture with Trichoderma viride- NRRL-2473 [17α-OH] and Wojnowicia graminis - NRRL- 2472 [21-OH])	MCC	4-pregnene-3,20-dione	11β-OH	M-566
OOSPORA				
aurantii	TNAES	17α,21-dihydroxy-4-pregnene- 3,20-dione	—	S-849
lactis	UC	not given	oxidation	M-601; M-636

TABLE III

Transformations by Genus: OPHIOBOLUS   (Asco. - Sphaeriales)

SPECIES	SOURCE	SUBSTRATE	REACTION	REF.
graminis	NARI	17α,21-dihydroxy-4-pregnene-3,20-dione	11α-OH	S-849
herpotrichus	C	d,1-19-<u>nor</u>-4-pregnene-3,20-dione	d,1 → d-21-OH + 1	W-1102
		4-pregnene-3,20-dione	21-OH	M-584; W-1101
		d,1-4-pregnene-3,20-dione	d,1 → d-21-OH + 1	W-1102
		17α-hydroxy-4-pregnene-3,20-dione	21-OH	M-584; W-1101
		d,1-9α-fluoro-11β-hydroxy-4-pregnene-3,20-dione	d,1 →d-21-OH + 1	W-1102
		d,1-11β,18β-dihydroxy-4-pregnene-3,20-dione	d,1 →d-21-OH + 1	W-1102
		4-pregnene-3,11,20-trione	21-OH	M-584; W-1101
		d,1-11β-hydroxy-3,20-diketo-4-pregnen-18-oic acid (18 →11) lactone	d,1 →d-21-OH + 1	W-1101; W-1102
			d,1 → d-21-OH + 1	V-1055
		11β,16α-dihydroxy-3,20-diketo-4-pregnen-18-oic acid (18 →11) lactone	21-OH	W-1091
		d,1-11β-hydroxy-3,20-diketo-4-pregnen-18-al (18 → 11) hemiacetal	d,1 →d-21-OH + 1	W-1102
		1,4-pregnadiene-3,20-dione	21-OH	W-1101
		11β,17α-dihydroxy-1,4-pregnadiene-3,20-dione	21-OH	W-1101
		17α-hydroxy-1,4-pregnadiene-3,11,20-trione	21-OH	W-1101
(in mixed culture with one of the following: Curvularia blakesleanna [11β-OH; 11-C=O] - Curvularia brachyospora [11β-OH] - Curvularia lunata [11β-OH] - Rhizopus nigricans [11α-OH])		4-pregnene-3,20-dione	21-OH	W-1106

TABLE III

Transformations by Genus: OPHIOBOLUS

SPECIES	SOURCE	SUBSTRATE	REACTION	REF.
herpotrichus (in mixed culture with Trichothecium roseum [17α-OH])	C	4-pregnene-3,20-dione	21-OH	W-1106
(in mixed culture with one of the following: Calonectria decora [Δ¹]-Curvularia brachyspora [11β- OH]-Trichothecium roseum [17α-OH])			21-OH	W-1107
(in mixed culture with Trichothecium roseum [17α-OH]		11β-hydroxy-4-pregnene-3,20- dione	21-OH	W-1106; W-1107
Calonectria decora [Δ¹])			21-OH	W-1107
(in mixed culture with Calonectria decora [Δ¹]-Tricothecium roseum [17α-OH])		4-pregnene-3,11,20-trione	21-OH	W-1106; W-1107
(in mixed culture with Cunninghamella blakesleeana [11β- OH]-Trichothecium roseum [17α-OH])		1,4-pregnadiene-3,20-dione	21-OH	W-1106
(in mixed culture with Trichothecium roseum [17α-OH])		11β-hydroxy-1,4-pregnadiene- 3,20-dione	21-OH	W-1106
(in mixed culture with Trichothecium roseum [17α-OH])		1,4-pregnadiene-3,11,20-trione	21-OH	W-1106
(in mixed culture with Curvularia brachy- spora [11β-OH])		4-pregnene-3,18,20-trione	21-OH	W-1106
	PIRI .	4-pregnene-3,20-dione	21-OH	<u>W-1081</u>
			$\Delta^4 \rightarrow 5\alpha$-H	<u>W-1081</u>
	SCH	3β-hydroxy-5,16-pregnadien- 20-one	21-OH	<u>H-388</u>; <u>O-700</u>
		11β,17α-dihydroxy-1,4-pregna- diene-3,20-dione	21-OH	<u>H-388</u>; <u>O-700</u>
		17α-hydroxy-1,4-pregnadiene- 3,11,20-trione	21-OH	<u>H-388</u>; <u>O-700</u>
		11α-hydroxy-1,4,16-pregna- triene-3,20-dione	21-OH	<u>H-388</u>; <u>O-700</u>
		11β-hydroxy-1,4,16-pregna- triene-3,20-dione	21-OH	<u>H-388</u>; <u>O-700</u>

TABLE III

Transformations by Genus: OPHIOBOLUS

SPECIES	SOURCE	SUBSTRATE	REACTION	REF.
herpotrichus	UC	4,14-pregnadiene-3,20-dione	21-OH	M-576; M-577
	WFEB	4-pregnene-3,20-dione	21-OH (O_2^{18})	H-374
heterostrophus	C	3β-hydroxy-5-androsten-17-one	Δ^1	W-1105
		4-androstene-3,17-dione	Δ^1	W-1105
		3β-hydroxy-5-pregnen-20-one	Δ^1	W-1105
		4-pregnene-3,20-dione	Δ^1	W-1105
		21-hydroxy-4-pregnene-3,20-dione	Δ^1	W-1105
		$11\alpha,21$-dihydroxy-4-pregnene-3,20-dione	Δ^1	W-1105
		$11\beta,21$-dihydroxy-4-pregnene-3,20-dione	Δ^1	W-1105
		$17\alpha,21$-dihydroxy-4-pregnene-3,20-dione	Δ^1	W-1105
		$11\alpha,17\alpha,21$-trihydroxy-4-pregnene-3,20-dione	Δ^1	W-1105
		$11\beta,17\alpha,21$-trihydroxy-4-pregnene-3,20-dione	Δ^1	W-1105
		$17\alpha,21$-dihydroxy-4-pregnene-3,11,20-trione	Δ^1	W-1105
		17α-hydroxy-3,20-diketo-4-pregnen-18-al	Δ^1	W-1105
		$11\beta,21$-dihydroxy-3,20-diketo-4-pregnen-18-al (18→11) hemiacetal	Δ^1	W-1105
	NIHJ	$17\alpha,21$-dihydroxy-4-pregnene-3,20-dione	Δ^1	S-849
	S	21-hydroxy-4-pregnene-3,20-dione	Δ^1	S-849; S-857
		$11\beta,21\alpha$-dihydroxy-4-pregnene-3,20-dione	Δ^1	S-849; S-857
		$17\alpha,21$-dihydroxy-4-pregnene-3,20-dione	Δ^1	S-849; S-857
		$11\beta,17\alpha,21$-trihydroxy-4-pregnene-3,20-dione	——	S-849; S-857

TABLE III

Transformations by Genus: OPHIOBOLUS

SPECIES	SOURCE	SUBSTRATE	REACTION	REF.
heterostrophus	S	$17\alpha,21$-dihydroxy-4-pregnene-3,11,20-trione	Δ^1	S-849; S-857
miyabeanus	C	3β-hydroxy-5-androsten-17-one	Δ^1	W-1105
		4-androstene-3,17-dione	Δ^1	W-1105
		3β-hydroxy-5-pregnen-20-one	Δ^1	W-1105
		$3\beta,21$-dihydroxy-5-pregnen-20-one	Δ^1	W-1105
		4-pregnene-3,20-dione	Δ^1	W-1105
		21-hydroxy-4-pregnene-3,20-dione	Δ^1	W-1105
		$11\alpha,21$-dihydroxy-4-pregnene-3,20-dione	Δ^1	W-1105
		$11\beta,21$-dihydroxy-4-pregnene-3,20-dione	Δ^1	W-1105
		$17\alpha,21$-dihydroxy-4-pregnene-3,20-dione	Δ^1	W-1105
		$11\alpha,17\alpha,21$-trihydroxy-4-pregnene-3,20-dione	Δ^1	W-1105
		$11\beta,17\alpha,21$-trihydroxy-4-pregnene-3,20-dione	Δ^1	W-1105
		$17\alpha,21$-dihydroxy-4-pregnene-3,11,20-trione	Δ^1	W-1105
		17α-hydroxy-3,20-diketo-4-pregnen-18-al	Δ^1	W-1105
		$11\beta,21$-dihydroxy-3,20-diketo-4-pregnen-18-al (18→11) hemiacetal	Δ^1	W-1105
	FRI	$17\alpha,21$-dihydroxy-4-pregnene-3,20-dione	11α-OH	S-849
	S	4-pregnene-3,20-dione	——	S-859
		17α-hydroxy-4-pregnene-3,20-dione	——	S-859
		$17\alpha,21$-dihydroxy-4-pregnene-3,20-dione	Δ^1	S-849; S-859
sativus	NARI	$17\alpha,21$-dihydroxy-4-pregnene-3,20-dione	6β-OH	S-849

TABLE III

Transformations by Genus:

OPHIOBOLUS
OPHIOSTOMA
PAECILOMYCES
PANAEOLUS

<u>TAXONOMY</u>

(Asco. -Sphaeriales)
(Imperf. - Moniliales)
(Basidio. - Agaricales)

SPECIES	SOURCE	SUBSTRATE	REACTION	REF.
species	C	4-pregnene-3,20-dione	Δ^1; 17β-Ac→ 17-C=O	V-1053
		21-hydroxy-4-pregnene-3,20-dione	Δ^1	V-1053
		11β,21-dihydroxy-4-pregnene-3,20-dione	Δ^1	V-1053
		17α,21-dihydroxy-4-pregnene-3,20-dione	Δ^1	V-1053
		17α,21-dihydroxy-4-pregnene-3,11,20-trione	Δ^1	V-1053
<u>OPHIOSTOMA</u>				
catanianum	NG	5-cholesten-3β-ol (sole carbon source)	utilization	S-793c
		24β-methyl-5,7,22-cholesta-trien-3β-ol (sole carbon source)	utilization	S-793c
<u>PAECILOMYCES</u>				
species	NG (Sandoz-904)	3β,6β,8β,14β-tetrahydroxy-4,20,22 -bufatrienolide 6-acetate 3-glucoside	3β[1^1ξ-gluco-side] → 3β-OH	<u>S-936a</u>
		3β,14β-dihydroxy-5β-20(22)-cardenolide-3-[glucosyl-digitoxosyl-digitoxosyl-digitoxoside]	glucosyl-digitoxosyl-digitoxosyl → digitoxosyl-digitoxosyl-digitoxoside	<u>S-936a</u>
		Digilanid A	selective cleavage of glucose from sugar chain	S-936a
	NRRL	plant saponins	—	K-478
varitoi	FRI	17α,21-dihydroxy-4-pregnene-3,20-dione	—	S-849
<u>PANAEOLUS</u>				
papilionaceus	AL (G-60)	4-pregnene-3,20-dione	oxidation - products not identified	S-825

TABLE III

ransformations by Genus:

PANELLUS	(Basidio. - Agaricales)
PARASITELLA	(Phyco. - Mucorales)
PARENDOMYCES	(Imperf. - Moniliales)
PAXILLUS	(Basidio. - Agaricales)
PELLICULARIA	(Basidio. - Agaricales)

SPECIES	SOURCE	SUBSTRATE	REACTION	REF.
PANELLUS				
stypticus (stipticus)	AL (C-224)	4-pregnene-3,20-dione	oxidation - products not identified	S-825
PARASITELLA				
simplex	FRI	17α,21-dihydroxy-4-pregnene-3,20-dione	——	S-849
PARENDOMYCES				
asteroides	FRI	17α,21-dihydroxy-4-pregnene-3,20-dione	——	S-849
PAXILLUS				
involutus	AL (H-19)	4-pregnene-3,20-dione	oxidation - products not identified	S-825
vernalis	AL (H-25)	4-pregnene-3,20-dione	oxidation - products not identified	S-825
PELLICULARIA (see Corticium)				
filamentosa f.s. timsii	IFO (6259)	17α,21-dihydroxy-4-pregnene-3,20-dione	6β-OH; 11α-OH	T-957
f.s. sasakii			6β-OH; 11α-OH; 11β-OH; 19-OH	T-957
f.s. solani			Δ^1; 6β-OH; 11α-OH	T-957
f.s. microsclerotia	IFO (6298)	9α-hydroxy-4-androstene-3,17-dione	6β-OH; 14α-OH	T-955
		11β-hydroxy-4-androstene-3,17-dione	11β-OH $\rightarrow$ 11-C=O; 14α-OH	T-955
		14α-hydroxy-4-androstene-3,17-dione	11α-OH; 11β-OH	T-955

NOTE: f.s. = forma seciaus

TABLE III

Transformations by Genus: PELLICULARIA
PENICILLIUM   (Imperf. - Moniliales)

SPECIES	SOURCE	SUBSTRATE	REACTION	REF.
filamentosa f.s. microsclerotia	IFO (6298)	15α-hydroxy-4-androstene-3,17-dione	11β-OH; 11-C=O (via 11β-OH)	T-955
		4-androstene-3,11,17-trione	14α-OH	T-955
		1,4-androstadiene-3,17-dione	14α-OH; 11β-OH; 11-C=O (via 11β-OH)	T-955
		11β-hydroxy-1,4-androstadiene-3,17-dione	14α-OH; 11β-OH → 11-C=O	T-955
		17α,21-dihydroxy-4-pregnene-3,20-dione	11α-OH; 11β-OH; 19-OH	T-957
		17α,20α,21-trihydroxy-4-pregnen-3-one	11β-OH; 19-OH	T-953; T-954
		11β,17α,21-trihydroxy-4-pregnene-3,20-dione	20-C=O → 20β-OH	T-953; T-954
PENICILLIUM				
aculeatum	CZAS	4-pregnene-3,20-dione	—	C-99
adametzi	ATCC-10407	5β-pregnane-3,20-dione	oxidation - product not identified	M-602
		4-pregnene-3,20-dione	oxidation - product not identified	M-602
		17α-hydroxy-4-pregnene-3,20-dione	oxidation - product not identified	M-602
		21-hydroxy-4-pregnene-3,20-dione	oxidation - product not identified	M-602
		17α,21-dihydroxy-4-pregnene-3,20-dione	oxidation - product not identified	M-602
		4,16-pregnadiene-3,20-dione	oxidation - product not identified	M-602
*	CZAS	4-pregnene-3,20-dione	17β-Ac → 17a-oxa-17-C=O	C-99

NOTE: f.s. = forma
        seciaus

TABLE III

ansformations by Genus: PENICILLIUM

SPECIES	SOURCE	SUBSTRATE	REACTION	REF.
adametzi (in mixed culture with Trichoderma lignorum [17α-OH] and Wojnowicia graminis [21-OH])	MCC	4-pregnene-3,20-dione	11α-OH	M-566
	NRRL	Sarsasapogenin	—	M-587
		Diosgenin	—	M-587
		4-dehydrotigogenone	—	M-587
	UC	4-pregnene-3,20-dione	17β-Ac→17a-oxa-17-C=O	P-726
lbidum *	ASRI	4-pregnene-3,20-dione	17β-Ac→17a-oxa-17-C=O	C-99
*	CZAA	4-pregnene-3,20-dione	17β-Ac→17a-oxa-17-C=O	C-99
*	CZAS	4-pregnene-3,20-dione	17β-Ac→17a-oxa-17-C=O	C-99
*	FCUTS	4-pregnene-3,20-dione	17β-Ac→17a-oxa-17-C=O	C-99
	MCC	4-pregnene-3,20-dione	none at C-11	D-190
sperum *	CZAS	4-pregnene-3,20-dione	17β-Ac→17a-oxa-17-C=O	C-99
	MCC	4-pregnene-3,20-dione	none at C-11	D-190
tramentosum *	ASRI	4-pregnene-3,20-dione	11α-OH	C-99
*	CZAS	4-pregnene-3,20-dione	11α-OH	C-99
	MCC	4-pregnene-3,20-dione	none at C-11	D-190
urantio-violaceum	MCC	4-pregnene-3,20-dione	none at C-11	D-190
urantio-virens	MCC	4-pregnene-3,20-dione	none at C-11	D-190
vellaneum[f]	CZAS	4-pregnene-3,20-dione	—	C-99
iforme	ASRI	4-pregnene-3,20-dione	—	C-99
	CZAS	4-pregnene-3,20-dione	—	C-99
	FCUTS	4-pregnene-3,20-dione	—	C-99
	MCC	4-pregnene-3,20-dione	none at C-11	D-190
refeldianum	MCC	4-pregnene-3,20-dione	none at C-11	D-190
revi-compactum	ATCC-9056	4-pregnene-3,20-dione	oxidation - products not identified	M-602

TABLE III

Transformations by Genus: PENICILLIUM

SPECIES	SOURCE	SUBSTRATE	REACTION	REF.
brevi-compactum	ATCC-9056	4-pregnene-3,20-dione	17β-Ac→ 17-C=O	M-637
		(revision of structure - 20α to 20β - Ref. S-832)	20-C=O → 20β-OH	M-637
	CZAS	4-pregnene-3,20-dione	—	C-99
	MCC	4-pregnene-3,20-dione	none at C-11	D-190
camemberti	CZAS	4-pregnene-3,20-dione	—	C-99
	MCC	4-pregnene-3,20-dione	none at C-11	D-190
canescens	ATCC-10419	5β-pregnane-3,20-dione	17β-Ac → 17-C=O	M-637
		4-pregnene-3,20-dione	oxidation - products not identified	M-602
		21-hydroxy-4-pregnene-3,20-dione acetate	17β-(20-C=O- 21-OAc) → 17-C=O	M-637
*		21-hydroxy-4-pregnene-3,20-dione acetate (revision of structure - 20α to 20β - Ref. S-832)	20-C=O → 20β-OH 21-OAc → 21-OH	M-637
*	ASRI	4-pregnene-3,20-dione	17β-Ac→17a-oxa-17-C=O	C-99
*	CZAS	4-pregnene-3,20-dione	17β-Ac→17a-oxa-17-C=O	C-99
	MCC	4-pregnene-3,20-dione	none at C-11	D-190
casei	ASRI	4-pregnene-3,20-dione	—	C-99
	FCUTS	4-pregnene-3,20-dione	—	C-99
caseicolum	MCC	4-pregnene-3,20-dione	none at C-11	D-190
charlesii	ASRI	4-pregnene-3,20-dione	—	C-99
	CZAA	4-pregnene-3,20-dione	—	C-99
	CZAS	4-pregnene-3,20-dione	—	C-99
	FCUTS	4-pregnene-3,20-dione	—	C-99
	UC	21-hydroxy-4-pregnene-3,20-dione acetate	17β-(20-C=O - 21-OAc) → 17-C=O	M-637
		(revision of structure - 20α to 20β-Ref. S-832)	20-C=O → 20β-OH; 21-OAc → 21-OH	M-637

TABLE III

SPECIES		SOURCE	SUBSTRATE	REACTION	REF.
chermesinum		CZAS	4-pregnene-3,20-dione	—	C-99
		FCUTS	4-pregnene-3,20-dione	—	C-99
		MCC	4-pregnene-3,20-dione	none at C-11	D-190
chrysogenum	*	ASRI	4-pregnene-3,20-dione	17β-Ac→17a-oxa-17-C=O	C-99
		AY	17α,21-dihydroxy-4-pregnene-3,20-dione (use of conidia)	17α-OH-17β-(20-C=O-21-OH) → 17-C=O	V-1048
	*	CZAS	4-pregnene-3,20-dione	17β-Ac→17a-oxa-17-C=O	C-99
		IPβ	4-pregnene-3,20-dione	17β-Ac→17-C=O	C-102
		MCC	4-pregnene-3,20-dione	none at C-11	D-190
		MCC(MF-2133)	Diosgenin (dioscorea tuber pulp)	3β-glycoside (Dioscin) → 3β-OH; 3β-OH →3-C=O; Δ^5→Δ^4	R-781
	*	NRRL	plant saponins	hydrolysis of glycosides to aglycones (sapogenins)	K-478; K-479
		SQ	3β-hydroxy-5-pregnen-20-one	Δ^5→Δ^4; 3β-OH →3-C=O	P-710
		WISC(48-701)	21-hydroxy-4-pregnene-3,20-dione	11β-OH	H-328
		WISC(49-133)	4-androstene-3,17-dione	no testolic acid	H-398
	*		17a-oxa-D-homo-4-androstene-3,17-dione	17a-oxa-17-C=O →13,17-seco-13α-OH-16-COOH	H-398
			4-pregnene-3,20-dione	17β-Ac→17a-oxa-17-C=O	F-270; F-284
	*			17β-Ac→13,17-seco-13α-OH-16-COOH	H-398
citreo-viride	*	CZAS	4-pregnene-3,20-dione	17β-Ac→17a-oxa-17-C=O	C-99
		MCC	4-pregnene-3,20-dione	none at C-11	D-190

TABLE III

Transformations by Genus: PENICILLIUM

SPECIES		SOURCE	SUBSTRATE	REACTION	REF.
citrinum	*	ASRI	4-pregnene-3,20-dione	17β-Ac→17β-OH	C-99
		ATCC-8506	A-<u>nor</u>-17β-hydroxy-3-androsten-2-one	17β-OH→17a-oxa-17-C=O	L-500
			4-androstene-3,17-dione	no testolic acid	H-398
	*		17a-oxa-D-<u>homo</u>-4-androstene-3,17-dione	17a-oxa-17-C=O →13,17-<u>seco</u>-13α-OH-16-COOH	H-398
			4-pregnene-3,20-dione	17β-Ac→17a-oxa-17-C=O	F-270
	*			17β-Ac→13,17-<u>seco</u>-13α-OH-16-COOH	H-398
		ATCC-10105	4-pregnene-3,20-dione	oxidation - products not identified	M-602
			6β-hydroxy-4-pregnene-3,20-dione	17β-Ac → 17-C=O	M-637
	*	CZAS	4-pregnene-3,20-dione	17β-Ac→ 17β-OH	C-99
		FRI	17α,21-dihydroxy-4-pregnene-3,20-dione	—	S-849
		IPβ (THOM)	4-androstene-3,17-dione	17-C=O → 17β-OH	H-336
	*		4-pregnene-3,20-dione	17β-Ac → 17β-OH	H-336
	*			17β-Ac → 17-C=O	C-102
			11α-hydroxy-4-pregnene-3,20-dione	17β-Ac → 17β-OH	H-336
	*		17α-hydroxy-4-pregnene-3,20-dione	17α-OH-17β-Ac→17β-OH	H-336
			4-pregnene-3,11,20-trione	17β-Ac → 17β-OH	H-336
		MCC	4-pregnene-3,20-dione	none at C-11	D-190
		S	4-androstene-3,17-dione	17-C=O → 17a-oxa-17-C=O	S-846
			4-pregnene-3,20-dione	17β-Ac→17a-oxa-17-C=O	S-846

TABLE III

Transformations by Genus: PENICILLIUM

SPECIES	SOURCE	SUBSTRATE	REACTION	REF.
citrinum	S	17α-hydroxy-4-pregnene-3,20-dione	17α-OH-17β-Ac →17a-oxa-17-C=O	S-846
		21-hydroxy-4-pregnene-3,20-dione	17β-(20-C=O-21-OH) →17a-oxa-17-C=O	S-846
		11β,21-dihydroxy-4-pregnene-3,20-dione	—	S-846
		17α,21-dihydroxy-4-pregnene-3,20-dione	20-C=O → 20β-OH	S-846
		11β,17α,21-trihydroxy-4-pregnene-3,20-dione	—	S-846
		17α,21-dihydroxy-4-pregnene-3,11,20-trione	—	S-846
	SQ	A-nor-17β-hydroxy-3-androsten-2-one	17β-OH →17a-oxa-17-C=O	L-502
		A-nor-3-pregnene-2,20-dione	17β-Ac→17a-oxa-17-C=O	L-502
		4-pregnene-3,11,20-trione	17β-Ac→17a-oxa-17-C=O	L-492
		9α-fluoro-4-pregnene-3,11,20-trione	17β-Ac→17a-oxa-17-C=O	L-492
claviforme	·CZAA	4-pregnene-3,20-dione	—	C-99
	CZAS	4-pregnene-3,20-dione	—	C-99
	RIDPI	4-pregnene-3,20-dione	—	C-99
clavigerum	ASRI	4-pregnene-3,20-dione	—	C-99
	CZAS	4-pregnene-3,20-dione	—	C-99
commune *	ASRI	4-pregnene-3,20-dione	17β-Ac→17a-oxa-17-C=O	C-99
*	CZAS	4-pregnene-3,20-dione	17β-Ac→17a-oxa-17-C=O	C-99
corylophilum *	ASRI	4-pregnene-3,20-dione	17β-Ac→17β-OH	C-99
*	CZAS	4-pregnene-3,20-dione	17β-Ac→17β-OH	C-99
	MCC	4-pregnene-3,20-dione	11α-OH	D-190
corymbiferum	ASRI	4-pregnene-3,20-dione	—	C-99

TABLE III

Transformations by Genus: PENICILLIUM

SPECIES		SOURCE	SUBSTRATE	REACTION	REF.
corymbiferum		CZAS	4-pregnene-3,20-dione	—	C-99
		MCC	4-pregnene-3,20-dione	none at C-11	D-190
crustosum		CZAS	4-pregnene-3,20-dione	—	C-99
		MCC	4-pregnene-3,20-dione	none at C-11	D-190
cyaneofulvum	*	ASRI	4-pregnene-3,20-dione	17β-Ac→17a-oxa-17-C=O	C-99
	*	CZAS	4-pregnene-3,20-dione	17β-Ac→17a-oxa-17-C=O	C-99
		MCC	4-pregnene-3,20-dione	none at C-11	D-190
cyaneum		MCC	4-pregnene-3,20-dione	none at C-11	D-190
cyclopium		CZAS	4-pregnene-3,20-dione	—	C-99
		MCC	4-pregnene-3,20-dione	none at C-11	D-190
(Westling)	*	NG	plant saponins	hydrolysis of glycosides to aglycones (sapogenin)	K-479
		NRRL-942, 1888, 1889, ERRL-1292	plant saponins	hydrolysis of glycosides to aglycones (sapogenin)	K-478
daleae		MCC	4-pregnene-3,20-dione	none at C-11	D-190
	*	RIDPI	4-pregnene-3,20-dione	17β-Ac→17a-oxa-17-C=O	C-99
decumbens	*	ASRI	4-pregnene-3,20-dione	17β-Ac→17a-oxa-17-C=O	C-99
	*	CZAS	4-pregnene-3,20-dione	17β-Ac→17a-oxa-17-C=O	C-99
	*	FCUTS	4-pregnene-3,20-dione	17β-Ac→17a-oxa-17-C=O	C-99
		IPB	4-androstene-3,17-dione	17-C=O → 17β-OH	H-336
	*		4-pregnene-3,20-dione	17β-Ac→17β-OH	H-332; H-336
			11α-hydroxy-4-pregnene-3,20-dione	17β-Ac→17β-OH	H-336
			17α-hydroxy-4-pregnene-3,20-dione	17α-OH-17β-Ac →17β-OH	H-336
			4-pregnene-3,11,20-trione	17β-Ac→17β-OH	H-336

TABLE III

Transformations by Genus: PENICILLIUM

SPECIES		SOURCE	SUBSTRATE	REACTION	REF.
decumbens		MCC	4-pregnene-3,20-dione	none at C-11	D-190
digitatum		CZAS	4-pregnene-3,20-dione	—	C-99
		MCC	4-pregnene-3,20-dione	none at C-11	D-190
		NC (Sandoz-872)	$3\beta,6\beta,8\beta,14\beta$-tetrahydroxy-4, 20,22-bufatrienolide 6-acetate 3-glucoside	3β-[$1^1\xi$-gluco-side]$\rightarrow 3\beta$-OH	S-936a
			$3\beta,14\beta$-dihydroxy-5β-20(22)-cardenolide 3[glucosyl-digitoxosyl-digitoxosyl-digitoxoside]	glucosyl-digitoxosyl-digitoxosyl-digitoxoside $\rightarrow$ digitoxosyl-digitoxosyl-digitoxoside	S-936a
diversum	*	CZAS	4-pregnene-3,20-dione	15β-OH	C-99
	*	FCUTS	4-pregnene-3,20-dione	15β-OH	C-99
duponti		MCC	4-pregnene-3,20-dione	none at C-11	D-190
egyptaceum	*	ASRI	4-pregnene-3,20-dione	17β-Ac$\rightarrow$17a-oxa-17-C=O	C-99
	*	CZAS	4-pregnene-3,20-dione	17β-Ac$\rightarrow$17a-oxa-17-C=O	C-99
	*	FCUTS	4-pregnene-3,20-dione	17β-Ac$\rightarrow$17a-oxa-17-C=O	C-99
	*	SSSR	4-pregnene-3,20-dione	17β-Ac$\rightarrow$17a-oxa-17-C=O	C-99
ehrlichii		MCC	4-pregnene-3,20-dione	none at C-11	D-190
expansum		ASRI	4-pregnene-3,20-dione	—	C-99
		ATCC-7861	4-pregnene-3,20-dione	oxidation - products not identified	M-602
			4-pregnene-3,11,20-trione	17β-Ac $\rightarrow$ 17-C=O	M-637
		CZAA	4-pregnene-3,20-dione	—	C-99
		CZAS	4-pregnene-3,20-dione	—	C-99
		FCUTS	4-pregnene-3,20-dione	—	C-99
		MCC	4-pregnene-3,20-dione	none at C-11	D-190
		NRRL	Sarsasapogenin	—	M-587
			Diosgenin	—	M-587
			4-dehydrotigogenone	—	M-587

TABLE III

Transformations by Genus: PENICILLIUM

SPECIES		SOURCE	SUBSTRATE	REACTION	REF.
fellutanum		MCC	4-pregnene-3,20-dione	none at C-11	D-190
		SSSR	4-pregnene-3,20-dione	—	C-99
frequentans	*	ASRI	4-pregnene-3,20-dione	17β-Ac→17a-oxa-17-C=O	C-99
		ATCC-10444	4-pregnene-3,20-dione	17β-Ac→17-C=O	M-637
	*	CZAS	4-pregnene-3,20-dione	17β-Ac→17a-oxa-17-C=O	C-99
		MCC	4-pregnene-3,20-dione	none at C-11	D-190
funiculosum		MCC	4-pregnene-3,20-dione	none at C-11	D-190
		NRRL	Sarsasapogenin	—	M-587
			Diosgenin	—	M-587
			4-dehydrotigogenone	—	M-587
fuscum	*	CZAS	4-pregnene-3,20-dione	17β-Ac→17a-oxa-17-C=O	C-99
gladioli		MCC	4-pregnene-3,20-dione	none at C-11	D-190
godlewskii	*	CZAS	4-pregnene-3,20-dione	17β-Ac→17a-oxa-17-C=O	C-99
granulatum		CZAS	4-pregnene-3,20-dione	—	C-99
		MCC	4-pregnene-3,20-dione	none at C-11	D-190
helicum		CZAS	4-pregnene-3,20-dione	—	C-99
herquei		MCC	4-pregnene-3,20-dione	none at C-11	D-190
humuli		ASRI	4-pregnene-3,20-dione	—	C-99
		CZAS	4-pregnene-3,20-dione	—	C-99
		MCC	4-pregnene-3,20-dione	none at C-11	D-190
implicatum	*	FCUTS	4-pregnene-3,20-dione	17β-Ac→17a-oxa-17-C=O	C-99
		MCC	4-pregnene-3,20-dione	none at C-11	D-190
islandicum		MCC	4-pregnene-3,20-dione	none at C-11	D-190
italicum		CZAS	4-pregnene-3,20-dione	—	C-99
		MCC	4-pregnene-3,20-dione	none at C-11	D-190
janthinellum	*	ASRI	4-pregnene-3,20-dione	17β-Ac→17a-oxa-17-C=O	C-99

TABLE III

Transformations by Genus: PENICILLIUM

SPECIES		SOURCE	SUBSTRATE	REACTION	REF.
janthinellum		ATCC-10455	4-pregnene-3,20-dione	oxidation - products not identified	M-602
		CZAS	4-pregnene-3,20-dione	17β-Ac→17a-oxa-17-C=O	C-99
		MCC	4-pregnene-3,20-dione	none at C-11	D-190
javanicum	*	ASRI	4-pregnene-3,20-dione	17β-Ac→17a-oxa-17-C=O	C-99
	*	CZAS	4-pregnene-3,20-dione	17β-Ac→17a-oxa-17-C=O	C-99
		MCC	4-pregnene-3,20-dione	none at C-11	D-190
		NRRL	Sarsasapogenin	—	M-587
			Diosgenin	—	M-587
			4-dehydrotigogenone	—	M-587
jensenii	*	ASRI	4-pregnene-3,20-dione	17β-Ac→17a-oxa-17-C=O	C-99
	*	CZAS	4-pregnene-3,20-dione	17β-Ac→17a-oxa-17-C=O	C-99
	*	FCUTS	4-pregnene-3,20-dione	17β-Ac→17a-oxa-17-C=O	C-99
		MCC	4-pregnene-3,20-dione	none at C-11	D-190
	*	SSSR	4-pregnene-3,20-dione	17β-Ac→17a-oxa-17-C=O	C-99
kapuscinskii	*	SSSR	4-pregnene-3,20-dione	17β-Ac→17a-oxa-17-C=O	C-99
lanoso-coeruleum		MCC	4-pregnene-3,20-dione	none at C-11	D-190
		NRRL	Sarsasapogenin	—	M-587
			Diosgenin	—	M-587
			4-dehydrotigogenone	—	M-587
lanoso-griseum		MCC	4-pregnene-3,20-dione	none at C-11	D-190
lanoso-viride		MCC	4-pregnene-3,20-dione	none at C-11	D-190
lanosum		CZAS	4-pregnene-3,20-dione	—	C-99
lavendulum		ASRI	4-pregnene-3,20-dione	—	C-99
		NRRL	Sarsasapogenin	—	M-587
			Diosgenin	—	M-587
			4-dehydrotigogenone	—	M-587

TABLE III

Transformations by Genus: PENICILLIUM

SPECIES	SOURCE	SUBSTRATE	REACTION	REF.
levitum	ASRI	4-pregnene-3,20-dione	—	C-99
	CZAS	4-pregnene-3,20-dione	—	C-99
lilacinum *	ASRI	4-pregnene-3,20-dione	17β-Ac→17a-oxa-17-C=O	C-99
	ATCC-10114	17β-hydroxy-4-androsten-3-one	17β-OH→17-C=O	P-737
			17β-OH→17a-oxa-17-C=O	P-737
			17β-OH→13,17-seco-13α-OH-16-COOH	P-737
		4-androstene-3,17-dione	17-C=O→17a-oxa-17-C=O	P-737
			17-C=O→13,17-seco-13α-OH-16-COOH	P-737
		5α-pregnane-3,11,20-trione	17β-Ac → 17-C=O	M-637
		5β-pregnane-3,12,20-trione	17β-Ac → 17-C=O	M-637
		$3\alpha,11\alpha,17\alpha$-trihydroxy-5$\beta$-pregnan-20-one	17α-OH-17β-Ac →17-C=O	M-637
		4-pregnene-3,20-dione	oxidation - products not identified	M-602
			20-C=O → 20β-OH	M-637
			17β-Ac→17-C=O	M-637
		14α-hydroxy-4-pregnene-3,20-dione	17β-Ac→17-C=O	E-204; M-637
		17α-hydroxy-4-pregnene-3,20-dione	17α-OH-17β-Ac →17-C=O	M-637
		$14\alpha,21$-dihydroxy-4-pregnene-3,20-dione	17β-(20-C=O-21-OH)→17-C=O	M-637
		$17\alpha,21$-dihydroxy-4-pregnene-3,20-dione	17α-OH-17β-(20-C=O-21-OH)→17-C=O	M-637
			20-C=O →20β-OH	M-637
		$11\alpha,17\alpha,21$-trihydroxy-4-pregnene-3,20-dione	17α-OH-17β-(20-C=O-21-OH)→17-C=O	M-637

TABLE III

Transformations by Genus: PENICILLIUM

SPECIES	SOURCE	SUBSTRATE	REACTION	REF.
lilacinum	ATCC-10114	14α,17α,21-trihydroxy-4-preg-nene-3,20-dione	17α-OH-17β-(20-C=O-21-OH)→17-C=O	M-637
		17α,21-dihydroxy-4-pregnene-3,11,20-trione	17α-OH-17β-(20-C=O-21-OH)→17-C=O	M-637
		17α,21-dihydroxy-4-pregnene-3,11,20-trione 21-acetate	17α-OH-17β-(20-C=O-21-OAc)→17-C=O	M-637
		3-ketobisnor-4-cholen-22-al	20-H-C=O → 20β-CH₂OH	E-202; W-1068
*	CZAA	4-pregnene-3,20-dione	17β-Ac→17a-oxa-17-C=O	C-99
*	CZAS	4-pregnene-3,20-dione	17β-Ac→17a-oxa-17-C=O	C-99
	MCC	4-pregnene-3,20-dione	11α-OH	D-109
	NRRL	Sarsasapogenin	—	M-587
		Diosgenin	—	M-587
		4-dehydrotigogenone	—	M-587
	UC	4-pregnene-3,20-dione	17β-Ac→17a-oxa-17-C=O	P-726; S-832
			17β-Ac→17β-OH	S-832
			17β-Ac→17-C=O	P-726; S-832
		11α-hydroxy-4-pregnene-3,20-dione	17β-Ac→17a-oxa-17-C=O	S-832
			17β-Ac→17β-OH	S-832
			20-C=O → 20β-OH	S-832
			17β-Ac → 17-C=O	S-831; S-832
(in mixed culture with Rhizopus nigricans [11α-OH])		4-pregnene-3,20-dione	17β-Ac→17-C=O	S-831
(in mixed culture with Rhizopus nigricans [11α-OH])		11α-hydroxy-4-pregnene-3,20-dione	17β-Ac→17-C=O	S-831

TABLE III

Transformations by Genus: PENICILLIUM

SPECIES		SOURCE	SUBSTRATE	REACTION	REF.
lividum		ATCC-10102	21-hydroxy-4-pregnene-3,20-dione acetate	17β-(20-C=O-21-OAc) → 17-C=O	M-637
			(revision of structure - 20α to 20β - Ref. S-832)	20-C=O → 20β-OH;21-OAc →21-OH	M-637
	*	MCC	4-pregnene-3,20-dione	none at C-11	D-190
		SSSR	4-pregnene-3,20-dione	17β-Ac→17a-oxa-17-C=O	C-99
luteum		ATCC-10465	4-pregnene-3,20-dione	oxidation - products not identified	M-602
		CZAS	4-pregnene-3,20-dione	—	C-99
		FRI	17α,21-dihydroxy-4-pregnene-3,20-dione	—	S-849
martensii		CZAS	4-pregnene-3,20-dione	—	C-99
		MCC	4-pregnene-3,20-dione	none at C-11	D-190
melearginum	*	ASRI	4-pregnene-3,20-dione	17β-Ac→17a→oxa-17-C=O	C-99
	*	CZAS	4-pregnene-3,20-dione	17β-Ac→17a-oxa-17-C=O	C-99
		MCC	4-pregnene-3,20-dione	none at C-11	D-190
melinii	*	CZAS	4-pregnene-3,20-dione	17β-Ac→17a-oxa-17-C=O	C-99
		MCC	4-pregnene-3,20-dione	none at C-11	D-190
miczynskii	*	CZAS	4-pregnene-3,20-dione	17β-Ac→17a-oxa-17-C=O	C-99
	*	FCUTS	4-pregnene-3,20-dione	17β-Ac→17a-oxa-17-C=O	C-99
		MCC	4-pregnene-3,20-dione	none at C-11	D-190
multicolor	*	FCUTS	4-pregnene-3,20-dione	17β-Ac→17a-oxa-17-C=O	C-99
	*	SSSR	4-pregnene-3,20-dione	17β-Ac→17a-oxa-17-C=O	C-99
nalgiovensis		MCC	4-pregnene-3,20-dione	none at C-11	D-190
	*	SSSR	4-pregnene-3,20-dione	17β-Ac→17a-oxa-17-C=O	C-99

TABLE III

ransformations by Genus: PENICILLIUM

SPECIES		SOURCE	SUBSTRATE	REACTION	REF.
namyslowskii		MCC	4-pregnene-3,20-dione	none at C-11	D-190
nigricans	*	ASRI	4-pregnene-3,20-dione	17β-Ac→17a-oxa-17-C=O	C-99
		ATCC-10115	4-pregnene-3,20-dione	oxidation - products not identified	M-636
			21-hydroxy-4-pregnene-3,20-dione	17β-(20-C=O-21-OH) → 17-C=O	M-637
			(revision of structure - 20α to 20β - Ref. S-832)	20-C=O → 20β-OH	M-637
	*	CZAA	4-pregnene-3,20-dione	17β-Ac→17a-oxa-17-C=O	C-99
	*	CZAS	4-pregnene-3,20-dione	17β-Ac→17a-oxa-17-C=O	C-99
		MCC	4-pregnene-3,20-dione	none at C-11	D-190
notatum	*	ASRI	4-pregnene-3,20-dione	17β-Ac→17β-OH	C-99
		ATCC-9479	4-pregnene-3,20-dione	oxidation - products not identified	M-602
	*	CZAS	4-pregnene-3,20-dione	17β-Ac → 17β-OH	C-99
		FARMIT	4-pregnene-3,20-dione	15α-OH	C-86
				3-C=O→3β-OH; Δ^4→5α-H	C-86
			21-hydroxy-4-pregnene-3,20-dione	15α-OH	C-86
	*	FCUTS	4-pregnene-3,20-dione	17β-Ac→17β-OH	C-99
(Westling)		IPB	5-androstene-3β,17α-diol	3β-OH→3-C=O; Δ^5→Δ^4	H-337
			5-androstene-3β,17β-diol	3β-OH→3-C=O; Δ^5→Δ^4	H-337
			4-androstene-3,17-dione	17-C=O → 17β-OH	H-336
			4-pregnene-3,20-dione	17β-Ac → 17β-OH	H-332; H-336
			11α-hydroxy-4-pregnene-3,20-dione	17β-Ac → 17β-OH	H-336

TABLE III

Transformations by Genus: PENICILLIUM

SPECIES	SOURCE	SUBSTRATE	REACTION	REF.
notatum *▴	IPβ	17α-hydroxy-4-pregnene-3,20-dione	17α-OH-17β-Ac→17β-OH	H-336
		4-pregnene-3,11,20-trione	17β-Ac→17β-OH	H-336
	MCC	4-pregnene-3,20-dione	none at C-11	D-190
	NG	5-cholesten-3β-ol (sole carbon source)	utilization	S-793c
		24β-methyl-5,7,22-cholesta-trien-3β-ol (sole carbon source)	utilization	S-793c
	(Sandoz-831)	$3\beta,6\beta,8\beta,14\beta$-tetrahydroxy-4-20,22 -bufatrienolide 6-acetate 3-glucoside	3β-[$1^{1}\xi$-gluco-side] → 3β-OH	S-936a
		$3\beta,14\beta$-dihydroxy-5β-20(22)-cardenolide-3-[glucosyl-digitoxosyl-digitoxosyl-digitoxoside]	glucosyl-digitoxosyl-digitoxosyl-digitoxoside → digitoxosyl-digitoxosyl-digitoxoside	S-936a
novae-zeelandia	ATCC-10473	5β-pregnane-3,6,20-trione	17β-Ac→17-C=O	M-637
		4-pregnene-3,20-dione	oxidation - products not identified	M-602
ochraceum	CZAS	4-pregnene-3,20-dione	—	C-99
	FCUTS	4-pregnene-3,20-dione	—	C-99
	MCC	4-pregnene-3,20-dione	none at C-11	D-190
ochro-chlorum *	ASRI	4-pregnene-3,20-dione	17β-Ac→17a-oxa-17-C=O	C-99
*	CZAS	4-pregnene-3,20-dione	17β-Ac→17a-oxa-17-C=O	C-99
	MCC	4-pregnene-3,20-dione	none at C-11	D-190
olivino-viride	MCC	4-pregnene-3,20-dione	none at C-11	D-190
oxalicum	ATCC-10576	4-pregnene-3,20-dione	oxidation - products not identified	M-636
*	CZAS	4-pregnene-3,20-dione	11α-OH	C-99
*	FCUTS	4-pregnene-3,20-dione	11α-OH	C-99
	MCC	4-pregnene-3,20-dione	none at C-11	D-190
palitans	CZAS	4-pregnene-3,20-dione	—	C-99
	MCC	4-pregnene-3,20-dione	none at C-11	D-190
pallidum	ASRI	4-pregnene-3,20-dione	—	C-99
parvum *	ASRI	4-pregnene-3,20-dione	17β-Ac→17a-oxa-17-C=O	C-99

TABLE III

Transformations by Genus: PENICILLIUM

SPECIES		SOURCE	SUBSTRATE	REACTION	REF.
parvum	*	FCUTS	4-pregnene-3,20-dione	17β-Ac→17a-oxa-17-C=O	C-99
patulum		NG (Sandoz-815)	3β,6β,8β,14β-tetrahydroxy-4,20,22-bufatrienolide 6-acetate 3-glucoside	3β-[1^1ξ-gluco-side] → 3β-OH	S-936a
			3β,14β-dihydroxy-5β-20(22)-cardenolide 3-[glucosyl-digitoxosyl-digitoxosyl-digitoxoside]	glucosyl-digitoxosyl-digitoxosyl-digitoxoside→digitoxosyl-digitoxosyl-digitoxoside	S-936a
phoenicum		FCUTS	4-pregnene-3,20-dione	—	C-99
piscarium	*	CZAS	4-pregnene-3,20-dione	17β-Ac→17a-oxa-17-C=O	C-99
		MCC	4-pregnene-3,20-dione	none at C-11	D-190
psittacinum	*	CZAS	4-pregnene-3,20-dione	17β-Ac→17a-oxa-17-C=O	C-99
puberulum		ASRI	4-pregnene-3,20-dione	—	C-99
		MCC	4-pregnene-3,20-dione	none at C-11	D-190
pulvillorum	*	ASRI	4-pregnene-3,20-dione	17β-Ac→17a-oxa-17-C=O	C-99
	*	CZAS	4-pregnene-3,20-dione	17β-Ac→17a-oxa-17-C=O	C-99
purpurescens	*	CZAS	4-pregnene-3,20-dione	17β-Ac→17a-oxa-17-C=O	C-99
		MCC	4-pregnene-3,20-dione	none at C-11	D-190
		SSSR	4-pregnene-3,20-dione	17β-Ac→17a-oxa-17-C=O	C-99
purpurogenum		ASRI	4-pregnene-3,20-dione	—	C-99
		CZAS	4-pregnene-3,20-dione	—	C-99
		MCC	4-pregnene-3,20-dione	none at C-11	D-190
pusillum	*	FCUTS	4-pregnene-3,20-dione	17β-Ac→17a-oxa-17-C=O	C-99
	*	SSSR	4-pregnene-3,20-dione	17β-Ac→17a-oxa-17-C=O	C-99
raciborskii	*	ASRI	4-pregnene-3,20-dione	17β-Ac→17a-oxa-17-C=O	C-99
	*	CZAS	4-pregnene-3,20-dione	17β-Ac→17a-oxa-17-C=O	C-99

TABLE III

Transformations by Genus: PENICILLIUM

SPECIES		SOURCE	SUBSTRATE	REACTION	REF.
raistrickii	*	ASRI	4-pregnene-3,20-dione	17β-Ac→17a-oxa-17-C=O	C-99
		ATCC-10490	4-pregnene-3,20-dione	oxidation - products not identified	M-602
	*	CZAA	4-pregnene-3,20-dione	17β-Ac→17a-oxa-17-C=O	C-99
	*	CZAS	4-pregnene-3,20-dione	17β-Ac→17a-oxa-17-C=O	C-99
		MCC	4-pregnene-3,20-dione	none at C-11	D-190
restrictum	*	ASRI	4-pregnene-3,20-dione	17β-Ac→17a-oxa-17-C=O	C-99
	*	CZAS	4-pregnene-3,20-dione	17β-Ac→17a-oxa-17-C=O	C-99
	*	FCUTS	4-pregnene-3,20-dione	17β-Ac→17a-oxa-17-C=O	C-99
		MCC	4-pregnene-3,20-dione	none at C-11	D-190
restrictulosum	*	ASRI	4-pregnene-3,20-dione	17β-Ac→17a-oxa-17-C=O	C-99
	*	CZAS	4-pregnene-3,20-dione	17β-Ac→17a-oxa-17-C=O	C-99
rolfsii		· MCC	4-pregnene-3,20-dione	none at C-11	D-190
roqueforti		CZAS	4-pregnene-3,20-dione	—	C-99
		FCUTS	4-pregnene-3,20-dione	—	C-99
		MCC	4-pregnene-3,20-dione	none at C-11	D-190
		NRRL	Sarsasapogenin	—	M-587
			Diosgenin	—	M-587
			4-dehydrotigogenone	—	M-587
roseo-purpureum		MCC	4-pregnene-3,20-dione	none at C-11	D-190
rubrum		CZAS	4-pregnene-3,20-dione	—	C-99
rugulosum	*	ASRI	4-pregnene-3,20-dione	15β-OH	C-99
	*	CZAS	4-pregnene-3,20-dione	15β-OH	C-99
		MCC	4-pregnene-3,20-dione	none at C-11	D-190
sclerotiorum	*	SSSR	4-pregnene-3,20-dione	17β-Ac→17a-oxa-17-C=O	C-99

TABLE III

ansformations by Genus: PENICILLIUM

SPECIES	SOURCE	SUBSTRATE	REACTION	REF.
implicissimum *	CZAS	4-pregnene-3,20-dione	17β-Ac→17a-oxa-17-C=O	C-99
	MCC	4-pregnene-3,20-dione	none at C-11	D-190
olitum	MCC	4-pregnene-3,20-dione	none at C-11	D-190
oppi *	CZAS	4-pregnene-3,20-dione	17β-Ac→17a-oxa-17-C=O	C-99
	MCC	4-pregnene-3,20-dione	none at C-11	D-190
pecies	ATCC-11598	17β-hydroxy-4-estren-3-one	15α-OH; 17β-OH→ 17-C=O	D-151
			15α-OH	D-151
		D-homo-17a-oxa-1,4-androsta-diene-3,17-dione	15α-OH	D-158
		4-pregnene-3,20-dione	15α-OH	F-285; F-287
			products of un-known or questionable structure	F-285; F-287
	ATCC-12556	3α-hydroxy-5β-androstan-17-one	7β-OH	F-290
		5α-androstane-3,17-dione	1α-OH	D-163
		5β-androstane-3,17-dione	7β-OH	F-290
		17β-hydroxy-4-androsten-3-one	1α-OH	T-1036
			6β-OH	T-1036
			12β-OH	T-1036
			15β-OH	T-1036
			$1\alpha,6\beta$-diOH	T-1036
		3β-hydroxy-5-androsten-17-one	1α-OH	D-163; D-164; D-168; G-293
			1α-OH; 3β-OH→ 3-C=O; Δ^5→Δ^4	D-163; D-168
		4-androstene-3,17-dione	1α-OH	D-163; D-167; D-168
			2β-OH	D-163; D-167; D-168

TABLE III

Transformations by Genus: PENICILLIUM

SPECIES	SOURCE	SUBSTRATE	REACTION	REF.
species	ATCC-12556	4-androstene-3,17-dione	1α-OH; $\Delta^4 \rightarrow$ 5α-H	D-163
			1α-OH; $\Delta^4 \rightarrow$ 5α-H; 3-C=O→ 3β-OH	D-163
		17a-oxa-D-homo-4-androstene-3,17-dione	2β-OH	T-1036
		4-pregnene-3,20-dione	2β-OH	T-1036
			15β-OH	T-1036
			$2\beta,15\beta$-diOH	T-1036
			$7\beta,15\beta$-diOH	D-177; T-1036 T-1037
			6β-OH; 15-C=O (via 15β-OH)	T-1036
		16α,17α-oxido-4-pregnene-3,20-dione	7β-OH	T-1036
		17β,21-dihydroxy-4-pregnene-3,20-dione	7β-OH	T-1036 T-1037
			15β-OH	T-1036
	ATCC-13001	17α-methyl-5-androsten-1α,3β,17β-triol	3β-OH→3-C=O; $\Delta^5 \rightarrow \Delta^4$	G-293
	EM	17α,21-trihydroxy-16-methylene-1,4-pregnadiene-3,20-dione	11α-OH	M-558
	IPB	4-androstene-3,17-dione	17-C=O → 17β-OH	H-336
		4-pregnene-3,20-dione	17β-Ac→17-C=O	C-102
			17β-Ac→17a-oxa-17-C=O	C-99; C-102
			15β-OH	C-99
			11α-OH	C-99; D-190
			17β-Ac→17β-OH	C-99; C-102; H-336
		17α-hydroxy-4-pregnene-3,20-dione	17α-OH-17β-Ac→17β-OH	H-336
	NG	1,3,5(10)-estratriene-3,17β-diol (sole carbon source)	—	T-1033
		3-hydroxy-1,3,5(10)-estratrien-17-one (sole carbon source)	—	T-1033
		3α-hydroxy-5β-cholanic acid (sole carbon source)	utilization	T-1033

TABLE III

nsformations by Genus: PENICILLIUM

SPECIES	SOURCE	SUBSTRATE	REACTION	REF.
species	NG	$3\alpha, 7\alpha, 12\alpha$-trihydroxy-$5\beta$-cholanic acid (sole carbon source)	utilization	T-1033
	(Sandoz-822, 825,833,834, 838,841,851, 858,860,889, 890,909)	$3\beta, 6\beta, 8\beta, 14\beta$-tetrahydroxy-4, 20,22 -bufatrienolide 6-acetate 3-glucoside	3β-[$1^1\xi$-gluco-side]→3β-OH	S-936a
	(Sandoz-822, 833,834,838, 851,858,889, 909)	$3\beta, 14\beta$-dihydroxy-5β-20(22)-cardenolide-3-[glucosyl-digitoxosyl-digitoxosyl-digitoxoside]	glucosyl-digitoxosyl-digitoxosyl-digitoxoside → digitoxosyl-digitoxosyl-digitoxoside	S-936a
	(Sandoz-858, 889)	Digilanid A	selective cleavage of glucose from sugar chain	S-936a
	(Univ. of Texas - Sp. 17,18,19,20)	5-cholesten-3β-ol (suggested precautions to be taken before concluding sterol is modified by a culture)	utilization	P-732
(in mixed culture with Rhizopus nigricans [11α-OH] - Sporotrichum sulfurescens [11α-OH])	NG	4-pregnene-3,20-dione	17β-Ac→17-C=O	S-922
	NRRL	plant saponins	hydrolysis of glycosides to aglycones (sapogenin)	K-478
	Searle	3β-hydroxy-5-androsten-17-one	1α-OH; Δ^5→Δ^4; 3β-OH→3-C=O	D-162
		4-androstene-3,17-dione	1α-OH; 2β-OH	D-162
	SQ	17α-oxa-D-homo-1,4-androsta-diene-3,17-dione	15α-OH	P-706
	UC	4-pregnene-3,20-dione (revision of structure -20α to 20β - Ref. S-832)	20-C=O→ 20β-OH	M-637
		21-hydroxy-4-pregnene-3,20-dione acetate (revision of structure - 20α to 20β- Ref. S-832)	20-C=O → 20β-OH; 21-OAc→21-OH	M-637
spiculisporum	CZAS	4-pregnene-3,20-dione	—	C-99
spinulosum *	ASRI	4-pregnene-3,20-dione	17β-Ac→17a-oxa-17-C=O	C-99

TABLE III

Transformations by Genus: PENICILLIUM

SPECIES		SOURCE	SUBSTRATE	REACTION	REF.
spinulosum	*	CZAA	4-pregnene-3,20-dione	17β-Ac→17a-oxa-17-C=O	C-99
	*	CZAS	4-pregnene-3,20-dione	17β-Ac→17a-oxa-17-C=O	C-99
		MCC	4-pregnene-3,20-dione	none at C-11	D-190
steckii	*	ASRI	4-pregnene-3,20-dione	17β-Ac→17a-oxa-17-C=O	C-99
	*	CZAS	4-pregnene-3,20-dione	17β-Ac→17a-oxa-17-C=O	C-99
	*	FCUTS	4-pregnene-3,20-dione	17β-Ac→17a-oxa-17-C=O	C-99
	*	IPβ	4-pregnene-3,20-dione	17β-Ac→17-C=O	C-102
	*			17β-Ac→17a-oxa-17-C=O	C-102
		MCC	4-pregnene-3,20-dione	none at C-11	D-190
	*	SSSR	4-pregnene-3,20-dione	17β-Ac→17a-oxa-17-C=O	C-99
stoloniferum		SSSR	4-pregnene-3,20-dione	—	C-99
striatum		CZAS	4-pregnene-3,20-dione	—	C-99
subalteritium	*	ASRI	4-pregnene-3,20-dione	17β-Ac→17a-oxa-17-C=O	C-99
	*	FCUTS	4-pregnene-3,20-dione	17β-Ac→17a-oxa-17-C=O	C-99
tardum		MCC	4-pregnene-3,20-dione	11α-OH	D-190
	*	SSSR	4-pregnene-3,20-dione	15β-OH	C-99
terlikowski	*	ASRI	4-pregnene-3,20-dione	17β-Ac→17a-oxa-17-C=O	C-99
		MCC	4-pregnene-3,20-dione	none at C-11	D-190
terrestre		ASRI	4-pregnene-3,20-dione	—	C-99
		CZAS	4-pregnene-3,20-dione	—	C-99
		MCC	4-pregnene-3,20-dione	none at C-11	D-190
thomii	*	ASRI	4-pregnene-3,20-dione	17β-Ac→17a-oxa-17-C=O	C-99
		ATCC-10506	4-pregnene-3,20-dione	oxidation - products not identified	M-602
			11α,17α-dihydroxy-4-pregnene-3,20-dione	17α-OH-17β-Ac→17-C=O	M-637
	*	CZAS	11α,17α-dihydroxy-4-pregnene-3,20-dione	17α-Ac→17a-oxa-17-C=O	C-99
	*	FCUTS	11α,17α-dihydroxy-4-pregnene-3,20-dione	17α-Ac→17a-oxa-17-C=O	C-99
		MCC	11α,17α-dihydroxy-4-pregnene-3,20-dione	none at C-11	D-190

TABLE III

Transformations by Genus: PENICILLIUM

SPECIES	SOURCE	SUBSTRATE	REACTION	REF.
thomii	WISC	$14\beta,19$-dihydroxy-3-keto-4, 20(22)-cardadienolide	19-OH→ 19-C=O	S-892
		14β-hydroxy-3,19-dioxo-4, 20(22)-cardadienolide	19-C=O→ 19-OH	S-892
trzebinskii	MCC	4-pregnene-3,20-dione	none at C-11	D-190
turbatum	MCC	4-pregnene-3,20-dione	none at C-11	D-190
urticae	ATCC-10120	17β-hydroxy-4-estren-3-one	15ξ-OH	M-639
		17β-hydroxy-4-androsten-3-one	15α-OH	M-639
		4-pregnene-3,20-dione	15α-OH	E-202; F-250; M-576; M-577; M-602
			6β-OH	E-202
		4-pregnene-3,11,20-trione	15α-OH	A-31; B-44
		6α-fluoro-4-pregnene-3,11, 20-trione	15α-OH	A-31
		9α-fluoro-4-pregnene-3,11, 20-trione	15α-OH	A-31
		6α-methyl-4-pregnene-3,11, 20-trione	15α-OH	A-31
		$6\alpha,9\alpha$-difluoro-4-pregnene-3, 11,20-trione	15α-OH	A-31
		9α-fluoro-6α-methyl-4-preg- nene-3,11,20-trione	.15α-OH	A-31
	CZAA	4-pregnene-3,20-dione	—	C-99
	CZAS	4-pregnene-3,20-dione	—	C-99
variabile	ASRI	4-pregnene-3,20-dione	—	C-99
vermiculatum	MCC	4-pregnene-3,20-dione	none at C-11	D-190
	NRRL	Sarsasapogenin	—	M-587
		Diosgenin	—	M-587
		4-dehydrotigogenone	—	M-587
verruculosum	MCC	4-pregnene-3,20-dione	none at C-11	D-190
vinaceum	MCC	4-pregnene-3,20-dione	none at C-11	D-190
viridicatum	CZAS	4-pregnene-3,20-dione	—	C-99
	MCC	4-pregnene-3,20-dione	none at C-11	D-190
waksmanni	MCC	4-pregnene-3,20-dione	none at C-11	D-190
wortmanni	MCC	4-pregnene-3,20-dione	none at C-11	D-190

TABLE III

Transformations by Genus: PENTATRICHOMONAS   (Zoomastigina - Polymastigina)
                                    PESTALOTIA   (Imperf. - Melanconiales)

SPECIES	SOURCE	SUBSTRATE	REACTION	REF.
PENTATRICHOMONAS (Protozoa)				
gallinarum	UC	11α-hydroxy-4-androstene-3,17-dione	17-C=O$\rightarrow$ 17β-OH	S-830
		1,4-androstadiene-3,17-dione	17-C=O$\rightarrow$ 17β-OH	S-830
hominis	UC	1,4-androstadiene-3,17-dione	17-C=O$\rightarrow$ 17β-OH	S-830
PESTALOTIA				
diospyri	FRI	$17\alpha,21$-dihydroxy-4-pregnene-3,20-dione	11α-OH	S-849
foedans	ATCC-11817 (QM-795)	4-pregnene-3,20-dione	11α-OH	S-882
		16α-ethyl-$17\alpha,21$-dihydroxy-1,4-pregnadiene-3,20-dione 21-acetate	11α-OH; 21-OAc$\rightarrow$ 21-OH	O-703
		$17\alpha,21$-dihydroxy-16α-methyl-1,4-pregnadiene-3,20-dione	11α-OH	O-702
funerea	AY	$17\alpha,21$-dihydroxy-4-pregnene-3,20-dione (with spores)	16α-OH	S-835
	C	$11\beta,21$-dihydroxy-3,20-diketo-4-pregnen-18-oic acid ($18\rightarrow$ 11) lactone	16α-OH	W-1091
	KSC	17β-hydroxy-4-androsten-3-one	16α-OH	F-265; F-266
	C	3β-hydroxy-5α-pregnane-11,20-dione	16α-OH	W-1092
			X-OH; 16α-OH	F-266
	KSC	4-pregnene-3,20-dione	16α-OH	F-265; F-266
	TNAES	$17\alpha,21$-dihydroxy-4-pregnene-3,20-dione	——	S-849
royenae	ATCC-11816 (QM-531)	4-pregnene-3,20-dione	11α-OH	S-882

TABLE III

TAXONOMY

nsformations by Genus:

PEZIZA	(Asco. - Pezizales)	
PHIALOPHORA	(Imperf. - Moniliales)	
PHOLIOTA	(Basidio. - Agaricales)	
PHOMA	(Imperf. - Sphaeropsidales)	

SPECIES	SOURCE	SUBSTRATE	REACTION	REF.
:ZIZA				
ecies	C (ETH-M-23)	21-hydroxy-4-pregnene-3,20-dione	7α-OH	M-585
	(ETH-M-26)	d,1-21-hydroxy-4-pregnene-3,20-dione	d,1 → d-7α-OH + 1	W-1102
HIALOPHORA				
rrucosa	FRI	17α,21-dihydroxy-4-pregnene-3,20-dione	——	S-849
IOLIOTA				
iposa	FRI	17α,21-dihydroxy-4-pregnene-3,20-dione	——	S-849
uarrosoides	AL (H-140)	4-pregnene-3,20-dione	oxidation - products not identified	S-825
IOMA				
ecies	ATCC-13145	16α-tert-butyl-17α,21-dihydroxy-5α-pregnane-3,20-dione	11α-OH	I-422
			11β-OH	I-42.
		16β-ethyl-17α,21-dihydroxy-5α-pregnane-3,20-dione	11α-OH	I-422
			11β-OH	I-422
		17α,21-dihydroxy-16α-methyl-5α-pregnane-3,20-dione	11α-OH	I-422
			11β-OH	I-422
		17α,21-dihydroxy-16β-methyl-5α-pregnane-3,20-dione	11α-OH	I-422
			11β-OH	I-422
		17α,21-dihydroxy-4-pregnene-3,20-dione	6β-OH	I-422
			11α-OH	I-422
			11β-OH	I-422

TABLE III

Transformations by Genus: PHOMA
PHOMOPSIS
PHYCOMYCES (Imperf. - Sphaeropsidales)
(Phyco. - Mucorales)

SPECIES	SOURCE	SUBSTRATE	REACTION	REF.
species	ATCC-13145	$17\alpha,21$-dihydroxy-4-pregnene-3,20-dione	15β-OH	I-422
		$17\alpha,21$-dihydroxy-16α-methyl-4-pregnene-3,20-dione	11α-OH	I-422
			11β-OH	I-422
		$17\alpha,21$-dihydroxy-16β-methyl-4-pregnene-3,20-dione	11α-OH	I-422
			11β-OH	I-422
		16α-tert. butyl-$17\alpha,21$-dihydroxy-1,4-pregnadiene-3,20-dione	11α-OH	I-422
			11β-OH	I-422
		16β-ethyl-$17\alpha,21$-dihydroxy-1,4-pregnadiene-3,20-dione	11α-OH	I-422
			11β-OH	I-422
		$17\alpha,21$-dihydroxy-16α-methyl-1,4-pregnadiene-3,20-dione	11α-OH	I-422
			11β-OH	I-422
		$17\alpha,21$-dihydroxy-16β-methyl-1,4-pregnadiene-3,20-dione	11α-OH	I-422
			11β-OH	I-422
	FAHU	$17\alpha,21$-dihydroxy-4-pregnene-3,20-dione	——	S-849
PHOMOPSIS				
citri	FRI	$17\alpha,21$-dihydroxy-4-pregnene-3,20-dione	11α-OH	S-849
	TNAES	$17\alpha,21$-dihydroxy-4-pregnene-3,20-dione	——	S-849
PHYCOMYCES				
blakesleeanus	NRRL	Sarsasapogenin	——	M-587
		Diosgenin	——	M-587
		4-dehydrotigogenone	——	M-587
	PF	$17\alpha,21$-dihydroxy-4,14-pregnadiene-3,20-dione	$\Delta^{14} \rightarrow 14\alpha,15\alpha$-oxide	S-865

TABLE III

Transformations by Genus: PHYCOMYCES

SPECIES	SOURCE	SUBSTRATE	REACTION	REF.
lakesleeanus	SQ	3β-hydroxy-5-pregnen-20-one	$\Delta^5 \rightarrow \Delta^4$; 3β-OH $\rightarrow$3-C=O	P-710
		4-pregnene-3,20-dione	7α-OH	F-285; F-286; F-288
			15β-OH	F-285; F-286; F-287; F-288
	UC	4-pregnene-3,20-dione	11-oxygenation	M-601; M-636
		17α-hydroxy-4-pregnene-3,20-dione	11-oxygenation	M-601; M-636
		21-hydroxy-4-pregnene-3,20-dione	11-oxygenation	M-601; M-636
		$17\alpha,21$-dihydroxy-4-pregnene-3,20-dione	11-oxygenation	M-601; M-636
tens	SSSR	$17\alpha,21$-dihydroxy-4-pregnene-3,20-dione	11α-OH	E-224
rottianus	SSSR	$17\alpha,21$-dihydroxy-4-pregnene-3,20-dione	—	E-224
ecies	ATCC-14163	4-pregnene-3,20-dione	6β-OH	H-400
		11α-hydroxy-4-pregnene-3,20-dione	6β-OH	H-400
		$17\alpha,21$-dihydroxy-4-pregnene-3,20-dione	6β-OH	H-400
		$11\beta,17\alpha,21$-trihydroxy-4-pregnene-3,20-dione	6β-OH	H-400
		$17\alpha,21$-dihydroxy-$9\beta,11\beta$-oxido-4-pregnene-3,20-dione	6β-OH	H-400
		9α-fluoro-$11\beta,16\alpha,17\alpha,21$-tetrahydroxy-4-pregnene-3,20-dione 16,17-acetonide	6β-OH; 6β-OH; 11β-OH $\rightarrow$11-C=O	H-400; H-400
		9α-fluoro-$11\beta,16\alpha,17\alpha,21$-tetrahydroxy-1,4-pregnadiene-3,20-dione 16,17-acetonide	6β-OH	H-400
		$17\alpha,21$-dihydroxy-4-pregnene-3,11,20-trione	6β-OH	H-400
		9α-fluoro-$16\alpha,17\alpha,21$-trihydroxy-4-pregnene-3,11,20-trione 16,17-acetonide	6β-OH	H-400

TABLE III

TABLE III

Transformations by Genus:

PHYCOMYCES
PHYTOMONAS
PHYTOPHTHORA
PICHIA

TAXONOMY

(Schizo. - Pseudomonadales)
(Phyco. - Peronosporales)
(Asco. - Endomycetales)

SPECIES	SOURCE	SUBSTRATE	REACTION	REF.
species	NG	5-cholesten-3β-ol (sole carbon source)	utilization	S-793c
		24β-methyl-5,7,22-cholesta-trien-3β-ol (sole carbon source)	utilization	S-793c
theobromatus	UC	4-pregnene-3,20-dione	11-oxygenation	M-601; M-636
		17α-hydroxy-4-pregnene-3,20-dione	11-oxygenation	M-601; M-636
		21-hydroxy-4-pregnene-3,20-dione	11-oxygenation	M-601; M-636
		17α,21-dihydroxy-4-pregnene-3,20-dione	11-oxygenation	M-601; M-636
PHYTOMONAS (see Xanthomonas)				
citri	TNAES	17α,21-dihydroxy-4-pregnene-3,20-dione	—	S-849
eicobatryae	TNAES	17α,21-dihydroxy-4-pregnene-3,20-dione	—	S-849
malvacearum	NG	5-cholesten-3β-ol (sole carbon source)	—	T-1030
PHYTOPHTHORA				
citrophthora	TNAES (CI-16)	17α,21-dihydroxy-4-pregnene-3,20-dione	—	S-849
parasitica	FAKU	17α,21-dihydroxy-4-pregnene-3,20-dione	—	S-849
PICHIA				
membranaefaciens	NRRL	Sarsasapogenin	—	M-587
		Diosgenin	—	M-587
		4-dehydrotigogenone	—	M-587
rosa	FRI	17α,21-dihydroxy-4-pregnene-3,20-dione	—	S-849

TABLE III

ransformations by Genus: PILAIRA (Phyco. - Mucorales)
PIRICULARIA (Imperf. - Moniliales)
PLEOSPORA (Asco. - Sphaeriales)

SPECIES	SOURCE	SUBSTRATE	REACTION	REF.
PILAIRA				
anomala	NRRL	Sarsasapogenin	—	M-587
		Diosgenin	—	M-587
		4-dehydrotigogenone	—	M-587
PIRICULARIA				
oryzae	FAKU	$17\alpha,21$-dihydroxy-4-pregnene-3,20-dione	6β-OH	S-849
	FRI	$17\alpha,21$-dihydroxy-4-pregnene-3,20-dione	6β-OH; 11α-OH	S-849
	S	$17\alpha,21$-dihydroxy-4-pregnene-3,20-dione	11α-OH	S-849
PLEOSPORA				
gaeumanni	C	11β-hydroxy-3,20-diketo-4-pregnen-18-oic acid $(18 \rightarrow 11)$ lactone	14α-OH	W-1108
		$11\beta,21$-dihydroxy-3,20-diketo-4-pregnen-18-al	14α-OH	W-1108
		d,l-21-hydroxy-4-pregnene-3,20-dione	d,l$\rightarrow$d-14α-OH + l	W-1102
		12α-fluoro-11β-hydroxy-4-pregnene-3,20-dione	14α-OH	W-1103
		12α-fluoro-$11\beta,17\alpha$-dihydroxy-4-pregnene-3,20-dione	14α-OH	W-1103
		9α-fluoro-$11\beta,17\alpha,21$-trihydroxy-4-pregnene-3,20-dione	14α-OH	W-1108a
		9α-fluoro-4-pregnene-3,11,20-trione	14α-OH	W-1108a
		$11\beta,21$-dihydroxy-3,20-diketo-1,4-pregnadien-18-al	14α-OH	W-1108
		12α-fluoro-$11\beta,17\alpha$-dihydroxy-1,4-pregnadiene-3,20-dione	14α-OH	W-1103
		9α-fluoro-$11\beta,17\alpha,21$-trihydroxy-1,4-pregnadiene-3,20-dione	14α-OH	W-1108a

TABLE III

Transformations by Genus:

PLEUROTUS	(Basidio. - Agaricales)
PLUTEUS	(Basidio. - Agaricales)
POLYPORUS	(Basidio. - Agaricales)

SPECIES	SOURCE	SUBSTRATE	REACTION	REF.
PLEUROTUS				
japonicus	IAM	17α,21-dihydroxy-4-pregnene-3,20-dione	—	S-849
ostreatus	FAKU	17α,21-dihydroxy-4-pregnene-3,20-dione	—	S-849
	FRI	17α,21-dihydroxy-4-pregnene-3,20-dione	—	S-849
	NRRL-2366	4-pregnene-3,20-dione	oxidation - products not identified	R-778
PLUTEUS				
granularis	AL(C-123)	4-pregnene-3,20-dione	17β-Ac→17a-oxa-17-C=O	S-825
POLYPORUS				
abietinus	UC	not given	oxidation	M-601; M-636
brumalis	AL(G-67)	4-pregnene-3,20-dione	oxidation - products not identified	S-825
caeruleoporus	AL(H-126)	4-pregnene-3,20-dione	oxidation - products not identified	S-825
cinnabarinus	AL(G-90)	4-pregnene-3,20-dione	oxidation - products not identified	S-825
	LED (D-6)	21-hydroxy-4-pregnene-3,20-dione	6β-OH; 14α-OH; 15β-OH	B-63
conchifer	AL(C-255)	4-pregnene-3,20-dione	oxidation - products not identified	S-825
frondosus	IAM	17α,21-dihydroxy-4-pregnene-3,20-dione	—	S-849
pubescens	IAM	17α,21-dihydroxy-4-pregnene-3,20-dione	6β-OH; 11α-OH	S-849
radicata	AL(H-139)	4-pregnene-3,20-dione	oxidation - products not identified	S-825

TABLE III

ransformations by Genus: POLYPORUS
POLYSTICTUS   (Basidio. - Agaricales)
PORIA   (Basidio. - Agaricales)

SPECIES	SOURCE	SUBSTRATE	REACTION	REF.
squamosus	AL (C-180)	4-pregnene-3,20-dione	oxidation - products not identified	S-825
sulfureus	AL (C-6)	4-pregnene-3,20-dione	oxidation - products not identified	S-825
	IAM	17α,21-dihydroxy-4-pregnene-3,20-dione	—	S-849
ulipiferus	ATCC-13489	21-hydroxy-4-pregnene-3,20-dione	6β-OH; 14α-OH; 15β-OH	B-63
		17α,21-dihydroxy-4-pregnene-3,20-dione	6β-OH	B-63
			14α-OH	B-63
			15β-OH	B-63
POLYSTICTUS				
innabarius	FAKU	17α,21-dihydroxy-4-pregnene-3,20-dione	—	S-849
irstus	IAM	17α,21-dihydroxy-4-pregnene-3,20-dione	—	S-849
olyzonus	IAM	17α,21-dihydroxy-4-pregnene-3,20-dione	6β-OH; 11α-OH	S-849
anguineus	IAM	17α,21-dihydroxy-4-pregnene-3,20-dione	—	S-849
	FRI	17α,21-dihydroxy-4-pregnene-3,20-dione	11α-OH	S-849
ersicola	IAM	17α,21-dihydroxy-4-pregnene-3,20-dione	11α-OH	S-849
	S	4-pregnene-3,20-dione	—	S-859
		17α-hydroxy-4-pregnene-3,20-3,20-dione	—	S-859
		17α,21-dihydroxy-4-pregnene-3,20-dione	6β-OH; 11α-OH	S-859
ersicolorpus	S	17α,21-dihydroxy-4-pregnene-3,20-dione	6β-OH; 11α-OH	S-849
PORIA				
ocos	ATCC-13490	21-hydroxy-4-pregnene-3,20-dione	6β-OH; 14α-OH; 15β-OH	B-63
		17α,21-dihydroxy-4-pregnene-3,20-dione	6β-OH	B-63
			14α-OH	B-63
			15β-OH	B-63
pecies	FRI	17α,21-dihydroxy-4-pregnene-3,20-dione	—	S-849

TABLE III

Transformations by Genus: PORIA
PROACTINOMYCES (Schizo. - Actinomycetales)

SPECIES	SOURCE	SUBSTRATE	REACTION	REF.
PORIA				
vaporaria	FRI	17α,21-dihydroxy-4-pregnene-3,20-dione	——	S-849
PROACTINOMYCES (Synonym - Nocardia)				
actinomorphus	NG	5-cholesten-3β-ol (sole carbon source)	utilization	T-1030
agrestis	NG	5-cholesten-3β-ol (sole carbon source)	utilization	T-1030
aquosus	NG	5-cholesten-3β-ol (sole carbon source)	utilization	T-1030
coeliacus	NG	5-cholesten-3β-ol (sole carbon source)	utilization	T-1030
crystallophagus	NG	5-cholesten-3β-ol (sole carbon source)	utilization	T-1030
erythropolis	NG	1,3,5(10)-estratriene-3,17β-diol	17β-OH$\rightarrow$ 17-C=O	T-1034
		5-androstene-3β,17β-diol	$\Delta^5\rightarrow\Delta^4$; 3$\beta$-OH$\rightarrow$ 3-C=O	T-1032
			$\Delta^5\rightarrow\Delta^4$; 3$\beta$-OH$\rightarrow$ 3-C=O; 17β- OH$\rightarrow$17-C=O	T-1032
		3β-hydroxy-5-androsten-17-one	$\Delta^5\rightarrow\Delta^4$; 3$\beta$-OH$\rightarrow$ 3-C=O	T-1032
		17β-hydroxy-4-androsten-3-one	17β-OH$\rightarrow$ 17-C=O	T-1032
		3β-hydroxy-5-cholenic acid	$\Delta^5\rightarrow\Delta^4$; 3$\beta$-OH$\rightarrow$ 3-C=O	T-1032
		3-keto-4-cholenic acid	17β-CH (CH$_3$)CH$_2$CH$_2$ COOH$\rightarrow$ 17β-COOH	T-1034
		3β-hydroxy-4-cholenic acid	3β-OH$\rightarrow$ 3-C=O	T-1034
		5β-cholestan-3β-ol	3β-OH$\rightarrow$ 3-C=O	T-1032; T-1034
		5-cholesten-3β-ol	$\Delta^5\rightarrow\Delta^4$; 3$\beta$-OH$\rightarrow$ 3-C=O	T-1030; T-1031; T-1032; T-1034

TABLE III

Transformations by Genus: PROACTINOMYCES

SPECIES	SOURCE	SUBSTRATE	REACTION	REF.
erythropolis	NG	5-cholesten-3β-ol (sole carbon source)	utilization	T-1030; T-1031
		5-cholesten-3β-ol acetate	—	T-1032
		4-cholesten-3-one	cholestenone → ring A cleavage	T-1034
			17β-CH(CH$_3$) CH$_2$CH$_2$CH$_2$CH (CH$_3$)$_2$ → 17β-COOH	T-1034
		5-stigmasten-3β-ol	3β-OH→3-C=O; Δ^5→Δ^4	T-1032
		5,22-stigmastadien-3β-ol	3β-OH→3-C=O; Δ^5 → Δ^4	T-1032
globerulus	NG	5-cholesten-3β-ol (sole carbon source)	utilization	T-1030
minimus	NG	5-cholesten-3β-ol (sole carbon source)	utilization	T-1030
paraffinae	NG	5-cholesten-3β-ol (sole carbon source)	utilization	T-1030
polychromogenes	NG	5-cholesten-3β-ol (sole carbon source)	utilization	T-1030
restrictus	NG	5-cholesten-3β-ol (sole carbon source)	utilization	T-1030
roseus	NG	5-cholesten-3β-ol (sole carbon source)	7ξ-OH	K-474; K-475
			Δ^5→Δ^4; 3β-OH→ 3-C=O	K-474; K-475
rubropertinctus	NG	5-cholesten-3β-ol (sole carbon source)	utilization	T-1030
species	NG	1,3,5(10)-estratriene-3,17β-diol (all substrates-Ref. T-1033) (sole carbon source)	utilization	T-1033
		3-hydroxy-1,3,5(10)-estratrien-17-one	utilization	T-1033
		3α-hydroxy-5α-androstan-17-one	utilization	T-1033
		3β-hydroxy-5-androsten-17-one	utilization	T-1033
		4-pregnene-3,20-dione	utilization	T-1033
		3α,7α,12α-trihydroxy-5β-cholanic acid	utilization	T-1033
		3β-hydroxy-5-cholenic acid	utilization	T-1033

TABLE III

Transformations by Genus: PROACTINOMYCES
PROTAMINOBACTER   (Schizo. - Pseudomonadales)

SPECIES	SOURCE	SUBSTRATE	REACTION	REF.
species	NG	cholestan-3α-ol	utilization	T-1033
		cholestan-3β-ol	utilization	T-1033
		5β-cholestan-3α-ol	utilization	T-1033
		5β-cholestan-3β-ol	utilization	T-1033
		5β-cholestan-3β-ol acetate	utilization	T-1033
		5α,6β-dibromocholestan-3β-ol	—	T-1033
		3β-chloro-5-cholestene	—	T-1033
		5-cholesten-3β-ol	$\Delta^5 \to \Delta^4$; 3β-OH→ 3-C=O	H-406; H-407
		5-cholesten-3β-ol acetate	utilization	T-1033
		dicholesteryl ether	utilization	T-1033
		4-cholesten-3-one	utilization	T-1033
		24β-methyl-5,7,22-cholestatrien-3β-ol	utilization	T-1033
		5-stigmasten-3β-ol	utilization	T-1033
		5,22-stigmastadien-3β-ol	utilization	T-1033
PROTAMINOBACTER				
alboflavum (alboflavus)	ATCC-8458	estran-3-one	$\Delta^{1,4}$; enol.	S-866
		5α-androstan-3-one	$\Delta^{1,4}$	S-866
		17α-hydroxy-5α-androstan-3-one	$\Delta^{1,4}$	S-866
		5α-androstane-3,17-dione	$\Delta^{1,4}$	S-866
		5β-androstane-3,17-dione	$\Delta^{1,4}$	S-866
		17β-hydroxy-4-estren-3-one	Δ^1; enol.	S-863
		4-androstene-3,17-dione	Δ^1	S-863
		4,6-androstadiene-3,17-dione	Δ^1	S-863
		5α-pregnan-3-one	$\Delta^{1,4}$	S-866
		5β-pregnan-3-one	$\Delta^{1,4}$	S-866
		11β-hydroxy-5β-pregnan-3-one	$\Delta^{1,4}$	S-866
		14α-hydroxy-5β-pregnan-3-one	$\Delta^{1,4}$	S-866
		17α-hydroxy-5β-pregnan-3-one	$\Delta^{1,4}$	S-866
		20-hydroxy-5β-pregnan-3-one	$\Delta^{1,4}$	S-866

TABLE III

ransformations by Genus: PROTAMINOBACTER

SPECIES	SOURCE	SUBSTRATE	REACTION	REF.
alboflavum (aiboflavus)	ATCC-8458	5α-pregnane-3,11-dione	Δ[1,4]	S-866
		5α-pregnane-3,20-dione	Δ[1,4]	S-866
		11β-hydroxy-5β-pregnane-3,20-dione	Δ[1,1]	S-866
		14α-hydroxy-5β-pregnane-3,20-dione	Δ[1,4]	S-866
		17α-hydroxy-5β-pregnane-3,20-dione	Δ[1,1]	S-866
		21-hydroxy-5β-pregnane-3,20-dione	Δ[1,4]	S-866
		21-hydroxy-5ξ-pregnane-3,20-dione	Δ[4]	S-863; S-866
		11β,21-dihydroxy-5β-pregnane-3,20-dione	Δ[1,4]	S-866
		11β,21-dihydroxy-5ξ-pregnane-3,20-dione	Δ[1]	S-866
		11β,17α,21-trihydroxy-5β-pregnane-3,20-dione	Δ[1,4]	S-866
		11β,14α,17α,21-tetrahydroxy-5β-pregnane-3,20-dione	Δ[1,4]	S-866
		5α-pregnane-3,11,20-trione	Δ[1,4]	S-866
		17α,21-dihydroxy-5β-pregnane-3,11,20-trione	Δ[1,4]	S-866
		17α-hydroxy-4-pregnene-3,20-dione	Δ[1]	S-863
		11β,17α-dihydroxy-4-pregnene-3,20-dione	Δ[1]	S-863
		17α,21-dihydroxy-4-pregnene-3,20-dione	Δ[1]	S-863
		11β,17α,21-trihydroxy-4-pregnene-3,20-dione	Δ[1]	S-863
		9α-fluoro-11β,17α,21-trihydroxy-4-pregnene-3,20-dione	Δ[1]	S-863
		16β-fluoro-11β,17α,21-trihydroxy-4-pregnene-3,20-dione	Δ[1]	B-51
		11β,14α,17α,21-tetrahydroxy-4-pregnene-3,20-dione	Δ[1]	S-863

TABLE III

Transformations by Genus: PROTAMINOBACTER

SPECIES	SOURCE	SUBSTRATE	REACTION	REF.
alboflavum (alboflavus)	ATCC-8458	$17\alpha,21$-dihydroxy-$14\alpha,15\alpha$-oxido-4-pregnene-3,20-dione	Δ^1	S-863
		$11\beta,17\alpha,21$-trihydroxy-$14\alpha,15\alpha$-oxido-4-pregnene-3,20-dione	Δ^1	S-863
		4-pregnene-3,11,20-trione	Δ^1	S-863
		$17\alpha,21$-dihydroxy-4-pregnene-3,11,20-trione	Δ^1	S-863
		2α-fluoro-$17\alpha,21$-dihydroxy-4-pregnene-3,11,20-trione	Δ^1	H-401
		$14\alpha,17\alpha,21$-trihydroxy-4-pregnene-3,11,20-trione	Δ^1	S-863
		4,16-pregnadiene-3,20-dione	Δ^1	S-863
		$17\alpha,21$-dihydroxy-4,9(11)-pregnadiene-3,20-dione	Δ^1	S-863
		$17\alpha,21$-dihydroxy-4,14-pregnadiene-3,20-dione	Δ^1	S-863
	NRRL	Sarsasapogenin	—	M-587
		Diosgenin	—	M-587
		4-dehydrotigogenone	—	M-587
rubrum	ATCC-8457	estran-3-one	$\Delta^{1,4}$; enol.	S-866
		5α-androstan-3-one	$\Delta^{1,4}$	S-866
		17α-hydroxy-5α-androstan-3-one	$\Delta^{1,4}$	S-866
		5α-androstane-3,17-dione	$\Delta^{1,4}$	S-866
		5β-androstane-3,17-dione	$\Delta^{1,4}$	S-866
		17β-hydroxy-4-estren-3-one	Δ^1; enol.	S-863
		4-androstene-3,17-dione	Δ^1	S-863
		4,6-androstadiene-3,17-dione	Δ^1	S-863
		5α-pregnan-3-one	$\Delta^{1,4}$	S-866
		5β-pregnan-3-one	$\Delta^{1,4}$	S-866
		11β-hydroxy-5β-pregnan-3-one	$\Delta^{1,4}$	S-866
		14α-hydroxy-5β-pregnan-3-one	$\Delta^{1,4}$	S-866
		17α-hydroxy-5β-pregnan-3-one	$\Delta^{1,4}$	S-866
		20-hydroxy-5β-pregnan-3-one	$\Delta^{1,4}$	S-866
		5α-pregnane-3,11-dione	$\Delta^{1,4}$	S-866

TABLE III

ransformations by Genus: PROTAMINOBACTER

SPECIES	SOURCE	SUBSTRATE	REACTION	REF.
rubrum	ATCC-8457	5α-pregnane-3,20-dione	$\Delta^{1,4}$	S-866
		11β-hydroxy-5β-pregnane-3,20-dione	$\Delta^{1,4}$	S-866
		14α-hydroxy-5β-pregnane-3,20-dione	$\Delta^{1,4}$	S-866
		17α-hydroxy-5β-pregnane-3,20-dione	$\Delta^{1,4}$	S-866
		21-hydroxy-5β-pregnane-3,20-dione	$\Delta^{1,4}$	S-866
		21-hydroxy-5ξ-pregnane-3,20-dione	Δ^{1}	S-863; S-866
		11β,21-dihydroxy-5β-pregnane-3,20-dione	$\Delta^{1,4}$	S-866
		11β,21-dihydroxy-5ξ-pregnane-3,20-dione	Δ^{4}	S-866
		11β,17α,21-trihydroxy-5β-pregnane-3,20-dione	$\Delta^{1,4}$	S-866
		11β,14α,17α,21-tetrahydroxy-5β-pregnane-3,20-dione	$\Delta^{1,4}$	S-866
		5α-pregnane-3,11,20-trione	$\Delta^{1,4}$	S-866
		17α,21-dihydroxy-5β-pregnane-3,11,20-trione	$\Delta^{1,4}$	S-866
		17α-hydroxy-4-pregnene-3,20-dione	Δ^{1}	S-863
		11β,17α-dihydroxy-4-pregnene-3,20-dione	Δ^{1}	S-863
		17α,21-dihydroxy-4-pregnene-3,20-dione	Δ^{1}	S-863
		11β,17α,21-trihydroxy-4-pregnene-3,20-dione	Δ^{1}	S-863
		9α-fluoro-11β,17α,21-trihydroxy-4-pregnene-3,20-dione	Δ^{1}	S-863
		11β,14α,17α,21-tetrahydroxy-4-pregnene-3,20-dione	Δ^{1}	S-863
		17α,21-dihydroxy-14α,15α-oxido-4-pregnene-3,20-dione	Δ^{1}	S-863
		11β,17α,21-trihydroxy-14α,15α-oxido-4-pregnene-3,20-dione	Δ^{1}	S-863
		4-pregnene-3,11,20-trione	Δ^{1}	S-863
		17α,21-dihydroxy-4-pregnene-3,11,20-trione	Δ^{1}	S-863

TABLE III

Transformations by Genus: PROTAMINOBACTER
                               PROTEUS   (Schizo. - Eubacteriales)
                               PSEUDOMONAS   (Schizo. - Pseudomonadiales)

SPECIES	SOURCE	SUBSTRATE	REACTION	REF.
rubrum	ATCC-8457	$14\alpha,17\alpha,21$-trihydroxy-4-pregnene-3,11,20-trione	Δ^1	S-863
		$17\alpha,21$-dihydroxy-4,9(11)-pregnadiene-3,20-dione	Δ^1	S-863
		$17\alpha,21$-dihydroxy-4,14-pregnadiene-3,20-dione	Δ^1	S-863
		4,16-pregnadiene-3,20-dione	Δ^1	S-863
PROTEUS				
species	rat caecum	$3\alpha,7\alpha,12\alpha$-trihydroxy-5β-cholanic acid	——	N-675
	IAM (HX-19)	$17\alpha,21$-dihydroxy-4-pregnene-3,20-dione	11β-OH	S-849
	NG	5-cholesten-3β-ol (sole carbon source)	utilization	T-1030
PSEUDOMONAS				
aeruginosa	IAM (MT)	$17\alpha,21$-dihydroxy-4-pregnene-3,20-dione	——	S-849
	IAM (Baltimore)		——	S-849
	IFO (3505)	$11\beta,17\alpha,21$-trihydroxy-4-pregnene-3,20-dione	——	I-428
(in mixed culture with Mycococcus sp. A_1)			Δ^1	I-428
	IAM	4-pregnene-3,20-dione	oxidation	I-414; I-415
	IAM	$17\alpha,21$-dihydroxy-4-pregnene-3,20-dione	——	I-414; I-415
	NG	5-cholesten-3β-ol (sole carbon source)	utilization	T-1030
aureofaciens	IAM	4-pregnene-3,20-dione	——	I-414; I-415
	IAM	$17\alpha,21$-dihydroxy-4-pregnene-3,20-dione	——	I-414; I-415
	NRRL B-1543		——	S-849
azoformicans	IAM	4-pregnene-3,20-dione	oxidation	I-414; I-415

TABLE III

Transformations by Genus: PSEUDOMONAS

SPECIES	SOURCE	SUBSTRATE	REACTION	REF.
azoformicans	IAM	$17\alpha,21$-dihydroxy-4-pregnene-3,20-dione	——	I-414; I-415
boreopolis	ATCC-13476	$17\alpha,21$-dihydroxy-4-pregnene-3,20-dione	Δ^1	T-960
			Δ^1; 20-C=O → 20β-OH	T-960
			11β-OH	T-960
	IAM	4-pregnene-3,20-dione	——	I-414; I-415
	IAM	$17\alpha,21$-dihydroxy-4-pregnene-3,20-dione	——	I-414; I-415
	Takeda (109)		Δ^1; 20-C=O → 20β-OH	N-652
			11β-OH	N-652
irradiated mutant	Takeda (109)		Δ^1; 11β-OH	T-961
caudata	IAM	4-pregnene-3,20-dione	——	I-414; I-415
	IAM	$17\alpha,21$-dihydroxy-4-pregnene-3,20-dione	——	I-414; I-415
chlororaphis	IAM (1511)	3α-hydroxy-5α-androstan-17-one	——	N-648
		3β-hydroxy-5-androsten-17-one	——	N-648
		17β-hydroxy-4-androsten-3-one	Δ^1; 17β-OH → 17-C=O	N-648
			17β-OH → 17-C=O	N-648
		1,4-androstadiene-3,17-dione	——	N-648
		4-pregnene-3,20-dione	——	N-648
		17α-hydroxy-4-pregnene-3,20-dione	——	N-648
		21-hydroxy-4-pregnene-3,20-dione	——	N-648
		$11\beta,21$-dihydroxy-4-pregnene-3,20-dione	——	N-648
		$17\alpha,21$-dihydroxy-4-pregnene-3,20-dione	Δ^1; 17α-OH-17β-(20-C=O-21-OH) →17a-oxa-17-C=O	N-648
			Δ^1	N-648

TABLE III

Transformations by Genus: PSEUDOMONAS

SPECIES	SOURCE	SUBSTRATE	REACTION	REF.
chlororaphis	IAM (1511)	17α,21-dihydroxy-4-pregnene-3,20-dione	17α-OH-17β-(20-C=O-21-OH) $\rightarrow$ 17-C=O	N-648
		11β,17α,21-trihydroxy-4-pregnene-3,20-dione	Δ^1	N-648
			17α-OH-17β-(20-C=O-21-OH) $\rightarrow$ 17-C=O	N-648
			Δ^1; 17α-OH-17β-(20-C=O-21-OH) $\rightarrow$17-C=O	N-648
		15α,17α,21-trihydroxy-4-pregnene-3,20-dione	17α-OH-17β-(20-C=O-21-OH) $\rightarrow$ 17-C=O	N-648
		11β,17α,21-trihydroxy-1,4-pregnadiene-3,20-dione	17α-OH-17β-(20-C=O-21-OH)$\rightarrow$ 17-C=O	N-648
cohaerens	IAM	4-pregnene-3,20-dione	oxidation	I-414; I-415
		17α,21-dihydroxy-4-pregnene-3,20-dione	—	I-414; I-415
cruciviae	ATCC-13262	4-androstene-3,17-dione	9α-OH; Δ^1; rev. aldol., enol.	M-597
		19-hydroxy-4-androstene-3,17-dione	Δ^1; rev. aldol. (Formaldehyde↑) enol.	M-597
	IAM	4-pregnene-3,20-dione	oxidation	I-414; I-415
		17α,21-dihydroxy-4-pregnene-3,20-dione	Δ^1	I-414; I-415; S-849
dacunhae	ATCC-13261	4-androstene-3,17-dione	Δ^1	M-597
		19-hydroxy-4-androstene-3,17-dione	Δ^1; rev. aldol. (Formaldehyde↑) enol.	M-597
	IAM (A-6-3)	21-hydroxy-4-pregnene-3,20-dione	Δ^1	S-848
		11β,21-dihydroxy-4-pregnene-3,20-dione	Δ^1	S-848
		17α,21-dihydroxy-4-pregnene-3,20-dione	Δ^1	S-848; S-849

TABLE III

Transformations by Genus: PSEUDOMONAS

SPECIES	SOURCE	SUBSTRATE	REACTION	REF.
dacunhae	IAM (A-6-3)	$11\beta,17\alpha,21$-trihydroxy-4-pregnene-3,20-dione	—	S-848
		$17\alpha,21$-dihydroxy-4-pregnene-3,11,20-trione	—	S-848
	IAM (C-1-7) (G-1-13) (R-10-2)	$17\alpha,21$-dihydroxy-4-pregnene-3,20-dione	Δ^1	S-849
	S	4-pregnene-3,20-dione	—	S-859
		17α-hydroxy-4-pregnene-3,20-dione	—	S-859
		21-hydroxy-4-pregnene-3,20-dione	Δ^1	S-849
		$11\beta,21$-dihydroxy-4-pregnene-3,20-dione	Δ^1	S-849
		$17\alpha,21$-dihydroxy-4-pregnene-3,20-dione	Δ^1	S-849; S-859
		$11\beta,17\alpha,21$-trihydroxy-4-pregnene-3,20-dione	—	S-849
		$17\alpha,21$-dihydroxy-4-pregnene-3,11,20-trione	—	S-849
desmolytica	IAM	4-pregnene-3,20-dione	oxidation	I-414; I-415
		$17\alpha,21$-dihydroxy-4-pregnene-3,20-dione	—	I-414; I-415
docunhae (probably dacunhae)	IAM	4-pregnene-3,20-dione	oxidation	I-414; I-415
		$17\alpha,21$-dihydroxy-4-pregnene-3,20-dione	—	I-414; I-415
fluorescens	ATCC-13475	$17\alpha,21$-dihydroxy-4-pregnene-3,20-dione	20-C=O → 20β-OH	T-960; U-1039
	IAM (A-3-8)	$17\alpha,21$-dihydroxy-4-pregnene-3,20-dione	—	S-849
	IAM (A-3-12)	$17\alpha,21$-dihydroxy-4-pregnene-3,20-dione	Δ^1	S-849
(in mixed culture with Mycococcus sp. A_1)	IAM	4-pregnene-3,20-dione	oxidation	I-414; I-415
(in mixed culture with Mycococcus sp. A_1)		$17\alpha,21$-dihydroxy-4-pregnene-3,20-dione	—	I-414; I-415

TABLE III

Transformations by Genus: PSEUDOMONAS

SPECIES	SOURCE	SUBSTRATE	REACTION	REF.
fluorescens	IFO (3081)	$17\alpha,21$-dihydroxy-4-pregnene-3,20-dione	—	S-849
	IFO (3459)	$17\alpha,21$-dihydroxy-4-pregnene-3,20-dione	—	S-849
		$11\beta,17\alpha,21$-trihydroxy-4-pregnene-3,20-dione	—	I-428
(in mixed culture with Mycococcus sp. A_1)			Δ^1	I-428
	NG	5-cholesten-3β-ol	—	T-1030
	NRRL	Sarsasapogenin	—	M-587
		Diosgenin	—	M-587
		4-dehydrotigogenone	—	M-587
	Takeda (M-8)	$17\alpha,21$-dihydroxy-4-pregnene-3,20-dione	20-C=O → 20β-OH	N-652
fragi	IFO (3458)	$11\beta,17\alpha,21$-trihydroxy-4-pregnene-3,20-dione	—	I-428
(in mixed culture with Mycococcus sp. A_1)			Δ^1	I-428
gaegeri	IAM	4-pregnene-3,20-dione	oxidation	I-414; I-415
		$17\alpha,21$-dihydroxy-4-pregnene-3,20-dione	oxidation	I-414; I-415
gelidicola	IAM	4-pregnene-3,20-dione	oxidation	I-414; I-415
		$17\alpha,21$-dihydroxy-4-pregnene-3,20-dione	—	I-414; I-415; S-849
graveolens	IFO (3460)	$11\beta,17\alpha,21$-trihydroxy-4-pregnene-3,20-dione	—	I-428
(in mixed culture with Mycococcus sp. A_1)			Δ^1	I-428
	NRRL	Sarsasapogenin	—	M-587
		Diosgenin	—	M-587
		4-dehydrotigogenone	—	M-587
indoloxidans	NRRL	Sarsasapogenin	—	M-587
		Diosgenin	—	M-587
		4-dehydrotigogenone	—	M-587

TABLE III

Transformations by Genus: PSEUDOMONAS

SPECIES	SOURCE	SUBSTRATE	REACTION	REF.
inertia	IAM	4-pregnene-3,20-dione	oxidation	I-414; I-415
		17α,21-dihydroxy-4-pregnene-3,20-dione	—	I-414; I-415
jaegeri	IAM (AHH-23) (AHH-27) (AHH-28)	17α,21-dihydroxy-4-pregnene-3,20-dione	—	S-849
	rat feces	5-cholesten-3β-ol	utilization	W-1067
lacunogenes	IAM	4-pregnene-3,20-dione	oxidation	I-414; I-415
		17α,21-dihydroxy-4-pregnene-3,20-dione	—	I-414; I-415
melanogenes	IAM	4-pregnene-3,20-dione	—	I-414; I-415
		17α,21-dihydroxy-4-pregnene-3,20-dione	—	I-414; I-415
myxogenes	IAM	4-pregnene-3,20-dione	—	I-414; I-415
		17α,21-dihydroxy-4-pregnene-3,20-dione	—	I-414; I-415
nitroreductans	IAM	4-pregnene-3,20-dione	oxidation	I-414; I-415
		17α,21-dihydroxy-4-pregnene-3,20-dione	—	I-414; I-415
ochracea	IAM	4-pregnene-3,20-dione	—	I-414; I-415
		17α,21-dihydroxy-4-pregnene-3,20-dione	—	I-414; I-415
oleovorans	ATCC-13474	17α,21-dihydroxy-4-pregnene-3,20-dione	Δ^1	T-960
			Δ^1; 11β-OH	T-960
			Δ^1; 20-C=O $\rightarrow$ 20β-OH	T-960
	Takeda (SP-125)	17α,21-dihydroxy-4-pregnene-3,20-dione	Δ^1	N-652

TABLE III

Transformations by Genus: PSEUDOMONAS

SPECIES	SOURCE	SUBSTRATE	REACTION	REF.
ovalis	IAM(A-10-3; CB-3; S-5)	17α,21-dihydroxy-4-pregnene-3,20-dione	—	S-849
	IAM	4-pregnene-3,20-dione	oxidation	I-414; I-415
*		17α,21-dihydroxy-4-pregnene-3,20-dione	Δ^1	I-414; I-415
	NRRL	Sarsasapogenin	—	M-587
		Diosgenin	—	M-587
		4-dehydrotigogenone	—	M-587
pavonacea	IAM	4-pregnene-3,20-dione	oxidation	I-414; I-415
		17α,21-dihydroxy-4-pregnene-3,20-dione	—	I-414; I-415
perlurida	IAM	4-pregnene-3,20-dione	—	I-414; I-415
		17α,21-dihydroxy-4-pregnene-3,20-dione	—	I-414; I-415
pictorum	NC	5-cholesten-3β-ol	—	T-1030
putida	IAM	4-pregnene-3,20-dione	—	I-414; I-415
		17α,21-dihydroxy-4-pregnene-3,20-dione	—	I-414; I-415
	NRRL	Sarsasapogenin	—	M-587
		Diosgenin	—	M-587
		4-dehydrotigogenone	—	M-587
pyocyanea	rat cecum	3α,7α,12α-trihydroxy-5β-cholanic acid	—	N-675
rathonis	IAM	4-pregnene-3,20-dione	oxidation	I-414; I-415
		17α,21-dihydroxy-4-pregnene-3,20-dione	Δ^1	I-414; I-415
riboflavinus	IAM	4-pregnene-3,20-dione	oxidation	I-414; I-415
		17α,21-dihydroxy-4-pregnene-3,20-dione	—	I-414; I-415; S-849

TABLE III

ansformations by Genus: PSEUDOMONAS

SPECIES	SOURCE	SUBSTRATE	REACTION	REF.
roseum	IAM	4-pregnene-3,20-dione	oxidation	I-414; I-415
		17α,21-dihydroxy-4-pregnene-3,20-dione	—	I-414; I-415
schuylkill	IAM (CB-6; B-6)	17α,21-dihydroxy-4-pregnene-3,20-dione	—	S-849
schuylkilliensis	IAM	4-pregnene-3,20-dione	oxidation	I-414; I-415
		17α,21-dihydroxy-4-pregnene-3,20-dione	—	I-414; I-415
species	ATCC-13261	4-androstene-3,17-dione	Δ^1	D-171
			9α-OH; Δ^1; rev. aldol; enol.	D-171
	ATCC-13262	4-androstene-3,17-dione	7β-OH	D-171; M-597
	ATCC-13263	4-androstene-3,17-dione	11α-OH	D-171; M-597
			9α-OH; Δ^1; rev. aldol.; enol.	D-171; M-597
			9α-OH; Δ^1; rev. aldol; enol.; 17-C=O →17β-OH	D-171; M-597
		19-hydroxy-4-androstene-3,17-dione	Δ^1; rev. aldol; (Formaldehyde ↑); enol.	D-171; M-597
(later - testosteroni, ATCC-11966 - Ref. M-560)	Ben May Lab Chicago	1,3,5(10)-estratriene-3,17β-diol (all substrates, this reference using testosterone adapted cells)	—	T-968
		3-hydroxy-1,3,5(10)-estratrien-17-one	—	T-968
		5α-androstane-3,17-dione	oxidation	T-968
		3α-hydroxy-5α-androstan-17-one	oxidation	T-968
		3β-hydroxy-5-androsten-17-one	oxidation	T-968
		3α-hydroxy-5-androsten-17-one	oxidation	T-968
		17α-hydroxy-4-androsten-3-one	oxidation	T-968
		17β-hydroxy-4-androsten-3-one (sole carbon source)	17β-OH →17-C=O	T-968
		17β-hydroxy-17α-methyl-4-androsten-3-one	—	T-968

TABLE III

Transformations by Genus: PSEUDOMONAS

SPECIES	SOURCE	SUBSTRATE	REACTION	REF.
species (later - testosteroni, ATCC-11966 - Ref. M-560)	Ben May Lab Chicago	4-androstene-3,17-dione	oxidation	T-968
		21-hydroxy-4-pregnene-3,20-dione	—	T-968
		11β,17α,21-trihydroxy-4-pregnene-3,20-dione	—	T-968
		17α,21-dihydroxy-4-pregnene-3,11,20-trione	—	T-968
	C	3α-hydroxy-5α-androstan-17-one	d,1-3α-OH → d-3-C=O + 1-3α-OH	W-1102
	IAM	17α,21-dihydroxy-4-pregnene-3,20-dione	—	S-849
	NG	1,3,5(10)-estratriene-3,17β-diol (sole carbon source - all substrates - T-1033, S-786, S-787)	—	T-1033
		3-hydroxy-1,3,5(10)-estratrien-17-one	—	T-1033
		3α-hydroxy-5α-androstan-17-one	utilization	T-1033
		3β-hydroxy-5-androsten-17-one	utilization	T-1033
		17β-hydroxy-4-androsten-3-one	utilization	S-786; S-787
		4-pregnene-3,20-dione	utilization	S-787; T-1033
		3α,7α,12α-trihydroxy-5β-cholanic acid	utilization	T-1033
		3-hydroxy-5-cholenic acid	utilization	T-1033
		5,6-dibromo-cholestane-3β-ol acetate	—	T-1033
		3β-chloro-5-cholestene	—	T-1033
		24β-methyl-5,7,22-cholesta-trien-3β-ol	utilization	T-1033
	Searle	4-androstene-3,17-dione	9α-OH; Δ^1; rev. aldol.; enol.	D-169
		19-hydroxy-4-androstene-3,17-dione	Δ^1; rev. aldol. (Formaldehyde ↑); enol.	D-169
	Takeda (109)	17α,21-dihydroxy-4-pregnene-3,20-dione	11β-OH	N-652; U-1038

TABLE III

Transformations by Genus: PSEUDOMONAS

SPECIES	SOURCE	SUBSTRATE	REACTION	REF.
species	Takeda (109)	$17\alpha,21$-dihydroxy-4-pregnene-3,20-dione	Δ^1; 20-C=O → 20β-OH	U-1038
	(109-mutant)		Δ^1; 20-C=O 20β-OH	U-1040
			Δ^1; 11β-OH	T-961; U-1040
	(M-8)	$17\alpha,21$-dihydroxy-4-pregnene-3,20-dione	Δ^1	N-652; U-1039
			Δ^1; 20-C=O → 20β-OH	N-652; U-1039
	(125)	$17\alpha,21$-dihydroxy-4-pregnene-3,20-dione	Δ^1	U-1039
			Δ^1; 20-C=O → 20β-OH	U-1039
(in mixed culture with one of the following: Mycococcus sp. A_1, A_{10}, A_{14}, A_{15}, A_{18}, A_{24}, A_{25}, A_{26}, A_{27}, A_{30}, A_{31}, A_{32}	(B-1)		Δ^1	I-428
striafaciens	IFO (3309)	$11\beta,17\alpha,21$-trihydroxy-4-pregnene-3,20-dione	—	I-428
(in mixed culture with Mycococcus sp. A_1)			—	I-428
stutzeri	IAM	4-pregnene-3,20-dione	oxidation	I-414; I-415
		$17\alpha,21$-dihydroxy-4-pregnene-3,20-dione	—	I-414; I-415
synxantha	IAM	4-pregnene-3,20-dione	—	I-414; I-415
		$17\alpha,21$-dihydroxy-4-pregnene-3,20-dione	—	I-414; I-415
taetrolens	IAM	4-pregnene-3,20-dione	—	I-414; I-415
		$17\alpha,21$-dihydroxy-4-pregnene-3,20-dione	—	I-414; I-415

TABLE III

Transformations by Genus: PSEUDOMONAS

SPECIES	SOURCE	SUBSTRATE	REACTION	REF.
testosteroni	ATCC-11996	<u>Type Reaction for β-hydroxy steroid dehydrogenase</u> 3β-hydroxy-5-androsten-17-one + DPN$^+$ $\rightleftharpoons$ 4-androstene-3,17-dione + DPNH + H$^+$ 17β-hydroxy-4-androsten-3-one + DPN$^+$ $\rightleftharpoons$ 4-androstene-3,17-dione + DPNH + H$^+$ (see references for isolation, purification, specificity, kinetics and inhibition of enzymes.)	3β-OH$\rightarrow$3-C=O; 17β-OH$\rightarrow$ 17-C=O	D-155; F-241; F-242; M-559; M-560; T-964; T-965; T-966; T-967; T-969
		<u>Type Reaction for 3α-hydroxy steroid dehydrogenase</u> 3α-hydroxy-5α-androstan-17-one + DPN$^+$ $\rightleftharpoons$ androstane-3,17-dione + DPNH + H$^+$ (see references for isolation, purification, specificity, kinetics and inhibition of enzymes.)	3α-OH$\rightarrow$3-C=O	D-155; M-560; R-767; T-964; T-965; T-971
		<u>Type Reaction for Δ^5-3-keto-steroid isomerase</u> 5-androstene-3,17-dione $\rightarrow$ 4-androstene-3,17-dione (see references for isolation purification, specificity, kinetics and inhibition of enzymes.)	$\Delta^5 \rightarrow \Delta^4$	K-437; K-438; T-583; T-964; T-972; W-1064
		<u>Ring A dehydrogenation</u> Δ^1-dehydrogenase Δ^4-5α-dehydrogenase Δ^4-5β-dehydrogenase (see references for isolation, purification, specificity, kinetics and inhibition of enzymes and Ref. T-1005 for comparison with "steroid ring dehydrogenase" from Nocardia.)	Δ^1; Δ^4	L-507; L-508; L-509; T-1005
		3α-hydroxy-5α-androstan-17-one	3α-OH$\rightarrow$3-C=O	D-155
		5α-androstane-3,17-dione-(cell free extracts - Ref. L-507)	Δ^1	L-507; L-508; L-509
			$\Delta^{1,4}$	L-507; L-508

TABLE III

ansformations by Genus: PSEUDOMONAS

SPECIES	SOURCE	SUBSTRATE	REACTION	REF.
estosteroni	ATCC-11996	5α-androstane-3,17-dione (cell free extracts - Ref. L-507)	$\Delta^{1,4}$	L-508
		17β-hydroxy-5β-androstan-3-one	$\Delta^{1,4}$ 17β-OH→17-C=O	L-507
			$\Delta^{1,4}$	L-508
			17β-OH→17-C=O; Δ^4	L-508
		A-nor-17β-hydroxy-3-androsten-2-one	9α-OH; 17β-OH →17-C=O	S-885
		17β-hydroxy-5α-estran-3-one	Δ^1; 17β-OH → 17-C=O	L-508
		17β-hydroxy-4-estren-3-one	Δ^1; enol. 17β-OH→17-C=O	L-507; L-508; L-509
			Δ^1; enol.	L-508
		5-androstene-3β,17β-diol	$\Delta^5\to\Delta^4$; 3β-OH→3-C=O; 17β-OH →17-C=O	T-966
		17α-methyl-5-androstene-3β,17β-diol	$\Delta^5\to\Delta^4$; 3β-OH→3-C=O	T-966
		17β-hydroxy-4-androsten-3-one	Δ^1	L-507
			17β-OH→17-C=O; Δ^1	L-507
			17β-OH→17-C=O	D-155; L-508; T-966
		11β,17β-dihydroxy-4-androsten-3-one	17β-OH→17-C=O	T-966
		3β-hydroxy-5-androsten-17-one	$\Delta^5\to\Delta^4$; 3β-OH→3-C=O	T-966
			$\Delta^5\to\Delta^4$; 3β-OH→3-C=O; 17-C=O →17β-OH	T-966
		1-androstene-3,17-dione	Δ^4; 17-C=O → 17β-OH	L-508
		4-androstene-3,17-dione	Δ^1; 17-C=O → 17β-OH	L-508
			Δ^1	L-507; L-508
			17-C=O → 17β-OH	T-966

TABLE III

Transformations by Genus: PSEUDOMONAS
<u>TAXONOMY</u>
                              PSEUDOMYCODERMA   (Imperf. - Moniliales)
                              PSILOCYBE   (Basidio. - Agaricales)

SPECIES	SOURCE	SUBSTRATE	REACTION	REF.
testosteroni	ATCC-11996	17β-hydroxy-17α-methyl-4-androsten-3-one	Δ^1	<u>L-508</u>
		5α-1-estrene-3,17-dione	$\overset{4}{\Delta}$; enol.	<u>L-508</u>
		4-estrene-3,17-dione	$\overset{1}{\Delta}$; enol.	<u>L-508</u>; L-509
		1,3,5(10)-estratriene-3,17β-diol	17β-OH→17-C=O	D-155; T-966
		3-hydroxy-1,3,5(10)-estratrien-17-one	17-C=O →17β-OH	T-966
		21-hydroxy-4-pregnene-3,20-dione	9α-OH	<u>P-740</u>
		(use of inhibitors to increase 9α-OH)	9α-OH	<u>S-898</u>
		4-pregnene-3,20-dione	9α-OH	<u>S-885</u>
		11β,17α,21-trihydroxy-4-pregnene-3,20-dione (use of dried cells)	Δ^1	F-231
		3β-hydroxy-5-pregnen-20-one	$\overset{5}{\Delta}\to\overset{4}{\Delta}$; 3$\beta$-OH→3-C=O	T-966
trifolii	IAM	4-pregnene-3,20-dione	—	I-414; I-415
		17α,21-dihydroxy-4-pregnene-3,20-dione	—	I-414; I-415
xanthe	IAM	4-pregnene-3,20-dione	—	I-414; I-415
		17α,21-dihydroxy-4-pregnene-3,20-dione	—	I-414; I-415
<u>PSEUDOMYCODERMA</u>				
miso	FRI	17α,21-dihydroxy-4-pregnene-3,20-dione	—	S-849
<u>PSILOCYBE</u>				
caerulescens (var. mazatecorum)	S$_1$	3β-hydroxy-5-pregnen-20-one	3β-OH→3-C=O; Δ^5→Δ^4; 11α-OH	<u>C-113</u>
			3β-OH→3-C=O; Δ^5→Δ^4; 11α-OH; 21-OH; 11α,21-diOH	<u>C-113</u>
		4-pregnene-3,20-dione	11α-OH	<u>C-113</u>
			11α-OH; 21-OH; 11α,21-diOH	<u>C-113</u>

TABLE III

ansformations by Genus: PSILOCYBE

SPECIES	SOURCE	SUBSTRATE	REACTION	REF.
aerulescens * (var. mazatecorum)	SY	$17\alpha,21$-dihydroxy-4-pregnene-3,20-dione	11α-OH	C-113
aerulipes	AL (C-236)	4-pregnene-3,20-dione	oxidation - products not identified	S-825
mexicana *	SY	$17\alpha,21$-dihydroxy-4-pregnene-3,20-dione	11α-OH	C-113
	UB	4-androstene-3,17-dione	oxidation - products not identified	W-1075
		4-pregnene-3,20-dione	oxidation - products not identified	W-1075
		14β-hydroxy-3-keto-5β-20(22)-cardenolide	7β-OH	W-1075
		$3\beta,14\beta$-dihydroxy-5β-20(22)-cardenolide	3β-OH $\rightarrow$ 3-C=O	W-1075
			7β-OH; 3β-OH $\rightarrow$3-C=O	W-1075
			7β-OH	W-1075
			12β-OH	W-1075
		$3\beta,5\beta,14\beta$-trihydroxy-19-oxo-20(22)-cardenolide	oxidation - products not identified	W-1075
		$3\beta,11\alpha,14\beta$-trihydroxy-5β-20(22)-cardenolide	oxidation - products not identified	W-1075
		$3\beta,14\beta,16\beta$-trihydroxy-5β-20(22)-cardenolide	oxidation - products not identified	W-1075
		$3\beta,5\beta,14\beta,19$-tetrahydroxy-20(22)-cardenolide	oxidation - products not identified	W-1075
semperviva	UB	21-hydroxy-4-pregnene-3,20-dione	oxidation - products not identified	W-1075
		14β-hydroxy-3-keto-5β-20(22)-cardenolide	3-C=O$\rightarrow3\beta$-OH	W-1075
			12β-OH; 3-C=O $\rightarrow3\beta$-OH	W-1075

TABLE III

Transformations by Genus: PSILOCYBE
PULLULARIA   (Imperf. - Moniliales)
PYCNODOTHIS   (Imperf. - Sphaeropsidales)

SPECIES	SOURCE	SUBSTRATE	REACTION	REF.
semperviva	UB	$3\beta,14\beta$-dihydroxy-5β-20(22)-cardenolide	12β-OH	W-1075
		$3\beta,11\alpha,14\beta$-trihydroxy-5β-20(22)-cardenolide	oxidation - products not identified	W-1075
		$3\beta,14\beta,16\beta$-trihydroxy-5β-20(22)-cardenolide	oxidation - products not identified	W-1075
		$3\beta,5\beta,14\beta$-trihydroxy-19-oxo-20(22)-cardenolide	19-C=O → 19-OH	W-1075
PULLULARIA				
pullulans	FRI	$17\alpha,21$-dihydroxy-4-pregnene-3,20-dione	—	S-849
	NG (Sandoz)	$3\beta,6\beta,8\beta,14\beta$-tetrahydroxy-4,20,22-bufatrienolide 6-acetate 3-glucoside	3β-[$1^1\xi$-glucoside] → 3β-OH	S-936a
		$3\beta,14\beta$-dihydroxy-5β-20(22)-cardenolide 3-[glucosyl-digitoxosyl-digitoxosyl-digitoxoside]	—	S-936a
		Digilanid - A	—	S-936a
species	NRRL	plant saponins	hydrolysis of glycosides to aglycones (sapogenins)	K-478
PYCNODOTHIS				
species	ATCC-11721	4-androstene-3,17-dione	Δ^1	K-450
		4-pregnene-3,20-dione	17β-Ac→17-C=O	K-450
			Δ^1; 17β-Ac → 17-C=O	K-450
			Δ^1; 17β-Ac → 17β-OH	K-450
		21-hydroxy-4-pregnene-3,20-dione	17β-(20-C=O-21-OH) → 17-C=O; Δ^1	K-450

TABLE III <u>TAXONOMY</u>

ansformations by Genus:

PYCNODOTHIS	
PYCNOSPORIUM	(Imperf. - Sphaeropsidales)
PYRENOPHORA	(Asco. - Sphaeriales)
PYRONEMA	(Asco. - Pezizales)
PYTHIUM	(Phyco. - Peronosporales)

SPECIES	SOURCE	SUBSTRATE	REACTION	REF.
pecies	ATCC-11721	4,16-pregnadiene-3,20-dione	Δ^{16}-17-Ac $\rightarrow$ 17-C=O; Δ^{1}	K-450
YCNOSPORIUM				
pecies	ATCC-12231 (QM-703)	4-pregnene-3,20-dione	11β-OH	D-147
		21-hydroxy-4-pregnene-3,20-dione	11β-OH	D-147
		17α,21-dihydroxy-4-pregnene-3,20-dione	11β-OH	D-147
YRENOPHORA				
reminea	FRI	17α,21-dihydroxy-4-pregnene-3,20-dione	2β-OH	S-849
eres	NIHJ(A-17)	17α,21-dihydroxy-4-pregnene-3,20-dione	—	S-849
	NIHJ(A-29)	17α,21-dihydroxy-4-pregnene-3,20-dione	6β-OH; 11α-OH	S-849
YRONEMA				
confluens	FRI	17α,21-dihydroxy-4-pregnene-3,20-dione	11α-OH	S-849
PYTHIUM				
ltimum	FRI	17α,21-dihydroxy-4-pregnene-3,20-dione	11β-OH	S-849
	S	4-androstene-3,17-dione	17-C=O $\rightarrow$ 17a-oxa-17-C=O	S-846
		4-pregnene-3,20-dione	17β-Ac $\rightarrow$ 17a-oxa-17-C=O	S-846; S-849
		17α-hydroxy-4-pregnene-3,20-dione	17α-OH-17β-Ac $\rightarrow$ 17a-oxa-17-C=O	S-846; S-849
		21-hydroxy-4-pregnene-3,20-dione	17β-(20-C=O-21-OH) $\rightarrow$ 17a-oxa-17-C=O	S-846; S-849
		11β,21-dihydroxy-4-pregnene-3,20-dione	—	S-846; S-849

TABLE III

Transformations by Genus: PYTHIUM
RAMULARIA   (Imperf. - Moniliales)
RHACODIUM   (Imperf. - Mycelia Sterilia)
RHIZOBIUM   (Schizo. - Eubacteriales)

SPECIES	SOURCE	SUBSTRATE	REACTION	REF.
ultimum	S	$17\alpha,21$-dihydroxy-4-pregnene-3,20-dione	20-C=O → 20β-OH	S-846; S-849
		$11\beta,17\alpha,21$-trihydroxy-4-pregnene-3,20-dione	—	S-846; S-849
		$17\alpha,21$-dihydroxy-4-pregnene-3,11,20-trione	—	S-846; S-849
RAMULARIA				
robusta	Leo Pharm. Products, Denmark	17β-hydroxy-4-androsten-3-one	Δ^1	L-525
		17β-hydroxy-17α-methyl-4-androsten-3-one	Δ^1	L-525
RHACODIUM				
cellare	ATCC-13243†	$17\alpha,21$-dihydroxy-4-pregnene-3,20-dione	11α-OH	G-313
RHIZOBIUM				
leguminosarum	SY	3-hydroxy-1,3,5(10)-estratrien-17-one	17-C=O → 17β-OH	C-114
		4-androstene-3,17-dione	17-C=O → 17β-OH	C-114
		19-nor-4-pregnene-3,20-dione	—	C-114
		4-pregnene-3,20-dione	—	C-114
		11α-hydroxy-4-pregnene-3,20-dione	—	C-114
		17α-hydroxy-4-pregnene-3,20-dione	—	C-114
		$17\alpha,21$-dihydroxy-4-pregnene-3,20-dione	20-C=O → 20ξ-OH	C-114
		$11\beta,17\alpha,21$-trihydroxy-4-pregnene-3,20-dione	20-C=O → 20ξ-OH	C-114
		$17\alpha,21$-dihydroxy-4-pregnene-3,11,20-trione	20-C=O → 20ξ-OH	C-114
		4,16-pregnadiene-3,20-dione	—	C-114

TABLE III

Transformations by Genus: RHIZOBIUM

SPECIES	SOURCE	SUBSTRATE	REACTION	REF.
meliloti	SY	3-hydroxy-1,3,5(10)-estratrien-17-one	17-C=O → 17β-OH	C-114
		4-androstene-3,17-dione	17-C=O → 17β-OH	C-114
		19-nor-4-pregnene-3,20-dione	—	C-114
		4-pregnene-3,20-dione	—	C-114
		11α-hydroxy-4-pregnene-3,20-dione	—	C-114
		17α-hydroxy-4-pregnene-3,20-dione	—	
		17α,21-dihydroxy-4-pregnene-3,20-dione	20-C=O → 20ξ-OH	C-114
		11β,17α,21-trihydroxy-4-pregnene-3,20-dione	20-C=O → 20ξ-OH	C-114
		17α,21-dihydroxy-4-pregnene-3,11,20-trione	20-C=O → 20ξ-OH	C-114
		4,16-pregnadiene-3,20-dione	—	C-114
phaseoli	SY	3-hydroxy-1,3,5(10)-estratrien-17-one	17-C=O → 17β-OH	C-114
		4-androstene-3,17-dione	17-C=O → 17β-OH	C-114
		19-nor-4-pregnene-3,20-dione	—	C-114
		4-pregnene-3,20-dione	—	C-114
		11α-hydroxy-4-pregnene-3,20-dione	—	C-114
		17α-hydroxy-4-pregnene-3,20-dione	—	C-114
		17α,21-dihydroxy-4-pregnene-3,20-dione	20-C=O → 20ξ-OH	C-114
		11β,17α,21-trihydroxy-4-pregnene-3,20-dione	20-C=O → 20ξ-OH	C-114
		17α,21-dihydroxy-4-pregnene-3,11,20-trione	20-C=O → 20ξ-OH	C-114
		4,16-pregnadiene-3,20-dione	—	C-114
trifolii	SY	3-hydroxy-1,3,5(10)-estratrien-17-one	17-C=O → 17β-OH	C-114
		4-androstene-3,17-dione	17-C=O → 17β-OH	C-114

568

TABLE III

Transformations by Genus: RHIZOBIUM
                              RHIZOCTONIA   (Imperf. - Mycelia Sterilia)

SPECIES	SOURCE	SUBSTRATE	REACTION	REF.
trifolii	SY	19-<u>nor</u>-4-pregnene-3,20-dione	—	C-114
		4-pregnene-3,20-dione	—	C-114
		11α-hydroxy-4-pregnene-3,20-dione	—	C-114
		17α-hydroxy-4-pregnene-3,20-dione	—	C-114
		17α,21-dihydroxy-4-pregnene-3,20-dione	20-C=O → 20ξ-OH	<u>C-114</u>
		11β,17α,21-trihydroxy-4-pregnene-3,20-dione	20-C=O → 20ξ-OH	<u>C-114</u>
		17α,21-dihydroxy-4-pregnene-3,11,20-trione	20-C=O → 20ξ-OH	<u>C-114</u>
		4,16-pregnadiene-3,20-dione	—	C-114
RHIZOCTONIA (See - Corticium)				
ferrugena	ATCC-13246t or CBS	17β-hydroxy-4-androsten-3-one	1β-OH; 2β-OH	G-313
		4-pregnene-3,20-dione	1β-OH; 2β-OH	G-313
		21-hydroxy-4-pregnene-3,20-dione	1β-OH; 2β-OH	G-313
		11β,21-dihydroxy-4-pregnene-3,20-dione	1β-OH; 2β-OH	G-313
		17α,21-dihydroxy-4-pregnene-3,20-dione	1β-OH	G-312; <u>G-313</u>; G-315
			2β-OH	G-312; <u>G-313</u>; G-315
		11α,17α,21-trihydroxy-4-pregnene-3,20-dione	1β-OH; 2β-OH	G-313
		11β,17α,21-trihydroxy-4-pregnene-3,20-dione	1β-OH; 2β-OH	G-313
		9α-fluoro-11β,17α,21-trihydroxy-4-pregnene-3,20-dione	1β-OH; 2β-OH	G-313
		11β,17α,21-trihydroxy-6α-methyl-4-pregnene-3,20-dione	1β-OH; 2β-OH	G-313
		9α-fluoro-11β,16α,17α,21-tetrahydroxy-4-pregnene-3,20-dione	1β-OH; 2β-OH	G-313

TABLE III

ansformations by Genus: RHIZOCTONIA

SPECIES	SOURCE	SUBSTRATE	REACTION	REF.
errugena	ATCC-13246t	$17\alpha,21$-dihydroxy-4,9(11)-pregnadiene-3,20-dione	1β-OH; 2β-OH	G-313
		$17\alpha,21$-dihydroxy-4-pregnene-3,11,20-trione	1β-OH; 2β-OH	G-313
uneratii	ATCC-13247t	17β-hydroxy-4-androsten-3-one	1ξ-OH; 11α-OH; 11β-OH; 11-C=O (via 11β-OH)	G-313
		4-pregnene-3,20-dione	1ξ-OH; 11α-OH; 11β-OH; 11-C=O (via 11β-OH	G-313
		21-hydroxy-4-pregnene-3,20-dione	1ξ-OH; 11α-OH; 11β-OH; 11-C=O (via 11β-OH)	G-313
		$17\alpha,21$-dihydroxy-4-pregnene-3,20-dione	1β-OH; 11α-OH	G-313
olani	ATCC-10154, 10157, 10187	17β-hydroxy-4-androsten-3-one	1ξ-OH; 11α-OH; 11β-OH; 11-C=O (via 11β-OH)	G-313
		4-pregnene-3,20-dione	1ξ-OH; 11α-OH; 11β-OH; 11-C=O (via 11β-OH)	G-313
		21-hydroxy-4-pregnene-3,20-dione	1ξ-OH; 11α-OH; 11β-OH; 11-C=O (via 11β-OH)	G-313
		$17\alpha,21$-dihydroxy-4-pregnene-3,20-dione	1ξ-OH; 11α-OH	G-313
		$11\alpha,17\alpha,21$-trihydroxy-4-pregnene-3,20-dione	—	G-313
		$11\beta,17\alpha,21$-trihydroxy-4-pregnene-3,20-dione	—	G-313
		9α-fluoro-$11\beta,17\alpha,21$-trihydroxy-4-pregnene-3,20-dione	—	G-313
	ATCC-10157, 10187	$11\beta,17\alpha,21$-trihydroxy-6-methyl-4-pregnene-3,20-dione	—	G-313
		$11\beta,16\alpha,17\alpha,21$-tetrahydroxy-4-pregnene-3,20-dione	—	G-313
		$17\alpha,21$-dihydroxy-4-pregnene-3,11,20-trione	—	G-313
		$17\alpha,21$-dihydroxy-4-pregnene-3,11,20-trione 21-acetate	—	G-313
		$17\alpha,21$-dihydroxy-1,4-pregnadiene-3,20-dione	—	G-313

TABLE III

Transformations by Genus: RHIZOCTONIA

SPECIES	SOURCE	SUBSTRATE	REACTION	REF.
solani	ATCC-13248t; CBS	17β-hydroxy-4-androsten-3-one	11α-OH; 11β-OH	G-313
		4-pregnene-3,20-dione	11α-OH; 11β-OH	G-313
		17α,21-dihydroxy-4-pregnene-3,20-dione	11α-OH; 11β-OH; 11-C=O (via 11β-OH)	G-313
		11α,17α,21-trihydroxy-4-pregnene-3,20-dione	—	G-313
		11β,17α,21-trihydroxy-4-pregnene-3,20-dione	1ξ-OH	G-313
		9α-fluoro-11β,17α,21-trihydroxy-4-pregnene-3,20-dione	—	G-313
		11β,17α,21-trihydroxy-6-methyl-4-pregnene-3,20-dione	—	G-313
		11β,16α,17α,21-tetrahydroxy-4-pregnene-3,20-dione	—	G-313
		17α,21-dihydroxy-4-pregnene-3,11,20-trione	1ξ-OH	G-313
		17α,21-dihydroxy-4-pregnene-3,11,20-trione 21-acetate	1ξ-OH	G-313
		17α,21-dihydroxy-1,4-pregnadiene-3,20-dione	11α-OH; 11β-OH; 11-C=O (via 11β-OH)	G-313
	ATCC-13249t; CBS	17β-hydroxy-4-androsten-3-one	1ξ-OH; 2β-OH	G-313
		4-pregnene-3,20-dione	1ξ-OH; 2β-OH	G-313
		17α,21-dihydroxy-4-pregnene-3,20-dione	1ξ-OH; 2β-OH	G-313
		11α,17α,21-trihydroxy-4-pregnene-3,20-dione	—	G-313
		11β,17α,21-trihydroxy-4-pregnene-3,20-dione	1ξ-OH; 2β-OH	G-313
		9α-fluoro-11β,17α,21-trihydroxy-4-pregnene-3,20-dione	1ξ-OH; 2β-OH	G-313
		11β,17α,21-trihydroxy-6-methyl-4-pregnene-3,20-dione	1ξ-OH; 2β-OH	G-313
		11β,16α,17α,21-tetrahydroxy-4-pregnene-3,20-dione	1ξ-OH; 2β-OH	G-313
		17α,21-dihydroxy-4-pregnene-3,11,20-trione	1ξ-OH; 2β-OH	G-313

TABLE III

ransformations by Genus: RHIZOCTONIA

SPECIES	SOURCE	SUBSTRATE	REACTION	REF.
solani	ATCC-13249t; CBS	$17\alpha,21$-dihydroxy-4-pregnene-3,11,20-trione 21-acetate	1ξ-OH; 2β-OH	G-313
		$17\alpha,21$-dihydroxy-1,4-pregna-diene-3,20-dione	—	G-313
	ATCC-13250t; CBS	17β-hydroxy-4-androsten-3-one	1ξ-OH; 2β-OH	G-313
		4-pregnene-3,20-dione	1ξ-OH; 2β-OH	G-313
			$1\xi,15\xi$-diOH	G-312
			$6\beta,15\xi$-diOH; 20-C=O $\rightarrow$ 20ξ-OH	G-312
		$11\beta,21$-dihydroxy-4-pregnene-3,20-dione	oxidation - products not identified	G-312
		$17\alpha,21$-dihydroxy-4-pregnene-3,20-dione	1ξ-OH	G-313
			2β-OH; 11-C=O (via 11β-OH)	G-312
			6β-OH; 11-C=O (via 11β-OH)	G-312
			6β-OH	S-793b
		$11\alpha,17\alpha,21$-trihydroxy-4-preg-nene-3,20-dione	1ξ-OH; 2β-OH	G-313
		$11\beta,17\alpha,21$-trihydroxy-4-preg-nene-3,20-dione	1ξ-OH	G-313
		9α-fluoro-$11\beta,17\alpha,21$-trihydroxy-4-pregnene-3,20-dione	—	G-313
		$11\beta,17\alpha,21$-trihydroxy-6-methyl-4-pregnene-3,20-dione	—	G-313
		$11\beta,16\alpha,17\alpha,21$-tetrahydroxy-4-pregnene-3,20-dione	—	G-313
		$17\alpha,21$-dihydroxy-4-pregnene-3,11,20-trione	1ξ-OH; 2β-OH	G-313
		$17\alpha,21$-dihydroxy-4-pregnene-3,11,20-trione 21-acetate	1ξ-OH; 2β-OH	G-313
			$2\beta,6\beta$-diOH	G-312
		$17\alpha,21$-dihydroxy-1,4-pregna-diene-3,20-dione	—	G-313
	C	11β-hydroxy-4-androstene-3,17-dione	6β-OH	U-1043

TABLE III

Transformations by Genus: RHIZOCTONIA

SPECIES	SOURCE	SUBSTRATE	REACTION	REF.
solani (var. lycopersici)	CBS	$17\alpha,21$-dihydroxy-4-pregnene-3,20-dione	1ξ-OH	G-313
	FAKU(B-5; P-20)	$17\alpha,21$-dihydroxy-4-pregnene-3,20-dione	—	S-849
	IFO (6521)	$17\alpha,21$-dihydroxy-4-p regnene-3,20-dione	Δ^1	T-956
			6β-OH	T-956
species	ATCC-13245 or CBS	17β-hydroxy-4-androsten-3-one	2β-OH; 11α-OH	G-313
		4-pregnene-3,20-dione	2β-OH; 11α-OH	G-313
		$17\alpha,21$-dihydroxy-4-pregnene-3,20-dione	1β-OH	G-313; S-793b
			2β-OH	G-312
			6β-OH	G-312
			2β-OH; 11α-OH	G-313
		$11\alpha,17\alpha,21$-trihydroxy-4-pregnene-3,20-dione	—	G-313
		$11\beta,17\alpha,21$-trihydroxy-4-pregnene-3,20-dione	2β-OH	G-313
		9α-fluoro-$11\beta,17\alpha,21$-trihydroxy-4-pregnene-3,20-dione	—	G-313
		$11\beta,17\alpha,21$-trihydroxy-6-methyl-4-pregnene-3,20-dione	—	G-313
		$11\beta,16\alpha,17\alpha,21$-tetrahydroxy-4-pregnene-3,20-dione	—	G-313
		$17\alpha,21$-dihydroxy-4-pregnene-3,11,20-trione	2β-OH	G-313
		$17\alpha,21$-dihydroxy-4-pregnene-3,11,20-trione 21-acetate	2β-OH	G-313
		$17\alpha,21$-dihydroxy-1,4-pregnadiene-3,20-dione	—	G-313
	NRRL-2573	17β-hydroxy-4-androsten-3-one	11α-OH; 11β-OH	G-313
		4-pregnene-3,20-dione	11α-OH; 11β-OH	G-313
		$17\alpha,21$-dihydroxy-4-pregnene-3,20-dione	11α-OH	G-312; G-313; S-793b
			11β-OH	G-312; G-313; S-793b
			11β-OH; 11- C=O(via 11β-OH)	G-312; G-313

TABLE III

ansformations by Genus: RHIZOCTONIA
                            RHIZOPUS   (Phyco. - Mucorales)

SPECIES	SOURCE	SUBSTRATE	REACTION	REF.
species	NRRL-2573	11α,17α,21-trihydroxy-4-pregnene-3,20-dione	—	G-313
		11β,17α,21-trihydroxy-4-pregnene-3,20-dione	1ξ-OH	G-313
		9α-fluoro-11β,17α,21-trihydroxy-4-pregnene-3,20-dione	—	G-313
		11β,17α,21-trihydroxy-6-methyl-4-pregnene-3,20-dione	—	G-313
		11β,16α,17α,21-tetrahydroxy-4-pregnene-3,20-dione	—	G-313
		17α,21-dihydroxy-4-pregnene-3,11,20-trione	1ξ-OH	G-313
		17α,21-dihydroxy-4-pregnene-3,11,20-trione 21-acetate	1ξ-OH	G-313
		17α,21-dihydroxy-1,4-pregnadiene-3,20-dione	11α-OH; 11β-OH; 11-C=O (via 11β-OH)	G-313
	FAHU	17α,21-dihydroxy-4-pregnene-3,20-dione	2β-OH	S-849
(from apple)	Rutgers (Dr. Haenseler)	17α,21-dihydroxy-4-pregnene-3,20-dione	7ξ-OH	G-312
			15α-OH	G-312
RHIZOPUS				
arrhizus	ATCC-11145 UC (RH-176)	17β-hydroxy-4-androsten-3-one	6β-OH	E-201
			11α-OH	E-201
		17β-hydroxy-17α-methyl-4-androsten-3-one	6β-OH	E-201
			11α-OH	E-201
		4-androstene-3,17-dione	6β-OH	E-201
			11α-OH	E-201; M-601; M-604; M-636; P-728
			$\Delta^4 \rightarrow 5\alpha$-H; 6-C=O	M-601; M-604; M-636
		4-androstene-3,17-dione 6α,7ξ-H^3	6β-OH	B-32
			11α-OH	B-32

TABLE III

Transformations by Genus: RHIZOPUS

SPECIES	SOURCE	SUBSTRATE	REACTION	REF.
arrhizus	ATCC-11145	4-pregnene-3,20-dione	11α-OH	F-247; F-248; H-340; L-518; L-519; M-528; M-601; M-611; M-636; N-649; N-682; P-728; P-729; S-906
			6β,11α-diOH	H-343; M-601; M-616; N-682; O-697; O-698; P-729
*		17α-hydroxy-4-pregnene-3,20-dione	6β-OH	M-580
			11α-OH	M-601; M-636; M-580
		21-hydroxy-4-pregnene-3,20-dione	6β-OH	E-203; M-601; M-631; M-636
			11α-OH	E-203; P-728
		21-hydroxy-4-pregnene-3,20-dione acetate	6β-OH; 21-OAc →21-OH	E-203
			11α-OH; 21-OAc → 21-OH	E-203
		3β-hydroxy-5α-pregnan-20-one	7β-OH	E-202; M-601; M-636
		3β-hydroxy-5β-pregnan-20-one	11-OH	M-601; M-636
		3β-hydroxy-5-pregnen-20-one	7β,11α-diOH	E-202; M-601; M-628; M-629
			7β,11α-diOH	E-202; M-601; M-630

TABLE III

ransformations by Genus: RHIZOPUS

SPECIES	SOURCE	SUBSTRATE	REACTION	REF.
arrhizus	ATCC-11145	19-nor-4-pregnene-3,20-dione	oxidation - products not identified	B-71
		21-hydroxy-4-pregnene-3,20-dione	6β-OH (O_2^{18})	H-374
		17α,21-dihydroxy-4-pregnene-3,20-dione	6β-OH	M-601; M-615; M-636; N-682; P-725
*				
*			11α-OH	N-682
			6β,11α-diOH	N-682
		17α,21-dihydroxy-4-pregnene-3,20-dione 21-acetate	11α-OH; 21-OAc → 21-OH	M-645
		17α,21-dihydroxy-4,9(11)-pregnadiene-3,20-dione	no epoxidation	B-66
		17α,21-dihydroxy-4,14-pregnadiene-3,20-dione	no epoxidation	B-66
		11β,21-dihydroxy-4,17(20)-pregnadien-3-one	6β-OH; 11β-OH → 11-C=O	H-341; H-344
		3α,14β-dihydroxy-5β-20(22)-cardenolide	3α-OH → 3-C=O	N-681
*		3β,14β-dihydroxy-5β-20(22)-cardenolide (Ref. N-683 - method to accelerate rate of hydroxylation)	1β-OH	N-682
			5β-OH	N-678; N-682
			7β-OH	I-425; J-432; N-678; N-682; N-683
*				
*				
			X-OH	J-432
			7β-OH; 3β-OH → 3-C=O	N-678
*			1β,7β-diOH	N-682
*			5β,7β-diOH	N-682
		3β,14β-dihydroxy-5β-20(22)-cardenolide 3-acetate	3β-OAc→3-C=O; 7β-OH	N-678
*		3β,14β-dihydroxy-5β,17α-20(22)-cardenolide	3β-OH → 3-C=O	N-681; N-682
		14-hydroxy-3-keto-5β-20(22)-cardenolide	3-C=O →3α-OH; 7β-OH	N-678

TABLE III

Transformations by Genus: RHIZOPUS

SPECIES	SOURCE	SUBSTRATE	REACTION	REF.
arrhizus	ATCC-11145	14β-hydroxy-3-keto-5β-20(22)-cardenolide	7β-OH	N-678
		3β,7β,14β-trihydroxy-5β-20(22)-cardenolide	3β-OH→3-C=O	N-678
		3-keto-<u>bisnor</u>-4-cholen-22-al	6β,11α-diOH; 22-C=O → 22-OH	M-578
	C	(20S)-20-hydroxy-18,20-<u>cyclo</u>-4-pregnen-3-one	11α-OH	W-1071
	IAM (R-5-6)	4-pregnene-3,20-dione	11α-OH	A-29
	NRRL-R-16	11β,21-dihydroxy-4,17(20)-pregnadien-3-one	6β-OH; 11β-OH →11-C=O	<u>H-341</u>
		Sarsasapogenin	—	M-587
		Diosgenin	—	M-587
		4-dehydrotigogenone	—	M-587
	SSSR	17α,21-dihydroxy-4-pregnene-3,20-dione	6β-OH	E-224
cambodjae	FARMIT	4-pregnene-3,20-dione	11α-OH	<u>C-84</u>
			6β,11α-diOH	<u>C-84</u>
	SSSR	4-pregnene-3,20-dione	6β,11α-diOH	E-224
chinensis (-)	ATCC-1227b	4-pregnene-3,20-dione	oxidation	M-601; M-636
		17α-hydroxy-4-pregnene-3,20-dione	oxidation	M-601; M-636
		21-hydroxy-4-pregnene-3,20-dione	oxidation	M-601; M-636
		17α,21-dihydroxy-4-pregnene-3,20-dione	oxidation	M-601; M-636
	IAM (10-10)	4-pregnene-3,20-dione	11α-OH	<u>A-26</u>; <u>A-29</u>
	SSSR	17α,21-dihydroxy-4-pregnene-3,20-dione	6β-OH	E-224
chiuniang (Yamazaki)	IAM(14-14B)	4-pregnene-3,20-dione	11α-OH	A-29
cohnii	ATCC-8996	11β,21-dihydroxy-4,17(20)-pregnadien-3-one	6β-OH; 11β-OH →11-C=O	H-431
	CZAS(I; II)	4-pregnene-3,20-dione	11α-OH	T-1028

TABLE III

Transformations by Genus: RHIZOPUS

SPECIES	SOURCE	SUBSTRATE	REACTION	REF.
cohnii	SSSR	$17\alpha,21$-dihydroxy-4-pregnene-3,20-dione	6β-OH; 11α-OH; 11β-OH	E-224
	U	4-pregnene-3,20-dione	oxidation	M-601; M-636
		17α-hydroxy-4-pregnene-3,20-dione	oxidation	M-601; M-636
		21-hydroxy-4-pregnene-3,20-dione	oxidation	M-601; M-636
		$17\alpha,21$-dihydroxy-4-pregnene-3,20-dione	oxidation	M-601; M-636
delemar	ATCC-4858	$11\beta,21$-dihydroxy-4,17(20)-pregnadien-3-one	6β-OH; 11β-OH $\rightarrow$11-C=O	H-341
	IAM (19-27)	4-pregnene-3,20-dione	11α-OH	A-29
*	NI	4-pregnene-3,20-dione	11α-OH	N-682
			$6\beta,11\alpha$-diOH	N-682
*		$17\alpha,21$-dihydroxy-4-pregnene-3,20-dione	6β-OH	N-682
*			11α-OH	N-682
*		$3\beta,14\beta$-dihydroxy-5β-20(22)-cardenolide	1β-OH	N-682
*			3β-OH$\rightarrow$3-C=O	N-682
			7β-OH	N-682
*			$5\beta,7\beta$-diOH	N-682
		14β-hydroxy-3-keto-5β-20(22)-cardenolide	7β-OH	N-682
delemar	U	4-pregnene-3,20-dione	oxidation	M-601; M-636
		17α-hydroxy-4-pregnene-3,20-dione	oxidation	M-601; M-636
		21-hydroxy-4-pregnene-3,20-dione	oxidation	M-601; M-636
		$17\alpha,21$-dihydroxy-4-pregnene-3,20-dione	oxidation	M-601; M-636
formosensis (formosaensis)	IAM(24-29C) (Nakazawa)	4-pregnene-3,20-dione	11α-OH	A-29
japonicus	ATCC-8446	$11\beta,21$-dihydroxy-4,17(20)-pregnadien-3-one	6β-OH; 11β-OH $\rightarrow$11-C=O	H-341

TABLE III

Transformations by Genus: RHIZOPUS

SPECIES	SOURCE	SUBSTRATE	REACTION	REF.
japonicus	IAM(24-14; 24-14B)	4-pregnene-3,20-dione	11α-OH	A-29
	U	4-pregnene-3,20-dione	oxidation	M-601; M-636
		17α-hydroxy-4-pregnene-3,20-dione	oxidation	M-601; M-636
		21-hydroxy-4-pregnene-3,20-dione	oxidation	M-601; M-636
		17α,21-dihydroxy-4-pregnene-3,20-dione	oxidation	M-601; M-636
javanicus	IAM(26-23)	4-pregnene-3,20-dione	11α-OH	A-29
*	NI	4-pregnene-3,20-dione	6β,11α-diOH	N-682
			11α-OH	N-682
*		17α,21-dihydroxy-4-pregnene-3,20-dione	6β-OH	N-682
*			11α-OH	N-682
*		3β,14β-dihydroxy-5β-20(22)-cardenolide	7β-OH	N-682
*			1β-OH	N-682
*			3β-OH→3-C=O	N-682
		14β-hydroxy-3-keto-5β-20(22)-cardenolide	7β-OH	N-682
kansho (Yamamoto)	IAM(28-14)	4-pregnene-3,20-dione	11α-OH	A-29
			6β,11α-diOH	A-26
kasanensis	ATCC-8998	11β,21-dihydroxy-4,17(20)-pregnadien-3-one	6β-OH; 11β-OH →11-C=O	H-341
	U	4-pregnene-3,20-dione	oxidation	M-601; M-636
		17α-hydroxy-4-pregnene-3,20-dione	oxidation	M-601; M-636
		21-hydroxy-4-pregnene-3,20-dione	oxidation	M-601; M-636
		17α,21-dihydroxy-4-pregnene-3,20-dione	oxidation	M-601; M-636
nigricans	ATCC-6227a	3β-hydroxy-5-pregnen-20-one	oxidation - products not identified	T-1028

TABLE III

ransformations by Genus: RHIZOPUS

SPECIES	SOURCE	SUBSTRATE	REACTION	REF.
nigricans	ATCC-6227a	4-pregnene-3,20-dione	11α-OH	M-601; M-636; T-1028
		17α-hydroxy-4-pregnene-3,20-dione	11α-OH	M-636
		21-hydroxy-4-pregnene-3,20-dione	11α-OH	M-636
			oxidation - products not identified	T-1028
		17α,21-dihydroxy-4-pregnene-3,20-dione	11α-OH	M-636
			oxidation - products not identified	T-1028
(see stolonifer)	ATCC-6227b	17β-hydroxy-4-estren-3-one	6β-OH	M-642; P-708
			10β-OH	M-642; P-708
			11α-OH	M-619; M-620; P-708
		17β-hydroxy-17α-methyl-4-estren-3-one	11α-OH	M-575; M-608
		17β-hydroxy-4-androsten-3-one	6β-OH	E-201
			11α-OH	E-201; M-601; M-619; M-620; M-636
		17β-hydroxy-17α-methyl-4-androsten-3-one	6β-OH	E-198; E-201; M-619
			11α-OH	E-201; M-575; M-608; M-624; M-626; M-638
(in mixed culture with Penicillium lilacinum [17β-Ac→ 17β-OH])			11α-OH	S-831

TABLE III

Transformations by Genus: RHIZOPUS

SPECIES	SOURCE	SUBSTRATE	REACTION	REF.
nigricans	ATCC-6227b	4-androstene-3,17-dione	6β-OH	E-201
			11α-OH	E-201; M-601; M-636
(in mixed culture with Penicillium lilacinum [17β-Ac→ 17-C=O])			11α-OH	S-831
		3β-hydroxy-5α-pregnan-20-one	11α-OH	M-601; M-636
			7β,11α-diOH	M-601; M-636
		6β-hydroxy-3α,5α-cyclopregnan-20-one	11α-OH	W-1069; W-1070
		5α-pregnane-3,20-dione	11α-OH	E-209; M-601; M-636
		5β-pregnane-3,20-dione	11α-OH	E-209; M-601; M-636
		5β-pregnane-3,20-dione 11α,12α-H^3	11α-H^3→ 11α-OH	H-371
		5β-pregnane-3,20-dione-11α-D	11α-OH (loss of 11α-D)	C-137
		5β-pregnane-3,20-dione-11β-D	11α-OH (11β-D)	C-137
		16α,17α-oxido-5α-pregnane-3,20-dione	11α-OH	K-439
		16α,17α-oxido-5β-pregnane-3,20-dione	11α-OH	K-440; W-1066
		3β-hydroxy-5-pregnen-20-one	7β-OH	E-202
		20α-hydroxy-4-pregnen-3-one	11α-OH	S-832
		20β-hydroxy-4-pregnen-3-one	11α-OH	S-832
		(20S)-20-hydroxy-18,20-cyclo-4-pregnen-3-one	no oxidation at C-11	W-1071
		19-nor-4-pregnene-3,20-dione	11α-OH	B-71; B-73; C-117; C-118; M-636

TABLE III

Transformations by Genus: RHIZOPUS

SPECIES	SOURCE	SUBSTRATE	REACTION	REF.
nigricans	ATCC-6227b	4-pregnene-3,20-dione	11α-OH	E-200; M-601; M-611; M-636; N-650; N-682; P-729; R-766; T-1028; W-1069; W-1106
			11α-OH; $\Delta^4 \to$ 5α-H	P-729
*			6β,11α-diOH	N-682; P-729; W-1069
(in mixed culture with Penicillium lilacinum [17β-Ac→ 17-C=O])			11α-OH	S-831
		17α-hydroxy-4-pregnene-3,20-dione	6β-OH	M-580; M-601; M-607; M-613
			11α-OH	E-200; H-391; M-580; M-601; M-607; M-627; M-636
		21-hydroxy-4-pregnene-3,20-dione	11α-OH	E-203; M-601; M-636
			11α-OH (O_2^{18})	H-374
		21-hydroxy-4-pregnene-3,20-dione acetate	11α-OH; 21-OAc →21-OH	E-203; M-601; M-636
		16α-methyl-4-pregnene-3,20-dione	11α-OH	C-141; L-515; L-517; S-804
		16β-methyl-4-pregnene-3,20-dione	11α-OH	L-517
		6β-fluoro-17α-hydroxy-4-pregnene-3,20-dione	11α-OH	H-391
*		17α,21-dihydroxy-4-pregnene-3,20-dione	6β-OH	M-615; N-682; P-725

TABLE III

Transformations by Genus: RHIZOPUS

SPECIES	SOURCE	SUBSTRATE	REACTION	REF.
nigricans *	ATCC-6227b	17α,21-dihydroxy-4-pregnene-3,20-dione	11α-OH	E-200; M-601; M-636; M-641; M-645; N-682; P-725
			11α-OH; $\Delta^4 \rightarrow$ 5β-H	M-601; M-606; M-636; P-725
		17α,21-dihydroxy-4-pregnene-3,20-dione 21-acetate	11α-OH; 21-OAc $\rightarrow$21-OH	M-601; M-636; M-641; M-645
		17α-hydroxy-21-methyl-4-pregnene-3,20-dione	11α-OH	H-391
		21-hydroxy-17α-methyl-4-pregnene-3,20-dione acetate	11α-OH	H-377
		6α,16α-dimethyl-4-pregnene-3,20-dione	11α-OH	S-923
		16α,17α-methylene-4-pregnene-3,20-dione	11α-OH	C-92
		16α,17α-oxido-4-pregnene-3,20-dione	11α-OH	B-52; D-160; D-161; E-223; M-644; P-727
		6α-chloro-16α,17α-methylene-4-pregnene-3,20-dione	11α-OH	C-92
		6β-fluoro-17α-hydroxy-21-methyl-4-pregnene-3,20-dione	11α-OH	H-391
		6α-fluoro-16α,17α-methylene-4-pregnene-3,20-dione	11α-OH	C-92
		6β-fluoro-16α,17α-methylene-4-pregnene-3,20-dione	11α-OH	C-92
		21-hydroxy-16α,17α-oxido-4-pregnene-3,20-dione acetate	11α-OH; 21-OAc $\rightarrow$21-OH	A-8
		17α,21-dihydroxy-7-methyl-4-pregnene-3,20-dione 21-acetate	11α-OH; 21-OAc $\rightarrow$21-OH	B-33
		6α-methyl-16α,17α-methylene-4-pregnene-3,20-dione	11α-OH	C-92

TABLE III

Transformations by Genus: RHIZOPUS

SPECIES	SOURCE	SUBSTRATE	REACTION	REF.
nigricans	ATCC-6227b	6α-fluoro-17α,21-dihydroxy-16-methylene-4-pregnene-3,20-dione 21-acetate	11α-OH; 21-OAc→21-OH	A-7
		17α,21-dihydroxy-6α,16α-dimethyl-4-pregnene-3,20-dione	11α-OH	S-903
		21-hydroxy-16α,17α-oxido-4-pregnene-3,20-dione	11α-OH	F-243
		21-hydroxy-17α-methyl-1,4-pregnadiene-3,20-dione acetate	11α-OH	H-377
		16α,17α-methylene-1,4-pregnadiene-3,20-dione	11α-OH	C-92
		6α-chloro-16α,17α-methylene-1,4-pregnadiene-3,20-dione	11α-OH	C-92
		6α-fluoro-16α,17α-methylene-1,4-pregnadiene-3,20-dione	11α-OH	C-92
		6β-fluoro-16α,17α-methylene-1,4-pregnadiene-3,20-dione	11α-OH	C-92
		6α-methyl-16α,17α-methylene-1,4-pregnadiene-3,20-dione	11α-OH	C-92
		17α,21-dihydroxy-6α,16α-dimethyl-1,4-pregnadiene-3,20-dione 21-acetate	11α-OH; 21-OAc→21-OH	S-903
		6α-fluoro-16α,17α,21-trihydroxy-1,4-pregnadiene-3,20-dione	11α-OH	R-771
		4,6-pregnadiene-3,20-dione	11α-OH	D-178; M-601; M-621; M-636; P-730
		6-chloro-16α,17α-methylene-4,6-pregnadiene-3,20-dione	11α-OH	C-92
		16α,17α-methylene-4,6-pregnadiene-3,20-dione	11α-OH	C-92
		6-methyl-16α,17α-methylene-4,6-pregnadiene-3,20-dione	11α-OH	C-92
		17α,21-dihydroxy-4,14-pregnadiene-3,20-dione	no epoxidation	B-66
		4,16-pregnadiene-3,20-dione	11α-OH; Δ^{16}-17-Ac→17α-Ac	M-579; M-601; M-605; M-612; M-636

TABLE III

Transformations by Genus: RHIZOPUS

SPECIES	SOURCE	SUBSTRATE	REACTION	REF.
nigricans	ATCC-6227b	1,4,6-pregnatriene-3,20-dione	11α-OH	H-388; O-700
		16α,17α-methylene-1,4,6-pregnatriene-3,20-dione	11α-OH	C-92
		6-chloro-16α,17α-methylene-1,4,6-pregnatriene-3,20-dione	11α-OH	C-92
		6-fluoro-16α,17α-methylene-1,4,6-pregnatriene-3,20-dione	11α-OH	C-92
		6-methyl-16α,17α-methylene-1,4,6-pregnatriene-3,20-dione	11α-OH	C-92
		14β-hydroxy-3-keto-5β-20(22)-cardenolide	7β-OH	N-682
*		3β,14β-dihydroxy-5β-20(22)-cardenolide (Ref. N-683 - method to	1β-OH	N-682; N-683
* *		accelerate hydroxylation)	7β-OH	N-682; N-683
*			1β,7β-diOH	N-682
*			5β,7β-diOH	N-682
*			3β-OH→3-C=O	N-682
		bisnor-4-cholen-22-al-3-one	11α-OH; 22-C=O→22-OH	M-578; M-601; M-622; M-636
			6β,11α-diOH; 22-C=O →22-OH	M-578; M-601; M-636
			15α-OH; 22-C=O → 22-OH	E-202
	ATCC-7577	4-pregnene-3,20-dione	11α-OH	M-601
		17α-hydroxy-4-pregnene-3,20-dione	11α-OH	M-636
		21-hydroxy-4-pregnene-3,20-dione	11α-OH	M-636
		17α,21-dihydroxy-4-pregnene-3,20-dione	11α-OH	M-636
	ATCC-10404	4-pregnene-3,20-dione	11α-OH	M-601
		17α-hydroxy-4-pregnene-3,20-dione	11α-OH	M-636

TABLE III

ansformations by Genus: RHIZOPUS

SPECIES	SOURCE	SUBSTRATE	REACTION	REF.
nigricans	ATCC-10404	21-hydroxy-4-pregnene-3,20-dione	11α-OH	M-636
		17α,21-dihydroxy-4-pregnene-3,20-dione	11α-OH	M-636
		19-<u>nor</u>-4-pregnene-3,20-dione	oxidation - products not identified	B-71
		11β,21-dihydroxy-4,17(20)-pregnadien-3-one	6β-OH; 11β-OH → 11-C=O	H-341
		3β,21-dihydroxy-5α-pregnan-20-one	7β-OH	K-433
		d,1-4-pregnene-3,20-dione	d,1→d-11α-OH + l	<u>W-1102</u>
(in mixed culture with Ophiobolus herpotrichus [21-OH] and Tricothecium roseum [17α-OH])		4-pregnene-3,20-dione	11α-OH	W-1106
		18-hydroxy-4-pregnene-3,20-dione	11α-OH	<u>W-1100</u>
		21-hydroxy-4-pregnene-3,20-dione	11α-OH	K-433
		17α,21-dihydroxy-4-pregnene-3,20-dione	11α-OH	K-433
	Charles	4-pregnene-3,20-dione	11α-OH	T-1028
	CZAS	3β-hydroxy-B-<u>nor</u>-5-androsten-17-one	Δ⁵ → 5ξ , 6ξ-oxide	<u>P-741</u>
			11α-OH	<u>P-741</u>
			11α-OH; Δ⁵ → 5ξ , 6ξ-oxide	<u>P-741</u>
			Δ⁵ →5ξ, 6ξ-oxide →5α,6β-diol	<u>P-741</u>
			15α-OH	P-741
			X-OH	<u>P-741</u>
	FRI	17α,21-dihydroxy-4-pregnene-3,20-dione	6β-OH; 11α-OH	S-849
(in mixed culture with low yielding strain of Bacillus subtlis -Δ¹)	Hoechst	17α,21-dihydroxy-4-pregnene-3,20-dione	Δ¹ (increased yield)	L-521

TABLE III

Transformations by Genus: RHIZOPUS

SPECIES	SOURCE	SUBSTRATE	REACTION	REF.
nigricans (in mixed culture with low yielding strain of Bacillus subtilis $[\Delta^1]$)	Hoechst	$11\beta,17\alpha,21$-trihydroxy-4-pregnene-3,20-dione	Δ^1	L-521
		$17\alpha,21$-dihydroxy-4-pregnene-3,11,20-trione	Δ^1	L-521
(Yamazaki) (Ehrenberg)	IAM (R-5-4; R-5-7; 37-12; 37-27)	4-pregnene-3,20-dione	11α-OH	A-29
	IPB	(use of Warburg studies as indicator of transformation - Ref. C-106)	11α-OH	C-103; C-106; C-107
		20β-hydroxy-3-keto-4-pregnen-18-oic acid (18→20) lactone	$7\,\xi$-OH	L-488; L-489
			11α-OH	L-488; L-489
	NG (Brit. Drug Houses - No. 153)	17β-hydroxy-4-methyl-4-androsten-3-one	6β-OH	K-445
			7α-OH	K-445
			7β-OH	K-445
			11α-OH	K-445
	NG	$16\alpha,17\alpha$-oxido-4-pregnene-3,20-dione	11α-OH	E-223
	NG (Sandoz)	$3\beta,6\beta,8\beta,14\beta$-tetrahydroxy-4,20,22-bufatrienolide 6-acetate 3-glucoside	3β-$[1^1\xi$-glucoside→3β-OH]	S-936a
	NRRL-1478	$16\alpha,17\alpha,21$-[3,1,1-(2-pyrazolino)]-4-pregnene-3,20-dione	11α-OH	W-1113
	NRRL	Sarsasapogenin	——	M-587
		Diosgenin	——	M-587
		4-dehydrotigogenone	——	M-587
	PIRI	4-pregnene-3,20-dione	11α-OH; $6\beta,11\alpha$-diOH	W-1115
	SSSR (VNIKH-F-1-7)	4-pregnene-3,20-dione	11α-OH	B-42
	(F-1)		11α-OH	T-1011

TABLE III

Transformations by Genus: RHIZOPUS

SPECIES	SOURCE	SUBSTRATE	REACTION	REF.
nigricans	Moscow (very active strains - 1, 7, 10, 16, 17, 18, 19, 58) (poorly active - 2, 5, 6, 8, 11, 12, 13, 14)	4-pregnene-3, 20-dione	11α-OH; 6β, 11α-diOH	T-1010
	SSSR		11α-OH	E-224; S-946; T-1009
			6β, 11α-diOH; 11β-OH; 11α-OH	T-1009; E-224
	WC(86)	6β-fluoro-17α, 21-dihydroxy-4-pregnene-3, 20-dione	11α-OH	F-268
	TSURUMI	4, 11-pregnadiene-3, 20-dione	no epoxidation	K-484
niveus (Yamazaki)	IAM (R-5-5)	4-pregnene-3, 20-dione	11α-OH	A-29
nodosus (Namyslowski)	IAM (32-29)		11α-OH	A-29
oryzae	ATCC-9363 and 10260	4-pregnene-3, 20-dione	11-oxygenation	M-601; M-636
		17α-hydroxy-4-pregnene-3, 20-dione	11-oxygenation	M-601; M-636
		21-hydroxy-4-pregnene-3, 20-dione	11-oxygenation	M-601; M-636
		17α, 21-dihydroxy-4-pregnene-3, 20-dione	11-oxygenation	M-601; M-636
	IAM (R-5-7)	4-pregnene-3, 20-dione	11α-OH	A-29
pseudochinensis	CZAS	4-pregnene-3, 20-dione	11α-OH	T-1028
(Yamalaki)	IAM		11α-OH	A-29
pygmaeus	SSSR	17α, 21-dihydroxy-4-pregnene-3, 20-dione	6β-OH	E-224
reflexus	ATCC-1225	17β-hydroxy-4-estren-3-one	6β-OH; Δ⁴→Δ⁵; ketoniz.	M-623
			6β-OH	M-618; M-620
			11α-OH	M-618; M-620

TABLE III

Transformations by Genus: RHIZOPUS

SPECIES	SOURCE	SUBSTRATE	REACTION	REF.
reflexus	ATCC-1225	17β-hydroxy-4-androsten-3-one	6β-OH	E-201; M-618
			3-C=O-$\Delta^4 \rightarrow$ 5α-H-3,6-di- C=O (via 6β- OH; $\Delta^4 \rightarrow \Delta^5$; ketoniz.)	E-201; M-623
			11α-OH	E-201
		17β-hydroxy-17α-methyl-4- androsten-3-one	6β-OH	E-201
			11α-OH	E-201
		4-androstene-3,17-dione	6β-OH	E-201
			11α-OH	E-201
		$16\alpha,17\alpha$-oxido-4-pregnene-3,20- dione	11α-OH	M-644
	U	4-pregnene-3,20-dione	11-OH	M-601; M-636
		17α-hydroxy-4-pregnene-3,20- dione	11-OH	M-601; M-636
		21-hydroxy-4-pregnene-3,20- dione	11-OH	M-601; M-636
		$17\alpha,21$-dihydroxy-4-pregnene- 3,20-dione	11-OH	M-601; M-636
shanghaiesis (shanghaiensis)	ATCC-10329	$11\beta,21$-dihydroxy-4,17(20)- pregnadien-3-one	6β-OH; 11β-OH $\rightarrow$ 11-C=O	H-341
		3β-hydroxy-$14\alpha,15\alpha$-oxido-20(22)- cardenolide acetate	3β-OAc $\rightarrow 3\beta$- OH	M-576; M-577
	U	4-pregnene-3,20-dione	11-oxygenation	M-601; M-636
		17α-hydroxy-4-pregnene-3,20- dione	11-oxygenation	M-601; M-636
		21-hydroxy-4-pregnene-3,20- dione	11-oxygenation	M-601; M-636
		$17\alpha,21$-dihydroxy-4-pregnene- 3,20-dione	11-oxygenation	M-601; M-636
species	C	$3\beta,21$-dihydroxy-5α-pregnan-20- one	7β-OH	K-433
		4-pregnene-3,20-dione	11α-OH	K-433
		21-hydroxy-4-pregnene-3,20- dione	11α-OH	K-433

TABLE III

Transformations by Genus: RHIZOPUS

SPECIES	SOURCE	SUBSTRATE	REACTION	REF.
species	C	d,1-21-hydroxy-4-pregnene-3, 20-dione	d,l→d-6β-OH + l	W-1102
		17α,21-hydroxy-4-pregnene-3,20-dione	11α-OH	K-433
	IAM	4-pregnene-3,20-dione	11α-OH	A-29
	NRRL	plant saponins	——	K-478
	Searle	3β-hydroxy-5-androsten-17-one	7α-OH	D-175
			7β-OH	D-175
			7-C=O	D-175
		4-androstene-3,17-dione	6β-OH; 11α-OH	D-175
	SSSR	4-pregnene-3,20-dione	11α-OH	T-1010
			6β,11α-diOH	T-1010
	SY	4-pregnene-3,20-dione	11α-OH	M-554
stolonifer (synonym for nigricans)	ATCC-6227b	4-androstene-3,17-dione	7β-OH	T-1037
		17α-methylthio-4-androsten-3-one	11α-OH; 17α-SCH$_3$→17α-S(O)CH$_3$	D-174; D-176
			17α-SCH$_3$ → 17α-S(O)CH$_3$ (stereochemistry at S unknown)	D-174
			17α-SCH$_3$→ 17α-S(O)CH$_3$ (opposite stereochemistry at S from preceding compound)	D-174
		17β-methylsulfinyl-4-androsten-3-one	11α-OH (stereochemistry at S unknown)	D-176
			11α-OH (opposite stereochemistry at S from preceding compound)	D-176
		17β-methylsulfonyl-4-androsten-3-one	11α-OH	D-176
stolonifer in abstract (nigricans–in Ref. T-1011)	SSSR (No. 7,16)	4-pregnene-3,20-dione	11α-OH	T-1011

590

TABLE III

Transformations by Genus: RHIZOPUS
RHODOSEPTORIA

TAXONOMY

(Imperf. - Sphaeropsidales)

SPECIES	SOURCE	SUBSTRATE	REACTION	REF.
suinus	C	21-hydroxy-4-pregnene-3,20-dione	17β-(20-C-O-21-OH)→ 17-C=O	W-1095
tonkinensis	IAM (65-10)	4-pregnene-3,20-dione	11α-OH	A-29
	SSSR	17α,21-dihydroxy-4-pregnene-3,20-dione	6β-OH	E-224
	U	4-pregnene-3,20-dione	11-oxygenation	M-601; M-676
		17α-hydroxy-4-pregnene-3,20-dione	11-oxygenation	M-601; M-636
		21-hydroxy-4-pregnene-3,20-dione	11-oxygenation	M-601; M-636
		17α,21-dihydroxy-4-pregnene-3,20-dione	11-oxygenation	M-601; M-636
tritici	ATCC-1230	11β,21-dihydroxy-4,17(20)-pregnadien-3-one	6β-OH; 11β-OH→ 11-C=O	H-341
	IAM (65-5a; 66-14c; 66-27)	4-pregnene-3,20-dione	11α-OH	A-29
	U		oxidation	M-601; M-636
		17α-hydroxy-4-pregnene-3,20-dione	oxidation	M-601; M-636
		21-hydroxy-4-pregnene-3,20-dione	oxidation	M-601; M-636
		17α,21-dihydroxy-4-pregnene-3,20-dione	oxidation	M-601; M-636
RHODOSEPTORIA				
species	ATCC-11833 QM-704	17α-hydroxy-4-pregnene-3,20-dione	11β-OH	K-446
		21-hydroxy-4-pregnene-3,20-dione	11β-OH	K-446
		17α,21-dihydroxy-4-pregnene-3,20-dione (use of whole broth or washed mycelium)	11β-OH	K-446

TABLE III

ansformations by Genus: RHODOTORULA   (Imperf. - Moniliales)

SPECIES	SOURCE	SUBSTRATE	REACTION	REF.
RHODOTORULA				
glutinis	IFO (0395)	$11\beta,17\alpha$-dihydroxy-4-pregnene-3,20-dione	20-C=O → 20α-OH	T-958
		$17\alpha,21$-dihydroxy-4-pregnene-3,20-dione	20-C=O → 20α-OH	T-958
		$17\alpha,19,21$-trihydroxy-4-pregnene-3,20-dione	20-C=O → 20α-OH	T-958
		$17\alpha,21$-dihydroxy-1,4-pregnadiene-3,20-dione	20-C=O → 20α-OH	T-958
	NRRL	Sarsasapogenin	—	M-587
		Diosgenin	—	M-587
		4-dehydrotigogenone	—	M-587
gracilis	SQ (SC-2218)	4-pregnene-3,20-dione	—	T-1005
		5-cholesten-3β-ol	$\Delta^5 \to \Delta^4$; 3β-OH →3-C=O	T-1005
longissima	NRRL-Y-2343	4-pregnene-3,20-dione	20-C=O → 20α-OH	C-122
		11α-hydroxy-4-pregnene-3,20-dione	20-C=O → 20α-OH	C-122
		11β-hydroxy-4-pregnene-3,20-dione	20-C=O → 20α-OH	C-122
		17α-hydroxy-4-pregnene-3,20-dione	20-C=O → 20α-OH	C-122
		17β-hydroxy-17α-4-pregnene-3,20-dione	—	C-122
		21-hydroxy-4-pregnene-3,20-dione	—	C-122
		$11\beta,17\alpha$-dihydroxy-4-pregnene-3,20-dione	20-C=O → 20α-OH	C-122
		$11\beta,21$-dihydroxy-4-pregnene-3,20-dione	—	C-122
		$17\alpha,21$-dihydroxy-4-pregnene-3,20-dione	20-C=O → 20α-OH	C-110; C-122
		$11\alpha,17\alpha,21$-trihydroxy-4-pregnene-3,20-dione	20-C=O → 20α-OH	C-122
		$11\beta,17\alpha,21$-trihydroxy-4-pregnene-3,20-dione	20-C=O → 20α-OH	C-122
		4-pregnene-3,11,20-trione	20-C=O → 20α-OH	C-122

TABLE III

Transformations by Genus: RHODOTORULA
ROSSELLINIA   (Asco. - Sphaeriales)
RUSSULA   (Basidio. - Agaricales)
SACCHAROMYCES   (Asco. - Endomycetales)

SPECIES	SOURCE	SUBSTRATE	REACTION	REF.
longissima	NRRL-Y-2343	17α-hydroxy-4-pregnene-3,11,20-trione	20-C=O→ 20α-OH	C-122
		17α,21-dihydroxy-4-pregnene-3,11,20-trione	20-C=O→ 20α-OH	C-122; C-110
		17α,21-dihydroxy-1,4-pregnadiene-3,11,20-trione	20-C=O→ 20α-OH	C-110
(rubra)		17α-hydroxy-9β,11β-oxido-1,4,6-pregnatriene-3,20-dione	20-C=O→ 20α-OH	G-303
		17α,21-dihydroxy-9β,11β-oxido-1,4,6-pregnatriene-3,20-dione	20-C=O→ 20α-OH	G-303
ROSSELLINIA				
necatrix	TNAES	17α,21-dihydroxy-4-pregnene-3,20-dione	——	S-849
RUSSULA				
delicans	AL(C-173)	4-pregnene-3,20-dione	oxidation - product not identified	S-825
SACCHAROMYCES				
NOTE: Literature is not always clear on name of species; top or bottom yeast, bakers, brewers or impoverished yeast, nor is it certain that all were strains of cerevisiae. Wherever possible the original source and type are given.		Note on Reactions Attributed to Yeast: In the years 1937-1938 many oxidations of steroids were erroneously reported to be carried out by yeast (see Ref. V-1047). Later work showed that these reactions were due to species of corynebacteria and flavobacteria which were contaminants in the yeast preparations (see Ref. A-17).		A-17; K-457; M-552; M-594; V-1047
		Transformations reported in this table show only those reactions actually carried out by yeast. All others may be found under the appropriate bacterial genus.		A-17; E-219; E-220; M-538; M-546; M-553
cerevisiae	ATCC-4125	1,4-androstadiene-3,17-dione	17-C=O→ 17β-OH	C-128
		9α-fluoro-11β-hydroxy-1,4-androstadiene-3,17-dione	17-C=O→ 17β-OH	N-666

TABLE III

ansformations by Genus: SACCHAROMYCES

SPECIES	SOURCE	SUBSTRATE	REACTION	REF.
cerevisiae	ATCC-4125	9α-fluoro-11β-hydroxy-16α-methyl-1,4-androstadiene-3,17-dione	17-C=O → 17β-OH	R-752
		9α-bromo-16α-methyl-1,4-androstadiene-3,11,17-trione	17-C=O → 17β-OH	R-752
		9α-chloro-16α-methyl-1,4-androstadiene-3,11,17-trione	17-C=O → 17β-OH	R-752
		9α-fluoro-16α-methyl-1,4-androstadiene-3,11,17-trione	17-C=O → 17β-OH	R-752
		11β-hydroxy-1,4,6-androstatriene-3,17-dione	17-C=O → 17β-OH	G-305
		9α-fluoro-11β-hydroxy-1,4,6-androstatriene-3,17-dione	17-C=O → 17β-OH	G-305
		1,4,6-androstatriene-3,11,17-trione	17-C=O → 17β-OH	G-305
		9α-fluoro-1,4,6-androstatriene-3,11,17-trione	17-C=O → 17β-OH	G-305
		1,4,9(11)-androstatriene-3,17-dione	17-C=O → 17β-OH	R-775
(distillers)	FARMIT	3β-hydroxy-16α,17α-oxido-5α-pregnan-20-one	16α,17α-oxide →16α-OH; 13β-CH$_3$→17β-CH$_3$; 20-C=O →20α-OH; Δ^{13}	C-88
		11α-hydroxy-5α-pregnane-3,20-dione	3-C=O →3β-OH	C-83; C-89
		11α-hydroxy-5α-pregnane-3,20-dione acetate	no reduction	C-83
		11α-hydroxy-5β-pregnane-3,20-dione	no reduction	C-83
		17α-hydroxy-5β-pregnane-3,20-dione	no reduction	C-83
		21-hydroxy-5β-pregnane-3,20-dione	no reduction	C-83
		16α,17α-oxido-5β-pregnane-3,20-dione	16α,17α-oxide→ 16α-OH; 13β-CH$_3$ →17β-CH$_3$; 20-C=O→20α-OH; Δ^{13}	C-88; C-90
		11β,17α,21-trihydroxy-5α-pregnane-3,20-dione 21-acetate	no reduction	C-83

TABLE III

Transformations by Genus: SACCHAROMYCES

SPECIES	SOURCE	SUBSTRATE	REACTION	REF.
cerevisiae (distillers)	FARMIT	5α-pregnane-3,11,20-trione	3-C=O → 3α-OH	C-83; C-89
		5β-pregnane-3,11,20-trione	3-C=O → 3α-OH	C-83; C-89
		17α,21-dihydroxy-5α-pregnane-3,11,20-trione 21-acetate	no reduction	C-83
		3β-hydroxy-16α,17α-oxido-5-pregnen-20-one	16α,17α-oxide→ 16α-OH; 13β-CH$_3$ →17β-CH$_3$; 20-C=O→20α-OH; Δ^{13}	C-88; C-90
		20β-hydroxy-16α,17α-oxido-4-pregnen-3-one	—	C-88
		11α-hydroxy-16α,17α-oxido-4-pregnene-3,20-dione	—	C-88
		16α,17α-oxido-4-pregnene-3,20-dione	16α,17α-oxide→ 16α-OH; 13β-CH$_3$ → 17β-CH$_3$; 20-C=O→20α-OH; Δ^{13}	C-88; C-90
		4-pregnene-3,11,20-trione	no reduction	C-83
(bread yeast)	FARMIT	3β,20β-dihydroxy-4β,5β-oxido-pregnane	4β,5β-oxido→ 4β,5α-diol	C-87
		3β-hydroxy-5α,6α-oxido-pregnan-20-one	5α,6α-oxido→ 5α,6β-diol	C-87
		3β,21-dihydroxy-16α,17α-oxido-5-pregnen-20-one 21-acetate	16α,17α-oxide→ 16α-OH; 13β-CH$_3$ → 17β-CH$_3$; 20-C=O→20α-OH; Δ^{13}	C-90
		4β,5β-oxidopregnane-3,20-dione	3-C=O→3β-OH; 4β,5β-oxido→ 4β,5α-diol	C-87; C-90
(bakers yeast)	Kaiser Wihelm Inst., Berlin	1,3,5(10)-estratriene-3,17β-diol propionate	3-OPr→3-OH	M-539
		3-hydroxy-1,3,5(10)-estratrien-17-one acetate	3-OAc → 3-OH	M-539
			3-OAc → 3-OH; 17-C=O→17β-OH	M-539
		3-hydroxy-1,3,5(10)-estratrien-17-one propionate	3-OPr→3-OH	M-539
			3-OPr→3-OH; 17-C=O→17β-OH	M-539

TABLE III

SACCHAROMYCES

SPECIES	SOURCE	SUBSTRATE	REACTION	REF.
erevisiae (bakers yeast)	Kaiser Wihelm Inst., Berlin	3-hydroxy-1,3,5(10)-estratrien-17-one butyrate	3-OBu → 3-OH	M-539
			3-OBu → 3-OH; 17-C=O → 17β-OH	M-539
		3α,5α-cycloandrostane-6,17-dione	17-C=O→17β-OH	B-81
		3β-hydroxy-5-androsten-17-one acetate	17-C=O→17β-OH	M-539
		17β-hydroxy-5α-1-androsten-3-one	Δ^1→H; 3-C=O → 3β-OH	B-80
		5α-1-androstene-3,17-dione	17-C=O → 17β-OH	B-78
			Δ^1→H; 17-C=O →17β-OH; 3-C=O →3β-OH	B-80
		4-androstene-3,17-dione	Δ^4→5β-H; 3-C=O →3α-OH; 17-C=O →17β-OH	S-808
		5α-1-pregnene-3,20-dione	—	B-80
		5α-1-cholesten-3-one	—	B-80
	IPB	4-androstene-3,17-dione	17-C=O → 17β-OH	C-106
	Max Planck Inst. for Biochem., Munchen	1,4-androstadiene-3,17-dione	17-C=O → 17β-OH	D-143
	SCH	3-hydroxy-1,3,5(10)-estratrien-17-one	17-C=O → 17β-OH	S-806
		5α-androstane-3,17-dione	3-C=O→3β-OH; 17-C=O → 17β-OH	M-543
		3β-hydroxy-5-androsten-17-one	17-C=O → 17β-OH	M-543
		4-androstene-3,17-dione	17-C=O → 17β-OH	M-543
		4-androstene-3,11,17-trione	17-C=O → 17β-OH	H-385
		1,4,9(11)-androstatriene-3,17-dione	17-C=O → 17β-OH	G-308
		3,12-diketo-5β-cholanic acid	3-C=O→3α-OH	M-543
		5α-cholestan-3-one	3-C=O→3β-OH	M-543

TABLE III

Transformations by Genus: SACCHAROMYCES

SPECIES	SOURCE	SUBSTRATE	REACTION	REF.
cerevisiae (compressed yeast)	ATCC-4125	15β-hydroxy-4-androstene-3,17-dione	17-C=O → 17β-OH	H-382
		3β-hydroxy-16,17-oxido-5α-pregnan-20-one	16,17-oxide → 16α-OH; 13β-Me →17β-Me; 20-C=O→20α-OH; Δ^{13}	C-85; C-88
		16α-methyl-1,4,9(11)-androsta-triene-3,17-dione	17-C=O → 17β-OH	R-775
	C	3-hydroxy-1,3,5(10)-estratrien-17-one	17-C=O → 17β-OH	W-1085
(pressed yeast)	C	d,l-3-hydroxy-1,3,5(10)-estra-trien-17-one	d,l-17-C=O → d-17β-OH + l-17-C=O	V-1055; W-1094
	IPβ	4-androstene-3,17-dione	17-C=O → 17β-OH	H-335; H-337
	NG	3-keto-5β-cholanic acid	—	E-221
		3,6-diketo-5β-cholanic acid	3-C=O → 3α-OH	E-221
	(Sandoz)	3β,6β,8β,14β-tetrahydroxy-4,20,22-oufatrienolide 6-acetate 3-glucoside	—	S-936a
	NRRL	Sarsasapogenin	—	M-587
		Diosgenin	—	M-587
		4-dehydrotigogenone	—	M-587
	SAG	12β-hydroxy-4-androstene-3,17-dione	17-C=O → 17β-OH	R-749
(mailand-flockige fermente)	Instituto Perezion-amento	5α-androstane-3,17-dione	3-C=O→3β-OH; 17-C=O→17β-OH	M-551; V-1046
		3β-hydroxy-5-androsten-17-one	17-C=O→17β-OH	M-549
		4-androstene-3,17-dione	17-C=O→17β-OH	M-550
		5-androstene-3,17-dione	Δ^5→5α-H; 3-C=O→3β-OH; 17-C=O →17β-OH	M-551
		5α-cholestan-3-one	no reduction	M-550

TABLE III

ansformations by Genus:

SACCHAROMYCES
SACCHAROMYCODES   (Asco. - Endomycetales)
SANSEVIERIA   (Spermatophyta - Liliiflorae)

SPECIES	SOURCE	SUBSTRATE	REACTION	REF.
cerevisiae (brewers yeast)	Phys. Chem. Inst., Okayama	3,12-diketo-5β-cholanic acid	3-C=O →3α-OH	K-441
		12α-hydroxy-3-keto-5β-cholanic acid acetate	3-C=O →3α-OH	K-442
(Fleishmann)	PF	11β,17β-dihydroxy-21-methyl-1,4-pregnadiene-3,20,21-trione	21-C=O→21-OH	A-6
		6α,9α-difluoro-11β,17β-dihydroxy-21-methyl-1,4-pregnadiene-3,20,21-trione	21-C=O→21-OH	A-6
ellipsoideus	NG	4-androstene-3,17-dione	17-C=O → 17β-OH	A-17
fragilis	ATCC-10022	4-androstene-3,17-dione	17-C=O → 17β-OH	M-572
			17-C=O → 17β-OAc	M-572
	NRRL	Sarsasapogenin	—	M-587
		Diosgenin	—	M-587
		4-dehydrotigogenone	—	M-587
lactis	NRRL	Sarsasapogenin	—	M-587
		Diosgenin	—	M-587
		4-dehydrotigogenone	—	M-587
pastorianus	ATCC-2366	21-hydroxy-4-pregnene-3,20-dione	oxidation - products not identified	H-328
SACCHAROMYCODES				
ludwigii	NRRL	Sarsasapogenin	—	M-587
		Diosgenin	—	M-587
		4-dehydrotigogenone	—	M-587
SANSEVIERIA (Plant)				
zeylanica (cellular extract)	PF	17β-hydroxy-4-androsten-3-one	Δ^1	N-658a
		17α,21-dihydroxy-4-pregnene-3,20-dione	Δ^1	N-658a
			$\Delta^4 \rightarrow 5\beta$-H	N-658a

TABLE III

Transformations by Genus:

SARCINA	(Schizo. - Eubacteriales)
SARCINOMYCES	(Imperf. - Moniliales)
SCENEDESMUS	(Chlorphyta - Chlorococcales)
SCHIZOPHYLLUM	(Basidio. - Agaricales)

SPECIES	SOURCE	SUBSTRATE	REACTION	REF.
SARCINA				
albida	IFO (3063)	11β,17α,21-trihydroxy-4-pregnene-3,20-dione	—	I-428
(in mixed culture with Mycococcus sp. A₁)			—	I-428
albiden	IAM	17α,21-dihydroxy-4-pregnene-3,20-dione	11α-OH	S-849
aurentiace	IAM	17α,21-dihydroxy-4-pregnene-3,20-dione	11α-OH	S-849
lutea	IAM (PCI-1001)	17α,21-dihydroxy-4-pregnene-3,20-dione	—	S-849
	IFO (3232)	11β,17α,21-trihydroxy-4-pregnene-3,20-dione	—	I-428
(in mixed culture with Mycococcus sp. A₁)			—	I-428
	NG	5-cholesten-3β-ol (sole carbon source)	—	T-1030
	NRRL	Sarsasapogenin	—	M-587
		Diosgenin	—	M-587
		4-dehydrotigogenone	—	M-587
marginata	IAM	17α,21-dihydroxy-4-pregnene-3,20-dione	—	S-849
variabilis	IAM	17α,21-dihydroxy-4-pregnene-3,20-dione	11α-OH	S-849
SARCINOMYCES				
crustaceum	FRI	17α,21-dihydroxy-4-pregnene-3,20-dione	—	S-849
SCENEDESMUS (Algae)				
species	SCH (J9-A-21)	17α,21-dihydroxy-4-pregnene-3,20-dione	6β-OH	L-527
			11α-OH; 11β-OH	L-527
SCHIZOPHYLLUM				
commune	IAM	17α,21-dihydroxy-4-pregnene-3,20-dione	—	S-849

TABLE III

ansformations by Genus: SCHIZOSACCHAROMYCES   (Asco. - Endomycetales)
                                SCLEROTINIA   (Asco. - Helotiales)

SPECIES	SOURCE	SUBSTRATE	REACTION	REF.
CHIZOSACCHARO- MYCES				
ctosporus	NRRL	Sarsasapogenin	—	M-587
		Diosgenin	—	M-587
		4-dehydrotigogenone	—	M-587
CLEROTINIA				
lii	TNAES	17α,21-dihydroxy-4-pregnene- 3,20-dione	—	S-849
ucticola	C	4-pregnene-3,20-dione	21-OH	W-1101
		17α-hydroxy-1,4-pregnadiene- 3,11,20-trione	21-OH	W-1101
uctigena	TNAES	17α,21-dihydroxy-4-pregnene- 3,20-dione	—	S-849
bertiana	IAM	17α,21-dihydroxy-4-pregnene- 3,20-dione	2β-OH; 11β-OH	S-849
	S	4-pregnene-3,20-dione	2β,15β-DIOH	S-849; S-850; S-859; T-983
			2β,X-DIOH	T-983
			products of un- known or questionable structure	T-983
		17α-hydroxy-4-pregnene-3,20- dione	2β-OH	S-849; S-859; T-983
			11α-OH	S-849; S-859; T-983
			15β-OH	S-850; T-983
		21-hydroxy-4-pregnene-3,20- dione	2β,15β-DIOH	S-849
		21-hydroxy-4-pregnene-3,20- dione acetate	2β,15β-DIOH; 21-OAc→21-OH	S-840; S-849; S-853
		11β,21-dihydroxy-4-pregnene- 3,20-dione	2β-OH	S-840; S-849; S-853
			15β-OH	S-840; S-849; S-853

TABLE III

Transformations by Genus: SCLEROTINIA
SCLEROTIUM   (Imperf. - Mycelia Sterilia)

SPECIES	SOURCE	SUBSTRATE	REACTION	REF.
libertiana	S	$17\alpha,21$-dihydroxy-4-pregnene-3,20-dione	2β-OH	S-849; S-859; S-860; T-983
			11α-OH	S-849; S-859; S-860
			11β-OH	S-849; S-859; S-860
			X-OH	T-983
	TNAES	$17\alpha,21$-dihydroxy-4-pregnene-3,20-dione	2β-OH; 11β-OH	S-849
sclerotiorum	FAHU		2β-OH; 11β-OH	S-849
	S	$17\alpha,21$-dihydroxy-4-pregnene-3,20-dione	2β-OH	S-860
			11α-OH	S-860
			11β-OH	S-860
SCLEROTIUM				
coffeicolum	OR	17β-hydroxy-17α-propyl-4-androsten-3-one	16β-OH	S-950
hydrophilum	NARI	$17\alpha,21$-dihydroxy-4-pregnene-3,20-dione	6β-OH; 11α-OH	S-849
	S	4-pregnene-3,20-dione	$6\beta,11\alpha$-DIOH	S-849; S-856; S-859
		17α-hydroxy-4-pregnene-3,20-dione	6β-OH	S-856; S-859
			11α-OH	S-849; S-856; S-859
		21-hydroxy-4-pregnene-3,20-dione	6β-OH; 11α-OH	S-856
		21-hydroxy-4-pregnene-3,20-dione acetate	6β-OH; 21-OAc → 21-OH	S-856
			11α-OH; 21-OAc → 21-OH	S-856

TABLE III

ansformations by Genus: SCLEROTIUM
SCOPULARIOPSIS   (Imperf. - Moniliales)

SPECIES	SOURCE	SUBSTRATE	REACTION	REF.
hydrophilum	S	21-hydroxy-4-pregnene-3,20-dione acetate	$6\beta,11\alpha$-diOH; 21-OAc → 21-OH	S-856
		$11\beta,21$-dihydroxy-4-pregnene-3,20-dione	6β-OH; 11β-OH → 11-C=O	S-849; S-856
			15β-OH; 11β-OH → 11-C=O	S-856
		$17\alpha,21$-dihydroxy-4-pregnene-3,20-dione	6β-OH	S-849; S-856; S-859
			11α-OH	S-849; S-856; S-859
oryzae (var. irregularis)	CBS QM-93-A	17β-hydroxy-4-androsten-3-one	11α-OH; 11β-OH	G-313
		4-pregnene-3,20-dione	11α-OH; 11β-OH	G-313
		$17\alpha,21$-dihydroxy-4-pregnene-3,20-dione	1ξ-OH; 11α-OH; 11β-OH; 11-C=O (via 11β-OH)	G-313
rolfsii	ATCC-12450	17β-hydroxy-4-androsten-3-one	1ξ-OH; 11α-OH; 11β-OH; 11-C=O (via 11β-OH)	G-313
		4-pregnene-3,20-dione	1ξ-OH; 11α-OH; 11β-OH; 11-C=O (via 11β-OH)	G-313
		21-hydroxy-4-pregnene-3,20-dione	1ξ-OH; 11α-OH; 11β-OH; 11-C=O (via 11β-OH)	G-313
		$17\alpha,21$-dihydroxy-4-pregnene-3,20-dione	1ξ-OH; 11α-OH	G-313
SCOPULARIOPSIS				
americana	FRI	$17\alpha,21$-dihydroxy-4-pregnene-3,20-dione	——	S-849
brevicaulis	NRRL-1103	4-pregnene-3,20-dione	$11\alpha,17\alpha$-diOH	D-188

TABLE III

Transformations by Genus: SCOPULARIOPSIS
                              SEPEDONIUM   (Imperf. - Moniliales)
                              SEPTOMYXA   (Imperf. - Melanconiales)

SPECIES	SOURCE	SUBSTRATE	REACTION	REF.
brevicaulis	NRRL	Sarsasapogenin	—	M-587
		Diosgenin	—	M-587
		4-dehydrotigogenone	—	M-587
SEPEDONIUM				
ampullosporum	NRRL-2877	5β-pregnane-3,11,20-trione	16α-OH	F-252
		11α-hydroxy-4-pregnene-3,20-dione	17α-OH	M-646
	PH	retro-4-pregnene-3,20-dione	16α-OH	P-735
		retro-4,6-pregnadiene-3,20-dione	16α-OH	P-735
chrysospermum	PH	17β-hydroxy-retro-4-androsten-3-one	16α-OH	P-735
		retro-4,6-pregnadiene-3,20-dione	16α-OH	P-735
SEPTOMYXA				
aesculi	U	17β-hydroxy-19-nor-4-androsten-4-estrone	Δ^1; enol.	W-1072
			Δ^1; enol.; 17β-OH→ 17-C=O	W-1072
		17β-hydroxy-4-androsten-3-one	Δ^1	W-1072
			Δ^1; 17β-OH→ 17-C=O	W-1072
		17β-hydroxy-17α-methyl-4-androsten-3-one	Δ^1	W-1072
		11β,17β-dihydroxy-17α-methyl-4-androsten-3-one	Δ^1	E-206
		4-androstene-3,17-dione	Δ^1	W-1072
			Δ^1; 17-C=O → 17a-oxa-17-C =O	W-1072
			Δ^1; 17-C=O→ 17β-OH	W-1072
		5α-pregnane-3,11,20-trione	Δ^1; 17β-Ac→ 17-C=O	W-1072

TABLE III

ransformations by Genus: SEPTOMYXA

SPECIES	SOURCE	SUBSTRATE	REACTION	REF.
aesculi	U	4-pregnene-3,20-dione (use of washed mycelium and various additives changes proportion of products)	Δ^1	W-1072
			Δ^1; 17β-Ac → 17β-OH	W-1072
			Δ^1; 17β-Ac → 17-C=O	W-1072
			Δ^1; 17β-Ac → 17a-oxa-17-C =O	W-1072
		11α-hydroxy-4-pregnene-3,20-dione	Δ^1	W-1072
			Δ^1; 17β-Ac → 17β-OH	W-1072
			Δ^1; 17β-Ac → 17-C=O	W-1072
		11β-hydroxy-4-pregnene-3,20-dione	Δ^1; 17β-Ac → 17β-OH	W-1072
			Δ^1; 17β-Ac → 17-C=O	W-1072
		17α-hydroxy-4-pregnene-3,20-dione	Δ^1	W-1072
			Δ^1; 17α-OH-17β-Ac → 17β-OH	W-1072
		21-hydroxy-4-pregnene-3,20-dione	Δ^1	W-1072
			Δ^1; 17β-(20-C =O-21-OH) → 17β-OH	W-1072
			Δ^1; 17β-(20-C =O-21-OH) → 17-C=O	W-1072
			Δ^1; 17β-(20-C =O-21-OH) → 17a-oxa-17-C =O	W-1072
		17α,21-dihydroxy-4-pregnene-3,20-dione	Δ^1	W-1072
		11β,17α,21-trihydroxy-4-pregnene-3,20-dione	Δ^1	W-1072
		11β,17α,21-trihydroxy-6α-methyl-4-pregnene-3,20-dione	Δ^1	W-1072
		4-pregnene-3,11,20-trione	Δ^1	W-1072

TABLE III

Transformations by Genus: SEPTOMYXA

SPECIES	SOURCE	SUBSTRATE	REACTION	REF.
aesculi	UC	4-pregnene-3,11,20-trione	Δ^1; 17β-Ac $\rightarrow$ 17-C=O	W-1072
			Δ^1; 17β-Ac $\rightarrow$ 17β-OH	W-1072
		$17\alpha,21$-dihydroxy-4-pregnene-3,11,20-trione	Δ^1	W-1072
		$11\beta,21$-dihydroxy-4,17(20)-pregnadien-3-one	Δ^1	W-1072
affinis	ATCC-6737	In the following reactions the use of one or the other of the following "accelerators," "inducers" or "promoters" will be designated by the symbol (+ A) under substrate. List of Accelerators 1,4-androstadiene-3,17-dione 17β-hydroxy-1,4-androstadiene-3,17-dione 17a-oxa-D-homo-1,4-androstadiene-3,17-dione 4-pregnene-3,20-dione 11α-hydroxy-4-pregnene-3,20-dione $11\beta,21$-dihydroxy-4,17(20)-pregnadiene-3,20-dione 3-keto-bisnor-4-cholen-22-al 3-keto-bisnor-4-cholen-22-ol 3-keto-bisnor-1,4-choladien-22-al 3-keto-bisnor-1,4-choladien-22-ol 3-keto-bisnor-1,4-choladien-22-oic acid		B-43; B-44; F-249; F-251; F-253; H-395; L-513; L-517; M-530; M-531; M-532; M-534; M-647; P-709; S-833; S-922; S-924; S-925; S-926; S-927
		17β-hydroxy-4-estren-3-one	Δ^1; enol.	M-573; W-1072
			Δ^1; enol.; 17β-OH $\rightarrow$ 17-C=O	M-573; W-1072

TABLE III

Transformations by Genus: SEPTOMYXA

SPECIES	SOURCE	SUBSTRATE	REACTION	REF.
affinis	ATCC-6737	17β-hydroxy-2α-methyl-4-estren-3-one	Δ^1; enol.; 17β-OH $\rightarrow$ 17-C=O	P-731
		17β-hydroxy-4-methyl-4-estren-3-one	Δ^1; enol.; 17β-OH $\rightarrow$ 17-C=O	P-731
		17α-ethinyl-6α-fluoro-17β-hydroxy-4-estren-3-one	Δ^1; enol.	C-93
		6α-fluoro-17β-hydroxy-17α-methyl-4-estren-3-one	Δ^1; enol.	C-93
		6α-fluoro-17β-hydroxy-17α-methylethinyl-4-estren-3-one	Δ^1; enol.	C-93
		6α-fluoro-4-estrene-3,17-dione	Δ^1; enol.	P-709
		6β-fluoro-4-estrene-3,17-dione	Δ^1; enol.	P-709
		6α-fluoro-4-estrene-3,11,17-trione	Δ^1; enol.	P-709
		6β-fluoro-4-estrene-3,11,17-trione	Δ^1; enol.	P-709
		4,7-estradiene-3,17-dione	Δ^1; enol.	B-72
		17β-hydroxy-4-androsten-3-one	Δ^1	W-1072
			Δ^1; 17β-OH $\rightarrow$ 17-C=O	W-1072
			Δ^1; 17β-OH $\rightarrow$ 17a-oxa-17-C=O	W-1072
		$2\alpha,17\beta$-dihydroxy-4-androsten-3-one diacetate	2α-OAc $\rightarrow$ 2α-OH; 17β-OAc $\rightarrow$ 17β-OH	H-399
		$2\beta,17\beta$-dihydroxy-4-androsten-3-one diacetate	2β-OAc $\rightarrow$ 2β-OH; 17β-OAc $\rightarrow$ 17β-OH	H-399
			2β-OAc $\rightarrow$ 2β-OH; 17β-OAc $\rightarrow$ 17-C=O	H-399
		17β-hydroxy-17α-methyl-4-androsten-3-one	Δ^1	E-205; W-1072
		17α-bromethinyl-6α-fluoro-4-androsten-3-one	Δ^1	O-694; O-695
		17α-bromethinyl-17β-hydroxy-4-androsten-3-one	Δ^1	O-694; O-695

606

TABLE III

Transformations by Genus: SEPTOMYXA

SPECIES	SOURCE	SUBSTRATE	REACTION	REF.
affinis	ATCC-6737	17α-bromethinyl-17β-methoxy-4-androsten-3-one	Δ^1	O-694; O-695
		17α-chlorethinyl-17β-hydroxy-4-androsten-3-one	Δ^1	O-694; O-695
		17α-chlorethinyl-17β-methoxy-4-androsten-3-one	Δ^1	O-694; O-695
		17α-ethinyl-6α-fluoro-17β-hydroxy-4-androsten-3-one	Δ^1	C-93
		17α-ethyl-6α-fluoro-17β-hydroxy-4-androsten-3-one	Δ^1	C-93
		11β,17β-dihydroxy-17α-methyl-4-androsten-3-one	Δ^1	E-206
		6α-fluoro-17β-hydroxy-17α-methyl-4-androsten-3-one	Δ^1	C-93
		17α-bromethinyl-6α-chloro-17β-hydroxy-4-androsten-3-one	Δ^1	O-694; O-695
		17α-bromethinyl-6α-fluoro-17β-methoxy-4-androsten-3-one	Δ^1	O-694; O-695
		17α-bromethinyl-17β-hydroxy-6α-methyl-4-androsten-3-one	Δ^1	O-694; O-695
		6α-chloro-17α-chlorethinyl-17β-hydroxy-4-androsten-3-one	Δ^1	O-694; O-695
		17α-chlorethinyl-6α-fluoro-17β-hydroxy-4-androsten-3-one	Δ^1	O-694; O-695
		17α-chlorethinyl-6α-fluoro-17β-methoxy-4-androsten-3-one	Δ^1	O-694; O-695
		17α-chlorethinyl-17β-hydroxy-6α-methyl-4-androsten-3-one	Δ^1	O-694; O-695
		9α-fluoro-11β,17β-dihydroxy-17α-methyl-4-androsten-3-one (+A)	Δ^1	M-647
		6α-fluoro-17β-hydroxy-17α-methylethinyl-4-androsten-3-one	Δ^1	C-93
		17β-hydroxy-17α-methyl-9β,11β-oxido-4-androsten-3-one (+A)	Δ^1	M-647
		6α-fluoro-17β-hydroxy-4-androstene-3,11-dione	Δ^1	P-709
		4-androstene-3,17-dione (testolic acid was not produced by cultures forming lactone- Ref. H-398)	Δ^1	H-399; W-1072

TABLE III

Transformations by Genus: SEPTOMYXA

SPECIES	SOURCE	SUBSTRATE	REACTION	REF.
affinis	ATCC-6737	4-androstene-3,17-dione (testolic acid was not produced by cultures forming lactone- Ref. H-398)	Δ^1; 17-C=O → 17β-OH	W-1072
			Δ^1; 17-C=O → 17a-oxa-17-C =O	H-398; W-1072
		6α-fluoro-11β-hydroxy-4-andro- stene-3,17-dione (+A)	Δ^1	P-709
		6β-fluoro-11β-hydroxy-4-andro- stene-3,17-dione (+A)	Δ^1	P-709
		6α-fluoro-4-androstene-3,11,17- trione	Δ^1	P-709
		17a-oxa-D-homo-4-androstene- 3,17-dione	no testolic acid	H-398
		17α-chlorethinyl-6-fluoro-17β- hydroxy-4,6-androstadien-3- one	Δ^1	O-694; O-695
		17α-chlorethinyl-6-fluoro-17β- methoxy-4,6-androstadien-3- one	Δ^1	O-694; O-695
		17α-chlorethinyl-17β-hydroxy- 6-methyl-4,6-androstadien-3- one	Δ^1	O-694; O-695
		6-chloro-17α-chlorethinyl-17β- hydroxy-4,6-androstadien-3- one	Δ^1	O-694; O-695
		6-chloro-17α-chlorethinyl-17β- methoxy-4,6-androstadien-3- one	Δ^1	O-694; O-695
		17α-bromethinyl-6-chloro-17β- hydroxy-4,6-androstadien-3- one	Δ^1	O-694; O-695
		17α-bromo-6-chloro-17β- methoxy-4,6-androstadien-3- one	Δ^1	O-694; O-695
		17α-bromethinyl-6-fluoro-17β- hydroxy-4,6-androstadien-3- one	Δ^1	O-694; O-695
		17α-bromethinyl-6-fluoro-17β- methoxy-4,6-androstadien-3- one	Δ^1	O-694; O-695
		17α-bromethinyl-17β-hydroxy- 6-methyl-4,6-androstadien-3- one	Δ^1	O-694; O-695

TABLE III

Transformations by Genus: SEPTOMYXA

SPECIES	SOURCE	SUBSTRATE	REACTION	REF.
affinis	ATCC-6737	4,7-androstadiene-3,17-dione	Δ^1	B-72
		6α-fluoro-17α-hydroxy-5α-pregnane-3,20-dione	Δ^1	B-34
		3β-hydroxy-5α-pregnane-11,20-dione 20-cycloethyleneketal (+A)	Δ^1; 3β-OH → 3-C=O	F-251
		3β,17α-dihydroxy-5α-pregnane-11,20-dione 20-cycloethyleneketal (+A)	Δ^1; 3β-OH → 3-C=O	F-251
		3β,21-dihydroxy-5α-pregnane-11,20-dione 20-cycloethyleneketal (+A)	Δ^1; 3β-OH → 3-C=O	F-251
		3β,17α,21-trihydroxy-5α-pregnane-11,20-dione 20-cycloethyleneketal (+A)	Δ^1; 3β-OH → 3-C=O	F-251
		5α-pregnane-3,11,20-trione (+A)	Δ^1; 17β-Ac → 17-C=O	E-207; M-573; W-1072
		6β-fluoro-3β,5α-dihydroxy-pregnan-20-one 20-cycloethyleneketal (+A)	Δ^1; 3β-OH → 3-C=O	F-251
		3β,5α-dihydroxy-6β-methyl-pregnan-20-one 20-cycloethyleneketal (+A)	Δ^1; 3β-OH → 3-C=O	F-251
		6α-fluoro-17α-hydroxy-5β-pregnane-3,20-dione	Δ^1	B-34
		5β-pregnane-3,11,20-trione (compare with ethyleneketal derivative - Ref. R-251)	oxidized to androstane series Δ^1; 17β-Ac → 17-C=O	F-251 E-207; M-573; W-1072
		5β-pregnane-3,11,20-trione 20-cycloethyleneketal (+A)	Δ^1	F-249; F-251; F-253
		3β-hydroxy-5-pregnen-20-one (+A)	oxidized to androstane series	F-251
		3β-hydroxy-5-pregnen-20-one 20-cycloethyleneketal (+A)	Δ^1; $\Delta^5 \to \Delta^4$; 3β-OH→3-C=O	F-251
		3β-hydroxy-5-pregnen-20-one 20-methyl enol ether (+A)	Δ^1; $\Delta^5 \to \Delta^4$; 3β-OH → 3-C=O	F-251

TABLE III

Transformations by Genus: SEPTOMYXA

SPECIES	SOURCE	SUBSTRATE	REACTION	REF.
affinis	ATCC-6737	3β-hydroxy-16α-methyl-5-preg-nen-20-one 20-cycloethylene-ketal	Δ^1; $\Delta^5 \to \Delta^4$; 3β-OH $\to$ 3-C=O	F-251
		4-pregnene-3,20-dione	Δ^1	H-399; S-901; W-1072
		[occurrence of testolic acid by cultures reported to produce testololactone-Ref. H-398; with spores - Ref. S-901; use of washed mycelium and changing proportion of products by various additives-Ref. W-1072]	Δ^1; 17β-Ac $\to$ 17β-OH	S-901; W-1072
			Δ^1; 17β-Ac $\to$ 17-C=O	S-901; W-1072
			Δ^1; 17β-Ac $\to$ 17a-oxa-17-C=O	H-398; S-901; W-1072
		11α-hydroxy-4-pregnene-3,20-dione	Δ^1	E-208; W-1072
			Δ^1; 17β-Ac $\to$ 17β-OH	W-1072
			Δ^1; 17β-Ac $\to$ 17-C=O	W-1072
		11β-hydroxy-4-pregnene-3,20-dione	Δ^1	W-1072
			Δ^1; 17β-Ac $\to$ 17β-OH	W-1072
			Δ^1; 17β-Ac $\to$ 17-C=O	W-1072
		17α-hydroxy-4-pregnene-3,20-dione (with spores - Ref. S-901)	Δ^1	W-1072
			Δ^1; 17α-OH-17β-Ac $\to$ 17β-OH	S-901; W-1072
			Δ^1; 17α-OH-17β-Ac $\to$ 17-C=O	S-901
			Δ^1; 17α-OH-17β-Ac $\to$ 17a-oxa-17-C=O	S-901
		17α-hydroxy-4-pregnene-3,20-dione acetate	Δ^1	B-36

TABLE III

Transformations by Genus: SEPTOMYXA

SPECIES	SOURCE	SUBSTRATE	REACTION	REF.
affinis	ATCC-6737	21-hydroxy-4-pregnene-3,20-dione (with spores -Ref. S-901)	Δ^1	W-1072
			Δ^1; 17β-(20-C =O-21-OH) → 17β-OH	S-901; W-1072
			Δ^1; 17β-(20-C =O-21-OH) → 17-C=O	S-901; W-1072
			Δ^1; 17β-(20-C = O-21-OH) → 17a-oxa-17-C =O	S-901; W-1072
		17α-ethyl-4-pregnene-3,20-dione (with spores)	Δ^1	S-901
		17α-methyl-4-pregnene-3,20-dione (with spores)	Δ^1	S-901
		21-fluoro-4-pregnene-3,20-dione (with spores)	Δ^1; 17β-(20-C =O-21-F) → 17β-OH	S-901
			Δ^1; 17β-(20-C =O-21-F) → 17-C=O	S-901
			Δ^1; 17β-(20-C =O-21-F) → 17a-oxa-17-C =O	S-901
		6α-fluoro-11α-hydroxy-4-pregnene-3,20-dione	Δ^1	C-91
		6α-fluoro-11β-hydroxy-4-pregnene-3,20-dione	Δ^1	C-91
		6α-fluoro-17α-hydroxy-4-pregnene-3,20-dione	Δ^1	B-34
		6β-fluoro-11α-hydroxy-4-pregnene-3,20-dione	Δ^1	C-91
		6β-fluoro-11β-hydroxy-4-pregnene-3,20-dione	Δ^1	C-91
		6β,11α-dihydroxy-4-pregnene-3,20-dione (+A)	Δ^1	M-647
		11α,17α-dihydroxy-4-pregnene-3,20-dione (+A)	Δ^1	M-647
		11β,17α-dihydroxy-4-pregnene-3,20-dione (+A)	Δ^1	M-647

TABLE III

ransformations by Genus: SEPTOMYXA

SPECIES	SOURCE	SUBSTRATE	REACTION	REF.
affinis	ATCC-6737	11β,21-dihydroxy-4-pregnene-3,20-dione	Δ^1; 17β-(20-C=O-21-OH) → 17β-OH	S-901
			Δ^1; 17β-(20-C=O-21-OH) → 17-C=O	S-901
		17α,21-dihydroxy-4-pregnene-3,20-dione (with spores - Ref. S-901)	Δ^1	S-901; W-1072
			Δ^1; 17α-OH-17β-(20-C=O-21-OH) → 17β-OH	S-901
			Δ^1; 17α-OH-17β-(20-C=O-21-OH) → 17-C=O	S-901
		21-fluoro-17α-methyl-4-pregnene-3,20-dione (with spores)	Δ^1	S-901
		21-hydroxy-17α-methyl-4-pregnene-3,20-dione acetate (with spores)	Δ^1; 21-OAc → 21-OH	S-901
		6α,17α-dimethyl-4-pregnene-3,20-dione	Δ^1	S-901
		9α-chloro-11β,21-dihydroxy-4-pregnene-3,20-dione	Δ^1; 17β-(20-C=O-21-OH) → 17-C=O	H-399
		9α-fluoro-11β-hydroxy-6α-methyl-4-pregnene-3,20-dione (+A)	Δ^1	S-923; S-927
		11β,17α,21-trihydroxy-4-pregnene-3,20-dione [(+A)- Ref. M-647, reaction kinetics, washed cells-Ref. C-132, use of dried thalli Ref.-F-231]	Δ^1	C-132; F-231; M-647; W-1072
		6α- isobutyl-11β,17α,21-trihydroxy-4-pregnene-3,20-dione (+A)	Δ^1	H-395
		7α-cyano-11β,17α,21-trihydroxy-4-pregnene-3,20-dione	Δ^1	B-75
		7β-cyano-11β,17α,21-trihydroxy-4-pregnene-3,20-dione	Δ^1	B-75
		6α-fluoro-11β,17α-dihydroxy-2α-methyl-4-pregnene-3,20-dione (+A)	Δ^1	B-43

TABLE III

Transformations by Genus: SEPTOMYXA

SPECIES	SOURCE	SUBSTRATE	REACTION	REF.
affinis	ATCC-6737	9α-fluoro-11β,17α-dihydroxy-6α-methyl-4-pregnene-3,20-dione (+A)	Δ^1	L-513
		9α-fluoro-11β-hydroxy-6α,16α-dimethyl-4-pregnene-3,20-dione	Δ^1	S-923
		6α-fluoro-11β,17α,21-trihydroxy-4-pregnene-3,20-dione 21-acetate [(+A)-Ref. M-530,531,532, 647]	Δ^1; 21-OAc → 21-OH	H-396; M-530; M-531; M-532; M-647; S-924; S-926
		6β-fluoro-11β,17α,21-trihydroxy-4-pregnene-3,20-dione 21-acetate (+A)	Δ^1; 21-OAc → 21-OH	S-925; S-926
		6α-hexyl-11β,17α,21-trihydroxy-4-pregnene-3,20-dione (+A)	Δ^1	H-395
		11α,17α,21-trihydroxy-6ξ-methyl-4-pregnene-3,20-dione (+A)	Δ^1	S-833
		11β,17α,21-trihydroxy-2α-methyl-4-pregnene-3,20-dione (+A-Ref. M-647)	Δ^1	H-394; M-573; M-647
		11β,17α,21-trihydroxy-6α-methyl-4-pregnene-3,20-dione (+A-Ref. H-395; S-833; S-922)	Δ^1	H-395; L-512; M-573; M-647; S-833; S-922; W-1072
		11β,17α,21-trihydroxy-6β-methyl-4-pregnene-3,20-dione (+A-Ref. H-395; S-833)	Δ^1	H-395; L-512; S-833
		11β,17α,21-trihydroxy-6-methylene-4-pregnene-3,20-dione	Δ^1	F-264
		11β,17α,21-trihydroxy-6α-pentyl-4-pregnene-3,20-dione (+A)	Δ^1	H-395
		11β,17α,21-trihydroxy-6α-phenyl-4-pregnene-3,20-dione (+A)	Δ^1	H-395
		11β,17α,21-trihydroxy-6α-iso-propyl-4-pregnene-3,20-dione (+A)	Δ^1	H-395
		11β,15α,17α,21-tetrahydroxy-4-pregnene-3,20-dione (+A)	Δ^1	B-44

TABLE III

Transformations by Genus: SEPTOMYX A

SPECIES	SOURCE	SUBSTRATE	REACTION	REF.
affinis	ATCC-6737	$11\beta,15\beta,17\alpha,21$-tetrahydroxy-4-pregnene-3,20-dione (+A)	Δ^1	B-44
		9α-bromo-6α-fluoro-11β,17α-dihydroxy-2α-methyl-4-pregnene-3,20-dione (+A)	Δ^1	B-43
		9α-bromo-6β-fluoro-11β,17α,21-trihydroxy-4-pregnene-3,20-dione 21-acetate	Δ^1; 21-OAc→21-OH	S-926
		9α-chloro-6α-fluoro-11β,17α-dihydroxy-2α-methyl-4-pregnene-3,20-dione (+A)	Δ^1	B-43
		9α-chloro-6β-fluoro-11β,17α,21-trihydroxy-4-pregnene-3,20-dione 21-acetate	Δ^1; 21-OAc→21-OH	S-926
		6α-fluoro-11β,17α,21-trihydroxy-2α-methyl-4-pregnene-3,20-dione (+A)	Δ^1	B-43
		6α-fluoro-11β,17α,21-trihydroxy-16α-methyl-4-pregnene-3,20-dione 21-acetate	Δ^1; 21-OAc→21-OH	L-517
		6α-fluoro-11β,17α,21-trihydroxy-16β-methyl-4-pregnene-3,20-dione 21-acetate	Δ^1; 21-OAc→21-OH	L-517
		6β-fluoro-11β,17α,21-trihydroxy-2α-methyl-4-pregnene-3,20-dione (+A)	Δ^1	B-43
		9α-fluoro-11β,17α,21-trihydroxy-6α-methyl-4-pregnene-3,20-dione (+A)	Δ^1	S-921
		9α-fluoro-11β,15α,17α,21-tetrahydroxy-4-pregnene-3,20-dione (+A)	Δ^1	B-44
		9α-fluoro-11β,15β,17α,21-tetrahydroxy-4-pregnene-3,20-dione (+A)	Δ^1	B-44
		$6\alpha,9\alpha$-difluoro-11β,17α-dihydroxy-2α-methyl-4-pregnene-3,20-dione (+A)	Δ^1	B-43
		$6\alpha,21$-difluoro-11β,17α-dihydroxy-2α-methyl-4-pregnene-3,20-dione (+A)	Δ^1	B-43
		$6\alpha,9\alpha,21$-trifluoro-11β,17α-dihydroxy-4-pregnene-3,20-dione (+A)	Δ^1	M-534

TABLE III

Transformations by Genus: SEPTOMYXA

SPECIES	SOURCE	SUBSTRATE	REACTION	REF.
affinis	ATCC-6737	$6\beta,9\alpha$-difluoro-$11\beta,17\alpha,21$-tri-hydroxy-4-pregnene-3,20-dione 21-acetate	Δ^1; 21-OAc $\rightarrow$ 21-OH	S-926
		$11\beta,17\alpha,21$-trihydroxy-16α-methyl-6-methylene-4-preg-nene-3,20-dione	Δ^1	F-264
		$11\beta,15\beta,17\alpha,21$-tetrahydroxy-$15\alpha$-methyl-4-pregnene-3,20-dione (+A)	Δ^1	B-44
		$11\beta,16\alpha,17\alpha,21$-tetrahydroxy-$6\alpha$-methyl-4-pregnene-3,20-dione	Δ^1	L-517
		9α-bromo-$6\alpha,21$-difluoro-$11\beta,17\alpha$-dihydroxy-2α-methyl-4-pregnene-3,20-dione (+A)	Δ^1	B-43
		9α-chloro-$6\alpha,21$-difluoro-$11\beta,17\alpha$-dihydroxy-2α-methyl-4-pregnene-3,20-dione (+A)	Δ^1	B-43
		9α-fluoro-$11\beta,15\beta,17\alpha,21$-tetra-hydroxy-$15\alpha$-methyl-4-preg-nene-3,20-dione	Δ^1	B-44
		9α-fluoro-$11\beta,16\alpha,17\alpha,21$-tetra-hydroxy-$6\alpha$-methyl-4-preg-nene-3,20-dione	Δ^1	L-517
		$6\alpha,9\alpha,21$-trifluoro-$11\beta,17\alpha$-di-hydroxy-2α-methyl-4-preg-3,20-dione	Δ^1	B-43
		4-pregnene-3,11,20-trione	Δ^1	E-208; M-574; W-1072
			Δ^1; 17β-Ac $\rightarrow$ 17β-OH	W-1072
			Δ^1; 17β-Ac $\rightarrow$ 17-C=O	W-1072
		6α-fluoro-4-pregnene-3,11,20-trione	Δ^1	C-91
		6β-fluoro-4-pregnene-3,11,20-trione	Δ^1	C-91
		6α-methyl-4-pregnene-3,11,20-trione	Δ^1; 17β-Ac $\rightarrow$ 17β-OH	R-780
			Δ^1; 17β-Ac $\rightarrow$ 17-C=O	R-780
		6β-methyl-4-pregnene-3,11,20-trione	Δ^1; 17β-Ac $\rightarrow$ 17β-OH	R-780

TABLE III

ransformations by Genus: SEPTOMYXA

SPECIES	SOURCE	SUBSTRATE	REACTION	REF.
affinis	ATCC-6737	6β-methyl-4-pregnene-3,11,20-trione	Δ^1; 17β-Ac → 17-C=O	R-780
		9α-fluoro-6α-methyl-4-pregnene-3,11,20-trione	Δ^1	S-923; S-927
		17α,21-dihydroxy-4-pregnene-3,11,20-trione (with spores - Ref. S-901)	Δ^1	S-901; W-1072
			Δ^1; 17α-OH-17β-(20-C=O-21-OH) → 17β-OH	S-901
			Δ^1; 17α-OH -17β-(20-C=O-21-OH) → 17-C=O	S-901
		6α-fluoro-17α-hydroxy-2α-methyl-4-pregnene-3,11,20-trione	Δ^1	B-43
		2α-fluoro-17α,21-dihydroxy-4-pregnene-3,11,20-trione	Δ^1	H-401
		6α-fluoro-17α,21-dihydroxy-4-pregnene-3,11,20-trione 21-acetate (+A)	Δ^1; 21-OAc → 21-OH	M-530; M-531; M-532; S-924; S-926
		6β-fluoro-17α,21-dihydroxy-4-pregnene-3,11,20-trione 21-acetate (+A)	Δ^1; 21-OAc → 21-OH	S-925; S-926
		9α-fluoro-6α,16α-dimethyl-4-pregnene-3,11,20-trione	Δ^1	S-923
		17α,21-dihydroxy-6α-methyl-4-pregnene-3,11,20-trione (+A-Ref. L-512)	Δ^1	L-512; S-833
		17α,21-dihydroxy-6β-methyl-4-pregnene-3,11,20-trione	Δ^1	S-833
		15α,17α,21-trihydroxy-4-pregnene-3,11,20-trione	Δ^1	B-44
		15β,17α,21-trihydroxy-4-pregnene-3,11,20-trione	Δ^1	B-44
		9α-bromo-6α-fluoro-17α-hydroxy-2α-methyl-4-pregnene-3,11,20-trione (+A)	Δ^1	B-43
		9α-bromo-6β-fluoro-17α,21-dihydroxy-4-pregnene-3,11,20-trione 21-acetate	Δ^1; 21-OAc → 21-OH	S-926

TABLE III

Transformations by Genus: SEPTOMYXA

SPECIES	SOURCE	SUBSTRATE	REACTION	REF.
affinis	ATCC-6737	9α-chloro-6α-fluoro-17α-hydroxy-2α-methyl-4-pregnene-3,11,20-trione (+A)	Δ^1	B-43
		9α-chloro-6β-fluoro-17α,21-dihydroxy-4-pregnene-3,11,20-trione 21-acetate	Δ^1 ; 21-OAc → 21-OH	S-926
		6α-fluoro-17α,21-dihydroxy-2α-methyl-4-pregnene-3,11,20-trione (+A)	Δ^1	B-43
		6β-fluoro-17α,21-dihydroxy-2α-methyl-4-pregnene-3,11,20-trione (+A)	Δ^1	B-43
		9α-fluoro-15α,17α,21-trihydroxy-4-pregnene-3,11,20-trione (+ A)	Δ^1	B-44
		9α-fluoro-15β,17α,21-trihydroxy-4-pregnene-3,11,20-trione (+A)	Δ^1	B-44
		6α,9α-difluoro-17α-hydroxy-2α-methyl-4-pregnene-3,11,20-trione (+A)	Δ^1	B-43
		6β,9α-difluoro-17α,21-dihydroxy-4-pregnene-3,11,20-trione 21-acetate	Δ^1 ; 21-OAc → 21-OH	S-926
		6α,21-difluoro-17α-hydroxy-2α-methyl-4-pregnene-3,11,20-trione (+A)	Δ^1	B-43
		15β,17α,21-trihydroxy-15α-methyl-4-pregnene-3,11,20-trione (+A)	Δ^1	B-44
		9α-bromo-6α,21-difluoro-17α-hydroxy-2α-methyl-4-pregnene-3,11,20-trione (+A)	Δ^1	B-43
		9α-chloro-6α,21-difluoro-17α-hydroxy-2α-methyl-4-pregnene-3,11,20-trione (+A)	Δ^1	B-43
		9α-fluoro-15β,17α,21-trihydroxy-15α-methyl-4-pregnene-3,11,20-trione (+A)	Δ^1	B-44
		6α,9α,21-trifluoro-17α-hydroxy-2α-methyl-4-pregnene-3,11,20-trione	Δ^1	B-43
		20-methoxy-4,17(20)-pregnadien-3-one	Δ^1	E-251

TABLE III

ransformations by Genus: SEPTOMYXA

SPECIES	SOURCE	SUBSTRATE	REACTION	REF.
affinis	ATCC-6737	11β,21-dihydroxy-4,17(20)-pregnadien-3-one (use of incremental addition for dehydrogenation at concentrations exceeding solubility of substrate - Ref. C-130, reaction kinetics and use of washed cells - Ref. C-132, continuous transformation - Ref. R-766 (+A) - Ref. M-647)	Δ^1	C-130; C-132; M-647; R-766; S-922; W-1072
		6α-fluoro-11β,21-dihydroxy-4,17(20)-pregnadien-3-one 21-acetate (+A)	Δ^1; 21-OAc $\rightarrow$ 21-OH	L-517
		11β,21-dihydroxy-2α-methyl-4,17(20)-pregnadien-3-one	Δ^1	H-394; M-573; S-927
		11β,21-dihydroxy-6α-methyl-4,17(20)-pregnadien-3-one	Δ^1	M-573; S-928
		11β,16α,21-trihydroxy-4,17(20)-cis-pregnadien-3-one 21-acetate	Δ^1	M-529
		11β,21-dihydroxy-6α,16α-dimethyl-4,17(20)-pregnadien-3-one (+A)	Δ^1	L-517
		11β,21-dihydroxy-6α,16β-dimethyl-4,17(20)-pregnadien-3-one (+A)	Δ^1	L-517
		6,17α-dimethyl-4,6-pregnadiene-3,20-dione (with conidia)	Δ^1	S-901
		11β,17α,21-trihydroxy-6-methyl-4,6-pregnadiene-3,20-dione (+A)	Δ^1	H-395
		17α,21-dihydroxy-6-methyl-4,6-pregnadiene-3,11,20-trione (+A)	Δ^1	H-395
	ATCC-13425	11α-hydroxy-4-pregnene-3,20-dione (demonstration of inducible enzyme - Ref. K-456)	Δ^1	K-456
		11β,17α,21-trihydroxy-4-pregnene-3,20-dione (see note above)	Δ^1	K-456
		11β,17α,21-trihydroxy-6α-methyl-4-pregnene-3,20-dione (see note above)	Δ^1	K-456

TABLE III

Transformations by Genus: SEPTOMYXA

SPECIES	SOURCE	SUBSTRATE	REACTION	REF.
affinis	ATCC-13425	17α,21-dihydroxy-4-pregnene-3,11,20-trione (see note above)	Δ^1	K-456
		11β,21-dihydroxy-4,17(20)-pregnadien-3-one (see note above)	Δ^1	K-456
	AY	17β-hydroxy-4-androstene-3,17-dione (with conidia)	Δ^1; 17β-OH→17-C=O	S-835
		4-pregnene-3,20-dione (with conidia)	Δ^1	S-835; V-1048
		17α,21-dihydroxy-4-pregnene-3,20-dione (with conidia)	Δ^1	S-835; V-1048
		11α,17α,21-trihydroxy-4-pregnene-3,20-dione	Δ^1	S-835
corni	ATCC-13416 CBS	17β-hydroxy-4-estren-3-one	Δ^1; enol.	W-1072
			Δ^1; enol.; 17β-OH→17-C=O	W-1072
		17β-hydroxy-4-androsten-3-one	Δ^1	W-1072
			Δ^1; 17β-OH→17-C=O	W-1072
		17β-hydroxy-17α-methyl-4-androsten-3-one	Δ^1	W-1072
		11β,17β-dihydroxy-17α-methyl-4-androsten-3-one	Δ^1	E-206
		4-androstene-3,17-dione	Δ^1	W-1072
			Δ^1; 17-C=O→17a-oxa-17-C=O	W-1072
			Δ^1; 17-C=O→17β-OH	W-1072
		5α-pregnane-3,11,20-trione	Δ^1; 17β-Ac→17-C=O	W-1072
		4-pregnene-3,20-dione · (use of washed mycelium and various additives changes proportion of products)	Δ^1	W-1072
			Δ^1; 17β-Ac→17β-OH	W-1072
			Δ^1; 17β-Ac→17-C=O	W-1072

TABLE III

ransformations by Genus: SEPTOMYXA

SPECIES	SOURCE	SUBSTRATE	REACTION	REF.
corni	ATCC-13416 CBS	4-pregnene-3,20-dione (use of washed mycelium and various additives changes proportion of products)	Δ^1; 17β-Ac → 17a-oxa-17-C =O	W-1072
		11α-hydroxy-4-pregnene-3,20-dione	Δ^1	W-1072
			Δ^1; 17β-Ac → 17β-OH	W-1072
			Δ^1; 17β-Ac → 17-C=O	W-1072
		11β-hydroxy-4-pregnene-3,20-dione	Δ^1; 17β-Ac → 17β-OH	W-1072
			Δ^1; 17β-Ac → 17-C=O	W-1072
		17α-hydroxy-4-pregnene-3,20-dione	Δ^1	W-1072
			Δ^1; 17α-OH-17β-Ac → 17β-OH	W-1072
		21-hydroxy-4-pregnene-3,20-dione	Δ^1	W-1072
			Δ^1; 17β-(20-C =O-21-OH) → 17β-OH	W-1072
			Δ^1; 17β-(20-C =O-21-OH) → 17-C=O	W-1072
			Δ^1; 17β-(20-C =O-21-OH) → 17a-oxa-17-C =O	W-1072
		17α,21-dihydroxy-4-pregnene-3,20-dione	Δ^1	W-1072
		11β,17α,21-trihydroxy-4-pregnene-3,20-dione	Δ^1	W-1072
		11β,17α,21-trihydroxy-6α-methyl-4-pregnene-3,20-dione	Δ^1	W-1072
		4-pregnene-3,11,20-trione	Δ^1	W-1072
			Δ^1; 17β-Ac → 17-C=O	W-1072
			Δ^1; 17β-Ac → 17β-OH	W-1072

TABLE III

Transformations by Genus: SEPTOMYXA

SPECIES	SOURCE	SUBSTRATE	REACTION	REF.
corni	ATCC-13416 CBS	$17\alpha, 21$-dihydroxy-4-pregnene-3,11,20-trione	Δ^1	W-1072
		$11\beta, 21$-dihydroxy-4,17(20)-pregnadien-3-one	Δ^1	W-1072
salicina	U	17β-hydroxy-4-estren-3-one	Δ^1; enol.	W-1072
			Δ^1; enol.; 17β-OH $\rightarrow$ 17-C=O	W-1072
		17β-hydroxy-4-androsten-3-one	Δ^1	W-1072
			Δ^1; 17β-OH $\rightarrow$ 17-C=O	W-1072
		17β-hydroxy-17α-methyl-4-androsten-3-one	Δ^1	W-1072
		$11\beta, 17\beta$-dihydroxy-17α-methyl-4-androsten-3-one	Δ^1	E-206
		4-androstene-3,17-dione	Δ^1	W-1072
			Δ^1; 17-C=O $\rightarrow$ 17a-oxa-17-C=O	W-1072
			Δ^1; 17-C=O $\rightarrow$ 17β-OH	W-1072
		5α-pregnane-3,11,20-trione	Δ^1; 17β-Ac $\rightarrow$ 17-C=O	W-1072
		4-pregnene-3,20-dione (use of washed mycelium and various additives changes proportion of products)	Δ^1	W-1072
			Δ^1; 17β-Ac $\rightarrow$ 17β-OH	W-1072
			Δ^1; 17β-Ac $\rightarrow$ 17-C=O	W-1072
			Δ^1; 17β-Ac $\rightarrow$ 17a-oxa-17-C=O	W-1072
		11α-hydroxy-4-pregnene-3,20-dione	Δ^1	W-1072
			Δ^1; 17β-Ac $\rightarrow$ 17β-OH	W-1072
			Δ^1; 17β-Ac $\rightarrow$ 17-C=O	W-1072
		11β-hydroxy-4-pregnene-3,20-dione	Δ^1; 17β-Ac $\rightarrow$ 17β-OH	W-1072

TABLE III

Transformations by Genus: SEPTOMYXA

SPECIES	SOURCE	SUBSTRATE	REACTION	REF.
salicina	U	11β-hydroxy-4-pregnene-3,20-dione	Δ^1; 17β-Ac → 17-C=O	W-1072
		17α-hydroxy-4-pregnene-3,20-dione	Δ^1	W-1072
			Δ^1; 17α-OH-17β-Ac → 17β-OH	W-1072
		21-hydroxy-4-pregnene-3,20-dione	Δ^1	W-1072
			Δ^1; 17β-(20-C=O-21-OH) → 17β-OH	W-1072
			Δ^1; 17β-(20-C=O-21-OH) → 17-C=O	W-1072
			Δ^1; 17β-(20-C=O-21-OH) → 17a-oxa-17-C=O	W-1072
		17α,21-dihydroxy-4-pregnene-3,20-dione	Δ^1	W-1072
		11β,17α,21-trihydroxy-4-pregnene-3,20-dione	Δ^1	W-1072
		11β,17α,21-trihydroxy-6α-methyl-4-pregnene-3,20-dione	Δ^1	W-1072
		4-pregnene-3,11,20-trione	Δ^1	W-1072
			Δ^1; 17β-Ac → 17-C=O	W-1072
			Δ^1; 17β-Ac → 17β-OH	W-1072
		17α,21-dihydroxy-4-pregnene-3,11,20-trione	Δ^1	W-1072
		11β,21-dihydroxy-4,17(20)-pregnadien-3-one	Δ^1	W-1072
tulasnei		17β-hydroxy-4-estren-3-one	Δ^1; enol.	W-1072
			Δ^1; enol.; 17β-OH → 17-C=O	W-1072
		17β-hydroxy-4-androsten-3-one	Δ^1	W-1072
			Δ^1; 17β-OH → 17-C=O	W-1072

TABLE III

Transformations by Genus: SEPTOMYXA

SPECIES	SOURCE	SUBSTRATE	REACTION	REF.
tulasnei	U	17β-hydroxy-17α-methyl-4-androsten-3-one	Δ^1	W-1072
		$11\beta,17\beta$-dihydroxy-17α-methyl-4-androsten-3-one	Δ^1	E-206
		4-androstene-3,17-dione	Δ^1	W-1072
			Δ^1; 17-C=O → 17a-oxa-17-C =O	W-1072
			Δ^1; 17-C=O → 17β-OH	W-1072
		5α-pregnane-3,11,20-trione	Δ^1; 17β-Ac → 17-C=O	W-1072
		4-pregnene-3,20-dione (use of washed mycelium and various additives changes proportion of products)	Δ^1	W-1072
			Δ^1; 17β-Ac → 17β-OH	W-1072
			Δ^1; 17β-Ac → 17-C=O	W-1072
			Δ^1; 17β-Ac → 17a-oxa-17-C =O	W-1072
		11α-hydroxy-4-pregnene-3,20-dione	Δ^1	W-1072
			Δ^1; 17β-Ac → 17β-OH	W-1072
			Δ^1; 17β-Ac → 17-C=O	W-1072
		11β-hydroxy-4-pregnene-3,20-dione	Δ^1; 17β-Ac → 17β-OH	W-1072
			Δ^1; 17β-Ac → 17-C=O	W-1072
		17α-hydroxy-4-pregnene-3,20-dione	Δ^1	W-1072
			Δ^1; 17α-OH-17β-Ac → 17β-OH	W-1072
		21-hydroxy-4-pregnene-3,20-dione	Δ^1	W-1072
			Δ^1; 17β-(20-C= O-21-OH) → 17β-OH	W-1072

TABLE III

Transformations by Genus: SEPTOMYXA
SERRATIA   (Schizo. - Eubacteriales)

SPECIES	SOURCE	SUBSTRATE	REACTION	REF.
tulasnei	U	21-hydroxy-4-pregnene-3,20-dione	Δ^1; 17β-(20-C=O-21-OH) $\rightarrow$ 17-C=O	W-1072
			Δ^1; 17β-(20-C=O-21-OH) $\rightarrow$ 17a-oxa-17-C=O	W-1072
		17α,21-dihydroxy-4-pregnene-3,20-dione	Δ^1	W-1072
		11β,17α,21-trihydroxy-4-pregnene-3,20-dione	Δ^1	W-1072
		11β,17α,21-trihydroxy-6α-methyl-4-pregnene-3,20-dione	Δ^1	W-1072
		4-pregnene-3,11,20-trione	Δ^1	W-1072
			Δ^1; 17β-Ac $\rightarrow$ 17-C=O	W-1072
			Δ^1; 17β-Ac $\rightarrow$ 17β-OH	W-1072
		17α,21-dihydroxy-4-pregnene-3,11,20-trione	Δ^1	W-1072
		11β,21-dihydroxy-4,17(20)-pregnadien-3-one	Δ^1	W-1072
SERRATIA				
marcescens	ATCC-13477	17α,21-dihydroxy-4-pregnene-3,20-dione	Δ^1	T-960
	IAM (1-2; 1-3; 1-7; 1-9; 1-10)		Δ^1 Δ^1 Δ^1 Δ^1 Δ^1 2β-OH	S-849 S-849
	(2-1 2-2)		—	S-849
	(2-3)		2β-OH	S-849
	(2-5; 2-7)		Δ^1	S-849
	(2-10)		Δ^1; 11α-OH	S-849
	IFO (3046)	17α,21-dihydroxy-4-pregnene-3,20-dione	—	S-849

624

TABLE III

TAXONOMY

Transformations by Genus:

SERRATIA
SHIYUDAKE (Taxonomy Unclear)
SORDARIA (Asco. - Sphaeriales)
SPHACELOMA (Imperf. - Melanconiales)
SPICARIA (Imperf. - Moniliales)

SPECIES	SOURCE	SUBSTRATE	REACTION	REF.
marcescens	IFO (3046)	$11\beta,17\alpha,21$-trihydroxy-4-preg-nene-3,20-dione	—	I-428
(in mixed culture with Mycococcus sp. A_1)			—	I-428
	IFO (3048)	$17\alpha,21$-dihydroxy-4-pregnene-3,20-dione	—	S-849
	NG	5-cholesten-3β-ol (sole carbon source)	—	S-793c; T-1030
		24β-methyl-5,7,22-cholestatrien-3β-ol (sole carbon source)	—	S-793c
plymuthica	ATCC-13478	$11\beta,17\alpha,21$-trihydroxy-4-preg-nene-3,20-dione	Δ^1	T-960
SHIYUDAKE				
species	S	$17\alpha,21$-dihydroxy-4-pregnene-3,20-dione	11α-OH	S-849
SORDARIA				
species	NRRL	plant saponins	—	K-478
SPHACELOMA				
species	TNAES	$17\alpha,21$-dihydroxy-4-pregnene-3,20-dione	—	S-849
SPICARIA				
simplicissima	ATCC-13595	$17\alpha,21$-dihydroxy-4-pregnene-3,20-dione	15β-OH	A-9; B-58
species	LED(Z-118)	$17\alpha,21$-dihydroxy-4-pregnene-3,20-dione	15β-OH	B-56
	NRRL	plant saponins	—	K-478
violacea	NRRL	Sarsasapogenin	—	M-587

TABLE III

ransformations by Genus: SPICARIA
SPONDYLOCLADIUM   (Imperf. - Moniliales)

SPECIES	SOURCE	SUBSTRATE	REACTION	REF.
violacea	NRRL	Diosgenin	——	M-587
		4-dehydrotigogenone	——	M-587
viridans	FRI	17α,21-dihydroxy-4-pregnene-3,20-dione	11α-OH; 11β-OH	S-849
SPONDYLOCLADIUM				
australe	ATCC-12728	17β-hydroxy-4-androsten-3-one	11β-OH	S-790
		4-androstene-3,20-dione	11β-OH	S-790
		20-hydroxy-5α-pregnan-3-one	11β-OH	S-790
		20-hydroxy-5β-pregnan-3-one	11β-OH	S-790
		3β-hydroxy-5-pregnen-20-one	11β-OH	S-790
		4-pregnene-3,20-dione	11β-OH	S-790
		17α-hydroxy-4-pregnene-3,20-dione	11β-OH	H-391; S-790
		17α,21-dihydroxy-4-pregnene-3,20-dione	11β-OH	H-391; S-790
		6α-fluoro-17α,21-dihydroxy-16-methylene-4-pregnene-3,20-dione 21-propionate	11β-OH; 21-Pr→21-OH	A-7
		1,4-pregnadiene-3,20-dione	11β-OH	S-790
		17α,21-dihydroxy-1,4-pregnadiene-3,20-dione	11β-OH	S-790
xylogenum	ATCC-12727	17β-hydroxy-4-androsten-3-one	11β-OH	S-790
		4-androstene-3,17-dione	11β-OH	S-790
		20-hydroxy-5α-pregnan-3-one	11β-OH	S-790
		20-hydroxy-5β-pregnan-3-one	11β-OH	S-790
		3β-hydroxy-5-pregnen-20-one	11β-OH	S-790
		4-pregnene-3,20-dione	11β-OH	S-790
		17α-hydroxy-4-pregnene-3,20-dione	11β-OH	S-790
		17α,21-dihydroxy-4-pregnene-3,20-dione	11β-OH	S-790
		1,4-pregnadiene-3,20-dione	11β-OH	S-790
		17α,21-dihydroxy-1,4-pregnadiene-3,20-dione	11β-OH	S-790

TABLE III

Transformations by Genus: SPOROBOLOMYCES   (Imperf. - Moniliales)
                             SPORORMIA   (Asco. - Sphaeriales)
                             SPOROTRICHUM (Imperf. - Moniliales)

SPECIES	SOURCE	SUBSTRATE	REACTION	REF.
roseum	FRI	$17\alpha,21$-dihydroxy-4-pregnene-3,20-dione	——	S-849
SPORORMIA				
fasciculata	PH	<u>retro</u>-4-pregnene-3,20-dione	17β-Ac → 17β-OH	P-734
leporina	PH	<u>retro</u>-4-pregnene-3,20-dione	17β-Ac → 17β-OH	P-734
minima	NRRL-2475	4-pregnene-3,20-dione	17α-OH	D-182a
		11β-hydroxy-4-pregnene-3,20-dione	17α-OH	D-182a
		21-hydroxy-4-pregnene-3,20-dione	17α-OH	D-182a
		$11\beta,21$-dihydroxy-4-pregnene-3,20-dione	17α-OH	D-182a
montana	PH	<u>retro</u>-4-pregnene-3,20-dione	17β-Ac → 17β-OH	P-734
pollaccii	PH		17β-Ac → 17β-OH	P-734
SPOROTRICHUM				
asteroides	FRI	$17\alpha,21$-dihydroxy-4-pregnene-3,20-dione	——	S-849
bombycinum	ATCC-7139	1,4-androstadiene-3,17-dione	11α-OH	M-582
epigaeum	ATCC-7145	5α-androstane-3,17-dione	11α-OH	M-582
		5β-pregnane-3,20-dione (reaction depends on air rate- <u>low</u>-hydroxylation only-<u>high</u>-hydroxylation + side chain cleavage - Ref. M-582) air rate not critical if substrate has no side chain at C-17)	11α-OH; or 11α-OH; 17β-Ac → 17β-OH	M-582
		4-pregnene-3,20-dione (see note this ref.)	11α-OH; or 11α-OH; 17β-Ac → 17β-OH	M-582
		4-pregnene-3,20-dione 20-cyclo-ethyleneketal	11α-OH	F-251
		11α-hydroxy-4-pregnene-3,20-dione	17β-Ac → 17β-OH	M-582

TABLE III

ansformations by Genus: SPOROTRICHUM

SPECIES	SOURCE	SUBSTRATE	REACTION	REF.
epigaeum	ATCC-7145	17α-hydroxy-4-pregnene-3,20-	17α-OH-17β-Ac → 17β-OH	M-582
		21-hydroxy-4-pregnene-3,20-dione	17β-(20-C=O-21-OH) → 17β-OH	M-582
		11α,21-dihydroxy-4-pregnene-3,20-dione	17β-(20-C=O-21-OH) → 17β-OH	M-582
		17α,21-dihydroxy-4-pregnene-3,20-dione	17α-OH-17β-(20-C=O-21-OH) → 17β-OH	M-582
		21-hydroxy-1,4-pregnadiene-3,20-dione (low air rate)	11α-OH	M-582
		(high air rate)	11α-OH; 17β-(20-C=O-21-OH) → 17β-OH	M-582
gougeroti	IFO (5982)	17α,21-dihydroxy-4-pregnene-3,20-dione	20-C=O → 20β-OH	T-958
		17α,21-dihydroxy-1,4-pregnadiene-3,20-dione	20-C=O → 20β-OH	T-958
sulfurescens	ATCC-7159	5β-androstane-3,17-dione	11α-OH	M-582
		17β-hydroxy-17α-methyl-4-androsten-3-one	11α-OH	M-582
		17β-hydroxy-1,4-androstadien-3-one	11α-OH	M-582
		17α,21-dihydroxy-4-pregnene-3,20-dione (low air rate)	11α-OH	M-582
		(high air rate)	11α-OH; 17α-OH-17β-(20-C=O - 21-OH) → 17β-OH	M-582
		3-keto-bisnor-4-cholenic acid	11α-OH	M-582
		22-hydroxy-bisnor-4-cholen-3-one	11α-OH	M-582
var. beyman	CBS	17β-hydroxy-17α-methyl-4-androsten-3-one	11α-OH	M-582
		17β-hydroxy-17α-methyl-1,4-androstadien-3-one	11α-OH	E-205; M-582
		17α,21-dihydroxy-4-pregnene-3,20-dione	11α-OH	M-582
	U	4-pregnene-3,20-dione	11α-OH; 17β-Ac → 17β-OH	S-831

TABLE III

Transformations by Genus: SPQROTRICHUM
STACHYBOTRYS   (Imperf. - Moniliales)
STACHYLIDIUM   (Imperf. - Moniliales)

SPECIES	SOURCE	SUBSTRATE	REACTION	REF.
sulfurescens in sequential fermentation with Penicillium sp. (initial substrate 4-pregnene-3,20-dione)	U	17β-hydroxy-4-androsten-3-one	11α-OH	S-831
STACHYBOTRYS				
species	NRRL	plant saponins	——	K-478
	NG (Sandoz)	$3\beta,6\beta,8\beta,14\beta$-tetrahydroxy-4,20,22-bufatrienolide 6-acetate 3-glucoside	$3\beta\,[1^1\xi$-glucoside$]\to 3\beta$-OH	S-936a
STACHYLIDIUM (possible synonym - Verticillium)				
bicolor	ATCC-12672	$17\alpha,21$-dihydroxy-4-pregnene-3,20-dione	11β-OH	D-146
	FRI	$17\alpha,21$-dihydroxy-4-pregnene-3,20-dione	11α-OH; 11β-OH	S-849
	IFO (6647)	$17\alpha,21$-dihydroxy-4-pregnene-3,20-dione	11α-OH; 11β-OH	K-468; K-468
(in mixed culture with Bacillus sphaericus ATCC-7055 [Δ^1])			11α-OH; 11β-OH	K-468
	S	21-hydroxy-4-pregnene-3,20-dione	11β-OH	S-843; S-849
			14α-OH	S-843; S-849
		$11\beta,21$-dihydroxy-4-pregnene-3,20-dione	——	S-843; S-849
		$14\alpha,21$-dihydroxy-4-pregnene-3,20-dione	11β-OH	S-841; S-843; S-849; S-851
		$17\alpha,21$-dihydroxy-4-pregnene-3,20-dione	11β-OH	S-843; S-849
theobromae	ATCC-12474	17α-hydroxy-4-pregnene-3,20-dione	11β-OH	D-146
		$17\alpha,21$-dihydroxy-4-pregnene-3,20-dione	11α-OH; 11β-OH	D-146
		$17\alpha,21$-dihydroxy-4-pregnene-3,20-dione 21-acetate	11β-OH; 21-OAc $\to$ 21-OH	D-146

TABLE III

TAXONOMY

ansformations by Genus: STACHYLIDIUM
STAGONOSPORA (Imperf. - Sphaeropsidales)
STAPHYLOCOCCUS (Schizo. - Eubacteriales)
STAUROPHOMA (Imperf. - Sphaeropsidales)

SPECIES	SOURCE	SUBSTRATE	REACTION	REF.
theobromae	AY	4-pregnene-3,20-dione (use of conidia)	11α-OH; 14α-OH	S-835; V-1048
			14α-OH	S-835; V-1048
		17α,21-dihydroxy-4-pregnene-3,20-dione (use of conidia)	11β-OH	S-835
	CBS	17α,21-dihydroxy-4-pregnene-3,20-dione (use of conidia)	11α-OH; 11β-OH	D-146
STAGONOSPORA				
curtisii	PH	retro-17β-hydroxy-4-androsten-3-one	16α-OH	P-736
		retro-4-pregnene-3,20-dione	16α-OH	P-736
		retro-4,6-pregnadiene-3,20-dione	16α-OH	P-736
STAPHYLOCOCCUS				
albus	NG (rat cecum)	3α,7α,12α-trihydroxy-5β-cholanic acid	—	N-675
aureus (Pyogenes aureus)	IAM (FAD-209p)	17α,21-dihydroxy-4-pregnene-3,20-dione	11β-OH	S-849
	NG (rat cecum)	3α,7α,12α-trihydroxy-5β-cholanic acid	—	N-675
	NG	5-cholesten-3β-ol (sole carbon source)	—	S-793c; T-1030
		24β-methyl-5,7,22-cholesta-trien-3β-ol	—	S-793c
STAUROPHOMA				
species	ATCC-14288	17β-hydroxy-4-androsten-3-one	16α-OH	H-397
		4-androstene-3,17-dione	16α-OH	H-397
		4-pregnene-3,20-dione	16α-OH	H-397

TABLE III

Transformations by Genus:

STEMPHYLIUM	(Imperf. - Moniliales)
STEREUM	(Basidio. - Agaricales)
STERIGMATOCYSTIS	(Imperf. - Moniliales)
STIGMINA	(Imperf. - Moniliales)
STREPTOCOCCUS	(Schizo. - Eubacteriales)

SPECIES	SOURCE	SUBSTRATE	REACTION	REF.
STEMPHYLIUM				
botryosum	FRI	$17\alpha,21$-dihydroxy-4-pregnene-3,20-dione	—	S-849
	Takeda	4-pregnene-3,20-dione	14α-OH	N-661
		$17\alpha,21$-dihydroxy-4-pregnene-3,20-dione	14α-OH	N-661
species	NG (Sandoz)	$3\beta,6\beta,8\beta,14\beta$-tetrahydroxy-4,20(22)-bufatrienolide 6-acetate 3-glucoside	3β-$[1^1\xi$-gluco-side$] \to 3\beta$-OH	S-936a
	NRRL	plant saponins	—	K-478
STEREUM				
fasciatum	IFO (9994)	17β-hydroxy-17α-methyl-4-androsten-3-one	Δ^1	T-959
		$17\alpha,21$-dihydroxy-4-pregnene-3,20-dione	Δ^1	T-959
			Δ^1; 20-C=O $\to$ 20β-OH	T-959
induratum	IAM	$17\alpha,21$-dihydroxy-4-pregnene-3,20-dione	—	S-849
STERIGMATOCYSTIS				
japonica	FRI	$17\alpha,21$-dihydroxy-4-pregnene-3,20-dione	—	S-849
STIGMINA				
platani (in mixed culture with Hendersonia rubra [21-OH] or Tricho-derma nigrovirens [17α-OH])	MCC	4-pregnene-3,20-dione	11β-OH	M-566
STREPTOCOCCUS				
pyogenes	NG	5-cholesten-3β-ol (sole carbon source)	—	T-1030

TABLE III

ansformations by Genus: STREPTOMYCES   (Schizo. - Actinomycetales)

SPECIES	SOURCE	SUBSTRATE	REACTION	REF.
TREPTOMYCES (occasionally Actinomyces)				
lbidoflavus	Shionogi	$17\alpha,21$-dihydroxy-4-pregnene-3,20-dione	20-C=O → 20β-OH	K-470
		$11\beta,17\alpha,21$-trihydroxy-4-pregnene-3,20-dione	20-C=O → 20β-OH	K-470
lbidus * (Actinomyces)	CZAS	4-pregnene-3,20-dione	16α-OH	V-1060
lbosporeus	ATCC-3003	$17\alpha,21$-dihydroxy-4-pregnene-3,20-dione	20-C=O → 20β-OH	K-470
		$11\beta,17\alpha,21$-trihydroxy-4-pregnene-3,20-dione	20-C=O → 20β-OH	K-470
lbus	ATCC-3004, 3351	$17\alpha,21$-dihydroxy-4-pregnene-3,20-dione	20-C=O → 20β-OH	K-470
		$11\beta,17\alpha,21$-trihydroxy-4-pregnene-3,20-dione	20-C=O → 20β-OH	K-470
	C	d,1-1,3,5(10)-estratriene-3,17β-diol	d,1-17β-OH → d-17-C=O + 1-17β-OH	W-1102
	CZAS	4-pregnene-3,20-dione	use of oscillo-polarographic detection of transformations of steroids	S-929
	NG	1,3,5(10)-estratriene-3,17β-diol	17β-OH → 17-C=O	W-1082
	NRRL	Sarsasapogenin	—	M-587
		Diosgenin	—	M-587
		4-dehydrotigogenone	—	M-587
(Rossi-Doria)	Shionogi	$17\alpha,21$-dihydroxy-4-pregnene-3,20-dione	20-C=O → 20β-OH	K-470
		$11\beta,17\alpha,21$-trihydroxy-4-pregnene-3,20-dione	20-C=O → 20β-OH	K-470
(Actinomyces)	SSSR (3006)	$17\alpha,21$-dihydroxy-4-pregnene-3,20-dione	20-C=O → 20β-OH	K-458
		$11\beta,17\alpha,21$-trihydroxy-4-pregnene-3,20-dione	20-C=O → 20β-OH	K-459
		$17\alpha,21$-dihydroxy-4-pregnene-3,11,20-trione	20-C=O → 20β-OH	K-459
		$11\beta,17\alpha,21$-trihydroxy-1,4-pregnadiene-3,20-dione	20-C=O → 20β-OH	K-459

TABLE III

Transformations by Genus: STREPTOMYCES

SPECIES	SOURCE	SUBSTRATE	REACTION	REF.
albus	SSSR	17α,21-dihydroxy-1,4-pregna-diene-3,11,20-trione	20-C=O → 20β-OH	K-459
annulatus * (Actinomyces)	CZAS	4-pregnene-3,20-dione	16α-OH	V-1060
antibioticus	ATCC-8663	17α,21-dihydroxy-4-pregnene-3,11,20-trione	Δ^1	C-125
	ATCC-11891	4-pregnene-3,20-dione	1ξ-OH	F-234
		21-hydroxy-4-pregnene-3,20-dione	1ξ-OH	F-234
		17α,21-dihydroxy-4-pregnene-3,20-dione	1ξ-OH	F-234
		11β,17α,21-trihydroxy-4-pregnene-3,20-dione	1ξ-OH	F-234
		9α-fluoro-11β,17α,21-trihydroxy-4-pregnene-3,20-dione	1ξ-OH	F-234
		11β,16α,17α,21-tetrahydroxy-4-pregnene-3,20-dione	1ξ-OH	F-234
		9α-fluoro-11β,16α,17α,21-tetra-hydroxy-4-pregnene-3,20-dione	1ξ-OH	F-234
		9α-fluoro-11β,17α,21-trihydroxy-6α-methyl-1,4-pregnadiene-3,20-dione	1ξ-OH	F-234
	NG	5-cholesten-3β-ol	—	S-793c
		24β-methyl-5,7,22-cholestatrien-3β-ol	—	S-793c
argenteolus (species ATCC-11009 Ref. F-265, H-380, P-716,P-719 -ident-ified as argenteolus in Ref. F-267)	ATCC-11009 SQ (MD-248)	4-androstene-3,17-dione	16α-OH	F-265; F-267
*		3β-hydroxy-5-pregnen-20-one	$\Delta^5 \to \Delta^4$; 3β-OH →3-C=O	F-267; P-710; P-712; P-716
			$\Delta^5 \to \Delta^4$; 3β-OH →3-C=O; 16α-OH	F-265; F-267; P-712; P-716

TABLE III

ansformations by Genus: STREPTOMYCES

SPECIES	SOURCE	SUBSTRATE	REACTION	REF.
rgenteolus	ATCC-11009 (SQ-MD-248)	4-pregnene-3,20-dione (effect of antibiotics - Ref. P-719 - adaptive enzyme inhibitors - Ref. P-711)	16α-OH	F-265; F-267; P-711; P-716; P-718; P-719
			2β,16α-diOH	F-267; P-716; P-718
			$\Delta^4 \to 5\beta$-H; 16α-OH	F-267; P-716; P-718
		21-hydroxy-4-pregnene-3,20-dione	16α-OH	F-288
		21-hydroxy-4-pregnene-3,20-dione acetate	16α-OH; 21-OAc $\to$21-OH	F-265; F-267; P-716
			16α-OH; 21-OAc $\to$21-OH; $\Delta^4 \to$ 5β-H	F-267
		17α,21-dihydroxy-4-pregnene-3,20-dione 21-acetate	2β-OH; 21-OAc $\to$21-OH	F-265; F-267; P-716
		12α-fluoro-11β,17α,21-trihydroxy-4-pregnene-3,20-dione	16α-OH	H-380
		9α-fluoro-11β,17α,21-trihydroxy-2ξ-methyl-4-pregnene-3,20-dione	16α-OH	H-380
		12α-fluoro-11β,17α,21-trihydroxy-1,4-pregnadiene-3,20-dione	16α-OH	H-380
		9α-fluoro-11β,17α,21-trihydroxy-2-methyl-1,4-pregnadiene-3,20-dione	16α-OH	H-380
ureofaciens	ATCC-10762	4-pregnene-3,20-dione	1ξ-OH	F-234
		17α,21-dihydroxy-4-pregnene-3,20-dione	1ξ-OH	F-234
		11β,17α,21-trihydroxy-4-pregnene-3,20-dione	1ξ-OH	F-234
		9α-fluoro-11β,17α,21-trihydroxy-4-pregnene-3,20-dione	1ξ-OH	F-234
		9α-fluoro-11β,16α,17α,21-tetrahydroxy-4-pregnene-3,20-dione	1ξ-OH	F-234
		9α-fluoro-11β,16α,17α,21-tetrahydroxy-1,4-pregnadiene-3,20-dione	1ξ-OH	F-234

TABLE III

Transformations by Genus: STREPTOMYCES

SPECIES	SOURCE	SUBSTRATE	REACTION	REF.
aureofaciens	ATCC-10762	$3\beta,14\beta$-dihydroxy-5β-20(22)-cardenolide	7β-OH	T-1013
	NRRL-2209	3β-hydroxy-5-pregnen-20-one	$\Delta^5 \rightarrow \Delta^4$; 3β-OH $\rightarrow$3-C=O	P-712
		4-pregnene-3,20-dione	6β-OH	F-288; P-713
			9α-OH	F-288; P-713
			$6\beta,9\alpha$-diOH	P-714
		$17\alpha,21$-dihydroxy-4-pregnene-3,20-dione	9α-OH	P-715
	SQ	3β-hydroxy-5-pregnen-20-one	$\Delta^5 \rightarrow \Delta^4$; 3β-OH $\rightarrow$3-C=O	P-710
aureus	ATCC-3309	4-pregnene-3,20-dione	1ξ-OH	F-234
			16α-OH	P-745
		21-hydroxy-4-pregnene-3,20-dione	16α-OH	P-745
		$17\alpha,21$-dihydroxy-4-pregnene-3,20-dione	16α-OH	P-745
			$\Delta^4 \rightarrow 5\alpha$-H; 3-C=O$\rightarrow 3\beta$-OH	K-471
		$11\beta,17\alpha,21$-trihydroxy-4-pregnene-3,20-dione	1ξ-OH; 16α-OH	F-234; P-745
		9α-fluoro-$11\beta,17\alpha,21$-trihydroxy-4-pregnene-3,20-dione	16α-OH	P-745
		$11\beta,17\alpha,21$-trihydroxy-1,4-pregnadiene-3,20-dione	16α-OH	P-745
*	CZAS	4-pregnene-3,20-dione	16α-OH	V-1060
	WC(3569, 3676)	4-pregnene-3,20-dione	15α-OH	F-285; F-287
bikiniensis	NG	1,3,5(10)-estratriene-3,17α-diol	16α-OH	S-935
		1,3,5(10)-estratriene-3,17β-diol	16α-OH	S-935
		3-hydroxy-1,3,5(10)-estratrien-17-one	16α-OH	S-935
	SSSR (11062)	$17\alpha,21$-dihydroxy-4-pregnene-3,20-dione	20-C=O $\rightarrow$ 20β-OH	K-458
bobilae	(E-55-LL) Shionogi	$17\alpha,21$-dihydroxy-4-pregnene-3,20-dione	20-C=O $\rightarrow$ 20β-OH	K-470

TABLE III

ransformations by Genus: STREPTOMYCES

SPECIES	SOURCE	SUBSTRATE	REACTION	REF.
bobilae	(E-55-LL) Shionogi	$11\beta,17\alpha,21$-trihydroxy-4-pregnene-3,20-dione	$20\text{-C=O} \rightarrow 20\beta\text{-OH}$	K-470
californicus	Shionogi (5119)	$17\alpha,21$-dihydroxy-4-pregnene-3,20-dione	$20\text{-C=O} \rightarrow 20\beta\text{-OH}$	K-470
		$11\beta,17\alpha,21$-trihydroxy-4-pregnene-3,20-dione	$20\text{-C=O} \rightarrow 20\beta\text{-OH}$	K-470
		3α-hydroxy-5β-cholanic acid (sole carbon source)	utilization	S-785
		$3\alpha,7\alpha,12\alpha$-trihydroxy-5β-cholanic acid (sole carbon source)	utilization	H-357; S-784; S-785
		$3\alpha,7\alpha,12\alpha$-trihydroxy-5β-cholanic acid conjugated with glycine-glycocholic acid (sole carbon source)	utilization	S-785
		$3\alpha,7\alpha,12\alpha$-trihydroxy-5β-cholanic acid conjugated with taurine-taurocholic acid (sole carbon source)	utilization	S-785
		3,7,12-triketo-5β-cholanic acid (sole carbon source)	utilization	S-785
	WC (3312)	3-hydroxy-1,3,5(10)-estratrien-17-one	16α-OH	L-491
		4-androstene-3,17-dione	16α-OH	L-491
*		4-pregnene-3,20-dione	16α-OH	L-491
		21-hydroxy-4-pregnene-3,20-dione acetate	16α-OH; 21-OAc $\rightarrow$21-OH	L-491
		$17\alpha,21$-dihydroxy-4-pregnene-3,20-dione 21-acetate	16α-OH; 21-OAc $\rightarrow$21-OH	L-491
		9α-fluoro-$11\beta,17\alpha,21$-trihydroxy-4-pregnene-3,20-dione	16α-OH	L-491
		$11\beta,17\alpha,21$-trihydroxy-1,4-pregnadiene-3,20-dione	16α-OH	L-491
		9α-fluoro-$11\beta,17\alpha,21$-trihydroxy-1,4-pregnadiene-3,20-dione	16α-OH	L-491
celluloflavus	AMCY	4-pregnene-3,20-dione	1ξ-OH	F-234
		$17\alpha,21$-dihydroxy-4-pregnene-3,20-dione	1ξ-OH	F-234
		$11\beta,17\alpha,21$-trihydroxy-4-pregnene-3,20-dione	1ξ-OH	F-234

TABLE III

Transformations by Genus: STREPTOMYCES

SPECIES	SOURCE	SUBSTRATE	REACTION	REF.
celluloflavus	AMCY	$11\beta,16\alpha,17\alpha,21$-tetrahydroxy-4-pregnene-3,20-dione	1ξ-OH	F-234
		9α-fluoro-$11\beta,16\alpha,17\alpha,21$-tetrahydroxy-4-pregnene-3,20-dione	1ξ-OH	F-234
		$11\beta,17\alpha,21$-trihydroxy-6α-methyl-1,4-pregnadiene-3,20-dione	1ξ-OH	F-234
chartreusis	Shionogi	$17\alpha,21$-dihydroxy-4-pregnene-3,20-dione	20-C=O → 20β-OH	K-470
		$11\beta,17\alpha,21$-trihydroxy-4-pregnene-3,20-dione	20-C=O → 20β-OH	K-470
chrysomallus *	CZAS	4-pregnene-3,20-dione	16α-OH	V-1060
coelicolor	C	d,1-$17\alpha,21$-dihydroxy-4-pregnene-3,20-dione	d,1-20-C=O → d-20β-OH + 1	W-1094
	CZAS	$17\alpha,21$-dihydroxy-4-pregnene-3,20-dione	20-C=O → 20β-OH	K-470
		$11\beta,17\alpha,21$-trihydroxy-4-pregnene-3,20-dione	20-C=O → 20β-OH	K-470
*	WC (3593)	4-pregnene-3,20-dione	16α-OH	L-491
		21-hydroxy-4-pregnene-3,20-dione acetate	16α-OH; 21-OAc →21-OH	L-491
diastaticus (Krainsky)	ATCC-3315	$17\alpha,21$-dihydroxy-4-pregnene-3,20-dione	20-C=O→ 20β-OH	K-470
		$11\beta,17\alpha,21$-trihydroxy-4-pregnene-3,20-dione	20-C=O → 20β-OH	K-470
	AY	1,3,5(10)-estratriene-3,17β-diol (using spores)	17β-OH → 17-C=O	S-835; V-1048
*	CZAS	4-pregnene-3,20-dione	16α-OH	V-1060
diastatochromogenes	CZAS	4-pregnene-3,20-dione	6β-OH; 6β,11α-diOH	S-929
endus	U (9-20)	21-hydroxy-4-pregnene-3,20-dione	11-oxygenation	H-328
erythreus	PF	$11\beta,17\alpha$-dihydroxy-21-methyl-1,4-pregnadiene-3,20,21-trione	20-C=O → 20β-OH	A-6
exfoliatus	CZAS	4-pregnene-3,20-dione	6β-OH; 6β,11α-diOH	S-929

TABLE III

Transformations by Genus: STREPTOMYCES

SPECIES	SOURCE	SUBSTRATE	REACTION	REF.
fimicarius	CBS	4-pregnene-3,20-dione	16α-OH	P-745
		21-hydroxy-4-pregnene-3,20-dione	16α-OH	P-745
		17α,21-dihydroxy-4-pregnene-3,20-dione	16α-OH	P-745
		11β,17α,21-trihydroxy-4-pregnene-3,20-dione	16α-OH	P-745
		9α-fluoro-11β,17α,21-trihydroxy-4-pregnene-3,20-dione	16α-OH	P-745
*	CZAS	4-pregnene-3,20-dione	16α-OH	V-1060
flaveolus *	CZAS	4-pregnene-3,20-dione	16α-OH	V-1060
	Shionogi (D-551)	17α,21-dihydroxy-4-pregnene-3,20-dione	Δ^1	K-470
			Δ^1; 20-C=O → 20β-OH	K-470
		11β,17α,21-trihydroxy-4-pregnene-3,20-dione	Δ^1	K-470
			Δ^1; 20-C=O → 20β-OH	K-470
flavogriseus	Shionogi (H-4449)	17α,21-dihydroxy-4-pregnene-3,20-dione	20-C=O → 20β-OH	K-470
		11β,17α,21-trihydroxy-4-pregnene-3,20-dione	20-C=O → 20β-OH	K-470
	Tokyo Univ. (4449)	3α,7α,12α-trihydroxy-5β-cholanic acid	3α-OH→3-C=O; 12α-OH → 12-C=O; Δ^4	H-357
			3α-OH→3-C=O; 12α-OH→12-C=O; 17β-CH(CH$_3$)-CH$_2$CH$_2$COOH →17β-CH(CH$_3$)-COOH	S-784; S-785
fradiae	C	d,l-3β-hydroxy-5-pregnen-20-one	d,l-3β-OH →d-3-C=O +l-3β-OH; d,l-Δ^5→ d-Δ^4+ l-Δ^5	W-1102
	CZAS (6,9; 6,10; 6,11; 6,15; 6,16; 6,17)	4-pregnene-3,20-dione	6β-OH; 6β,11α-diOH	S-929; V-1061
		11α-hydroxy-4-pregnene-3,20-dione	6β-OH	V-1061
		11β-hydroxy-4-pregnene-3,20-dione	6β-OH	V-1061

TABLE III

Transformations by Genus: STREPTOMYCES

SPECIES	SOURCE	SUBSTRATE	REACTION	REF.
fradiae	CZAS (6,9; 6,10; 6,11; 6,15; 6,16; 6,17)	17α-hydroxy-4-pregnene-3,20-dione	6β-OH; $6\beta,11\alpha$-diOH	V-1061
		21-hydroxy-4-pregnene-3,20-dione	6β-OH; $6\beta,11\alpha$-diOH	V-1061
		$17\alpha,21$-dihydroxy-4-pregnene-3,20-dione	6β-OH; $6\beta,11\alpha$-diOH	V-1061
		$11\beta,17\alpha,21$-trihydroxy-4-pregnene-3,20-dione	6β-OH	V-1061
		4-pregnene-3,11,20-trione	6β-OH	V-1061
		$17\alpha,21$-dihydroxy-4-pregnene-3,11,20-trione	6β-OH	V-1061
	SQ	3β-hydroxy-5-pregnen-20-one	$\Delta^5 \to \Delta^4$; 3β-OH $\to$ 3-C=O	P-710
	WC (3535)	3β-hydroxy-5-pregnen-20-one	$\Delta^5 \to \Delta^4$; 3β-OH $\to$ 3-C=O	P-712
		21-hydroxy-4-pregnene-3,20-dione	6β-OH	H-328
			11β-OH	C-134
		$17\alpha,21$-dihydroxy-4-pregnene-3,20-dione	11β-OH	C-112; C-134; C-135; H-328
			11β-OH; 11-C=O (via 11β-OH)	C-134; C-135; H-328
fulvissimus	NRRL B-1453	9α-fluoro-$11\beta,17\alpha,21$-trihydroxy-4-pregnene-3,20-dione	1ξ-OH	F-234
gelaticus (Actinomyces)	Okayama Univ. Med. School (1164)	3α-hydroxy-5β-cholanic acid	17β-CH(CH$_3$)-CH$_2$CH$_2$COOH$\to$17β-COOH; 3β-OH$\to$3-C=O; $\Delta^5 \to \Delta^4$; X-OH	H-364
		$3\alpha,7\alpha,12\alpha$-trihydroxy-5β-cholanic acid	3α-OH$\to$3-C=O; 12α-OH$\to$12-C=O; Δ^4; 17β-CH(CH$_3$)-CH$_2$-CH$_2$-COOH$\to$17β-CH(CH$_3$)-COOH	H-354; H-355; H-356; H-360; S-785
			12α-OH$\to$12-C=O; 17β-CH(CH$_3$)-CH$_2$-CH$_2$-COOH$\to$17β-CH(CH$_3$)-COOH	H-359
			3α-OH$\to$3-C=O; 7α-OH$\to\Delta^6$; 12α-OH$\to$12-C=O; Δ^4	H-359; H-361

TABLE III

Transformations by Genus: STREPTOMYCES

SPECIES	SOURCE	SUBSTRATE	REACTION	REF.
gelaticus (Actinomyces)	Okayama Univ. Med. School(1164)	$3\alpha,7\alpha,12\alpha$-trihydroxy-5β-cholanic acid	7α-OH$\to\Delta^6$; 3α-OH$\to$3-C=O; Δ^4; 17β-CH(CH$_3$)-(CH$_2$)$_2$-COOH$\to$ 17β-CH(CH$_3$)-COOH	H-359
			3α-OH$\to$3-C=O	H-366
			12α-OH $\to$ 12-C=O	H-366
			3α-OH$\to$3-C=O; 12α-OH $\to$12-C=O	H-366
			3α-OH$\to$3-C=O; 12ι-OH$\to$12-C=O; 7α-OH $\to \Delta^6$; Δ^4	H-366
		$3\alpha,7\alpha,12\alpha$-trihydroxy-5β-cholanic acid (sole carbon source)	utilization	S-784
		$3,7,12$-triketo-5β-cholanic acid	7-C=O$\to$7α-OH; Δ^4	H-363
			7-C=O$\to$7α-OH; Δ^4; 17β-CH(CH$_3$)-(CH$_2$)$_2$-COOH$\to$ 17β-CH(CH$_3$)-COOH	H-363
	Shionogi (1164)	$17\alpha,21$-dihydroxy-4-pregnene-3,20-dione	20-C=O $\to$ 20β-OH	K-470
		$11\beta,17\alpha,21$-trihydroxy-4-pregnene-3,20-dione	20-C=O $\to$ 20β-OH	K-470
globisporus	IPB	5-androstene-3β,17α-diol	$\Delta^5\to\Delta^4$; 3β-OH$\to$ 3-C=O	H-337
		5-androstene-3β,17β-diol	$\Delta^5\to\Delta^4$; 3β-OH$\to$ 3-C=O	H-337
			$\Delta^5\to\Delta^4$; 3β-OH$\to$ 3-C=O; 17β-OH $\to$17-C=O	H-337
		3β-hydroxy-5-androsten-17-one (influence of steroid on microbial respiration)	$\Delta^5\to\Delta^4$; 3β-OH $\to$3-C=O	C-106; C-107
		3β-hydroxy-5-androsten-17-one acetate	$\Delta^5\to\Delta^4$; 3β-OAc $\to$3-C=O	H-335
			$\Delta^5\to\Delta^4$; 3β-OAc $\to$3-C=O; 17-C=O $\to$17β-OH	H-335

TABLE III

Transformations by Genus: STREPTOMYCES

SPECIES	SOURCE	SUBSTRATE	REACTION	REF.
globosus * (Actinomyces)	CZAA	4-pregnene-3,20-dione	16α-OH	V-1060
griseocarneus	ATCC-12628	$11\beta,17\alpha,21$-trihydroxy-4-preg-nene-3,20-dione	1ξ-OH	F-234
		9α-fluoro-$11\beta,17\alpha,21$-trihydroxy-4-pregnene-3,20-dione	1ξ-OH	F-234
		$11\beta,16\alpha,17\alpha,21$-tetrahydroxy-4-pregnene-3,20-dione	1ξ-OH	F-234
		9α-fluoro-$11\beta,16\alpha,17\alpha,21$-tetra-hydroxy-4-pregnene-3,20-dione	1ξ-OH	F-234
	CZAS	4-pregnene-3,20-dione	6β-OH	S-929
			$6\beta,11\alpha$-diOH	S-929
griseolus	AMCY (LED-AD-1431)	4-pregnene-3,20-dione	16α-OH	P-745
		21-hydroxy-4-pregnene-3,20-dione	16α-OH	P-745
		$17\alpha,21$-dihydroxy-4-pregnene-3,20-dione	16α-OH	P-745
		9α-fluoro-$11\beta,17\alpha,21$-trihydroxy-4-pregnene-3,20-dione	16α-OH	P-745
		$11\beta,17\alpha,21$-trihydroxy-1,4-pregnadiene-3,20-dione	16α-OH	P-745

griseus
  (var. casteneous)
  (var. cinnibarinus)
  (var. violaceus)
  (WC)
	AMCY (LED)	4-pregnene-3,20-dione	16α-OH	P-745

		21-hydroxy-4-pregnene-3,20-dione	16α-OH	P-745
		$17\alpha,21$-dihydroxy-4-pregnene-3,20-dione	16α-OH	P-745
		$11\beta,17\alpha,21$-trihydroxy-4-preg-nene-3,20-dione	16α-OH	P-745
		9α-fluoro-$11\beta,17\alpha,21$-trihydroxy-4-pregnene-3,20-dione	16α-OH	P-745
		$11\beta,17\alpha,21$-trihydroxy-1,4-pregnadiene-3,20-dione	16α-OH	P-745
	ATCC-13968	$11\beta,16\alpha,17\alpha,21$-tetrahydroxy-4-pregnene-3,20-dione 16,17-acetonide	2β-OH	F-235; F-236
		9α-fluoro-$11\beta,16\alpha,17\alpha,21$-tetra-hydroxy-4-pregnene-3,20-dione 16, 17- acetonide	2β-OH	F-235; F-236

TABLE III

Transformations by Genus: STREPTOMYCES

SPECIES	SOURCE	SUBSTRATE	REACTION	REF.
griseus	ATCC-13968	$6\alpha,9\alpha$-difluoro-$11\beta,16\alpha,17\alpha,21$-tetrahydroxy-4-pregnene-3,20-dione 16,17-acetonide	2β-OH	F-235; F-236
		9α-fluoro-$11\beta,16\alpha,17\alpha,21$-tetra-hydroxy-1,4-pregnadiene-3,20-dione 16,17-acetonide	2-OH	F-235; F-236
	C	5α-androstane-3,17-dione	3-C=O $\rightarrow 3\beta$-OH	V-1059; W-1097
		4-androstene-3,17-dione	$\Delta^4 \rightarrow 5\alpha$-H	V-1059; W-1097
			$\Delta^4 \rightarrow 5\alpha$-H; 3-C=O$\rightarrow 3\beta$-OH	V-1059; W-1097
		5α-pregnane-3,20-dione	3-C=O$\rightarrow 3\beta$-OH	V-1059; W-1097
		21-hydroxy-5α-pregnane-3,20-dione	3-C=O $\rightarrow 3\beta$-OH	V-1059; W-1097
		$17\alpha,21$-dihydroxy-5α-pregnane-3,20-dione	3-C=O$\rightarrow 3\beta$-OH	V-1059; W-1097
		4-pregnene-3,20-dione	$\Delta^4 \rightarrow 5\alpha$-H	V-1059; W-1097
			$\Delta^4 \rightarrow 5\alpha$-H; 3-C=O$\rightarrow 3\beta$-OH	V-1059; W-1097
		16α-hydroxy-4-pregnene-3,20-dione	$\Delta^4 \rightarrow 5\alpha$-H; 3-C=O$\rightarrow 3\beta$-OH	V-1059; W-1097
		21-hydroxy-4-pregnene-3,20-dione	$\Delta^4 \rightarrow 5\alpha$-H	V-1051; V-1059; W-1097
			$\Delta^4 \rightarrow 5\alpha$-H; 3-C=O$\rightarrow 3\beta$-OH	V-1059; W-1097
		$11\beta,21$-dihydroxy-4-pregnene-3,20-dione	$\Delta^4 \rightarrow 5\alpha$-H; 3-C=O$\rightarrow 3\beta$-OH	V-1059; W-1097
		$17\alpha,21$-dihydroxy-4-pregnene-3,20-dione	$\Delta^4 \rightarrow 5\alpha$-H	V-1059; W-1097
			$\Delta^4 \rightarrow 5\alpha$-H; 3-C=O $\rightarrow 3\beta$-OH	V-1059; W-1097
		$11\beta,17\alpha,21$-trihydroxy-4-pregnene-3,20-dione	3-C=O$\rightarrow 3\beta$-OH; $\Delta^4 \rightarrow 5\alpha$-H	W-1097
		$17\alpha,21$-dihydroxy-4-pregnene-3,11,20-trione	3-C=O$\rightarrow 3\beta$-OH; $\Delta^4 \rightarrow 5\alpha$-H	W-1097

TABLE III

Transformations by Genus: STREPTOMYCES

SPECIES	SOURCE	SUBSTRATE	REACTION	REF.
griseus *	CZAS	4-pregnene-3,20-dione	16α-OH	V-1060
	NG	1,3,5(10)-estratriene-3,17α-diol	16α-OH	S-935
		1,3,5(10)-estratriene-3,17β-diol	16α-OH	S-935
		3-hydroxy-1,3,5(10)-estratrien-17-one	16α-OH	S-935
		5-cholesten-3β-ol (sole carbon source)	—	S-793c
		24β-methyl-5,7,22-cholestatrien-3β-ol (sole carbon source)	—	S-793c
	SCH (FC-103)	11β,17α,21-trihydroxy-4-pregnene-3,20-dione	20-C=O → 20β-OH	C-110
		17α,21-dihydroxy-4-pregnene-3,11,20-trione	20-C=O → 20β-OH	C-110
		11β,17α,21-trihydroxy-1,4-pregnadiene-3,20-dione	20-C=O → 20β-OH	C-110
		17α,21-dihydroxy-1,4-pregnadiene-3,11,20-trione	20-C=O → 20β-OH	C-110
	Shionogi	17α,21-dihydroxy-4-pregnene-3,20-dione	20-C=O → 20β-OH	K-470
		11β;17α,21-trihydroxy-4-pregnene-3,20-dione	20-C=O → 20β-OH	K-470
	SQ	3β-hydroxy-5-pregnen-20-one	$\Delta^5 \to \Delta^4$; 3β-OH →3-C=O	P-710
	WC (No. 4; 3478)	3β-hydroxy-5-pregnen-20-one	$\Delta^5 \to \Delta^4$; 3β-OH →3-C=O	P-712
halstedii	ATCC-13499	1,3,5(10)-estratriene-3,17β-diol	16α-OH	K-448
			16α-OH; 17β-OH →17-C=O	K-448
		3-hydroxy-1,3,5(10)-estratrien-17-one	16α-OH	K-448
			16α-OH; 17-C=O→17β-OH	K-448
		17α,21-dihydroxy-4-pregnene-3,20-dione	16α-OH	K-447
		9α-fluoro-11β,17α,21-trihydroxy-4-pregnene-3,20-dione 21-acetate	16α-OH; 21-OAc →21-OH	K-447
		9α-fluoro-11β,17α,21-trihydroxy-4-pregnene-3,20-dione 21-propionate	16α-OH; 21-OPr→21-OH	K-447

TABLE III

Transformations by Genus: STREPTOMYCES

SPECIES	SOURCE	SUBSTRATE	REACTION	REF.
halstedii	CBS	4-pregnene-3,20-dione	1ξ-OH	F-234
		21-hydroxy-4-pregnene-3,20-dione	1ξ-OH	F-234
		17α,21-dihydroxy-4-pregnene-3,20-dione	1ξ-OH	F-234
		11β,17α,21-trihydroxy-4-pregnene-3,20-dione	1ξ-OH	F-234
		9α-fluoro-11β,17α,21-trihydroxy-4-pregnene-3,20-dione	1ξ-OH	F-234
		9α-fluoro-11β,16α,17α,21-tetrahydroxy-4-pregnene-3,20-dione	1ξ-OH	F-234
	IAM (3199)	3α,7α,12α-trihydroxy-5β-cholanic acid (sole carbon source)	utilization	H-357; S-784
		several bile acids	utilization	S-785
	NRRL B-2138	1,3,5(10)-estratriene-3,17β-diol	16α-OH	K-448
			16α-OH; 17β-OH →17-C=O	K-448
		3-hydroxy-1,3,5(10)-estratrien-17-one	16α-OH	K-448
			16α-OH; 17-C=O →17β-OH	K-448
		9α-fluoro-11β,17α,21-trihydroxy-4-pregnene-3,20-dione 21-acetate	16α-OH; 21-OAc →21-OH	K-447
hydrogenans	Hoechst (FAM) (FHP-678)	4-pregnene-3,20-dione	—	L-522
		21-hydroxy-4-pregnene-3,20-dione	—	L-522
		17α,21-dihydroxy-4-pregnene-3,20-dione (induction of 20β-hydroxy-dehydrogenase, Ref. N-656 - isolation and specificity, Ref. N-657 - purification and crystallization, Ref. H-408; H-409; H-410; S-802; S-803)	20-C=O → 20β-OH	H-408; L-522; N-656
		11α,17α,21-trihydroxy-4-pregnene-3,20-dione	20-C=O → 20β-OH	H-408; L-522

TABLE III

Transformations by Genus: STREPTOMYCES

SPECIES	SOURCE	SUBSTRATE	REACTION	REF.
hydrogenans	Hoechst (FAM) (FHP-678)	$11\beta,17\alpha,21$-trihydroxy-4-pregnene-3,20-dione	20-C=O → 20β-OH	H-408; L-522; S-801
		$17\alpha,21$-dihydroxy-4-pregnene-3,11,20-trione	20-C=O → 20β-OH	L-522
		$11\beta,17\alpha,21$-trihydroxy-1,4-pregnadiene-3,20-dione	20-C=O → 20β-OH	H-408; L-522
		$17\alpha,21$-dihydroxy-1,4-pregnadiene-3,11,20-trione	20-C=O → 20β-OH	L-522
hygroscopicus	AMCY	$11\beta,17\alpha,21$-trihydroxy-4-pregnene-3,20-dione	1ξ-OH	F-234
		9α-fluoro-$11\beta,17\alpha,21$-trihydroxy-4-pregnene-3,20-dione	1ξ-OH	F-234
		$11\beta,16\alpha,17\alpha,21$-tetrahydroxy-4-pregnene-3,20-dione	1ξ-OH	F-234
		9α-fluoro-$11\beta,16\alpha,17\alpha,21$-tetrahydroxy-4-pregnene-3,20-dione	1ξ-OH	F-234
		$11\beta,17\alpha,21$-trihydroxy-6α-methyl-1,4-pregnadiene-3,20-dione	1ξ-OH	F-234
lavendulae	AMCY (LED)	$11\beta,17\alpha,21$-trihydroxy-4-pregnene-3,20-dione	1ξ-OH	F-234
		9α-fluoro-$11\beta,17\alpha,21$-trihydroxy-4-pregnene-3,20-dione	1ξ-OH	F-234
	ATCC-8664	19-nor-4-pregnene-3,20-dione	Δ^1; enol.	G-317
			17β-Ac → 17-C=O	G-317
			Δ^1; enol. 17β-Ac→17β-OH	G-317
			17β-Ac→17a-oxa-17-C=O; Δ^1; enol.	G-317
		4-pregnene-3,20-dione (adaptive enzyme; effect of antibiotics)	Δ^1; 17β-Ac → 17-C=O	P-719
	SQ (SC-1620)	4-pregnene-3,20-dione	Δ^1	T-1005
		5-cholesten-3β-ol	$\Delta^5 \to \Delta^4$; 3β-OH →3-C=O	T-1005
	AY	$17\alpha,21$-dihydroxy-4-pregnene-3,20-dione	Δ^1	S-835; V-1048
			20-C=O → 20β-OH	S-835

TABLE III

Transformations by Genus: STREPTOMYCES

SPECIES	SOURCE	SUBSTRATE	REACTION	REF.
lavendulae	C	d,1-17α,21-dihydroxy-4-preg- nene-3,20-dione	d,1-20-C=O → d-20β-OH + l	W-1094
	CZAS	4-pregnene-3,20-dione	16α-OH	V-1060
	NG	5-cholesten-3β-ol	—	S-793c
		24β-methyl-5,7,22-cholestatrien- 3β-ol	—	S-793c
	Shionogi (O-20-60)	17α,21-dihydroxy-4-pregnene- 3,20-dione	Δ^1; 20-C=O → 20β-OH	K-470
		11β,17α,21-trihydroxy-4-preg- nene-3,20-dione	Δ^1; 20-C=O → 20β-OH	K-470
	(Waksman strain)	17α,21-dihydroxy-4-pregnene- 3,20-dione	20-C=O → 20β-OH	K-470
		11β,17α,21-trihydroxy-4-preg- nene-3,20-dione	20-C=O → 20β-OH	K-470
	WC (3440-14)	17β-hydroxy-1,4-androstadien- 3-one	17β-OH → 17-C=O	P-733
		4-pregnene-3,20-dione	17β-Ac→17-C =O; Δ^1	F-251
			17β-Ac→17β-OH; Δ^1	F-251
			Δ^1; 17β-Ac → 17-C=O	F-271; F-284; P-733
			Δ^1; 17β-Ac → 17β-OH	F-271; F-284; P-733
			20-C=O → 20β-OH	F-271; F-284
		4-pregnene-3,20-dione 20- cycloethyleneketal	Δ^1	F-251
		16α-hydroxy-4-pregnene-3,20- dione	17β-Ac→17β-OH	F-271; F-288
			Δ^1; 20-C=O → 20β-OH	F-271; F-273; F-288
			20-C=O → 20β-OH	F-271; F-273; F-288
		11β,17α,21-trihydroxy-4-preg- nene-3,20-dione	Δ^1	F-272

TABLE III

Transformations by Genus: STREPTOMYCES

SPECIES	SOURCE	SUBSTRATE	REACTION	REF.
lipmanii	ATCC-3331	4-pregnene-3,20-dione	16α-OH	P-745
		21-hydroxy-4-pregnene-3,20-dione	16α-OH	P-745
		17α,21-dihydroxy-4-pregnene-3,20-dione	16α-OH	P-745
		11β,17α,21-trihydroxy-4-pregnene-3,20-dione	16α-OH	P-745
		9α-fluoro-11β,17α,21-trihydroxy-4-pregnene-3,20-dione	16α-OH	P-745
*	CZAS	4-pregnene-3,20-dione	16α-OH	V-1060
mediocidicus	ATCC-13278	1,3,5(10)-estratriene-3,17β-diol	16α-OH	K-448; S-788
			16α-OH; 17β-OH $\rightarrow$17-C=O	K-448
		3-hydroxy-1,3,5(10)-estratrien-17-one	16α-OH	K-448
			16α-OH; 17-C=O $\rightarrow$17β-OH	K-448
*		4-pregnene-3,20-dione	16α-OH	S-788
*		9α-fluoro-11β,17α,21-trihydroxy-4-pregnene-3,20-dione	16α-OH	S-788
*		9α-fluoro-17α,21-dihydroxy-4-pregnene-3,11,20-trione	16α-OH	S-788
*	ATCC-13279	1,3,5(10)-estratriene-3,17β-diol	16α-OH	S-788
*		17β-hydroxy-4-androsten-3-one	16α-OH	S-788
microflavus	ATCC-3332	11β,17α,21-trihydroxy-4-pregnene-3,20-dione	16α-OH	P-745
		9α-fluoro-11β,17α,21-trihydroxy-4-pregnene-3,20-dione	16α-OH	P-745
*	CZAS	4-pregnene-3,20-dione	16α-OH	V-1060
nitrosporeus	AMCY	21-hydroxy-4-pregnene-3,20-dione	1ξ-OH	F-234
		17α,21-dihydroxy-4-pregnene-3,20-dione	1ξ-OH	F-234
		9α-fluoro-11β,17α,21-trihydroxy-4-pregnene-3,20-dione	1ξ-OH	F-234
		11β,17α,21-trihydroxy-6α-methyl-1,4-pregnadiene-3,20-dione	1ξ-OH	F-234

TABLE III

Transformations by Genus: STREPTOMYCES

SPECIES	SOURCE	SUBSTRATE	REACTION	REF.
nitrosporeus	IAM (O-20)	3α-hydroxy-5β-cholanic acid (sole carbon source)	utilization	S-785
		$3\alpha,7\alpha,12\alpha$-trihydroxy-5β-cholanic acid (sole carbon source)	utilization	H-357; S-784
		$3\alpha,7\alpha,12\alpha$-trihydroxy-5β-cholanic acid conjugated with glycine-glycocholic acid (sole carbon source)	utilization	S-785
		$3\alpha,7\alpha,12\alpha$-trihydroxy-5β-cholanic acid conjugated with taurine-taurocholic acid (sole carbon source)	utilization	S-785
		3,7,12-triketo-5β-cholanic acid (sole carbon source)	utilization	S-785
olivaceus *	CZAS	4-pregnene-3,20-dione	16α-OH	S-929; V-1060
	WC (3688)	17β-hydroxy-4-androsten-3-one	16α-OH	F-265
		4-androstene-3,17-dione	16α-OH	F-265; F-267
		4-pregnene-3,20-dione	16α-OH	F-265; F-267
		21-hydroxy-4-pregnene-3,20-dione	16α-OH	F-265; F-267
olivochromogenus	ATCC-3336	$11\beta,17\alpha,21$-trihydroxy-4-pregnene-3,20-dione	Δ^1	C-125
		$17\alpha,21$-dihydroxy-4-pregnene-3,11,20-trione	Δ^1	C-125
	ATCC-13025 MCC (MA-320)	9α-fluoro-$11\beta,17\alpha,21$-trihydroxy-4-pregnene-3,20-dione 21-acetate	1ξ-OH; 21-OAc $\rightarrow$21-OH	M-569; S-941
			20-C=O $\rightarrow$20β-OH; 21-OAc $\rightarrow$ 21-OH	M-569; S-941
			6β-OH; 21-OAc $\rightarrow$21-OH	M-569; S-941
			21-OAc$\rightarrow$21-OH	S-941
parvus *	CZAS	4-pregnene-3,20-dione	16α-OH	V-1060
	NRRL	Sarsasapogenin	—	M-587
		Diosgenin	—	M-587
		4-dehydrotigogenone	—	M-587
purpureochromogenus	ATCC-3133	4-pregnene-3,20-dione	16α-OH	P-745

TABLE III

Transformations by Genus: STREPTOMYCES

SPECIES	SOURCE	SUBSTRATE	REACTION	REF.
purpureochromogenus	ATCC-3133	21-hydroxy-4-pregnene-3,20-dione	16α-OH	P-745
		17α,21-dihydroxy-4-pregnene-3,20-dione	16α-OH	P-745
		11β,17α,21-trihydroxy-4-pregnene-3,20-dione	16α-OH	F-234; P-745
		9α-fluoro-11β,17α,21-trihydroxy-4-pregnene-3,20-dione	16α-OH	P-745
*	CZAS	4-pregnene-3,20-dione	16α-OH	V-1060
rimosus	AY	1,3,5(10)-estratriene-3,17β-diol (with spores)	17β-OH → 17-C=O	S-835; V-1048
	CZAS	4-pregnene-3,20-dione	6β-OH	S-929
			6β,11α-diOH	S-929
	LED (T-1686B)	9α-fluoro-11β,17α,21-trihydroxy-4-pregnene-3,20-dione	6β-OH	S-909
	NG	1,3,5(10)-estratriene-3,17α-diol	16α-OH	S-935
		1,3,5(10)-estratriene-3,17β-diol	16α-OH	S-935
		3-hydroxy-1,3,5(10)-estratrien-17-one	16α-OH	S-935
	NRRL-2234	3β-hydroxy-5-pregnen-20-one	$\Delta^5 \to \Delta^4$; 3β-OH →3-C=O	P-712
		4-pregnene-3,20-dione	Δ^1	T-1005
		5-cholesten-3β-ol	$\Delta^5 \to \Delta^4$; 3β-OH →3-C=O	T-1005
	SQ	3β-hydroxy-5-pregnen-20-one	$\Delta^5 \to \Delta^4$; 3β-OH →3-C=O	P-710
roseochromogenus	AMCY (LED)	9α-fluoro-11β,17α,21-trihydroxy-4-pregnene-3,20-dione	21-OH→21-AcNH	S-911
		21-(n-acetylamino)-9α-fluoro-11β,17α-dihydroxy-4-pregnene-3,20-dione	2β-OH (tentative)	S-911
		21-amino-9α-fluoro-11β,17α-dihydroxy-4-pregnene-3,20-dione hydrochloride	21-NH$_2$→ 21-AcNH	S-911
		9α-fluoro-11β,17α,21-trihydroxy-1,4-pregnadiene-3,20-dione	21-OH→21-AcNH	S-911
		21-(n-acetylamino)-9α-fluoro-11β,17α-dihydroxy-1,4-pregnadiene-3,20-dione	—	S-911

TABLE III

Transformations by Genus: STREPTOMYCES

SPECIES	SOURCE	SUBSTRATE	REACTION	REF.
roseochromogenus	AMCY (LED-409)	9α-fluoro-11β-hydroxy-4-androstene-3,17-dione	16α-OH	B-62
	ATCC-3347	4-estren-3-one	16α-OH	S-793a
			16β-OH	S-793a
			16-C=O (via either 16α or 16β-OH)	S-793a
		16α-hydroxy-4-estren-3-one	16α-OH→16β-OH (via 16-C=O)	S-793a
			16α-OH→16-C=O	S-793a
		16β-hydroxy-4-estren-3-one	16β-OH → 16-C=O	S-793a
		4-estren-3,16-dione	16-C=O → 16β-OH	S-793a
		3β-bromo-19-nor-5-pregnen-20-one	16α-OH	Z-1128
		3β-chloro-19-nor-5-pregnen-20-one	16α-OH	Z-1128
		3β-fluoro-19-nor-5-pregnen-20-one	16α-OH	Z-1128
		3β-hydroxy-19-nor-5-pregnen-20-one	16α-OH	Z-1128; Z-1129
		11β,21-dihydroxy-4-pregnene-3,20-dione	16α-OH	H-399
		17α,21-dihydroxy-4-pregnene-3,20-dione	16α-OH	H-399
		9α-fluoro-11β,21-dihydroxy-4-pregnene-3,20-dione	16α-OH	H-403
		11α,17α,21-trihydroxy-4-pregnene-3,20-dione	16α-OH	G-295; G-297
			16α-OH; 16α,17α-diOH-17β-(20-C=O-21-OH) →D-homo-16α,$17a\alpha$-diOH-$17a\beta$-CH$_2$OH-17-C=O	G-297
		11β,17α,21-trihydroxy-4-pregnene-3,20-dione	16α-OH	G-295; G-297; H-399

TABLE III

Transformations by Genus: STREPTOMYCES

SPECIES	SOURCE	SUBSTRATE	REACTION	REF.
roseochromogenus	ATCC-3347	$11\beta,17\alpha,21$-trihydroxy-4-pregnene-3,20-dione	16α-OH; 16α, 17α-diOH-17β- (20-C=O-21-OH) →D-<u>homo</u>-16α- $17a\alpha$-diOH-$17a\beta$- CH_2OH-17-C=O	G-297
		9α-chloro-$11\beta,17\alpha,21$-trihydroxy-4-pregnene-3,20-dione	2β-OH	S-913
		6α-cyano-9α-fluoro-$11\beta,17\alpha,21$-trihydroxy-4-pregnene-3,20-dione	16α-OH	B-74
		9α-fluoro-$11\beta,17\alpha,21$-trihydroxy-4-pregnene-3,20-dione	2β-OH	G-298; S-913
		(strain variation - Ref. G-298)	2β-OH	S-912
		(Ref. G-297, presence of ferric or ferrous ion leads to a non-biologic isomerization of this substrate to D-<u>homo</u> compound)	16α-OH	G-295; G-297; L-505; S-913
			16α-OH; 17α-OH- 17β-(20-C=O- 21-OH)→$17a\alpha$- OH-$17a\beta$-CH_2OH- 17-C=O	G-295; G-297; G-298; L-505; S-910; S-912; S-913
			$2\beta,16\alpha$-diOH	G-298; S-912; S-913
		9α-chloro-$2\beta,11\beta,17\alpha,21$-tetrahydroxy-4-pregnene-3,20-dione	16α-OH	S-913
		9α-chloro-$11\beta,16\alpha,17\alpha,21$-tetrahydroxy-4-pregnene-3,20-dione	2β-OH	S-913
		9α-fluoro-$2\beta,11\beta,17\alpha,21$-tetrahydroxy-4-pregnene-3,20-dione (see note Ref. G-297)	16α-OH	S-912; G-297
		9α-fluoro-$11\beta,16\alpha,17\alpha,21$-tetrahydroxy-4-pregnene-3,20-dione	2β-OH	S-913
		6α-cyano-$17\alpha,21$-dihydroxy-4-pregnene-3,11,20-trione	16α-OH	B-74
		$11\beta,17\alpha,21$-trihydroxy-1,4-pregnadiene-3,20-dione (see note Ref. G-297)	16α-OH	G-295; G-297
		6α-fluoro-$11\beta,17\alpha,21$-trihydroxy-1,4-pregnadiene-3,20-dione	16α-OH	H-399

TABLE III

ransformations by Genus: STREPTOMYCES

SPECIES	SOURCE	SUBSTRATE	REACTION	REF.
roseochromogenus	ATCC-3347	9α-fluoro-11β,17α,21-trihydroxy-1,4-pregnadiene-3,20-dione (Δ^1 of substrate blocks 2β-OH)	16α-OH	G-298
		6α-cyano-17α,21-dihydroxy-1,4-pregnadiene-3,11,20-trione	16α-OH	B-74
			16α-OH; 17α-OH -17β-(20-C=O-21-OH)$\rightarrow$$17a\alpha$-OH-$17a\beta$-CH$_2$OH -$17$-C=O	G-297
	AY	17α,21-dihydroxy-4-pregnene-3,20-dione (with conidia)	16α-OH	S-835; V-1048
	C	3β-hydroxy-19-nor-5α-pregnan-20-one	16α-OH	W-1093
		3β-hydroxy-5α-pregnan-20-one acetate	3β-OAc$\rightarrow$$3\beta$-OH; 16α-OH	W-1092
		11β,21-dihydroxy-4-pregnene-3,20-dione 18-oic acid ($18\rightarrow11$)-lactone	16α-OH	W-1091
*	CZAS	4-pregnene-3,20-dione	16α-OH	V-1060
(Krainsky)	Shionogi (O-36)	17α,21-dihydroxy-4-pregnene-3,20-dione	Δ^1; 20-C=O $\rightarrow$ 20β-OH	K-470
		11β,17α,21-trihydroxy-4-pregnene-3,20-dione	Δ^1; 20-C=O $\rightarrow$ 20β-OH	K-470
	SQ	D-homo-$17a$-oxa-1,4-androstadiene-3,17-dione	16α-OH	P-706
		A-nor-3-pregnene-2,20-dione	16α-OH	L-502
		4-androstene-3,17-dione	16α-OH	F-288
		17β-hydroxy-4-androsten-3-one	16α-OH	F-288
		21-hydroxy-4-pregnene-3,20-dione	16α-OH	F-288
	WC(3689)	17β-hydroxy-4-androsten-3-one	16α-OH	F-265
		4-androstene-3,17-dione	16α-OH	F-265; F-267
		A-nor-D-homo-$17a$-oxa-3-androstene-2,17-dione	16α-OH	L-503
		D-homo-$17a$-oxa-1,4-androstadiene-3,17-dione	16α-OH	T-1000
		9α-fluoro-11β-hydroxy-4-androstene-3,17-dione	16α-OH	T-1008

TABLE III

Transformations by Genus: STREPTOMYCES

SPECIES	SOURCE	SUBSTRATE	REACTION	REF.
roseochromogenus	WC (3689)	9α-chloro-4-androstene-3,11,17-trione	16α-OH	T-1008
		9α-fluoro-4-androstene-3,11,17-trione	16α-OH	T-1008
		A-nor-3-pregnene-2,20-dione	16α-OH	L-506
		4-pregnene-3,20-dione	16α-OH	F-265; F-267
		21-hydroxy-4-pregnene-3,20-dione	16α-OH	F-265; F-267
		12α-bromo-11β-hydroxy-4-pregnene-3,20-dione	16α-OH	F-256
		12α-chloro-11β-hydroxy-4-pregnene-3,20-dione	16α-OH	F-256
		6α-fluoro-11β-hydroxy-4-pregnene-3,20-dione	16α-OH	B-35
		12α-fluoro-11β-hydroxy-4-pregnene-3,20-dione	16α-OH	F-256; F-257
		12α-fluoro-21-hydroxy-4-pregnene-3,20-dione	16α-OH	F-256
		11β,17α-dihydroxy-4-pregnene-3,20-dione	16α-OH	F-256
		11β-hydroxy-6α-methyl-4-pregnene-3,20-dione	16α-OH	S-834
		11β-hydroxy-12α-methyl-4-pregnene-3,20-dione	16α-OH	F-257
		21-hydroxy-11β,12β-oxido-4-pregnene-3,20-dione	16α-OH	D-156; D-157
		6α-fluoro-11β,17α-dihydroxy-4-pregnene-3,20-dione	16α-OH	M-530
		9α-fluoro-11β,17α-dihydroxy-3,20-diketo-4-pregnene-21-al	21-C=O → 21-OH	S-907
			21-C=O → 21-OH; 20-C=O →20β-OH	S-907
		11β,17α-dihydroxy-6α-methyl-4-pregnene-3,20-dione	16α-OH	L-511
		9α-fluoro-11β,17α-dihydroxy-6α-methyl-4-pregnene-3,20-dione	16α-OH	L-511
		21-fluoro-11β,17α-dihydroxy-6α-methyl-4-pregnene-3,20-dione	16α-OH	L-510

TABLE III

Transformations by Genus: STREPTOMYCES

SPECIES	SOURCE	SUBSTRATE	REACTION	REF.
roseochromogenus	WC (3689)	6α, 21-difluoro-11β, 17α-di-hydroxy-4-pregnene-3, 20-dione	16α-OH	M-532
		6α-fluoro-11β, 17α, 21-trihydroxy-4-pregnene-3, 20-dione	16α-OH	M-533; M-534; M-586
		9α-fluoro-11β, 17α, 21-trihydroxy-4-pregnene-3, 20-dione (strain variation, Ref. G-298)	2β-OH	G-298; S-913
			16α-OH	G-298; S-913; T-1002
			2β, 16α-diOH	G-298
			20-C=O → 20β-OH	S-907
			16α-OH; 20-C=O→20β-OH	S-907
		12α-fluoro-11β, 17α, 21-trihydroxy-4-pregnene-3, 20-dione	16α-OH	F-256; F-257
		6α-fluoro-11β, 17α, 21-trihydroxy-9α-methyl-4-pregnene-3, 20-dione	16α-OH	F-260
		9α-fluoro-11β, 17α, 21-trihydroxy-12α-methyl-4-pregnene-3, 20-dione	16α-OH	F-260
		6α, 9α-difluoro-11β, 17α, 21-trihydroxy-4-pregnene-3, 20-dione	16α-OH	M-533; M-586
		6α, 12α-difluoro-11β, 17α, 21-trihydroxy-4-pregnene-3, 20-dione	16α-OH	F-261
		9α, 21-difluoro-11β, 17α-dihydroxy-6α-methyl-4-pregnene-3, 20-dione	16α-OH	L-510
		6α, 9α, 21-trifluoro-11β, 17α-di-hydroxy-4-pregnene-3, 20-dione	16α-OH	M-532
		12α-bromo-4-pregnene-3, 11, 20-trione	16α-OH	F-256
		12α-chloro-4-pregnene-3, 11, 20-trione	16α-OH	F-257
		6α-fluoro-4-pregnene-3, 11, 20-trione	16α-OH	B-35

654

TABLE III

Transformations by Genus: STREPTOMYCES

SPECIES	SOURCE	SUBSTRATE	REACTION	REF.
roseochromogenus	WC (3689)	12α-fluoro-4-pregnene-3,11,20-trione	16α-OH	F-256
		6α-methyl-4-pregnene-3,11,20-trione	16α-OH	S-834
		12α-fluoro-21-hydroxy-4-pregnene-3,11,20-trione	16α-OH	F-256
		12α-chloro-17α,21-dihydroxy-4-pregnene-3,11,20-trione	16α-OH	F-256; F-257
		12α-fluoro-17α,21-dihydroxy-4-pregnene-3,11,20-trione	16α-OH	F-256
		12α-chloro-6α-fluoro-17α,21-dihydroxy-4-pregnene-3,11,20-trione	16α-OH	F-261
		21-hydroxy-11β,12β-oxido-1,4-pregnadiene-3,20-dione	16α-OH	D-157
		11β,17α-dihydroxy-6α-methyl-1,4-pregnadiene-3,20-dione	16α-OH	L-511
		11β,17α,21-trihydroxy-1,4-pregnadiene-3,20-dione	16α-OH	F-257
		6α-fluoro-11β,17α,21-trihydroxy-1,4-pregnadiene-3,20-dione	16α-OH	M-531
		9α-fluoro-11β,17α,21-trihydroxy-1,4-pregnadiene-3,20-dione (Δ^1 of substrate blocks 2β-OH - Ref. G-298)	16α-OH	G-298; T-1002
		12α-fluoro-11β,17α,21-trihydroxy-1,4-pregnadiene-3,20-dione	16α-OH	F-256; F-257
		9α-fluoro-11β,17α-dihydroxy-6α-methyl-1,4-pregnadiene-3,20-dione	16α-OH	L-511
		21-fluoro-11β,17α-dihydroxy-6α-methyl-1,4-pregnadiene-3,20-dione	16α-OH	L-510
		6α,21-difluoro-11β,17α-dihydroxy-1,4-pregnadiene-3,20-dione	16α-OH	M-532
		11β,17α,21-trihydroxy-6α-methyl-1,4-pregnadiene-3,20-dione	16α-OH	F-257
		9α-fluoro-11β,17α,21-trihydroxy-6α-methyl-1,4-pregnadiene-3,20-dione	16α-OH	F-257
		9α,21-difluoro-11β,17α-dihydroxy-6α-methyl-1,4-pregnadiene-3,20-dione	16α-OH	L-510

TABLE III

ransformations by Genus: STREPTOMYCES

SPECIES	SOURCE	SUBSTRATE	REACTION	REF.
roseochromogenus	WC (6389)	$6\alpha,9\alpha,21$-trifluoro-$11\beta,17\alpha$-dihydroxy-$1,4$-pregnadiene-$3,20$-dione	16α-OH	M-532
		12α-fluoro-$17\alpha,21$-dihydroxy-$1,4$-pregnadiene-$3,11,20$-trione	16α-OH	F-256
ruber	NRRL (B - 1268)	4-pregnene-$3,20$-dione	1ξ-OH	F-234
		$17\alpha,21$-dihydroxy-4-pregnene-$3,20$-dione	1ξ-OH	F-234
		$11\beta,17\alpha,21$-trihydroxy-4-pregnene-$3,20$-dione	1ξ-OH	F-234
		9α-fluoro-$11\beta,17\alpha,21$-trihydroxy-4-pregnene-$3,20$-dione	1ξ-OH	F-234
		9α-fluoro-$11\beta,16\alpha,17\alpha,21$-tetrahydroxy-$4$-pregnene-$3,20$-dione	1ξ-OH	F-234
		9α-fluoro-$11\beta,16\alpha,17\alpha,21$-tetrahydroxy-$1,4$-pregnadiene-$3,20$-dione	1ξ-OH	F-234
rubescens	IAM (Z-52)	3α-hydroxy-5β-cholanic acid (sole carbon source)	utilization	S-785
		$3\alpha,7\alpha,12\alpha$-trihydroxy-5β-cholanic acid (sole carbon source)	utilization	H-357; S-784
			3α-OH$\rightarrow$3-C=O; 7α-OH$\rightarrow\Delta^6$; 12α-OH$\rightarrow$12-C=O; 5β-H$\rightarrow\Delta^4$	H-365
			3α-OH$\rightarrow$3-C=O; Δ^4-(5β-H)	H-365
			3α-OH$\rightarrow$3-C=O; 12α-OH$\rightarrow$12-C=O Δ^4-(5β-H)	H-365
			3α-OH$\rightarrow$3-C=O; 7α-OH$\rightarrow\Delta^6$; Δ^4-(5β-H)	H-362
		$3\alpha,7\alpha,12\alpha$-trihydroxy-5β-cholanic acid conjugated with glycine-glycocholic acid (sole carbon source)	utilization	S-785
		$3\alpha,7\alpha,12\alpha$-trihydroxy-5β-cholanic acid conjugated with taurine-taurocholic acid (sole carbon source)	utilization	S-785
		$3,7,12$-triketo-5β-cholanic acid (sole carbon source)	utilization	S-785

TABLE III

Transformations by Genus: STREPTOMYCES

SPECIES	SOURCE	SUBSTRATE	REACTION	REF.
rubrireticuli	AMCY (LED)	$11\beta,17\alpha,21$-trihydroxy-4-pregnene-3,20-dione	1ξ-OH	F-234
		9α-fluoro-$11\beta,17\alpha,21$-trihydroxy-4-pregnene-3,20-dione	1ξ-OH	F-234
rubrocyanodiastaticus	Shionogi	$17\alpha,21$-dihydroxy-4-pregnene-3,20-dione	20-C=O → 20β-OH	K-470
		$11\beta,17\alpha,21$-trihydroxy-4-pregnene-3,20-dione	20-C=O → 20β-OH	K-470
rutgersensis	NRRL	Sarsasapogenin	—	M-587
		Diosgenin	—	M-587
		4-dehydrotigogenone	—	M-587
scabies	IAM (3111)	3α-hydroxy-5β-cholanic acid (sole carbon source)	utilization	S-785
		$3\alpha,7\alpha,12\alpha$-trihydroxy-5β-cholanic acid (sole carbon source - Ref. S-784)	utilization	H-357; S-784
		$3\alpha,7\alpha,12\alpha$-trihydroxy-5β-cholanic acid conjugated with glycine-glycocholic acid (sole carbon source)	utilization	S-785
		$3\alpha,7\alpha,12\alpha$-trihydroxy-5β-cholanic acid conjugated with taurine-taurocholic acid (sole carbon source)	utilization	S-785
		3,7,12-triketo-5β-cholanic acid (sole carbon source)	utilization	S-785
setonii *	CZAS	4-pregnene-3,20-dione	16α-OH	V-1060
species	AMCY (LED-AC-209)	2-fluoro-$17\alpha,21$-dihydroxy-1,4-pregnadiene-3,11,20-trione	Δ^1→H (2α-F)	H-402
(species later identified as argenteolus)	ATCC-11009	3β-hydroxy-5-pregnen-20-one	3β-OH→3-C=O; Δ^5→Δ^4	F-267; P-710; P-712; P-716
	C (A-7747)	3β-hydroxy-19-<u>nor</u>-5α-pregnan-20-one	16α-OH	W-1093
		3β-hydroxy-5α-pregnan-20-one	16α-OH	N-653; W-1092
		3β-hydroxy-5β-pregnan-20-one	16α-OH	W-1092
		9α-fluoro-$3\beta,11\beta$-dihydroxy-5α-pregnan-20-one	16α-OH	W-1092

TABLE III

ransformations by Genus: STREPTOMYCES

SPECIES	SOURCE	SUBSTRATE	REACTION	REF.
species	C (A-7747)	3β-hydroxy-5α-9(11)-pregnen-20-one acetate	16α-OH; 3β-OAc $\rightarrow 3\beta$-OH	W-1092
		21-hydroxy-4-pregnene-3,20-dione	16α-OH	V-1054
		d,1-21-hydroxy-4-pregnene-3,20-dione	d,1$\rightarrow$d-16α-OH +1	W-1102
		11β,21-dihydroxy-4-pregnene-3,20-dione 18-oic acid (18$\rightarrow$11) lactone	16α-OH	W-1091
	MCC (MA-449)	17α,21-dihydroxy-4-pregnene-3,11,20-trione	$\Delta^4 \rightarrow 5\beta$-H; 3-C=O$\rightarrow 3\alpha$-OH	B-41
	NG	5-cholesten-3β-ol	utilization	D-145
		5-cholesten-3β-ol 4-C^{14}	utilization	D-145
		5-cholesten-3β-ol 26-C^{14}	utilization	D-145
	QM-1086	17α,21-dihydroxy-4-pregnene-3,20-dione	20-C=O $\rightarrow$ 20β-OH	C-110
		11β,17α,21-trihydroxy-4-pregnene-3,20-dione	20-C=O $\rightarrow$ 20β-OH	C-110
		17α,21-dihydroxy-4-pregnene-3,11,20-trione	20-C=O $\rightarrow$ 20β-OH	C-110
		11β,17α,21-trihydroxy-1,4-pregnadiene-3,20-dione	20-C=O $\rightarrow$ 20β-OH	C-110
		17α,21-dihydroxy-1,4-pregnadiene-3,11,20-trione	20-C=O$\rightarrow$ 20β-OH	C-110
	S (8)	4-pregnene-3,20-dione	16α-OH	S-847; S-849; S-859
		17α-hydroxy-4-pregnene-3,20-dione	—	S-859
		17α,21-dihydroxy-4-pregnene-3,20-dione	—	S-859
	(27)	4-pregnene-3,20-dione	16α-OH	S-847; S-859
		17α-hydroxy-4-pregnene-3,20-dione	—	S-849; S-859
		21-hydroxy-4-pregnene-3,20-dione	—	S-849
		17α,21-dihydroxy-4-pregnene-3,20-dione	—	S-849; S-859

TABLE III

Transformations by Genus: STREPTOMYCES

SPECIES	SOURCE	SUBSTRATE	REACTION	REF.
species (strain 8, 27, 41, 44 - Actinomyces)	S (41)	4-pregnene-3, 20-dione	$6\beta, 11\alpha$-diOH	S-859
		17α-hydroxy-4-pregnene-3, 20-dione	—	S-859
		$17\alpha, 21$-dihydroxy-4-pregnene-3, 20-dione	—	S-859
	(44)	4-pregnene-3, 20-dione	16α-OH	S-847; S-859
		17α-hydroxy-4-pregnene-3, 20-dione	—	S-859
		$17\alpha, 21$-dihydroxy-4-pregnene-3, 20-dione	—	S-859
	(72)	4-pregnene-3, 20-dione	16α-OH	S-847
	(103)	4-pregnene-3, 20-dione	6β-OH	S-847; S-854; S-859
			$6\beta, 11\alpha$-diOH	S-847; S-854; S-859
		17α-hydroxy-4-pregnene-3, 20-dione	—	S-859
		21-hydroxy-4-pregnene-3, 20-dione	6β-OH	S-847; S-849
			11α-OH	S-847; S-849
		$17\alpha, 21$-dihydroxy-4-pregnene-3, 20-dione	6β-OH	S-847; S-849; S-854
			11α-OH	S-847; S-854
	(161)	4-pregnene-3, 20-dione	16α-OH	S-847
	SCH (DS-81B, FC-6-53S, FC-7-206)	$17\alpha, 21$-dihydroxy-4-pregnene-3, 20-dione	2β-OH	H-383
	(FC-B-222)		20-C=O → 20β-OH	C-110
	Shionogi (I-13)	$17\alpha, 21$-dihydroxy-4-pregnene-3, 20-dione	Δ^1	K-470
			20-C=O → 20β-OH	K-470
			Δ^1; 20-C=O → 20β-OH	K-470

TABLE III

ransformations by Genus: STREPTOMYCES

SPECIES	SOURCE	SUBSTRATE	REACTION	REF.
species	Shionogi (I-13)	11β,17α,21-trihydroxy-4-preg-nene-3,20-dione	Δ^1; 20-C=O → 20β-OH	K-470
			20-C=O → 20β-OH	K-470
			Δ^1	K-470
	SQ (SC-1646, SC-3309, SC-3310, SC-3311)	4-pregnene-3,20-dione	Δ^1	T-1005
		5-cholesten-3β-ol	$\Delta^5 \rightarrow \Delta^4$; 3β-OH →3-C=O	T-1005
	SY (J-6-11)	17α,21-dihydroxy-4-pregnene-3,20-dione	6β-OH	C-112
			11β-OH	C-112
			6β,11β-diOH	C-112
	UC	21-hydroxy-4-pregnene-3,20-dione (revision of structure at 20 - see Ref. S-832)	20-C=O → 20β-OH	E-202
	(BC-17,H-39,K-93,W-4)		11-oxygenation	H-328
	(H-39)	17α,21-dihydroxy-4-pregnene-3,20-dione	oxidation	H-328
	WC (3676)	4-pregnene-3,20-dione	15α-OH	F-285; F-287
	WC (3808)	17α,21-dihydroxy-1,4-pregna-diene-3,11,20-trione	$\Delta^4 \rightarrow 5\beta$-H	G-314
		17α,21-dihydroxy-16α-methyl-1,4-pregnadiene-3,11,20-trione	$\Delta^4 \rightarrow 5\beta$-H	G-314
tanashiensis	Shionogi	17α,21-dihydroxy-4-pregnene-3,20-dione	Δ^1; 20-C=O → 20β-OH	K-470
		11β,17α,21-trihydroxy-4-pregnene-3,20-dione	Δ^1; 20-C=O → 20β-OH	K-470
tendae	Shionogi (ETH-11313)	17α,21-dihydroxy-4-pregnene-3,20-dione	20-C=O → 20β-OH	K-470
		11β,17α,21-trihydroxy-4-preg-nene-3,20-dione	20-C=O → 20β-OH	K-470
thioluteus	Shionogi (OKAMI)	17α,21-dihydroxy-4-pregnene-3,20-dione	20-C=O → 20β-OH	K-470
		11β,17α,21-trihydroxy-4-preg-nene-3,20-dione	20-C=O → 20β-OH	K-470

TABLE III

Transformations by Genus: STREPTOMYCES

SPECIES	SOURCE	SUBSTRATE	REACTION	REF.
vinaceus *	ATCC-11861	4-pregnene-3,20-dione	16α-OH	L-491
		21-hydroxy-4-pregnene-3,20-dione acetate	16α-OH; 21-OAc →21-OH	L-491
viridans	Shionogi	17α,21-dihydroxy-4-pregnene-3,20-dione	20-C=O → 20β-OH	K-470
		11β,17α,21-trihydroxy-4-pregnene-3,20-dione	20-C=O → 20β-OH	K-470
viridifaciens	ATCC-11389	17α,21-dihydroxy-4-pregnene-3,20-dione	1ξ-OH	F-234
		11β,17α,21-trihydroxy-4-pregnene-3,20-dione	1ξ-OH	F-234
		9α-fluoro-11β,17α,21-trihydroxy-4-pregnene-3,20-dione	1ξ-OH	F-234
		17α,21-dihydroxy-4,9(11)-pregnadiene-3,20-dione	1ξ-OH	F-234
viridis	AY	17α,21-dihydroxy-4-pregnene-3,20-dione (with spores)	16α-OH	S-835; V-1048
*	CZAS	4-pregnene-3,20-dione	16α-OH	V-1060
	WC (3690)	17β-hydroxy-4-androsten-3-one	16α-OH	F-265
		4-androstene-3,17-dione	16α-OH	F-265; F-267
		4-pregnene-3,20-dione	16α-OH	F-265; F-267
		21-hydroxy-4-pregnene-3,20-dione	16α-OH	F-265; F-267
viridochromogenes (Actinomyces)	CZAS	4-pregnene-3,20-dione	—	S-929
	IPB	5-androstene-3β,17β-diol	3β-OH→3-C=O; Δ^5→Δ^4; 17β-OH →17-C=O	H-337
		5-androstene-3β,17α-diol	3β-OH→3-C=O; Δ^5→Δ^4	H-337
		3β-hydroxy-5-androsten-17-one acetate	3β-OAc→3-C=O; Δ^5→Δ^4	H-335
			3β-OAc→3-C=O; Δ^5→Δ^4; 17-C=O →17β-OH	H-335

TABLE III

<u>TAXONOMY</u>

Transformations by Genus:
STREPTOMYCES
STROPHARIA   (Basidio. - Agaricales)
STYSANUS   (Imperf. - Moniliales)
SYNCEPHALASTRUM   (Phyco. - Mucorales)

SPECIES	SOURCE	SUBSTRATE	REACTION	REF.
viridochromogenes	NRRL	Sarsasapogenin	—	M-587
		Diosgenin	—	M-587
		4-dehydrotigogenone	—	M-587
willmorei	NRRL B-1332	$11\beta,17\alpha,21$-trihydroxy-4-preg-nene-3,20-dione	16α-OH	P-745
		9α-fluoro-$11\beta,17\alpha,21$-trihydroxy-4-pregnene-3,20-dione	16α-OH	P-745
STROPHARIA				
cubensis	SY	$17\alpha,21$-dihydroxy-4-pregnene-3,20-dione	11α-OH	C-113
nordmanii	AL (SS-74)	4-pregnene-3,20-dione	oxidation - products not identified	S-825
STYSANUS				
medius	FRI	$17\alpha,21$-dihydroxy-4-pregnene-3,20-dione	6β-OH; 11α-OH	S-849
SYNCEPHALASTRUM				
cincereum (cinereum)	SSSR	$17\alpha,21$-dihydroxy-4-pregnene-3,20-dione	11α-OH	E-224
racemosum	IAM (6801)	4-pregnene-3,20-dione (Ref. T-1025 corrects con-figuration at 7 to 7β in Ref. A-26,27,30; T-1020,1021) (species identified as racemosum in Ref. A-27)	15β-OH	S-793
			$6\beta,11\alpha$-diOH	S-793
			$6\beta,15\beta$-diOH	S-793
			$7\beta,15\beta$-diOH	A-26; A-27; A-30; S-793; T-1020; T-1025
			$7\beta,14\alpha,15\beta$-triOH	A-26; A-27; A-30; S-793; T-1021; T-1025
			$\Delta^4 \rightarrow 5\alpha$-H; 15β-OH; 6-C=O (via 6β-OH)	S-793

TABLE III

Transformations by Genus:　SYNCEPHALASTRUM
　　　　　　　　　　　　　SYNCEPHALIS　　(Phyco. - Mucorales)
　　　　　　　　　　　　　TAPHRINA　　　(Asco. - Taphrinales)
　　　　　　　　　　　　　THAMNIDIUM　　(Phyco. - Mucorales)

SPECIES	SOURCE	SUBSTRATE	REACTION	REF.
racemosum	IAM (6801)	11α-hydroxy-4-pregnene-3,20-dione	6β-OH	A-27; T-1020
		6β,11α-dihydroxy-4-pregnene-3,20-dione	—	A-27
		7β,15β-dihydroxy-4-pregnene-3,20-dione	14α-OH	T-1021
		17α,21-dihydroxy-4-pregnene-3,20-dione	11α-OH	A-27; T-1020
		11β,17α,21-trihydroxy-4-pregnene-3,20-dione	—	A-27
	SSSR	17α,21-dihydroxy-4-pregnene-3,20-dione	6β-OH; 11α-OH; 11β-OH	E-224
species	NRRL	plant saponins	—	K-478
SYNCEPHALIS				
nodosa	UC	not given	oxidation	M-601; M-636
reflexa	UC	not given	oxidation	M-601; M-636
TAPHRINA				
diformans (deformans)	TNAES	17α,21-dihydroxy-4-pregnene-3,20-dione	—	S-849
pruni	TNAES	17α,21-dihydroxy-4-pregnene-3,20-dione	—	S-849
THAMNIDIUM				
elegans	SQ	4,9(11)-pregnadiene-3,20-dione	6β,12α-diOH	F-277; F-279
	SSSR	17α,21-dihydroxy-4-pregnene-3,20-dione	11α-OH; 11β-OH; 11-C=O (via 11β-OH)	E-224

TABLE III

ansformations by Genus:

THIELAVIA	(Asco. - Eurotiales)
THYROSPORA	(Imperf. - Moniliales)
TIEGHEMELLA	(Phyco. - Mucorales)
TILLETIOPSIS	(Imperf. - Moniliales)

SPECIES	SOURCE	SUBSTRATE	REACTION	REF.
THIELAVIA				
asicola	FRI	$17\alpha,21$-dihydroxy-4-pregnene-3,20-dione	6β-OH	S-849
erricola	C	no specific substrate - used in mixed culture	17α-OH	W-1106; W-1107
THYROSPORA				
stragali	FRI	$17\alpha,21$-dihydroxy-4-pregnene-3,20-dione	2β-OH	S-849
TIEGHEMELLA (synonym - Absidia)				
oerulea	SSSR	$17\alpha,21$-dihydroxy-4-pregnene-3,20-dione	11α-OH; 11β-OH; 11-C=O (via 11β-OH)	E-224
ylindrospora	SSSR	$17\alpha,21$-dihydroxy-4-pregnene-3,20-dione	11α-OH	E-224
yalospora	SSSR	$17\alpha,21$-dihydroxy-4-pregnene-3,20-dione	11α-OH; 11β-OH	E-224
rchidis	SSSR	$17\alpha,21$-dihydroxy-4-pregnene-3,20-dione	11α-OH; 11β-OH; 11-C=O (via 11β-OH	E-224
epens	SSSR	$17\alpha,21$-dihydroxy-4-pregnene-3,20-dione	11α-OH	E-224
pinosa	SSSR	$17\alpha,21$-dihydroxy-4-pregnene-3,20-dione	11α-OH; 11β-OH	E-224
eghemii	SSSR	$17\alpha,21$-dihydroxy-4-pregnene-3,20-dione	11α-OH; 11β-OH	E-224
rkestanica	SSSR	$17\alpha,21$-dihydroxy-4-pregnene-3,20-dione	11α-OH; 11β-OH; 11-C=O (via 11β-OH)	E-224
ILLETIOPSIS				
lacina	FRI	$17\alpha,21$-dihydroxy-4-pregnene-3,20-dione	—	S-849

TABLE III

Transformations by Genus:

TOMENTELLA	(Basidio. - Agaricales)
TORULA	(Imperf. - Moniliales)
TORULOPSIS	(Imperf. - Moniliales)
TRAMETES	(Basidio. - Agaricales)
TRICHODERMA	(Imperf. - Moniliales)

SPECIES	SOURCE	SUBSTRATE	REACTION	REF.
TOMENTELLA				
species	FRI	17α,21-dihydroxy-4-pregnene-3,20-dione	—	S-849
TORULA				
species	NG	5-cholesten-3β-ol	—	S-793c
		24β-methyl-5,7,22-cholesta-trien-3β-ol	—	S-793c
TORULOPSIS				
aeria	FRI	17α,21-dihydroxy-4-pregnene-3,20-dione	—	S-849
candida	NRRL	Sarsasapogenin	—	M-587
		Diosgenin	—	M-587
		4-dehydrotigogenone	—	M-587
TRAMETES				
dickinsii	IAM	17α,21-dihydroxy-4-pregnene-3,20-dione	—	S-849
pini	IAM	17α,21-dihydroxy-4-pregnene-3,20-dione	—	S-849
TRICHODERMA				
album (in mixed culture with Aspergillus niger [11α-OH]-Hendersonia acicola [21-OH])	MCC	4-pregnene-3,20-dione	17α-OH	M-566
glaucum	LED (Z-696)	17β-hydroxy-4-androsten-3-one	17β-OH → not esterified	H-404
		21-hydroxy-4-pregnene-3,20-dione	21-OH → not esterified	H-404
		16α,21-dihydroxy-4-pregnene-3,20-dione	21-OH → not esterified	H-404
		16α,17α,21-trihydroxy-4-pregnene-3,20-dione 16,17-acetonide	21-OH → 21-OAc	H-404

TABLE III

ransformations by Genus: TRICHODERMA

SPECIES	SOURCE	SUBSTRATE	REACTION	REF.
glaucum	LED (Z-696)	$11\beta,16\alpha,17\alpha,21$-tetrahydroxy-4-pregnene-3,20-dione 16,17-acetonide	21-OH → 21-OAc	H-404
		9α-fluoro-$11\beta,16\alpha,17\alpha,21$-tetrahydroxy-4-pregnene-3,20-dione	21-OH → not esterified	H-404
		9α-fluoro-$11\beta,16\alpha,17\alpha,21$-tetrahydroxy-4-pregnene-3,20-dione $16\alpha,17\alpha$-borate (sodium salt)	21-OH → not esterified	H-404
		9α-fluoro-$11\beta,16\alpha,17\alpha,21$-tetrahydroxy-4-pregnene-3,20-dione 16,17-acetonide	21-OH → 21-OAc	H-404
		9α-fluoro-$11\beta,16\alpha,17\alpha,21$-tetrahydroxy-1,4-pregnadiene-3,20-dione $16\alpha,17\alpha$-orthoformate	21-OH → not esterified	H-404
		9α-fluoro-$11\beta,16\alpha,17\alpha,21$-tetrahydroxy-1,4-pregnadiene-3,20-dione 16,17-acetonide	21-OH → 21-OAc	H-404
(in mixed culture with Cunninghamella blakesleeana [11β-OH] Wojnowicia graminis [21-OH])	MCC	4-pregnene-3,20-dione	17α-OH	M-566
koningi *	SSSR (8,23)	4-pregnene-3,20-dione	$6\beta,11\alpha$-diOH	T-1010
	(23)	4-pregnene-3,11,20-trione	17α-OH	T-1010
lignorum (in mixed culture with Penicillium adametzi [11α-OH] Wojnowicia graminis [21-OH])	MCC	4-pregnene-3,20-dione	17α-OH	M-566
*	SSSR (2,3,4,5,10,16,22)	4-pregnene-3,20-dione	$6\beta,11\alpha$-diOH	T-1010
		4-pregnene-3,11,20-trione	oxidation - products not identified	T-1010
nigrovirens (in mixed culture with Hendersonia rubi [21-OH] Stigmina platana[11β-OH])	MCC	4-pregnene-3,20-dione	17α-OH	M-566
species	NRRL	plant saponins	—	K-478
iride	MCC	4-pregnene-3,20-dione	17α-OH	M-565
	NRRL-2473	4-pregnene-3,20-dione	17α-OH	D-185

TABLE III

Transformations by Genus: TRICHODERMA
TRICHOLOMA (Basidio. - Agaricales)
TRICHOMONAS (Zoomastigina - Polymastigina)

SPECIES	SOURCE	SUBSTRATE	REACTION	REF.
viride (in mixed culture with Curvularia lunata [11β-OH] Omphaliatra lucida [11β-OH] and Wojnowicia graminis [17α-OH])	NRRL-2473	4-pregnene-3,20-dione	17α-OH	M-566; M-567
		11β-hydroxy-4-pregnene-3,20-dione	17α-OH	D-185
		21-hydroxy-4-pregnene-3,20-dione	17α-OH	D-185
	PIRI (FA-3-1)	4-pregnene-3,20-dione	11α-OH	W-1119
		3α-hydroxy-5β-cholanic acid	oxidation	W-1119
*	SSSR	4-pregnene-3,20-dione	6β,11α-diOH	T-1010
			17α-OH	T-1010
		4-pregnene-3,11,20-trione	oxidation - products not identified	T-1010
TRICHOLOMA				
nudum	NRRL-2371	4-pregnene-3,20-dione	oxidation - products not identified	R-778
species	AL (G-88)	4-pregnene-3,20-dione	oxidation - products not identified	S-825
TRICHOMONAS (Protozoa)				
foetus	NG	3-hydroxy-1,3,5(10)-estratrien-17-one	17-C=O → 17β-OH	S-829
		17β-hydroxy-4-estren-3-one	17β-OH → 17-C=O	S-829
		4-estrene-3,17-dione	17-C=O → 17β-OH	S-830
		11β-hydroxy-4-estrene-3,17-dione	17-C=O → 17β-OH; Δ¹; enol.	S-830
		4-estrene-3,11,17-trione	17-C=O → 17β-OH	S-830
		3α-hydroxy-5β-androstan-17-one	17-C=O → 17β-OH	S-830

TABLE III

Transformations by Genus: TRICHOMONAS

SPECIES	SOURCE	SUBSTRATE	REACTION	REF.
foetus	NG	3α-hydroxy-5β-androstan-17-one acetate	17-C=O → 17β-OH; 3α-OAc →3α-OH	S-830
		3β-hydroxy-5-androsten-17-one	17-C=O → 17β-OH	S-829; S-830
		3β-hydroxy-5-androsten-17-one acetate	17-C=O → 17β-OH; 3β-OAc →3β-OH	S-829
		17β-hydroxy-4-androsten-3-one	17β-OH → 17-C=O	S-829
		11β,17β-dihydroxy-4-androsten-3-one	17β-OH → 17-C=O	S-829
		4-androstene-3,17-dione	17-C=O → 17β-OH	S-829
		17β-hydroxy-4-androstene-3,11-dione	17β-OH → 17-C=O	S-829
		11α-hydroxy-4-androstene-3,17-dione	17-C=O → 17β-OH	S-829
		11β-hydroxy-4-androstene-3,17-dione	17-C=O → 17β-OH	S-829
		4-androstene-3,11,17-trione	17-C=O → 17β-OH	S-829; S-830
		1,4-androstadiene-3,17-dione	17-C=O → 17β-OH	S-829
(in mixed culture with Corynebacterium equi [Δ¹])		4-androstene-3,17-dione	17-C=O → 17β-OH	S-830
(in mixed culture with Corynebacterium equi [Δ¹])		4-estrene-3,11,17-trione	17-C=O → 17β-OH	S-830
gallinae	NG	3-hydroxy-1,3,5(10)-estratrien-17-one	17-C=O → 17β-OH	S-829; S-830
		17β-hydroxy-4-estren-3-one	17β-OH → 17-C=O	S-829
		4-estrene-3,17-dione	17-C=O → 17β-OH	S-830
		11β-hydroxy-4-estren-3,17-dione	17-C=O → 17β-OH; Δ¹; enol.	S-830
		4-estrene-3,11,17-trione	17-C=O → 17β-OH	S-830
		3α-hydroxy-5β-androstan-17-one	17-C=O → 17β-OH	S-830

TABLE III

Transformations by Genus: TRICHOMONAS

SPECIES	SOURCE	SUBSTRATE	REACTION	REF.
gallinae	NG	3α-hydroxy-5β-androstan-17-one acetate	17-C=O $\rightarrow$ 17β-OH	S-830
		3β-hydroxy-5-androsten-17-one	17-C=O $\rightarrow$ 17β-OH	S-829
		3β-hydroxy-5-androsten-17-one acetate	3β-OAc$\rightarrow$3β-OH	S-829
			17-C=O $\rightarrow$ 17β-OH	S-829; S-830
			17-C=O $\rightarrow$ 17β-OH; 3β-OAc $\rightarrow$3β-OH	S-829
		17β-hydroxy-4-androsten-3-one	17β-OH $\rightarrow$ 17-C=O	S-829
		11β,17β-dihydroxy-4-androsten-3-one	17β-OH $\rightarrow$ 17-C=O	S-829
		4-androstene-3,17-dione	17-C=O $\rightarrow$ 17β-OH	S-829; S-830
		17β-hydroxy-4-androstene-3,11-dione	17β-OH $\rightarrow$ 17-C=O	S-829
		11α-hydroxy-4-androstene-3,17-dione	17-C=O $\rightarrow$ 17β-OH	S-829; S-830
		11β-hydroxy-4-androstene-3,17-dione	17-C=O $\rightarrow$ 17β-OH	S-829; S-830
		4-androstene-3,11,17-trione	17-C=O $\rightarrow$ 17β-OH	S-829; S-830
		1,4-androstadiene-3,17-dione	17-C=O $\rightarrow$ 17β-OH	S-829
(in mixed culture with Corynebacterium simplex[Δ^1])		4-androstene-3,11,17-trione	17-C=O $\rightarrow$ 17β-OH	S-830
		11β-hydroxy-4-androstene-3,17-dione	17-C=O $\rightarrow$ 17β-OH	S-830
(in mixed culture with Corynebacterium equi [Δ^1])		11β-hydroxy-4-estrene-3,17-dione	17-C=O $\rightarrow$ 17β-OH	S-830
vaginalis	NG	3α-hydroxy-5β-androstan-17-one	17-C=O $\rightarrow$ 17β-OH	S-830
		1,4-androstadiene-3,17-dione	17-C=O $\rightarrow$ 17β-OH	S-830

TABLE III

Transformations by Genus: TRICOPHYTON (Imperf. - Moniliales)
TRICHOTHECIUM (Imperf. - Moniliales)

SPECIES	SOURCE	SUBSTRATE	REACTION	REF.
TRICOPHYTON				
concentricum	FRI	17α,21-dihydroxy-4-pregnene-3,20-dione	6β-OH; 11α-OH; 11β-OH	S-849
TRICHOTHECIUM (see Cephalothecium)				
arrhenopum	UC	4-pregnene-3,20-dione	17α-OH	M-600
		11β-hydroxy-4-pregnene-3,20-dione	17α-OH	M-600
		21-hydroxy-4-pregnene-3,20-dione acetate	17α-OH	M-600
		4-pregnene-3,11,20-trione	17α-OH	M-600
candidum	UC	4-pregnene-3,20-dione	17α-OH	M-600
		11β-hydroxy-4-pregnene-3,20-dione	17α-OH	M-600
		21-hydroxy-4-pregnene-3,20-dione acetate	17α-OH	M-600
		4-pregnene-3,11,20-trione	17α-OH	M-600
cystosporium	CBS	4-pregnene-3,20-dione	17α-OH	M-600
		11β-hydroxy-4-pregnene-3,20-dione	17α-OH	M-600
		21-hydroxy-4-pregnene-3,20-dione acetate	17α-OH	M-600
		4-pregnene-3,20-dione	17α-OH	M-600
domesticum	CBS	4-pregnene-3,20-dione	17α-OH	M-600
		11β-hydroxy-4-pregnene-3,20-dione	17α-OH	M-600
		21-hydroxy-4-pregnene-3,20-dione acetate	17α-OH	M-600
		4-pregnene-3,11,20-trione	17α-OH	M-600
luteum	CBS	4-pregnene-3,20-dione	17α-OH	M-600
		11β-hydroxy-4-pregnene-3,20-dione	17α-OH	M-600
		21-hydroxy-4-pregnene-3,20-dione acetate	17α-OH	M-600
		4-pregnene-3,11,20-trione	17α-OH	M-600

TABLE III

Transformations by Genus: TRICHOTHECIUM

SPECIES	SOURCE	SUBSTRATE	REACTION	REF.
plasmoparae	UC	4-pregnene-3,20-dione	17α-OH	M-600
		11β-hydroxy-4-pregnene-3,20-dione	17α-OH	M-600
		21-hydroxy-4-pregnene-3,20-dione acetate	17α-OH	M-600
		4-pregnene-3,11,20-trione	17α-OH	M-600
polybrochum	UC	4-pregnene-3,20-dione	17α-OH	M-600
		11β-hydroxy-4-pregnene-3,20-dione	17α-OH	M-600
		21-hydroxy-4-pregnene-3,20-dione acetate	17α-OH	M-600
		4-pregnene-3,11,20-trione	17α-OH	M-600
roseum	Armour and Co.	4-pregnene-3,20-dione (treatment of nutrients; sterilization with H_2O_2 - use of catalase)	11α-OH	W-1122
	ATCC-8685	9α-fluoro-11β,21-dihydroxy-4-pregnene-3,20-dione	17α-OH	N-668
		9α-fluoro-21-hydroxy-1,4-pregnadiene-3,11,20-trione	17α-OH	N-668
		3β,14β-dihydroxy-5β-20(22)-cardenolide	7β-OH	T-1013
			11α-OH	T-1013
			Δ^{16}	T-1013
	ATCC-12519	21-hydroxy-4-pregnene-3,20-dione	11β-OH	T-1003
		17α,21-dihydroxy-4-pregnene-3,20-dione	11α-OH	T-1003
			11β-OH	T-1003
	ATCC-12543 (QM-102E)	17α,21-dihydroxy-4-pregnene-3,20-dione	11β-OH	S-878
	C	21-hydroxy-4-pregnene-3,20-dione	6β-OH	M-584
			17α-OH	M-584
		11β,21-dihydroxy-4-pregnene-3,20-dione	6β-OH	N-654
			17α-OH	M-584
			17α-OH; 11β-OH $\rightarrow$11-C=O	F-584

TABLE III

Transformations by Genus: TRICHOTHECIUM

SPECIES	SOURCE	SUBSTRATE	REACTION	REF.
roseum	C	21-hydroxy-4-pregnene-3,11,20-trione	17α-OH	M-584
		d,l-11β,21-dihydroxy-3,20-diketo-4-pregnen-18-al (18→11) hemiacetal	d,l→d-17α-OH + l	W-1102
(in mixed culture with Cunninghamella blakesleeana [11β-OH; 11-C=O via 11β-OH] Ophiobolus herpotrichus [21-OH] and Rhizopus nigricans [11α-OH])		4-pregnene-3,20-dione	17α-OH	W-1106
(in mixed culture with Calonectria decora [Δ¹] Curvularia lunata [11β-OH] and Didymella lycopersici [Δ¹])		4-pregnene-3,20-dione	17α-OH	W-1107
		11β-hydroxy-4-pregnene-3,20-dione	17α-OH	W-1106
(in mixed culture with Ophiobolus herpotrichus [21-OH])		11β-hydroxy-4-pregnene-3,20-dione	17α-OH	W-1106
(in mixed culture with Calonectria decora [Δ¹] Ophiobolus herpotrichus [21-OH])		11β-hydroxy-4-pregnene-3,20-dione	17α-OH	W-1107
(in mixed culture with Cunninghamella blakesleeana [11β-OH; 11-C=O- via 11β-OH])		21-hydroxy-4-pregnene-3,20-dione	17α-OH	W-1106
(in mixed culture with Calonectria decora [Δ¹] Cunninghamella blakesleeana [11β-OH; 11-C=O - via 11β-OH])		21-hydroxy-4-pregnene-3,20-dione	17α-OH	W-1107
(in mixed culture with Cunninghamella blakesleeana [11β-OH; 11-C=O-via 11β-OH])		d,l-21-hydroxy-4-pregnene-3,20-dione	d,l→d-17α-OH + l	W-1102
		21-hydroxy-9β,11β-oxido-4-pregnene-3,20-dione acetate	17α-OH	W-1107
(in mixed culture with Didymelia lycopersici [Δ¹])		9α-fluoro-11β,21-dihydroxy-4-pregnene-3,20-dione 21-acetate	17α-OH	W-1107
(in mixed culture with Ophiobolus herpotrichus [21-OH] Wojnowicia graminis [21-OH])		4-pregnene-3,11,20-trione	17α-OH	W-1106

TABLE III

Transformations by Genus: TRICHOTHECIUM

SPECIES	SOURCE	SUBSTRATE	REACTION	REF.
roseum (in mixed culture with Cunninghamella blakesleeana [11β-OH; 11-C=O] Ophiobolus herpotrichus [21-OH])	C	1,4-pregnadiene-3,20-dione	17α-OH	W-1106
(in mixed culture with Ophiobolus herpo-trichus [21-OH])		11β-hydroxy-1,4-pregnadiene-3,20-dione	17α-OH	W-1106
(in mixed culture with Ophiobolus herpo-trichus [21-OH])		1,4-pregnadiene-3,11,20-trione	17α-OH	W-1106
(Link) (also pseudoverticillium form)	CβS	4-pregnene-3,20-dione	17α-OH	M-600
		11β-hydroxy-4-pregnene-3,20-dione	17α-OH	M-600
		21-hydroxy-4-pregnene-3,20-dione acetate	17α-OH	M-600
		4-pregnene-3,11,20-trione	17α-OH	M-600
		3β,14β-dihydroxy-5β-20(22)-cardenolide	3β-OH→3-C=O	J-432
			7β-OH	J-432
			12β-OH	J-432
	FRI	17α,21-dihydroxy-4-pregnene-3,20-dione	—	S-849
	NRRL	Sarsasapogenin	—	M-587
		Diosgenin	—	M-587
		4-dehydrotigogenone	—	M-587
(= Cephalothecium roseum - ATCC-8685)	NRRL-1665	4-pregnene-3,20-dione	17α-OH	M-600
		11β-hydroxy-4-pregnene-3,20-dione	17α-OH	M-600
		21-hydroxy-4-pregnene-3,20-dione acetate	6β,17α-diOH; 21-OAc→21-OH	M-600
			11α,17α-diOH; 21-OAc→21-OH	M-600
		11β,21-dihydroxy-4-pregnene-3,20-dione	17α-OH; 11β-OH→11-C=O	M-600
		17α,21-dihydroxy-4-pregnene-3,20-dione	11α-OH	M-600
		4-pregnene-3,11,20-trione	17α-OH	M-600

TABLE III

Transformations by Genus: TRICHOTHECIUM
                              TRITIRACHIUM   (Imperf. - Moniliales)
                              TUBARIA   (Basidio. - Agaricales)
                              UNIDENTIFIED

SPECIES	SOURCE	SUBSTRATE	REACTION	REF.
roseum	NRRL-1665	21-hydroxy-4-pregnene-3,11,20-trione	17α-OH	M-600
	NRRL-2576 (QM-936)	4-pregnene-3,20-dione	11α,17α-diOH	D-188
	NRRL-2577 (QM-599)	4-pregnene-3,20-dione	11α,17α-diOH	D-188
	SQ	6α-chloro-16α,17α,21-tri-hydroxy-4-pregnene-3,20-dione 16,17-acetophenonide	11α-OH	D-159
		6α-fluoro-16α,17α,21-tri-hydroxy-4-pregnene-3,20-dione 16,17-acetonide	11α-OH	D-159
	SSSR (strains 17 through 26)	4-pregnene-3,20-dione	6β,11α-diOH	T-1010
			11α,17α-diOH	T-1010
		11α-hydroxy-4-pregnene-3,20-dione	—	T-1010
		4-pregnene-3,11,20-trione	—	T-1010
	VEB	4-pregnene-3,20-dione	6β,14α-diOH	S-811
TRITIRACHIUM				
purureum	FRI	17α,21-dihydroxy-4-pregnene-3,20-dione	—	S-849
TUBARIA				
conspersa	AL(SS-32)	4-pregnene-3,20-dione	oxidation - products not identified	S-825
UNIDENTIFIED (listed alphabetically by reference)				
bacterium	SCH (FC-C-78)	17α,21-dihydroxy-4-pregnene-3,20-dione	20-C=O → 20β-OH	C-110
		11β,17α,21-trihydroxy-4-pregnene-3,20-dione	20-C=O → 20β-OH	C-110
		17α,21-dihydroxy-4-pregnene-3,11,20-trione	20-C=O → 20β-OH	C-110

TABLE II;

Transformations by Genus: UNIDENTIFIED

SPECIES	SOURCE	SUBSTRATE	REACTION	REF.
bacterium (listed alphabetically by reference)	SCH (FC-C-78)	$11\beta,17\alpha,21$-trihydroxy-1,4-pregnadiene-3,20-dione	20-C=O → 20β-OH	C-110
		$17\alpha,21$-dihydroxy-1,4-pregnadiene-3,11,20-trione	20-C=O → 20β-OH	C-110
	Univ. of Milan (IK; IKC; IKR O-4, Y-12)	5-cholesten-3β-ol	utilization	C-136
		4-cholesten-3-one	utilization	C-136
		cholesteryl acetate	utilization	C-136
(actually gram + coccus.)	Okayama Univ. Med. School (CE-1)	$3\alpha,7\alpha,12\alpha$-trihydroxy-5β-cholanic acid (sole carbon source)	3α-OH→3-C=O; Δ^4	E-194; H-357
	NG	not given	Δ^1	H-387
	TAKEDA (A,B,C)	$11\beta,17\alpha,21$-trihydroxy-4-pregnene-3,20-dione	Δ^1; further oxidation	I-427
bacterium isolated from yeast cake	NG	3β-hydroxy-5-androsten-17-one (product then reduced by yeast - 17-C=O →17β-OH - to testosterone - 17β-hydroxy-4-androsten-3-one)	$\Delta^5 \to \Delta^4$; 3β-OH →3-C=O	M-538
		17α-methyl-5-androstene-3β,17β-diol	$\Delta^5 \to \Delta^4$; 3β-OH →3-C=O	M-542
		3β-hydroxy-5-pregnen-20-one	$\Delta^5 \to \Delta^4$; 3β-OH →3-C=O	M-540
		5-cholesten-3β-ol	—	M-540
"faulnis bacterien" (putrefactive - anaerobic)	NG	5α-androstane-3,17-dione	3-C=O →3α-OH; 3-C=O→3β-OH	M-548
		17β-hydroxy-4-androsten-3-one	$\Delta^4 \to 5\beta$-H; 3-C=O →3α-OH	M-547; M-548
			$\Delta^4 \to 5\alpha$-H; 3-C=O→3β-OH	M-547; M-548
		4-androstene-3,17-dione	$\Delta^4 \to 5\alpha$-H	M-547
intestinal microorganisms (from male albino rats)	NG	5-cholesten-3α-ol	$\Delta^5 \to 5\beta$-H; 3α-OH→3β-OH	N-655
		5-cholesten-3β-ol	$\Delta^5 \to 5\beta$-H	N-655
		5-cholesten-3-one	$\Delta^5 \to 5\beta$-H; 3-C=O→3β-OH	N-655
		4,4-dimethyl-5-cholesten-3β-ol	—	N-655
		5,7-cholestadien-3β-ol	$\Delta^5 \to 5\beta$-H	N-655
		24-ethyl-5,22-cholestadien-3β-ol	$\Delta^5 \to 5\beta$-H	N-655

TABLE III

Transformations by Genus: UNIDENTIFIED

SPECIES	SOURCE	SUBSTRATE	REACTION	REF.
intestinal microorganisms (from male albino rats)	NG	24β-methyl-5,7,22-cholesta-trien-3β-ol	$\Delta^5 \to 5\beta$-H	N-655
		$3\alpha,7\alpha,12\alpha$-trihydroxy-5β-cholanic acid	7α-OH$\to$7-C=O	N-676
			7α-OH $\to$ H	N-676
			12α-OH$\to$12-C=O; 7α-OH$\to$H	N-676
			3α-OH$\to$3-C=O; 12α-OH$\to$12-C=O; 7α-OH$\to$H	N-676
bacteria - (22 isolates from 10 different source materials) (cholesterol - sole carbon source) (particularly active bacterium no. 5)	NG	1,3,5(10)-estratriene-3,17β-diol	utilization	S-793c
		1,3,5(10)-estratriene-3,16α,17β-triol	utilization	S-793c
		17β-hydroxy-4-androsten-3-one	utilization	S-793c
		3β-hydroxy-5-androsten-17-one	—	S-793c
		4-pregnene-3,20-dione	—	S-793c
		5-cholesten-3β-ol	utilization	S-793c
		5-cholesten-3β-ol acetate	utilization	S-793c
		5-cholesten-3β-ol palmitate	—	S-793c
		24β-methyl-5,7,22-cholesta-trien-3β-ol	—	S-793c
		3α-hydroxy-5β-cholanic acid	utilization	S-793c
		3α,6α-dihydroxy-5β-cholanic acid	—	S-793c
		3α,12α-dihydroxy-5β-cholanic acid	—	S-793c
		3α,7α,12α-trihydroxy-5β-cholanic acid	utilization	S-793c
basidiomycete (MEX - 25; 228)	AL (SS-70) (SS-50)	4-pregnene-3,20-dione	oxidation - products not identified	S-825
	AL (Z-9; 12)	4-pregnene-3,20-dione	oxidation - products not identified	S-825
bacterium (feces)	NG	5-cholesten-3β-ol	$\Delta^5 \to 5\beta$-H	S-914
soil microorganisms	NG	potassium 5α-cholestan-3β-ol sulfate	A ring cleavage	S-940

TABLE III

Transformations by Genus:

UNIDENTIFIED
USTILAGO (Basidio. - Ustilaginales)
VENTURIA (Asco. - Sphaeriales)
VERTICILLIUM (Imperf. - Moniliales)

SPECIES	SOURCE	SUBSTRATE	REACTION	REF.
soil microorganisms	NG	5-cholesten-3β-ol	$\Delta^5 \rightarrow \Delta^4$; 3β-OH $\rightarrow$3-C=O	S-940
		potassium 5-cholesten-3β-ol sulfate (substrate used to divert attack from 3-C position)	7-C=O (probably not microbiological)	S-940
bacteria (soil)	NG	5-cholesten-3β-ol (substrate added to soil to demonstrate degradation is the result of microbial action)	utilization	T-1029
fungus belonging to family - Dematiaceae	NG	17α,21-dihydroxy-4-pregnene-3,20-dione	20-C=O $\rightarrow$ 20β-OH	V-1045
fungus belonging to order - Melanconiales and Moniliales	Lepetit	17α,21-dihydroxy-1,4-pregna-diene-3,20-dione	11α-OH	T-990
			11β-OH	T-990
			14α-OH	T-990
USTILAGO				
zeae	NG	3β-hydroxy-5-pregnen-20-one	$\Delta^5 \rightarrow \Delta^4$; 3β-OH $\rightarrow$3-C=O	P-710
	NRRL	Sarsasapogenin	—	M-587
		Diosgenin	—	M-587
		4-dehydrotigogenone	—	M-587
VENTURIA				
pirma (pirina)	TNAES	17α,21-dihydroxy-4-pregnene-3,20-dione	—	S-849
VERTICILLIUM				
albo-atrum	IFO (5922)	17α,21-dihydroxy-4-pregnene-3,20-dione	—	K-468
dahliae	IFO (5916; 6119; 6126; 6150)	17α,21-dihydroxy-4-pregnene-3,20-dione	—	K-468
malthousii	IFO (6624)	17α,21-dihydroxy-4-pregnene-3,20-dione	6β-OH	K-468
			11α-OH	K-468

TABLE III

Transformations by Genus:

VERTICILLIUM
VIBRIO (Schizo. - Pseudomonadales)
VOLUTELLA (Imperf. - Moniliales)
WOJNOWICIA (Imperf. - Sphaeropsidales)

SPECIES	SOURCE	SUBSTRATE	REACTION	REF.
nieveostratosum	FRI	$17\alpha,21$-dihydroxy-4-pregnene-3,20-dione	—	S-849
	IFO (6625)	$17\alpha,21$-dihydroxy-4-pregnene-3,20-dione	6β-OH	K-468
species	NG	5-cholesten-3β-ol (sole carbon source)	—	S-793c
		24β-methyl-5,7,22-cholestatrien-3β-ol (sole carbon source)	—	S-793c
theobromae	CBS	$17\alpha,21$-dihydroxy-4-pregnene-3,20-dione	11α-OH	K-468
			11β-OH	K-468
(in mixed culture with Bacillus sphaericus - ATCC-7055 $[\Delta^1]$)			11α-OH; 11β-OH	K-468
VIBRIO				
cyclosites	NG	5-cholesten-3β-ol (sole carbon source)	—	T-1030
metschnikovu	IAM	$17\alpha,21$-dihydroxy-4-pregnene-3,20-dione	—	S-849
percolans	IFO (3348)	$11\beta,17\alpha,21$-trihydroxy-4-preg-nene-3,20-dione	—	I-428
(but in mixed culture with Mycococcus sp. A_1)			Δ^1	I-428
tyrogenes	IAM	$17\alpha,21$-dihydroxy-4-pregnene-3,20-dione	—	S-849
VOLUTELLA				
ciliata	Leo Pharm. Products, Denmark	17β-hydroxy-4-androsten-3-one	Δ^1	L-525
		17β-hydroxy-17α-methyl-4-androsten-3-one	Δ^1	L-525
		$17\alpha,21$-dihydroxy-4-pregnene-3,20-dione	Δ^1	L-525
WOJNOWICIA				
graminis	C	d,1-11β-hydroxy-3,20-diketo-4-pregnen-18-oic acid (18→11) lactone	d,1—d-21-OH + 1	W-1102
(in mixed culture with Trichothecium roseum $[17\alpha$-OH$]$)		d,1-11β-hydroxy-4-pregnene-3,18,20-trione	d,1—d-21-OH +1	W-1102

TABLE III

Transformations by Genus: WOJNOWICIA

SPECIES	SOURCE	SUBSTRATE	REACTION	REF.
graminis	CBS	17β-hydroxy-4-androsten-3-one	6β-OH	H-381
			12α-OH	H-381
			14α-OH ; 17β-OH $\rightarrow$17-C=O	H-381
			16α-OH	H-381
			16β-OH	H-381
			16-C=O	H-381
			17β-OH $\rightarrow$ 17-C=O	H-381
			Δ^{14}; 12α-OH	H-381
			16α-OH; $\Delta^{4}\rightarrow$ 5ξ-H; 3-C=O ?	H-381
		4-androstene-3,17-dione	6β-OH	H-381
			17-C=O $\rightarrow$ 17β-OH	H-381
			16α-OH; 17-C=O $\rightarrow17\beta$-OH	H-381
		4-pregnene-3,20-dione	21-OH	M-564
	NRRL -2472	4-pregnene-3,20-dione	21-OH	D-183; D-184
		11α-hydroxy-4-pregnene-3,20-dione	21-OH	D-183; D-184
		11β-hydroxy-4-pregnene-3,20-dione	21-OH	D-184
		17α-hydroxy-4-pregnene-3,20-dione	21-OH	D-184
		17α,21-dihydroxy-4-pregnene-3,20-dione	21-OH	D-184
		11β,12β-oxido-4-pregnene-3,20-dione	21-OH	D-156; D-157
		11β,12β-oxido-1,4-pregnadiene-3,20-dione	21-OH	D-157
(in sequential fermentation with one or the other of Curvularia lunata [11β-OH] Trichoderma [17α-OH] Cunninghamella [11β-OH] Penicillium [11α-OH] Omphaliatra [11β-OH])		4-pregnene-3,20-dione	21-OH	M-566; M-567

TABLE III

Transformations by Genus: WOJNOWICIA
XANTHOMONAS   (Schizo. - Pseudomonadales)
XEROMPHALINA   (Basidio. - Agaricales)
XYLARIA   (Asco. - Sphaeriales)
YEAST

SPECIES	SOURCE	SUBSTRATE	REACTION	REF.
graminis (in sequential fermentation with Curvularia lunata [11β-OH])	NRRL-2472	17α-hydroxy-4-pregnene-3,20-dione	21-OH	M-566; M-567
XANTHOMONAS (see Phytomonas)				
citri	FAKU	17α,21-dihydroxy-4-pregnene-3,20-dione	Δ^1	S-849
malvacerum	IFO (3383)	11β,17α,21-trihydroxy-4-pregnene-3,20-dione	—	I-428
(in mixed culture with Mycococcus sp. A₁)			—	I-428
XEROMPHALINA				
tenuipes	AL (SS-6)	4-pregnene-3,20-dione	oxidation - products not identified	S-825
XYLARIA				
polymorpha	FRI	17α,21-dihydroxy-4-pregnene-3,20-dione	11α-OH	S-849
species	Searle (M-40-6)	4-androstene-3,17-dione	1β-OH	D-165
			7β-OH	D-165
			15β-OH	D-165
			1β,6β-diOH	D-165
YEAST				

see under the following
genera:
  CANDIDA
  DEBARYOMYCES
  ENDOMYCES
  EREMASCUS
  HANSENULA
  KLOECKERA
  MONILIA
  NADSONIA
  OIDIUM
  OOSPORA
  PICHIA
  PSEUDOMYCODERMA
  RHODOTORULA

(continued)

TABLE III

Transformations by Genus: YEAST
ZYGORHYNCHUS (Phyco. - Mucorales)

SPECIES	SOURCE	SUBSTRATE	REACTION	REF.
see under the following genera: SACCHAROMYCES SACCHAROMYCODES SPOROBOLOMYCES TORULA TORULOPSIS ' ' ZYGORHYNCHUS				
heterogamus	SSSR	$17\alpha,21$-dihydroxy-4-pregnene-3,20-dione	6β-OH; 11α-OH	E-224
	U	4-pregnene-3,20-dione	oxidation	M-601; M-636
		17α-hydroxy-4-pregnene-3,20-dione	oxidation	M-601; M-636
		21-hydroxy-4-pregnene-3,20-dione	oxidation	M-601; M-636
		$17\alpha,21$-dihydroxy-4-pregnene-3,20-dione	oxidation	M-601; M-636
moelleri	SSSR	$17\alpha,21$-dihydroxy-4-pregnene-3,20-dione	6β-OH	E-224
	U	4-pregnene-3,20-dione	oxidation	M-601; M-636
		17α-hydroxy-4-pregnene-3,20-dione	oxidation	M-601; M-636
		21-hydroxy-4-pregnene-3,20-dione	oxidation	M-601; M-636
		$17\alpha,21$-dihydroxy-4-pregnene-3,20-dione	oxidation	M-601; M-636

CHAPTER VI

BIBLIOGRAPHY

References A-1 through Z-1134 are included in this chapter.

A-1   Adams, W. J., Patel, D. K., Petrow, V., and Stuart-Webb, I. A., J. Chem. Soc., p. 297 (1956).

A-2   Agnello, E. J., Bloom, B. M., and Laubach, G. D., J. Am. Chem. Soc. 77, 4684 (1955).

A-3   Agnello, E. J., Bloom, B. M., and Laubach, G. D., U.S. Patent 2,835,683 (May 20, 1958).

A-4   Agnello, E. J., Bloom, B. M., and Laubach, G. D., U.S. Patent 2,835,684 (May 20, 1958).

A-5   Agnello, E. J., Bloom, B. M., and Laubach, G. D., U.S. Patent 2,976,283 (March 21, 1961).

A-6   Agnello, E. J., Figdor, S. K., Hughes, G. M. K., Ordway, H. W., Pinson, R., Jr., Bloom, B. M., and Laubach, G. D., J. Org. Chem. 28, 1531 (1963).

A-7   Agnello, E. J., Laubach, G. D., and Moreland, W. T., U.S. Patent 3,067,197 (December 4, 1962).

A-8   Allen, W. S., Bernstein, S., Feldman, L. I., and Weiss, M. J., J. Am. Chem. Soc. 82, 3696 (1960).

A-9   Allen, W. S., and Feldman, L. I., U.S. Patent 3,010,877 (November 28, 1961).

A-10   Amiard, G., and Heymes, R., U.S. Patent 3,005,816 (October 24, 1961).

A-11   Amiard, G., and Heymes, R., U.S. Patent 3,033,863 (May 8, 1962).

A-12   Amiard, G., and Heymes, R., U.S. Patent 3,052,697 (September 4, 1962).

A-13   Amiard, G., Heymes, R., and Thuong, T. V., U.S. Patent 3,081,300 (March 12, 1963).

A-14   Arnaudi, C., Boll. Sez. Ital. Soc. Intern. Microbiol. 11, 208 (1939).

A-15   Arnaudi, C., Boll. Ist. Sieroterap. Milan. 21, 1 (1942).

A-16   Arnaudi, C., Zentr. Bakteriol., Parasitenk., Abt. I. Orig. 105, 352 (1942).

A-17   Arnaudi, C., Boll. Ist. Sieroterap. Milan. 21, 1-12 (1942).

A-18   Arnaudi, C., Experientia 2, 138 (1946).

A-19   Arnaudi, C., Rend. Ist. Lombardo Sci. Lettere, Pt. I 83, 151-164 (1950).

A-20   Arnaudi, C., Experientia 7, 81 (1951). REVIEW.

A-21   Arnaudi, C., Appl. Microbiol. 2, 274 (1954). REVIEW.

A-22   Arnaudi, C., and Colla, C., Experientia 5, 120 (1949).

A-23   Arnaudi, C., and Ercoli, A., Boll. Ist. Sieroterap. Milan. 20, 137 (1941).

A-24   Arth, G. E., Beyler, R. E., and Sarett, L. H., U.S. Patent 3,004,994
            (October 17, 1961).

A-25   Arth, G. E., Beyler, R. E., and Sarett, L. H., U.S. Patent 3,054,811
            (September 18, 1962).

A-26   Asai, T., Aida, K., Ohki, E., Tanaka, T., and Hattori, M., J. Agr. Chem. Soc.
            Japan 32, 723 (1958).

A-27   Asai, T., Aida, K., Tanaka, T., Ohki, E., Matsuhisa, T., Takeda, Y., and Inui,
            T., J. Gen. Appl. Microbiol. (Tokyo) 5, 127 (1959).

A-28   Asai, T., Aida, K., Tanaka, T., and Sato, Yoshihiro, J. Agr. Chem. Soc. Japan
            35, 122 (1961).

A-29   Asai, T., Tsuda, K., Aida, K., Ohki, E., Tanaka, T., Hattori, M., and Machida,
            H., J. Gen. Appl. Microbiol. (Tokyo) 4, 63 (1958).

A-30   Asai, T., Tsuda, K., Aida, K., Ohki, E., Tanaka, T., and Hattori, M., J. Gen.
            Appl. Microbiol. (Tokyo), 4, 79 (1958).

A-31   Ayer, D. E., U.S. Patent 3,056,808 (October 2, 1962).

B-32   Baba, S., Brodie, H. J., Hayano, M., Peterson, D. H., and Sebek, O. K.,
            Steroids 1, 151 (1963).

B-33   Babcock, J. C., and Campbell, J. A., U.S. Patent 2,838,534 (June 10, 1958).

B-34   Babcock, J. C., Campbell, J. A., and Hogg, J. A., U.S. Patent 2,838,531
            (June 10, 1958).

B-35   Babcock, J. C., Campbell, J. A., Hogg, J. A., and Sebek, O. K., U.S. Patent
            2,838,544 (June 10, 1958).

B-36   Babcock, J. C., and Pederson, R. L., U.S. Patent 2,971,886 (February 14, 1961).

B-37   Badia, D. J., and Sardinas, J. L., U.S. Patent 3,010,876 (November 28, 1961).

B-38   Bagli, J. P., Morand, P. F., Wiesner, K., and Gaudry, R., Tetrahedron Letters,
            p. 387 (1964).

B-39   Baichikov, A. G., Barmenkov, A. S., and Eroshin, V. K., Med. Prom. SSSR 13,
            15 (1959). REVIEW.

B-40   Barber, G. W., Peterson, D. H., and Ehrenstein, M., J. Org. Chem. 25, 1168
            (1960).

B-41   Barkemeyer, H. R., Stoudt, T. H., Chemerda, J. M., Kozlowski, M. A., and
            McAleer, W. J., Appl. Microbiol. 8, 237 (1960).

B-42   Barmenkov, A. S., Fedotiva, M. V., Eroshin, V. K., Gusakova, E. G., and
            Ogareva, O. B., Med. Prom. SSSR 15, 39 (1961).

B-43   Beal, P. F., Hogg, J. A., and Jackson, R. W., U.S. Patent 2,989,523 (June 20,
            1961).

B-44   Beal, P. F., and Kagan, F., U.S. Patent 3,053,864 (September 11, 1962).

B-45   Beesch, S. C., and Shull, G. M., Ind. Eng. Chem. 47, 1857 (1955). REVIEW.

B-46   Beesch, S. C., and Shull, G. M., Ind. Eng. Chem. 48, 1585 (1956). REVIEW.

B-47   Beesch, S. C., and Shull, G. M., Ind. Eng. Chem. 49, 1491 (1957). REVIEW.

B-48   Beesch, S. C., and Tanner, F. W., Jr., Ind. Eng. Chem. 50, 1341 (1958). REVIEW.

B-49   Beesch, S. C., and Tanner, F. W., Jr., Ind. Eng. Chem. 51, 1086 (1959). REVIEW.

B-50   Benetti, R. T., Ann. Microbiol. 5, 1 (1952).

B-51   Berg, R. G., and Laubach, G. D., U.S. Patent 3,022,297 (February 20, 1962).

B-52   Bergstrom, C. G., U.S. Patent 2,703,799 (March 8, 1955).

B-53   Bernhauer, K., Ergeb. Enzymforsch. 11, 219 (1944). REVIEW.

B-54   Bernstein, S., and Allen, W. S., U.S. Patent 2,806,043 (September 10, 1957).

B-55   Bernstein, S., Allen, W. S., Heller, M., Lenhard, R. H., Feldman, L. I., and Blank, R. H., J. Org. Chem. 24, 286 (1959).

B-56   Bernstein, S., Feldman, L. I., Allen, W. S., and Blank, R. H., U.S. Patent 2,962,512 (November 29, 1960).

B-57   Bernstein, S., Feldman, L. I., Allen, W. S., Blank, R. H., and Linden, C. E., Chem. & Ind. (London), p. 111 (1956).

B-58   Bernstein, S., Heller, M., Feldman, L. I., Allen, W. S., Blank, R. H., and Linden, C. E., J. Am. Chem. Soc. 82, 3685 (1960).

B-59   Bernstein, S., Lenhard, R. H., and Allen, W. S., U.S. Patent 2,789,118 (April 16, 1957).

B-60   Bernstein, S., Lenhard, R. H., Allen, W. S., Heller, M., Littell, R., Stolar, S. M., Feldman, L. I., and Blank, R. H., J. Am. Chem. Soc. 78, 5693 (1956).

B-61   Bernstein, S., Lenhard, R. H., Allen, W. S., Heller, M., Littell, R., Stolar, S. M., Feldman, L. I., and Blank, R. H., J. Am. Chem. Soc. 81, 1689 (1959).

B-62   Bernstein, S., Lenhard, R. H., Rigler, N. E., and Darken, M. A., J. Org. Chem. 25, 297 (1960).

B-63   Blank, R. H., Shay, A. J., Pruess, L. M., and Rigler, N. E., U.S. Patent 2,982,695 (May 2, 1961).

B-64   Bloom, B. M., Hayano, M., Saito, A., Stone, D., and Dorfman, R. I., Federation Proc. 15, 222 (1956).

B-65   Bloom, B. M., Kita, D. A., Laubach, G. D., and Shull, G. M., U.S. Patent 2,891,080 (June 16, 1959).

B-66   Bloom, B. M., and Shull, G. M., J. Am. Chem. Soc. 77, 5767 (1955).

B-67   Bodanszky, A., Kollonitsch, J., and Wix, G., Experientia 11, 384 (1955).

B-68   Bork, K. H., Bruckner, K., Mannhardt, H. J., Metz, H., and von Werder, F., U.S. Patent 3,064,015 (November 13, 1962).

B-69   Bork, K. H., Bruckner, K., and Metz, H., Naturwiss. 50, 42 (1963).

B-70   Bourgain, L., Ph. D. Thesis, University of Nancy, France (1956).

B-71   Bowers, A., Casas-Campillo, C., and Djerassi, C., Tetrahedron 2, 165 (1958).

B-72   Bowers, A., Casas-Campillo, C., Zderic, J. A., and Djerassi, C., U.S. Patent 3,067,212 (December 4, 1962).

B-73   Bowers, A., Mills, J. S., Casas-Campillo, C., and Djerassi, C., J. Org. Chem. 27, 361 (1962).

B-74   Bowers, A., and Ringold, H. J., U.S. Patent 3,037,976 (June 5, 1962).

B-75   Bowers, A., and Ringold, H. J., U.S. Patent 3,050,534 (August 21, 1962).

B-75a   Brodie, H. J., Hayano, M., and Gut, M., J. Am. Chem. Soc. 84, 3766 (1962).

B-76   Bruckner, K., Irmscher, K., von Werder, F., Bork, K. H., and Metz, H., Ber. 94, 2897 (1961).

B-77   Burn, D., Ellis, B., and Petrow, V., J. Chem. Soc., p. 795 (1958).

B-78   Butenandt, A., and Dannenberg, H., Ber. 71, 1681 (1938).

B-79   Butenandt, A., and Dannenberg, H., Naturwiss. 30, 52 (1942).

B-80   Butenandt, A., Dannenberg, H., and Suranyi, L. A., Ber. 73, 818 (1940).

B-81   Butenandt, A., and Suranyi, L. A., Ber. 75, 591 (1942).

C-82   Camerino, B., Alberti, C. G., and Vercellone, A., Gazz. Chim. Ital. 83, 684 (1953).

C-83   Camerino, B., Alberti, C. G., and Vercellone, A., Helv. Chim. Acta 36, 1945 (1953).

C-84   Camerino, B., Alberti, C. G., Vercellone, A., and Ammannati, F., Gazz. Chim. Ital. 84, 301 (1954).

C-85   Camerino, B., and Modelli, R., Gazz. Chim. Ital. 86, 1219 (1956).

C-86   Camerino, B., Modelli, R., and Spalla, C., Gazz. Chim. Ital. 86, 1226 (1956).

C-87   Camerino, B., and Sciaky, R., Gazz. Chim. Ital. 89, 654 (1959).

C-88   Camerino, B., and Vercellone, A., Gazz. Chim. Ital., 86, 260 (1956).

C-89   Camerino, B., and Vercellone, A., U.S. Patent 2,866,736 (December 30, 1958).

C-90   Camerino, B., and Vercellone, A., U.S. Patent 2,880,141 (March 31, 1959).

C-91   Campbell, J. A., Babcock, J. C., and Hogg, J. A., U.S. Patent 3,004,044 (October 10, 1961).

C-92   Campbell, J. A., Babcock, J. C., and Wechter, W. J., U.S. Patent 3,086,029 (April 16, 1963).

C-93   Campbell, J. A., Pederson, R. L., Babcock, J. C., and Hogg, J. A., U.S. Patent 2,877,240 (March 10, 1959).

C-94   Canonica, L., Pacini, N., Scolastico, C., and Valcavi, U., Gazz. Chim. Ital. 93, 301 (1963).

C-95   Canonica, L., Pacini, N., Scolastico, C., and Valcavi, U., Gazz. Chim. Ital. 93, 787 (1963).

C-96   Canonica, L., Valcavi, U., and Scolastico, C., Gazz. Chim. Ital. 93, 368 (1963).

C-97   Čapek, A., and Hanč, O., Folia Microbiol. (Prague) 5, 251 (1960).

C-98   Čapek, A., and Hanč, O., Folia Microbiol. (Prague) 6, 237 (1961).

C-99   Čapek, A., and Hanč, O., Folia Microbiol. (Prague) 7, 121 (1962).

C-100   Čapek, A., and Hanč, O., Folia Microbiol. (Prague) 7, 181 (1962).

C-101   Čapek, A., Hanč, O., Kakác, B., and Tadra, M., Folia Microbiol. (Prague) 7, 175 (1962).

C-102   Čapek, A., Hanč, O., Macek, K., Tadra, M., and Riedl-Tumová, E., Naturwiss. 43, 471 (1956).

C-103   Čapek, A., Hanč, O., and Malíková, E., Cesk. Mikrobiol. 2, 282 (1957).

C-104   Čapek, A., Hanč, O., and Pavlu, H., Cesk. Mikrobiol. 2, 168 (1957).

C-105   Čapek, A., Hanč, O., and Tadra, M., Folia Microbiol. (Prague) 8, 120 (1963).

C-106   Čapek, A., Pavlu, H., and Hanč, O., Naturwiss. 45, 89 (1958).

C-107   Čapek, A., Pavlu, H., and Hanč, O., Folia Biol. (Prague) 4, 337 (1958).

C-108   Carvajal, F., U.S. Patent 2,887,499 (May 19, 1959).

C-109   Carvajal, F., U.S. Patent 2,985,563 (May 23, 1961).

C-110   Carvajal, F., Vitale, O. F., Gentles, M. J., Herzog, H. L., and Hershberg,
        E. B., J. Org. Chem. 24, 695 (1959).

C-111   Casas-Campillo, C., Rev. Latinoam. Microbiol. Suppl. 6, 1 (1960). REVIEW.

C-112   Casas-Campillo, C., and Bautista, M., Proc. 4th Natl. Mex. Congr. Microbiol.,
        p. 45 (1962).

C-113   Casas-Campillo, C., and Esparza, F., Proc. 8th Intl. Congr. Microbiol., Montreal,
        1962, Abstr., p. 71. Univ. of Toronto Press, Toronto, 1963.

C-114   Casas-Campillo, C., Esparza, F., and Balandrano, D., Bacteriol. Proc. p. 11
        (1964).

C-115   Casas-Campillo, C., and Jimenez, L., Proc. 4th Natl. Mex. Congr. Microbiol.,
        p. 17 (1962).

C-116   Casas-Campillo, C., and Magana-Plaza, I., Bacteriol. Proc., p. 170 (1961).

C-117   Casas-Campillo, C., and Ruiz-Herrera, J., Rev. Latinoam. Microbiol. 3, 213
        (1960).

C-118   Casas-Campillo, C., and Ruiz-Herrera, J., Rev. Latinoam. Microbiol. 3, 151
        (1960).

C-119   Casas-Campillo, C., Ruiz-Herrera, J., and Balandrano, D., Bacteriol. Proc.,
        p. 33 (1960).

C-120   Caspi, E., Schmid, W., and Khan, B. T., Tetrahedron 18, 767 (1962).

C-121   Cella, J. A., U.S. Patent 2,900,383 (August 18, 1959).

C-122   Chang, V. M., and Idler, D. R., Can. J. Biochem. Physiol. 39, 1277 (1961).

C-123   Charney, W., Abstr. 130th Meeting Am. Chem. Soc. Atlantic City, 1956 p. 32A.

C-124   Charney, W., Proc. 7th Intern. Congr. Microbiol., Stockholm, 1958, p. 401.
        Almqvist & Wiksell, Uppsala, 1958.

C-125   Charney, W., U.S. Patent 2,951,016 (August 30, 1960).

C-126   Charney, W., Herzog, H. L., and Sutter, D., U.S. Patent 2,958,631 (November 1,
        1960).

C-127   Charney, W., Herzog, H. L., and Sutter, D., U.S. Patent 3,014,051
        (December 19, 1961).

C-128   Charney, W., Nobile, A., Federbush, C., Sutter, D., Perlman, P. L., Herzog,
        H. L., Payne, C. C., Tully, M. E., Gentles, M. J., and Hershberg, E. B.,
        Tetrahedron 18, 591 (1962).

C-129   Charney, W., Weber, L., and Oliveto, E., Arch. Biochem. Biophys. 79, 402
        (1959).

C-130   Chen, J. W., Hills, F. J., Koepsell, H. J., and Maxon, W. D., Abstr. 145th
        Meeting Am. Chem. Soc., New York, 1963, p. 16 P.

C-131   Christensen, B. G., Hirschmann, R. F., and Chemerda, J. M., U. S. Patent 3,
        087,925 (April 30, 1963).

C-132   Chen, J. W., Koepsell, H. J., and Maxon, W. D., Biotechnol. Bioeng. 4, 65
         (1962).

C-133   Coleman, D. L., and Baumann, C. A., Arch. Biochem. Biophys. 72, 219 (1957).

C-134   Colingsworth, D. R., Brunner, M. P., and Haines, W. J., J. Am. Chem. Soc.
         74, 2381 (1952).

C-135   Colingsworth, D. R., Karnemaat, J. N., Hanson, F. R., Brunner, M. P., Mann,
         K. M., and Haines, W. J., J. Biol. Chem. 203, 807 (1953).

C-136   Colla, C., Ann. Microbiol. 5, 207 (1953).

C-137   Corey, E. J., Gregoriou, G. A., and Peterson, D. H., J. Am. Chem. Soc. 80,
         2338 (1958).

C-138   Coronelli, C., Kluepfel, D., and Sensi, P., Experientia 20, 208 (1964).

C-139   Crabbe, P., and Casas-Campillo, C., J. Org. Chem. 29, 2731 (1964).

C-140   Curran, G. L., and Brewster, K. C., Bull. Johns Hopkins Hosp. 91, 68 (1952).

C-141   Cutler, F. A., Jr., and Chemerda, J. M., U.S. Patent 3,116,290 (December 31,
         1963).

D-142   Damiens, R., Pharmazie 11, 81 (1956). REVIEW.

D-143   Dannenberg, H., and Neumann, H.G., Ann. 646, 148 (1961).

D-144   Davidson, S. J., and Talalay, P., Federation Proc. 23, 275 (1964).

D-145   Davis, J. R., Brown, R. L., Lewis, H. L., and Peterson, G. E., Bacteriol.
         Proc., p. 105 (1964).

D-146   Davisson, J. W., U.S. Patent 2,830,937 (April 15, 1958).

D-147   Davisson, J. W., Kita, D. A., and Routien, J. B., U.S. Patent 2,848,370
         (August 19, 1958).

D-148   de Flines, J., Marx, A. F., van der Waard, E. P., and van der Sijde, D., Tetra-
         hedron Letters, p. 1257 (1962).

D-149   de Flines, J., van der Waard, W. F., Mijs, W., and Szpilfogel, S., Rec. Trav.
         Chim. 82, 121 (1963).

D-150   de Flines, J., van der Waard, W. F., Mijs, W. J., and Szpilfogel, S. A., Rev.
         Trav. Chim. 82, 129 (1963).

D-151   de Flines, J., van der Waard, W. F., Mijs, W. J., and Szpilfogel, S. A., Rec.
         Trav. Chim. 82, 143 (1963).

D-152   de Flines, J., van der Waard, W. F., Mijs, W. J., van Dijck, L. A., and
         Szpilfogel, S. A., Rev. Trav. Chim. 82, 139 (1963).

D-153   de Flines, J., van der Waard, W. F., Mijs, W. J., van Dijck, L. A., and
         Szpilfogel, S. A., Rec. Trav. Chim. 82, 149 (1963).

D-154   Deindoerfer, F. H., Mateles, R. I., and Humphrey, A. E., Appl. Microbiol. 11,
         273 (1963). REVIEW.

D-155   Delin, S., and Porath, J., Biochim. Biophys. Acta 67, 197 (1963).

D-156   Diassi, P. A., U.S. Patent 3,093,637 (June 11, 1963).

D-157   Diassi, P. A., Laskin, A. I., and Principe, P. A., U.S. Patent 3,060,176
         (October 23, 1962).

D-158   Diassi, P. A., and Pan, S. C., U.S. Patent 3,083,210 (March 26, 1963).

D-159   Diassi, P. A., and Principe, P. A., U.S. Patent 3,079,384 (February 26, 1963).

D-160   Dodson, R. M., and Bergstrom, C. G., U.S. Patent 2,705,711 (April 5, 1955).

D-161   Dodson, R. M., and Bergstrom, C. G., U.S. Patent 2,951,857 (September 6, 1960).

D-162   Dodson, R. M., Goldkamp, A. H., and Muir, R. D., J. Am. Chem. Soc. $\underline{79}$, 3921 (1957).

D-163   Dodson, R. M., Goldkamp, A. H., and Muir, R. D., J. Am. Chem. Soc. $\underline{82}$, 4026 (1960).

D-164   Dodson, R. M., Goldkamp, A. H., and Pappo, R., U.S. Patent 2,833,792 (May 6, 1958).

D-165   Dodson, R. M., Kraychy, S., Nicholson, R. T., and Mizuba, S., J. Org. Chem. $\underline{27}$, 3159 (1962).

D-166   Dodson, R. M., and Mizuba, S., J. Org. Chem. $\underline{27}$, 698 (1962).

D-167   Dodson, R. M., and Muir, R. D., U.S. Patent 2,805,231 (September 3, 1957).

D-168   Dodson, R. M., and Muir, R. D., U.S. Patent 2,833,793 (May 6, 1958).

D-169   Dodson, R. M., and Muir, R. D., J. Am. Chem. Soc. $\underline{80}$, 5004 (1958).

D-170   Dodson, R. M., and Muir, R. D., J. Am. Chem. Soc. $\underline{80}$, 6148 (1958).

D-171   Dodson, R. M., and Muir, R. D., J. Am. Chem. Soc. $\underline{83}$, 4627 (1961).

D-172   Dodson, R. M., and Muir, R. D., J. Am. Chem. Soc. $\underline{83}$, 4631 (1961).

D-173   Dodson, R. M., and Muir, R. D., U.S. Patent 3,029,233 (April 10, 1962).

D-174   Dodson, R. M., Newman, N., and Tsuchiya, H. M., J. Org. Chem. $\underline{27}$, 2707 (1962).

D-175   Dodson, R. M., Nicholson, R. T., and Muir, R. D., J. Am. Chem. Soc. $\underline{81}$, 6295 (1959).

D-176   Dodson, R. M., and Sollman, P. B., U.S. Patent 2,999,101 (September 5, 1961).

D-177   Dodson, R. M., and Tweit, R. C., U.S. Patent 2,924,611 (February 9, 1960).

D-178   Donia, R. A., and Johnson, B. A., U.S. Patent 2,817,670 (December 24, 1957).

D-179   Donin, M. N., Fried, J., and Thoma, R. W., U.S. Patent 2,881,189 (April 7, 1959).

D-180   Donin, M. N., Fried, J., and Thoma, R. W., U.S. Patent 2,960,435 (November 15, 1960).

D-181   Dulaney, E. L., U.S. Patent 2,905,593 (September 22, 1959).

D-182   Dulaney, E. L., and McAleer, W. J., U.S. Patent 2,802,775 (August 13, 1957).

D-182a   Dulaney, E. L., and McAleer, W. J., U.S. Patent 2,813,060 (November 12, 1957).

D-183   Dulaney, E. L., and McAleer, W. J., U.S. Patent 2,819,200 (January 7, 1958).

D-184   Dulaney, E. L., and McAleer, W. J., U.S. Patent 2,819,201 (January 7, 1958).

D-185   Dulaney, E. L., and McAleer, W. J., U.S. Patent 2,863,806 (December 9, 1958).

D-186   Dulaney, E. L., and McAleer, W. J., U.S. Patent 2,875,133 (February 24, 1959).

D-187   Dulaney, E. L., and McAleer, W. J., U.S. Patent 2,888,469 (May 26, 1959).

D-188   Dulaney, E. L., and McAleer, W. J., U.S. Patent 2,970,085 (January 31, 1961).

D-189   Dulaney, E. L., McAleer, W. J., Barkemeyer, H. R., and Hlavac, C., Appl.
           Microbiol. 3, 372 (1955).

D-190   Dulaney, E. L., McAleer, W. J., Koslowski, M., Stapley, E. O., and Jaglom, J.,
           Appl. Microbiol. 3, 336 (1955).

D-191   Dulaney, E. L., McAleer, W. J., and Stoudt, T., U.S. Patent 2,960,434
           (November 15, 1960).

D-192   Dulaney, E. L., and Stapley, E. O., Appl. Microbiol. 7, 276 (1959).

D-193   Dulaney, E. L., Stapley, E. O., and Hlavac, C., Myclogia 47, 464 (1955).

E-194   Eguchi, T., J. Biochem. (Tokyo) 44, 81 (1957).

E-195   El-Tayeb, O. M., and Sih, C. J., Bacteriol. Proc. (Soc. Am. Bacteriologists),
           63, 106 (1963).

E-195a   Emerman, S. L., and Levitz, M., Steroids 3, 351 (1964).

E-196   Enthoven, R. H., Chem. Weekblad 52, 166 (1956). REVIEW.

E-197   Eppstein, S. H., and Leigh, H. M., U.S. Patent 2,697,715 (December 21, 1954).

E-198   Eppstein, S. H., and Leigh, H. M., U.S. Patent 2,697,716 (December 21, 1954).

E-199   Eppstein, S. H., and Leigh, H. M., U.S. Patent 2,742,486 (April 17, 1956).

E-200   Eppstein, S. H., and Leigh, H. M., U.S. Patent 2,759,004 (August 14, 1956).

E-201   Eppstein, S. H., Meister, P. D., Leigh, H. M., Peterson, D. H., Murray, H. C.,
           Reineke, L. M., and Weintraub, A., J. Am. Chem. Soc. 76, 3174 (1954).

E-202   Eppstein, S. H., Meister, P. D., Murray, H. C., and Peterson, D. H., Vitamins
           Hormones 14, 359 (1956). REVIEW.

E-203   Eppstein, S. H., Meister, P. D., Peterson, D. H., Murray, H. C., Leigh, H. M.,
           Lyttle, D. A., Reineke, L. M., and Weintraub, A., J. Am. Chem. Soc. 75, 408
           (1953).

E-204   Eppstein, S. H., Meister, P. D., Peterson, D. H., Murray, H. C., Osborn,
           H. M. Leigh, Weintraub, A., Reineke, L. M., and Meeks, R. C., J. Am. Chem.
           Soc. 80, 3382 (1958).

E-205   Eppstein, S. H., Meister, P. D., and Weintraub, A., U.S. Patent 2,864,831
           (December 16, 1958).

E-206   Eppstein, S. H., Meister, P. D., and Weintraub, A., U.S. Patent 2,864,832
           (December 16, 1958).

E-207   Eppstein, S. H., Meister, P. D., and Weintraub, A., U.S. Patent 2,874,169
           (February 17, 1959).

E-208   Eppstein, S. H., Meister, P. D., and Weintraub, A., U.S. Patent 2,883,400
           (April 21, 1959).

E-209   Eppstein, S. H., Peterson, D. H., Leigh, H. M., Murray, H. C., Weintraub, A.,
           Reineke, L. M., and Meister, P. D., J. Am. Chem. Soc. 75, 421 (1953).

E-210   Ercoli, A. Ber. 71, 650 (1938).

E-211   Ercoli, A., Ber. 72, 190 (1939).

E-212   Ercoli, A., Chim. Ind. (Milan) 22, 449 (1940).

E-213   Ercoli, A., Chim. Ind. (Milan) 22, 14 (1940).

E-214   Ercoli, A., Boll. Sci. Fac. Chim. Ind. Bologna 18, 279 (1940).

E-215   Ercoli, A., Biochim. Terap. Sper. 28, 125 (1941).

E-216   Ercoli, A., Biochim. Terap. Sper. 28, 215 (1941).

E-217   Ercoli, A., Z. Physiol. Chem. 270, 266 (1941).

E-218   Ercoli, A., and Mamoli, L., Ber. 71, 156 (1938).

E-219   Ercoli, A., and Molina, L., Boll. Ist. Sieroterap. Milan. 23, 158 (1944).

E-220   Ercoli, A., and Molina, L., Boll. Ist. Sieroterap. Milan. 23, 175 (1944).

E-221   Ercoli, A., and de Ruggieri, P., Boll. Soc. Ital. Biol. Sper. 28, 611 (1952).

E-222   Ercoli, A., and de Ruggieri, P., Gazz. Chim. Ital. 84, 479 (1954).

E-223   Ercoli, A., de Ruggieri, P., and Della Morte, D., Gazz. Chim. Ital. 85, 628 (1955).

E-224   Eroshin, V. K., Mikrobiologiya 31, 608 (1962).

E-225   Eroshin, V. K., and Krasilnikov, N. A., Dokl. Akad. Nauk SSSR 137, 968 (1961).

E-226   Esparza, F., Balandrano, D., and Servin, B., Proc. 4th Natl. Mex. Congr. Micro-
         biol., p. 46 (1962).

E-227   Esparza, F., and Servin, B., Proc. 4th Natl. Mex. Congr. Microbiol., p. 47
         (1962).

F-228   Federbush, C., M. S. Thesis, New York University (1959).

F-229   Feldman, L. I., and Allen, W. S., U.S. Patent 2,789,940 (April 23, 1957).

F-230   Feldman, L. I., Holmlund, C. E., and Barbacci, N. L., Abstr. 140th Meeting Am.
         Chem. Soc., Chicago, 1961, p. 1 P.

F-231   Feldman, L. I., Holmlund, C. E., and Barbacci, N. L., U.S. Patent 3,087,864
         (April 30, 1963).

F-232   Feldman, L. I., Holmlund, C. E., and Barbacci, N. L., U.S. Patent 3,091,575
         (May 28, 1963).

F-233   Feldman, L. I., Nielsen, B. E., and Mowat, J. H., U.S. Patent 3,037,914
         (June 5, 1962).

F-234   Feldman, L. I., Pruess, L. M., and Rigler, N. E., U.S. Patent 3,039,937
         (June 19, 1962).

F-235   Feldman, L. I., Rigler, N. E., Holmlund, C. E., and Nielsen, B., U.S. Patent
         3,063,991 (November 13, 1962).

F-236   Feldman, L. I., Rigler, N. E., Holmlund, C. E., and Nielsen, B., U.S. Patent
         3,091,576 (May 28, 1963).

F-237   Feldman, L. I., Rigler, N. E., and Shay, A. J., U.S. Patent 2,962,423
         (November 29, 1960).

F-238   Feldman, L. I., Rigler, N. E., Shay, A. J., and Nielsen, B., U.S. Patent
         3,037,912 (June 5, 1962).

F-239   Feldman, L. I., Rigler, N. E., Shay, A. J., and Nielsen, B., U.S. Patent
         3,060,101 (October 23, 1962).

F-240   Feldman, L. I., Shay, A. J., and Rigler, N. E., U.S. Patent 3,037,913 (June 5,
         1962).

F-241   Ferrari, R. A., and Arnold, A., Biochim. Biophys. Acta 77, 349 (1963).

F-242   Ferrari, R. A., and Arnold, A., Biochim. Biophys. Acta 77, 357 (1963).

F-243   Figdor, S. K., Pinson, E. R., Jr., Bloom, B. M., and Laubach, G. D., U.S.
           Patent 3,045,010 (July 17, 1962).

F-244   Finch, C. A., Mfg. Chemist 25, 247 (1954). REVIEW.

F-245   Fischer, F. G., "Newer Methods of Preparative Organic Chemistry," Vol. I,
           p. 159. Wiley (Interscience), New York, 1948. REVIEW.

F-246   Florey, K., Chimia 8, 81 (1954). REVIEW.

F-247   Fonken, G. S., Levin, R. H., and McIntosh, A. V., Jr., U.S. Patent 2,714,599
           (August 2, 1955).

F-248   Fonken, G. S., Levin, R. H., and McIntosh, A. V., Jr., U.S. Patent 2,714,600
           (August 2, 1955).

F-249   Fonken, G. S., and Murray, H. C., U.S. Patent 2,913,457 (November 17, 1959).

F-250   Fonken, G. S., and Murray, H. C., U.S. Patent 2,967,803 (January 10, 1961).

F-251   Fonken, G. S., and Murray, H. C., U.S. Patent 2,981,659 (April 25, 1961).

F-252   Fonken, G. S., and Murray, H. C., U.S. Patent 3,007,950 (November 7, 1961).

F-253   Fonken, G. S., and Murray, H. C., J. Org. Chem. 27, 1102 (1962).

F-254   Fonken, G. S., Murray, H. C., and Reineke, L. M., J. Am. Chem. Soc. 82, 550
           (1960).

F-255   Fox, S. M., Origoni, V. E., and Smith, L. L., J. Am. Chem. Soc. 82, 2580 (1960).

F-256   Fried, J., U.S. Patent 3,047,595 (July 31, 1962).

F-257   Fried, J., U.S. Patent 3,048,581 (August 7, 1962).

F-258   Fried, J., U.S. Patent 3,050,519 (August 21, 1962).

F-259   Fried, J., U.S. Patent 3,050,535 (August 21, 1962).

F-260   Fried, J., U.S. Patent 3,053,834 (September 11, 1962).

F-261   Fried, J., U.S. Patent 3,053,837 (September 11, 1962).

F-262   Fried, J., U.S. Patent 3,069,418 (December 18, 1962).

F-263   Fried, J., U.S. Patent 3,069,439 (December 18, 1962).

F-264   Fried, J., Nutile, A. N., and Arth, G. E., U.S. Patent 3,090,781 (May 21, 1963).

F-265   Fried, J., Perlman, D., Langlykke, A. F., and Titus, E. O., U.S. Patent
           2,855,410 (October 7, 1958).

F-266   Fried, J., Perlman, D., Langlykke, A. F., and Titus, E. O., U.S. Patent
           2,872,381 (February 3, 1959).

F-267   Fried, J., Perlman, D., Langlykke, A. F., and Titus, E. O., U.S. Patent
           2,855,343 (October 7, 1958).

F-268   Fried, J., and Principe, P. A., U.S. Patent 3,004,047 (October 10, 1961).

F-269   Fried, J., and Thoma, R. W., U.S. Patent 2,744,120 (May 1, 1956).

F-270   Fried, J., and Thoma, R. W., U.S. Patent 2,768,928 (October 30, 1956).

F-271   Fried, J., and Thoma, R. W., U.S. Patent 2,756,179 (July 24, 1956).

F-272   Fried, J., and Thoma, R. W., U.S. Patent 2,793,164 (May 21, 1957).

F-273   Fried, J., and Thoma, R. W., U.S. Patent 2,799,690 (July 16, 1957).

F-274   Fried, J., and Thoma, R. W., U.S. Patent 2,823,171 (February 11, 1958).

F-275   Fried, J., and Thoma, R. W., U.S. Patent 2,868,694 (January 13, 1959).

F-276   Fried, J., and Thoma, R. W., U.S. Patent 2,902,498 (September 1, 1959).

F-277   Fried, J., and Thoma, R. W., U.S. Patent 2,914,543 (November 24, 1959).

F-278   Fried, J., and Thoma, R. W., U.S. Patent 2,946,807 (July 26, 1960).

F-279   Fried, J., and Thoma, R. W., U.S. Patent 2,964,450 (December 13, 1960).

F-280   Fried, J., and Thoma, R. W., U.S. Patent 2,964,523 (December 13, 1960).

F-281   Fried, J., and Thoma, R. W., U.S. Patent 3,058,889 (October 16, 1962).

F-282   Fried, J., and Thoma, R. W., U.S. Patent 3,083,211 (March 26, 1963).

F-283   Fried, J., Thoma, R. W., Gerke, J. R., Herz, J. E., Donin, M. N., and Perl-
          man, D., J. Am. Chem. Soc. 74, 3962 (1952).

F-284   Fried, J., Thoma, R. W., and Klingsberg, A., J. Am. Chem. Soc. 75, 5764 (1953).

F-285   Fried, J., Thoma, R. W., Perlman, D., and Gerke, J. R., U.S. Patent 2,753,290
          (July 3, 1956).

F-286   Fried, J., Thoma, R. W., Perlman, D., and Gerke, J. R., U.S. Patent 2,836,608
          (May 27, 1958).

F-287   Fried, J., Thoma, R. W., Perlman, D., and Gerke, J. R., U.S. Patent 2,879,280
          (May 24, 1959).

F-288   Fried, J., Thoma, R. W., Perlman, D., Herz, J. E., and Borman, A., Recent
          Prog. Hormone Res. 11, 149 (1955). REVIEW.

F-289   Fukui, T., J. Biochem. (Tokyo) 25, 61 (1937).

F-290   Fukushima, D. K., J. Biol. Chem. 239, 1748 (1964).

G-291   Gale, P. H., Page, A. C., Stoudt, T. H., and Folkers, K., Biochemistry 1, 788
          (1962).

G-292   Gnoj, O., Oliveto, E. P., Robinson, C. H., and Barton, D. H. R., Proc. Chem.
          Soc., p. 207 (1961).

G-293   Goldkamp, A. H., and Dodson, R. M., U.S. Patent 2,833,794 (May 6, 1958).

G-294   Goodman, J. J., U.S. Patent 2,938,834 (May 31, 1960).

G-295   Goodman, J. J., and Matrishin, M., U.S. Patent 2,982,693 (May 2, 1961).

G-296   Goodman, J. J., May, M., and Smith, L. L., J. Biol. Chem. 235, 965 (1960).

G-297   Goodman, J. J., and Smith, L. L., Appl. Microbiol. 8, 363 (1960).

G-298   Goodman, J. J., and Smith, L. L., Appl. Microbiol. 9, 372 (1961).

G-299   Gould, D. H., U.S. Patent 2,814,631 (November 26, 1957).

G-300   Gould, D. H., U.S. Patent 3,053,832 (September 11, 1962).

D-301   Gould, D. H., Hershberg, E. B., and Shapiro, E. L., U.S. Patent 2,864,835
          (December 16, 1958).

G-302   Gould, D. H., Hershberg, E. B., and Shapiro, E. L., U.S. Patent 2,900,400
          (August 18, 1959).

G-303   Gould, D. H., and Herzog, H. L., U.S. Patent 2,819,264 (January 7, 1958).

G-304   Gould, D. H., Herzog, H. L., and Hershberg, E. B., U.S. Patent 2,816,121
          (December 10, 1957).

G-305   Gould, D. H., Herzog, H. L., and Hershberg, E. B., U.S. Patent 2,899,447
          (August 11, 1959).

G-306   Gould, D., Ilavsky, J., Gutekunst, R., and Hershberg, E. B., J. Org. Chem. $\underline{22}$,
          829 (1957).

G-307   Gould, D. H., Reimann, H., and Finckenor, L. E., U.S. Patent 3,009,938
          (November 21, 1961).

G-308   Gould, D. H., and Robinson, C. H., U.S. Patent 3,032,564 (May 1, 1962).

G-309   Gould, D. H., and Shapiro, E. L., U.S. Patent 2,816,902 (December 17, 1957).

G-310   Gould, D. H., Shapiro, E. L., Herzog, H. L., Gentles, M. J., Hershberg, E. B.,
          Charney, W., Gilmore, M., Tolksdorf, S., Eisler, M., Perlman, P. L., and
          Pechet, M. M., J. Am. Chem. Soc. $\underline{79}$, 502 (1957).

G-311   Grant, J. K., Annual Rept. Progr. Chem. (Chem. Soc. London) $\underline{52}$, 316 (1955).
          REVIEW.

G-312   Greenspan, G., Ph. D. Thesis, Rutgers University (1960).

G-313   Greenspan, G., and Schaffner, C. P., U.S. Patent 2,968,595 (January 17, 1961).

G-314   Greenspan, G., Schaffner, C. P., Charney, W., Gentles, M. J., and Herzog,
          H. L., J. Org. Chem. $\underline{26}$, 1676 (1961).

G-315   Greenspan, G., Schaffner, C. P., Charney, W., Herzog, H. L., and Hershberg,
          E. B., J. Am. Chem. Soc. $\underline{79}$, 3922 (1957).

G-316   Groger, D., Pharmazie $\underline{18}$, 725 (1963).

G-317   Gual, C., Dorfman, R. I., and Stitch, S. R., Biochim. Biophys. Acta $\underline{49}$, 387
          (1961).

G-318   Gual, C., Stitch, S. R., Gut, M., and Dorfman, R. I., J. Org. Chem. $\underline{24}$, 418
          (1959).

G-319   Gubler, A., and Tamm, C., Helv. Chim. Acta $\underline{41}$, 301 (1958).

G-320   Gubler, A., and Tamm, C., Helv. Chim. Acta $\underline{41}$, 297 (1958).

G-321   Guehler, P. F., Dodson, R. M., and Tsuchiya, H. M., Proc. Natl. Acad. Sci.
          U.S. $\underline{48}$, 377 (1962).

G-322   Guehler, P. F., Tsuchiya, H. M., and Dodson, R. M., Abstr. 148th Meeting Am.
          Chem. Soc., Chicago, 1964, p. 6Q.

G-323   Gut, M., and Hayano, M., Atomlight $\underline{23}$, 1 (1962).

H-324   Hagemann, G., Nomine, G., and Warnant, J., U.S. Patent 2,805,978
          (September 10, 1957).

H-325   Hagiwara, H., J. Pharm. Soc. Japan $\underline{80}$, 962 (1960).

H-326   Hagiwara, H., J. Pharm. Soc. Japan $\underline{80}$, 965 (1960).

H-327   Hagiwara, H., J. Pharm. Soc. Japan $\underline{80}$, 1667 (1960).

H-328   Haines, W. J., and Colingsworth, D. R., U.S. Patent 2,649,401 (August 18, 1953).

H-329   Haines, W. J., and Drake, N. A., Federation Proc. $\underline{9}$, 180 (1950).

H-330   Halperin, A. H., Quastel, J. H., and Scholefield, P. G., Arch Biochem. Biophys.
          $\underline{52}$, 5 (1954).

H-331   Hanč, O., Global Impacts Appl. Microbiol., p. 420. Almqvist & Wiksell, Uppsala,
          1964.

H-332 Hanč, O., and Čapek, A., 7th Intern. Congr. Microbiol., Stockholm, Abstr., p. 403. Almqvist & Wiksell, Uppsala, 1958.

H-333 Hanč, O. and Čapek, A. Pharmacotherapeutica 1950-1959, Collection Papers 10th Anniversary Res. Inst. Pharm. Biochem., Prague, 1960, p. 157 (1961).

H-334 Hanč, O., Čapek, A., and Kakáč, B., Folia Microbiol. (Prague) 6, 392 (1961).

H-335 Hanč, O., Čapek, A., and Tadra, M., Cesk. Farm. 6, 373 (1957).

H-336 Hanč, O., Čapek, A., Tadra, M., Macek, K., and Simek, K., Arzneimittel-Forsch. 7, 175 (1957).

H-337 Hanč, O., Jirát, E., Čapek, A., and Tadra, M., Collection Czech. Chem. Commun. 23, 982 (1958).

H-338 Hanč, O., and Riedl-Tumová, E., Pharmazie 9, 877 (1954). REVIEW.

H-339 Hanson, F. R., Mann, K. M., Nielson, E. D., Anderson, H. V., Brunner, M. P., Karnemaat, J. N., Colingsworth, D. R., and Haines, W. J., J. Am. Chem. Soc. 75, 5369 (1953).

H-340 Hanze, A. R., U.S. Patent 2,676,181 (April 20, 1954).

H-341 Hanze, A. R., Murray, H. C., and Sebek, O. K., U.S. Patent 2,935,521 (May 3, 1960).

H-342 Hanze, A. R., Murray, H. C., and Sebek, O. K., U.S. Patent 3,038,913 (June 12, 1962).

H-343 Hanze, A. R., and Ogilvie, R. B., U.S. Patent 2,672,467 (March 16, 1954).

H-344 Hanze, A. R., Sebek, O. K., and Murray, H. C., J. Org. Chem. 25, 1968 (1960).

H-345 Hartsell, S. E., and Rettger, L. F., J. Bacteriol. 27, 497 (1934).

H-346 Hasegawa, T., J. Agr. Chem. Soc. Japan 32, A63 (1958). REVIEW.

H-347 Hasegawa, T., and Takahashi, T., Bull. Agr. Chem. Soc. Japan 22, 212 (1958).

H-348 Hasegawa, T., and Takahashi, T., Bull. Agr. Chem. Soc. Japan 23, 137 (1959).

H-349 Hasegawa, T., Takahashi, T., Nishikawa, M., and Hagiwara, H., Bull. Agr. Chem. Soc. Japan 21, 390 (1957).

H-350 Hasegawa, T., Takahashi, T., Nishikawa, M., and Hagiwara, H., U.S. Patent 2,966,444 (December 27, 1960).

H-351 Hassall, C. H., and Smith, B. S. W., Chem. & Ind. (London), p. 1570 (1957).

H-352 Hayaishi, O., Sato, Y., Jakoby, W. B., and Stohlman, E. F., Arch. Biochem. Biophys. 56, 554 (1955).

H-353 Hayaishi, O., Slaughter, C., and Jakoby, W. B., J. Bacteriol. 79, 145 (1960).

H-354 Hayakawa, S., Proc. Japan Acad. 30, 128 (1954).

H-355 Hayakawa, S., Proc. Japan Acad. 30, 133 (1954).

H-356 Hayakawa, S., Proc. Japan Acad. 30, 139 (1954).

H-357 Hayakawa, S., Fujii, T., Saburi, Y., and Eguchi, T., Nature 179, 537 (1957).

H-358 Hayakawa, S., and Kurokawa, K., Nature 199, 490 (1963).

H-359 Hayakawa, S., Saburi, Y., and Akaeda, I., J. Biochem. (Tokyo) 44, 109 (1957).

H-360 Hayakawa, S., Saburi, Y., Fujii, T., and Sonoda, Y., J. Biochem. (Tokyo) 43, 723 (1956).

H-361   Hayakawa, S., Saburi, Y., Fujii, T., and Sonada, Y., J. Biochem. (Tokyo) $\underline{43}$,
          731 (1956).

H-362   Hayakawa, S., Saburi, Y., and Hoshijima, H., J. Biochem. (Tokyo) $\underline{45}$, 465 (1958).

H-363   Hayakawa, S., Saburi, Y., and Tamaki, K., Proc. Japan Acad. $\underline{33}$, 221 (1957).

H-364   Hayakawa, S., Saburi, Y., and Tamaki, K., Proc. Japan Acad. $\underline{33}$, 225 (1957).

H-365   Hayakawa, S., Saburi, Y., and Tamaki, K., J. Biochem. (Tokyo) $\underline{45}$, 419 (1958).

H-366   Hayakawa, S., Saburi, Y., and Teraoka, H., Proc. Japan Acad. $\underline{32}$, 519 (1956).

H-367   Hayakawa, S., and Samuelsson, B., J. Biol. Chem. $\underline{239}$, 94 (1964).

H-368   Hayakawa, S., and Sato, Y., J. Org. Chem. $\underline{27}$, 704 (1962).

H-369   Hayakawa, S., and Sato, Y., J. Org. Chem. $\underline{28}$, 2742 (1963).

H-370   Hayano, M., Gut, M., Dorfman, R. I., Schubert, A., and Siebert, R., Biochim.
          Biophys. Acta $\underline{32}$, 269 (1959).

H-371   Hayano, M., Gut, M., Dorfman, R. I., Sebek, O. K., and Peterson, D. H., J.
          Am. Chem. Soc. $\underline{80}$, 2336 (1958).

H-372   Hayano, M., Lindberg, M. G., Dorfman, R. I., Hancock, J. E. H., and Doering,
          W. E., Arch. Biochem. Biophys. $\underline{59}$, 529 (1955).

H-373   Hayano, M., Ringold, H. J., Stefanovic, V., Gut, M., and Dorfman, R. I.,
          Biochem. Biophys. Res. Commun. $\underline{4}$, 454 (1961).

H-374   Hayano, M., Saito, A., Stone, D., and Dorfman, R. I., Biochim. Biophys. Acta
          $\underline{21}$, 380 (1956).

H-375   Hayano, M., Stefanovic, V., Kurosawa, Y., Gut, M., and Dorfman, R. I.,
          Federation Proc. $\underline{20}$, 238 (1961).

H-376   Hershberg, E. B., U.S. Patent 2,833,797 (May 6, 1958).

H-377   Hershberg, E. B., U.S. Patent 2,860,148 (November 11, 1958).

H-378   Hershberg, E. B., and Gebert, W., U.S. Patent 3,009,936 (November 21, 1961).

H-379   Herzog, H. L., U.S. Patent 2,854,383 (September 30, 1958).

H-380   Herzog, H. L., U.S. Patent 2,979,517 (April 11, 1961).

H-381   Herzog, H. L., Gentles, M. J., Basch, A., Coscarelli, W., Zeitz, M. E. A.,
          and Charney, W., J. Org. Chem. $\underline{25}$, 2177 (1960).

H-382   Herzog, H. L., Gentles, M. J., Charney, W., Sutter, D., Townley, E., Yudis,
          M., Kabasakalian, P., and Hershberg, E. B., J. Org. Chem. $\underline{24}$, 691 (1959).

H-383   Herzog, H. L., Gentles, M. J., Hershberg, E. B., Carvajal, F., Sutter, D.,
          Charney, W., and Schaffner, C. P., J. Am. Chem. Soc. $\underline{79}$, 3921 (1957).

H-384   Herzog, H. L., and Gould, D. H., U.S. Patent 2,957,893 (October 25, 1960).

H-385   Herzog, H. L., Jevnik, M. A., Perlman, P. L., Nobile, A., and Hershberg,
          E. B., J. Am. Chem. Soc. $\underline{75}$, 266 (1953).

H-386   Herzog, H. L., and Nobile, A., U.S. Patent 2,928,850 (March 15, 1960).

H-387   Herzog, H. L., Nobile, A., Tolksdorf, S., Charney, W., Hershberg, E. B.,
          Perlman, P. L., and Pechet, M. M., Science $\underline{121}$, 176 (1955).

H-388   Herzog, H. L., and Oliveto, E. P., U.S. Patent 2,874,172 (February 17, 1959).

H-389   Herzog, H. L., Payne, C. C., Hughes, M. T., Gentles, M. J., Hershberg, E. B.,
         Nobile, A., Charney, W., Federbush, C., Sutter, D., and Perlman, P. L., Tetra-
         hedron 18, 581 (1962).

H-390   Hess, H. J. E., Figdor, S. K., Hughes, G. M. K., and Moreland, W. T., U.S.
         Patent 3,042,691 (July 3, 1962).

H-391   Hess, H. J. E., Hughes, G. M. K., and Laubach, G. D., U.S. Patent 3,047,594
         (July 31, 1962).

H-392   Hirschmann, R. F., U.S. Patent 3,049,556 (August 14, 1962).

H-393   Hoehn, W. M., Schmidt, L. H., and Hughes, H. B., J. Biol. Chem. 152, 59 (1944).

H-394   Hogg, J. A., and Lincoln, F. H., U.S. Patent 3,009,937 (November 21, 1961).

H-395   Hogg, J. A., and Nathan, A. H., U.S. Patent 3,031,476 (April 24, 1962).

H-396   Hogg, J. A., Spero, G. B., Thompson, J. L., Magerlein, B. J., Schneider, W. P.,
         Peterson, D. H., Sebek, O. K., Murray, H. C., Babcock, J. C., Pederson, R. L.,
         and Campbell, J. A., Chem. & Ind. (London), p. 1002 (1958).

H-397   Holmlund, C. E., Blank, R. H., and Evans, R. H., U.S. Patent 3,071,516
         (January 1, 1963).

H-398   Holmlund, C. E., Blank, R. H., Sax, K. J., and Evans, R. H., Jr., Arch.
         Biochem. Biophys. 103, 105 (1963).

H-399   Holmlund, C. E., Feldman, L. I., Blank, R. H., Barbacci, N., and Nielsen,
         B. E., Sci. Rept. Ist. Super. Sanita 1, 289 (1961). REVIEW.

H-400   Holmlund, C. E., Feldman, L. I., Evans, R. H., Jr., Bernstein, S., and Dusza,
         J. P., U.S. Patent 3,071,580 (January 1, 1963).

H-401   Holmlund, C. E., Feldman, L. I., Kissman, H. M., and Weiss, M. J., U.S.
         Patent 3,047,569 (July 31, 1962).

H-402   Holmlund, C. E., Feldman, L. I., Kissman, H. M., and Weiss, M. J., J. Org.
         Chem. 27, 2122 (1962).

H-403   Holmlund, C. E., Feldman, L. I., Rigler, N. E., Evans, R. H., Jr., Blank,
         R. H., and Nielsen, B. E., J. Med. Chem. 6, 611 (1963).

H-404   Holmlund, C. E., Feldman, L. I., Rigler, N. E., Nielsen, B. E., and Evans,
         R. H., Jr., J. Am. Chem. Soc. 83, 2568 (1961).

H-405   Holmlund, C. E., Sax, K. J., Nielsen, B. E., Hartman, R. E., Evans, R. H.,
         Jr., and Blank, R. H., J. Org. Chem. 27, 1468 (1962).

H-406   Horvath, J., and Kramli, A., Nature 160, 639 (1947).

H-407   Horvath, J., and Kramli, A., Arch. Biol. Hung. [2] 18, 19 (1948).

H-408   Hübener, H. J., and Lehmann, C. O., Z. Physiol. Chem. 313, 124 (1958).

H-409   Hübener, H. J., and Sahrholz, F. G., Biochem. Z. 333, 95 (1960).

H-410   Hübener, H. J., Sahrholz, F. G., Schmidt-Thome, J., Nesemann, G., and Junk,
         R., Biochim. Biophys. Acta 35, 270 (1959).

H-411   Hughes, H. B., and Schmidt, L. H., Proc. Soc. Exptl. Biol. Med. 51, 162 (1942).

H-412   Humphrey, A. E., and Deindoerfer, F. H., Ind. Eng. Chem. 53, 934 (1961).
         REVIEW.

H-413   Humphrey, A. E., and Deindoerfer, F. H., Appl. Microbiol. 10, 359 (1962).
         REVIEW.

I-413a   Idler, D. R., Fagerland, U. H. M., and Ronald, A., Biochem. Biophys. Res. Commun. 2, 133 (1960).

I-414   Iizuka, H., and Naito, A., J. Gen. Appl. Microbiol. (Tokyo) 6, 169 (1960).

I-415   Iizuka, H., and Naito, A., J. Agr. Chem. Soc. Japan 34, 469 (1960).

I-416   Iizuka, H., Naito, A., and Hattori, M., J. Agr. Chem. Soc. Japan 32, 674 (1958).

I-417   Iizuka, H., Naito, A., and Hattori, M., J. Gen. Appl. Microbiol. (Tokyo) 4, 67 (1958).

I-418   Iizuka, H., Naito, A., Ohki, E., Sato, Yoshihiro and Nattori, M., J. Agr. Chem. Soc. Japan 34, 472 (1960).

I-419   Iizuka, H., Naito, A., and Sato, Yoshihiro, J. Agr. Chem. Soc. Japan 35, 430 (1961).

I-420   Iizuka, H., Naito, A., and Sato, Yoshihiro, J. Gen. Appl. Microbiol. (Tokyo) 7, 118 (1961).

I-421   Ilavsky, J., and Herzog, H. L., U.S. Patent 3,013,945 (December 19, 1961).

I-422   Ilavsky, J., and Herzog, H. L., U.S. Patent 3,054,725 (September 18, 1962).

I-423   Ishii, H., J. Pharm. Soc. Japan 81, 153 (1961).

I-424   Ishii, H., Chem. & Pharm. Bull. (Tokyo) 10, 354 (1962).

I-425   Ishii, H., Nozaki, Y., Okumura, T., and Sato, D., J. Pharm. Soc. Japan 80, 1150 (1961).

I-426   Ishii, H., Nozaki, Y., Okumura, T., and Sato, D., J. Pharm. Soc. Japan 81, 1051 (1961).

I-427   Isono, M., and Abe, M., J. Agr. Chem. Soc. Japan 35, 672 (1961).

I-428   Isono, M., and Abe, M., J. Agr. Chem. Soc. Japan 35, 677 (1961).

I-429   Isono, M., and Abe, M., U.S. Patent 3,056,731 (October 2, 1962).

I-430   Isono, M., and Abe, M., U.S. Patent 3,086,919 (April 23, 1963).

I-431   Isono, M., and Abe, M., U.S. Patent 3,086,920 (April 23, 1963).

J-432   Juhasz, G., and Tamm, C., Helv. Chim. Acta 44, 1063 (1961).

K-433   Kahnt, F., Meystre, C., Neher, R., Vischer, E., and Wettstein, A., Experientia 8, 422 (1952).

K-434   Kamiya, T., and Yamano, T., Chem. & Pharm. Bull. (Tokyo) 9, 579 (1961).

K-435   Karow, E. O., and Petsiavas, D. N., Abstr. 128th Meeting Am. Chem. Soc., Minneapolis, 1955, p. 21A.

K-436   Karow, E. O., and Petsiavas, D. N., Ind. Eng. Chem. 48, 2213 (1956).

K-437   Kawahara, F. S., and Talalay, P., J. Biol. Chem. 235, PC1 (1960).

K-438   Kawahara, F. S., Wang, S.-F., and Talalay, P., J. Biol. Chem. 237, 1500 (1962).

K-439   Kenney, H. E., Serota, S., Weaver, E. A., and Wall, M. E., J. Am. Chem. Soc. 82, 3689 (1960).

K-440   Kenney, H. E., Weaver, E. A., and Wall, M. E., J. Am. Chem. Soc. 80, 5568 (1958).

K-441   Kim, C. H., Enzymologia 4, 119 (1937).

K-442   Kim, C. H., Enzymologia 6, 105 (1939).

K-443   Kimura, T., Ann. Repts. Shionogi Res. Lab. 12, 166 (1962).

K-444   Kimura, T., Ann. Repts. Shionogi Res. Lab. 12, 180 (1962).

K-445   Kirk, D. N., Petrow, V., and Williamson, M. H., J. Chem. Soc., p. 3872 (1960).

K-446   Kita, D. A., U.S. Patent 2,936,264 (May 10, 1960).

K-447   Kita, D. A., U.S. Patent 2,991,230 (July 4, 1961).

K-448   Kita, D. A., Sardinas, J. L., and Shull, G. M., Nature 190, 627 (1961).

K-449   Kita, D. A., and Shull, G. M., U.S. Patent 2,830,936 (April 15, 1958).

K-450   Kita, D. A., and Shull, G. M., U.S. Patent 2,903,398 (September 8, 1959).

K-451   Kluepfel, D., and Coronelli, C., Experientia 18, 441 (1962).

K-452   Kluger, B., Siebert, R., and Schubert, A., Naturwiss. 44, 40 (1957).

K-453   Kluyver, A. J., and Hooft, F. V., U.S. Patent 1,833,716 (November 24, 1931).

K-454   Knight, S. G., U.S. Patent 3,031,379 (April 24, 1962).

K-455   Knight, S. G., U.S. Patent 3,031,382 (April 24, 1962).

K-456   Koepsell, H. J., Biotechnol. Bioeng. 4, 57 (1962).

K-457   Koester, H., Mamoli, L., and Vercellone, A., U.S. Patent 2,236,574 (April 1, 1941).

K-458   Kogan, L. M., Oranskaya, M. S., Suvorov, N. N., Skryabin, G. K., and Torgov, I. V., Izv. Akad. Nauk SSSR, Otd. Khim. Nauk, p. 302 (1962).

K-459   Kogan, L. M., Ulezlo, I. V., Skryabin, G. K., Suvorov, N. N., and Torgov, I. V., Izv. Akad. Nauk SSSR, Otd. Khim. Nauk, p. 328 (1963).

K-460   Kondo, E., J. Agr. Chem. Soc. Japan 34, 762 (1960).

K-461   Kondo, E., Ann. Rept. Shionogi Res. Lab. 10, 91 (1960).

K-462   Kondo, E., Ann. Rept. Shionogi Res. Lab. 10, 95 (1960).

K-463   Kondo, E., Agr. Biol. Chem. (Tokyo) 27, 69 (1962).

K-464   Kondo, E., and Masuo, E., J. Agr. Chem. Soc. Japan 34, 759 (1960).

K-465   Kondo, E., and Masuo, E., J. Agr. Chem. Soc. Japan 34, 847 (1960).

K-466   Kondo, E., and Masuo, E., Ann. Rept. Shionogi Res. Lab. 10, 103 (1960).

K-467   Kondo, E., and Masuo, E., J. Gen. Appl. Microbiol. (Tokyo) 7, 113 (1961).

K-468   Kondo, E., and Masuo, E., Ann. Rept. Shionogi Res. Lab. 12, 157 (1962).

K-469   Kondo, E., and Mitsugi, T., J. Agr. Chem. Soc. Japan 35, 521 (1961).

K-470   Kondo, E., Mitsugi, T., and Masuo, E., Agr. Biol. Chem. (Tokyo) 26, 16 (1962).

K-471   Kondo, E., Mitsugi, T., and Masuo, E., Agr. Biol. Chem. (Tokyo) 26, 22 (1962).

K-472   Kondo, E., Morihara, K., Nozaki, Y., and Masuo, E., J. Agr. Chem. Soc. Japan 34, 844 (1960).

K-473   Kondo, E., and Tori, K., J. Am. Chem. Soc. 86, 736 (1964).

K-474   Kramli, A., and Horvath, J., Nature 162, 619 (1948).

K-475   Kramli, A., and Horvath, J., Nature 163, 219 (1949).

K-476   Krassilnikov, N. A., Skryabin, G. K., Aseeva, I. V., and Korsunskaya, L. O., Dokl. Akad. Nauk SSSR 128, 836 (1959).

K-477   Krassilnikov, N. A. , Skryabin, G. K. , Aseeva, I. V. , and Korsunskaya, L. O. ,
         Dokl. Akad. Nauk SSSR 128, 1063 (1959).

K-478   Krider, M. M. , Cordon, T. C. , and Wall, M. E. , J. Am. Chem. Soc. 76, 3515
         (1954).

K-479   Krider, M. M. , Cordon, T. C. , and Wall, M. E. , U.S. Patent 2,784,144
         (March 5, 1957).

K-480   Kroll, H. A. , Pagano, J. F. , and Thoma, R. W. , U.S. Patent 2,822,318
         (February 4, 1958).

K-481   Kupchan, S. M. , Sih, C. J. , Katsui, N. , and El-Tayeb, O. , J. Am. Chem. Soc.
         84, 1752 (1962).

K-482   Kurosawa, Y. , J. Agr. Chem. Soc. Japan 31, 478 (1957).

K-483   Kurosawa, Y. , J. Agr. Chem. Soc. Japan 32, 515 (1958).

K-484   Kurosawa, Y. , Hayano, M. , and Bloom, B. M. , Agr. Biol. Chem. (Tokyo) 25,
         838 (1961).

K-485   Kurosawa, Y. , Hayano, M. , Gut, M. , Dorfman, R. I. , Schubert, A. , and Bunton,
         C. A. , Agr. Biol. Chem. (Tokyo) 25, 424 (1961).

K-486   Kurosawa, Y. , and Sawai, M. , Japanese Patent 25379 (1963).

K-487   Kushinsky, S. , J. Biol. Chem. 230, 31 (1958).

L-488   Labler, L. , and Sorm, F. , Chem. & Ind. (London), p. 1114 (1961).

L-489   Labler, L. , and Sorm, F. , Collection Czech. Chem. Commun. 27, 276 (1962).

L-490   Laskin, A. I. , U.S. Patent 3,056,730 (October 2, 1962).

L-491   Laskin, A. I. , U.S. Patent 3,098,796 (July 23, 1963).

L-492   Laskin, A. I. , and Diassi, P. A. , Federation Proc. 22, 354 (1963).

L-493   Laskin, A. I. , and Fried, J. , U.S. Patent 3,115,443 (December 24, 1963).

L-494   Laskin, A. I. , and Fried, J. , U.S. Patent 3,115,444 (December 24, 1963).

L-495   Laskin, A. I. , and Fried, J. , Bacteriol. Proc., p. 106 (1963).

L-496   Laskin, A. I. , Fried, J. , and Diassi, P. A. , U.S. Patent 3,063,992 (November 13,
         1962).

L-497   Laskin, A. I. , Grabowich, B. , Junta, B. , Meyers, C. deL. , and Fried, J. , J.
         Org. Chem. 29, 1333 (1964).

L-498   Laskin, A. I. , Guiducci, M. A. , and Fried, J. , U.S. Patent 2,977,286 (March 28,
         1961).

L-499   Laskin, A. I. , Junta, B. , Meyers, C. deL. , and Pan, S. C. , Abstr. 145th
         Meeting Am. Chem. Soc. , New York, 1963, p. 16 P.

L-500   Laskin, A. I. , Lerner, L. J. , and Weisenborn, F. L. , U.S. Patent 2,998,428
         (August 29, 1961).

L-501   Laskin, A. I. , Thoma, R. W. , and Trejo, W. H. , Bacteriol. Proc., p. 34 (1960).

L-502   Laskin, A. I. , and Weisenborn, F. L. , Bacteriol. Proc. , p. 26 (1962).

L-503   Laskin, A. I. , and Weisenborn, F. L. , U.S. Patent 3,098,079 (July 16, 1963).

L-503a   Laskin, A. I. , and Weisenborn, F. L. , U.S. Patent 3,143,480 (August 4, 1964).

L-504   Ledingham, G. A. , Ann. Rev. Microbiol. 7, 433 (1953). REVIEW.

L-504a   Lee, S. S., and Sih, C. J., Biochemistry $\underline{3}$, 1267 (1964).

L-505   Leeson, L. J., Muller, S. A., and Sieger, G. M., U.S. Patent 3,005,839
           (October 24, 1961).

L-506   Lerner, L. J., Laskin, A. I., and Weisenborn, F. L., U.S. Patent 3,005,017
           (October 17, 1961).

L-507   Levy, H. R., and Talalay, P., J. Am. Chem. Soc. $\underline{79}$, 2658 (1957).

L-508   Levy, H. R., and Talalay, P., J. Biol. Chem. $\underline{234}$, 2009 (1959).

L-509   Levy, H. R., and Talalay, P., J. Biol. Chem. $\underline{234}$, 2014 (1959).

L-510   Lincoln, F. H., Schneider, W. P., Sebek, O. K., and Spero, G. B., U.S. Patent
           2,864,836 (December 16, 1958).

L-511   Lincoln, F. H., Schneider, W. P., Sebek, O. K., and Spero, G. B., U.S. Patent
           2,864,838 (December 16, 1958).

L-512   Lincoln, F. H., Schneider, W. P., and Spero, G. B., U.S. Patent 2,867,634
           (January 6, 1959).

L-513   Lincoln, F. H., Schneider, W. P., and Spero, G. B., U.S. Patent 2,867,637
           (January 6, 1959).

L-514   Lincoln, F. H., Schneider, W. P., and Spero, G. B., U.S. Patent 2,867,638
           (January 6, 1959).

L-515   Lincoln, F. H., Schneider, W. P., and Spero, G. B., U.S. Patent 3,005,838
           (October 24, 1961).

L-516   Lincoln, F. H., Schneider, W. P., and Spero, G. B., U.S. Patent 3,030,360
           (April 17, 1962).

L-517   Lincoln, F. H., Schneider, W. P., and Spero, G. B., U.S. Patent 3,105,083
           (September 24, 1963).

L-518   Lincoln, F. H., and Spero, G. B., U.S. Patent 2,671,093 (March 2, 1954).

L-519   Lincoln, F. H., and Spero, G. B., U.S. Patent 2,671,094 (March 2, 1954).

L-520   Lincoln, F. H., and Spero, G. B., U.S. Patent 2,970,156 (January 31, 1961).

L-521   Lindner, F., Junk, R., Kehl, H., Nesemann, G., and Schmidt-Thome, J.,
           Naturwiss. $\underline{43}$, 39 (1956).

L-522   Lindner, F., Junk, R., Nesemann, G., and Schmidt-Thome, J., Z. Physiol.
           Chem. $\underline{313}$, 117 (1958).

L-523   Logemann, W., Inhoffen, H. H., and Eysenbach, H., U.S. Patent 2,322,809
           (June 29, 1943).

L-524   Loomeijer, F. J., Biochim. Biophys. Acta $\underline{29}$, 168 (1958).

L-525   Lorck, H., Proc. 8th Intern. Congr. Microbiol., Montreal, 1962, Abstr., p. 81.
           Univ. of Toronto Press, Toronto, 1963.

L-526   Luedemann, G., Charney, W., Mitchell, A., and Herzog, H. L., J. Org. Chem.
           $\underline{24}$, 1385 (1959).

L-527   Luedemann, G., Charney, W., Woyciesjes, A., Pettersen, E., Peckham, W. D.,
           Gentles, M. J., Marshall, H., and Herzog, H. L., J. Org. Chem. $\underline{26}$, 4128 (1961).

M-528   Magerlein, B. J., U.S. Patent 2,752,341 (June 26, 1956).

M-529   Magerlein, B. J., Birkenmeyer, R. D., and Kagan, F., J. Org. Chem. $\underline{28}$, 3474
           (1963).

M-530 Magerlein, B. J., Schneider, W. P., Sebek, O. K., and Spero, G. B., U.S. Patent 2,838,545 (June 10, 1958).

M-531 Magerlein, B. J., Schneider, W. P., Sebek, O. K., and Spero, G. B., U.S. Patent 2,838,546 (June 10, 1958).

M-532 Magerlein, B. J., Schneider, W. P., Sebek, O. K., and Spero, G. B., U.S. Patent 2,838,547 (June 10, 1958).

M-533 Magerlein, B. J., Schneider, W. P., Sebek, O. K., and Spero, G. B., U.S. Patent 2,838,548 (June 10, 1958).

M-534 Magerlein, B. J., Spero, G. B., Schneider, W. P., and Hogg, J. A., U.S. Patent 2,838,539 (June 10, 1958).

M-535 Malhotra, S. K., and Ringold, H. J., J. Am. Chem. Soc. 86, 1997 (1964).

M-536 Mallett, G. E., U.S. Patent 3,128,238 (April 7, 1964).

M-537 Mallett, G. E., and Fukuda, D. S., Bacteriol. Proc., p. 26 (1962).

M-538 Mamoli, L., Ber. 71, 2278 (1938).

M-539 Mamoli, L., Ber. 71, 2696 (1938).

M-540 Mamoli, L., Ber. 71, 2701 (1938).

M-541 Mamoli, L., Ber. 72, 1863 (1939).

M-542 Mamoli, L., Gazz. Chim. Ital. 69, 237 (1939).

M-543 Mamoli, L., U.S. Patent 2,186,906 (January 9, 1940).

M-544 Mamoli, L., U.S. Patent 2,341,110 (February 8, 1944).

M-545 Mamoli, L., Koch, R., and Teschen, H., Z. Physiol. Chem. 261, 287 (1939).

M-546 Mamoli, L., Koch, R., and Teschen, H., Naturwiss. 27, 319 (1939).

M-547 Mamoli, L., and Schramm, G., Ber. 71, 2083 (1938).

M-548 Mamoli, L., and Schramm, G., Ber. 71, 2698 (1938).

M-549 Mamoli, L., and Vercellone, A., Z. Physiol. Chem. 245, 93 (1937).

M-550 Mamoli, L., and Vercellone, A., Ber. 70, 470 (1937).

M-551 Mamoli, L., and Vercellone, A., Ber. 70, 2079 (1937).

M-552 Mamoli, L., and Vercellone, A., Ber. 71, 154 (1938).

M-553 Mamoli, L., and Vercellone, A., Ber. 71, 1686 (1938).

M-554 Mancera, O., Zaffaroni, A., Rubin, B. A., Sondheimer, F., Rosenkranz, G., and Djerassi, C., J. Am. Chem. Soc. 74, 3711 (1952).

M-555 Mann, K. M., Hanson, F. R., and O'Connell, P. W., Federation Proc. 14, 251 (1955).

M-556 Mann, K. M., Hanson, F. R., O'Connell, P. W., Anderson, H. V., Brunner, M. P., and Karnemaat, J. N., Appl. Microbiol. 3, 14 (1955).

M-557 Mannhardt, H. J., and Metz, H., U.S. Patent 2,950,226 (August 23, 1960).

M-558 Mannhardt, H. J., Bork, K. H., Bruckner, K., and Metz, H., U.S. Patent 3,074,977 (January 22, 1963).

M-559 Marcus, P. I., and Talalay, P., Proc. Roy. Soc. B144, 116 (1955).

M-560 Marcus, P. I., and Talalay, P., J. Biol. Chem. 218, 661 (1956).

M-561   Mateles, R. I., Deindoerfer, F. H., and Humphrey, A. E., Biotechnol. Bioeng. 6, 73 (1964). REVIEW.

M-562   Mateles, R. I., and Fuld, G. J., J. Microbiol. Serol. 27, 33 (1961).

M-563   Mazur, R. H., and Muir, R. D., J. Org. Chem. 28, 2442 (1963).

M-564   McAleer, W. J., and Dulaney, E. L., Arch. Biochem. Biophys. 62, 109 (1956).

M-565   McAleer, W. J., and Dulaney, E. L., Arch. Biochem. Biophys. 62, 111 (1956).

M-566   McAleer, W. J., and Dulaney, E. L., U.S. Patent 2,831,798 (April 22, 1958).

M-567   McAleer, W. J., and Dulaney, E. L., U.S. Patent 2,875,132 (February 24, 1959).

M-568   McAleer, W. J., Jacob, T. A., Turnbull, L. B., Schoenewaldt, E. F., and Stoudt, T. H., Arch. Biochem. Biophys. 73, 127 (1958).

M-569   McAleer, W. J., Kozlowski, M. A., Stoudt, T. H., and Chemerda, J. M., J. Org. Chem. 23, 508 (1958).

M-570   McAleer, W. J., Kozlowski, M. A., Stoudt, T. H., and Chemerda, J. M., J. Org. Chem. 23, 958 (1958).

M-571   McAleer, W. J., and Stoudt, T. H., U.S. Patent 2,954,326 (September 27, 1960).

M-572   McGuire, J. S., Maxwell, E. S., and Tomkins, G. M., Biochim. Biophys. Acta 45, 392 (1960).

M-573   Meeks, R. C., Meister, P. D., Eppstein, S. H., Rosselet, J. P., Weintraub, A., Murray, H. C., Sebek, O. K., Reineke, L. M., and Peterson, D. H., Chem. & Ind. (London), p. 391 (1958).

M-574   Meeks, R. C., Meister, P. D., and Murray, H. C., U.S. Patent 2,952,693 (September 13, 1960).

M-575   Meister, P. D., U.S. Patent 2,678,933 (May 18, 1954).

M-576   Meister, P. D., and Murray, H. C., U.S. Patent 2,930,791 (March 29, 1960).

M-577   Meister, P. D., and Murray, H. C., U.S. Patent 2,968,596 (January 17, 1961).

M-578   Meister, P. D., Peterson, D. H., Eppstein, S. H., Murray, H. C., Reineke, L. M., Weintraub, A., and Osborn, H. M. Leigh, J. Am. Chem. Soc. 76, 5679 (1954).

M-579   Meister, P. D., Peterson, D. H., Murray, H. C., Eppstein, S. H., Reineke, L. M., Weintraub, A., and Leigh, H. M., J. Am. Chem. Soc. 75, 55 (1953).

M-580   Meister, P. D., Peterson, D. H., Murray, H. C., Spero, G. B., Eppstein, S. H., Weintraub, A., Reineke, L. M., and Leigh, H. M., J. Am. Chem. Soc. 75, 416 (1953).

M-581   Meister, P. D., Reineke, L. M., Meeks, R. C., Murray, H. C., Eppstein, S. H., Osborn, H. M. Leigh, Weintraub, A., and Peterson, D. H., J. Am. Chem. Soc. 76, 4050 (1954).

M-582   Meister, P. D., and Weintraub, A., U.S. Patent 2,877,162 (March 10, 1959).

M-583   Meystre, C., Vischer, E., Kahnt, F., Neher, R., and Wettstein, A., Chimia (Aarau) 9, 119 (1955). REVIEW.

M-584   Meystre, C., Vischer, E., and Wettstein, A., Helv. Chim. Acta 37, 1548 (1954).

M-585   Meystre, C., Vischer, E., and Wettstein, A., Helv. Chim. Acta 38, 381 (1955).

M-586   Mills, J. S., Bowers, A., Djerassi, C., and Ringold, H. J., J. Am. Chem. Soc. 82, 3399 (1960).

M-587   Mininger, R. F., Wall, M. E., Dworschack, R. G., and Jackson, R. W., Arch.
          Biochem. Biophys. <u>60</u>, 427 (1956).

M-588   Misei, A., and Szabo, A., J. Biochem. Microbiol. Technol. Eng. <u>2</u>, 411 (1960).

M-589   Misei, A., and Szabo, A., J. Biochem. Microbiol. Technol. Eng. <u>3</u>, 21 (1961).

M-590   Misei, A., and Szabo, A., J. Biochem. Microbiol. Technol. Eng. <u>3</u>, 119 (1961).

M-591   Molina, L., Boll. Ist. Sieroterap. Milan. <u>23</u>, 168 (1944).

M-592   Molina, L., and Ercoli, A., Boll. Ist. Sieroterap. Milan. <u>23</u>, 164 (1944).

M-593   Moore, J. A., Holton, W. F., and Wittle, E. L., J. Am. Chem. Soc. <u>84</u>, 390
          (1962).

M-594   Mueller, A. O., Schmitt, H. P., and Mueller, G. P., J. Tenn. Acad. Sci. <u>26</u>, 157
          (1951).

M-595   Mueller, A. O., Schmitt, H. P., and Mueller, G. P., J. Tenn. Acad. Sci. <u>26</u>, 249
          (1951).

M-596   Muir, R. D., and Dodson, R. M., U.S. Patent 2,823,170 (February 11, 1958).

M-597   Muir, R. D., and Dodson, R. M., U.S. Patent 3,023,229 (February 27, 1962).

M-598   Muller, G., U.S. Patent 3,115,491 (December 24, 1963).

M-599   Murray, H. C., and Meister, P. D., U.S. Patent 2,889,255 (June 2, 1959).

M-600   Murray, H. C., and Meister, P. D., U.S. Patent 2,925,366 (February 16, 1960).

M-601   Murray, H. C., and Peterson, D. H., U.S. Patent 2,602,769 (July 8, 1952).

M-602   Murray, H. C., and Peterson, D. H., U.S. Patent 2,649,400 (August 18, 1953).

M-603   Murray, H. C., and Peterson, D. H., U.S. Patent 2,649,402 (August 18, 1953).

M-604   Murray, H. C., and Peterson, D. H., U.S. Patent 2,656,370 (October 20, 1953).

M-605   Murray, H. C., and Peterson, D. H., U.S. Patent 2,659,741 (November 17, 1953).

M-606   Murray, H. C., and Peterson, D. H., U.S. Patent 2,659,743 (November 17, 1953).

M-607   Murray, H. C., and Peterson, D. H., U.S. Patent 2,660,585 (November 24, 1953).

M-608   Murray, H. C., and Peterson, D. H., U.S. Patent 2,660,586 (November 24, 1953).

M-609   Murray, H. C., and Peterson, D. H., U.S. Patent 2,660,587 (November 24, 1953).

M-610   Murray, H. C., and Peterson, D. H., U.S. Patent 2,662,089 (December 8, 1953).

M-611   Murray, H. C., and Peterson, D. H., U.S. Patent 2,666,070 (January 12, 1954).

M-612   Murray, H. C., and Peterson, D. H., U.S. Patent 2,666,071 (January 12, 1954).

M-613   Murray, H. C., and Peterson, D. H., U.S. Patent 2,670,357 (February 23, 1954).

M-614   Murray, H. C., and Peterson, D. H., U.S. Patent 2,670,358 (February 23, 1954).

M-615   Murray, H. C., and Peterson, D. H., U.S. Patent 2,671,096 (March 2, 1954).

M-616   Murray, H. C., and Peterson, D. H., U.S. Patent 2,672,466 (March 16, 1954).

M-617   Murray, H. C., and Peterson, D. H., U.S. Patent 2,673,866 (March 30, 1954).

M-618   Murray, H. C., and Peterson, D. H., U.S. Patent 2,683,725 (July 13, 1954).

M-619   Murray, H. C., and Peterson, D. H., U.S. Patent 2,686,791 (August 17, 1954).

M-620   Murray, H. C., and Peterson, D. H., U.S. Patent 2,686,792 (August 17, 1954).

BIBLIOGRAPHY 703

M-621   Murray, H. C., and Peterson, D. H., U.S. Patent 2,691,030 (October 5, 1954).

M-622   Murray, H. C., and Peterson, D. H., U.S. Patent 2,691,031 (October 5, 1954).

M-623   Murray, H. C., and Peterson, D. H., U.S. Patent 2,692,273 (October 19, 1954).

M-624   Murray, H. C., and Peterson, D. H., U.S. Patent 2,695,260 (November 23, 1954).

M-625   Murray, H. C., and Peterson, D. H., U.S. Patent 2,695,907 (November 30, 1954).

M-626   Murray, H. C., and Peterson, D. H., U.S. Patent 2,697,110 (December 14, 1954).

M-627   Murray, H. C., and Peterson, D. H., U.S. Patent 2,698,331 (December 28, 1954).

M-628   Murray, H. C., and Peterson, D. H., U.S. Patent 2,702,809 (February 22, 1955).

M-629   Murray, H. C., and Peterson, D. H., U.S. Patent 2,702,810 (February 22, 1955).

M-630   Murray, H. C., and Peterson, D. H., U.S. Patent 2,703,326 (March 1, 1955).

M-631   Murray, H. C., and Peterson, D. H., U.S. Patent 2,703,327 (March 1, 1955).

M-632   Murray, H. C., and Peterson, D. H., U.S. Patent 2,703,806 (March 8, 1955).

M-633   Murray, H. C., and Peterson, D. H., U.S. Patent 2,721,828 (October 25, 1955).

M-634   Murray, H. C., and Peterson, D. H., U.S. Patent 2,727,910 (December 20, 1955).

M-635   Murray, H. C., and Peterson, D. H., U.S. Patent 2,727,911 (December 20, 1955).

M-636   Murray, H. C., and Peterson, D. H., U.S. Patent 2,735,800 (February 21, 1956).

M-637   Murray, H. C., and Peterson, D. H., U.S. Patent 2,762,747 (September 11, 1956).

M-638   Murray, H. C., and Peterson, D. H., U.S. Patent 2,771,474 (November 20, 1956).

M-639   Murray, H. C., and Peterson, D. H., U.S. Patent 2,793,216 (May 21, 1957).

M-640   Murray, H. C., and Peterson, D. H., U.S. Patent 2,800,490 (July 23, 1957).

M-641   Murray, H. C., and Peterson, D. H., U.S. Patent 2,861,088 (November 18, 1958).

M-642   Murray, H. C., and Peterson, D. H., U.S. Patent 2,888,384 (May 26, 1959).

M-643   Murray, H. C., and Peterson, D. H., U.S. Patent 2,889,255 (June 2, 1959).

M-644   Murray, H. C., and Peterson, D. H., U.S. Patent 2,920,073 (January 5, 1960).

M-645   Murray, H. C., and Peterson, D. H., U.S. Patent 2,992,972 (July 18, 1961).

M-646   Murray, H. C., and Reineke, L. M., U.S. Patent 3,011,951 (December 5, 1961).

M-647   Murray, H. C., and Sebek, O. K., U.S. Patent 2,902,411 (September 1, 1959).

N-648   Naito, A., Sato, Yoshihiro, Iizuka, H., and Tsuda, K., Steroids 3, 327 (1964).

N-649   Nathan, A. H., U.S. Patent 2,647,135 (July 28, 1953).

N-650   Nathan, A. H., Hogg, J. A., and Lyttle, D. A., U.S. Patent 2,713,588 (July 19, 1955).

N-651   Nawa, H., Uchibayashi, M., Kamiya, T., Yamano, T., Arai, H., and Abe, M., Nature 184, 469 (1959).

N-652   Nawa, H., Uchibayashi, M., Takeda, R., Nakanishi, I., Kusaka, T., Terumichi, J., Uchida, M., Katsumata, M., Yoshino, K., and Fujitani, H., Tetrahedron 4, 201 (1958).

N-653   Neher, R., Desaulles, P., Vischer, E., Wieland, P., and Wettstein, A., Helv. Chim. Acta 41, 1667 (1958).

N-654   Neher, R., and Wettstein, A., Helv. Chim. Acta $\underline{39}$, 2062 (1956).

N-655   Neiderhiser, D. H., Ph. D. Thesis, University of Wisconsin (1963).

N-656   Nesemann, G., Hübener, H. J., Junk, R., and Schmidt-Thome, J., Biochem. Z.,
           $\underline{333}$, 88 (1960).

N-657   Nesemann, G., Hübener, H. J., and Schmidt-Thome, J., Biochem. Z. $\underline{336}$, 329
           (1962).

N-658   Neuberg, C., Advan. Carbohydrate Chem. $\underline{4}$, 75 (1949). REVIEW.

N-658a   Nickell, L. G., U.S. Patent 2,962,422 (November 29, 1960).

N-659   Nielson, E. D., Abstr. 126th Meeting Am. Chem. Soc., New York, 1954, p. 9A.

N-660   Nishikawa, M., and Hagiwara, H., Chem. & Pharm. Bull. (Tokyo) $\underline{6}$, 226 (1958).

N-661   Nishikawa, M., and Hagiwara, H., J. Pharm. Soc. Japan $\underline{78}$, 1256 (1958).

N-662   Nishikawa, M., and Noguchi, S., U.S. Patent 3,094,465 (June 18, 1963).

N-663   Nishikawa, M., Noguchi, S., and Hasegawa, T., Chem. & Pharm. Bull. (Tokyo)
           $\underline{3}$, 322 (1955).

N-664   Nishikawa, M., Noguchi, S., Hasegawa, T., and Banno, I., J. Pharm. Soc. Japan
           $\underline{76}$, 383 (1956).

N-665   Nobile, A., U.S. Patent 2,837,464 (June 3, 1958).

N-666   Nobile, A., U.S. Patent 2,955,118 (October 4, 1960).

N-667   Nobile, A., U.S. Patent 3,010,957 (November 28, 1961).

N-667a   Nobile, A., U.S. Patent 3,060,092 (October 23, 1962).

N-668   Nobile, A., U.S. Patent 3,084,103 (April 2, 1963).

N-669   Nobile, A., U.S. Patent 3,105,795 (October 1, 1963).

N-670   Nobile, A., U.S. Patent 3,134,718 (May 26, 1964).

N-671   Nobile, A., Charney, W., Perlman, P. L., Herzog, H. L., Payne, C. C., Tully,
           M. E., Jevnik, M. A., and Hershberg, E. B., J. Am. Chem. Soc. $\underline{77}$, 4184 (1955).

N-672   Noguchi, S., J. Pharm. Soc. Japan $\underline{81}$, 381 (1961).

N-673   Noguchi, S., J. Pharm. Soc. Japan $\underline{81}$, 385 (1961).

N-674   Noguchi, S., Morita, K., and Nishikawa, M., Chem. & Pharm. Bull. (Tokyo) $\underline{8}$,
           563 (1960).

N-675   Norman, A., and Bergman, S., Acta Chem. Scand. $\underline{14}$, 1781 (1960).

N-676   Norman, A., and Sjovall, J. Biochim. Biophys. Acta $\underline{29}$, 467 (1958).

N-677   Nozaki, Y., Agr. Biol. Chem. (Tokyo) $\underline{25}$, 461 (1961).

N-678   Nozaki, Y., Agr. Biol. Chem. (Tokyo) $\underline{25}$, 559 (1961).

N-679   Nozaki, Y., Agr. Biol. Chem. (Tokyo) $\underline{25}$, 879 (1961).

N-680   Nozaki, Y., Agr. Biol. Chem. (Tokyo) $\underline{25}$, 884 (1961).

N-681   Nozaki, Y., Agr. Biol. Chem. (Tokyo) $\underline{25}$, 890 (1961).

N-682   Nozaki, Y., Masuo, E., Ishii, H., Okumura, T., and Satoh, D., Ann. Rept.
           Shionogi Res. Lab. $\underline{11}$, 9 (1961).

N-683   Nozaki, Y., Masuo, E., and Satoh, D., Agr. Biol. Chem. (Tokyo) $\underline{26}$, 399 (1962).

N-684   Nozaki, Y., and Okumura, T., Agr. Biol. Chem. (Tokyo) $\underline{25}$, 515 (1961).

N-685   Nussbaum, A. L., U.S. Patent 2,814,632 (November 26, 1957).

N-686   Nussbaum, A. L., U.S. Patent 3,045,011 (July 17, 1962).

N-687   Nussbaum, A. L., Brabazon, G., Popper, T. L., and Oliveto, E. P., J. Am. Chem. Soc. $\underline{80}$, 2722 (1958).

N-688   Nussbaum, A. L., Carlon, F. E., Gould, D., Oliveto, E. P., Hershberg, E. B., Gilmore, M. L., and Charney, W., J. Am. Chem. Soc. $\underline{79}$, 4814 (1957).

N-689   Nussbaum, A. L., Carlon, F. E., Gould, D., Oliveto, E. P., Hershberg, E. B., Gilmore, M. L., and Charney, W., J. Am. Chem. Soc. $\underline{81}$, 5230 (1959).

N-690   Nussbaum, A. L., and Oliveto, E. P., U.S. Patent 2,908,696 (October 13, 1959).

N-691   Nussbaum, A. L., and Oliveto, E. P., U.S. Patent 3,013,011 (December 12, 1961).

N-692   Nussbaum, A. L., and Oliveto, E. P., U.S. Patent 3,013,033 (December 12, 1961).

N-693   Nussbaum, A. L., Yuan, E., Oliveto, E. P., Federbush, C., and Charney, W., Chem. & Ind. (London), p. 836 (1960).

O-694   Oberster, A. E., Beyler, R. E., and Sarett, L. H., U.S. Patent 3,067,214 (December 4, 1962).

O-695   Oberster, A. E., Beyler, R. E., and Sarett, L. H., U.S. Patent 3,100,204 (August 6, 1963).

O-696   O'Connell, P. W., Mann, K. M., Nielson, E. D., and Hanson, F. R., Appl. Microbiol. $\underline{3}$, 16 (1955).

O-697   Ogilvie, R. B., and Hanze, A. R., U.S. Patent 2,671,091 (March 2, 1954).

O-698   Ogilvie, R. B., and Hanze, A. R., U.S. Patent 2,672,468 (March 16, 1954).

O-699   Okada, M., Yamada, A., and Ishidate, M., Chem. & Pharm. Bull. (Tokyo) $\underline{8}$, 530 (1960).

O-699a   Okumura, T., Nozaki, Y., and Satoh, D., Chem. & Pharm. Bull. (Tokyo) $\underline{11}$, 1340 (1963).

O-700   Oliveto, E. P., and Herzog, H. L., U.S. Patent 2,932,639 (April 12, 1960).

O-701   Oliveto, E. P., and Rausser, R., U.S. Patent 3,010,959 (November 28, 1961).

O-702   Oliveto, E. P., Rausser, R., Weber, L., Nussbaum, A. L., Gebert, W., Coniglio, C. T., Hershberg, E. B., Tolksdorf, S., Eisler, M., Perlman, P. L., and Pechet, M. M., J. Am. Chem. Soc. $\underline{80}$, 4431 (1958).

O-703   Oliveto, E. P., and Weber, L., Chem. & Ind. (London), p.514 (1961).

O-704   Origoni, V. E., Fox, S., and Smith, L. L., U.S. Patent 3,002,010 (September 26, 1961).

O-705   Origoni, V. E., Rigler, N. E., and Goodman, J. J., U.S. Patent 3,047,468 (July 31, 1962).

P-706   Pan, S. C., Thoma, R. W., and Principe, P., Abstr. 142nd Meeting Am. Chem. Soc., Atlantic City, 1962, p.11P.

P-706a   Pan, S. C., Laskin, A. I., Junta, B., Principe, P., and Weisenborn, F., Abstr. 148th Meeting, Am. Chem. Soc., Chicago, 1964, p. 14Q.

P-707   Pasqualini, J. R., Ann. Chim. (Paris) [13] $\underline{8}$, 27 (1963). REVIEW.

P-708   Pederson, R. L., Campbell, J. A., Babcock, J. C., Eppstein, S. H., Murray, H. C., Weintraub, A., Meeks, R. C., Meister, P. D., Reineke, L. M., and Peterson, D. H., J. Am. Chem. Soc. $\underline{78}$, 1512 (1956).

P-709   Pederson, R. L., Herr, M. E., Babcock, J. C., Campbell, J. A., and Hogg,
         J. A., U.S. Patent 2,867,630 (January 6, 1959).

P-710   Perlman, D., Science 115, 529 (1952).

P-711   Perlman, D., Abstr. 130th Meeting Am. Chem. Soc., Atlantic City, 1956, p. 33A.

P-712   Perlman, D., U.S. Patent 2,915,439 (December 1, 1959).

P-713   Perlman, D., Dutcher, J. D., Fried, J., and Titus, E. O., U.S. Patent
         2,840,578 (June 24, 1958).

P-714   Perlman, D., Dutcher, J. D., Fried, J., and Titus, E. O., U.S. Patent
         2,840,579 (June 24, 1958).

P-715   Perlman, D., Dutcher, J. D., Fried, J., and Titus, E. O., U.S. Patent
         2,840,580 (June 24, 1958).

P-716   Perlman, D., Fried, J., Titus, E. O., and Langlykke, A. F., U.S. Patent
         2,709,705 (May 31, 1955).

P-717   Perlman, D., Jackson, P. W., Giuffre, N., and Fried, J., Can. J. Biochem.
         Physiol. 38, 393 (1960).

P-718   Perlman, D., Titus, E., and Fried, J., J. Am. Chem. Soc. 74, 2126 (1952).

P-719   Perlman, D., Weinstein, M. J., and Peterson, G. E., Can. J. Microbiol. 3, 841
         (London) (1957).

P-720   Peterson, D. H., Research 6, 309 (1953). REVIEW.

P-721   Peterson, D. H., Record Chem. Progr. (Kresge-Hooker Sci. Lib.) 17, 211 (1956).
         REVIEW.

P-722   Peterson, D. H., Proc. 4th Intern. Congr. Biochem., Vienna, 1958, Vol 4, p. 83.
         Pergamon Press, Oxford, 1959. REVIEW.

P-723   Peterson, D. H., in "Biochemistry of Industrial Microorganisms" (C. Rainbow and
         A. H. Rose, eds.), Chapter 16. Academic Press, New York, 1963. REVIEW.

P-724   Peterson, D. H., Global Impacts Appl. Microbiol., p. 439. Almquist & Wiksell,
         Stockholm, 1964.

P-725   Peterson, D. H., Eppstein, S. H., Meister, P. D., Magerlein, B. J., Murray,
         H. C., Leigh, H. M., Weintraub, A., and Reineke, L. M., J. Am. Chem. Soc.
         75, 412 (1953).

P-726   Peterson, D. H., Eppstein, S. H., Meister, P. D., Murray, H. C., Leigh, H. M.,
         Weintraub, A., and Reineke, L. M., J. Am. Chem. Soc. 75, 5768 (1953).

P-727   Peterson, D. H., Meister, P. D., Weintraub, A., Reineke, L. M., Eppstein,
         S. H., Murray, H. C., and Osborn, H. M., Leigh, J. Am. Chem. Soc. 77, 4428
         (1955).

P-728   Peterson, D. H., and Murray, H. C., J. Am. Chem. Soc. 74, 1871 (1952).

P-729   Peterson, D. H., Murray, H. C., Eppstein, S. H., Reineke, L. M., Weintraub,
         A., Meister, P. D., and Leigh, H. M., J. Am. Chem. Soc. 74, 5933 (1952).

P-730   Peterson, D. H., Nathan, A. H., Meister, P. D., Eppstein, S. H., Murray, H. C.,
         Weintraub, A., Reineke, L. M., and Leigh, H. M., J. Am. Chem. Soc. 75, 419
         (1953).

P-731   Peterson, D. H., Reineke, L. M., Murray, H. C., and Sebek, O. K., Chem. &
         Ind. (London), p. 1301 (1960).

P-732   Peterson, G. E., Mandy, W. J., Futch, H., and Luckey, D., Can. J. Microbiol.
         8, 193 (1962).

P-733   Peterson, G. E., Thoma, R. W., Perlman, D., and Fried, J., J. Bacteriol. 74, 684 (1957).

P-734   Philips, N. V., Co., Irish Patent 1008 (1963).

P-735   Philips, N. V., Co., Irish Patent 1009 (1963).

P-736   Philips, N. V., Co., Irish Patent 1010 (1963).

P-737   Prairie, R. L., and Talalay, P., Biochemistry 2, 203 (1963).

P-738   Prescott, S. C., and Dunn, C. G., "Industrial Microbiology," p. 723. McGraw-Hill, New York (1959). REVIEW.

P-739   Prevot, A.-R., Janot, M.-M., and Tam, N. D., Compt. Rend. 256, 3785 (1963).

P-740   Principe, P. A., and Diassi, P. A., U.S. Patent 3,080,298 (March 5, 1963).

P-741   Prochazka, Z., Fajkos, J., Joska, J., and Sorm, F., Collection Czech. Chem. Commun. 26, 2068 (1961).

P-742   Protiva, J., Schwarz, V., and Syhora, K., Tetrahedron Letters, p. 805 (1962).

P-743   Protiva, J., Schwarz, V., and Syhora, K., Folia Microbiol. (Prague) 8, 186 (1963).

P-744   Protiva, J., Schwarz, V., and Syhora, K., Folia Microbiol. (Prague) 9, 218 (1964).

P-745   Pruess, L. M., Feldman, L. I., and Rigler, N. E., U.S. Patent 3,116,219 (December 31, 1963).

P-746   Pruess, L. M., Pidacks, C., and Rigler, N. E., U.S. Patent 3,047,470 (July 31, 1962).

R-747   Rao, P. G., Indian J. Pharm. 25, 131 (1963).

R-748   Rao, P. G., Indian J. Chem. 1, 314 (1963).

R-749   Raspe, G., and Kieslich, K., Naturwiss. 48, 479 (1961).

R-750.   Raspe, G., Kieslich, K., Olivar, E., Muller, R., and Wagner, B., U.S. Patent 3,102,080 (August 27, 1963).

R-751   Rausser, R., and Oliveto, E. P., U.S. Patent 2,999,103 (September 5, 1961).

R-752   Rausser, R., and Oliveto, E. P., U.S. Patent 3,010,958 (November 28, 1961).

R-753   Reichstein, T., Wettstein, A., Anner, G., Billeter, J.-R., Heusler, K., Neher, R., Schmidlin, J., Ueberwasser, H., and Wieland, P., U.S. Patent 2,904,545 (September 15, 1959).

R-754   Reimann, H., and Gould, D. H., U.S. Patent 3,009,927 (November 21, 1961).

R-755   Reimann, H., and Gould, D. H., U.S. Patent 3,009,928 (November 21, 1961).

R-756   Reimann, H., and Gould, D. H., U.S. Patent 3,009,929 (November 21, 1961).

R-757   Reimann, H., and Gould, D. H., U.S. Patent 3,009,929 (November 21, 1961).

R-758   Reimann, H., and Gould, D. H., U.S. Patent 3,009,931 (November 21, 1961).

R-759   Reimann, H., and Gould, D. H., U.S. Patent 3,009,932 (November 21, 1961).

R-760   Reimann, H., and Shapiro, E. L., U.S. Patent 3,085,088 (April 9, 1963).

R-761   Reimann, H., and Gould, D. H., U.S. Patent 3,087,938 (April 30, 1963).

R-762   Reimann, H., and Robinson, C. H., U.S. Patent 3,076,829 (February 5, 1963).

R-763   Reimann, H., Schneider, H., Sarre, O. Z., Federbush, C., Towne, C., Charney, W., and Oliveto, E. P., Chem. & Ind. (London), p. 334 (1963).

R-764   Reimann, H., and Shapiro, E. L., U.S. Patent 2,988,557 (June 13, 1961).

R-765   Reineke, L. M., Anal. Chem. 28, 1853 (1956).

R-766   Reusser, F., Koepsell, H. J., and Savage, G. M., Appl. Microbiol. 9, 346 (1961).

R-767   Ringold, H. J., Graves, J., Hayano, M., and Lawrence, H., Jr., Biochem.
             Biophys. Res. Commun. 13, 162 (1963).

R-768   Ringold, H. J., Gut, M., Hayano, M., and Turner, A., Tetrahedron Letters, p. 835.
             (1962).

R-769   Ringold, H. J., Hayano, M., and Stefanovic, V., J. Biol. Chem. 238, 1960 (1963).

R-770   Ringold, H. J., Mancera, O., Djerassi, C., Bowers, A., Batres, E., Martinez,
             H., Necoechea, E., Edwards, J., Velasco, M., Casas-Campillo, C., and
             Dorfman, R. I., J. Am. Chem. Soc. 80, 6464 (1958).

R-771   Ringold, H. J., and Rosenkranz, G., U.S. Patent 3,107,240 (October 15, 1963).

R-772   Roberts, H. R., and Robison, R. S., Nature 194, 88 (1962).

R-773   Robinson, C. H., U.S. Patent 3,009,933 (November 21, 1961).

R-774   Robinson, C. H., Bruce, N. F., and Oliveto, E. P., J. Org. Chem. 28, 975 (1963).

R-775   Robinson, C. H., Finckenor, L. E., Tiberi, R., Eisler, M., Neri, R., Watnick,
             A., Perlman, P. L., Holroyd, P., Charney, W., and Oliveto, E. P., J. Am.
             Chem. Soc. 82, 4611 (1960).

R-776   Robinson, C. H., Gnoj, O., Charney, W., Gilmore, M. L., and Oliveto, E. P.,
             J. Am. Chem. Soc. 81, 408 (1959).

R-777   Robinson, C. H., and Oliveto, E. P., U.S. Patent 3,081,299 (March 12, 1963).

R-778   Roland, J. F., Jr., and Weiner, B. A., Science 121, 803 (1955).

R-779   Ross, J. W., U.S. Patent 3,022,226 (February 20, 1962).

R-780   Rosselet, J. P., U.S. Patent 2,842,566 (July 8, 1958).

R-781   Rothrock, J. W., Stoudt, T. H., and Garber, J. D., Arch. Biochem. Biophys. 57,
             151 (1955).

R-782   Routien, J. B., and Shull, G. M., U.S. Patent 2,875,134 (February 24, 1959).

R-783   Rubin, B. A., Casas-Campillo, C., Hendrichs, G., Cordova, F., and Zaffaroni,
             A., Bacteriol. Proc., p. 33 (1956).

S-784   Saburi, Y., Hayakawa, S., and Fujii, T., Japan. J. Exptl. Med. 25, 151 (1955).

S-785   Saburi, Y., Hayakawa, S., Fujii, T., and Akaeda, I., J. Biochem. (Tokyo) 43,
             711 (1956).

S-786   Santer, M., and Ajl, S. J., J. Biol. Chem. 199, 85 (1952).

S-787   Santer, M., Ajl, S. J., and Turner, R. A., J. Biol. Chem. 198, 397 (1952).

S-788   Sardinas, J. L., U.S. Patent 3,032,475 (May 1, 1962).

S-789   Sardinas, J. L., Routien, J. B., and Shull, G. M., U.S. Patent 2,882,205
             (April 14, 1959).

S-790   Sardinas, J. L., and Shull, G. M., U.S. Patent 2,876,170 (March 3, 1959).

S-791   Sato, Yoshio, and Hayakawa, S., J. Org. Chem. 26, 4181 (1961).

S-792   Sato, Yoshihiro, Naito, A., Kato, M., Iizuka, H., and Tsuda, K., Chem. & Pharm.
             Bull. (Tokyo) 9, 932 (1961).

S-793   Sato, Yoshihiro, Tanaka, T. , Kuto, M. , and Tsuda, K. , Chem. & Pharm. Bull.
           (Tokyo) 11, 1579 (1963).

S-793a   Sax, K. J. , Blank, R. H. , Evans, R. H. , Jr. , Feldman, L. I. , and Holmlund,
           C. E. , J. Org. Chem. 29, 2351 (1964).

S-793b   Schaffner, C. P. , Greenspan, G. , Charney, W. , and Herzog, H. L. , Proc. 7th
           Intern. Congr. Microbiol. , Stockholm, Paper No. 23h. Almqvist & Wiksell,
           Uppsala, 1958.

S-793c   Schatz, A. , Savard, K. , and Pintner, I. J. , J. Bacteriol. 58, 117 (1949).

S-794   Schiesser, A. , Ric. Sci. 22, 449 (1952).

S-795   Schiesser, A. , Ric. Sci. 23, 638 (1953).

S-796   Schiesser, A. , Ann. Microbiol. 7, 1 (1956).

S-797   Schleg, M. C. , and Knight, S. G. , Mycologia 54, 317 (1962).

S-798   Schmidt, L. H. , and Hughes, H. B. , J. Biol. Chem. 143, 771 (1942).

S-799   Schmidt, L. H. , and Hughes, H. B. , U.S. Patent 2,360,447 (October 17, 1944).

S-800   Schmidt, L. H. , Hughes, H. B. , Green, M. H. , and Cooper, E. , J. Biol. Chem.
           145, 229 (1942).

S-801   Schmidt-Thome, J. , Angew. Chem. 69, 238 (1957).

S-802   Schmidt-Thome, J. , and Hübener, H. J. , Angew. Chem. 73, 44 (1961).

S-803   Schmidt-Thome, J. , Nesemann, G. , Hübener, H. J. , and Alester, I. , Biochem.
           Z. 336, 322 (1962).

S-804   Schneider, W. P. , Lincoln, F. H. , Spero, G. B. , Murray, H. C. , and Thompson,
           J. L. , J. Am. Chem. Soc. 81, 3167 (1959).

S-805   Schneider, W. P. , and Murray, H. C. , Chem. & Ind. (London), p. 1163 (1960).

S-806   Schoeller, W. , U.S. Patent 2,184,167 (December 19, 1939).

S-806a   Schoeller, W. , Inhoffen, H. H. , and Eysenbach, H. , U.S. Patent 2,322,809
           (June 29, 1943).

S-807   Schoeller, W. , Serini, A. , and Inhoffen, H. H. , U.S. Patent 2,264,861
           (December 2, 1941).

S-808   Schramm, G. , and Mamoli, L. , Ber. 71, 1322 (1938).

S-809   Schubert, A. , Proc. 4th Intern. Congr. Biochem. , Vienna, 1958, Vol. 6, p. 120.
           Pergamon Press, Oxford, 1959.

S-810   Schubert, A. , Heller, K. , Koppe, L. , Onken, D. , and Siebert, R. , Z. Naturforsch.
           17b, 436 (1962).

S-811   Schubert, A. , Heller, K. , Onken, D. , Zetsche, K. , and Kluger, B. , Z. Naturforsch.
           15b, 269 (1960).

S-812   Schubert, A. , Heller, K. , and Siebert, R. , Tetrahedron 18, 993 (1962).

S-813   Schubert, A. , Heller, K. , Siebert, R. , Zetsche, K. , and Langbein, G. , Naturwiss.
           45, 264 (1958).

S-814   Schubert, A. , Langbein, G. , and Siebert, R. , Ber. 90, 2576 (1957).

S-815   Schubert, A. , Onken, D. , Siebert, R. , and Heller, K. , Ber. 91, 2549 (1958).

S-816   Schubert, A. , and Siebert, R. , Ber. 91, 1856 (1958).

S-817   Schubert, A., Siebert, R., and Koppe, L., Angew. Chem. 70, 742 (1958).

S-818   Schubert, K., Böhme, K.-H., and Hörhold, C., Z. Naturforsch. 15b, 584 (1960).

S-819   Schubert, K., Böhme, K.-H., and Hörhold, C., Z. Physiol. Chem. 325, 260 (1961).

S-820   Schubert, K., Böhme, K.-H., and Hörhold, C., Z. Naturforsch. 16b, 595 (1961).

S-820a Schubert, K., Böhme, K.-H., and Hörhold, C., Z. Naturforsch. 18b, 988 (1963).

S-821   Schubert, K., Böhme, K.-H., and Hörhold, C., Steroids 4, 581 (1964).

S-822   Schubert, K., Schlegel, J., and Hörhold, C., Z. Naturforsch. 17b, 84 (1962).

S-823   Schubert, K., Schlegel, J., and Hörhold, C., Z. Naturforsch. 18b, 284 (1963).

S-824   Schubert, K., Schlegel, J., and Hörhold, C., Z. Physiol. Chem. 332, 310 (1963).

S-825   Schuytema, E. C., Hargie, M. P., Siehr, D. J., Merits, I., Schenck, J. R., Smith, M. S., and Varner, E. L., Appl. Microbiol. 11, 256 (1963).

S-826   Sebek, O. K., Proc. 7th Intern. Congr. Microbiol., Stockholm, 1958, Abstr., p. 405. Almqvist & Wiksell, Uppsala, 1958.

S-827   Sebek, O. K., Am. Perfumer 76, 27 (1961). REVIEW.

S-828   Sebek, O. K., U.S. Patent 3,116,220 (December 31, 1963).

S-829   Sebek, O. K., and Michaels, R. M., Nature 179, 210 (1957).

S-830   Sebek, O. K., and Michaels, R. M., U.S. Patent 2,877,161 (March 10, 1959).

S-831   Sebek, O. K., Reineke, L. M., and Peterson, D. H., Bacteriol. Proc., p. 15 (1959).

S-832   Sebek, O. K., Reineke, L. M., and Peterson, D. H., J. Bacteriol. 83, 1327 (1962).

S-833   Sebek, O. K., and Spero, G. B., U.S. Patent 2,897,218 (July 28, 1959).

S-834   Sebek, O. K., Spero, G. B., and Thompson, J. L., U.S. Patent 2,864,837 (December 16, 1958).

S-835   Sehgal, S. N., Singh, K., Bourchier, W. F., and Vezina, C., Proc. 8th Intern. Congr. Microbiol., Montreal, 1962 Abstr., p. 81. Univ. of Toronto Press, Toronto, 1963; also Vezina, C., private communication.

S-836   Sehgal, S. N., Singh, K., and Vezina, C., Steroids 2, 93, (1963).

S-837   Shapiro, E., Legatt, T., Weber, L., Steinberg, M., Watnick, A., Eisler, M., Hennessey, M. G., Coniglio, C. T., Charney, W., and Oliveto, E. P., J. Med. Pharm. Chem. 5, 975 (1962).

S-838   Shapiro, E. L., and Reimann, H., U.S. Patent 3,089,873 (May 14, 1963).

S-839   Shapiro, E. L., Steinberg, M., Gould, D., Gentles, M. J., Herzog, H. L., Gilmore, M., Charney, W., Hershberg, E. B., and Mandell, L., J. Am. Chem. Soc. 81, 6483 (1959).

S-840   Shirasaka, M., Chem. & Pharm. Bull. (Tokyo) 9, 54 (1961).

S-841   Shirasaka, M., Chem. & Pharm. Bull. (Tokyo) 9, 59 (1961).

S-842   Shirasaka, M., Chem. & Pharm. Bull. (Tokyo) 9, 152 (1961).

S-843   Shirasaka, M., Chem. & Pharm. Bull. (Tokyo) 9, 203 (1961).

S-844   Shirasaka, M., Hayashi, R., and Tsuruta, M., Bull. Agr. Chem. Soc. Japan 23, 244 (1959).

S-845   Shirasaka, M., and Ozaki, M., J. Agr. Chem. Soc. Japan 35, 200 (1961).

S-846   Shirasaka, M., and Ozaki, M., J. Agr. Chem. Soc. Japan 35, 206 (1961).

S-847   Shirasaka, M., and Ozaki, M., J. Ferment. Assoc. Japan 19, 389 (1961).

S-848   Shirasaka, M., Ozaki, M., and Sugawara, S., J. Ferment. Assoc. Japan 19, 335
         (1961).

S-849   Shirasaka, M., Ozaki, M., and Sugawara, S., J. Gen. Appl. Microbiol. (Tokyo) 7,
         341 (1961).

S-850   Shirasaka, M., Takasaki, R., Hayashi, R., and Tsuruta, M., Bull. Agr. Chem.
         Soc. Japan 23, 245 (1959).

S-851   Shirasaka, M., Takasaki, R., and Tsuruta, M., Nature 186, 390 (1960).

S-852   Shirasaka, M., and Tsuruta, M., Arch. Biochem. Biophys. 85, 277 (1959).

S-853   Shirasaka, M., and Tsuruta, M., Arch. Biochem. Biophys. 87, 338 (1960).

S-854   Shirasaka, M., and Tsuruta, M., Nature 185, 845 (1960).

S-855   Shirasaka, M., and Tsuruta, M., Chem. & Pharm. Bull. (Tokyo) 9, 159 (1961).

S-856   Shirasaka, M., and Tsuruta, M., Chem. & Pharm. Bull. (Tokyo) 9, 196 (1961).

S-857   Shirasaka, M., and Tsuruta, M., Chem. & Pharm. Bull. (Tokyo) 9, 207 (1961).

S-858   Shirasaka, M., and Tsuruta, M., Chem. & Pharm. Bull. (Tokyo) 9, 238 (1961).

S-859   Shirasaka, M., Tsuruta, M., Naito, A., Sugawara, S., and Nakamura, M., Ann.
         Rept. Takamine Lab. 10, 52 (1958).

S-860   Shirasaka, M., Tsuruta, M., and Nakamura, M., Bull. Agr. Chem. Soc. Japan 22,
         273 (1958).

S-861   Shull, G. M., Abstr. 130th Meeting Am. Chem. Soc., Atlantic City, 1956,
         p. 32A.

S-862   Shull, G. M., N. Y. Acad. Sci. [2] 19, 147 (1956). REVIEW.

S-863   Shull, G. M., U.S. Patent 2,776,927 (January 8, 1957).

S-864   Shull, G. M., U.S. Patent 2,809,919 (October 15, 1957).

S-865   Shull, G. M., and Bloom, B. M., U.S. Patent 2,830,935 (April 15, 1958).

S-866   Shull, G. M., U.S. Patent 2,876,171 (March 3, 1959).

S-867   Shull, G. M., U.S. Patent 2,890,153 (June 9, 1959).

S-868   Shull, G. M., U.S. Patent 2,908,616 (October 13, 1959).

S-869   Shull, G. M., U.S. Patent 3,039,926 (June 19, 1962).

S-870   Shull, G. M., U.S. Patent 3,040,038 (June 19, 1962).

S-871   Shull, G. M., and Kita, D. A., J. Am. Chem. Soc. 77, 763 (1955).

S-872   Shull, G. M., and Kita, D. A., U.S. Patent 2,831,876 (April 22, 1958).

S-873   Shull, G. M., and Kita, D. A., U.S. Patent 2,905,592 (September 22, 1959).

S-874   Shull, G. M., and Kita, D. A., U.S. Patent 2,932,606 (April 12, 1960).

S-875   Shull, G. M., Kita, D. A., and Davisson, J. W., U.S. Patent 2,658,023
         (November 3, 1953).

S-876   Shull, G. M., Kita, D. A., and Davisson, J. W., U.S. Patent 2,702,812
         (February 22, 1955).

S-877   Shull, G. M., Kita, D. A., and Davisson, J. W., U.S. Patent 2,745,784 (May 15,
         1956).

S-878   Shull, G. M. , Kita, D. A. , and Davisson, J. W. , U.S. Patent 2,765,258
         (October 2, 1956).

S-879   Shull, G. M. , Kita, D. A. , and Davisson, J. W. , U.S. Patent 2,783,255
         (February 26, 1957).

S-880   Shull, G. M. , and Routien, J. B. , U.S. Patent 2,866,737 (December 30, 1958).

S-881   Shull, G. M. , and Routien, J. B. , U.S. Patent 2,872,380 (February 3, 1959).

S-882   Shull, G. M. , Sardinas, J. L. , and Routien, J. B. , U.S. Patent 2,721,163
         (October 18, 1955).

S-883   Sih, C. J. , J. Pharm. Sci. 50, 712 (1961).

S-884   Sih, C. J. , Biochem. Biophys. Res. Commun. 7, 87 (1962).

S-885   Sih, C. J. , Biochim. Biophys. Acta 62, 541 (1962).

S-886   Sih, C. J. , J. Bacteriol. 84, 382 (1962).

S-887   Sih, C. J. , and Bennett, R. E. , Federation Proc. 19, 25 (1960).

S-888   Sih, C. J. , and Bennett, R. E. , Biochim. Biophys. Acta 38, 378 (1960).

S-889   Sih, C. J. , and Bennett, R. E. , Biochim. Biophys. Acta 56, 584 (1962).

S-890   Sih, C. J. , and Bennett, R. E. , U.S. Patent 3,047,469 (July 31, 1962).

S-891   Sih, C. J. , Kupchan, S. M. , El Tayeb, O. , and Afonso, A. , J. Med. Pharm.
         Chem. 5, 629 (1962).

S-892   Sih, C. J. , Kupchan, S. M. , Katsui, N. , and El Tayeb, O. M. , J. Org. Chem. 28,
         854 (1963).

S-893   Sih, C. J. , Laval, J. , and Rahim, M. A. , J. Biol. Chem. 238, 566 (1963).

S-894   Sih, C. J. , and Rahim, A. M. , J. Pharm. Sci. 52, 1075 (1963).

S-895   Sih, C. J. , and Wang, K. C. , J. Am. Chem. Soc. 85, 2135 (1963).

S-896   Sih, C. J. , Wang, K. C. , and Tsong, Y. Y. , Abstr. 148th Meeting Am. Chem.
         Soc. , Chicago, 1964, p. 6Q.

S-897   Sih, C. J. , and Weisenborn, F. L. , J. Am. Chem. Soc. 82, 2653 (1960).

S-898   Sih, C. J. , and Weisenborn, F. L. , U.S. Patent 3,065,146 (November 20, 1962).

S-899   Sihn, T. S. , J. Biochem. (Tokyo) 28, 165 (1938).

S-900   Singh, K. , Sehgal, S. N. , and Vezina, C. , Proc. 8th Intern. Congr. Microbiol. ,
         Montreal, 1962, Abstr. p. 81. Univ. of Toronto Press, Toronto, 1963.

S-901   Singh, K. , Sehgal, S. N. , and Vezina, C. , Steroids 2, 513 (1963).

S-902   Sletzinger, M. , and Karady, S. , U.S. Patent 2,951,075 (August 30, 1960).

S-903   Sletzinger, M. , and Reinhold, D. F. , U.S. Patent 3,094,523 (June 18, 1963).

S-904   Sletzinger, M. , Reinhold, D. F. , and Karady, S. , U.S. Patent 3,068,228
         (December 11, 1962).

S-905   Sletzinger, M. , Ruyle, W. V. , and Gaines, W. A. , U.S. Patent 2,964,541
         (December 13, 1960).

S-906   Slomp, G. , Jr. , U.S. Patent 2,665,517 (October 13, 1953).

S-907   Smith, L. L. , Foell, T. , and Goodman, J. J. , Biochemistry 1, 353 (1962).

S-908   Smith, L. L. , Garbarini, J. J. , Goodman, J. J. , Marx, M. , and Mendelsohn, H. ,
         J. Am. Chem. Soc. 82, 1437 (1960).

S-909   Smith, L. L. , Goodman, J. J. , Mendelsohn, H. , Dusza, J. P. , and Bernstein, S. ,
         J. Org. Chem. <u>26</u>, 974 (1961).

S-910   Smith, L. L. , Marx, M. , Garbarini, J. J. , Foell, T. , Origoni, V. E. , and
         Goodman, J. J. , J. Am. Chem. Soc. <u>82</u>, 4616 (1960).

S-911   Smith, L. L. , Marx, M. , Mendelsohn, H. , Foell, T. , and Goodman, J. J. , J. Am.
         Chem. Soc. <u>84</u>, 1265 (1962).

S-912   Smith, L. L. , Mendelsohn, H. , Foell, T. , and Goodman, J. J. , J. Org. Chem.
         <u>26</u>, 2859 (1961).

S-913   Smith, L. L. , Mendelsohn, H. , and Goodman, J. J. , U.S. Patent 3,063,989
         (November 13, 1962).

S-914   Snog-Kjaer, A. , Prange, I. , and Dam, H. , J. Gen. Microbiol. <u>14</u>, 256 (1956).

S-915   Sobel, H. , and Plaut, A. , J. Bacteriol. <u>57</u>, 377 (1949).

S-916   Sohngen, N. L. , Zentr. Bakteriol. , Parasitenk. Abt. II <u>37</u>, 595 (1913).

S-917   Sokolova, L. V. , Ryzhkova, V. M. , Skryabin, G. K. , and Suvorov, N. N. , Med.
         Prom. SSSR <u>15</u>, 29 (1961).

S-918   Spalla, C. , Amici, A. M. , and Bianchi, M. L. , Giorn. Microbiol. <u>9</u>, 249 (1961).

S-919   Spalla, C. , Amici, A. M. , and Bianchi, M. L. , Giorn. Microbiol. <u>9</u>, 255 (1961).

S-920   Spalla, C. , Modelli, R. , and Amici, A. M. , U.S. Patent 3,030,278 (April 17, 1962).

S-921   Spero, G. B. , U.S. Patent 2,928,851 (March 15, 1960).

S-922   Spero, G. B. , U.S. Patent 2,964,542 (December 13, 1960).

S-923   Spero, G. B. , U.S. Patent 3,100,777 (August 13, 1963).

S-924   Spero, G. B. , and Hogg, J. A. , U.S. Patent 2,838,497 (June 10, 1958).

S-925   Spero, G. B. , Magerlein, B. J. , Schneider, W. P. , and Hogg, J. A. , U.S. Patent
         2,838,499 (June 10, 1958).

S-926   Spero, G. B. , Magerlein, B. J. , Schneider, W. P. , and Hogg, J. A. , U.S. Patent
         2,838,537 (June 10, 1958).

S-927   Spero, G. B. , and Thompson, J. L. , U.S. Patent 3,045,031 (July 17, 1962).

S-928   Spero, G. B. , Thompson, J. L. , Magerlein, B. J. , Hanze, A. R. , Murray, H. C. ,
         Sebek, O. K. , and Hogg, J. A. , J. Am. Chem. Soc. <u>78</u>, 6213 (1956).

S-929   Srogl, M. , Sindelar, L. , and Vondrova, O. , Folia Microbiol. (Prague) <u>8</u>, 237 (1963).

S-930   Stadtman, T. C. , Cherkes, A. , and Anfinsen, C. B. , J. Biol. Chem. <u>206</u>, 511
         (1954).

S-931   Stadtman, E. R. , and Stadtman, T. C. , Ann. Rev. Microbiol. <u>7</u>, 143 (1953).
         REVIEW.

S-932   Stanley, A. R. , and Hickey, R. J. , "Industrial Fermentations," Vol. II, p. 398.
         Chem. Publ. Co. , New York, 1954. REVIEW.

S-933   Stefanovic, V. , Hayano, M. , and Dorfman, R. I. , Biochim. Biophys. Acta <u>71</u>, 429
         (1963).

S-934   Stein, A. M. , and Kaplan, N. O. , Science <u>129</u>, 1611 (1959).

S-935   Stimmel, B. F. , Bucknell, T. E. , and Notchev, V. , Federation Proc. <u>19</u>, 171
         (1960).

S-936   Stodola, F. H. , Abstr. 136th Meeting Am. Chem. Soc. , Atlantic City, 1959,
         p. 14A. REVIEW.

S-936a   Stoll, A., Renz, J., and Brack, A., Helv. Chim. Acta 34, 397 (1951).

S-937   Stone, D., Hayano, M., Dorfman, R. I., Hechter, O., Robinson, C. H., and
           Djerassi, C., J. Am. Chem. Soc. 77, 3926 (1955).

S-938   Stoudt, T. H., Advan. Appl. Microbiol. 2, 183 (1960). REVIEW.

S-939   Stoudt, T. H., U.S. Patent 3,016,335 (January 9, 1962).

S-940   Stoudt, T., and Brower, B., Abstr. 122nd Meeting Am. Chem. Soc., Atlantic City,
           1952, p. 10C.

S-941   Stoudt, T. H., Kozlowski, M. A., and McAleer, W. J., U.S. Patent 2,982,694
           (May 2, 1961).

S-942   Stoudt, T. H., McAleer, W. J., Chemerda, J. M., Kozlowski, M. A., Hirschmann,
           R. F., Marlatt, V., and Miller, R., Arch. Biochem. Biophys. 59, 304 (1955).

S-943   Stoudt, T. H., McAleer, W. J., Kozlowski, M. A., and Marlatt, V., Arch.
           Biochem. Biophys. 74, 280 (1958).

S-944   Sugawara, S., Tsuruta, M., Shirasaka, M., and Nakamura, M., Arch. Biochem.
           Biophys. 80, 383 (1959).

S-945   Sutter, D., Charney, W., O'Neill, P. L., Carvajal, F., Herzog, H. L., and
           Hershberg, E. B., J. Org. Chem. 22, 578 (1957).

S-946   Suvorov, N. N., Med. Prom. SSSR 6, 22 (1956).

S-947   Suvorov, N. N., Sokolova, L. V., Ryzhkova, V. M., and Dvoryantseva, G. G.,
           Dokl. Akad. Nauk SSSR 152, 1130 (1963).

S-948   Suvorov, N. N., Sokolova, L. V., Ryzhkova, V. M., and Saikina, D. N., Dokl.
           Akad. Nauk SSSR 132, 1325 (1960).

S-949   Szpilfogel, S. A., de Winter, M. S., and Alsche, W. J., Rec. Trav. Chim. 75,
           402 (1956).

S-950   Szpilfogel, S. A., Mijs, W. J., de Flines, J., and van der Waard, W. F., U.S.
           Patent 3,031,445 (April 24, 1962).

S-951   Szpilfogel, S. A., Van Hemert, P. A., and de Winter, M. S., Rec. Trav. Chim.
           75, 1227 (1956).

T-952   Tak, J. D., J. Microbiol. Serol. 8, 32 (1942).

T-953   Takahashi, T., Agr. Biol. Chem. 27, 633 (1963).

T-954   Takahashi, T., Agr. Biol. Chem. 27, 639 (1963).

T-955   Takahashi, T., Agr. Biol. Chem. 28, 38 (1964).

T-956   Takahashi, T., and Hasegawa, T., J. Agr. Chem. Soc. Japan 35, 1394 (1961).

T-957   Takahashi, T., and Hasegawa, T., J. Agr. Chem. Soc. Japan 35, 1399 (1961).

T-958   Takahashi, T., and Uchibori, Y., Agr. Biol. Chem. (Tokyo) 26, 89 (1962).

T-959   Takahashi, T., Uchibori, Y., and Hasegawa, T., J. Agr. Chem. Soc. Japan 36,
           67 (1962).

T-960   Takeda, R., Nakanishi, I., Nawa, H., Uchibayashi, M., Kusaka, T., Terumichi,
           J., Uchida, M., Katsumata, M., Yoshino, K., and Fujitani, H., U.S. Patent
           3,037,915 (June 5, 1962).

T-961   Takeda, R., Nakanishi, I., Terumichi, J., Uchida, M., Katsumata, M.,
           Uchibayashi, M., and Nawa, H., Tetrahedron Letters, p. 17 (1959).

T-962   Talalay, P., Federation Proc. 15, 368 (1956),

T-963   Talalay, P., Abstr. 130th Meeting Am. Chem. Soc., Atlantic City, 1956, p. 34A.

T-964   Talalay, P., Record Chem. Progr. (Kresge-Hooker Sci. Lib.) 18, 31 (1957). REVIEW.

T-965   Talalay, P., Physiol. Rev. 37, 362 (1957). REVIEW.

T-966   Talalay, P., U.S. Patent 2,796,382 (June 18, 1957).

T-967   Talalay, P., and Dobson, M. M., J. Biol. Chem. 205, 823 (1953).

T-968   Talalay, P., Dobson, M. M., and Tapley, D. F., Nature 170, 620 (1952).

T-969   Talalay, P., Loewus, F. A., and Vennesland, B., J. Biol. Chem. 212, 801 (1955).

T-970   Talalay, P., and Marcus, P. I., Nature 173, 1189 (1954).

T-971   Talalay, P., and Marcus, P. I., J. Biol. Chem. 218, 675 (1956).

T-972   Talalay, P., and Wang, V. S., Biochim. Biophys. Acta 18, 300 (1955).

T-973   Tam, N. D., Ann. Pharm. Franc. 20, 556 (1962).

T-974   Tamaki, K., J. Biochem. (Tokyo) 45, 299 (1958).

T-975   Tamaki, K., J. Biochem. (Tokyo) 45, 693 (1958).

T-976   Tamm, C., Planta Med. 8, 331 (1960). REVIEW.

T-977   Tamm, C., and Gubler, A., Helv. Chim. Acta 41, 1762 (1958).

T-978   Tamm, C., and Gubler, A., Helv. Chim. Acta 42, 239 (1959).

T-979   Tamm, C., and Gubler, A., Helv. Chim. Acta 42, 473 (1959).

T-980   Tamm, C., Gubler, A., Juhasz, G., Weiss-Berg, E., and Zurcher, W., Helv. Chim. Acta 46, 889 (1963).

T-981   Tanabe, M., U.S. Patent 3,116,289 (December 31, 1963).

T-982   Tanabe, K., Hayashi, R., Takasaki, R., and Shirasaka, M., Chem. & Pharm. Bull. (Tokyo) 7, 811 (1959).

T-983   Tanabe, K., Takasaki, R., Hayashi, R., and Shirasaka, M., Chem. & Pharm. Bull. (Tokyo) 7, 804 (1959).

T-984   Taub, D., Hoffsommer, R. D., and Wendler, N. L., J. Am. Chem. Soc. 78, 2912 (1956).

T-985   Taub, D., Hoffsommer, R. D., and Wendler, N. L., J. Am. Chem. Soc. 79, 452 (1957).

T-986   Taub, D., Wendler, N. L., and Slates, H. L., U.S. Patent 3,053,865 (September 11, 1962).

T-987   Taub, D., Wendler, N. L., and Slates, H. L., U.S. Patent 3,116,303 (December 31, 1963).

T-988   Teller, J. D., and Bongiovanni, A. M., Nature 197, 1112 (1963).

T-989   Terumichi, J., U.S. Patent 2,992,973 (July 18, 1961).

T-990   Testa, E., Ann. Chim. (Rome) 47, 1132 (1957).

T-991   Testa, E., U.S. Patent 2,865,813 (December 23, 1958).

T-992   Thoma, R. W., Abstr. 136th Meeting Am. Chem. Soc., Atlantic City, 1959, p. 14A. REVIEW.

T-993   Thoma, R. W., Frazier, W. R., Harris, G. C. M., and Brown, W. E., Bacteriol.
           Proc., p. 29, Abstr. A-38 (1962).

T-994   Thoma, R. W., and Fried, J., U.S. Patent 2,801,251 (July 30, 1957).

T-995   Thoma, R. W., and Fried, J., U.S. Patent 2,880,217 (March 31, 1959).

T-996   Thoma, R. W., and Fried, J., U.S. Patent 2,955,075 (October 4, 1960).

T-997   Thoma, R. W., and Fried, J., U.S. Patent 2,960,436 (November 15, 1960).

T-998   Thoma, R. W., and Fried, J., U.S. Patent 2,960,513 (November 15, 1960).

T-999   Thoma, R. W., and Fried, J., U.S. Patent 3,031,477 (April 24, 1962).

T-1000   Thoma, R. W., and Fried, J., U.S. Patent 3,083,212 (March 26, 1963).

T-1001   Thoma, R. W., and Fried, J., U.S. Patent 3,105,842 (October 1, 1963).

T-1002   Thoma, R. W., Fried, J., Bonanno, S., and Grabowich, P., J. Am. Chem. Soc.
           $\underline{79}$, 4818 (1957).

T-1003   Thoma, R. W., Gerke, J. R., and Fried, J., U.S. Patent 2,793,162 (May 21, 1957).

T-1004   Thoma, R. W., Gerke, J. R., and Fried, J., U.S. Patent 2,793,163 (May 21, 1957).

T-1005   Thoma, R. W., Laskin, A. I., Trejo, W. H., Kroll, H., Peterson, G. E., and
           Stickle, G. P., Sci. Rept. Ist. Super. Sanita $\underline{1}$, 326 (1961).

T-1006   Thoma, R. W., and Weisenborn, F. L., U.S. Patent 3,005,028 (October 17, 1961).

T-1007   Thoma, R. W., and Whitney, K. J., Bacteriol. Proc., p. 11 (1964).

T-1008   Thomas, G. H., and Thoma, R. W., U.S. Patent 2,853,502 (September 23, 1958).

T-1009   Timofeeva, A. G., Barmenkov, A. S., and Fedotova, M. V., Med. Prom. SSSR $\underline{7}$,
           23 (1957).

T-1010   Timofeeva, A. G., Gusakova, E. G., and Shpingis, A. A., Izv. Akad. Nauk SSSR,
           Ser. Biol. $\underline{26}$, 574 (1961).

T-1011   Timofeeva, A. G., Madaeva, O. S., Gusakova, E. G., Kovylkina, N. F., Men'shova,
           N. I., and Novikova, V. M., Izv. Akad. Nauk SSSR, Ser. Biol., p. 712 (1958).

T-1012   Titus, E., Advan. Appl. Microbiol. $\underline{3}$, 279 (1961).

T-1013   Titus, E., Murray, A. W., and Spiegel, H. E., J. Biol. Chem. $\underline{235}$, 3399 (1960).

T-1014   Tori, K., and Kondo, E., Tetrahedron Letters, p. 645 (1963).

T-1015   Toulmin, H. A., Jr., U.S. Patent 3,070,512 (December 25, 1962).

T-1016   Toulmin, H. A., Jr., U.S. Patent 3,070,513 (December 25, 1962).

T-1017   Townsley, J. D., Brodie, H. J., Hayano, M., and Dorfman, R. I., Steroids $\underline{3}$,
           341 (1964).

T-1018   Trelawny, G. S., Schatz, V., and Schatz, A., Proc. Penn. Acad. Sci. $\underline{29}$, 61
           (1955).

T-1019   Tsuda, K., Asai, T., Iizuka, H., Tanaka, T., Nakamura, M., Okazaki, H.,
           Shirasaka, M., and Naito, A., U.S. Patent 2,993,839 (July 25, 1961).

T-1020   Tsuda, K., Asai, T., Ohki, E., Tanaka, A., and Hattori, M., Chem. & Pharm.
           Bull. (Tokyo) $\underline{6}$, 387 (1958).

T-1021   Tsuda, K., Asai, T., Ohki, E., Tanaka, A., and Matsuhisa, T., Chem. & Pharm.
           Bull. (Tokyo) $\underline{7}$, 369 (1959).

T-1022   Tsuda, K., Asai, T., Sato, Yoshihiro, Tanaka, T., and Hasegawa, H., Chem. &
           Pharm. Bull. (Tokyo) $\underline{9}$, 735 (1961).

T-1023   Tsuda, K., Asai, T., Sato, Yoshihiro, Tanaka, T., and Kato, M., J. Gen. Appl. Microbiol. (Tokyo) 5, 1 (1959).

T-1024   Tsuda, K., Asai, T., Sato, Yoshihiro and Tanaka, T., Chem. & Pharm. Bull. (Tokyo) 7, 534 (1959).

T-1025   Tsuda, K., Asai, T., Sato, Yoshihiro, Tanaka, T., Matsuhisa, T., and Hasegawa, H., Chem. & Pharm. Bull. (Tokyo) 8, 626 (1960).

T-1026   Tsuda, K., Iizuka, H., Ohki, E., Sato, Yoshihiro, Naito, A., and Hattori, M., J. Gen. Appl. Microbiol. (Tokyo) 5, 7 (1959).

T-1027   Tsuda, K., Iizuka, H., Sato, Yoshihiro, Naito, A., and Kato, M., Chem. & Pharm. Bull. (Tokyo) 9, 925 (1961).

T-1028   Tumova, E., Siblikova-Zbudovska, O., and Hanc, O., Cesk. Farm. 4, 65 (1955).

T-1029   Turfitt, G. E., Biochem. J. 37, 115 (1943).

T-1030   Turfitt, G. E., J. Bacteriol. 47, 487 (1944).

T-1031   Turfitt, G. E., Biochem. J. 38, 492 (1944).

T-1032   Turfitt, G. E., Biochem. J. 40, 79 (1946).

T-1033   Turfitt, G. E., J. Bacteriol. 54, 557 (1947).

T-1034   Turfitt, G. E., Biochem. J. 42, 376 (1948).

T-1035   Tweit, R. C., U.S. Patent 3,063,993 (November 13, 1962).

T-1036   Tweit, R. C., Dodson, R. M., and Muir, R. D., J. Org. Chem. 27, 3654 (1962).

T-1037   Tweit, R. C., Goldkamp, A. H., and Dodson, R. M., J. Org. Chem. 26, 2856 (1961).

U-1038   Uchibayashi, M., Chem. & Pharm. Bull. (Tokyo) 8, 112 (1960).

U-1039   Uchibayashi, M., Chem. & Pharm. Bull. (Tokyo) 8, 117 (1960).

U-1040   Uchibayashi, M., Chem. & Pharm. Bull. (Tokyo) 8, 255 (1960).

U-1041   Uehleke, H., Naturwiss. 46, 77 (1959).

U-1042   Urech, J., Desaulles, P. A., Vischer, E., and Wettstein, A., Gazz. Chim. Ital. 93, 133 (1963).

U-1043   Urech, J., Vischer, E., and Wettstein, A., Helv. Chim. Acta 43, 1077 (1960).

U-1044   Urech, J., Vischer, E., and Wettstein, A., Helv. Chim. Acta 46, 2788 (1963).

V-1045   Valcavi, U., and Zannini, E., Gazz. Chim. Ital. 91, 958 (1961).

V-1046   Vercellone, A., and Mamoli, L., Z. Physiol. Chem. 248, 277 (1937).

V-1047   Vercellone, A., and Mamoli, L., Ber. 71, 152 (1938).

V-1048   Vezina, C., Sehgal, S. N., and Singh, K., Appl. Microbiol. 11, 50 (1963).

V-1049   Vezina, C., Singh, K., and Sehgal, S. N., Proc. 8th Intern. Congr. Microbiol., Montreal, 1962, Abstr. p. 41. Univ. of Toronto Press, Toronto, 1963.

V-1050   Vischer, E., Abstr. 130th Meeting Am. Chem. Soc., Atlantic City, 1956, p. 33A.

V-1051   Vischer, E., Abstr. 7th Intern. Congr. Microbiol., Stockholm, 1958 p. 407. Almquist & Wiksell, Uppsala, 1958.

V-1052   Vischer, E., Meystre, C., and Wettstein, A., Helv. Chim. Acta 38, 1502 (1955).

V-1053   Vischer, E., Meystre, C., and Wettstein, A., Helv. Chim. Acta 38, 835 (1955).

V-1054   Vischer, E., Schmidlin, J., and Wettstein, A., Helv. Chim. Acta 37, 321 (1954).

V-1055   Vischer, E., Schmidlin, J., and Wettstein, A., Experientia 12, 50 (1956).

V-1056   Vischer, E., and Wettstein, A., Experientia 9, 371 (1953).

V-1057   Vischer, E., and Wettstein, A., Angew. Chem. 69, 456 (1957). REVIEW.

V-1058   Vischer, E., and Wettstein, A., Advan. Enzymol. 20, 237 (1958). REVIEW.

V-1059   Vischer, E., and Wettstein, A., Experientia 16, 355 (1960).

V-1059a   Vondrová, O., and Capek, A., Folia Microbiol. (Prague) 8, 117 (1963).

V-1060   Vondrová, O., and Hanc, O., Folia Microbiol. (Prague) 5, 247 (1960).

V-1061   Vondrová, O., Tadra, M., and Capek, A., Folia Microbiol. (Prague) 8, 176 (1963).

W-1062   Wainfan, E., Henkin, G., Rittenberg, S. C., and Marx, W., J. Biol. Chem. 207, 843 (1954).

W-1062a   Wallen, L. L., Stodola, F. H., and Jackson, R. W., U.S. Dept. Agr., ARS-71-13 (1959). REVIEW.

W-1063   Wang, K. C., and Sih, C. J., Biochemistry 2, 1238 (1963).

W-1064   Wang, S.-F., Kawahara, F. S., and Talalay, P., J. Biol. Chem. 238, 576 (1963).

W-1065   Weaver, E. A., U.S. Patent 3,019,170 (January 30, 1962).

W-1066   Weaver, E. A., and Kenney, H. E., U.S. Patent 2,989,439 (June 20, 1961).

W-1067   Weaver, E. A., Kenney, H. E., and Wall, M. E., Appl. Microbiol. 8, 345 (1960).

W-1068   Wechter, W. J., U.S. Patent 3,070,611 (December 25, 1962).

W-1069   Wechter, W. J., and Murray, H. C., Chem. & Ind. (London), p. 411 (1962).

W-1070   Wechter, W. J., and Murray, H. C., J. Org. Chem. 28, 755 (1963).

W-1071   Wehrli, H., Cereghetti, M., Schaffner, K., Urech, J., and Vischer, E., Helv. Chim. Acta 44, 1927 (1961).

W-1072   Weintraub, A., Eppstein, S. H., and Meister, P. D., U.S. Patent 2,902,410 (September 1, 1959).

W-1073   Weintraub, A., and Meister, P. D., U.S. Patent 2,879,206 (March 24, 1959).

W-1074   Weiss-Berg, E., and Tamm, C., Helv. Chim. Acta 46, 1166 (1963).

W-1075   Weiss-Berg, E., and Tamm, C., Helv. Chim. Acta 46, 2435 (1963).

W-1076   Weisenborn, F. L., U.S. Patent 2,950,289 (August 23, 1960).

W-1077   Weisenborn, F. L., and Laskin, A. I., U.S. Patent 3,031,494 (April 24, 1962).

W-1078   Weisenborn, F. L., Lerner, L. J., and Laskin, A. I., U.S. Patent 3,005,018 (October 17, 1961).

W-1079   Weisenborn, F. L., and Sih, C. J., U.S. Patent 3,056,838 (October 2, 1962).

W-1080   Weisenborn, F. L., and Sih, C. J., U.S. Patent 3,110,733 (November 12, 1963).

W-1081   Weisz, E., Wix, G., and Bodanszky, M., Naturwiss. 43, 39 (1956).

W-1082   Welsch, M., and Heusghem, C., Compt. Rend. Soc. Biol. 142, 1074 (1948).

W-1083   Wendler, N. L., and Taub, D., U.S. Patent 2,973,375 (February 28, 1961).

W-1084   Werder, F. von Bruckner, K., Bork, K.-H., Metz, H., Hampel, B., and Mannhardt, H. J., Ber. 95, 2110 (1962).

W-1085   Wettstein, A., Helv. Chim. Acta <u>22</u>, 250 (1939).

W-1086   Wettstein, A., Abstr. 128th Meeting Am. Chem. Soc., Minneapolis, 1955, p. 16N.

W-1087   Wettstein, A., Experientia <u>11</u>, 465 (1955). REVIEW.

W-1088   Wettstein, A., Verhandl. Deut. Ges. Inn. Med. <u>62</u>, 214 (1956). REVIEW.

W-1089   Wettstein, A., Experientia <u>17</u>, 329 (1961). REVIEW.

W-1090   Wettstein, A., and Anner, G., Experientia <u>10</u>, 397 (1954). REVIEW.

W-1090a   Wettstein, A., Anner, G., and Kebrle, J., U.S. Patent 3,055,887 (September 25, 1962).

W-1091   Wettstein, A., Heusler, K., and Wieland, P., U.S. Patent 3,012,940 (December 12, 1961).

W-1092   Wettstein, A., Neher, R., DeSaulles, P. A., Vischer, E., and Wieland, P., U.S. Patent 3,033,748 (May 8, 1962).

W-1093   Wettstein, A., Neher, R., Vischer, E., and Wieland, P., U.S. Patent 3,033,749 (May 8, 1962).

W-1094   Wettstein, A., and Vischer, E., U.S. Patent 2,841,531 (July 1, 1958).

W-1095   Wettstein, A., and Vischer, E., U.S. Patent 2,904,472 (September 15, 1959).

W-1096   Wettstein, A., and Vischer, E., U.S. Patent 2,949,405 (August 16, 1960).

W-1097   Wettstein, A., and Vischer, E., U.S. Patent 2,972,568 (February 21, 1961).

W-1098   Wettstein, A., and Vischer, E., U.S. Patent 3,033,759 (May 8, 1962).

W-1100   Wettstein, A., Vischer, E., Kahnt, F. W., Meystre, C., and Neher, R., U.S. Patent 3,060,100 (October 23, 1962).

W-1101   Wettstein, A., Vischer, E., and Meystre, C., U.S. Patent 2,778,776 (January 22, 1957).

W-1102   Wettstein, A., Vischer, E., and Meystre, C., U.S. Patent 2,844,513 (July 22, 1958).

W-1103   Wettstein, A., Vischer, E., and Meystre, C., U.S. Patent 2,922,798 (January 26, 1960).

W-1104   Wettstein, A., Vischer, E., and Meystre, C., U.S. Patent 2,929,763 (March 22, 1960).

W-1105   Wettstein, A., Vischer, E., and Meystre, C., U.S. Patent 2,949,405 (August 16, 1960).

W-1106   Wettstein, A., Vischer, E., and Meystre, C., U.S. Patent 2,969,304 (January 24, 1961).

W-1107   Wettstein, A., Vischer, E., and Meystre, C., U.S. Patent 2,969,305 (January 24, 1961).

W-1108   Wettstein, A., Vischer, E., and Meystre, C., U.S. Patent 3,000,884 (September 19, 1961).

W-1108a   Wettstein, A., Vischer, E., and Meystre, C., U.S. Patent 3,076,828 (February 5, 1963).

W-1109   Wettstein, A., Vischer, E., Meystre, C., and Ehmann, L., U.S. Patent 2,871,245 (January 27, 1959).

W-1110   Wettstein, A., Vischer, E., Urech, J., and Jeger, O., U.S. Patent 3,055,806 (September 25, 1962).

W-1111   Whitmarsh, J. M., Biochem. J. 90, 23P (1964).

W-1112   Wiechert, R., Kerb, U., and Kieslich, K., Ber., 96, 2765 (1963).

W-1113   Wittle, E. L., and Moore, J. A., U.S. Patent 3,052,671 (September 4, 1962).

W-1114   Wix, G., "Ten Years Activity of the Research Institute for Pharmaceutical Industry
          1950 January 1 - December 31, 1959," pp. 97-149. Tech. Publ., Budapest, 1960.
          REVIEW.

W-1115   Wix, G., and Albrecht, K., Nature 183, 1279 (1959).

W-1116   Wix, G., and Albrecht, K., J. Biochem. Microbiol. Technol. Eng. 1, 239 (1959).

W-1117   Wix, G., and Albrecht, K., J. Biochem. Microbiol. Technol. Eng. 3, 325 (1961).

W-1118   Wix, G., and Albrecht, K., Acta Microbiol. Acad. Sci. Hung. 8, 339 (1961).

W-1119   Wix, G., Bodanszky, A., and Kollonitsch, J., Acta Microbiol. Acad. Sci. Hung. 3,
          333 (1956).

W-1120   Wix, G., Natonek, M., and Kovacs, M., Acta Microbiol. Acad. Sci. Hung. 6, 197
          (1959).

W-1121   Wix, G., Weisz, E., and Bodanszky, M., Acta Microbiol. Acad. Sci. Hung. 4, 9
          (1957).

W-1122   Wolnak, B., and Barrington, L. F., U.S. Patent 3,041,250 (June 26, 1962).

Z-1123   Zaffaroni, A., Casas-Campillo, C., Cordoba, F., and Rosenkranz, G., Experientia
          11, 219 (1955).

Z-1124   Zaffaroni, A., and Rubin, B. A., U.S. Patent 2,812,285 (November 5, 1957).

Z-1125   Zaffaroni, A., and Rubin, B. A., U.S. Patent 2,812,286 (November 5, 1957).

Z-1126   Zderic, J. A., Bowers, A., Carpio, H., and Djerassi, C., J. Am. Chem. Soc. 80,
          2596 (1958).

Z-1127   Zderic, J. A., Carpio, H., Bowers, A., and Djerassi, C., Steroids 1, 233 (1963).

Z-1128   Zderic, J. A., Halpern, O., and Iriarte, J., U.S. Patent 3,071,581 (January 1,
          1963).

Z-1129   Zderic, J. A., Halpern, O., and Iriarte, J., U.S. Patent 3,099,656 (July 30, 1963).

Z-1130   Zetsche, K., Naturwiss. 47, 232 (1960).

Z-1131   Zetsche, K., Naturwiss. 48, 407 (1961).

Z-1132   Zetsche, K., Arch. Mikrobiol. 38, 237 (1961).

Z-1133   Zimmermann, W., and May, G., Zentr. Bakteriol., Parasitenk., Abt. I. Orig.
          151, 462 (1944).

Z-1134   Zuidweg, M. H. J., van der Waard, W. F., and de Flines, J., Biochim. Biophys.
          Acta 58, 131 (1962).

CHAPTER VII

BIBLIOGRAPHICAL APPENDIX

References Ap-1 through Ap-100 are included in this chapter.

Ap-1   Afonso, A., Herzog, H. L., Federbush, C., and Charney, W., Steroids 7, 429 (1966). Conversion of 1,3,5(10) - cholestatrien-3-ol into estrone by Nocardia restrictus.

Ap-2   Bellet, P., Nomine, G., and Mathieu, J., Compt. Rend. 263C, 88 (1966). Stereo-specific reduction of an optically inactive ketonic precursor in a total synthesis of steroids using Rhizopus arrhizus to give an optically active intermediate which could be converted to estradiol of the natural series. Same principle as Gibian reference (Ap-24).

Ap-3   Benn, W. R., Tiberi, R., and Nussbaum, A. L., J. Org. Chem. 29, 3712 (1964). Oxidation of 5,16-pregnadiene-3β,20β-diol and the corresponding 20α-ol with Flavo-bacterium dehydrogenans to 16-dehydroprogesterone.

Ap-4   Bolt, C. C., Mijs, W. J., Zeelen, F. J., Szpilfogel, S. A., de Flines, J. and van der Waard, W. F., Rec. Trav. Chim. 84, 626 (1965). 1β-Hydroxylation of 19-nortestosterone with Botryodiplodia malorum.

Ap-5   Brannon, D. R., Martin, J., Oehlschlager, A. C., Durham, N. N., and Zalkow, L. H., J. Org. Chem. 30, 760 (1965). Aspergillus tamarii on progesterone gave testololactone and 11β-hydroxytestosterone. 11β-Hydroxyprogesterone gave 11β-hydroxytestosterone. 11α-Hydroxyprogesterone gave 11α-hydroxytestosterone. 4-Androstene-3,17-dione and testosterone gave testololactone.

Ap-6   Bridgeman, J. E., Cherry, P. C., Cottrell, W. R. T., Jones, E. R. H., Le Quesne, P. W., and Meakins, G. D., Chem. Commun. p. 561 (1966). 1β,6α-Dihydroxylation of 5α-androstan-17-one with unnamed organism.

Ap-7   Canonica, L., Jommi, G., Pagnoni, U. M., Pellizzoni, F., Ranzi, B. M., and Scolastico, C., Gazz. Chim. Ital. 96, 820 (1966). 7β-Hydroxylation and oxidation of 3-hydroxyl to ketone in glycyrrhetic acid by Curvularia lunata.

Ap-8   Capek, A., Hanc, O., Tadra, M., and Tuma, J., Cesk. Farm. 4, 198 (1966). Improved preparation of cortisone from Reichstein's Compound S.

Ap-9   Capek, A., Tadra, M., and Tuma, J., Folia Microbiol. (Prague) 9, 380-382 (1964).

Ap-10   Casas-Campillo, C., and Bautista, M., Appl. Microbiol. 13, 977 (1965). 15α-Hydroxylation of estrone and estradiol with Fusarium moniliforme. 6β-Hydroxyla-tion of estradiol 3-methyl ether with same organism.

Ap-11   Casas-Campillo, C., Esparza, F., and Balandrano, D., Bacteriol. Proc. p. 93 (1965).

Ap-12   Cherry, P. C., Jones, E. R. H., and Meakins, G. D., Chem. Commun. p. 587 (1966). 3β-Hydroxylation and 12β-hydroxylation of 5-androsten-7-one by Calonectria decora. Tentative 4β-hydroxylation of the same substrate by the same organism.

Ap-13   Coombe, R. G. , Tsong, Y. Y. , Hamilton, P. B. , and Sih, C. J. , J. Biol. Chem.
        241, 1587 (1966). Degradation of estrone by Nocardia sp. via 4-hydroxylation.

Ap-14   Curtis, P. J. , Biochem. J. 97, 148 (1965). Demethylation of totally-synthetic,
        phenolic 8-azasteroid 3-methyl ether by Aspergillus flavus and Cunninghamella
        blakesleeana. Reduction of 17a-carbonyl group in same substrate to 17aα-ol and
        17aβ-ol by Aspergillus ochraceus.

Ap-15   Davidson, S. J. , and Talalay, P. , J. Biol. Chem. 241, 906 (1966). Soluble 5β-
        dehydrogenase from Pseudomonas testosteroni.

Ap-16   de Flines, J. , van der Sijde, D. , and van der Waard, W. F. , Rec. Trav. Chim. 85,
        701 (1966). Fermentation of 9β,10α-progesterone with Sporomia pollaccii yielded
        mainly 9β,10α-testosterone. Fermentation with Helicosporium lumbricopsis
        afforded 9β,10α-androst-4-ene-3,17-dione. Fermentation with Colletotrichum
        gloeosporioides afforded 15α-hydroxy-9β,10α-progesterone. This product was
        converted with Helicosporium lumbricopsis to 15α-hydroxy-9β,10α-androst-4-ene-
        3,17-dione. Fermentation of 6-dehydro-9β,10α-progesterone with Mastigosporium
        heterosporium afforded 9β,10α-androsta-4,6-diene-3,17-dione.

Ap-17   Deghenghi, R. , Revesz, C. , and Gaudry, R. , J. Med. Chem. 6, 301 (1963).
        Failure of Septomyxa affinis and Streptomyces lavendulae to degrade the side chain
        to 17α-alkyl derivatives of progesterone.

Ap-18   Dodson, R. M. , Langbein, G. , Muir, R. D. , Schubert, A. , Siebert, R. , Tamm, C. ,
        and Weiss-Berg, E. , Helv. Chim. Acta 48, 1933 (1965). Identity of "6β,15α-di-
        hydroxyprogesterone" (G-319) and "11α,15β-dihydroxyprogesterone" (M-596) with
        12β,15α-dihydroxyprogesterone.

Ap-19   El-Tayeb, O. , Knight, S. G. , and Sih, C. J. , Biochim. Biophys. Acta 93, 402
        (1964). Cylindrocarpon radicicola on 16α,17α-oxidoprogesterone (I) gave 20α-
        hydroxy-16α,17α-oxido-4-pregnen-3-one (II), 20α-hydroxy-16α,17α-oxido-1,4-
        pregnadien-3-one (III), 16α-hydroxy-17a-oxa-1,4-androstadiene-3,17-dione (IV)
        and 16α,17α-dihydroxy-1,4-androstadien-3-one (V). Sequence and mechanism of
        degradation are discussed. 16α-Hydroxy-4-pregnene-3,20-dione gave (V) only.
        16α-Hydroxy-4-androstene-3,17-dione gave (IV) and (V).

Ap-20   El-Tayeb, O. , Knight, S. G. , and Sih, C. J. , Biochim. Biophys. Acta 93, 411
        (1964). 17α-Hydroxyprogesterone with Penicillium citrinum gave 12β-hydroxylation
        and 15β-hydroxylation. Cylindrocarpon radicicola gave 17a-oxa-1,4-androstadiene-
        3,17-dione from either 17α-hydroxyprogesterone or 16-dehydroprogesterone.

Ap-21   Eroshin, V. K. , Med. Prom. SSSR 16, 23-25 (1962).

Ap-22   Fukushima, D. K. , J. Biol. Chem. 239, 1748 (1964). 3α-Hydroxy-5β-androstane-
        17-one and 5β-androstane-3,17-dione were hydroxylated at 7β- by Penicillium sp.

Ap-23   Fukushima, D. K. , and Noguchi, S. , Federation Proc. 24, 414 (1964). Andro-
        sterone and Penicillium sp. gave 12β-hydroxylation. Epiandrosterone with the
        same organism gave 1α-hydroxylation. 5α-Androstane-3,17-dione gave some 1α,
        3β-dihydroxy-5α-androstan-17-one. 3β-Hydroxy-5β-androstan-17-one gave the
        7β-ol and 7β-hydroxy-5β-androstane-3,17-dione.

Ap-24   Gibian, H. , Kieslich, K. , Koch, H. J. , Kosmol, H. , Rufer, C. , Schröder, E. ,
        and Vossing, R. , Tetrahedron Letters 21, 2321 (1966). Asymmetric reduction
        with Saccharomyces sp. and Bacillus thuringiensis of a carbonyl group in a totally
        synthetic, optically inactive steroid precursor.

Ap-25   Gibson, D. T. , Wang, K. C. , Sih, C. J. , and Whitlock, H. , Jr. , J. Biol. Chem.
        241, 551 (1966). The structures of several nonsteroidal degradation products from
        the action of Nocardia restrictus on Δ⁴-3-ketosteroids, and insights into the mech-
        anism of degradation derived therefrom; also J. Am. Chem. Soc. 87, 1386 (1965).

Ap-26   Greenspan, G. , Rees, R. , Smith, L. L. , and Alburn, H. E. , J. Org. Chem. 30,
         4215 (1965). 11α-Hydroxylation and 12β-hydroxylation of steroidal alkaloids (funt-
         umine and funtumidine) by Aspergillus ochraceus.

Ap-27   Greenspan, G. , Smith, L. L. , Foell, T. J. , and Rees, R. , U. S. Patent 3,231,589
         (1966). Hydroxylation of 18-homo-19-nortestosterone at 1β, 6β, 10β, and 11α by
         Aspergillus ochraceus.

Ap-28   Greenspan, G. , Smith, L. L. , Rees, R. , Foell, T. J. , and Alburn, H. E. , J. Org.
         Chem. 31, 2512 (1966). Microbial transformation of steroids of the unnatural (l)
         series, and simultaneous transformation of other d- and l-substrates by the same
         cultures.

Ap-29   Grozdyak, P. I. , Med. Prom. SSSR 16, 26-28 (1962).

Ap-30   Holmlund, C. E. , Sax, K. J. , Blank, R. H. , and Evans, R. H. , Jr. Steroids 5,
         459 (1965). 7β-Hydroxylation and deacetylation of 16α-methyl-17α,21-dihydroxy-
         4-pregnene-3,20-dione 21-acetate with Rhizopus nigricans. 11α-Hydroxylation
         and deacetylation of the same substrate with Dactylium dendroides.

Ap-31   Iida, M. , Townsley, J. D. , Hayano, M. , and Brodie, H. J. , Steroids, Suppl. 1,
         p. 159 (1965). Reversible Δ^1-dehydrogenating-hydrogenating enzyme system iso-
         lated from Bacillus cyclo-oxydans. Dependence on cofactors and enzyme induction
         discussed.

Ap-32   Irmscher, K. , Bierstecher, W. , Metz, H. , Watzel, R. , and Bork, K. H. , Ber.
         97, 3363 (1964). Δ^1-Dehydrogenation of 7α-hydroxytestosterone and 7α-acetoxy-
         methyltestosterone by Corynebacterium simplex. 7α-Hydroxylation of methyltes-
         tosterone and testosterone by Curvularia lunata and Cunninghamella blakesleeana.

Ap-33   Jerussi, R. , and Ringold, H. J. , Biochemistry 4, 2113 (1965). Enzyme kinetics
         of 1,2-dehydrogenation using cellfree preparations of Bacillus sphaericus.
         Comments on mechanism.

Ap-34   Kogan, L. M. , Ulezlo, I. V. , Kozlova, I. K. , Suvorov, N. N. , Portnova, S. L. ,
         Skryabin, G. K. , and Torgov, I. V. , Izv. Akad. Nauk SSSR, Ser. Khim. No. 11,
         p. 2008-2015 (1964).

Ap-35   Kogan, L. M. , Vorshvillo, W. E. , Skryabin, G. K. , and Torgov, I. V. , Dokl.
         Akad. Nauk SSSR 160, 346-348 (1965).

Ap-36   Kondo, E. , Kogyo Kagaku Zasshi 67, 724-727 (1964).

Ap-37   Kondo, E. , and Mitsugi, T. , J. Am. Chem. Soc. 88, 4737 (1966). Degradation of
         spiroketal side chain in diosgenin and tigogenin by Fusarium solani and Corynebac-
         terium simplex. Formation of 1,4-androstadiene-3,16-dione in 65% yield. Dis-
         cussion of mechanism.

Ap-38   Kondo, E. , Mitsugi, T. , and Tori, K. , J. Am. Chem. Soc. 87, 4655 (1965). 18-
         Hydroxylation of corticosterone by Corynespora cassiicola and Corynespora melonis.
         Microbial synthesis of aldosterone.

Ap-39   Kurosawa, Y. , Shimojima, H. , and Osawa, Y. , Steroids Suppl. 1, p. 185 (1965).
         Resolution of totally synthetic steroid precursors by yeast and pancreatic enzymes.

Ap-40   Koscheenko, K. A. , Skryabin, G. K. , Eroshin, V. K. , Kogan, L. M. , and Torgov,
         I. V. , Prikl. Biokhim. i Mikrobiol. 1, 127-130 (1965).

Ap-41   Kuchaeva, A. G. , and Capek, A. , Microbiology (USSR) (English Transl.) 32,
         843-846 (1964).

Ap-42   Laskin, A. I. , Fried, J. , Cohen, A. I. , Meyers, C. , Grabowich, P. , Junta, B. ,
         Palmere, R. M. , and Diassi, P. A. , Steroids 5, 57 (1965). 2β-Hydroxylation of

deoxycorticosterone, 6α-fluoro-4-pregnene-16α,17α,21-triol-3,20-dione 16,17-acetonide, 16α-methyl-17α,21-dihydroxy-4-pregnene-3,20-dione, and progesterone with Gnomonia fragariae. 14α-Hydroxylation and 2β, 16α-dihydroxylation of progesterone by the same organism.

Ap-43   Laskin, A. I., Grabowich, P., Meyers, C. DeL., and Fried, J., J. Med. Chem. 7, 406 (1964). Eburicoic acid was transformed by Glomerella fusarioides into 3,4-seco-$\Delta^{8,24\,(28)}$-eburicadien-4-ol-3,21-dioic acid.

Ap-44   Malhotra, S. K., and Ringold, H. J., J. Am. Chem. Soc. 87, 3228 (1965). The mechanism of action of isomerase derived from Bacillus sphaericus.

Ap-45   Mallett, G. E., Fukuda, D. S., and Guynes, G. J., Abstr. 150th Meeting Am. Chem. Soc., Atlantic City, 1965, p. 12Q.

Ap-46   Manson, A. J., Sjogren, R. E., and Riano, M., J. Org. Chem. 30, 307 (1965). Reduction of 17α-ethinyl-17β-hydroxy-2-hydroxymethylene-4-androsten-3-one by Rhizopus stolonifer to the corresponding 2α-hydroxymethyl product.

Ap-47   Martinkova, J., and Dyr. J., Collection Czech. Chem. Commun. 30, 2994 (1965).

Ap-48   Marx, A. F., Beck, H. C., van der Waard, W. F., and de Flines, J., Steroids 8, 421 (1966). Incubation of concessine with stachybotrys parvispora gave Δ^{4}-conenin-3-one and 11α-hydroxy-Δ^{4}-conenin-3-one. Fermentation with Gloeosporium fructigenum gave 7α-hydroxyconessine, 7β-hydroxyconessine, and 11α-hydroxyconessine.

Ap-49   Marx, A. F., Beck, H. C., van der Waard, W. F., and de Flines, J., Steroids 8, 391 (1966). 9α-Hydroxylation and 12α-hydroxylation of conessine with Botryodiplodia theobromae.

Ap-50   Modelli, R., Ann. Chim. (Rome) 55, 205 (1965). 16α-Hydroxylation of 17α-methyltestosterone and 4-hydroxy-17α-methyltestosterone by Nocardia italica.

Ap-51   Modelli, R., Ann. Chim. (Rome) 55, 310 (1965). 2α-Hydroxylation and 16α-hydroxylation of 4-estrene-3,17-dione and 19-nortestosterone by Nocardia italica.

Ap-52   Neidleman, S. L., Diassi, P. A., Junta, B., Palmere, R. M., and Pan, S. C., Tetrahedron Letters, p. 5337 (1966). 17α-Chlorination and 17α-bromination of 16-ketoprogesterone and 16-keto-A-nor-progesterone by enzymes from Caldariomyces fumago together with hydrogen peroxide and a source of halide ion. 16,16-Dibromination of 15-keto-1-dehydrotestololactone under same conditions. Proofs of structure by comparison with samples prepared by nonenzymatic halogenation. No enzymatic halogenation occurred with substrates lacking the β-dicarbonyl structural element. Also 15α-hydroxylation of 1-dehydrotestololactone by Penicillium sp. Work by Brown and Hager [J. Am. Chem. Soc. 89, 719 (1967)] indicates that the enzymatic reaction involves generation of Cl^{+} from Cl^{-} and hydrogen peroxide. The inference may be drawn that there is no steroid-enzyme interaction required in the halogenation examples shown by Neidleman.

Ap-53   Noda Institute for Scientific Research, Netherlands Patent 6,502,883 (1965) (Japanese Patent 30915 (1964); Derwent Abstr. 19, 293). Degradation of cholesterol, sitosterol, or stigmasterol by Corynebacterium simplex and other known 1-dehydrogenating species, in the presence of agents which chelate copper or iron, to give 4-androstene 3,17-dione, 1,4-androstadiene-3,17-dione, and other products.

Ap-54   Noguchi, S., and Fukushima, D. K., J. Org. Chem. 30, 3552 (1965). Penicillium sp. with 3α-hydroxy-5α-androstan-17-one gave 12β-hydroxy product. The same organism with 3β-hydroxy-5α-androstan-17-one gave the 1α-hydroxy product and with 3β-hydroxy-5β-androstan-17-one gave the 7β-hydroxy product and 7β-hydroxy-5β-androstane-3,17-dione.

Ap-55   Okada, M., and Hasunuma, M., J. Pharm. Soc. Japan <u>86</u>, 67 (1966). 7β-Hydroxy-lation of digitoxigenin with <u>Cunninghamella</u> <u>blakesleeana</u>.

Ap-56   Okada, M., Hasunuma, M., and Saito, Y., J. Pharm. Soc. Japan <u>85</u>, 1092 (1965). 12β-Hydroxylation of bufalin and resibufogenin with <u>Gibberella</u> <u>saubinetti</u>.

Ap-57   Okada, M., and Saito, Y., Steroids <u>6</u>, 651 (1965). Assignment of structure to 7α, 15α-dihydroxylated product from <u>Gibberella</u> <u>saubinetti</u> on dehydroepiandrosterone.

Ap-58   Okada, M., Yamada, A., and Ishidate, J. Pharm. Soc. Japan <u>85</u>, 816 (1965). 7α-Hydroxylation of dehydroepiandrosterone with <u>Gibberella</u> <u>saubinetti</u>. 15α-Hydroxy-lation of progesterone, deoxycorticosterone, and testosterone with the same organism.

Ap-59   Okumura, T., Nozaki, Y., and Satoh, D., Chem. & Pharm. Bull. (Tokyo) <u>12</u>, 1143 (1964). 3β,14β,21-Trihydroxy-5β-pregnan-20-one gave 1β-hydroxylation with <u>Absidia</u> <u>orchidis</u>. From 4,5-dehydrodigitoxigenone the 7β-hydroxy and 7β,12β-dihydroxy products were characterized.

Ap-60   Peterson, G. E., and Davis, J. R., Steroids <u>4</u>, 677 (1964). Degradation of cho-lesterol by <u>Streptomyces</u> sp.

Ap-61   Prochazka, Z., and Sorm, F., Collection Czech. Chem. Commun. <u>30</u>, 1874 (1965). 11α-Hydroxylation of 14β,18-cycloprogesterone (10β-methyl-13β,14β-cyclomethy-lene-17β-acetyl-4-gonen-3-one) with <u>Rhizopus</u> <u>nigricans</u>.

Ap-62   Protiva, J., Schwartz, V., and Syhora, K., Folia Mikrobiol. (Prague) <u>9</u>, 218-221 (1964).

Ap-63   Rahim, M. A., and Sih, C. J., J. Biol. Chem. <u>241</u>, 3615 (1966). In <u>vitro</u> studies of oxygenase and esterase from <u>Cylindrocarpon</u> <u>radicicola</u>. Degradation of proges-terone, 17α-hydroxyprogesterone, 16-dehydroprogesterone, deoxycorticosterone, and 16α,17α-oxidoprogesterone to C-19 steroids.

Ap-64   Raman, P. B., and Peron, F. G., Steroids <u>5</u>, 249 (1965). 11β-Hydroxylation of 18,21-dihydroxy-4-pregnene-3,20-dione with <u>Cunninghamella</u> <u>blakesleeana</u>.

Ap-65   Reimann, H., Sarre, O. Z., and Oliveto, E. P., Steroids <u>7</u>, 505 (1966). Con-version of a 3β-hydroxy-Δ⁵-steroid to a 3-keto-Δ⁴-steroid with <u>Flavobacterium</u> <u>dehydrogenans</u>.

Ap-66   Sato, Y., Waters, J. A., and Kaneko, H., J. Org. Chem. <u>29</u>, 3732 (1964). 9α-Hydroxylation and 7β-hydroxylation of 5,6-dihydrosolasodine by <u>Helicosytum</u> <u>piri-forme</u>.

Ap-67   Saucy, G., Els, H., Miksch, F., and Furst, A., Helv. Chim. Acta <u>49</u>, 1529 (1966). 11α-Hydroxylation of 9β,10α-substrates ("retrosteroids") by <u>Aspergillus</u> <u>ochraceus</u>.

Ap-68   Sax, K. J., Holmlund, C. E., Feldman, L. I., Evans, R. H., Jr., Blank, R. H., Shay, A. J., Schultz, J. S., and Dann, M., Steroids <u>5</u>, 345 (1965). 1α,2α-Di-hydroxylation of 17α-ethynyl-17β-hydroxy-4-androsten-3-one, 9α-fluoro-11β,17β-dihydroxy-17α-methyl-4-androsten-3-one, and 11β,21-dihydroxy-16α,17α-isopro-pylidenedioxy-4-pregnene-3,20-dione by inducible enzyme from <u>Nocardia</u> <u>corallina</u>. Same reaction with a Δ¹-substrate, proposed as intermediate in this process.

Ap-69   Schubert, K., Böhme, K. H., and Hörhold, C., Z. Naturforsch. <u>18b</u>, 988 (1963). Degradation of deoxycorticosterone acetate by <u>Mycobacterium</u> <u>smegmatis</u>. Isolation of fragment with only C and D rings from original skeleton intact.

Ap-70   Schubert, K., Groh, H., and Hörhold, C., Naturwiss. <u>52</u>, 20 (1965). Degradation of cholesterol and 4-cholesten-3-one by <u>Mycobacterium</u> <u>smegmatis</u> to 9,10-seco-Δ¹,³,⁵(¹⁰)-androstatrien-3-ol-9,17-dione.

Ap-71   Schubert, K., Schlegel, J., and Hörhold, C., Steroids, Suppl. 1, p. 175 (1965). *Clostridium* paraputrificum reduces 3-keto-Δ^4-steroids to 3α-hydroxy-4,5β-di-hydrosteroids; 3-keto-$\Delta^{1,4}$-steroids to 3-keto-Δ^1-4,5β-dihydrosteroids and 3α-hydroxy-1,2,4,5β-tetrahydrosteroids; 3-keto-$\Delta^{4,6}$-steroids into Δ^6-3α-hydroxy-4,5β-dihydrosteroids; and 3-keto-$\Delta^{1,4,6}$-steroids to Δ^6-3α-hydroxy-1,2,4,5β-tetrahydrosteroids.

Ap-72   Schubert, A., and Schwarz, S., Experientia <u>21</u>, 562 (1965). Dehydrogenation at 1- with *Mycobacterium* sp. and 11α-hydroxylation with *Rhizopus nigricans* using several unusual twenty-carbon substrates.

Ap-73   Schupbach, M., and Tamm, C., Helv. Chim. Acta <u>47</u>, 2217 (1964). Incubation of 14β,15β-epoxy-14-anhydro-digitoxigenin with *Fusarium lini* gave the 12β-hydroxy product. The same organism with resibufogenin also gave 12β-hydroxy product.

Ap-74   Schupbach, M., and Tamm, C., Helv. Chim. Acta <u>47</u>, 2226 (1964). Marinobufagenin with *Fusarium lini* gave the 12β-hydroxy product.

Ap-75   Schuytema, E. C., Hargie, M. P., Merits, I., Schenck, J. R., Siehr, D. J., Smith, M. S., and Varner, E. L., Biotechnol. Bioeng. <u>8</u>, 275 (1966). Use of basidiomycetes to hydroxylate (6β,11α,17α), reduce (5α-H), and degrade (17β-Ac → 17a-oxa-17-ketone) progesterone.

Ap-76   Schwarz, V., Ulrich, M., and Syhora, K., Steroids <u>4</u>, 645 (1964). Production of the 1β-hydroxy product, along with cortisol and 11-epicortisol, by *Absidia orchidis* on Compound S.

Ap-77   Shaw, D. A., Borkenhagen, L. F., and Talalay, P., Proc. Natl. Acad. Sci. U.S. <u>54</u>, 837 (1965). Identification of amino acids into which fragments of androstenedione, formed by degradation with *Pseudomonas testosteroni*, are incorporated.

Ap-78   Shirasaka, M., Sankyo Kenyusho Nempo <u>15</u>, 1-35 (1963).

Ap-79   Sih, C. J., Lee, S. S., Tsong, Y. Y., and Wang, K. C., J. Am. Chem. Soc. <u>87</u>, 1385 (1965). *Nocardia restrictus* on 6β,19-oxido-4-androstene-3,17-dione gave the 9α-hydroxy product. 9α,19-Dihydroxy-4-androstene-3,17-dione gave 3,19-di-hydroxy-9,10-<u>seco</u>-1,3,5(10)-androstatriene-9,17-dione. 2,17β-Dihydroxy-1,4-androstadien-3-one gave 2ξ,9α-dihydroxy-4-androsten-3,17-dione. 2-Methoxy-17β-hydroxy-1,4-androstadien-3-one gave 2-methoxy-3,4-dihydroxy-9,10-<u>seco</u>-1,3,5(10)-androstatrien-9,17-dione. 4,9α,17β-Trihydroxy-4-androsten-3-one gave 3,4-dihydroxy-9,10-<u>seco</u>-1,3,5(10)-androstatriene-9,17-dione which in turn could be degraded further by <u>N</u>. <u>restrictus</u>. Comments on mechanism of degradation.

Ap-80   Sih, C. J., Lee, S. S., Tsong, Y. Y., and Wang, K. C., J. Biol. Chem. <u>241</u>, 540 (1966). Degradation mechanisms with *Nocardia restrictus*.

Ap-81   Sih, C. J., Lee, S. S., Tsong, Y. Y., Wang, K. C., and Chang, F. N., J. Am. Chem. Soc. <u>87</u>, 2765 (1965). 6β,19-Oxido-4-cholesten-3-one with *Nocardia restrictus* gave 6β,19-oxido-4-androsten-3,17-dione (I). 3β-Acetoxy-5-cholesten-19-ol with organism CSD-10 gave estrone in 72% yield. 3β-Acetoxy-5α-chloro-6β,19-oxidocholestane with CSD-10 gave (I).

Ap-82   Sih, C. J., Lee, S. S., Wang, K. C., and Tsong, Y. Y., Bacteriol. Proc. p. 93 (1965). Mechanism of A-ring degradation by *Nocardia restrictus*. See also Ap-79.

Ap-83   Sih, C. J., and Wang, K. C., J. Am. Chem. Soc. <u>87</u>, 1387 (1965). 19-Hydroxy-4-cholesten-3-one with *Nocardia restrictus* gave estrone. 19-Hydroxy-β-sitost-4-en-3-one gave estrone.

Ap-84   Singh, K., Sehgal, S. N., and Vezina, C., Can. J. Microbiol. <u>11</u>, 351 (1965). Detailed study of the influence of medium and other environmental conditions on the 1-dehydrogenation of Compound S by spores of *Septomyxa affinis*. Evidence that the required enzyme is constitutive and not induced. Mention of a variety of other spore-forming organisms, spores from which Δ^1-dehydrogenate Compound S.

Ap-85   Skryabin, G. K., Zryagintseva, I. S., and Sokolova, L. V., Izv. Akad. Nauk SSSR, Ser. Biol. 29, 715-20 (1964).

Ap-86   Smith, L. L., Greenspan, G., Rees, R., and Foell, T., J. Am. Chem. Soc. 88, 3120 (1966). Aspergillus ochraceus on racemic 19-nortestosterone gave l-1β-hydroxy, d-6β-hydroxy, l-10β-hydroxy, and d-11α-hydroxy products. Similar, but not identical, results with racemic higher 18-homologs.

Ap-87   Sokolova, L. V., Grinyuk, T. I., Yaroslavtseva, Z. A., Kovylkina, N. F., Gusakova, E. G., Skryabin, G. K., and Suvorov, N. N., Med. Prom. SSSR 16, 26-28 (1962).

Ap-88   Suvorov, N. N., Novikova, V. M., Sokolova, L. V., and Kovylkina, N. F., Med. Prom. SSSR 14, 22-24 (1960).

Ap-89   Talalay, P., and Boyer, J., Biochim. Biophys. Acta 105, 389 (1965). Preparation of crystalline Δ^5-isomerase from Pseudomonas testosteroni on a large scale.

Ap-90   Tori, K., and Kondo, E., Steroids 4, 713 (1964). NMR method for determination of position of hydroxyl group introduced by microbiological transformation. 15α-Hydroxylation from Helminthosporium sigmoideum on Compound S. 15β-Hydroxylation from Cercospora melonis on Compound S. 7α,14α-Dihydroxylation from Curvularia lunata on Compound S. 6β,11α-Dihydroxylation by Cunninghamella echinulata on progesterone.

Ap-91   Tsong, Y. Y., Wang, K. C., and Sih, C. J., Biochim. Biophys. Acta 93, 398 (1964). Reduction of Δ^6 in 17β-hydroxy-4,6-androstadien-3-one by Nocardia restrictus. Other products include 9α-hydroxy-4,6-androstadien-3,17-dione and 9α,17β-dihydroxy-4,6-androstadien-3-one.

Ap-92   van der Sijde, D., de Flines, J., and van der Waard, W. F., Rec. Trav. Chim. 85, 721 (1966). Fermentation of 17α,21-dihydroxy-9β,10α-pregn-4-ene-3,20-dione with Aspergillus ochraceus yielded 11α,17α,21-trihydroxy-9β,10α-pregn-4-ene-3,20-dione and 15α,17α,21-trihydroxy-9β,10α-pregn-4-ene-3,20-dione. Fermentation of 9β,10α-progesterone with Aspergillus ochraceus afforded 11α-hydroxy-9β,10α-progesterone. Fermentation of the latter product with Sporomia pollaccii and Helicosporium lumbricopsis afforded 11α-hydroxy-9β,10α-testosterone and 11α-hydroxy-9β,10α-androst-4-ene-3,17-dione. Fermentation of 9β,10α-testosterone with Aspergillus ochraceus yielded 11α-hydroxy-9β,10α-testosterone and 11α-hydroxy-9β,10α-androst-4-ene-3,17-dione. Fermentation of 17α-hydroxy-9β,10α-progesterone with Aspergillus ochraceus afforded 11α,17α-dihydroxy-9β,10α-progesterone and 11α-hydroxy-9β,10α-androst-4-ene-3,17-dione.

Ap-93   van der Waard, W. F., van der Sijde, D., and de Flines, J., Rec. Trav. Chim. 85, 712 (1966). Fermentation of progesterone, 9β,10α-progesterone, 6-dehydro-9β, 10α-progesterone, and 9β,10α-testosterone with Sepedonium ampullosporum afforded the respective 16α-hydroxy derivatives.

Ap-94   Wacker, A., Drews, J. Pratt, W. B., Lawrent, H., and Petzoldt, K., Z. Naturforsch. 20b, 547 (1965). Study of steroid-initiated enzyme induction in Pseudomonas testosteroni with respect to kinetics, strengths of various inducers, and other factors.

Ap-95   Wang, K. C., Lee, S. S., Tsong, Y. Y., Sih, C. J., Abstr. 150th Meeting Am. Chem. Soc., Atlantic City, 1965, p. 13Q. Failure of Nocardia and Mycobacteria sp. to convert 1,3,5(10)-cholestatrien-3-ol into estrone.

Ap-96   Wiechert, R., Kerb, U., and Kieslich, K., Ber. 96, 2765 (1963). 11β-Hydroxylation of 1α-methyl Compound S with Curvularia lunata.

Ap-97   Wiechert, R., Z. Naturforsch. <u>19b</u>, 944 (1964). 11β-Hydroxylation of 1α-methyl-
           testosterone and 1α-methyl Compound S with <u>Curvularia</u> <u>lunata</u>.

Ap-98   Wilson, J., and Vestling, C. S., Arch. Biochem. Biophys. <u>110</u>, 401 (1965). Prep-
           aration of a cellfree 15α-hydroxylating system from <u>Bacillus</u> <u>megaterium</u>.

Ap-99   Zakrzewski, Z., Raczkowska, S., and Lewenstein, W., Przemysl. Chem. <u>43</u>,
           564-565 (1964).

Ap-100   Zvyagintseva, I. S., and Skryabin, G. K., Izv. Akad. Nauk SSSR, Ser. Biol. <u>24</u>,
           525-532 (1964).